Chemistry

THIRD EDITION

J. V. QUAGLIANO AND L. M. VALLARINO

Florida State University

Chemistry

THIRD EDITION

Prentice-Hall, Inc., Englewood Cliffs, N.J.

Printed in the United States of America.
Library of Congress Catalog No. 69-10012

Illustrations by BMA Associates

Cover photo by John Pitkin

C

PRENTICE-HALL INTERNATIONAL, INC., *London*
PRENTICE-HALL OF AUSTRALIA, PTY., LTD., *Sydney*
PRENTICE-HALL OF CANADA, LTD., *Toronto*
PRENTICE-HALL OF INDIA, PVT., LTD., *New Delhi*
PRENTICE-HALL OF JAPAN, INC., *Tokyo*

Current printing (last digit):
10 9 8 7 6 5 4 3 2 1

To Professor John C. Bailar, Jr., Professor Raymond E. Kirk, Professor Wendell L. Latimer, and Professor Roland Ward

DEDICATED AND INSPIRING TEACHERS

PREFACE

TO THE FIRST EDITION

This book has been written for the beginning student, in terms that he can understand. I have tried to state the important concepts clearly and intelligibly, and to relate each concept to what has gone before and to what is yet to come. It is impossible, of course, to explain every topic in a way that will make it equally meaningful to every student. But this is at least the ideal toward which I have striven—to put in the hands of students an accurate, meaningful statement that will give them the descriptive material and the basic principles they need in order to claim competence as beginning students of chemistry.

I take genuine pleasure in acknowledging the contributions of many colleagues and associates in the development of the manuscript. I am particularly grateful to the late Dr. Wendell Latimer for his generous interest, encouragement, and recommendations. Dr. Kenneth Pitzer, has also taken a great personal interest in this book, and many of his frank criticisms, suggestions, and revisions have been incorporated into the text. I also appreciate the skill, patience, and understanding of Mr. Everett M. Sims during the development of the manuscript. Dr. Brother Columba, C.S.C., Dr. Patrick McCusker, Dr. Sister Mary Martinette, B.V.M., Dr. Robert Parry, and Dr. Jay Young have contributed significantly with their comments, suggestions, and generous help. Some of these colleagues have put their own notes at my disposal, for which I am most grateful. Dr. Charles White read part of the manuscript, and Dr. George Hennion read the chapter on organic chemistry; both have made valuable suggestions. Dr. John Teegan has read the proofs and has suggested many helpful changes. The contributions of all these associates are reflected in many, many pages of this book. Dr. Jack W. Eichinger, Jr., has generously allowed me to reproduce the chart showing the electron configuration of the elements.

The contribution of the artist, Mr. Richard Mikel, is self-evident. I appreciate the help of Mrs. Virginia Manges who has done an outstanding job in the typing of the manuscript. Finally, I would like to express my appreciation to Dr. Andrew J. Boyle, Administrative Head of the Department of Chemistry at Notre Dame, who has encouraged and helped me in every possible way during the writing of this book.

J. V. QUAGLIANO

TO THE THIRD EDITION

The principal aim of this third edition is the same as that of the previous ones: namely, to present a text for the beginning student in terms that he can understand, maintaining at the same time an accurate and logical development of the subject.

Chemistry is first of all an experimental science, but a rationalization of the experimental facts on a theoretical basis is essential to its understanding. Once a beginning student has been introduced to some of the fundamental facts of chemistry, it is important to provide him with guiding principles that may be of help not only in explaining the facts already learned but also in predicting the general structure and behavior of elements and compounds not yet familiar to him. Two guiding principles which are emphasized in this book are the structural aspects of chemical bonding and energetics. The former gives the student an insight into the microscopic representation of matter—of the interactions among elementary particles and of their spatial distribution in patterns of characteristic symmetry. Energetics, on the other hand, helps the student to correlate a vast number of macroscopic physical and chemical properties, and to find the answer to one of the fundamental questions of chemistry: Why do certain reactions occur and others do not? Why are some substances stable and others unstable under comparable conditions?

In this third edition, the presentation of atomic and molecular structure has been reorganized and extended. The chapter on atomic structure now includes a simple and yet accurate discussion of the energy levels of atoms and of the electron distribution of atomic orbitals. This discussion serves as the basis for a rationalization of the stereochemistry of covalent molecules and of the concepts of single and multiple bonding, which are considered in detail in the chapters on molecular structure.

Two new chapters deal with chemical energetics, and the concepts of energetics have been extensively applied in both the general and the descriptive chapters so that they constitute a unifying theme throughout the entire book.

Believing that chemistry can be presented to the beginning student in a more meaningful, logically acceptable, and stimulating manner in the light of these general principles of structure, energetics, and—whenever possible—kinetics, we have accordingly reworked all chapters of the book. In so doing, we have developed the discussion in a more quantitative manner and to a greater depth while attempting to maintain the sympathetic approach to the beginning student that has been characteristic of the preceding editions. Many other minor but important changes have been made throughout the book, all of which, we hope, will help to achieve the aim set out above. To the very many friends who have helped in this edition, we express here our deep gratitude.

J. V. QUAGLIANO AND L. M. VALLARINO

CONTENTS

Chemistry

THIRD EDITION

INTRODUCTION

1

To future historians the years we are living through will probably be known as the beginning of the "scientific age." During the last half-century scientists have made greater progress than man had made in all the centuries since he first became aware of his surroundings. And the application of the knowledge we have gained through scientific research has led to a dramatic increase in our ability to use the resources of nature. We are living in a time when men are producing a larger quantity and a greater variety of goods than ever before in history. New developments in science continue at a constantly accelerating pace to produce better products for better living. Atomic energy, jet propulsion, and man-made satellites have brought the dawn of a new scientific age which is bright with striking new developments. Whether they will be used to benefit or destroy the human race is a matter of grave concern to every thinking person, but at least the *potential* promise of scientific progress seems almost unlimited.

1-1 Natural Science: Its Scope and Limitations

It is difficult to define the term "natural science" adequately. In the pages that follow we shall use the term to mean the *area of inquiry* concerned with the phenomena of the world around and within us—as well as the organized, correlated body of knowledge which has emerged from such inquiry and is continuously being extended and *developed by observation, experimenta-*

tion, and thought. The aim of natural science is not only to observe and describe phenomena, but also to interpret them in terms of theories or laws.

Man's knowledge and his experiences fall into two distinct classes. First, he gains knowledge of the material things about him through physical contact with them. Second, by mental processes he elaborates on his experimentally acquired knowledge of the material things, and thus accumulates knowledge on non-material or intangible things. A beautiful piece of poetry, for example, cannot be described in physical terms, but its reality is apparent to every truly educated person. Scientists are aware that beyond the limits of their ability to observe the physical world, they undergo significant subjective experiences to which objective scientific methods cannot be adequately applied and of which scientific facts and theories are completely independent. We see, then, that all scientific facts and theories *must* be judged objectively.

1-2 The Scientific Method

The scientific method is any logical procedure for discovering a general truth from many individual observations. This process of reasoning from the particular to the general is known as inductive reasoning. It was largely the emphasis that Lord Francis Bacon (1561–1626) put on inductive reasoning in the study of natural phenomena that led to the development of modern science. The scientific method involves three steps:

1. The first step is the *collection of data* concerning particular phenomena. These data must be as free as possible from errors of observation and measurement and must be unaffected by personal prejudices. An experiment or an observation must be repeated to insure that data collected once can be obtained again.
2. The second step is the *examination of the facts* that have been collected to see if any significant relationships exist between them, and to use these relationships, if any, to develop hypotheses and theories to explain these phenomena and similar ones as well. Relationships of this sort are more useful if they can be expressed in mathematical terms.
3. The last step involves *testing these hypotheses and theories* by means of new experiments which may have been suggested by the hypotheses and theories themselves. In fact, hypotheses and theories are only means to an end. If a hypothesis or a theory proves untenable in the light of new experimental data, it is discarded or modified to conform to the new information. Then the new modified hypotheses and theories may suggest further experiments, and so forth, until after a sometimes long and difficult process of successive re-elaboration a theory is found which explains and correlates all known facts about the phenomena under study. Incorrect theories, therefore, are not always useless if they point the way to further useful investigations.

1-3 The Science of Chemistry

Chemistry is a study of the properties, the composition, and the structure of matter, the changes that occur in matter, and the energy that is released or absorbed during these changes. Chemistry, like all the natural sciences, is an experimental science.

The *general* aim of chemistry is to discover everything possible about all these characteristics of matter. Naturally, then, chemistry is undergoing constant expansion and refinement. Complete knowledge of any phase of chemistry—as of any of the other natural sciences—is many years away, if, indeed, it is attainable at all.

The *immediate* aim of chemistry is to make use of all the knowledge about matter that has already been acquired and to extend the limits of our present knowledge by means of new observations and improved theories. The process by which we extend our knowledge of facts and theories is known as research. In general terms, research is the discovery of any heretofore unknown or unapplied fact or theory.

FACT AND THEORY IN CHEMISTRY

In chemistry, fact and theory are closely related. The part of chemistry primarily concerned with the observation, tabulation, and correlation of facts is sometimes called descriptive chemistry. After the facts have been organized, theoretical chemistry comes into play. Using descriptive facts, a theoretical chemist tries to develop useful theories from them. Descriptive and theoretical chemistry must always go hand in hand, for accurate experimental work is always the basis of sound theory. Since the behavior of matter cannot be predicted on the basis of reasoning alone, theoretical predictions must constantly be guided and checked by experimental observations. Thus, it is often said that "theory guides but experiment decides." The continued expansion of our knowledge of chemistry depends directly on constant effort in both experimental and theoretical research.

1-4 The History of Chemistry

FROM THE PREHISTORIC PERIOD TO A.D. 500

Since one of the objectives of chemistry is to acquire knowledge of the properties of matter, every bit of information that prehistoric man found out about the materials around him was, in a sense, a contribution to chemical knowledge. When man first learned that wood burns and stone does not, and then passed this information along to others, he took the first step toward acquiring chemical knowledge. During man's early life on earth, he acquired a great deal of useful information about the properties of matter. We find direct and indirect evidence in early Biblical writings and in other records that, as the years passed, man continued to extend his knowledge of matter and to put it to more and more uses. He learned to dig metals out of the earth, particularly gold, silver, and copper, and to fashion them into useful articles, and he also learned to extract metals such as iron, mercury, and tin from their ores. He discovered how to make glass from sand and lime and how to employ medicines, oils, and dyes from plants. However, since there was no successful attempt to classify or correlate this new-found knowledge, little progress was made toward a science of chemistry.

THE PERIOD OF ALCHEMY, A.D. 500–1600

During the Middle Ages and even more during the Renaissance, many capable and inquiring men called *alchemists* turned their attention to the direct observation of matter. Alchemists engaged in a great deal of experimentation, but they severely limited the potential value of their findings by keeping them secret. Some alchemists sought unsuccessfully to discover a method of changing base metals such as lead into noble metals such as gold, and to discover an "elixir of life" which they believed would prolong life and heal disease. They succeeded, however, in preparing many new elements such as arsenic, antimony, bismuth, and some of their compounds, and in developing scores of useful pieces of apparatus (distillation flasks and heating furnaces, for example) and refining their experimental skills.

THE MEDICAL-CHEMICAL PERIOD, 1600–1750

In some ways this period was similar to the period of alchemy. In their search for effective medicines, men prepared and purified many new chemical substances. It was during these years that the experimental and the theoretical approaches began to be wedded. Francis Bacon urged that the experimental study of nature be combined with theoretical interpretation. This was the period of the successful application of mathematics to natural phenomena by Galileo and of Bacon's emphasis on the careful observation of nature and the application of the new knowledge for the improvement of materials for man's use. Then, as other scholars adopted this approach, scientific progress began its spectacular growth.

PERIOD OF THE PHLOGISTON THEORY, 1700–1777

The scientists of the eighteenth century were specially interested in and made an intensive study of the process of burning and developed several theories to explain it. In 1702 Georg Ernst Stahl, a German chemist, proposed that some substance actually was released during the burning of combustible matter. This substance was called "phlogiston," from the Greek word *phlogistos,* which means flammable. Stahl's theory was widely accepted for 75 years. One reason for its wide acceptance was the failure of chemists to realize the importance of using weighing devices to determine the exact weights of materials before and after they were burned. This is an interesting example of a theory that seems correct and consistent with a large body of observed facts but is proved incorrect by more careful quantitative experimental work.

THE MODERN PERIOD, 1777–PRESENT

Most historians of science trace the beginnings of the modern period of chemistry to the work of a French chemist, Antoine Lavoisier (1743–1794). So let us pause here a moment to give a brief account of his life. He was born in Paris, and at the age of 23 was awarded a gold medal by the Academy of Sciences (of Paris) in recognition of a report he compiled on the problem of city lighting. Most of his life was spent in Paris, and most of his research was done at the Sorbonne. His work on combustion we shall discuss later. In addition, he developed a theory of acids which, though erroneous, was a significant advance over earlier ideas. He also drew up a nomenclature of chemical substances close to that still in use. Apart from his scientific researches, he served as adviser on many public committees both national and municipal, activities, however, which during the French Revolution led to his death by the guillotine in 1794.

Lavoisier made the first extensive use of weighing devices (balances) in chemical studies, which led to the discovery of the fundamental importance of the mass of matter in chemical studies. Now chemists could measure accurately the amount of matter used and produced in chemical reactions. And on the basis of these exact experimental data, they could proceed to develop acceptable theories and precise chemical laws. This significant innovation was the first step toward making chemistry an exact science.

1-5 Chemistry as a Science

FROM THE BEGINNING OF THE NINETEENTH CENTURY TO OUR TIME

The beginning of the nineteenth century coincides in many ways with the birth of chemistry as an exact science, and the century itself represents an era of exciting discovery and vigorous growth. The great scientists of the nineteenth century laid the foundations on which our present age of advanced technology is largely based. These were men of many nations and of very diverse backgrounds, but they all possessed the attributes of the scientist—the power to observe, to think, to devise experiments and draw from them correct conclusions, and finally to pass on their discoveries and theories to others through their teaching and writings.

Among the outstanding scientists of the first half of the nineteenth century, were the Englishman, Dalton, who developed the atomic theory of matter, and the

Swede, Berzelius, to whom we owe our present scheme of chemical symbols. Berzelius, incidentally, also determined with amazing accuracy the atomic weights of many elements, some of which had been just discovered by his own contemporaries. Other eminent scientists of this time were two Englishmen, Sir Humphry Davy, who discovered the alkali metals and showed that chlorine and bromine were elements, and his pupil, Michael Faraday, who explored the effect of electricity on solutions and discovered the laws which now bear his name.

By the 1850's chemistry had developed to the point where its division into two branches was becoming clear. On the one hand there was inorganic chemistry—concerned with "inanimate matter"—and on the other, organic chemistry—concerned with those forms of matter associated with animal and vegetable life. It had been believed up to this time that organic substances required some kind of "living force" for their formation, and that they could not be prepared in a laboratory. This belief was shown to be erroneous by the brilliant work of a German chemist, Wöhler, who was the first to synthesize a typical organic substance (urea) from purely inorganic materials. Wöhler's discovery opened the new and exciting field of organic synthesis, with which were soon associated the names of such eminent scientists as Liebig, Kolbe, Cannizzaro, and Pasteur.

In the latter half of the nineteenth century another branch of chemistry—physical chemistry—began to emerge as a separate area of investigation. The study of the behavior of solutions by Van't Hoff, Raoult, and Ostwald; of electrolytic dissociation by Arrhenius; formulation of the rules governing the transformation of solids to liquids to gases, and vice-versa, by Gibbs and of the concept of chemical equilibrium by Guldeberg and Waage; investigation of the factors that cause the release of heat energy during chemical reactions by Hess and Andrews—these are some of the most important advances made during that period and constitute the foundations of much of our present understanding of chemical phenomena.

Throughout this period, while new elements and compounds were being discovered, constant efforts were made to find some order among the elements, the building blocks of chemistry. The early work of Dobereiner, Lothar Mayer, and Newlands finally culminated in the periodic classification of the elements by the Russian, Mendeleef, in 1869, a classification which still forms the basis of systematic descriptive chemistry.

The advent of the present century saw startling discoveries in physics, many of which were to have a profound effect on the development of chemistry. Among the most significant were the discovery of radioactivity by Becquerel and Dr. and Mme. Curie in 1897; the probe into atomic structure by Thomson, Rutherford, and Bohr; and the identification and separation of isotopes by Aston. These discoveries led to a broader understanding of the behavior of matter, which in turn opened the way to investigations into the nature of chemical bonding by A. E. Werner, G. N. Lewis, I. Langmuir, L. Pauling, and R. S. Mulliken.

Many of these names will appear again in subsequent chapters where the discoveries and theories associated with them are discussed in detail. The reader should not regard this survey of the history of chemistry—or any other—as the tale of something that is now finished. Chemistry is a science that is continually developing and growing, and this growth, although based to a considerable degree on past investigations, is fed constantly by the efforts and original contributions of present-day scientists.

MATTER AND ENERGY

2

In this chapter we shall develop two concepts that are fundamental to chemistry: the concept of *matter* and the concept of *energy*. We shall also discuss how matter and energy are classified and measured. The definition of chemistry given in the introduction will serve as a good starting point for our discussion of these basic concepts: *Chemistry is a study of the properties, the composition, and the structure of matter, the changes that occur in matter, and the energy that is released or absorbed during these changes.* Let us look more closely at each of the terms used in this definition.

2-1 Matter and Its Properties

The concept of matter is intuitive and yet it is somewhat difficult to define. A common definition of matter is: *matter is anything that occupies space.* We may also define matter as the fundamental constituent of which all things are made. The amount of matter present in a given object is called its *mass*. The *weight* of a material object is measured by the force with which the object is pulled toward the center of the earth, and this force varies with the distance from the center of the earth. The weight of an object is directly proportional to its mass; hence the terms "weight" and "mass" are often used interchangeably, but they really mean different things—weight is a force, mass is a quantity of matter.

Any sample of matter can be described by a set of characteristics, or properties, either intensive or extensive. *Intensive* properties are common to all samples of the same kind of matter. For example, *all* samples of gold, large or small and of any shape, possess such properties as electrical conductivity, the same resistance to corrosion, the same characteristic color, and the same density. The mass and shape of a particular sample of gold, on the other hand, are characteristic only of that particular sample. Properties which depend on the amount of material are called *extensive* properties.

WHY CHEMISTS ARE CONCERNED WITH PROPERTIES. We must know the properties of matter before we can identify a material correctly or predict its behavior under particular conditions. Not only a chemist, but anyone who works with materials, must know the properties of the matter he uses. When we use a material for any purpose, we sometimes identify it subconsciously—by means of its characteristic properties. To a casual observer, for example, a bottle of clear, colorless, liquid benzene may look very much like a bottle of water. But anyone who has used benzene is familiar enough with the differences in properties between benzene and water to be able to tell them apart. The odor of a liquid, the manner in which it behaves when it is shaken, and many other observable properties, help us to identify it. And only after a liquid has been properly identified can it be properly used.

A chemist's concern with the properties of a material is fundamentally no different from that of any ordinary user of a material. Yet there is a difference of *degree.* For example, a chemist generally must make more careful observations and more exact measurements of the properties of benzene than an ordinary user. Most people need to know only that benzene is flammable and is an effective solvent for grease. But a chemist must also be aware, for example, of the temperature at which benzene will ignite, the temperature at which liquid benzene becomes a solid and at which it becomes a vapor, and the densities of solid, liquid, and vapor benzene under given conditions. Once a chemist knows the properties of benzene—or of any other material—he can use it to the best advantage under various conditions.

THE COMPOSITION AND STRUCTURE OF MATTER

A chemist also must know what materials are composed of. He must investigate what other kinds of materials may have been combined to form the particular material he is studying. He may find that the material is composed of two or more different materials, each having a characteristic set of properties which may be quite different from those of the material they compose. Benzene, for example, is composed of two elements, carbon and hydrogen, both of which have very different properties from the benzene itself.

What practical use can we make of our knowledge of the composition of material? For one thing, this knowledge may enable us to devise methods for changing one kind of material into a more useful kind of material. For example, before we can decide what materials can be obtained from a natural mineral deposit, we must know of what the mineral is composed.

The term "structure" refers in general to the manner in which the fundamental components of a material—its structural units—are put together. A knowledge of composition alone is often not enough to provide an insight into the behavior of a given material, because the two or more components or even the same single component can be combined in different ways, thereby producing materials with very different properties. Graphite and diamond are good examples of the influence of structure on the properties of a material. Both materials contain only one element, carbon. Graphite, which is used in ordinary pencils, is a soft, flaky material that can be spread out easily in a thin film. Diamond, on the other hand, is a very hard material that can be used for grinding and cutting other very hard materials. The differences in the *properties* of graphite and diamond can be traced to differences in the *arrangements* of the same kind of structural units—atoms of carbon—in the two materials—

that is, to differences in *structure.* In graphite the carbon atoms are joined together in a two-dimensional structure like a flat sheet. In diamond the carbon atoms are linked together to form a rigid three-dimensional structure (see p. 177). This difference in structure causes the observed difference in properties.

CHANGES THAT OCCUR IN MATTER

Every day we see examples of the conversion of one kind of matter into another. Think for a minute of the rusting of iron. Iron itself is a hard, rigid solid, of a dark, metallic color; but when an unprotected surface of iron is exposed to moist air, a slow change occurs. A flaky, reddish powder, which we know as rust, gradually forms on the surface. If the iron is exposed to moist air long enough, the rust continues to form and flake off until all the iron has been converted to rust.

This is an example of the kind of changes with which chemists are concerned. It is, in fact, an example of a chemical change. *A chemical change is any change in matter that results in the disappearance of one or more substances, and the appearance of one or more new substances, each with its own intensive properties.* In other words, chemical changes create substances (products) whose intensive properties are different from those of the substances (reactants) from which they were formed. For example, an iron ore of nearly the same composition as iron rust can be converted to iron metal by heating the ore with carbon.

ENERGY

The concept of energy, like that of matter, is very familiar and yet is very difficult to define simply. Energy is usually defined as the *capacity for doing work.* Let us consider several familiar examples. When a mechanical clock is wound up, energy is stored in its spring, and this stored energy is used to turn a series of gears in the clock, performing work. A machine in motion, such as a pile driver, utilizes energy to drive stakes into the ground or to pound rocks into powder. Movement of the gears and the hands of the clock against the forces of friction and inertia and the motion of the pile driver against an object represent work in the physical sense. Energy stored in the molecules of gasoline and oxygen represents potential chemical energy which can be released to drive the piston of a cylinder in an engine when the molecules react chemically with one another.

Chemical changes almost always involve the release or the absorption of energy, sometimes in considerable amounts. A familiar example is the combustion of fuels. When a fuel, for example natural gas, is burned in air, it reacts chemically with oxygen. New gases are formed as a result of the chemical reaction, and energy is released that may be used to heat a home, cook a meal, or operate a refrigerator. On the other hand, the melting of ice is a familiar example of a change of matter from one form (ice) to another (liquid water), which requires energy from some outside source. In general, the study of energy changes accompanying chemical changes belongs to the realm of chemistry.

2-2 The Chemical Classification of Matter

Remember that chemistry is an experimental science that depends for its data on observations and measurements of material objects. The chemical classification of matter is consequently based on the knowledge of the composition and structure of matter, obtained from experimental observations such as laboratory tests and measurements. The general scheme used in chemistry for classifying matter is shown in Table 2-1.

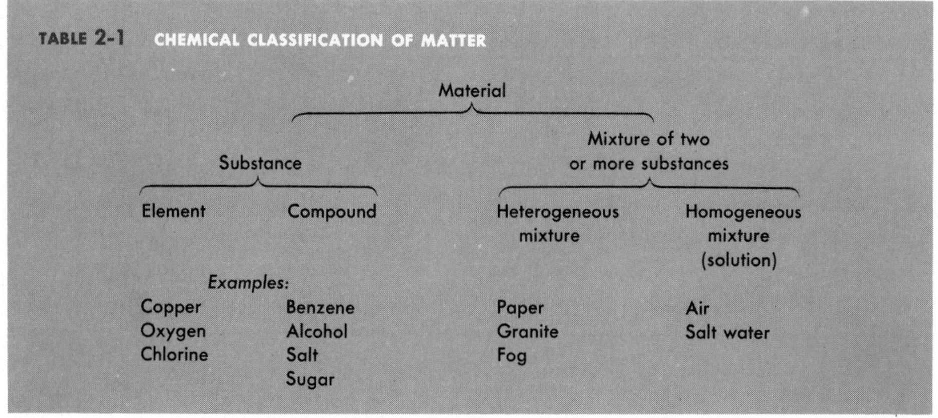

TABLE 2-1 CHEMICAL CLASSIFICATION OF MATTER

Material			
Substance		Mixture of two or more substances	
Element	Compound	Heterogeneous mixture	Homogeneous mixture (solution)
Examples:			
Copper	Benzene	Paper	Air
Oxygen	Alcohol	Granite	Salt water
Chlorine	Salt	Fog	
	Sugar		

PURE SUBSTANCES

As Table 2-1 shows, all forms of matter may be classified as either (pure) substances or mixtures. We can decide on the basis of laboratory tests and measurements whether or not a sample of matter is a pure substance. A pure substance is a form of matter whose composition is uniform—that is, all tangible samples, no matter how small, have the same intensive properties. A substance is a form of matter which cannot be separated into two or more other forms of matter having different intensive properties except by means of a chemical reaction.

MIXTURES

Any material that does not meet the above requirements of a pure substance is a mixture. Mixtures, in turn, are of two types: *heterogeneous* and *homogeneous.* A *heterogeneous mixture* is one whose composition is not uniform; that is, small samples of the same mixture have different compositions and hence different intensive properties.

Many materials can be classified as heterogeneous mixtures on the basis of rather superficial observation. Visual inspection of a piece of granite, for example, permits us to recognize distinct individual components, so granite is a heterogeneous (solid) mixture. A *homogeneous mixture* is one whose composition is uniform but which can be separated without chemical change into two or more different substances. At first glance, some homogeneous mixtures may appear to be pure substances because the two or more substances which compose the mixture are so intimately mixed that they are no longer individually recognizable. Homogeneous mixtures of this sort are generally called *solutions,* either solid, liquid, or gaseous. The different substances in a solution can be separated without resort to a chemical reaction. Salt water is an example of a homogeneous mixture (a solution), and the salt that has been dissolved in the water can be recovered simply by evaporating the water.

In classifying a sample of matter, then, the first step is to determine whether it is a pure substance or a mixture. If it is a mixture, the next step is to separate all the substances that are present. Each individual pure substance is then examined to determine whether it should be classified as an *element* or a *compound.*

ELEMENTS AND COMPOUNDS

We can determine whether a pure substance is an *element* or a *compound* by examining the sort of change it undergoes when it is subjected to various conditions and treatments. *If, from a definite mass of one pure substance, without the addition of any other substance, an equal total mass of two or more other substances can be obtained by chemical means, (involving energies well below those involved in nuclear reactions), the substance under consideration is classified as a compound.* In other words, a compound is a substance that can be decomposed by chemical methods into two or more different simpler substances. *A fundamental characteristic of a compound is its ability to undergo decomposition.*

If all efforts to obtain two or more substances, by chemical means, from any one pure substance fail, the substance is classified as an element. An element cannot be broken down into other substances by chemical means. Elements may be considered the building blocks for all other pure substances; they can be chemically combined with one another to produce compounds. A compound, therefore, is a substance obtained by the chemical combination of two or more elements.

NUMBER OF ELEMENTS AND COMPOUNDS

NUMBER OF ELEMENTS. Intensive research during the last 150 years has revealed that only a limited number of substances cannot be decomposed by ordinary chemical means and are therefore elements. In fact, a total of only 103 elements is now known; 15 of these do not occur naturally, but they have been produced in the laboratory by means of nuclear reactions. Many of the elements that are present in the physical world exist only in small amounts. As a result, only a few elements make up nearly the whole of our physical world. Of the material readily available to us for examination—namely, the crust of the earth, the atmosphere, and the oceans—more than 98 per cent of the total mass is made up of only 13 elements. This means that less than 2 per cent of the total mass of the earth's crust is made up of the remaining 75 naturally occurring elements.

These 13 most abundant elements are listed in decreasing order of abundance in Table 2-2. Notice that many of the familiar elements, such as lead, copper, silver, nitrogen, and iodine, are not even included. But the fact that an element is not relatively abundant does not necessarily mean that it is unimportant. In animals and plants, certain elements are essential to life even though they are present only in minute amounts. And in the manufacture of many industrial products, it is often essential to combine very small amounts of rare elements to obtain the desired product.

Although there are only 103 elements, the number of compounds that can be formed from them by chemical reactions is practically unlimited. A conservative estimate of the number of compounds that have been examined and identified by chemists is 2,000,000, and this number is continuously increasing as new compounds are being prepared and identified. Each individual chemical compound has its own set of properties, which differ to some extent from those of every other substance. It is one of the aims of chemists to classify and correlate the properties and behavior of this vast number of compounds so that they may study them on the basis of a relatively few fundamental principles.

2-3 The Measurement of Matter

THE METRIC SYSTEM

A system for relating various units of measurement is the *International (Metric) System*, often called the *metric system*, which was introduced at the beginning of the nineteenth century. Today, scientists of all nations use the metric system, in which the meter is the unit of length, the gram is the unit of mass, the second is the unit of time, and the cubic decimeter, also called the liter, is the unit of volume.

STANDARD MASS. The fundamental unit of mass in the metric system is the quantity of matter present in a particular block of platinum-iridium alloy called the *standard kilogram* (1,000 grams). This standard kilogram of mass is kept at the Inter-

TABLE 2-2 RELATIVE ABUNDANCE OF ELEMENTS IN EARTH'S CRUST

Element	Percentage
Oxygen	46.12
Silicon	25.75
Aluminum	7.51
Iron	4.70
Calcium	3.39
Sodium	2.64
Potassium	2.40
Magnesium	1.94
Chlorine	1.88
Hydrogen	0.88
Titanium	0.58
Phosphorus	0.120
Carbon	0.087

national Bureau of Weights and Measures at Sèvres, France, and an accurate duplicate is kept at the International Bureau of Standards at Washington, D.C. The objects of known mass used on a balance, and known simply as *weights*, are assigned mass values relative to the standard kilogram.

The total mass is one extensive property of matter that undergoes no *measurable* change during chemical reactions. This principle is expressed in the *Law of Conservation of Mass,** which states: *During chemical reactions there is no detectable loss or gain in total mass (weight).* In other words, in a chemical change the total mass of the reactants always equals the total mass of the products. Clearly, then, the measurement of mass is an essential operation in chemistry.

MEASUREMENT OF LENGTH AND VOLUME. The fundamental unit of *length* in the metric system is the wave length of orange-red light emitted by electrically excited krypton-86. (This is similar to the red light emitted by electrically excited neon in the familiar "neon sign.") The wave length of the light emitted by krypton-86 is very small —one inch is equivalent to 41,929,399 wave lengths. The meter, which was the earlier fundamental unit of length of the metric system, is equivalent to 1,650,763.73 wave lengths of the krypton-86 standard. Related units of length are the kilometer (1,000 meters; about 0.62 mile), the decimeter (1/10 of a meter), the centimeter (1/100 of a meter), and the millimeter (1/1,000 of a meter). In measuring area, we use such units as *square* meters, *square* centimeters, and so forth. In measuring volume, we use *cubic* meters, *cubic* decimeters, and *cubic* centimeters. The liter has been recently accepted as a special name for the volume occupied by one cubic decimeter. Thus 1 liter (1 l.) = 1 cubic decimeter (1 dm^3) = 1,000 cubic centimeters (1,000 cm^3 or 1,000 cc).

DENSITY. Density is a property of matter that relates to each other the mass and the volume of a piece of that matter. The density of an object is defined as the *mass per unit of volume.* Density may be expressed in any combination of units of mass and units of volume—for example, grams per cm^3 (cubic centimeter), or pounds per ft^3 (cubic foot). Since density is constant for all samples of the same substance under fixed conditions, it is an *intensive* property of matter.

2-4 Energy and Its Classification

LAW OF CONSERVATION OF ENERGY

Energy, like mass, is indestructible. The *Law of Conservation of Energy* states: *Energy may be changed from one form to another, but it cannot be created or destroyed.*

KINETIC ENERGY

The term "kinetic" comes from a Greek word meaning motion, and kinetic energy is the form of energy possessed by matter that is in motion. For example, flowing water is capable of doing work because of the energy associated with

* Both the *Law of Conservation of Mass* and the *Law of Conservation of Energy* (discussed in section 2-4) are of general validity in ordinary phenomena. However, mass and energy are actually interconvertible, although only in very special cases.

its motion. Kinetic energy or "motion energy," is acquired when a body at rest is put into motion; the quantity of kinetic energy is increased when the rate of motion of a body is increased. The kinetic energy (K.E.) of a moving body is defined as one-half the mass (m) of the body multiplied by the square of the velocity (v^2) of the body: K.E. $= \frac{1}{2}mv^2$.

Notice that kinetic energy depends on two properties of the moving body: (1) its mass, and (2) its velocity. Both factors contribute to the total kinetic energy. If two bodies are moving at the same velocity, then the one with the larger mass has the greater kinetic energy. A baseball possesses greater kinetic energy than a tennis ball moving at the same speed. Similarly, if two bodies have the same mass but move at different velocities, the object that moves faster has more kinetic energy. A rapidly moving baseball has greater kinetic energy than one that is moving slowly.

CAPACITY AND INTENSITY FACTORS. There are other forms of energy, in addition to kinetic energy that also are determined by two factors—the capacity factor and the intensity factor. In kinetic energy, the capacity factor is the mass and the intensity factor is the square of the velocity. Regardless of what form of energy we are considering, the capacity factor always depends on the *quantity* of matter involved. The intensity factor, however, is independent of the quantity of matter but does depend on the particular kind of energy considered.

CHEMICAL ENERGY

Chemical energy is a form of potential energy which depends on the ability of substances to undergo chemical change, thereby releasing energy in other forms. A familiar example is the potential chemical energy in coal and oxygen. When coal is heated in the presence of air, a chemical reaction occurs and stored (potential) energy is released in the form of heat and light. Much of the energy consumed in our everyday living originates from the chemical energy present in coal (and oxygen). For example, in many electrical generating stations, coal is burned and chemical energy is converted to heat energy, which is then used to convert water to high-pressure steam. The energy in the steam is next converted into kinetic energy in electrical generators. This kinetic energy is then converted into electrical energy, which can be transmitted long distances and converted into other forms of energy, such as heat, light, motion, and sound. Similarly, substances in a storage battery possess chemical energy that can be converted into electrical energy, heat energy, light energy, sound energy, or kinetic energy.

HEAT ENERGY

All other forms of energy can be readily converted into heat energy. When a moving object comes to rest, it may give up its kinetic energy through friction, and the energy that is "lost" through friction appears as heat energy. Chemical energy, too, in which we are particularly interested, usually is released as heat energy, an example being coal burning in air, a process we have just described. In fact, in describing chemical changes, we usually state the amount of heat energy that has been released or absorbed.

TEMPERATURE. Temperature expresses the intensity factor of heat energy. Temperature is an intensive property; it does not depend on the total mass of the object whose temperature we are measuring. In everyday life we use the terms "hot" and "cold" as a rough measure of this intensity factor. An object feels hot to the touch, for example, when its heat intensity is greater than the heat intensity of our hand. Similarly, an object feels cold when its heat intensity is less than the heat intensity of our hand.

Temperature is a measure of the vigor of the motion of the molecular particles in a substance and serves as a means of determining the direction in which heat energy will flow when two objects come into contact. If two objects have the same intensity of heat energy, they are at the same temperature and there is no transfer of heat energy from one to the other. But if the temperature of one object is higher than the temperature of another object, heat energy is transferred from the warmer object to the cooler one.

MEASURING TEMPERATURE. When we want to measure the temperature of an object, we usually bring it into contact with a measuring instrument called a thermometer and maintain the contact until the temperature of each is the same. By revealing its own temperature, the thermometer indicates the temperature of the object. Many different properties that vary regularly with temperature can be used as the basis for a thermometer, but the two most frequently used are the volume of a liquid and the electrical resistance of a metal.

THE CELSIUS TEMPERATURE SCALE. A mercury-column thermometer consists of a length of uniform fine-bore glass tubing attached to a bulb or reservoir (Fig. 2-1). This reservoir, *R*, and part of the fine-bore tubing, are filled with mercury, which appears in the illustration as a visible thread, *m*. As the temperature of the mercury in the reservoir changes, the mercury expands or contracts, and the mercury rises or falls. Thus, the rise or fall of the mercury thread indicates the temperature change.

The part of the fine-bore tubing above the mercury level contains a (Torricellian) vacuum (see Chapter 8). In order to read the temperature, we must translate the level of the mercury into numerical values, using some standard reference as a basis of comparison. Actually, for thermometers similar to the one illustrated in Fig. 2-1 we use two reference standards for the Celsius scale of temperature: (1) the freezing point of water, and (2) the boiling point of water, at normal atmospheric pressure. The freezing point of water in the presence of 1 atmosphere (1 atm) pressure of air is arbitrarily set at zero degrees Celsius: 0°C. The boiling point, under a pressure of one atmosphere (76 cm of mercury), is exactly 100 degrees Celsius: 100°C.

When the mercury in the bulb of the thermometer is at the same temperature as a mixture of ice and water (the freezing point of water), the height of the mercury corresponds to a temperature reading of 0°C, and the column is marked 0 at this point. When the mercury in the bulb of the thermometer is at the same temperature as water boiling at normal atmospheric pressure, the level of the mercury in the column is higher and corresponds to a temperature reading of 100°C; the column is marked exactly 100 at this point. The distance between these two marked positions of the mercury column is divided into 100 equal degrees and marked from 0 to 100. Lengths of the column above 100°C and below 0°C are also marked off, using degrees of the same size. This process of marking off the column is called *calibration*.

FIGURE 2-1 A Celsius thermometer.

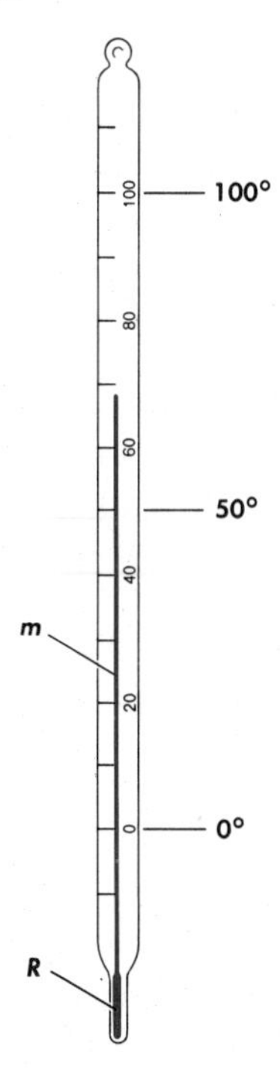

HEAT CAPACITY. The capacity factor of heat energy is represented by the quantity of heat needed to cause a definite increase in temperature for a definite quantity of material and is generally called *heat capacity*. Heat capacity is an extensive property. For example, if a certain quantity of heat energy is required to raise the temperature of 1 gram (g) of a material 1°C, exactly twice that amount of heat energy will be required to raise by 1°C the temperature of 2 g of the material.

The quantity of heat energy required to raise the temperature of 1 g of water from 14.5°C to 15.5°C is taken as the standard of heat quantity and is called a *calorie* (cal). Since almost the same quantity of heat, 1 cal, is needed to bring about a 1°C rise at other temperatures as long as water is liquid, we can say that the heat capacity of water is 1 cal per gram per degree (1 cal/g × deg). The number of calories required to raise the temperature of 1 g of any substance 1°C is called the *specific heat capacity* of the substance. The specific heat capacity of water is, by definition, 1, but the values for other substances are different. For metals, for example, the values range from a low of about 0.03 to a high of about 0.3 cal per gram per degree (0.3 cal/g × deg).

THE MEASUREMENT OF HEAT ENERGY. The heat absorbed or given off by a given mass of water surrounding another substance may be used to measure the quantity of heat energy given off or absorbed by the substance. If the substance is originally at a higher temperature than the surrounding mass of water, some heat energy will be given off by the substance and absorbed by the water until both have the same temperature. The change in temperature of the given mass of water is then a direct measure of the heat energy lost by the substance. In fact, the number of calories given off by the substance which is equal to the number of calories gained by the water, is obtained by multiplying the mass of water (in grams) by the increase in temperature (in degrees) of the water, since the specific heat capacity of water is 1 calorie per gram per degree (1 cal/g × deg). For example, if the temperature of the surrounding water (2000 g) increases from 20.0°C to 20.2°C, the number of calories given up by the substance is 2000 g × (20.2 − 20.0) deg × 1 cal/g × deg = 400 cal.

Similarly we can measure the heat energy released in a chemical reaction by arranging conditions so that the heat of the reaction will be absorbed by a known mass of water. The increase in the temperature of the water, multiplied by the mass of the water, then gives us the number of calories released in the chemical reaction.

THE RELATION BETWEEN MASS AND ENERGY

Any appearance of energy is accompanied by the disappearance of a small amount of matter. The relationship between the mass of the matter lost and the energy that is released is given by the equation: $E = mc^2$, where E is the energy, m is the mass, and c is the velocity of light. This relationship between mass and energy was first proposed in 1906 by the famous physicist and mathematician, Albert Einstein.

Apparently, energy and mass are equivalent and are different forms of the same thing. The Law of Conservation of Mass and the Law of Conservation of Energy must be combined, then, into one general law, called the *Law of Conservation of Mass-Energy*. This law states *that mass and energy may be converted from one to the other, but there is never any net loss of total mass-energy*. In other words, mass-energy is never created or destroyed. We are not usually concerned with this mass-energy interconversion, however, because in ordinary chemical reactions the quantities of energies involved are not large enough to correspond to detectable mass changes. However, in nuclear reactions such as those involving the disintegration of elements, enormous quantities of energy are given off and the resulting mass changes are detectable. A nuclear reactor and the explosion of an atomic bomb are examples of such nuclear changes. Since we are not usually concerned with mass-energy interconversion, we refer frequently to the *Law of Conservation of Mass-Energy* simply as the *Law of Conservation of Mass*.

2-5 Scientific Notation

In chemistry we often have to use very large and very small numbers. For example, we would have to use an enormously large number to express the number of atoms present in 1 g of iron. This number would actually be 108 followed by twenty zeros: 10,800,000,000,000,000,000,000. So we would have to use an extremely small number to express the weight in grams of one atom of iron; this number would be a decimal point followed by twenty-three zeros and then the number 926; that is: 0.000,000,000,000,000,000,000,009,26 g. To write out such numbers is very inconvenient. So mathematicians have worked out a shorthand method of expressing very large and very small numbers, called scientific notation. Expressed in scientific notation, the weight of 1 g of iron is 9.26×10^{-24} g, and the number of atoms in 1 g of iron is 1.08×10^{22}. A discussion of scientific notation can be found in Appendix 2-1.

Exercises

2-1 Define chemistry.

2-2 Define (a) matter, and (b) energy. (c) Make a distinction between matter and energy.

2-3 (a) List some of the *intensive properties* of any convenient object. (b) List some of its *extensive properties*.

2-4 Why is it desirable to know the *properties* of matter?

2-5 What is the process involved in the identification of any object?

2-6 Why is it desirable to know the *composition* of matter?

2-7 What possible utility would be lost if the properties but not the composition of a particular form of matter were known?

2-8 (a) Define chemical change. (b) Give three examples of chemical changes and three examples of non-chemical changes.

2-9 State clearly what you would observe in the way of change of properties when a chemical change occurs. Give several examples.

2-10 On what basis is a sample of matter classified as a pure substance or a mixture? Give three examples of pure substances and mixtures.

2-11 A sample of material is examined as closely as possible and appears to be the same throughout. What conclusion can you draw with respect to identifying the material as a pure substance or mixture?

2-12 State clearly in your own words how a pure substance is classified as an element or as a compound.

2-13 A 1-g sample of a pure substance is heated in the open air for 10 minutes and then reweighed. If the weight is unchanged and the properties are unchanged, what can be said about the substance being an element or a compound? Discuss.

2-14 A white crystalline substance is heated in an evacuated tube. If it is changed on heating to a black solid and a brownish liquid, is it an element or a compound? Why?

2-15 When 5 g of substance *A* is mixed with 10 g of substance *B* and heated in a sealed evacuated tube until chemical change occurs, as evidenced by a change in properties, what will be the mass of the resulting mixture? Why?

2-16 Without referring to the text, (a) how many elements have been discovered? (b) List the following elements in decreasing order of abundance: iron, aluminum, copper, magnesium, oxygen, silicon, phosphorus.

2-17 Compare the number of known elements with the number of possible compounds and the number of possible mixtures.

2-18 Explain the meaning of the statement, "The most fundamental property of matter is its mass."

2-19 Upon what kind of experimental evidence is the Law of the Conservation of Mass based?

2-20 Describe the relationship between mass and weight.

2-21 Explain the meaning of the term "standard mass."

2-22 What is the present international scientific standard of volume?

2-23 State two different sets of units in which density may be expressed.

2-24 Explain the difference between kinetic and potential energy.

2-25 List seven different varieties of energy.

2-26 Explain the meaning of the intensity factor and the capacity factor in heat energy.

2-27 If object *A* has a higher temperature than object *B* and they are brought into contact, can you be sure which way heat energy would flow? Discuss.

FUNDAMENTALS OF ATOMIC THEORY

3

In the preceding chapter we discussed the classification and measurement of matter and energy. We found that any sample of matter can be classified as a mixture, a substance, an element, or a compound on the basis of certain observable properties. If we wish to observe these properties, we need a sample of material that is large enough to be handled and measured. In other words, the observed properties and the classification of matter are concerned with *measurable quantities* of matter, and are quite independent of our knowledge about the ultimate constitution of matter. And yet the ultimate composition of matter is very important in chemistry. If we are to understand why matter behaves as it does, we must first understand the nature of the smallest particles of which matter is composed. So we turn now to some of the ideas concerning the ultimate structure of matter that have proved important in the development of chemistry.

3-1 Early Ideas on the Ultimate Structure of Matter

As early as 400 B.C., scholars began to speculate on the nature of matter. First the great Greek philosophers, Demokritos (468–370 B.C.), and Plato (427–347 B.C.), a pupil of Socrates, then Lucretius, a Roman (96–11 B.C.), and a host of others, conceived ideas about the fundamental structure of matter. These early thinkers speculated on the idea that matter was made up of extremely small particles, which, when combined in a piece of matter, gave it its characteristic properties. They reasoned that if they were able to subdivide any sample of matter into smaller and smaller pieces, they would ultimately come to a particle so small that further division would be impossible. Out of these speculations there arose a theory that matter was ultimately composed of small, indivisible particles, which were called atoms. The word "atom" is from a Greek word meaning indivisible. According to this early atomic theory, matter was discontinuous—that is, it was composed of small, separate particles. But not all the early thinkers accepted this atomic theory of matter. Some thought matter could be described better in terms of a continuous material.

All these early philosophers—both those who supported the atomic theory of matter and those who opposed it—arrived at their opinions through careful reasoning but had very limited factual knowledge with which to test their conclusions. It was not until 1620, when Francis Bacon (1561–1626) proposed a new way of investigating scientific problems based on the observation and collection of facts, that scientific investigators began to make important contributions to man's understanding of the world about him.

We judge an idea such as the atomic theory of matter on the basis of whether it generates conclusions which agree with experimental observations. In chemistry our main concern is whether a theory is *useful.* Does it help to correlate experimental facts and to predict the behavior of matter? Actually, once the atomic theory was adapted to scientific needs, it proved to be extremely useful in the development of chemistry. In fact, the whole of modern chemistry is based entirely on the atomic theory of matter.

3-2 Hypothesis, Theory, and Law

We have used the term "theory" in speaking of the ideas that were proposed to explain the ultimate nature of matter. Two other terms, "hypothesis" and "law," are also used to describe ideas intended to explain the behavior of matter. A *hypothesis* is an idea proposed to explain, or at least to correlate, a number of experimental facts. A hypothesis can first be accepted for the sake of testing its soundness and of uncovering new evidence. If the hypothesis is confirmed by a limited quantity of data, or if no data are found that definitely contradict it, then it becomes widely accepted. A *theory* is a more or less plausible and scientifically acceptable general principle offered to explain a rather wide range of experimental facts. When a set of facts can be formulated as a concise mathematical expression, so that the values calculated from this expression agree with the experimentally determined values, then we have a *law.* A law, then is a concise statement of fact, which is known to be true and which covers a wide range of facts.

Here is an example of the use of these terms. In 1811 the Italian scientist Amadeo Avogadro (1776–1856), Professor of Physics at the University of Turin, Italy, suggested that the number of molecules present in a given volume of any one gas would be exactly the same as the number of molecules present in an equal volume of any other gas, if the temperature and pressure of both gas samples were the same (see p. 126). This idea was known as *Avogadro's hypothesis.* At the time, the distinction between atoms and molecules was not clearly understood, so it was impossible to estimate the worth of Avogadro's hypothesis, and consequently the idea was not generally accepted for almost 50 years. Then, as the distinction between atoms and molecules became clear, Avogadro's idea proved able to account for and predict certain chemical facts. Today, the idea has been so well confirmed by experiments that it stands almost unquestioned, and chemists refer to it as *Avogadro's Law.*

3-3 Some Chemical Laws

Robert Boyle (1627–1691), an English scientist and philosopher who is perhaps better known for the law that bears his name (see p. 120), was the first to ascribe to the word "element" its modern meaning. But it was not until the end of the eighteenth century that chemists succeeded in identifying certain substances as elements and others as compounds, and began to establish experimentally various laws concerning the composition of matter and chemical reactions.

There are several laws that govern the composition of matter. The most fundamental of these is the *Law of Conservation of Mass-Energy,* already discussed. Acceptance of this statement as a law means that no deviations from this mass-energy balance are to be anticipated. In addition, there are two other fundamental laws concerning composition—the *Law of Constant Composition* and the *Law of Multiple Proportions.*

The Law of Constant Composition states that *the proportion by weight of the elements present in any pure compound is always the same.* In other words, once we have determined the composition of a pure substance, we know that the composition of all other pure specimens of the same substance will be the same. If, for example, we find that a sample of pure salt (sodium chloride) contains 39.34 per cent sodium and 60.66 per cent chlorine, we can rest assured that all pure samples of sodium chloride will contain exactly the same percentages of these elements.

A third fundamental law of composition concerns any series of compounds in which the same two elements combine in different proportions to form two or more different compounds. Thus from the same elements it is possible in many cases to derive more than one product. The *Law of Multiple Proportions* may be stated as follows: *Whenever the same two elements combine to form more than one compound, the weights of one element which combine with a fixed weight of the other are simple multiples of one another.* For example, copper and chlorine can combine in different proportions to produce two different compounds with different properties. And yet each compound contains only copper and chlorine. What is the relationship between the proportions of copper and chlorine present in these two different compounds? Experiments have shown that the weight of chlorine that combines with 1 g of copper to form the first of these two compounds is exactly *twice* the weight of chlorine that combines with 1 g of copper to form the second compound. In other words, the weights of chlorine that combine with the same weight of copper are in the ratio of 2 to 1. The formulas of the two chemical compounds containing the elements copper and chlorine are $CuCl_2$ and CuCl. These formulas, as we shall see, indicate that for the same weight of copper, the compound $CuCl_2$ contains twice the weight of chlorine that is present in the compound CuCl.

The elements nitrogen and oxygen react to form a series of compounds. Table 3-1 lists five oxides of nitrogen, which furnish an excellent illustration of the *Law of Multiple Proportions.*

But chemists are never satisfied with simply observing general laws such as the Law of Constant Composition and the Law of Multiple Proportions. Instead, they set about searching for some explanation of *why* matter "obeys" these laws of combination. In the early nineteenth century, John Dalton offered as an explanation of these laws of composition a scientific adaptation of the atomic theory that had been proposed long before. Dalton was for most of his early life a school teacher who had very little formal education, and yet his atomic theory made a great contribution to the understanding and progress of chemistry. Dalton's modified atomic theory, which was the first accepted chemical atomic theory, is summarized in the following section.

TABLE 3-1 EXAMPLES OF THE LAW OF MULTIPLE PROPORTIONS

Formula of Compound	Grams of Oxygen Combined with 1 g of Nitrogen	Ratio to 0.57
N_2O	0.57	0.57/0.57 = 1.00:1
NO	1.14	1.14/0.57 = 2.00:1
N_2O_3	1.71	1.71/0.57 = 3.00:1
NO_2	2.28	2.28/0.57 = 4.00:1
N_2O_5	2.85	2.85/0.57 = 5.00:1

3-4 Dalton's Atomic Theory

1. Elements are composed of extremely small, indivisible particles called atoms. Atoms retain their identity through all chemical changes.

2. Atoms of a particular element have the same average mass, and their other properties are also the same. Atoms of different elements generally have different average masses and different properties.

3. Compounds are formed by combinations of the atoms of different elements.

4. Atoms of two or more elements may combine in more than one ratio to form more than one compound.

Dalton's atomic theory proved completely satisfactory as an explanation of the three fundamental laws that had already been recognized:

EXPLANATION OF THE LAW OF CONSERVATION OF MASS

The indestructibility of atoms explained why all matter obeys the Law of Conservation of Mass. If chemical changes only rearrange atoms in various combinations, then, of course, the total mass of the material involved in these chemical transformations must remain unchanged.

EXPLANATION OF THE LAW OF CONSTANT COMPOSITION

The atomic theory was also consistent with the Law of Constant Composition. If compounds are formed by the combination of definite numbers of atoms of different elements, and if each atom has it own characteristic mass, the relative mass of each component in the compound must always be the same. Thus, in every pure sample of the same compound, the elements must always be present in the same proportions by mass.

EXPLANATION OF THE LAW OF MULTIPLE PROPORTIONS

The Law of Multiple Proportions is also understandable in the light of Dalton's atomic theory. If, in one compound, one atom of an element A is combined with one atom of the element B, and, in another compound, one atom of A is combined with two atoms of B, the masses of B that are combined with a fixed mass of A in the two compounds would be in the ratio of 1 to 2. The ability of one atom of an element to combine with one atom of another element to form a compound, or with two or more atoms to form other compounds, explains the Law of Multiple Proportions.

DEVELOPMENTS RESULTING FROM DALTON'S ATOMIC THEORY

As a result of Dalton's atomic theory, chemists were stimulated to work out explanations of other observed facts and to undertake rewarding new investigations. Soon they discovered the mass of an atom was one of its most fundamental properties. And because atomic mass (which chemists usually call atomic "weight") provided the best quantitative means of distinguishing between the atoms of different elements, chemists concentrated on working out accurate values for the *relative weights* of various atoms. They still had not devised an experimental method for determining actual atomic weights. Nevertheless, chemists worked out simple experimental procedures for determining what *weight* of one element would combine with a certain *weight* of another element. And these weights came to be known as equivalent, or combining, weights.

EQUIVALENT, OR COMBINING WEIGHTS

The weight of a given element that reacts with a fixed weight of another element can be determined by fairly simple laboratory experiments. *The combining weight, or the equivalent weight, of an element is the weight of that element that will combine with or displace 8.00 g of oxygen or 1.008 g of hydrogen.* Combining weights were carefully determined for a large number of elements, and it was found that many elements have more than one equivalent weight.

Since most elements "could be made to" react with oxygen or to liberate hydrogen, these two elements were taken as convenient standards of comparison for equivalent weights.

ATOMIC WEIGHTS

Working with these combining (equivalent) weights of the elements, and, later, with a knowledge of the number of atoms involved in each combination, chemists were able to work out exact relative weights for the atoms of various elements. These relative weights of the atoms are known as atomic weights.

The use of relative weights means that some reference value has to be selected as a basis of comparison. The standard is the stable isotope of carbon, ^{12}C, with an assigned value of 12. On this basis the atomic weight of an element is defined as *the weight of one atom of the element compared with the weight of one atom of (the isotope of) carbon, ^{12}C, exactly 12.* Thus, one atom of hydrogen which weighs approximately $\frac{1}{12}$ the weight of one atom of carbon (12), has an atomic weight of 1 ($\frac{1}{12} \times 12 = 1$). And one magnesium atom (^{24}Mg) that weighs twice as much as one carbon atom has an atomic weight of 24 ($2 \times 12 = 24$).

3-5 Modern Atomic Theory

Dalton's atomic theory assumed that the atoms of elements were indivisible and that no particles smaller than atoms existed. But, as in many theories in physical science, new experimental facts led to modifications, refinements, and extensions of Dalton's theory, which paved the way to our present modern atomic theory. And now we shall briefly discuss some fundamental particles now known to be present in an atom.

ELECTRONS

In the latter half of the nineteenth century, extensive studies were made of the rays that were found to pass from a negatively charged filament (cathode) through a vacuum to a positively charged plate (anode). The work was begun in Germany by Julius Plucker, Walter Kaufmann, and Emil Wiechert. In England, about 1886, Sir William Crookes designed a tube in which these rays

FIGURE 3-1 The formation of cathode rays.

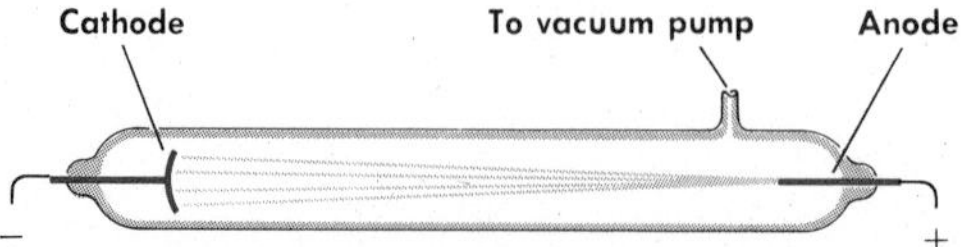

could be conveniently studied; and shortly thereafter it was shown that these rays, called cathode rays (see Fig. 3-1), consisted of negatively charged particles. In 1897, Sir J. J. Thomson (1856–1940), Professor of Physics at Cambridge, showed that these rays also had mass and hence that they consisted of negatively charged particles of very small mass. We now know these particles as *electrons*. It was also found that electrons could be obtained from many *elements*. Therefore it was concluded that these very small, negatively charged particles are present in the atoms of all elements. If negatively charged particles are present in an atom, positively charged particles must also be present, for all atoms are electrically neutral. Thus, the fundamental electrical character of the atom was first suggested by the study of cathode rays. The charge of an electron is conventionally assigned a value of -1, and its mass is approximately $\frac{1}{1840}$ the mass of a hydrogen atom or approximately $1/(1840 \times 12)$ of the mass of the carbon atom.

POSITIVELY CHARGED PARTICLES

The predicted presence of positively charged particles in atoms was confirmed in 1896 when Antoine Henri Becquerel, a French scientist, made the first studies of radioactivity. Becquerel (1852–1908), like his grandfather and his father, was Professor of Physics at the Musée d' Histoire Naturelle in Paris. He shared the Nobel Prize with Pierre and Marie Curie in 1903 for his work on the properties of uranium. Becquerel noticed that certain elements (notably uranium) spontaneously gave off positively charged particles, which he called alpha particles, and negatively charged particles (electrons), which he called beta particles. In addition, Becquerel observed in his study of these radioactive substances radiation that had neither mass nor electrical charge. Later on other investigators, by the dissociation and ionization of hydrogen gas under low pressure, discovered particles with a mass of 1 and a charge of $+1$. These particles were called *protons*.

THE ARRANGEMENT OF PARTICLES IN ATOMS

The general arrangement of the particles present in atoms was suggested by experiments performed by Ernest Rutherford (1871–1937) when he was Professor of Physics at Manchester University, England. Rutherford's career illustrates that the natural sciences (physics and chemistry in this case) overlap to some extent. His brilliant research as a physicist won for him the Nobel Prize in chemistry in 1908 and has enabled chemists to learn a great deal about the structure of matter.

Rutherford's experimental results indicated that the positively charged particles were concentrated in a small volume of the atom, which contained most of the mass of the atom. This small, positively charged core was called the *nucleus*. Rutherford assumed that the particles called protons were present in the nucleus and were responsible for the positive charge the nucleus carried. He considered the negatively charged electrons to be spread throughout a relatively large volume surrounding the nucleus, usually referred to as an *electron cloud* (or a charge cloud).

It may seem difficult at first to visualize how one or more electrons can form an electron cloud around the nucleus of an atom, but perhaps the following analogy will help. A stationary airplane propeller is distinctly visible, but when spinning rapidly it appears as a "blurred disk." Now assume that one or more electrons are present in the volume *outlined* by an imaginary airplane propeller; if we set this imaginary propeller spinning rapidly, the electrons can no longer be seen distinctly, but appear as a hazy cloud. In an atom, the electron cloud is not uniformly distributed in the space around the nucleus because the electrons tend to congregate near the positively charged nucleus. We may summarize by saying that an atom behaves as if it consisted of a small, positively charged nucleus surrounded by a diffuse electron cloud, which decreases in density as the distance from the nucleus increases. A schematic representation of this picture of the atom is given in Fig. 3-2 for the helium atom. The nucleus, though exceedingly small in volume, contains most of the mass of the atom, whereas the electron cloud surrounding the nucleus constitutes most of the volume of the atom but has a negligible mass.

As we shall discuss in more detail (Ch. 13), the electron cloud of an atom does not end abruptly, that is, it is not confined by a sharp distinct boundary. However, since the electron cloud becomes less and less dense as we proceed away from the nucleus, for the purpose of representation in our diagrams we shall usually terminate the electron cloud at a spherical boundary surface enclosing the greatest part (say 90 per cent) of the electron cloud.

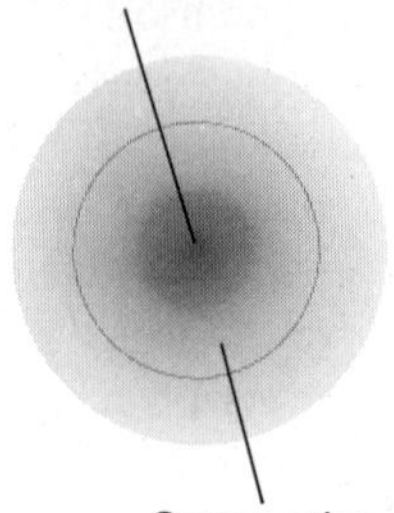

Nucleus (2 protons and 2 neutrons)

Outer portion (electron cloud, 2 electrons)

FIGURE 3-2 A schematic representation of an atom of helium $^4_2$He.

NEUTRONS

In 1932 another component of the nucleus was identified by an English physicist, Sir James Chadwick. This particle, the neutron, was electrically neutral, with a mass very nearly equal to the mass of a proton.*

ATOMIC STRUCTURE

Soon general features of atomic structure now became clear. Three components of the atom—the proton, the neutron, and the electron—had been identified, and their contributions to the mass and size of the atom were understood. The names, masses, and electrical charges of these three basic sub-atomic particles of matter are summarized in Table 3-2. The make-up of the nucleus differs from one element to another, and so do the number and arrangement of the electrons in the electron cloud.

TABLE 3-2 COMPONENTS OF THE ATOM

Name	Approx. Mass*	Electrical Charge
Electron	$\frac{1}{1840}$	−1
Proton	1	+1
Neutron	1	0

* Based on comparison with ^{12}C = 12.000.

The number of protons in the nucleus of an atom is known as the *atomic number*. The mass number of a given atom (an isotope) is the sum of the number of protons and neutrons present in the nucleus. The number of electrons in the electron cloud of an atom is equal to the number of protons in the nucleus. Schematic representations of the nuclei and the electron clouds for atoms of hydrogen, calcium, and cesium are given in Fig. 3-3. As will be explained later, the electron cloud tends to concentrate in regions at various distances from the nucleus.

There are precise numerical values for the atomic masses of the elements. A list of the elements with atomic numbers from 1 to 20, together with their symbols and atomic weights, is given in Table 3-3. (Symbols discussed in Ch. 4.) These 20 elements include the first three horizontal rows of the Periodic Table (Ch. 12).

MOLECULES AND MOLECULAR WEIGHT

Often two or more atoms come together and are held fast to one another by what we call chemical bonds. A group of chemically bonded atoms may form a structural unit called a *molecule*. The total weight of a group of combined

* The neutron, an elementary uncharged particle (having a mass nearly equal to that of a proton) is present in the nucleus of all known elements except the lightest isotope of hydrogen, ^{1}H.

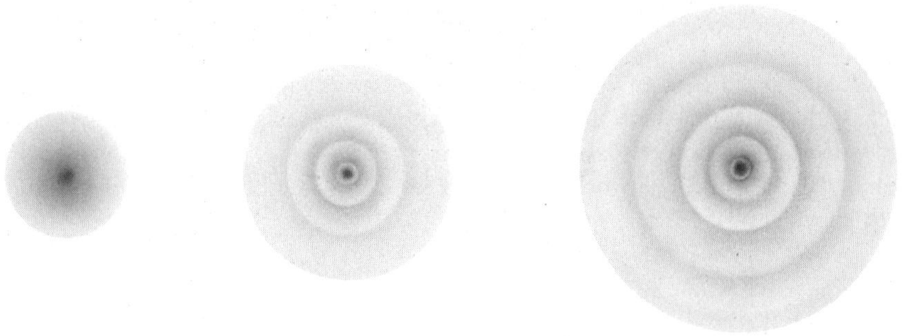

Hydrogen, $^{1}_{1}H$

Atomic mass 1
1 proton
1 electron

Calcium, $^{40}_{20}Ca$

Atomic mass 40
20 protons
20 electrons
20 neutrons

Cesium, $^{133}_{55}Cs$

Atomic mass 133
55 protons
55 electrons
78 neutrons

FIGURE 3-3 **Schematic representations of some atoms.**

atoms relative to the carbon atom (^{12}C isotope), which has a standard weight of exactly 12.000, is called its *molecular weight.* For example, if four atoms of hydrogen, each with an atomic weight of 1.008, are combined chemically with one atom of carbon, which has an atomic weight of 12.011, then one molecule of methane (CH_4), with a molecular weight of 16.043, is formed. Molecular weights vary from 2.016 for the lightest molecule—a molecule of hydrogen, H_2—to several hundred thousand for certain complex molecules.

CHANGES IN ATOMS DURING CHEMICAL REACTIONS

The electrons which surround the nucleus of an atom are arranged in such a way that only some of them—those in the outer parts of the electron cloud (valence electrons)—can interact with electrons of other atoms. (We shall look more closely at the arrangement of electrons in the atom in Chapter 12.) It is these outer electrons which are usually involved in chemical reactions. The number of valence electrons in an atom determines the ratio with which these atoms enter into chemical combination with one another. The electronic interactions leading to chemical reactions may be classified as two main types: (1) *the loss and gain of electrons,* and (2) *the sharing of electrons.*

TABLE 3-3 **SYMBOLS AND ATOMIC WEIGHTS OF THE FIRST TWENTY ELEMENTS**

Name	*Symbol*	*Atomic Weight*
Hydrogen	H	1.008
Helium	He	4.003
Lithium	Li	6.939
Beryllium	Be	9.012
Boron	B	10.811
Carbon	C	12.011
Nitrogen	N	14.007
Oxygen	O	15.999
Fluorine	F	18.998
Neon	Ne	20.183
Sodium	Na	22.990
Magnesium	Mg	24.312
Aluminum	Al	26.982
Silicon	Si	28.086
Phosphorus	P	30.974
Sulfur	S	32.066
Chlorine	Cl	35.453
Argon	Ar	39.948
Potassium	K	39.102
Calcium	Ca	40.080

IONIC COMPOUNDS

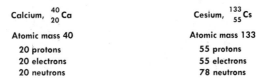

The loss and gain of electrons in a chemical reaction may be illustrated by the reaction between sodium and chlorine. Sodium metal is a silvery, soft, low-melting substance. Chlorine is a greenish, poisonous gas. And yet when these two elements come into contact, a chemical reaction occurs that produces a solid—sodium chloride. Sodium chloride is the harmless, stable compound that we know as ordinary table salt. The striking differences between the properties of sodium chloride and the properties of the elements of which it is composed are typical of the type of change that results from the interaction of electrons. The net reaction that occurs between solid sodium metal, $Na_{(solid)}$ and chlorine gas, $Cl_{2(gas)}$ to form the solid compound sodium chloride, $NaCl_{(solid)}$ is:

$$2\ Na_{(solid)} + Cl_{2(gas)} \longrightarrow 2\ NaCl_{(solid)}$$

We may imagine that sodium metal is first converted to individual sodium atoms, Na, and that the diatomic chlorine molecules are converted to individual chlorine atoms, Cl. What change can occur in the atoms of sodium and in the atoms of chlorine when they come into contact and how are the modified atoms held together to form sodium chloride? Experiments have established that sodium chloride is made up of positively charged sodium ions, Na^+, and negatively charged chloride ions, Cl^-. Hence we may conclude that the neutral sodium atom, Na, in the presence of a chlorine atom, Cl, gives up one electron, and the loss of this negatively charged particle upsets the electrical balance (neutrality) of the sodium atom. As a result, the neutral sodium atom, Na, becomes a *positively* charged particle, a sodium ion, Na^+. The neutral chlorine atom, Cl, takes on an electron. Again, the electrical balance of the atom is upset, but this time a *negatively* charged particle results, a chloride ion, Cl^-. Atoms that have lost or gained electrons and have thereby acquired an electric charge are called *ions.* The *loss* of electrons produces a *positive* ion, and the *gain* of electrons produces a *negative* ion. The electrical charge on an ion is indicated by the sign written as a right-hand superscript. The oppositely charged ions, Na^+ and Cl^-, attract each other with a strong force that gives the compound sodium chloride its stability. Positively charged sodium ions, Na^+, and negatively charged chloride ions, Cl^-, group themselves in a three-dimensional arrangement, creating an (ionic) crystal of sodium chloride.

Figure 3-4 shows schematically that when a neutral sodium atom, Na, gives up an electron it becomes a positive ion Na^+, with a charge of $+1$, because the sodium atom, Na, and the sodium ion, Na^+, each has the same number of protons, 11, but the sodium ion, Na^+, has one electron less. Notice, too, that the positive sodium ion, Na^+, is much smaller than the neutral sodium atom, Na. We shall explain the reason for this in a later chapter.

When the neutral chlorine atom, Cl, takes on one electron, it becomes a singly negatively charged (mononegative) chloride ion, Cl^-, because now it has one more negative electron than it has positive protons (Fig. 3-5). Figure 3-6 shows the reaction that takes place between the two atoms, Na and Cl, to form the ions, Na^+ and Cl^-. As we have stated, it is the electrostatic attraction between the oppositely charged Na^+ and Cl^- ions thus formed that makes the product of the reaction more stable than the reactants—neutral Na atom together with a neutral Cl atom. In fact, for an *assem-*

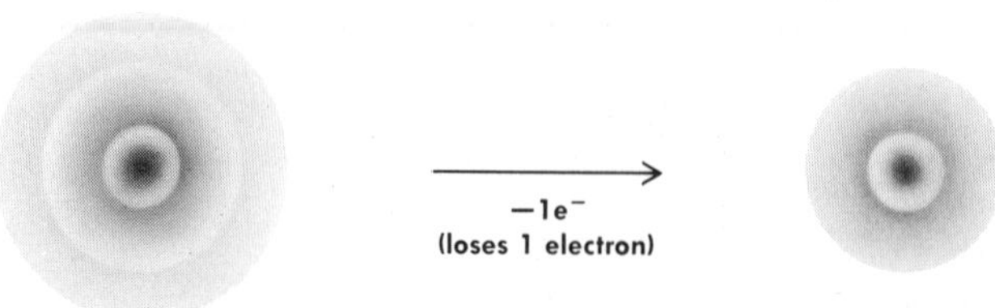

FIGURE 3-4 A schematic representation of the sodium atom, Na, and the sodium ion, Na^+.

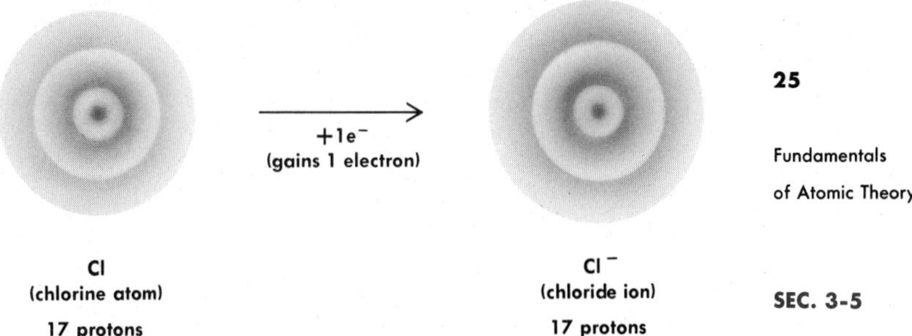

FIGURE 3-5 A schematic representation of the chlorine atom, Cl, and the chloride ion, Cl^-.

blage of Na^+ and Cl^- ions, this electrostatic attraction and thus the stability is greatest when the Na^+ ions and the Cl^- ions arrange themselves in the three-dimensional structure of crystalline sodium chloride. An *assemblage* of Na^+ ions and Cl^- ions in a crystal is very much more stable than a *collection* (equal number) of Na atoms and Cl atoms.

The ions Na^+ and Cl^- in solid sodium chloride are arranged according to a specific pattern; each ion is surrounded by six ions of opposite charge. This arrangement extends in three dimensions to produce a solid cubic structure, part of which is shown in Fig. 3-7. In this figure notice that the smaller (dark purple) sphere representing a positive sodium ion, Na^+, in the center of the cube, has six chloride ions, Cl^- (larger, light purple spheres), at equal distances from it. And each chloride ion, Cl^-, is equidistant from six sodium ions, Na^+. As a result of this arrangement, a continuous three-dimensional structure of positive ions and negative ions results.

Compounds that are made up of an assemblage of positive and negative ions, all held together by the attraction of their opposite electrical charges, are called *ionic compounds. A general characteristic of ionic compounds is that in the molten (liquid) state, or in solution, they are capable of conducting an electric current.* This electrical conduction depends on the movement of ions and cannot, therefore, occur unless ions are present.

Calcium oxide, $Ca^{++}O^{=}$, is another example of an ionic compound that results when one atom loses electrons to form a positive ion and another atom takes on the electrons to form a negative ion. This ionic compound consists of a three-dimensional network of calcium ions, Ca^{++}, formed from calcium atoms, Ca, that have lost two electrons each, and oxide ions, $O^{=}$, formed from oxygen atoms, O, that have gained two electrons each.

We see, then, that the formation of compounds may result from the *transfer* of one or more electrons from one atom to another. The compound formed is an *ionic compound* and the attraction arises from the opposite electrical charges.

But not all atoms yield or take on electrons readily to form ionic compounds.

FIGURE 3-6 The reaction between a sodium atom and a chlorine atom.

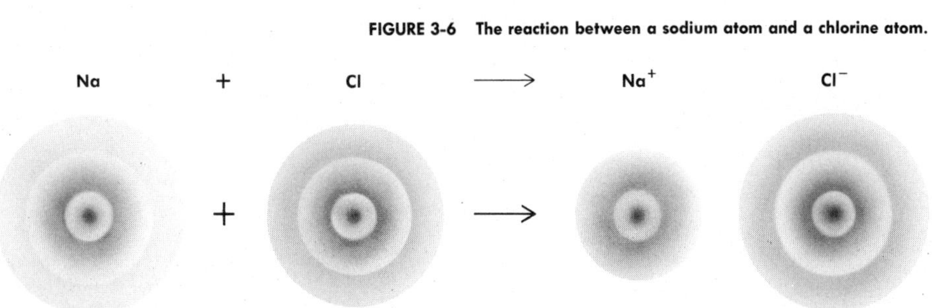

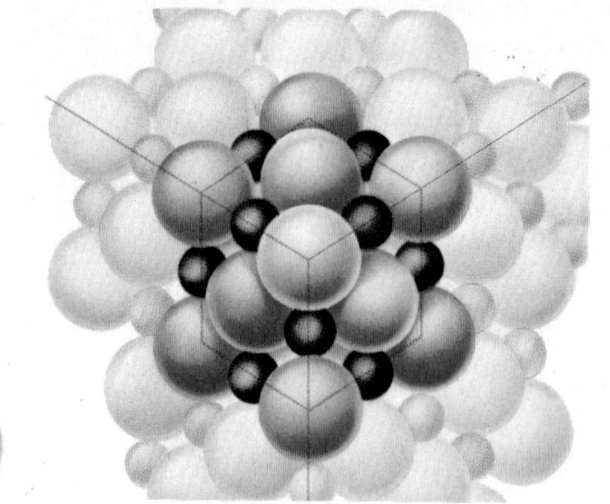

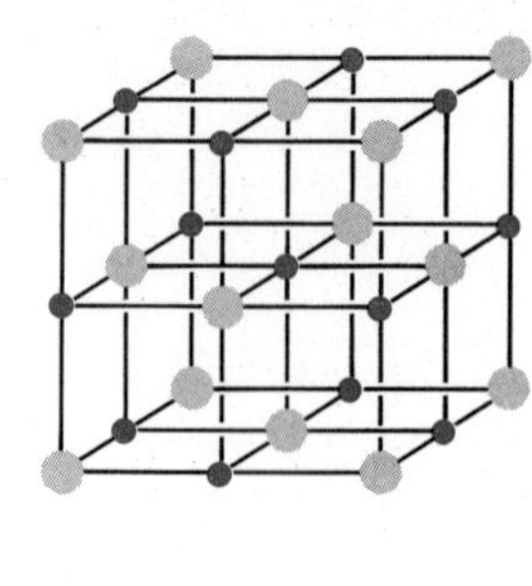

FIGURE 3-7 (Left) The arrangement of Na^+ ions and Cl^- ions in crystalline sodium chloride. (Right) schematic representation of the outlined cube.

Elements that can give up electrons with relatively little difficulty are called *electropositive elements;* these are the elements known as *metals.* Elements that do not easily yield electrons are known as *nonmetals.* If an element generally tends to take on electrons in compound formation, it is called *electronegative.*

COVALENT BONDING

Atoms can join together to form molecules of elements and molecules of compounds, however, even though they neither gain nor lose electrons, for two atoms can *share* electrons to form a compound. The molecule formed by a sharing of electrons is known as a *covalent molecule,* and the compound formed by a sharing of electrons is known as a *covalent compound.* In each case the bond between the bound atoms is known as a *covalent bond.* Covalent compounds do not conduct an electric current in the liquid state and do not therefore contain ions.

The hydrogen molecule, H_2, which is composed of two hydrogen atoms, is an example of a covalent molecule. In a molecule of hydrogen the electron clouds of each of the atoms of hydrogen overlap and hold the atoms together in chemical union, as illustrated in Fig. 3-8(a). Another example of a covalent molecule is chlorine, Cl_2, which is composed of two chlorine atoms. In a molecule of chlorine the outer electron clouds of each of the atoms overlap and hold the atoms together in chemical union, as illustrated in Fig. 3-8(b).

The best interpretation of this chemical bonding force is that the outermost electrons of each of the atoms are *shared* with the other atoms. *This sharing of electrons holds the molecule together.*

The compound hydrogen chloride gas, HCl, which is composed of hydrogen and chlorine, is an example of a covalent compound. In a molecule of hydrogen chloride the electron clouds of the hydrogen atom and the chlorine atom overlap and hold the atoms together in chemical union, as illustrated in Fig. 3-9(a). Another exam-

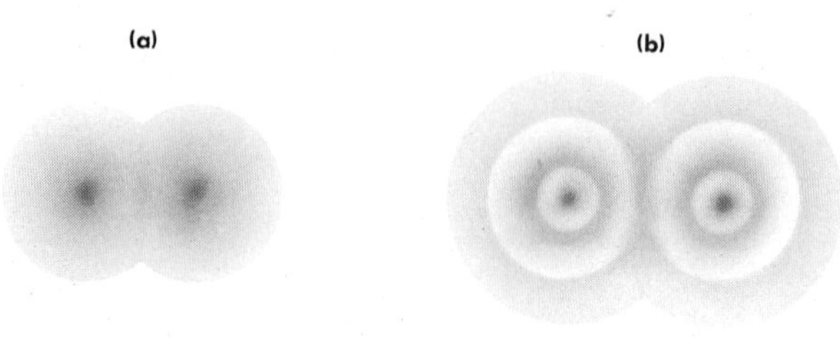

FIGURE 3-8 (a) The hydrogen molecule, H_2. (b) The chlorine molecule, Cl_2.

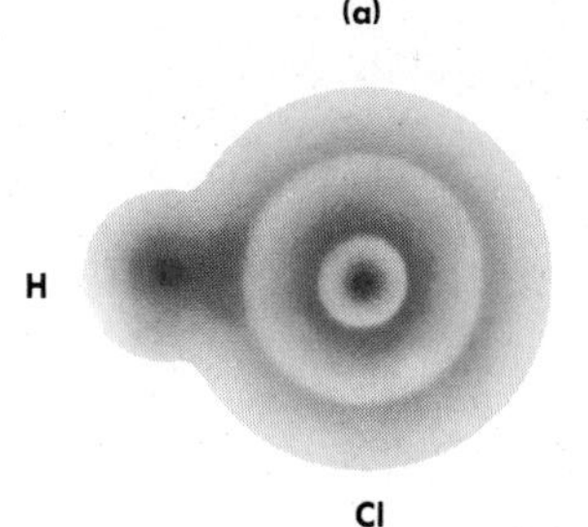

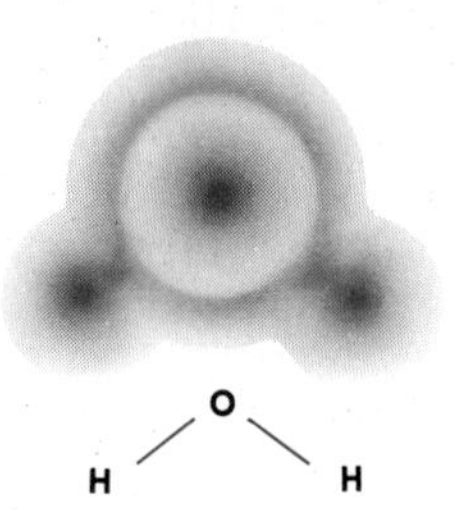

FIGURE 3-9 (a) The hydrogen chloride molecule, HCl. (b) The water molecule, H_2O.

ple of a covalent compound is water. A molecule of water, H_2O, contains two atoms of hydrogen and one atom of oxygen so strongly held together that considerable energy is required to decompose the molecule into its component elements. Since pure liquid water is not a very good conductor of electric current, apparently it does not contain appreciable numbers of ions. So we know that the atoms in the water molecule cannot be held together by ionic bonds, but are bonded covalently.

It is the sharing of electrons which binds together the atoms in the H_2O molecule. Figure 3-9(b) gives a simplified picture of the sharing of electrons between hydrogen and oxygen in the water molecule. The oxygen atom has two electrons available for covalent-bond formation, and the hydrogen atom has only one. Thus, one atom of oxygen can share its outermost electrons with two atoms of hydrogen. And in the water molecule, H_2O, the oxygen atom shares part of its electron cloud with the electron clouds of each of two hydrogen atoms.

In the hydrogen molecule, H_2, in the chlorine molecule, Cl_2, in the hydrogen chloride molecule, HCl, and in the water molecule, H_2O, the sharing of a pair of electrons constitutes the covalent bond between the atoms. To represent molecules held together by covalent bonds, we show the two shared electrons between the symbols of the chemically combined atoms, as in Fig. 3-10. In these formulas the symbols represent the core of the atoms (nucleus plus all electrons except the valence electrons); the dots represent the valence electrons.

In covalent molecules the electrons involved in the covalent bond surround both nuclei. The other electrons of each atom surround only their own nucleus. In the hydrogen molecule, however, the two shared electrons constitute the entire number of electrons in the system; there are no other electrons.

Although the concepts of ionic and covalent bonding are very important in the study of chemistry, few compounds fall sharply into one or the other of these two classes. Most bonds seem to be a blend of the two. We shall discuss this question at greater length in Chapter 14. Four useful statements to help you remember the nature of chemical bonds are:

1. Atoms of some elements usually react to form ionic compounds.
Examples: Na, K, Ca, e.g., in Na^+Cl^-, Na^+H^-, K^+F^-, $Ca^{++}O^=$

2. Atoms of other elements usually react to form covalent compounds.
Examples: H, C, N, e.g., in HCl, CO_2, NH_3

FIGURE 3-10 Sharing of a pair of electrons between atoms of molecules.

H:H	:C̤̈l:C̤̈l:	H:C̤̈l:	H:Ö: (with H below O)
H_2	Cl_2	HCl	H_2O

3. Some atoms may form either ionic or covalent compounds, depending on the properties of the atoms with which they combine.

Examples: Cl and H, e.g., in Na^+Cl^- and HCl, Na^+H^- and HCl

4. Some atoms combine with themselves to form metallic crystals (metallic bonds), see p. 180.

Examples: Cu (metal), Na (metal), zinc (metal).

3-6 Atomic Masses from Physical Measurements

We have already seen that the masses of the atoms of many elements were determined experimentally many years ago on the basis of combining, or equivalent, weights. More recently, atomic masses have been determined by direct measurements, particularly by an instrument called a mass spectrograph.

PRINCIPLE OF THE MASS SPECTROGRAPH

In the mass spectrograph, atoms are first converted into ions, which are then accelerated by electrical attraction to form a stream. This stream of ions is then deflected by means of electrical and magnetic fields. The degree by which an ion is deflected gives us a measure of its mass, and, consequently, also of the mass of the atom from which it was formed. The lighter the atom, the more its ion is deflected. The heavier the atom, the less its ion is deflected. By measuring precisely the degree to which the ions of various atoms are deflected under the same conditions, we can determine the relative masses of the atoms.

Here is a rough analogy to illustrate this principle: If several smooth balls of different weights but of approximately the same size are rolled at the same speed in a direction perpendicular to a strong wind, a lighter ball will be deflected much more than a heavier ball. This situation is illustrated in Fig. 3-11. By measuring the relative displacements of the three balls, we can calculate their relative weights.

The mass spectrograph operates on this same basic principle, with ions replacing the balls, and with a magnetic field replacing the wind. *Atomic weights of the elements can be determined directly by the use of this instrument.*

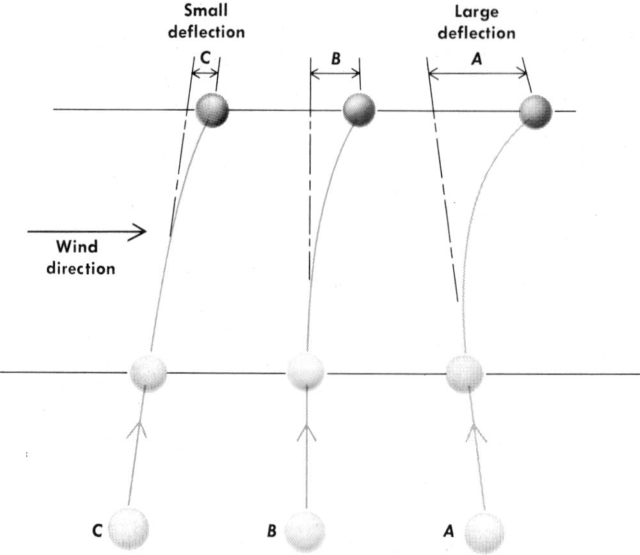

FIGURE 3-11 Principle of the mass spectrograph. Ball *A* has the least mass; ball *C*, the most, with ball *B*, intermediate. Note the differing magnitudes of deflection for each ball.

The modern mass spectrograph has been developed to a high degree of perfection. If a substance can be ionized at all, its mass can be determined by means of the mass spectrograph. Since this instrument also reveals the relative quantities of particles of different masses present in a given substance, it has become very useful in industry in analyzing complex mixtures of substances. The essential parts of a modern mass spectrograph are illustrated in Fig. 3-12.

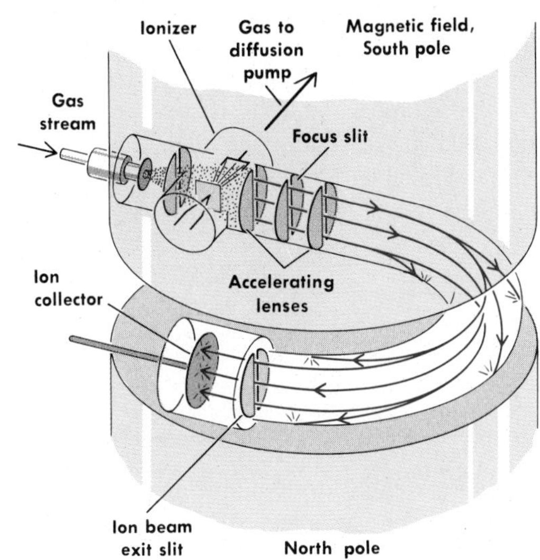

FIGURE 3-12 **A mass spectrograph.**

ISOTOPES

Many of the atomic weights determined by chemical methods are far from whole numbers, whereas others are quite close to whole numbers. The atomic weight of nitrogen, for example, is 14.0067, which is quite close to the whole number 14. The atomic weight of chlorine, on the other hand, is 35.453, about halfway between 35 and 36. Since the mass of an atom depends on the number of protons and neutrons in its nucleus, and since the mass of both the proton and the neutron is nearly 1, we would expect that the atomic weights of all elements would be close to whole numbers. Why is it, then, that the atomic weights of all the elements are not close to whole numbers? In 1919 F. W. Aston, an English physicist, found the answer to this question by determining the weights of individual atoms by physical measurements with the mass spectrograph. Aston discovered that some naturally occurring elements contain atoms that are identical chemically but have slightly different weights.

When atoms of any one of these elements were ionized and their deflections measured in the mass spectrograph, the beam of ions separated slightly into two or more paths. Since all the ions had the same electrical charge, apparently some had slightly different masses. Consequently, the atoms from which the ions were derived also had slightly different masses. Atoms of the same element with different masses are called *isotopes*. The isotopes of an element all have the same atomic number, because they have the same number of protons in their nucleus; but they have different atomic weights, because they have different numbers of neutrons in their nucleus. Other chemical evidence, based on the combining weights of elements from different mineral sources, also indicates the existence of isotopes. Isotopes have the same number of electrons in their electron clouds; chemical behavior depends primarily on electron cloud interactions. So the chemical properties of isotopes are almost identical. Since isotopes differ in their atomic weights, however, they have somewhat different physical properties.

Most but not all naturally occurring elements consist of a mixture of isotopes. And it is the existence of isotopes that explains why the atomic weight of many elements are far from whole numbers. An atomic weight determined by chemical methods gives the *average* weight of the atoms of the various isotopes present in an element as it occurs in nature. For example, chlorine as it occurs in nature consists of a mixture of isotopes of masses 35 and 37—75.53% of Cl 34.969, and 24.47% of Cl

36.966. And they are present in a proportion that gives chlorine an *average* atomic weight of 35.453.

Ordinarily, the weights of isotopes differ by only a few mass units from one another. The number of stable isotopes of a single element varies from two to as many as ten, although some elements exist as a single isotope.

The International Union of Pure and Applied Chemistry has decided that the carbon isotope, ^{12}C, shall be taken as the standard instead of (as was the case) either the *average* atomic weight of O = 16.0000 (standard of chemists) or isotope ^{16}O = 16.0000 (standard of physicists). The new standard is based on the value ^{12}C = 12.0000. The reason for the change is to make the atomic weight scale used by physicists identical with the scale used by chemists. However, the change to carbon as the standard changed the atomic weight values on the oxygen standard by only 4.3×10^{-3} per cent.

3-7 Absolute Weights of Atoms

So far, we have been talking only about the *relative* weights of the atoms of various elements, as compared with the weight 12 assigned to the C isotope 12. But these figures tell us nothing about the *actual,* or *absolute,* weight of a single atom of an element. A single atom of an element cannot be weighed directly, simply because it is too small. For example, a single atom of one of the isotopes of hydrogen would weigh only 1.67×10^{-24} g.

It would be a simple matter, however, to determine the absolute weight of one atom if we had some means of counting the number of atoms in a given weight of an element. If we could count the exact number of atoms in 1.008 g of hydrogen, for example, we could divide 1.008 by that number and come up with the weight, in grams, of one atom of hydrogen. Or if we could count the number of oxygen atoms in 16 g of oxygen, we could figure out the absolute weight of one atom of oxygen in grams. In fact, knowing the absolute weight of one atom of *any* element—carbon 12, for example—would enable us to calculate the absolute weights of all the other atoms, since we know the relative weights of other atoms compared with an atom of carbon 12.

Atoms are unimaginably small and it is impossible to see a single one even with the most powerful microscope. So we cannot count them directly. There are, however, certain indirect methods by which we can count the number of atoms in a known weight of an element, one, for example, being the diffraction of X rays by crystals. Since these methods are too complex to be presented at this stage, we must content ourselves simply with saying that an accurate count of atoms can be made experimentally.

AVOGADRO'S NUMBER

Through such indirect methods of counting, *the number of atoms in exactly 12 g of the carbon isotope,* ^{12}C, has been determined to be 6.02×10^{23}. This number is known as *Avogadro's Number.* The weight in grams of 6.02×10^{23} atoms of an element is called its *gram atomic weight* (g at wt). Thus, since 6.02×10^{23} atoms of carbon 12 weigh 12.0000 g, then 1 g at wt of carbon 12 is 12.0000 g. Since 6.02×10^{23} atoms of carbon weigh 12.0000 g, one atom of carbon 12 would weigh

$$\frac{12.0000 \text{ g}}{6.02 \times 10^{23} \text{ atoms}} = 1.99 \times 10^{-23} \frac{\text{g}}{1 \text{ atom}}$$

How could we calculate the weight of one atom of, say, magnesium? Each magnesium atom weighs twice as much as a carbon atom. Since the atomic weight of carbon is 12 and the atomic weight of magnesium is 24,* one atom of magnesium weighs $2.0 \times 1.99 \times 10^{-23}$ g $= 4.0 \times 10^{-23}$ g. Also, since 6.02×10^{23} atoms of carbon weigh 12 g, 6.02×10^{23} atoms of magnesium must weigh 24 g. Notice that 1 g at wt of carbon and 1 g at wt of magnesium each contain the same number of atoms, 6.02×10^{23}.

We can calculate the number of atoms in *any weight* of any element. For example, suppose we wanted to find out how many atoms of sulfur there are in 64 g of sulfur. We know that the relative, or atomic, weight of sulfur is 32, which means that 32 g of sulfur contain 6.02×10^{23} sulfur atoms. So in 64 g of sulfur there are twice as many atoms as in 32 g of sulfur—that is, $2 \times 6.02 \times 10^{23}$ atoms of sulfur. Each atom of sulfur weighs

$$\frac{32 \text{ g}}{6.02 \times 10^{23} \text{ atoms}} = 5.3 \times 10^{-23} \text{ g/atom}$$

Writing this number out will give some idea of how small it is: the weight in grams of one atom of sulfur is 0.000,000,000,000,000,000,000,053. For any element, the weight in grams of a single atom is equal to the atomic weight of the element divided by 6.02×10^{23}. Even an atom of the heaviest naturally occurring element, uranium, weighs only 0.000,000,000,000,000,000,000,39 g.

WEIGHT AND NUMBER OF ATOMS

The heavier an atom of an element is, the more the weight of 6.02×10^{23} atoms of that element. Also, the lighter an atom of an element is, the less the weight of 6.02×10^{23} atoms of that element. Therefore, the number of atoms in 1 g of a light element is greater than the number of atoms in 1 g of a heavy element. These relationships may be stated more exactly as follows:

1. *The weights of different elements that contain the* same number *of atoms are directly proportional to the atomic weights of the elements.*
2. *The number of atoms in* equal weights *of different elements is* inversely proportional to the atomic weights of the elements.

To summarize: *The number of atoms of any element present in 1 g at wt of the element is 6.02×10^{23} and is called Avogadro's Number.* The term "gram atomic weight" means the number of grams of an element that is numerically equal to its atomic weight. In other words, the gram atomic weight of any element always contains 6.02×10^{23} atoms. The atomic weight of nitrogen is 14.007; so 1 g at wt of nitrogen is 14.007 g, and this weight of nitrogen contains 6.02×10^{23} atoms.

THE MOLE

We have seen that 1 g at wt of an element contains one Avogadro's Number (6.02×10^{23}) of individual atoms of that element. For example, 1 g at wt (1.008 g) of hydrogen contains 6.02×10^{23} atoms of hydrogen. For convenience we speak of 6.02×10^{23} particles (of anything) as 1 mole (of that thing). Thus 1 mole of hydrogen atoms is 6.02×10^{23} individual atoms of hydrogen, H, and weighs 1.008 g.

In the same way, 1 mole (1 g at wt) (35.453 g) of the element chlorine is 6.02×10^{23} individual atoms of chlorine. We saw on page 26 that one atom of hydrogen, H, combines with one atom of chlorine, Cl, to form one molecule of the compound hydrogen chloride, HCl. Therefore, 6.02×10^{23} atoms of hydrogen combine with 6.02×10^{23} atoms of chlorine to form 6.02×10^{23} molecules of the compound hydrogen chloride. The quantity of hydrogen chloride that contains

* In some of the examples in this book, atomic weights are rounded off to the nearest whole number to simplify the calculations.

6.02×10^{23} individual HCl molecules is called one mole of hydrogen chloride, HCl. Thus up to this point, the term mole may refer to Avogadro's Number (6.02×10^{23}) of *atoms,* as 1 mole of hydrogen atoms, H, or to *molecules* of an element as 1 mole of hydrogen molecules, H_2, or to *molecules* of a compound as 1 mole of hydrogen chloride molecules, HCl. Notice that the particular units (atoms or molecules) referred to in any given case are usually stated or else are clear from the text. For example, 1 mole of the compound water is 1 mole of H_2O molecules, and also 2 moles of hydrogen atoms, H, and 1 mole of oxygen atoms, O, chemically combined as H_2O. Notice that in the above two cases we refer to "molecules" of water and to "atoms" of hydrogen and oxygen. Water *molecules* are the building units of the compound water, and hydrogen *atoms,* H, and oxygen *atoms,* O, are the building units of the elements hydrogen, H_2, and oxygen, O_2. We can extend the term mole to ionic compounds, such as sodium chloride (NaCl or Na^+Cl^-), for example. For an ionic compound the term mole is extended to indicate a number of ions, or pairs of ions, and therefore the weight in grams of these ions—the *gram formula weight.* For example, for the compound, sodium chloride, 1 mole of NaCl or Na^+Cl^- is 6.02×10^{23} sodium ions and 6.02×10^{23} chloride ions. These weigh 58.5 g or 1 mole of Na^+Cl^- is 1 mole of Na^+ ions, weighing 23.0 g *and* 1 mole of Cl^- ions, weighing 35.5 g. The term mole is also extended to include Avogadro's Number of various other units. When 1 mole (6.02×10^{23}) of Na atoms undergo a reaction in which they are transformed to 1 mole (6.02×10^{23}) of Na^+ ions, 1 mole (6.02×10^{23}) of electrons are involved in this (oxidation) process. That is, 1 mole of Na atoms give up 1 mole of electrons to form 1 mole of Na^+ ions. This use of the term mole is reflected in the following recommendation of the International Union of Pure and Applied Chemistry (IUPAC): "A mole is an amount of a substance, of specified chemical formula, containing the same number of formula units (atoms, molecules, ions, electrons, quanta, or other entities) as there are atoms in 12 grams (exactly) of the pure nuclide* ^{12}C." This definition intentionally avoids stating the exact number of units (particles) because it is possible that a still more precise value for Avogadro's number (6.0225×10^{23}) may be obtained as our laboratory techniques improve. In our discussions, however, we shall continue to say that the mole *is* a number (6.02×10^{23}) of the formula units considered.

ILLUSTRATIVE PROBLEMS

PROBLEM. How many grams of carbon are there in 4.7 mole (g at wt) of carbon? (At wt of carbon = 12)

SOLUTION. In 1 mole (g at wt) of carbon there are 12 g of carbon. Thus, the number of grams of carbon present in 4.7 mole (g at wt) of carbon is 4.7 times 12.

$$12 \text{ g of carbon} \times 4.7 = 56 \text{ g of carbon}$$

PROBLEM. How many moles (g at wt) are there in 50.0 g of aluminum? (At wt of aluminum = 27.0)

SOLUTION. In 27.0 g of aluminum there is 1 mole (g at wt). In 1 g of aluminum there is 1/27.0 mole (g at wt). Thus, the number of gram atomic weights of aluminum present in 50.0 g of aluminum is 50 times this value.

$$\frac{1.00 \text{ mole aluminum}}{27.0 \text{ g aluminum}} \times 50.0 \text{ g aluminum} = 1.85 \text{ mole aluminum}$$

PROBLEM. How many atoms of sulfur are there in 1.00 g of sulfur? (At wt of sulfur = 32.0)

SOLUTION. One mole (g at wt) of sulfur is 32.0 g. Therefore, 32.0 g of sulfur contain 6.02×10^{23} atoms. One g of sulfur will contain

* The term "nuclide" refers to any specific atomic species, such as ^{16}O, ^{19}F, or in this case, ^{12}C.

$$\frac{6.02 \times 10^{23} \text{ atoms of sulfur}}{32.0 \text{ g sulfur}} = \frac{1.88 \times 10^{22} \text{ atoms of sulfur}}{1.00 \text{ g sulfur}}$$

Thus, there are 1.88×10^{22} atoms of sulfur present in 1.00 g of sulfur.

PROBLEM. What is the weight in grams of 1.01×10^{22} atoms of nitrogen? (At wt of nitrogen = 14.0)

SOLUTION. 6.02×10^{23} atoms of nitrogen weigh 14.0 g. One atom of nitrogen weighs $14.0/6.02 \times 10^{23}$ g. Thus, the weight of 1.01×10^{22} atoms of nitrogen is 1.01×10^{22} times this value.

$$\frac{14.0 \text{ g of nitrogen}}{6.02 \times 10^{23} \text{ atoms of nitrogen}} \times 1.01 \times 10^{22} \text{ atoms of nitrogen} = 0.235 \text{ g of nitrogen}$$

PROBLEM. If there are X atoms in 5 g of carbon, how many atoms are there in 5 g of silicon? (At wt of carbon = 12; at wt of silicon = 28)

SOLUTION. The number of atoms in equal weights of two elements is inversely proportional to the atomic weights of the elements.

$$x \times \frac{12 \text{ g}}{28 \text{ g}} = 0.43 \text{ X atoms in 5 g of silicon}$$

PROBLEM. If 10 g of iron contain y atoms, how many grams of aluminum will contain y atoms? (At wt of iron = 56; at wt aluminum = 27.)

SOLUTION. The weights of elements that contain the same number of atoms are directly proportional to the atomic weights of the elements.

$$\frac{10 \text{ g}}{y \text{ atoms}} \times \frac{27 \text{ g}}{56 \text{ g}} = \frac{4.8 \text{ g}}{y \text{ atoms}} \text{ Al}$$

Exercises

3-1 State in your own words the Law of Constant Composition and the Law of Multiple Proportions.
3-2 Summarize Dalton's atomic theory.
3-3 How does Dalton's atomic theory explain the Law of Multiple Proportions?
3-4 Give the simplest statement of an atomic theory which would be adequate to explain fully the laws of Constant Composition and Multiple Proportions and justify your answer.
3-5 If the Law of Multiple Proportions is valid, what does that enable us to conclude about the possibility that an element may have variable combining power?
3-6 Define equivalent, or combining, weight. How is it determined experimentally?
3-7 Element *A* combines with oxygen when it is heated in air. Give experimental details for determining the equivalent weight of the element and show the necessary calculations.
3-8 State clearly the meaning of the term "atomic weight." Illustrate by examples.
3-9 What experimental evidence pointed to the existence of electrons in atoms?
3-10 When it was discovered that electrons were present in atoms, what further conclusion was necessary concerning the presence and nature of other particles in the atom?
3-11 In what way does the nucleus of an atom differ from the electron cloud?
3-12 If protons and neutrons are present in the nucleus of an atom and are surrounded by a much larger electron cloud, what parts of atoms are most likely to interact when atoms come together?
3-13 What are the properties of the neutron? When and by whom was it discovered?
3-14 List the mass and electrical charge of the proton and of the electron.
3-15 How are atomic number and atomic weight related to the number of protons and neutrons in the nucleus and the number of electrons outside the nucleus?
3-16 Draw schematic sketches illustrating the atoms of (a) sodium (b) chlorine, (c) magnesium (see Table 3-3).
3-17 What is the meaning of the term "ion"?

3-18 What electronic change occurs when atoms of different elements form an ionic bond?
3-19 When two or more atoms of the same element combine chemically, would you expect the resulting bond to be ionic or covalent? Justify your answer; give examples.
3-20 Draw a diagram showing the arrangement of ions in the compound NaCl.
3-21 What electronic change occurs when a covalent bond is formed?
3-22 State clearly the principles on which the operation of a mass spectrograph is based.
3-23 Explain the meaning of (a) Avogadro's Number and (b) the mole. Illustrate with examples.
3-24 Explain the meaning of the term "gram atomic weight."
3-25 State the relationships between and among weights, atomic weights, moles, and number of atoms.

Problems*

3-1 One g of hydrogen is found by measurement to combine with oxygen to form 9 g of water. If the atom of hydrogen and the atom of oxygen weighed the same, in what ratio would atoms of hydrogen and oxygen be present in water? If one atom of hydrogen combined with one atom of oxygen to form water, what would be the relative weights of the atoms of hydrogen and oxygen? If water is made up of oxygen and hydrogen atoms in the ratio 1:2 and if 1 g of hydrogen combines with 8 g of oxygen, what can we conclude about the relative weights of the atoms of hydrogen and oxygen?
3-2 The equivalent weight of an element is 20. What weight of the element would combine with 1 g of oxygen?
3-3 Calculate the weight in grams of the atoms of the following elements: helium, sodium, phosphorus, and magnesium.
3-4 If 1 lb. of iron contains *x* atoms, how many atoms are present in 5 lb. of phosphorus?
3-5 If *x* atoms of element A weigh 3 g, how much would 3*x* atoms of element *B* weigh?
3-6 Since 16.0 g of oxygen contain 6.02×10^{23} atoms, what would be the weight in grams of 6.02×10^{23} atoms of sulfur?
3-7 How many gram atomic weights are there in (a) 12 g of oxygen, (b) 16 g of helium, (c) 50 g of iron?
3-8 How many grams are there in (a) 2.5 g at wt of sodium, (b) 3.3 g at wt of gold?
3-9 Calculate the weight in grams of 1 million atoms of iron.
3-10 Calculate the weight in grams of 16,020,000,000 atoms of boron, B. Calculate the number of atoms in (a) 0.01 mole Fe, (b) 3.2 mole H, (c) 3.2 mole H_2, (d) 0.2 mole O, (e) 0.2 mole O_2, (f) 0.2 mole O_3, (g) 0.003 mole P_4, (h) 7.06×10^4 molecules of O_2.
3-11 Calculate the number of moles in (a) 6×10^{20} atoms of Zn; (b) 4.6×10^{30} molecules of CH_4; (c) 14.92 g of H_2O; (d) 0.01 g of K^+ ions; (e) 164 g of ozone, O_3.
3-12 Calculate the number of moles of ions in (a) 34.0 g of Cs^+F^-; (b) 20 g of $Ca^{++}O^=$; (c) 20.8 g $Ba^{++}\,(SO_4)^=$; (d) 6.9×10^{-4} g $Sr^{++}\,(Cl^-)_2$.
3-13 Calculate the weight of 1 mole of each of the following: (a) Br_2; (b) Cd; (c) NO; (d) SO_2; (e) Na; (f) Na^+; (g) Zn^{++}; (h) Cl; (i) Cl^-; (j) Na^+Cl^-; (k) $Zn^{++}(Cl^-)_2$.
3-14 Calculate the number of atoms of magnesium present in 4.2 milligrams of magnesium metal.
3-15 Compare the number of atoms in 1 mole of fluorine atoms, F, with the number of molecules in 1 mole of fluorine gas molecules, F_2, with the number of atoms in 1 mole of sodium, Na, and with the number of ions of sodium and the number of ions of fluorine (F^-) in 1 mole of sodium fluoride, (Na^+F^-).
3-16 Two isotopes of calcium are ^{39}Ca and ^{44}Ca. Draw schematic representations of these isotopes, showing the contents of the nucleus and the electron cloud for each isotope.

* For atomic weights, consult the table inside the front cover; round off to the nearest whole number.

SYMBOLS, FORMULAS, EQUATIONS, AND CALCULATIONS

4

In the last chapter, we learned that a compound is formed by electronic interactions between two or more different atoms, and that the elements in a compound are always present in the same proportions by weight. We also defined the term "mole"—mole of atoms, mole of ions, mole of molecules—which is essential to an understanding of chemical symbols, formulas, and equations, which we shall discuss in this chapter.

4-1 Symbols

To provide a convenient method for representing chemical changes, chemists have worked out a system based on symbols, formulas, and equations—a kind of chemical "shorthand."

DERIVATION

The great "organizer" of the science of chemistry in the early nineteenth century was Jöns Jakob Berzelius (1779–1848), professor of chemistry at Upsala University in Sweden. Berzelius was the first to distinguish clearly between an atom and a molecule and to propound clear ideas on what we now call "valence." Furthermore, he experimentally determined the atomic weights of many of the elements known at that time. In 1813 Berzelius hit on the use of letter symbols to represent the various elements. His system was rapidly adopted by other chemists, and ultimately an official symbol was designated for each of the known elements. These symbols, which are accepted by chemists the world over, are, with a few exceptions, the first two letters of the Latin, Greek, English, German, or French names for the elements. The first letter of the symbol is always capitalized. For example, Cu for copper, from the Latin cuprum, Dy for dysprosium, from the Greek dysprositos, and Ca for the English word calcium.

MEANING

The symbol for an element represents 1 mole (1 at wt) *of the element.* If you understand clearly the meaning of symbols, then you will understand the meaning of formulas and equations, the quantitative language of chemistry. When we write the symbol for any element, we are indicating a particular number of atoms of the element—namely, the Avogadro Number (6.02×10^{23})—or a number of parts by weight equal to the atomic weight of the element.

Here are some examples of the exact meaning of symbols in terms of moles and weight relationships. The symbol O stands for 1 mole of oxygen atoms—that is, 6.02×10^{23} atoms of oxygen—or for 15.999 g of oxygen. The symbol H stands for 1 mole of hydrogen atoms—that is, 6.02×10^{23} atoms of hydrogen—or 1.008 g of hydrogen. Similarly, the symbol S means 1 mole of sulfur atoms—6.02×10^{23}—or 32.064 g of sulfur. Table 4-1 lists the symbols for some of the more common elements, together with their atomic weights.

TABLE 4-1 SYMBOLS AND ATOMIC WEIGHTS OF SOME COMMON ELEMENTS

Symbol	What the Symbol Means
O	15.999 g oxygen
H	1.008 g hydrogen
C	12.011 g carbon
N	14.007 g nitrogen
Na	22.990 g sodium
Mg	24.312 g magnesium
Al	26.982 g aluminum
P	30.974 g phosphorus
S	32.064 g sulfur
Cl	35.453 g chlorine
Ca	40.08 g calcium
Cu	63.54 g copper
Fe	55.847 g iron
Zn	65.37 g zinc

ABBREVIATIONS AND SYMBOLS

There is a fundamental difference between the terms "abbreviation" and "symbol." An abbreviation is a shortened form of a word and has exactly the same meaning as the word. For example, g, lb, and ml are the *abbreviations* for the words gram, pound, and milliliter. But the *symbol* Ca stands for 1 mole of calcium atoms or 1 atomic weight or 40.08 g of calcium. It is not just an abbreviation for the word calcium. When a symbol is used, it represents a *definite number of atoms* or *a definite weight* of that particular element.

4-2 Formulas

Just as a definite weight of an element may be represented by a symbol, so a definite weight of a *compound* may be represented by a combination of symbols called a *formula.* Each symbol in the formula retains its individual meaning.

MEANING

The formula for a compound indicates the symbols of the elements that are present in the compound, and each symbol retains its original meaning. Thus a *formula* is a combination of the symbols for atoms or ions that are held together chemically. If we know the meaning of each symbol individually, we can easily interpret the meaning of a formula in which the symbols are combined.

SUBSCRIPTS

We know that the symbol for an element represents 1 mole of atoms of that element. If two or more atoms of an element are present in one molecule, we indicate them by a subscript following the symbol for the element. For example, a molecule of oxygen which has two atoms of oxygen chemically combined is represented by the formula O_2. The weight represented by the formula O_2 is $2 \times 16.00^* = 32.00$ g of oxygen, and the number of molecules represented by O_2 is 1 mole of molecules—that is, 6.02×10^{23} molecules. Similarly, the formula for ozone, O_3, represents $3 \times 16.00 = 48.00$ g of ozone or 1 mole (6.02×10^{23}) of molecules of ozone. The formula for a molecule of hydrogen gas, H_2, is simply a way of saying $2 \times 1.01 = 2.02$ g of hydrogen in the form of molecules, each containing two atoms of hydrogen chemically combined, or 6.02×10^{23} molecules of hydrogen.

EXAMPLES

The formula for hydrogen chloride gas, HCl, indicates 1 mole of HCl molecules; it also indicates 1 mole of H atoms (1.01 g) and 1 mole of Cl atoms (35.45 g) chemically combined as HCl molecules. Thus, the formula HCl stands for 1.01 g + 35.45 g = 36.46 g of hydrogen chloride.

The formula H_2SO_4 says that 2×1.01 g of hydrogen are chemically combined with 32.06 g of the element sulfur and with 4×16.00 g of the element oxygen, which gives a total of 2.02 + 32.06 + 64.00 = 98.08 g of hydrogen sulfate. This total of all the atomic weights in a compound is called the *formula weight.* Notice that a subscript applies only to the symbol immediately to the left, or to the symbols enclosed by the parentheses, ( ). Thus the formula $Al_2(SO_4)_3$ means that the compound consists of 2 moles of Al atoms and 3 moles of (SO_4) in chemical combination. With this information, we can work out the formula weight of $Al_2(SO_4)_3$:

$$\begin{aligned} 2\,\text{Al} &= 2 \times 26.98 &&= 53.96\text{ g} \\ 3(SO_4) &= 3 \times [32.06 + 4(16.00)] &&= 288.18\text{ g} \\ \hline & Al_2(SO_4)_3 &&= 342.14 \text{ parts by weight} \end{aligned}$$

In Table 4-2 you will find several examples of how formulas are used to represent the weights of chemical substances. A number written *before* a symbol or formula is called a coefficient. It simply acts as a multiplier, as in algebra. A coefficient multiplies every constituent (atom or group of atoms) of the formula that follows. Thus, when we write 2 H, we mean two moles of H atoms, or 2×1.01 g = 2.02 g of hydrogen existing as separate atoms.

Be sure that you understand the difference between H_2 and 2 H. Both represent the same total weight of hydrogen, namely 2.02 g. But the formula H_2 means that

* We round off 15.999 to 16.00, for convenience.

TABLE 4-2 FORMULAS AND WEIGHTS OF CHEMICAL SUBSTANCES

Substance	*Formula*	*What the Formula Means*
Hydrogen chloride	HCl	(1.01 + 35.45) = 36.46 g hydrogen chloride molecules
Hydrogen sulfate	H_2SO_4	$(2 \times 1.01) + 32.06 + (4 \times 16.00) = 98.08$ g hydrogen sulfate molecules
Zinc carbonate	$ZnCO_3$	$65.37 + 12.01 + (3 \times 16.00) = 125.38$ g zinc carbonate
Calcium phosphate	$Ca_3(PO_4)_2$	$(3 \times 40.08) + (2 \times 30.97) + (8 \times 16.00) = 310.18$ g calcium phosphate*

* You may prefer to calculate the weight of $2(PO_4)$ as: $2 \times (30.97 + 64.00) = 189.94$.

two atoms of hydrogen are *chemically combined* (the normal condition of hydrogen), whereas 2 H means that there are two *separate* atoms of hydrogen. Here is another example: 3 O_2 and 2 O_3 both represent the same total weight, 96.00 g. But 3 O_2 states that there are 3 moles of oxygen molecules present, each O_2 molecule containing two atoms of oxygen chemically combined. And 2 O_3 states that we have 2 moles of ozone molecules, each O_3 molecule containing three atoms of oxygen chemically combined. In writing formulas for compounds, we usually omit the coefficient 1 and the subscript 1. Thus, $ZnSO_4$ is the same as 1 $Zn_1S_1O_4$. To indicate 2 or more moles, however, we put the appropriate coefficient before the formula. Here is how we calculate the total weight represented by 2 $ZnSO_4$(Zn = 65.37; S = 32.06; O = 16.00):

		or		
Zn =	65.37 g		2 Zn =	130.74 g
S =	32.06 g	or	2 S =	64.12 g
4 O =	64.00 g		8 O =	128.00 g
$ZnSO_4$ =	161.43 g		2 $ZnSO_4$ =	322.86 g

Thus, 2 $ZnSO_4$ = 2 × 161.43 = 322.86 g

FORMULA WEIGHT AND MOLECULAR WEIGHT

To summarize: the formula of a substance tells us four things: (1) the elements present, (2) the number of atoms of each element present, (3) the weights of these atoms, and (4) the total weight represented by the formula (formula weight). The formula weight of a substance expressed in *grams* is called its *gram formula weight*, which is the same as the weight of a mole. For example, the formula of sulfur dioxide is SO_2, the formula weight of SO_2 is 64.06, and the gram formula weight of SO_2 is 64.06 g.

For sulfur dioxide, SO_2, the formula weight is also the molecular weight (see p. 23), because the formula SO_2 represents the smallest single structural unit of this compound—its molecule. *But a formula does not always represent a molecule.* For the compound sodium chloride, as an example, the formula NaCl does not represent a molecule, because, as we have seen in Chapter 3 (p. 25), sodium chloride in the crystalline state consists not of molecules but of sodium ions, Na^+, and chloride ions, Cl^-, arranged in a three-dimensional lattice. Thus, 1 mole of NaCl means 1 mole (6.02×10^{23}) of Na^+ ions and 1 mole (6.02×10^{23}) of Cl^- ions, combined together in the ionic compound NaCl; it also means, of course, a gram formula weight of NaCl or (22.990 + 35.453) = 58.443 g.

To summarize: the weight of a mole of units (atoms, molecules, ions) of any substance is its formula weight expressed in grams. For example, the formula weight of the element sodium, Na, is 22.990, and a mole of Na atoms weighs 22.990 g. The formula weight of Cl is 35.453, and a mole of Cl atoms weighs 35.453 g. The formula (ionic) weight of the sodium ion, Na^+, is 22.990, and a mole of sodium ions weighs 22.990 g. Similarly, the formula (ionic) weight of chloride ion, Cl^-, is 35.453, and a mole of chloride ions weighs 35.453 g. Also, the formula weight of sodium chloride, NaCl, is (22.990 + 35.453) = 58.443, and a mole of sodium chloride weighs 58.443 g.

For a substance made up of molecules a mole is the number of molecules (6.02×10^{23}) which weigh the formula (also molecular) weight expressed in grams. For example, the formula (molecular) weight of Cl_2 is 70.906, and a mole of chlorine molecules, Cl_2, weighs 70.906 g.

NUMBER OF PARTICLES (ATOMS, MOLECULES, IONS) IN A MOLE, AND THE WEIGHTS OF SINGLE PARTICLES. As we know, 1 mole of atoms of an element is that amount of the element which contains 6.02×10^{23} atoms. For example, 1 mole of calcium atoms, Ca, (40.08 g of calcium) contains 6.02×10^{23} individual Ca atoms. Therefore, the weight of one atom of calcium is 40.08 g/6.02×10^{23} atom = 6.66×10^{-23} g/1 atom. Similarly, since 1 mole of oxygen molecules (6.02×10^{23} O_2 molecules) weighs 32.00 g, the weight of 1 molecule of oxygen is 32.00 g/6.02×10^{23} molecules =

5.32×10^{-23} g/1 molecule. As an example of a molecular compound, the weight of a single molecule of methane, CH_4, is 16.0 g/6.02×10^{23} molecules = 2.66×10^{-23} g/molecule. For an ionic compound a mole is that amount which contains 6.02×10^{23} formula units of the compound. For example, 1 mole of calcium oxide, $Ca^{++}O^{=}$, contains 6.02×10^{23} formula units of CaO and weighs (40.08 g Ca^{++} + 16.00 g $O^{=}$) = 56.08 g. One mole of CaO contains 1 mole of Ca^{++} ions or 6.02×10^{23} Ca^{++} ions, and 1 mole of $O^{=}$ ions or 6.02×10^{23} $O^{=}$ ions; therefore, the weight of one Ca^{++} ion is 40.08 g/6.02×10^{23} ions = 6.66×10^{-23} g/ion, and the weight of one $O^{=}$ ion is 16.00 g/6.02×10^{23} ions = 2.66×10^{-23} g/ion. As another example, consider the ionic compound calcium chloride, $Ca^{++}(Cl^-)_2$. One mole of calcium chloride contains 6.02×10^{23} formula units of $CaCl_2$, that is, one mole of Ca^{++} ions, (6.02×10^{23} Ca^{++} ions), and two moles of Cl^- ions ($2 \times 6.02 \times 10^{23} = 12.04 \times 10^{23}$ Cl^- ions).

4-3 Equations

A chemical equation is a statement that describes a chemical reaction in terms of chemical symbols and formulas. If we know the meaning of the symbols, then we know the meaning of a formula. And if we know the meaning of formulas used in an equation, then we know the meaning of the equation.

When symbols and formulas appear in an equation, we interpret them just as we do when they stand by themselves. For example, the formula CH_4 stands for 16.0 g of methane, and the formula H_2O represents 18.0 g of water.

A chemical equation consists of the formulas of the reacting substances connected by plus signs, and an arrow followed by the formulas of the products connected by plus signs. The arrow may be read "to form." Consider, for example, the following equation:

$$H_2 + Cl_2 \longrightarrow 2\,HCl$$

If we are thinking in terms of the numbers of moles of the reactants and the product, the equation states that one mole of hydrogen molecules, H_2, reacts with one mole of chlorine molecules, Cl_2, to form two moles of hydrogen chloride molecules, HCl.

$$\underset{\text{1 mole}}{H_2} + \underset{\text{1 mole}}{Cl_2} \longrightarrow \underset{\text{2 moles}}{2\,HCl}$$

This equation also says that 2.016 (2×1.008) g of hydrogen react with 70.906 (2×35.453) g of chlorine to form 72.922 ($2 \times 1.008 + 2 \times 35.453$) g of hydrogen chloride.

$$\underset{\text{2.016 g}}{H_2} + \underset{\text{70.906 g}}{Cl_2} \longrightarrow \underset{\text{72.922 g}}{2\,HCl}$$

Here is another equation:

$$2\,NaOH + H_2SO_4 \longrightarrow Na_2SO_4 + 2\,H_2O$$

(Na = 22.99; O = 16.00; H = 1.01; S = 32.06)

We interpret this equation as follows:

$2\,NaOH$	+	H_2SO_4	$\longrightarrow$	Na_2SO_4	+	$2\,H_2O$
2 moles		1 mole		1 mole		2 moles
(2×22.99) + (2×16.00) + (2×1.01), or 80.00 g of sodium hydroxide	react with	(2×1.01) + 32.06 + (4×16.00), or 98.08 g of sulfuric acid	to form	(2×22.99) + 32.06 + (4×16.00), or 142.04 g of sodium sulfate	and	$2 \times (2 \times 1.01)$ + (2×16.00), or 36.04 g of water

Some of the various weight units that may be used in interpreting the chemical equation for the reaction of H_2 and O_2 to form H_2O are summarized in Table 4-3.

TABLE 4-3 INTERPRETATIONS OF EQUATION

Equation:	$2\ H_2$	+	O_2	⟶	$2\ H_2O$
Interpretation:	2 molecules	react with	1 molecule	to form	2 molecules
	2 × *Avogadro's Number* (6.02×10^{23}) of molecules	react with	1 × *Avogadro's Number* (6.02×10^{23}) of molecules	to form	2 × *Avogadro's Number* (6.02×10^{23}) of molecules
	2 moles	react with	1 mole	to form	2 moles
	4.04 g	react with	32.00 g	to form	36.03 g
	2 formula weights	react with	1 formula weight	to form	2 formula weights
	2 × 2(1.01) = 4.04 parts by weight	react with	2(16.00) = 32.00 parts by weight	to form	2 × [2(1.01) + 16.00] = 36.04 parts by weight

Study this table because you will find that if you can interpret its contents, you also will be able to interpret virtually *all* chemical equations.

BALANCING CHEMICAL EQUATIONS

Equations are *quantitative descriptions* of chemical reactions. If we know the composition (formulas) of all the reactants and all the products, we can arrive at a quantitative description of the reaction. Since we know that in a chemical reaction atoms are neither created nor destroyed, we can expect the number of moles of atoms of each element on one side of the equation to be equal to the number of moles of atoms of that element on the other side. This must be true if the equation is to agree with the Law of Conservation of Mass. Therefore, what we must be able to do somehow is to devise a simple procedure so that the number of moles of atoms of each element present both in the reacting substances and also in the products is the same.

When the equation is adjusted by the use of proper coefficients so that the number of moles of atoms of each element in the reactants is made equal to the number of the moles of atoms of that element in the products, the equation is *balanced.*

In other words, to "balance an equation" we place the appropriate coefficient before each formula so that the number of atoms of each element is the same on each side of the equation. Here are the steps to follow in balancing an equation:

Step 1. Write the formulas of the reactants on the left-hand side of the arrow and the formulas of the products on the other side.

Step 2. Count the number of times each symbol appears on the reactant side, and make a separate count of the number of times each symbol appears on the product side of the equation.

Step 3. If a symbol appears more times on one side than on the other, multiply the appropriate formulas by the smallest number that will make the number of symbols the same on both sides of the equation.

Step 4. Count all the symbols again, and, if necessary, change any coefficients again so that the number of symbols on the reactant side balances the number on the product side.

Step 5. Check to see that there are the same number of symbols of each element on both sides of the equation.

As an example of this procedure, let us balance the equation for the decomposition of a compound whose formula is $KClO_3$, into the products represented by the formulas KCl and O_2.

Step 1. $KClO_3 \longrightarrow KCl + O_2$

Step 2.
Symbols in Reactant: 1(K) 1(Cl) 3(O) $\longrightarrow$ *Symbols in Products:* 1(K) 1(Cl) 2(O)
There are three oxygen symbols on the reactant side, but only two oxygen symbols appear on the product side.

Step 3. To make the number of symbols for oxygen equal on both sides, place the coefficient 2 before the formula $KClO_3$, then place the coefficient 3 before the formula O_2. Thus,

Step 4. $2\ KClO_3 \longrightarrow KCl + 3\ O_2$
Symbols in Reactant: 2(K) 2(Cl) 6(O) $\longrightarrow$ *Symbols in Products:* 1(K) 1(Cl) 6(O)
Now the numbers of oxygen symbols are equal, but we have thrown the number of K and Cl symbols out of balance. We take care of this problem simply by placing the coefficient 2 before the formula KCl:

Step 5. $2\ KClO_3 \longrightarrow 2\ KCl + 3\ O_2$
Symbols in Reactant: 2(K) 2(Cl) 6(O) $\longrightarrow$ *Symbols in Products:* 2 (K) 2(Cl) 6(O)

Now the equation is balanced.

The following steps summarize the systematic procedure for balancing the equation:

$$KClO_3 \longrightarrow KCl + O_2$$
$$2\ KClO_3 \longrightarrow KCl + 3\ O_2$$
$$2\ KClO_3 \longrightarrow 2\ KCl + 3\ O_2 \text{ (balanced equation)}$$

In "balancing an equation," the important thing to keep in mind is that in a chemical reaction atoms can neither be created nor destroyed. So the same number of atoms of each element must appear both in the reactants and in the products.

THE EXPERIMENTAL BASIS FOR CHEMICAL EQUATIONS

Before we can write a chemical equation, *we must know the composition of all the reactants and all the products.* Otherwise, we cannot introduce the proper formulas into the equation. Even on this basis, however, it is possible to write balanced equations for reactions that do not actually occur (see Chapter 17). Consequently, even a balanced equation does *not necessarily* represent experimental facts.

The chemist does not need to memorize the coefficients of the formulas involved in a chemical equation, for he can work them out by balancing the equation. But he does have to know, or be able to find out, the *composition* of all the reactants and of all the products. And from the composition, he can derive the simplest (empirical) formula of the compounds involved.

EQUATIONS SHOWING THE HEAT OF REACTION. Nearly all chemical reactions involve some change in heat energy. It is therefore important to introduce here the conventions used to indicate the quantity of heat energy liberated or absorbed when a reaction occurs. For example, let us consider the reaction of carbon with oxygen to produce carbon dioxide. It is an experimental fact that when 1 mole (12.01 g) of carbon, C (graphite), reacts with (32.00 g) of oxygen, O_2, at 25°C and at 1 atm pressure, to produce 1 mole (44.01 g) of carbon dioxide gas, CO_2, 94.1 kcal of heat are released. The equation of the reaction can then be written in the following way, to indicate both the chemical change and the heat energy released in the reaction:

Equation:	C	+	O_2	$\longrightarrow$	CO_2	+		94.1 kcal
Interpretation:	12.01 g	react with	32.00 g	to form	44.01 g	and		94.1 kcal released

There is one important point to keep in mind in interpreting equations of this sort. Each symbol or formula of the reactants and products represents 1 *mole,* and the indicated quantity of heat energy (expressed in kilocalories or calories) represents the heat energy absorbed or released for, and only for, the number of moles of the reactants and products shown in the equation. For example, if we had considered the reaction of 2 moles (24.02 g) of graphite with 2 moles (64.00 g) of oxygen to give 2 moles (88.02 g) of carbon dioxide, at 25°C and 1 atm, the quantity of heat released would be *twice* that shown in the above equation—that is, $(2 \times 94.1) = 188.2$ kcal.

$$2\,C + 2\,O_2 \longrightarrow 2\,CO_2 + 188.2 \text{ kcal}$$

In general, we express the quantity of heat energy involved in a chemical reaction by placing its value in kilocalories or calories alongside the chemical equation, with a plus sign to indicate that heat energy is released (to the surroundings), or with a minus sign to indicate that heat energy is absorbed (from the surroundings).

Consider another example. The chemical combination of nitrogen gas, N_2, with oxygen gas, O_2, to form nitrogen oxide, NO, is expressed as:

$$N_2 + O_2 \longrightarrow 2\,NO - 43.0 \text{ kcal}$$

or

$$N_2 + O_2 + 43.0 \text{ kcal} \longrightarrow 2\,NO$$

Each of these equations indicates that 43.0 kcal of heat are absorbed when 1 mole (28.01 g) of N_2 react with 1 mole (32.00 g) of O_2 to form 2 moles (60.01 g) of NO.

The quantity of heat absorbed or liberated in a chemical reaction at constant temperature (25°C) and pressure (1 atm), is called the "change in enthalpy" for that reaction and is expressed as ΔH. When in a chemical reaction heat is *released* to the surroundings, as in the example of graphite reacting with oxygen to form carbon dioxide, the change in enthalpy is *negative,* and we write $\Delta H = -94.1$ kcal/mole of CO_2 formed. When in a reaction heat is *absorbed* from the surroundings, as in the example of N_2 and O_2 reacting to form NO, we say that the change in enthalpy is *positive,* and we write $\Delta H = +43.0$ kcal/per 2 moles of NO formed.

Here is an example of the two ways of expressing the heat transfer accompanying a reaction:

$$2\,H_2 + O_2 \longrightarrow 2\,H_2O + 136.6 \text{ kcal}$$

or

$$2\,H_2 + O_2 \longrightarrow 2\,H_2O \quad \Delta H = -136.6 \text{ kcal}$$

Both equations indicate that when 2 moles, $[2 \times (2.02)] = 4.04$ g of hydrogen gas, H_2, react with 1 mole, $[(2 \times 16.00)] = 32.00$ g of oxygen gas, O_2, to form 2 moles, (36.04 g) of water vapor, H_2O, then 136.6 kcal of heat are released. Since 136.6 kcal are released to the surroundings, the plus sign is used in the first equation. But the fact that heat is released to the surroundings in the reaction means that the enthalpy (heat content) H, of the product, is *less* than the enthalpy of the reactants, so that a decrease in enthalpy has taken place. We indicate this by using a minus sign with the ΔH value in the second equation ($\Delta H = -136.6$ kcal per 2 moles of H_2O vapor formed).

4-4 Calculations

Now that we have discussed at some length the quantitative meaning of symbols, formulas, and equations, we are ready to move on to some of the actual calculations. Wide experience with numerical problems is extremely valuable in your study of chemistry, for it gives you practice in thinking through problems which will deepen your understanding of the principles involved. But do not assume that just because you can solve a numerical problem correctly you necessarily understand the principles involved. *In fact, if you just go through the mechanical steps of a solution, giving no thought to the meaning of what you are doing, you may actually impair your understanding of the principles. In the following pages, we shall present a method of approaching common problems that emphasizes clear thinking rather than mere familiarity with a mechanical process.*

One principle underlies the discussion that follows: *In the types of problems considered in the remainder of this chapter, numbers are meaningless in themselves; only numbers associated with units have an exact meaning. Only numbers associated with units, therefore, are used in calculations. All the numbers used in the calculations must be associated with exact ideas that can be clearly expressed in words.*

As an example of the association of a number with a unit to express an exact idea, consider a distance expressed as 10 feet. In this example 10 is the number, and feet is the unit. But if this distance is expressed by the number 10 without a unit, the idea is not exactly stated—the distance could be 10 feet, 10 yards, 10 miles, or 10 "anything."

EXAMPLES OF UNITS

The mathematics involved in calculating weights in chemical reactions is very simple and familiar. Let us consider a problem involving familiar objects, and then consider an analogous chemical problem.

PROBLEM. If 9 pens cost 15 dollars, how many pens can be bought for 40 dollars?

SOLUTION.

$$\frac{9\text{ pens}}{15\text{ dollars}} \times 40\text{ dollars} = \frac{9\text{ pens}}{15\,\cancel{\text{dollars}}} \times 40\,\cancel{\text{dollars}} = 24\text{ pens}$$

Note that when the units are treated as arithmetical quantities (i.e., multiplied and divided), the answer comes out in the desired units.

PROBLEM. If the volume occupied by 27.0 g of mercury is 2.00 ml, (a) find the weight of 36.0 ml of mercury, and (b) find the volume occupied by 81.0 g of mercury.

SOLUTION.

$$\text{(a)}\quad \frac{27.0\text{ g mercury}}{2.00\,\cancel{\text{ml mercury}}} \times 36.0\,\cancel{\text{ml mercury}} = 486\text{ g mercury} = 4.86 \times 10^2\text{ g mercury}$$

$$\text{(b)}\quad \frac{2.00\text{ ml mercury}}{27.0\,\cancel{\text{g mercury}}} \times 81.0\,\cancel{\text{g mercury}} = 6.00\text{ ml mercury}$$

We have seen that a quantity of matter which contains 6.02×10^{23} units (atoms, molecules, or ions of whatever is the appropriate building unit of the type of-matter under discussion) is called a *mole*. Thus when we use the mole as the unit, we actually measure out quantities of matter in equal lots (6.02×10^{23}) of atoms or molecules or ions. The use of the mole as a unit in solving chemical problems often simplifies calculations, as illustrated by the following examples.

PROBLEM. If 18 g of carbon combine with 48 g of oxygen, how many moles of carbon will combine with 64 g of oxygen? (C = 12)*

SOLUTION. Since 1 mole of carbon weighs 12 g, the number of moles of carbon in 18 g of carbon is:

* Here and in similar problems that follow, the given numbers signify exactly the quantities indicated. The zeroes which should follow the decimal point to indicate such precision are omitted for simplicity; i.e., 18 = 18.000.

$$\frac{18 \text{ g carbon}}{\frac{12 \text{ g carbon}}{1 \text{ mole carbon}}} = 18 \text{ g carbon} \times \frac{1 \text{ mole carbon}}{12 \text{ g carbon}} = 1.5 \text{ mole carbon}$$ (this is the number of moles of carbon that combine with 48 g of oxygen)

$$\frac{1.5 \text{ moles carbon}}{48 \text{ g oxygen}} = \text{the number of moles of carbon that combine with 1 g of oxygen}$$

Thus, the number of moles of carbon that combine with 64 g of oxygen is 64 times this value.

$$\frac{1.5 \text{ moles carbon}}{48 \cancel{\text{ g oxygen}}} \times 64 \cancel{\text{ g oxygen}} = 2 \text{ moles carbon}$$

If you have difficulty in following the solution to this problem, refer to the solution of an analogous familiar problem and other problems in Appendix 4-1.

CALCULATIONS INVOLVING ENERGY

Let us proceed to consider the calculation of some problems in which we are interested in determining not only the weights of the substances involved in a chemical reaction, but also the energy change that accompanies the reaction. For example, iron reacts with sulfur to form iron(II) sulfide, FeS (see p. 59). When 55.85 g of iron react with 32.06 g of sulfur to form 87.91 g of iron(II) sulfide, FeS, 22.7 kcal of heat energy are liberated ($\Delta H = -22.7$ kcal). These facts are represented by the equation,*

$$\text{Fe} + \text{S} \longrightarrow \text{FeS} \qquad \Delta H = -22.7 \text{ kcal/mole}$$

PROBLEM. When 1 mole (55.85 g) of Fe reacts with S to form FeS, 22.7 kcal are liberated. If 11.17 g of Fe react completely, calculate the quantity of heat liberated

SOLUTION. The balanced equation is:

$$\underset{1 \text{ mole}}{\text{Fe}} + \underset{1 \text{ mole}}{\text{S}} \longrightarrow \underset{1 \text{ mole}}{\text{FeS}} \qquad \Delta H = -22.7 \text{ kcal/mole}$$

$$11.17 \text{ g Fe} = \frac{11.17 \text{ g Fe}}{\frac{55.85 \text{ g Fe}}{1 \text{ mole Fe}}} = \frac{11.17}{55.85} \text{ mole Fe}$$

According to the above equation, when 1 mole of Fe reacts with 1 mole of S to form 1 mole of FeS, 22.7 kcal are liberated. Therefore, when 11.17/55.85 mole Fe react, 11.17/55.85 times this value are liberated:

$$\frac{22.7 \text{ kcal}}{1 \cancel{\text{ mole Fe}}} \times \frac{11.17}{55.85} \cancel{\text{ mole Fe}} = 4.54 \text{ kcal (liberated)}$$

CALCULATING PERCENTAGE COMPOSITION FROM MOLECULAR FORMULA

If we know the formula for a compound, we can work out its percentage composition. For example, the formula for ammonia is NH_3, which tells us that 14 g of nitrogen and 3 g of hydrogen are present in 17 g of ammonia (here we are rounding off the atomic weights to whole numbers; N = 14; H = 1).

PROBLEM. Calculate the percentage by weight of nitrogen and the percentage by weight of hydrogen in ammonia, NH_3.

SOLUTION. To calculate the percentage by weight of nitrogen we must obtain the number of parts by weight of nitrogen present in 100 parts by weight of ammonia:

$$\frac{14 \text{ parts by wt nitrogen}}{17 \cancel{\text{ parts by wt}} \text{ ammonia}} \times 100 \cancel{\text{ parts by wt}} \text{ ammonia} = 82 \text{ per cent nitrogen (in ammonia)}$$

* According to the equation, 22.7 kcal are liberated for each mole of Fe that reacts (also for each mole of S that reacts and for each mole of FeS formed).

To calculate the percentage by weight of hydrogen, we must obtain the number of parts by weight of hydrogen present in 100 parts by weight of ammonia:

$$\frac{3 \text{ parts by wt hydrogen}}{17 \text{ ~~parts by wt~~ ammonia}} \times 100 \text{ ~~parts by wt~~ ammonia} = 18 \text{ per cent hydrogen (in ammonia)}$$

Thus, we have calculated that the compound NH_3 contains 82 per cent by weight of nitrogen and 18 per cent by weight of hydrogen.

The general procedure for calculating the percentage of an element in a compound from the formula of the compound is to divide the total weight of the element present in 1 formula weight of the compound by the formula weight of the compound, and then to multiply by 100.

CALCULATING EMPIRICAL (SIMPLEST) FORMULAS FROM PERCENTAGE COMPOSITION

We know that the formula of a compound expresses, by means of symbols, the weights of the elements present. Thus, to determine the formula of a substance, we must first determine its composition—that is, the kind and relative weights of the elements present. The formula of a compound obtained in this way is often called the *empirical formula* (from the Greek word meaning experimental) to indicate that it has been derived by experiment. The empirical formula gives only the relative numbers of each symbol expressed in the simplest whole number ratio and does not necessarily represent the molecular formula of the compound nor indicate the nature of the bonding present. Hence the empirical formula is also called the *simplest formula.*

INFORMATION NEEDED. We must know the following facts in order to determine the empirical formula of a compound:

1. All the elements present in the compound (and their atomic weights).
2. The percentage by weight, or the weight ratio, of the elements present in the compound.

THE EXPERIMENTAL BASIS OF FORMULAS. In order to emphasize the experimental basis of chemistry, we shall discuss the experiments involved in determining the composition of substances before we calculate empirical formulas. In chemistry, the general term for determining composition is "analysis." The branch of chemistry that deals with the detection of the components of a substance is known as *qualitative analysis.* The branch of chemistry that deals with the determination of the amounts of components present in a substance is known as *quantitative analysis.*

How does a chemist analyze a substance? He converts the substance into other substances that can be (easily) recognized. In order to do this, he must bring about a regrouping of the atoms, either by themselves or in combination with other atoms, into other substances whose composition he knows from physical or chemical tests.

Let us see how we could determine the exact composition of methane gas, the chief component of natural gas. We burn a known weight of methane gas in a known weight of oxygen and measure the weights of the (only) products formed: carbon dioxide, CO_2, and water, H_2O. From this chemical experiment we first satisfy ourselves that since the sum of the weights of the two products equals the sum of the weights of the reactants, these products must be the only ones present. Physical and chemical tests reveal that these products are carbon dioxide, CO_2, and water, H_2O. Now we determine the total weight of carbon dioxide obtained. From this figure we calculate the weight of carbon in the carbon dioxide, which must equal the weight of carbon in the original sample of methane. This is a simple weight problem just like those described previously. From this calculated weight of carbon, which was present in the original sample of methane, and from the weight of the water formed, we can calculate the weight and percentage of hydrogen in the compound.

In the case of methane, these calculations give us an experimental composition of 75 per cent carbon and 25 per cent hydrogen. (These percentages have been rounded off to the nearest whole number.) Since the compound contains only carbon and hydrogen, we can write the expression C_xH_y to represent methane. The problem is to determine the exact values of the subscripts x and y from the known percentage composition.

EXAMPLES OF CALCULATIONS OF EMPIRICAL FORMULAS: METHANE. The percentage composition of methane, rounded off to the nearest whole number, is 75 per cent carbon and 25 per cent hydrogen. This means that in 100 g of methane there are 75 g of carbon and 25 g of hydrogen. These facts may be expressed as: $\text{Carbon}_{(75\text{ g})}$ $\text{Hydrogen}_{(25\text{ g})}$. The formula of methane reveals the relative number of moles of atoms of carbon, C, and hydrogen, H. We must then convert the relative weights of carbon (75 g) and hydrogen (25 g) to relative numbers of moles of carbon atoms and hydrogen atoms. We proceed as follows:

$$\frac{75.0 \text{ g carbon}}{12.0 \text{ g carbon/1 mole C atoms}} = 6.25 \text{ moles C atoms (in 100 g of methane)}$$

Similarly,

$$\frac{25.0 \text{ g hydrogen}}{1.0 \text{ g hydrogen/1 mole H atoms}} = 25 \text{ moles H atoms (in 100 g of methane)}$$

Thus, in 100 g of methane there are 6.25 moles of carbon atoms and 25 moles of hydrogen atoms. These facts may be expressed as follows:

$$\text{Carbon}_{6.25\text{ moles of atoms}}\ \text{Hydrogen}_{25\text{ moles of atoms}}, \text{ or } C_{6.25}H_{25}$$

But since the simplest formula for a compound expresses its composition in terms of the *simplest relative* number of moles of atoms of the various elements present, we must simplify the mole ratio of 6.25/25 to the smallest whole numbers. We do this by dividing each number by the smaller one—that is, by 6.25—and we get 1.0/4.0. Thus, 6.25/6.25 = 1.0 g at wt, and 25/6.25 = 4.0 g at wt. The simplest ratio, then, is C_1H_4, and the empirical formula is CH_4.

Here is a summary of the steps that we followed in the above calculation:

$$\text{Carbon}_x \quad \text{Hydrogen}_y$$
$$\text{Carbon}_{(75\%)} \quad \text{Hydrogen}_{(25\%)}$$
$$\text{Carbon}_{(75\text{ g})} \quad \text{Hydrogen}_{(25\text{ g})}$$
$$\text{Carbon}\ \frac{75\text{ g}}{12\text{ g/mole of atoms}} \quad \text{Hydrogen}\ \frac{25\text{ g}}{1.0\text{ g/mole of atoms}}$$
$$\text{Carbon 6.25 moles of atoms} \quad \text{Hydrogen 25 moles of atoms}$$
$$\text{Carbon}\ \frac{6.25}{6.25} = 1.0 \text{ moles of atoms} \quad \text{Hydrogen}\ \frac{25}{6.25} = 4.0 \text{ moles of atoms}$$

$$\text{Formula: } C_{1.0\text{ mole}}H_{4.0\text{ moles}}, \text{ or } CH_4$$

As another example, let us consider a compound with the following composition: Sodium: 32.37%; Sulfur: 22.55%; Oxygen: 45.08%. Sum of percentages by weights: 100.00%. The atomic weights of the elements are: Na = 22.99, S = 32.06, O = 16.00. Knowing that the compound contains only sodium, sulfur, and oxygen, we can write the following expression for this compound:

$$\text{Sodium}_x\text{Sulfur}_y\text{Oxygen}_z$$

The problem is to find the relative values of x, y, and z. On the basis of weight composition, we can write the expression:

$$\text{Sodium}_{(32.37\ g)}\text{Sulfur}_{(22.55\ g)}\text{Oxygen}_{(45.08\ g)}$$

To find the relative numbers of moles of atoms of sodium, sulfur, and oxygen in the compound, we must divide the number of grams of each element by the number of grams in 1 mole of atoms of each element:

$$\frac{32.37\text{ g sodium}}{22.99\text{ g sodium/1 mole Na atoms}} = 1.408\text{ moles Na atoms}$$

$$\frac{22.55\text{ g sulfur}}{32.06\text{ g sulfur/1 mole S atoms}} = 0.7032\text{ mole S atoms}$$

$$\frac{45.08\text{ g oxygen}}{16.00\text{ g oxygen/1 mole O atoms}} = 2.813\text{ moles O atoms}$$

Thus, a formula expressed in symbols (number of moles of atoms) is:

$$Na_{1.408}S_{0.7032}O_{2.813}$$

Now we divide these figures by 0.7032, the smallest of the three numbers, to obtain the simplest whole-number mole ratio. The relationship then becomes:

$$Na = \frac{1.408}{0.7032} = 1.989 \qquad S = \frac{0.7031}{0.7031} = 1.000 \qquad O = \frac{2.813}{0.703} = 4.00$$

To one significant figure, Na = 2, S = 1, O = 4. So the *empirical formula* of the compound is $Na_2S_1O_4$, or simply Na_2SO_4.

Here is another example. We want to determine the empirical formula for the solid compound called ammonium chloride. When we heat this substance, we find that the only substances formed are two gases that are easily recognizable as ammonia, NH_3, and hydrogen chloride, HCl. We show by qualitative analysis that the only elements present in these two compounds are nitrogen, hydrogen, and chlorine; and we can therefore conclude that ammonium chloride itself contains only these three elements—N, H, and Cl. *Quantitative* analysis yields the following percentage composition: nitrogen, 26.10%; hydrogen, 7.42%; chlorine, 66.40%. The sum of the percentages is 99.92%.* Thus, a 100-g sample of ammonium chloride contains 26.10 g of nitrogen, 7.42 g of hydrogen, and 66.40 g of chlorine. Now, taking the atomic weight of nitrogen as 14.007, hydrogen as 1.008, and chlorine as 35.453, we can determine the empirical formula for the compound:

Number of moles of N atoms in 100 g of sample of ammonium chloride:

$$\frac{26.10\text{ g nitrogen}}{14.007\text{ g nitrogen/1 mole N atoms}} = 1.86\text{ moles N atoms}$$

Number of moles of H atoms in 100 g of sample of ammonium chloride:

$$\frac{7.42\text{ g hydrogen}}{1.008\text{ g hydrogen/1 mole H atoms}} = 7.41\text{ moles H atoms}$$

Number of moles of Cl atoms in 100 g of ammonium chloride:

$$\frac{66.40\text{ g chlorine}}{35.453\text{ g chlorine/1 mole Cl atoms}} = 1.87\text{ moles Cl atoms}$$

Thus, the formula expressed in symbols (number of atomic weights) is: $N_{1.86}H_{7.41}Cl_{1.87}$.

Dividing each number by the smallest number, 1.86, gives us the formula: $N_1H_4Cl_1$. The empirical formula for ammonium chloride, then, is $N_1H_4Cl_1$, or simply NH_4Cl.

* The small discrepancy of 0.08% between 99.92% and the theoretical total of 100% is due to experimental error.

Any (complete) quantitative information about the composition of a compound permits us to calculate its empirical formula. Thus it is not necessary to start with the percentage composition. For example, a 4.275 g sample of a compound is (completely) analyzed and contains 0.675 g of aluminum, 1.200 g of sulfur, and 2.40 g of oxygen. The weight ratio of the elements present, Al, S, O, is: *Aluminum,* 0.675 g; *Sulfur,* 1.200 g; *Oxygen,* 2.40 g. We need only to convert these weight ratios to mole ratios of the atoms, Al, S, and O: Al $= \frac{0.675\ \text{g}}{27.0\ \text{g/mole}} = 0.0250$ moles of atoms; S $= \frac{1.200\ \text{g}}{32.06\ \text{g/mole}} = 0.0375$ moles of atoms; O $= \frac{2.40\ \text{g}}{16.00\ \text{g/mole}} = 0.150$ moles of atoms. On this basis we may write the expression $Al_{0.0250}S_{0.0375}O_{0.150}$. If we divide each mole value by the smallest value, 0.0250, we have:

$$Al_{\frac{0.0250}{0.0250}} = Al_{1.00};\ S_{\frac{0.0375}{0.0250}} = S_{1.50};\ O_{\frac{0.150}{0.0250}} = O_{6.00}$$

Since all subscripts are not whole numbers or, rounding off to fewer significant figures, $Al_1S_{1.5}O_6$, we multiply each by 2 to get $Al_2S_3O_{12}$. This is generally written as $Al_2(SO_4)_3$.

Exercises

4-1 State the full meaning of (a) the symbol for an element, (b) the formula for a compound.

4-2 Distinguish between an atom of oxygen, O; a molecule of oxygen, O_2; and a molecule of ozone, O_3.

4-3 Complete the following statements:
(a) The atomic weight of an element is ______. (b) The gram atomic weight of an element is ______. (c) The molecular weight of an element is ______. (d) The gram molecular weight of an element is ______. (e) The mole of an element is ______.

4-4 If the reference atomic weight of carbon were 24 instead of 12, what would be (a) the atomic weight of calcium, (b) the formula weight of water?

4-5 State the full meaning of the following: (a) $MgCl_2$, (b) Na_2CO_3, (c) HCl, (d) $Ca(OH)_2 + 2\,HCl \longrightarrow CaCl_2 + 2\,H_2O$.

4-6 State the full meaning of the following: (a) Fe, (b) $CuCl_2$, (c) 2 Ca, (d) $4\,Fe_2(SO_4)_3$, (e) $Zn + 2\,HCl \longrightarrow ZnCl_2 + H_2$.

4-7 The following are statements in words of various chemical changes. Express the changes in terms of equations.
(a) Mercury (formula represents 1 mole of atoms of mercury) reacts with oxygen molecules (formula represents 1 mole of molecules, each containing 2 combined oxygen atoms) to produce mercuric oxide (formula represents 1 mole of molecules, each containing 1 atom of mercury and 1 atom of oxygen, combined together).
(b) Hydrogen (formula represents 2 moles of atoms of hydrogen) reacts with chlorine (formula represents 1 mole of molecules, each containing 2 combined chlorine atoms) to produce hydrogen chloride (formula represents 1 mole of molecules, each containing 1 atom of hydrogen and 1 atom of chlorine, combined together).
(c) Nitrogen (formula represents 2 moles of atoms of nitrogen) reacts with hydrogen to produce ammonia (formula represents 1 mole of molecules, each containing 1 atom of nitrogen and 3 atoms of hydrogen, combined together).
(d) Ethane (formula represents 1 mole of molecules, each containing 2 atoms of carbon and 6 atoms of hydrogen, combined together) reacts with oxygen (formula represents 1 mole of molecules, each containing 2 combined oxygen atoms) to produce carbon dioxide (formula represents 1 mole of molecules, each containing 1 atom of carbon and 2 atoms of oxygen, combined together) and water (formula represents 1 mole of molecules, each containing 2 atoms of hydrogen and 1 atom of oxygen, combined together).

(e) When potassium nitrate (formula represents 1 mole of molecules, each containing 1 atom of potassium, 1 atom of nitrogen, and 3 atoms of oxygen, combined together) is heated, it decomposes to potassium nitrite (formula represents 1 mole of molecules each containing 1 atom of potassium, 1 atom of nitrogen, and 2 atoms of oxygen, combined together) and oxygen (formula represents 1 mole of molecules, each containing 2 combined oxygen atoms).

4-8 The formula of acetylene (a gas used in welding) is C_2H_2. The formula of benzene (a liquid used as a solvent) is C_6H_6. Explain the difference in meaning of the formulas $3(C_2H_2)$ and $1(C_6H_6)$.

4-9 Given the equation $N_2 + 3\ H_2 \longrightarrow 2\ NH_3$; $\Delta H = -24.0$ kcal/mole, determine the kilocalories liberated when (a) 2 moles of N_2 completely react, (b) 4 moles of H_2 completely react, and (c) 10 moles of NH_3 are formed.

4-10 Explain the meaning of the following equations:

$$2\ Ca + O_2 \longrightarrow 2\ CaO \qquad \Delta H = -303.8 \text{ kcal}$$
$$Ca + Cl_2 \longrightarrow CaCl_2 \qquad \Delta H = -190.0 \text{ kcal}$$
$$2\ Zn + O_2 \longrightarrow 2\ ZnO \qquad \Delta H = -170.0 \text{ kcal}$$
$$Zn + Cl_2 \longrightarrow ZnCl_2 \qquad \Delta H = -99.4 \text{ kcal}$$
$$N_2 + O_2 \longrightarrow 2\ NO \qquad \Delta H = +43.2 \text{ kcal}$$

4-11 Balance the following equations:

(a) $KNO_3 \longrightarrow KNO_2 + O_2$
(b) $SO_2 + O_2 \longrightarrow SO_3$
(c) $Fe + O_2 \longrightarrow Fe_2O_3$
(d) $Fe_3O_4 + H_2 \longrightarrow Fe + H_2O$
(e) $C_2H_6 + O_2 \longrightarrow CO_2 + H_2O$
(f) $Al + H_2SO_4 \longrightarrow H_2 + Al_2(SO_4)_3$
(g) $Fe + H_2SO_4 \longrightarrow H_2 + FeSO_4$
(h) $Al + CuSO_4 \longrightarrow Cu + Al_2(SO_4)_3$

Problems

4-1 How many moles of atoms are there in (a) 1.6 g of sulfur, (b) 6.2 g of phosphorus?

4-2 Calculate the formula weights of the following compounds: (a) CCl_4, (b) Na_2SO_4, (c) H_2SO_4, (d) $Ca(HCO_3)_2$, (e) $(NH_4)_3PO_4$, (f) $Fe_2(SO_4)_3$.

4-3 How many *atoms* are present in: (a) 4.0 g of carbon, (b) 8.99 g of aluminum, (c) 5.0 g of hydrogen?

4-4 If 8.00 g of oxygen contain 3.01×10^{23} atoms, calculate the number of atoms present in 2.00 moles of oxygen.

4-5 Calculate the number of grams of sodium peroxide, Na_2O_2, that would be required to produce 50.0 g of oxygen by the following reaction:

$$2\ Na_2O_2 + 2\ H_2O \longrightarrow 4\ NaOH + O_2$$

4-6 Calculate the number of grams of KCl that would be formed along with 10 g of oxygen in the decomposition of potassium chlorate, $KClO_3$:

$$2\ KClO_3 \longrightarrow 2\ KCl + 3\ O_2$$

4-7 When 22.99 g of sodium react with oxygen, 16.00 g of oxygen combine with this weight of sodium. (a) How many grams of the resulting compound are formed? (b) Calculate the number of grams of sodium that would combine with 4.0 g of oxygen, and the number of grams of the compound so formed.

4-8 Calcium chloride, $CaCl_2$, is formed as shown by the following equation:

$$Ca(OH)_2 + 2\ HCl \longrightarrow CaCl_2 + 2\ H_2O$$

How many moles of calcium chloride are formed by the complete reaction of 37 g of calcium hydroxide, $Ca(OH)_2$?

4-9 If x grams of element A, atomic weight 20, contain n atoms, how many atoms are there in $2x$ grams of element B, atomic weight 37?

4-10 If n atoms of element C weigh 2.4 g and $2n$ atoms of element D, atomic weight 14, weigh 40 g, what is the atomic weight of element C?

4-11 Calculate the number of atoms in 0.01 lb of carbon.

4-12 Potassium chlorate, $KClO_3$, decomposes into potassium chloride, KCl, and oxygen, O_2. To obtain 100 l of oxygen gas at given conditions, how many grams of potassium chlorate would be necessary? (One l of oxygen gas at these conditions weighs 1.429 g).

4-13 Explain the meaning of this equation:

$$CH_4 + 2\,O_2 \longrightarrow CO_2 + 2\,H_2O \qquad \Delta H = -212.8 \text{ kcal/mole}$$

What weight of methane gas, CH_4, must react according to the above equation to liberate 3.0×10^8 kcal?

4-14 Copper metal reacts with sulfur according to the equation,

$$Cu + S \longrightarrow CuS \qquad \Delta H = -11.6 \text{ kcal/mole}$$

Calculate the number of kilocalories that would be liberated by the reaction of (a) 10.00 g of sulfur, (b) 63.54 g of copper, (c) 63.54 lb of copper, (d) 4.6 moles of copper.

4-15 When 1.00 mole of methane is burned with oxygen to form carbon dioxide and water, 212.8 kcal of heat are liberated. Calculate how many grams of methane would be required to raise the temperature of 1.50×10^3 g of water from 35.0°C to 50.0°C, assuming all the liberated heat could be transferred to the water.

4-16 Calculate the percentage of hydrogen and carbon in the compounds represented by the formulas C_2H_6 and C_2H_5OH.

4-17 Calculate the percentage of oxygen in the compounds represented by the following formulas: (a) $CaCO_3$, (b) $NaNO_3$, (c) HCOOH, (d) Na_2O_2.

4-18 Calculate the percentage composition of the compounds represented by the formulas (a) Na_3PO_4, (b) BaS.

4-19 If an iron-aluminum alloy containing 50% by weight of each element reacts with dilute sulfuric acid to liberate hydrogen, what weight of hydrogen would be obtained from 5.0 lb of the alloy?

4-20 One g of oxygen combines under certain conditions with 4.29 g of barium. Calculate the empirical formula of the resulting compound.

4-21 Calculate the percentage composition of the compounds represented by the formulas (a) K_2SO_4, (b) $Fe_3(PO_4)_2$, (c) Hg_2Cl_2, (d) C_3H_8O, (e) $C_{12}H_{22}O_{11}$.

4-22 A compound contains 68.5% chromium and 31.5% oxygen. Calculate its empirical formula.

4-23 Calculate the empirical formulas of the following compounds:

(a) A compound that contains 31.3% boron, B, and 68.7% oxygen, O.
(b) A compound that analyzes 68.4% chromium, Cr, and 31.6% oxygen, O.
(c) An oxide of rhenium that analyzes 76.9% rhenium, Re.
(d) A compound that analyzes 55.2% potassium, K, 14.6% phosphorus, P, and 30.2% oxygen, O.

4-24 Calculate the empirical formula of each of the following compounds:

(a) An oxide of lead that contains 9.4% oxygen.
(b) A compound that contains 31.2% boron and 68.8% oxygen.
(c) A compound that contains 60.0% carbon, 13.4% hydrogen, and 26.6% oxygen.
(d) The analysis of a compound that shows the presence of 26.67% carbon, 2.22% hydrogen and 71.11% oxygen.
(e) A compound that contains only nitrogen and hydrogen in the ratio of 0.30 g of hydrogen to 12.6 g of nitrogen.
(f) A compound that contains (only) nitrogen and hydrogen in the ratio of 0.60 g of hydrogen to 2.8 g of nitrogen.

4-25 How many moles of (a) K^+, (b) NO_3^-, (c) Rb^+, and (d) Cl^- ions are present in the (total) solution made by dissolving in water the following: 1 mole of K^+Cl^-, 2 moles of $Rb^+NO_3^-$, 1 mole of $Rb^+{}_2SO_4^=$, and 1 mole of $K^+NO_3^-$?

4-26 State the number of moles of Na^+, $SO_4^=$, and H_2O present in (a) 1 mole, (b) 5 moles, of $Na_2SO_4 \cdot 10\,H_2O$.

VALENCE, OXIDATION NUMBER, AND NOMENCLATURE

5

In the preceding chapter we discussed the use of symbols, formulas, and equations, and the manner of calculating the weights of substances involved in chemical reactions. Earlier, we also discussed briefly the equivalent (or combining) weights of the elements. In this chapter we shall develop the concept of *combining capacity* and see how numbers are used to express combining capacity. Also, we shall discuss a system of naming compounds (nomenclature) according to which a compound is given a name that is simply and systematically related to its formula. In chemistry, and in every science, a good system of nomenclature is a prime necessity.

5-1 The Combining Capacity of Elements

As we have seen, atoms have the ability to combine with other atoms to form molecules or ionic compounds. The *valence* of an element is the number of atoms of hydrogen, fluorine, or sodium that combine with 1 atom of the element; hydrogen, fluorine, and sodium being assigned by convention a valence of 1. Thus, valence is a number that describes the *combining capacity* of an element. For example, since the valence of hydrogen is 1 and the valence of fluorine is 1, we know that 1 atom of hydrogen will combine with 1 atom of fluorine, and hence that 1 mole of hydrogen atoms will combine with 1 mole of fluorine atoms to form 1 mole of hydrogen fluoride molecules, and that the formula of the resulting compound is HF. Similarly, the fact that H, F, and Na each has a valence of 1 and C has a valence of 4 explains the formulas NaF (Na_1F_1), HF, NaH, CH_4, and CF_4. An element that has a valence of 1 is called monovalent; a valence of 2, divalent; a valence of 3, trivalent; a valence of 4, tetravalent; and so on. The Greek prefixes mono-, di-, tri-, tetra-, and so on, are used to indicate the numerical value of the valence. The Latin prefixes uni-, bi-, ter-, and quadri- are also used to indicate valences of 1, 2, 3, and 4, respectively.

Different elements have different combining capacities. For example, the formulas of the compounds that the metals sodium, calcium, and aluminum form with fluorine are NaF, CaF_2, and AlF_3. Here we see that each of the three metal atoms has a different combining capacity, since 1 mole of sodium atoms combines with 1 mole of fluorine atoms, NaF; 1 mole of calcium atoms combines with 2 moles of fluorine atoms, CaF_2; and 1 mole of aluminum combines with 3 moles of fluorine atoms, AlF_3. This means that the relative combining capacities of sodium, calcium, and aluminum are in the ratio 1:2:3, and the valence of sodium is 1; of calcium, 2; and of aluminum, 3. This same difference in combining capacity also shows up in the formulas for the compounds which these elements form with oxygen, which itself has a valence of 2: Na_2O, CaO, and Al_2O_3. In general, if we examine the formulas of a series of compounds containing sodium, calcium and aluminum, we find that they exhibit the same combining capacities in all their compounds.

FIXED VALENCE OF CERTAIN ELEMENTS

When the element sodium reacts with other elements to form compounds, it always shows a valence of 1. Other elements, such as calcium and magnesium, show a valence of 2 in almost all their compounds. Thus, certain elements—actually, about one-fifth of all the elements—show only one valence in almost all their compounds. These elements have a *fixed valence.*

VARIABLE VALENCE OF CERTAIN ELEMENTS

As we saw in Chapter 3, there are certain elements, one atom of which can combine with either one atom or two atoms of another element to form two different compounds, composed only of these two elements. Thus, the valence of these certain elements can have more than one value. For example, two different compounds of copper with chlorine are represented by the formulas CuCl and $CuCl_2$. Thus, when it reacts with chlorine, copper has more than one combining power—more than one valence. Two different compounds of copper with oxygen are represented by the formulas Cu_2O and CuO. Clearly, then, copper, in its reaction with other elements, has *more than one valence.* Many other elements have more than one valence. For example, $FeCl_2$ and $FeCl_3$ are the formulas of two chlorides of iron; Hg_2Cl_2 and $HgCl_2$ are the formulas of two chlorides of mercury; and FeO and Fe_2O_3, and Hg_2O and HgO, are the formulas of the two oxides of iron and the two oxides of mercury respectively. An element that shows more than one valence has a *variable valence.* About four-fifths of all the elements have variable valence.

5-2 Oxidation Numbers

Up to this point we have expressed the combining capacity of elements by means of valence. A valence number without a plus or minus sign does express the combining capacity of an element, but it does *not* indicate whether the atoms of the element play a positive or negative role in compounds. Consequently, we need a term that will describe the combining capacity of an element and that will *also* indicate the positive or negative nature of its atoms in compounds. Such a term is called the *oxidation number.* The oxidation number is related to, but not identical with, valence, as we shall see in the following discussion. In particular, the oxidation number shows the positive or negative nature of the atoms present in a compound.

When two or more atoms combine to form a compound, certain changes occur in their electronic arrangement. As stated in Chapter 3, three different types of electronic rearrangement may occur, leading to the formation of either (1) ionic compounds, (2) covalent compounds, or (3) the metallic state (p. 28).

Let us first deal briefly with ionic compounds. When reacting to form ionic compounds, the atoms of *some* elements give up one or more electrons, thereby becoming positive ions, while the atoms of *other* elements take on one or more electrons, thereby becoming negative ions. A compound that is formed by two such elements, one of each kind, is an ionic compound. In ionic compounds, *positive oxidation numbers* are used to express the combining capacity of the elements present as *positive ions,* and *negative oxidation numbers* are used to express the combining capacity of the elements present as *negative ions.* For example, in the ionic compound NaCl, the oxidation number of sodium is +1 and that of chlorine is −1; in the ionic compound BaO, the oxidation number of barium is +2 and that of oxygen is −2. Notice also that, the *ionic charge* of the monopositive sodium ion, Na^+, is +1, and the *ionic charge* of the dipositive barium ion, Ba^{++}, is +2. The *ionic charge* of the mononegative chloride ion, Cl^-, is −1, and the *ionic charge* of the dinegative oxide ion, $O^=$, is −2. In positive or negative monoatomic ions, the oxidation number is the same as the charge on the ion.

Now we shall consider covalent compounds in which, as we have seen, the atoms of the elements are linked by covalent bonds. In a covalent bond the electron pair is normally not shared equally between the linked atoms. The atom which attracts the electron pair more strongly (the more electronegative element) is assigned a negative oxidation number, and the partner element is assigned a positive oxidation number.* For example, in the covalent compound hydrogen chloride, HCl, the oxidation number of hydrogen is +1 and the oxidation number of chlorine is −1, since chlorine attracts the electron pair more strongly than does hydrogen. As we shall see in this and following chapters, the use of positive and negative oxidation numbers is convenient in writing formulas and in balancing equations.

We can illustrate the use of the terms "valence" and "oxidation number" by the formulas of various compounds. For example, copper has a valence of 1 and an oxidation number of +1 in the compound CuCl; it has a valence of 2 and an oxidation number of +2 in the compound $CuCl_2$. Copper exhibits variable valence, and its oxidation number varies from one compound to the other. Similarly, in the compounds represented by the formulas $FeCl_2$ and $FeCl_3$, iron exhibits variable valence and has oxidation numbers of +2 and +3. Tables 5-1, 5-2, and 5-3 list the oxidation numbers of some of the common elements.

In addition to those listed in Table 5-2, many other elements, both metals and nonmetals, have variable oxidation numbers.

TABLE 5-1 SOME ELEMENTS WITH POSITIVE OXIDATION NUMBERS (Ox. No.)

Element	Ox. No.
H	+1
Li	+1
Na	+1
K	+1
Rb	+1
Cs	+1
Be	+2
Mg	+2
Ca	+2
Sr	+2
Zn	+2
Cd*	+2
B	+3
Al	+3
Ga	+3

* There is evidence for the existence of $(Cd_2)^{++}$ ion (dimer) in solution, in which the ox. no. of Cd is +1.

* The relative electronegatives of the elements will be discussed in Chapter 14.

Some elements have more than two oxidation numbers, and some have both negative and positive oxidation numbers. For example, the oxidation number of hydrogen may be +1 or −1; that of chlorine, −1, +1, +3, +5, or +7.

5-3 Electronic Explanation of Combining Capacity

Now we are ready to discuss the oxidation numbers of the elements in terms of the changes that occur in the electron clouds surrounding their atoms.

OXIDATION NUMBERS OF ELEMENTS IN IONIC COMPOUNDS: IONIC CHARGE

We have seen that an atom which gives up one electron to form an ion with a single positive charge is said to have an oxidation number of +1, and that an atom which gives up two electrons to form an ion with a double positive charge (a dipositive ion) is said to have an oxidation number of +2. For monoatomic positive ions, the charge of the ion is also called the *ionic charge* and has the same meaning and value as the term oxidation number. Thus, a sodium atom, Na, which has given up one electron to form a sodium ion, Na^+, has an oxidation number of +1 and an ionic charge of +1. A calcium atom, Ca, that has given up two electrons to form a dipositive calcium ion, Ca^{++}, has an oxidation number of +2 and the calcium ion, Ca^{++}, has an *ionic charge* of +2. Similarly a copper atom, Cu, which has given up one electron to form the positive ion, Cu^+, with an ionic charge of +1, has an oxidation number of +1, whereas a copper atom which has given up two electrons to form the dipositive ion, Cu^{++}, with an ionic charge of +2, has an oxidation number of +2. For the metals with *fixed* positive oxidation numbers the oxidation number corresponds to the number (Roman numeral) of their group in the Periodic Table (see Table 5-12) and hence can be easily remembered. As shown in Table 5-13, the oxidation number of these fixed-valence metals corresponds to the number of valence electrons of the metal atom.

TABLE 5-2 COMMON METALLIC ELEMENTS WITH VARIABLE OXIDATION NUMBERS

Element	*Common Variable Oxidation Numbers*
Cu	+1 and +2
Hg	+1 and +2
Fe	+2 and +3
Sn	+2 and +4
Pb	+2 and +4

TABLE 5-3 SOME ELEMENTS WITH NEGATIVE OXIDATION NUMBERS

Element	*Ox. No.*
H	−1
F	−1
Cl	−1
Br	−1
I	−1
O	−2
S	−2
N	−3
P	−3

For elements with variable oxidation numbers, the oxidation number must be specified. For example, the ions Fe^{++} and Fe^{+++} are formed when an iron atom, Fe, gives up two and three electrons, respectively. Thus, the Fe^{++} ion has an ionic charge of +2 and an oxidation number of +2, and the Fe^{+++} ion has an ionic charge of +3 and an oxidation number of +3.

An atom that takes on one electron to form an ion with a single negative charge has an oxidation number of −1; an atom that takes on two electrons to form an ion with a double negative charge (a dinegative ion) has an oxidation number of −2. Thus, a chlorine atom, Cl, that has taken on one electron to form a chloride ion, Cl^-, has an oxidation number of −1, and the chloride ion, Cl^-, has an ionic charge of −1. An oxygen atom, O, which has taken on two electrons to form a negatively charged oxide ion, $O^=$, has an oxidation number of -2; and the oxide ion, $O^=$, has an ionic charge of -2.

Many of the non-metals show variable oxidation numbers. If one selects for each such element its lowest negative oxidation number then it is possible to relate *this* oxidation number to the position of the element in the Periodic Table. This lowest possible negative oxidation number of a non-metal corresponds to the number of electrons that this element needs in order to attain the eight valence electrons (the octet) that characterize the noble gas electron configuration.

OXIDATION NUMBERS OF ELEMENTS IN COVALENT COMPOUNDS

In Chapter 3 we found that the molecule of a covalent compound is held together by a sharing of electrons between atoms. An atom that shares one of its electrons in a covalent bond with another atom has a valence of 1; an atom that shares two of its electrons in two covalent bonds with one or more other atoms has a valence of 2. As we have already mentioned, when two atoms are held together by a covalent bond it is customary to assign the negative value of the oxidation number to the element which has the greater attraction for the electron pair of the bond, that is the more *electronegative* element. In the covalent compound hydrogen chloride, HCl, the hydrogen atom shares its one electron with the chlorine atom, and the chlorine atom shares one of its electrons with the hydrogen atom. The *more electronegative* chlorine atom is assigned an oxidation number of -1, whereas the *less electronegative* hydrogen atom is assigned an oxidation number of $+1$. In the covalent compound H_2O, each hydrogen atom is assigned an oxidation number of $+1$, because hydrogen is *less electronegative* than oxygen. The oxygen atom shares two of its electrons in two covalent bonds, one with each hydrogen atom; the oxidation number of the *more electronegative* oxygen atom in H_2O is therefore -2.

OXIDATION NUMBERS OF COMBINED ELEMENTS

An uncombined atom of any element (for example, an isolated atom, as represented by the symbols Fe, Cu, Na, S, Cl, and O) has an oxidation number of zero. Actually, the oxidation number of an element in its elementary form (as an atom, a molecule, or a crystal) is always zero. In fact, in a covalent bond between identical atoms, as in H_2, or Cl_2, the electron pair is shared *equally* between the atoms, so that each atom is assigned an oxidation number of zero. The atoms in the molecules represented by the formulas, H_2, Cl_2, O_2, P_4, and S_8, as well as those in a crystal of sodium metal and diamond, for example, all have a zero oxidation number.

IONIC CHARGES OF POLYATOMIC IONS

To be more inclusive, we should define an ion as a single atom or a group of atoms which has given up or taken on one or more electrons and thereby carries either a positive charge or a negative charge. A group of (two or more) atoms which has a positive or negative charge is called a *polyatomic ion.* The most common polyatomic ion with a positive charge is the ammonium ion, NH_4^+. Two common examples of negative polyatomic ions are the hydroxide ion, OH^-, and the sulfate ion, $SO_4^=$. The fact that a polyatomic ion has a positive or negative charge means that the ion has one or more electrons less than or in excess of the number of electrons possessed by the assemblage of the corresponding neutral atoms. For example, the ammonium ion, NH_4^+, carries an ionic charge of $+1$ because, as a unit, it possesses one electron less than the assemblage of one neutral N atom and four neutral H atoms. The hydroxide ion, OH^-, has an ionic charge of -1 because it has one electron more than the neutral OH group. The sulfate ion, $SO_4^=$, has an ionic charge of -2 because it has two electrons more than neutral SO_4. In referring to positive or negative polyatomic ions, we speak of the *ionic charge* of the polyatomic ion itself but of the *oxidation number* of each of the atoms of the elements present. The names, formulas, and ionic charges of some common negative polyatomic ions are given in Table 5-4.

5-4 Writing Formulas

Every chemical formula is derived from chemical analysis based on actual experiments carried out in the laboratory. But a knowledge of the oxidation numbers of elements and of ionic charges of monatomic and polyatomic ions is helpful in *remembering* the formulas of a great many compounds. For example, we can write the formula of an ionic compound if we know the ionic charges of the two (or more) entities which make it up. In the ionic compound the sum of the ionic charges of all the positive ions must be equal to the sum of the ionic charges of all the negative ions. Thus, the ionic compound barium bromide is composed of barium ions, Ba^{++}, and bromide ions, Br^-, and its formula must be $Ba^{++}Br^-Br^-$, or simply $Ba^{++}(Br^-)_2$. Similarly, the ionic compound iron(II) phosphate is composed of iron(II) ions, Fe^{++}, and phosphate ions, $(PO_4^{\equiv})$, and its formula must be $(Fe^{++})_3(PO_4^{\equiv})_2$.

THE SUMMATION ZERO RULE

In a neutral compound the positive oxidation numbers and the negative oxidation numbers of the atoms present always add up to zero (Summation Zero Rule). Thus, in the compound represented by the formula $MgCl_2$, magnesium has an oxidation number of +2, and each chlorine atom has an oxidation number of −1. So the sum of the positive and negative oxidation numbers is zero. In the compound represented by the formula BCl_3, boron has an oxidation number of +3, and each chlorine atom has an oxidation number of −1. Again, the sum of the oxidation numbers is zero.

TABLE 5-4 NAMES, FORMULAS, AND IONIC CHARGES OF SOME POLYATOMIC NEGATIVE IONS

Polyatomic Ion	*Formula*	*Ionic Charge*
Hydroxide	OH^-	−1
Acetate	$C_2H_3O_2^-$	−1
Perchlorate	ClO_4^-	−1
Chlorate	ClO_3^-	−1
Nitrate	NO_3^-	−1
Nitrite	NO_2^-	−1
Permanganate	MnO_4^-	−1
Hydrogen carbonate	HCO_3^-	−1
Carbonate	$CO_3^=$	−2
Sulfate	$SO_4^=$	−2
Sulfite	$SO_3^=$	−2
Chromate	$CrO_4^=$	−2
Dichromate	$Cr_2O_7^=$	−2
(ortho) Phosphate	$PO_4^{\equiv}$	−3
Arsenate	$AsO_4^{\equiv}$	−3

We can always write the formula of a compound if we know the oxidation numbers of the elements present, even without knowing whether the compound is ionic, covalent, or a blend of both. For example, since the oxidation number of calcium in the calcium ion, Ca^{++}, is +2, and the oxidation number of iodine in the iodide ion, I^-, is −1, we know that the formula of the compound formed by these ions is CaI_2. Also, if we know that the oxidation number of potassium is +1, and that the ionic charge of the sulfate ion, $SO_4^=$, is −2, we can write the formula for the compound formed by these ions, K_2SO_4. Similarly, if we want to write the formula of the compound composed of iron with an oxidation number of +2, and of the sulfate ion with an ionic charge of −2, we know that it must be $FeSO_4$.

Similar considerations permit us to determine the oxidation number of any one element in a compound if we know the oxidation numbers of all other elements present in the compound. For example, let us determine the oxidation number of phosphorus, P, in the compound phosphoric acid, H_3PO_4. The oxidation number of each oxygen, O, atom is -2, and the sum of the four oxygen atoms is $4 \times (-2) = -8$. The sum of the oxidation numbers of the three hydrogen atoms, H, is $3 \times (+1) = +3$. Thus, in order that the sum of the positive and negative oxidation numbers be zero in the compound H_3PO_4, the phosphorus atom, P, must have an oxidation number of +5: H_3PO_4 $(+3 + 5 - 8 = 0)$. A similar calculation $(+2 + 6 - 8 = 0)$ reveals that the oxidation number of sulfur, S, in the compound Na_2SO_4 is +6.

THE SUMMATION CHARGE RULE

In a polyatomic ion, the sum of all the positive and negative oxidation numbers of the elements must equal the ionic charge (Summation Charge Rule). Therefore we can determine the oxidation number of any one element in a polyatomic ion if we know the ionic charge of the polyatomic ion and the oxidation numbers of all the other elements present. For example, let us determine the oxidation number of phosphorus in the phosphate ion, $(PO_4)^{\equiv}$. Since each oxygen atom has an oxidation number of -2, the sum of the oxidation numbers of the four oxygen atoms is $4 \times (-2)$, or -8. Consequently, since the sum of all the oxidation numbers of the elements in the polyatomic ion, $(PO_4)^{\equiv}$, must equal the ionic charge of -3, the one phosphorus atom must be +5 in the $(PO_4)^{\equiv}$ ion: $(+5 - 8 = -3)$. Notice that the oxidation number of phosphorus is +5 in the phosphate ion, $(PO_4)^{\equiv}$, in the H_3PO_4 molecule, and also in the ionic compounds sodium phosphate, Na_3PO_4; calcium phosphate, $Ca_3(PO_4)_2$; and iron(III) phosphate, $Fe(PO_4)$. Similarly, we calculate that the oxidation number of the nitrogen atom in the nitrate ion, NO_3^{-1}, is $+5 (+5 - 6 = -1)$, whereas in the ammonium ion, NH_4^+, each hydrogen atom has an oxidation number of +1, and the nitrogen atom has an oxidation number of -3. In the permanganate ion, $(MnO_4)^{-1}$, each oxygen atom has an oxidation number of -2, and the manganese atom must have an oxidation number of +7, since the charge on the ion (ionic charge) is -1. Notice that in almost all compounds and ions that contain hydrogen and/or oxygen, hydrogen has an oxidation number of +1 and oxygen has an oxidation number of -2.

5-5 Nomenclature of Chemical Compounds

A chemical formula shows concisely the number of atoms of each element present in the compound. Consequently, chemists usually use formulas in referring to various substances. But each compound also has its specific *name.* Thus, the name "water" identifies the compound whose formula is H_2O. However, the name "water" and the formula H_2O have no systematic connection, and names of this sort are called *trivial.* Many trivial names are in common use. Here are some examples: ammonia for NH_3; sugar for $C_{12}H_{22}O_{11}$; alcohol for C_2H_5OH; borax for $Na_2B_4O_7 \cdot 10\,H_2O$; baking soda for $NaHCO_3$; and lye or caustic soda for NaOH. Obviously, the only way to remember the formula corresponding to a trivial name is to memorize it.

But there is a more precise way of naming chemical compounds. For example, the name given to the specific chemical substance whose formula is SO_2 is "sulfur dioxide." This is an example of what we call a *systematic name,* since the name ("sulfur di-oxide") tells us, just as the formula SO_2 does, that each molecule of the compound SO_2, is made up of one sulfur atom and two oxygen atoms chemically combined. Clearly, systematic names are generally preferable to trivial names.

The modern nomenclature of compounds is based on a systematic procedure which insures that each name is uniquely associated with a particular formula. First, we shall discuss the naming of binary compounds (compounds containing 2 elements), then ternary and higher compounds (those containing 3 or more elements). The naming of the compounds of hydrogen will be given special consideration.

BINARY COMPOUNDS

A binary compound contains only two elements in chemical combination. With a very few exceptions, the less electronegative element (or, as we may say, the more electropositive element) is placed first both in the formula and in the name. The name of a binary compound is formed by the name of the first element followed by the stem of the name of the second element and the ending *-ide.*

All binary compounds that contain an electropositive element with a fixed oxidation number are named in this way. For example, the compound $BaBr_2$ is called (barium brom-ide) barium bromide; the compound $AlCl_3$ is called aluminum chloride; and the compound H_2Se is called hydrogen selenide. But we must know the oxidation numbers of the elements in order to derive the formula from the name. For example, we connect the name "barium bromide" with the formula $BaBr_2$ only if we know that barium has a fixed oxidation number of $+2$ and that the bromide ion has an oxidation number of -1. And we link the name "hydrogen selenide" with the formula H_2Se only if we know that the oxidation number of hydrogen is $+1$ and that of selenium is -2. Therefore, the name should also in some manner convey information about the number of atoms of each element present in the compound, particularly for compounds of elements with variable oxidation numbers.

For convenience, we shall discuss the nomenclature of binary compounds in this order: (1) binary compounds containing two non-metals, (2) binary compounds containing a metal and a non-metal. We shall also consider a special system for naming water solutions of compounds that are composed of hydrogen and a non-metal.

BINARY COMPOUNDS CONTAINING TWO NON-METALS. In naming binary compounds composed of non-metals, Greek prefixes (Table 5-5) are used to indicate the number of each of the atoms present in the compound. However, the prefix "mono" is usually omitted so that the absence of a prefix denotes the presence of a single atom. The name is formed as follows:

1. Give the Greek prefix (except mono-) that indicates the number of atoms of the first element in the formula. Then add the name of this element.

2. Give the prefix (except mono-) that indicates the number of atoms of the second element in the formula and add the stem of the name of this element, with the ending *-ide.*

TABLE 5-5 GREEK PREFIXES

Number	Greek Prefix
$\frac{1}{2}$	hemi-
1	mono-
$1\frac{1}{2}$	sesqui-
2	di-
3	tri-
4	tetra-
5	penta-
6	hexa-
7	hepta-
8	octa-
9	ennea-
10	deca-

Here are some examples: The compound of formula As_2S_3 is called (di-arsenic tri-sulf-ide) diarsenic trisulfide; the name of the compound represented by the formula SO_2 is (sulfur di-oxide) sulfur dioxide. Table 5-6 lists other examples of how binary compounds containing two non-metals are named. The hyphens are included here for clarity but are omitted in actual practice.

This system of nomenclature enables us to distinguish between different compounds that contain the same two elements, such as the chlorides of phosphorus (PCl_3 and PCl_5) and the oxides of nitrogen (NO and N_2O_3).

BINARY COMPOUNDS CONTAINING A METAL AND A NON-METAL. In forming the complete name of compounds containing a metal and a non-metal, the oxidation number of the metal should be specified for compounds of metals with variable oxidation numbers.

TABLE 5-6 FORMULAS AND NAMES OF SOME BINARY COMPOUNDS OF NON-METALS

Formula of Compound	Greek Prefix + Name of First Element	Greek Prefix + Stem of Second Element + Ending -ide	Name of Compound (Common names in parentheses)
P_2S_5	di-phosphorus	penta-sulf-ide	diphosphorus pentasulfide (phosphorus pentasulfide)
SO_3	sulfur	tri-ox-ide	sulfur trioxide
CCl_4	carbon	tetra-chlor-ide	carbon tetrachloride
BCl_3	boron	tri-chlor-ide	boron trichloride
PCl_3	phosphorus	tri-chlor-ide	phosphorus trichloride
PCl_5	phosphorus	penta-chlor-ide	phosphorus pentachloride
N_2O	di-nitrogen	ox-ide	dinitrogen oxide (nitrous oxide)
NO	nitrogen	ox-ide	nitrogen oxide (nitric oxide)
N_2O_3	di-nitrogen	tri-ox-ide	dinitrogen trioxide (nitrogen trioxide)
N_2O_4	di-nitrogen	tetra-ox-ide	dinitrogen tetroxide* (nitrogen tetroxide)
N_2O_5	di-nitrogen	penta-ox-ide	dinitrogen pentoxide* (nitrogen pentoxide)

* Note that the "a" of tetra and penta is omitted when followed by a vowel. This is purely in the interests of pronunciation.

Compounds of Metals with Fixed Oxidation Numbers. As already stated, the name of a binary compound containing a metal with a fixed oxidation number and a non-metal is formed by the name of the metal followed by the stem of the non-metal with the ending *-ide*. For example, the compound CsBr is called cesium bromide and the compound CaF_2 is called calcium fluoride.

Compounds of Metals with Variable Oxidation Numbers. The name of a binary compound in which the metal has a variable valence is formed according to the same simple rule for compounds of metals with fixed valence, except that we must specify the oxidation number of the metal in the name of each compound. This is done by writing after the (common) name of the metal, the Roman numeral (in parentheses) that indicates its oxidation number.

For example, the name of the compound represented by the formula $FeCl_2$, in which iron has an oxidation number of $+2$, is iron(II) chloride. And the compound whose formula is $FeCl_3$, in which iron has an oxidation number of $+3$, is named iron(III) chloride. Table 5-7 gives the formulas and names of several compounds containing metals with variable oxidation numbers.

TABLE 5-7 SOME BINARY COMPOUNDS OF METALS WITH VARIABLE OXIDATION NUMBERS

Formula	Ox. No. of Metal	Name of Compound
CuCl	+1	copper(I) chloride
$CuCl_2$	+2	copper(II) chloride
$FeCl_2$	+2	iron(II) chloride
$FeCl_3$	+3	iron(III) chloride
Hg_2Cl_2*	+1	mercury(I) chloride
$HgCl_2$	+2	mercury(II) chloride
$SnCl_2$	+2	tin(II) chloride
$SnCl_4$	+4	tin(IV) chloride

* The formula of the mercury(I) ion (mercurous ion) is Hg_2^{++}. This dimer ion, Hg_2^{++} ($Hg^+ + Hg^+ = Hg_2^{++}$), is present in all mercury(I) (mercurous) compounds and remains a dimer ion, Hg_2^{++}, when these compounds dissolve in water (if they are water soluble).

Although the rule we have just given has been universally accepted, an older method is still sometimes used, in which the suffixes *-ous* and *-ic* serve to indicate, respectively, the lower and higher oxidation numbers of the positive element. Thus, in this older system the compound represented by the formula $FeCl_2$ is called ferr*ous* chloride, and the compound represented by the formula $FeCl_3$ is called ferr*ic* chloride. Generally, the stem of the Latin word for the metal is used in this older method.

Notice that the endings *-ous* and *-ic* are relative. For example, the oxidation number of copper in the *-ous* compound of copper, cuprous chloride, CuCl, is +1; and in the *-ic* compound of copper, cupric chloride, $CuCl_2$, it is +2. But in the *-ous* compound of iron, ferrous chloride, $FeCl_2$, the oxidation number of iron is +2, and in the *-ic* compound, ferric chloride, $FeCl_3$, it is +3.

The simplest and most precise method of naming compounds which contain elements with variable oxidation numbers is to indicate the oxidation number by a Roman numeral (in parentheses) as explained above. But since the *-ous* and *-ic* terminology is still sometimes used and appears in older books and journals, the student of chemistry must be familiar with both systems.

BINARY COMPOUNDS CONTAINING HYDROGEN. When binary compounds of hydrogen and a non-metal are in their gaseous or pure liquid state—that is, when they exist as covalent compounds, they are named in the same way as other binary compounds of non-metals. For example, the gaseous compound, HCl, is called hydrogen chloride; HBr is called hydrogen bromide; and HI is called hydrogen iodide.

When certain binary compounds of hydrogen with non-metals are dissolved in water, however, the properties of the water solution of the compound are drastically different from the properties of the pure gas or liquid. For this reason, different names are used for water solutions of these compounds. In naming water solutions of binary compounds of hydrogen with non-metals which form acid solutions (see Chapter 20), we use the prefix *hydro-* followed by the *stem* of the name of the non-metal, plus the suffix *-ic*. This word is followed by the word *acid.* Thus, a water solution of hydrogen chloride, HCl, is called (hydro-chlor-ic acid), hydrochloric acid. The names of some common binary compounds of hydrogen with non-metals, together with those of their water solutions (acids), are listed in Table 5-10.

TERNARY AND HIGHER COMPOUNDS OF METALS

Many compounds contain a metal ion and a polyatomic anion.* In naming ternary compounds of this type, we follow the same rule used in naming binary compounds of metals, but instead of writing the name of the monoatomic anion, we write the name of the polyatomic anion. The names and formulas of some common polyatomic negative ions were given in Table 5-4 (p. 56). Thus we can name ternary and higher compounds by giving first the name of the metallic element (followed if necessary by the Roman numeral in parentheses to indicate its oxidation state), and then the name of the polyatomic anion. For example, the compound $Na(NO_3)$ is called sodium nitrate, the compound $Al_2(SO_4)_3$ is called aluminum sulfate, and $FeSO_4$ is called iron(II) sulfate. The formulas and names of some

TABLE 5-8 COMPOUNDS CONTAINING METALS WITH FIXED OXIDATION NUMBERS AND POLYATOMIC IONS

Formula	Name
$Mg(NO_3)_2$	magnesium nitrate
KOH	potassium hydroxide
Na_2SO_4	sodium sulfate
$Ca_3(PO_4)_2$	calcium phosphate
$Al_2(SO_4)_3$	aluminum sulfate
$NaHCO_3$	sodium hydrogen carbonate

* An anion equals a negatively charged ion.

common compounds containing polyatomic ions are given in Table 5-8; Table 5-9 lists the formulas and names of compounds that contain polyatomic ions together with metals with variable oxidation numbers.

In naming compounds that contain hydrogen and polyatomic negative ions, the word "hydrogen" is used followed by the name of the polyatomic anion. Thus, just as HCl is called hydrogen chloride, so HNO_3 is called hydrogen nitrate, and H_2SO_4 is called hydrogen sulfate.

TABLE 5-9 COMPOUNDS CONTAINING METALS WITH VARIABLE OXIDATION NUMBERS AND POLYATOMIC IONS

Formula	*Name*
$FeSO_4$	iron(II) sulfate
$Fe_2(SO_4)_3$	iron(III) sulfate
$Fe(NO_3)_3$	iron(III) nitrate
Cu_2SO_4	copper(I) sulfate
$CuSO_4$	copper(II) sulfate
$Cu_3(PO_4)_2$	copper(II) phosphate
$Ti_2(SO_4)_3$	titanium(III) sulfate
$Ti(SO_4)_2$	titanium(IV) sulfate
$Hg_2(NO_3)_2$	mercury(I) nitrate
$Hg(NO_3)_2$	mercury(II) nitrate

For compounds which contain both metal ions, hydrogen ions, and polyatomic negative ions, Greek prefixes are used to indicate the number of metal ions and the number of hydrogen ions present. For example, NaH_2PO_4 is called sodium dihydrogen phosphate, and $CaHPO_4$ is called calcium hydrogen phosphate; but Na_2HPO_4 is called disodium hydrogen phosphate.

OXYACIDS AND THEIR SALTS

As with the covalent binary compounds of hydrogen with non-metals, the properties of water solutions of ternary compounds that contain hydrogen and a polyatomic anion composed of a non-metal and oxygen, such as HNO_3 and H_2SO_4, are drastically different from the properties of these compounds in their pure gaseous or liquid states. Water solutions of this class of compounds are known as oxygen-acids, or simply oxyacids. In general, the names of the oxyacids are formed from the stem of the name of the non-metal present in the polyatomic anion, to which is added the ending *-ic* followed by the word "acid." For example, hydrogen sulfate, H_2SO_4, in water solution is called sulfuric acid; a water solution of hydrogen nitrate, HNO_3, is called nitric acid, and a water solution of hydrogen phosphate, H_3PO_4, is called phosphoric acid. Other examples of formulas and names of compounds containing hydrogen with polyatomic negative ions and their water solutions (acids) are given in Table 5-10.

When a non-metal forms two ternary oxyacids that contain a lower and a higher

TABLE 5-10 NAMES OF SOME COMMON BINARY AND HIGHER ACIDS

Name of Gas or Liquid	*Formula of Hydrogen Compound*	*Name of Water Solution of Hydrogen Compound, i.e., Acid*
hydrogen chloride	HCl	hydrochloric acid
hydrogen bromide	HBr	hydrobromic acid
hydrogen iodide	HI	hydriodic acid
hydrogen sulfide	H_2S	hydrosulfuric acid
hydrogen selenide	H_2Se	hydroselenic acid
hydrogen nitrate	HNO_3	nitric acid
hydrogen acetate	$HC_2H_3O_2$	acetic acid
hydrogen sulfate	H_2SO_4	sulfuric acid
hydrogen phosphate	H_3PO_4	phosphoric acid

oxidation number of the non-metal, the suffix terminology is used to differentiate between these two acids. The name of the acid containing the non-metal with the *higher* oxidation number carries the *-ic* suffix (as in naming the binary acids), and the name of the other acid containing this non-metal with the *lower* oxidation number ends in *-ous.* For example, the formulas of the two common oxyacids of sulfur are $H_2\overset{+6}{S}O_4$ and $H_2\overset{+4}{S}O_3$. And since sulfur has the higher oxidation number (+6) in the acid H_2SO_4, this acid is called sulfur*ic* acid; and the acid H_2SO_3, in which sulfur has the lower oxidation number (+4), is called sulfur*ous* acid. Similarly, HNO_3 and HNO_2 are the formulas of the two common oxyacids of nitrogen. The acid $H\overset{+5}{N}O_3$ is called nitr*ic* acid and the acid $H\overset{+3}{N}O_2$ is called nitr*ous* acid. Notice again that the endings *-ic* and *-ous* indicate only the *relative* oxidation numbers of the same non-metal in the two related oxyacids. Thus, for H_2SO_4 and H_2SO_3, the oxidation numbers of sulfur in the *-ic* and *-ous* compounds are +6 and +4, respectively, but the oxidation numbers of nitrogen in the nitr*ic* and nitr*ous* acids, HNO_3 and HNO_2, are +5 and +3, respectively.

The names of oxyacid anions are generally derived from the name of the oxyacid by changing the *-ic* suffix to *-ate;* if the name of the acid carries the *-ous* suffix, the *-ous* changes to *-ite* in the name of the anion. For example, the anion of nitr*ic* acid, $H\overset{+5}{N}O_3$ is called nitr*ate,* $\overset{+5}{N}O_3^-$, and the anion of nitr*ous* acid, $H\overset{+3}{N}O_2$ is called nitr*ite,* $\overset{+3}{N}O_2^-$. Similarly, the anion of sulfur*ic* acid $H_2\overset{+6}{S}O_4$, is called sulf*ate,* $\overset{+6}{S}O_4^=$, and the anion of sulfur*ous* acid, $H_2\overset{+4}{S}O_3$, is called sulf*ite* $\overset{+4}{S}O_3^=$.

Some non-metals form a series of three or more oxyacids in which the same (non-metal) element has three or more oxidation numbers. To name such acids we take as our reference the *-ous* and *-ic* suffixes assigned to two of the oxyacids of the non-metal under consideration. The member of the series of oxyacids which contains the non-metal with an oxidation number *lower* than the *-ous* acid is named by adding the prefix *hypo-* to the name of the *-ous* acid. For example, chlorine forms the series of oxyacids $H\overset{+1}{Cl}O_4$, $H\overset{+5}{Cl}O_3$, $H\overset{+3}{Cl}O_2$, $H\overset{+1}{Cl}O$. Of these, $H\overset{+5}{Cl}O_3$, is called chlor*ic* acid and

TABLE 5-11 NAMES AND FORMULAS OF SOME OXYACIDS AND THEIR METAL SALTS

Name of Acid	Formula of Acid	Formula of Metal Salt	Name of Metal Salt
nitrous acid	$H\overset{+3}{N}O_2$	$Ca(\overset{+3}{N}O_2)_2$	calcium nitrite
nitric acid	$H\overset{+5}{N}O_3$	$Fe(\overset{+5}{N}O_3)_3$	iron(III) nitrate
arsenious acid	$H_3\overset{+3}{As}O_3$	$K_3\overset{+3}{As}O_3$	potassium arsenite
arsenic acid	$H_3\overset{+5}{As}O_4$	$Zn_3(\overset{+5}{As}O_4)_2$	zinc arsenate
manganic acid	$H_2\overset{+6}{Mn}O_4$	$K_2\overset{+6}{Mn}O_4$	potassium manganate
permanganic acid	$H\overset{+7}{Mn}O_4$	$K\overset{+7}{Mn}O_4$	potassium permanganate
chloric acid	$H\overset{+5}{Cl}O_3$	$Na\overset{+5}{Cl}O_3$	sodium chlorate
perchloric acid	$H\overset{+7}{Cl}O_4$	$Sn(\overset{+7}{Cl}O_4)_2$	tin(II) perchlorate
hypophosphorous acid	$H_3\overset{+1}{P}O_2$	$NaH_2\overset{+1}{P}O_2$	sodium dihydrogen hypophosphite
phosphorous acid	$H_3\overset{+3}{P}O_3$	$CaH\overset{+3}{P}O_3$	calcium hydrogen phosphite
phosphoric acid	$H_3\overset{+5}{P}O_4$	$Cu_3(\overset{+5}{P}O_4)_2$	copper(II) phosphate

$H\overset{+3}{Cl}O_2$ is called chlor*ous*. The name of the compound HClO then becomes *hypo*-chlor*ous* acid. The prefix *hypo*- is a Greek word meaning *lower*, and generally oxyacids to which the prefix *hypo*- and the suffix *-ous* have been added have an oxidation number two units lower than the related oxyacid that ends in *-ous*. On the other hand, an oxyacid which contains the non-metal element with an oxidation number *higher* than the oxidation number of the *-ic* acid is named by adding the prefix *per*- to the name of the *-ic* acid. Thus, since the acid $H\overset{+5}{Cl}O_3$, is called chloric acid, $H\overset{+7}{Cl}O_4$ is called *per*chlor*ic* acid. The oxyacid of manganese represented by the formula $H_2\overset{+6}{Mn}O_4$ is called mangan*ic* acid, and the oxyacid $H\overset{+7}{Mn}O_4$, which contains manganese with a higher oxidation number (+7), is called *per*mangan*ic* acid. The names of the anions, and thus the names of the metal salts derived from oxyacids which carry the prefixes *hypo*- and *per*-, retain these prefixes. Again, the *-ous* suffix of the acid becomes *-ite* and the *-ic* suffix becomes *-ate*. The acid $H\overset{+1}{Cl}O$ is called *hypo*chlor*ous* acid, the $\overset{+1}{Cl}O^-$ ion is called *hypo*chlor*ite*, and the salt $Na\overset{+1}{Cl}O$ is called sodium *hypo*chlor*ite*. The acid $H\overset{+7}{Cl}O_4$ is called *per*chlor*ic* acid, the ClO_4^- ion is called *per*chlor*ate*, and the salt $Cu(ClO_4)_2$ is called copper(II) *per*chlor*ate*. Table 5-11 lists the formulas and the names of a number of oxyacids and their metal salts.

5-6 Introduction to the Periodic System (Table)

CLASSIFICATION OF THE ELEMENTS

Science, as we have said, is an organized body of knowledge. But one serious difficulty which always arises in presenting an introductory course in science is to find some systematic scheme of arrangement so that some topics are not presented as isolated facts and others are not introduced before a student has enough information at his disposal to understand them.

In the last few pages of this chapter we are going to introduce a classification of the elements known as the periodic system. Such a system will correlate in an orderly manner a number of facts you already have learned and it will help you to anticipate other facts that we have not yet covered. For the purposes of simplification, we shall limit our discussion of the periodic system to some 25 common elements, together with a group of 6 elements called the noble gases. In Chapter 12 we shall then consider the periodic system in more detail. The periodic system is an orderly arrangement of the elements which seeks to bring out certain physical and chemical relationships between and among the elements. Let us consider the first twenty elements, starting with hydrogen ($_1H$) and extending through calcium ($_{20}Ca$). The subscript preceding each chemical symbol represents the atomic number of the element, the number of protons in the nucleus, and the total number of electrons in the electron cloud of an atom of the element (see Table 5-12). When the elements are arranged in order of increasing atomic number (see p. 22), every ninth element (including the noble gas) exhibits similar physical and chemical properties, so we can arrange these elements in rows and columns, as shown in Table 5-12. Each of the first seven columns, or groups, shown in the table is denoted by a Roman numeral, I–VII; the last column is labeled 0. The first element, hydrogen, $_1H$, is included in the first vertical column, called Group I. The second element, helium, $_2He$, is at the top of the last column (that is, Group 0). Lithium, $_3Li$, is placed in Group I, below $_1H$, hydrogen; and $_4Be$, beryllium, appears in Group II. The next six elements, $_5B$, $_6C$, $_7N$, $_8O$, $_9F$, and $_{10}Ne$ occupy successively Groups III, IV, V, VI, VII, and 0. When we come to the next element, sodium, $_{11}Na$, we find that it can best be placed in Group I, under $_3Li$, an element very similar in physical and chemical properties. Next, $_{12}Mg$ falls into Group II, below $_4Be$—again, two elements that have many similar physical and chem-

TABLE 5-12 PERIODIC TABLE (PARTIAL LISTING)

Alkali Metals	Alkaline-Earth Metals				Oxygen-Sulfur Group	Halogens	Noble Gases
I	*II*	*III*	*IV*	*V*	*VI*	*VII*	*0*
$_1H$						$_1H$	$_2He$
$_3Li$	$_4Be$	$_5B$	$_6C$	$_7N$	$_8O$	$_9F$	$_{10}Ne$
$_{11}Na$	$_{12}Mg$	$_{13}Al$	$_{14}Si$	$_{15}P$	$_{16}S$	$_{17}Cl$	$_{18}Ar$
$_{19}K$	$_{20}Ca$					$_{35}Br$	$_{36}Kr$
$_{37}Rb$	$_{38}Sr$					$_{53}I$	$_{54}Xe$
$_{55}Cs$	$_{56}Ba$					$_{85}At$	$_{86}Rn$
$_{87}Fr$	$_{88}Ra$						

ical properties. Similarly for Group III—$_{13}Al$ falls under $_5B$. Then, in Group IV, $_{14}Si$ falls under $_6C$; in Group V, $_{15}P$ is under $_7N$; in Group VI, $_{16}S$ falls under $_8O$; in Group VII, $_{17}Cl$ lines up under $_9F$; and, finally, in Group 0, $_{18}Ar$ falls under $_{10}Ne$ and $_2He$. Thus, we find in each of Groups I, II, III, IV, V, VI, and VII two elements which are very similar in physical and chemical properties; and in Group 0, three elements—He, Ne, and Ar—which share common properties. Potassium, $_{19}K$, the nineteenth element, falls beneath $_{11}Na$ and $_3Li$ in Group I, all three elements exhibiting similar physical and chemical characteristics. The same is true of calcium, $_{20}Ca$, and of $_{12}Mg$ and $_4Be$ in Group II. For this introductory discussion, we will omit the next 14 elements and proceed to bromine, $_{35}Br$. This element falls into Group VII and again possesses physical and chemical properties similar to the elements above it in the same group—$_9F$, $_{17}Cl$. A comparable situation holds for the other elements listed in Table 5-12. Hence, such an arrangement reveals a periodic recurrence of physical and chemical properties among elements.

The elements of Group I: lithium, Li; sodium, Na; potassium, K; rubidium, Rb; cesium, Cs; and francium, Fr, are members of the same family and are known collectively as the *alkali metals.* The alkali metals are among the most electropositive (least electronegative) of all the elements, and in their compounds they always have an oxidation number of $+1$. These elements are extremely soft (they can be cut with a knife), have the lowest densities of all the metals, and have low melting points (all except Li melt below 100°C).

The Group II elements—beryllium, Be; magnesium, Mg; calcium, Ca; strontium, Sr; barium, Ba; and radium, Ra—constitute another family called the *alkaline-earth metals.* The first element of Group II, beryllium, Be, differs in some respects from the other members of this group, as does the second member, magnesium, Mg, though to a lesser extent than beryllium. Calcium, Ca; strontium, Sr; barium, Ba; and radium, Ra, the remaining members of Group II, are often called the principal members of the alkaline-earth family. Compared to the alkali metals, the alkaline-earth metals are much harder and have higher melting points.

The elements of Group VII—fluorine, F; chlorine, Cl; bromine, Br; iodine, I; and astatine, At—are called the *halogens.* Elements of Group 0—helium, He; neon, Ne; argon, Ar; krypton, Kr; xenon, Xe; and radon, Rn—are called the *noble gases.* Similar physical and chemical properties characterize all members of the same group, including Groups III, IV, V, VI, and VII, of which we have covered only the first two members. Hence, the word "periodic" in our classification indicates that when the elements are arranged in order of increasing atomic number, those with similar chemical and physical properties occur in the classification at periodic (or regular) intervals.

We shall now reconsider in the light of this partial listing of the periodic system some of the topics we have already discussed, such as metals and non-metals, oxidation numbers, ionic charges, ionic compounds, and covalent compounds. And as a result, we shall see how these topics can all be correlated.

METALS AND NON-METALS. All the elements listed in Group I (the alkali metals) and Group II (the alkaline-earth metals), together with aluminum, Al, and the other unlisted elements of Group III: gallium, Ga; indium, In; and thallium, Tl, are classified as metals and exhibit metallic properties. Furthermore, as we go down the list of a particular group, the elements in the group generally become more metallic, which permits us to generalize that the unlisted elements of Group III are metallic—in fact, more so than aluminum (or boron). The first member of Group III, boron, (B), is a border-line element which exhibits non-metallic as well as metallic properties. Generally, if any member of a given group displays properties different from the other members, it is the one listed at the top of the group. In fact, in Group I, lithium is less like sodium than any two successive metals of this group are like each other. And in Group II, beryllium is less like magnesium than any two successive members of this group are like each other.

All the elements in Groups IV to VII in this partial listing of the Periodic Table are non-metals. Moreover, the non-metallic properties of the non-metals grow more pronounced as we move across the Table from Group IV to Group VII (the halogens). Precisely the same is true of the first member of each of these groups as was true with Groups I to III; namely, that it exhibits some properties which are different from those of the other members of that Group.

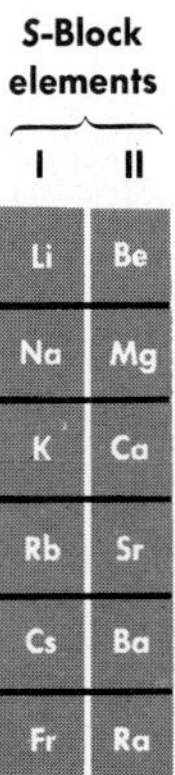

The elements of Group 0 exhibit unusual properties characteristic only of this group, and for this reason are considered separately. As the name "noble gas" implies, these elements are gases and in general their reactivity is very low, although some of them enter into chemical combination with some non-metals—for example, fluorine and oxygen.

OXIDATION NUMBERS, IONIC CHARGES, POSITIVE AND NEGATIVE IONS. The alkali metals (Li, Na, K, Rb, Cs, and Fr) have a fixed oxidation number of +1, and the alkaline-earth metals (Be, Mg, Ca, Sr, Ba, and Ra) have a fixed oxidation number of +2, and are often called S-block elements. A simple and effective way to understand and remember that the alkali metals form monopositive ions and that the alkaline-earth metals form dipositive ions is to refer to the dots about the symbols in Table 5-13,

TABLE 5-13 PERIODIC TABLE OF SOME ELEMENTS WITH THEIR ELECTRON-DOT FORMULAS

I	II	III	IV	V	VI	VII	0
H·						H·	He:
Li·	Be·	·B·	·C·	·N·	:O·	:F·	:Ne:
Na·	Mg·	·Al·	·Si·	·P·	:S·	:Cl·	:Ar:
K·	Ca·					:Br·	:Kr:
Rb·	Sr·					:I·	:Xe:
Cs·	Ba·					:At·	:Rn:
Fr·	Ra·						

which is the same partial listing of the elements as in Table 5-12. Hydrogen, $_1H$, is placed both in Group I (although a little aside from the alkali metals) and Group VII (although a little aside from the halogens) because as we shall see hydrogen has some properties in common with the members of both these groups. In Table 5-13 the symbols represent the core of the atom—its nucleus and all the electrons except the outermost ones—and each dot represents one of these outermost electrons. These outermost electrons, which may be involved in chemical reactions, are called valence electron(s) because they enable us to explain the combining power or valence of atoms (see pp. 51, 53). The symbol of an element together with its valence electron(s) is called the electron-dot formula. In Group I, the atom of each alkali metal has one valence electron and its electron-dot formula is represented by the symbol of the element together with one dot. In ionic compound formation, this one valence electron is given up to produce a monopositive ion. For example, the electron-dot formula of the sodium atom (of Group I) contains one valence electron, Na·, and in forming an ionic compound (such as Na^+Cl^-) the sodium atom gives up this one electron to form a monopositive ion, Na^+, as follows: $\text{Na}\cdot \longrightarrow \text{Na}^+ + 1\,e^-$.

Also, each of the atoms of the alkaline-earth metals in Group II has two valence electrons, and in the process of forming ionic compounds they give up these two electrons and form dipositive ions. For example, the electron-dot formula of the Group II calcium atom is $\dot{\text{Ca}}\cdot$, and the atom gives up these two electrons to form the dipositive calcium ion, Ca^{++}, as follows:

$$\dot{\text{Ca}}\cdot \longrightarrow \text{Ca}^{++} + 2\,e^-$$

The Group III aluminum atom, Al, has three valence electrons, and $\cdot\dot{\text{Al}}\cdot$ is its electron-dot formula. In forming ionic compounds, this atom has to give up these three electrons to become the tripositive aluminum ion, Al^{+++}.

$$\cdot\dot{\text{Al}}\cdot \longrightarrow \text{Al}^{+++} + 3\,e^-$$

Now let us summarize the material we have just covered. In forming ionic compounds, the atoms of the alkali metals of Group I give up their one valence electron to form monopositive ions, and the atoms of the alkaline-earth metals of Group II give up their two valence electrons to form dipositive ions. Similarly, in forming ionic compounds, aluminum and the metal atoms below it in Group III give up their three valence electrons to form tripositive ions.

Now let us focus our attention on the noble gases of Group 0. As we have already mentioned, the atoms of these elements do not combine readily with either the metals or the non-metals. These elements have eight valence electrons (except He, which has two, and which we will consider later). Since the atoms of these noble gases do not easily enter into chemical combination, we can conclude that an arrangement of eight valence electrons (octet) is particularly stable. The atoms of the elements of the halogen family of Group VII have seven valence electrons, and in forming ionic compounds, they take on one electron, thereby establishing an eight-electron shell (octet; Ch. 13) similar to the neighboring noble gas atoms in Group 0. Of course, when a halogen atom, X, takes on one electron, a mononegative halide ion, X^-, is formed. For example, when a chlorine atom, whose electron-dot formula is $:\ddot{\text{Cl}}\cdot$, takes on one electron in the formation of an ionic compound (Na^+Cl^-, for example), it forms the mononegative chloride ion, $:\ddot{\underset{..}{\text{Cl}}}:^-$, which has eight valence electrons similar to the eight valence electrons possessed by the argon atom, $:\ddot{\underset{..}{\text{Ar}}}:$ which is, of course, electrically neutral.

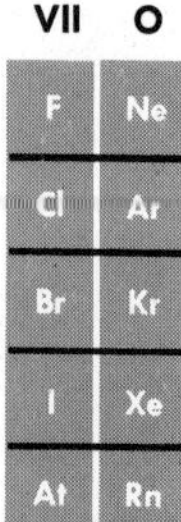

$$:\ddot{\underset{..}{\text{Cl}}}\cdot + 1\,e^- \longrightarrow :\ddot{\underset{..}{\text{Cl}}}:^-$$

Similarly, the atoms of each of the other halogens of Group VII take on one electron to form mononegative halide ions, ending up with eight valence electrons similar to the electronic arrangement of their neighboring noble gas atoms. This process is represented by the following general equation, where X stands for the halogen atom and X^- for the halide ion.

$$:\ddot{\underset{\cdot\cdot}{X}}\cdot + 1\,e^- \longrightarrow :\ddot{\underset{\cdot\cdot}{X}}:^-$$

The members of the oxygen-sulfur family of Group VI have six valence electrons. In forming ionic compounds, these atoms take on two electrons to form dinegative ions that have eight valence electrons similar to the atoms of the neighboring noble gases, neon and argon. Thus, the oxygen atom, whose electron-dot formula is $.\ddot{\underset{\cdot}{O}}:$, takes on *two* electrons in forming the dinegative oxide, ion, $(:\ddot{\underset{\cdot\cdot}{O}}:^{=})$.

$$.\ddot{\underset{\cdot}{O}}: + 2\,e^- \longrightarrow :\ddot{\underset{\cdot\cdot}{O}}:^{=}$$

And the sulfur atom, $.\ddot{\underset{\cdot}{S}}:$, in forming an ionic compound (e.g., $Ca^{++}S^{=}$), takes on two electrons to form the dinegative sulfide ion, $:\ddot{\underset{\cdot\cdot}{S}}:^{=}$. To summarize, the atoms of Group VII (the halogens) have seven valence electrons, and in forming ionic compounds, take on one electron to form mononegative ions. Similarly, the atoms of Group VI (the oxygen-sulfur group) have six valence electrons and take on two electrons to form dinegative ions.

IONIC COMPOUNDS. We have already pointed out that in forming compounds the atoms of the elements of Groups I and II give up one and two electrons to form monopositive and dipositive ions respectively, and that the atoms of Groups VII and VI take on one and two electrons to form mononegative and dinegative ions respectively. Consequently, we would expect that binary compounds composed of a Group I metal and a Group VII non-metal would be *ionic* compounds composed of a monopositive alkali metal ion, M^+, and a mononegative halide ion, X^-, arranged in a crystal, M^+X^-. And this is the case, for example, with sodium chloride, Na^+Cl^-, and potassium bromide, K^+Br^-, which are ionic compounds. In general, a binary compound composed of a Group I or Group II metal and a Group VI or Group VII non-metal will be an ionic compound. The ionic compounds rubidium oxide, $(Rb^+)_2O^{=}$, magnesium chloride, $Mg^{++}(Cl^-)_2$, and calcium oxide, $Ca^{++}O^{=}$, are examples.

Now let us return to the hydrogen atom, $H\cdot$, with its one (valence) electron. Hydrogen is placed in both Group I and Group VII, because, as we said, it has some properties in common with the elements of both groups. Like the alkali-metal atoms of Group I, the hydrogen atom has the capacity to give up its one valence electron in certain chemical reactions to form a monopositive hydrogen ion, (H^+):

$$H\cdot \longrightarrow H^+ + 1\,e^-$$

On the other hand, the hydrogen atom is similar to the halogen atoms of Group VII in that it can take on one electron (in certain other chemical reactions) to form a mononegative (hydride) ion, $(H:^-)$.

$$H\cdot + 1\,e^- \longrightarrow H:^-$$

Notice that when the hydrogen atom takes on one electron, the resulting hydride ion, $H:^-$, has two electrons similar to the two electrons of the helium atom, He:. Similarly, when a halogen atom takes on one electron to become a halide ion, it then has eight valence electrons similar to the nearest inert-gas atom in the Periodic Table. Of the atoms of the noble gases, only helium has a stable electron arrangement consisting of two valence electrons; all the others have eight. Examples of ionic compounds in which hydrogen is present as a mononegative hydride ion are sodium hydride, Na^+H^-, and calcium hydride, $Ca^{++}(H^-)_2$.

OXIDATION NUMBER; SHARING OF ELECTRONS; COVALENT COMPOUNDS. The Periodic Table is also very useful in helping to explain the formation of covalent molecules and compounds that result from the sharing of electrons. A Group VII halogen atom with seven valence electrons can, by sharing one of its electrons with another atom (of the same or a different element) and in turn sharing one electron from its new partner atom, achieve an arrangement of eight valence electrons. Thus, the halogen atom assumes an electronic configuration of eight valence electrons similar to that of a noble gas atom. For example, a chlorine atom with seven valence electrons can share one of its electrons with another chlorine atom that has seven valence electrons, so we assume that each chlorine atom in the chlorine molecule has eight valence electrons. In the diatomic molecule Cl_2, the chlorine atoms share a pair of electrons:

$$:\underset{\cdot\cdot}{\ddot{Cl}}\cdot + \cdot\underset{\cdot\cdot}{\ddot{Cl}}: \longrightarrow :\underset{\cdot\cdot}{\ddot{Cl}}:\underset{\cdot\cdot}{\ddot{Cl}}:$$

The molecules of the other halogens—F_2, Br_2, I_2, and At_2—are also diatomic and are held together by sharing a pair of electrons. Hydrogen bromide, HBr, is an example of a covalent compound containing two different atoms—hydrogen and bromine. In the covalent HBr molecule, the bromine atom has eight valence electrons, similar to the stable electronic configuration of the krypton atom, $:\underset{\cdot\cdot}{\ddot{Kr}}:$, and the hydrogen atom has two electrons, similar to the stable electronic configuration of the helium atom, (He:).

$$H\cdot + \cdot\underset{\cdot\cdot}{\ddot{Br}}: \longrightarrow H:\underset{\cdot\cdot}{\ddot{Br}}:$$

You will recall (p. 58) that in binary compounds formed by two non-metals, the less electronegative atom (written first in the formula) is assigned the positive oxidation number and the more electronegative atom (written last in the formula) is assigned the negative oxidation number. Thus in the covalent compound HBr, the hydrogen atom is assigned an oxidation number of $+1$, and the bromine atom an oxidation number of -1.

We know that a Group VII halogen atom can form a covalent bond with another atom (of the same or of a different element) to form a diatomic molecule. If the halogen atom is more electronegative than its partner atom, it is assigned an oxidation number of -1. If it is equally as electronegative as its partner atom (as in a diatomic molecule in which both atoms are the same, i.e., a homonuclear diatomic molecule), it is assigned an oxidation number of 0. If the halogen atom is less electronegative than its partner atom, it is assigned an oxidation number of $+1$. Thus, in the covalent compound BrCl, the bromine atom, which is less electronegative, is assigned an oxidation number of $+1$, and the chlorine atom, which is more electronegative, is assigned an oxidation number of -1.

The atoms of the elements of Group VI can share two of their valence electrons with one or two partner atoms. For example, one oxygen atom (the electron-dot formula is $\cdot\underset{\cdot}{\ddot{O}}:$) can share two of its electrons with two atoms of hydrogen (the electron-dot formula is $\cdot H$) to form the covalent water molecule H_2O.

$$\cdot\underset{\cdot}{\ddot{O}}: + \cdot H + \cdot H \longrightarrow \begin{array}{c} H:\ddot{O}: \\ \ \ \ \ \ \underset{\cdot\cdot}{} \\ H \end{array}$$

Hydrogen is the less electronegative element and therefore each hydrogen atom is assigned an oxidation number of $+1$, whereas the more electronegative oxygen atom is assigned an oxidation number of -2.

In their covalent compounds the atoms of Group V share three of their valence electrons with other atoms. The compound ammonia, NH_3, is an example of a covalent compound in which the nitrogen atom shares three of its valence electrons with three hydrogen atoms.

$$\cdot\underset{\cdot}{\ddot{N}}\cdot + \cdot H + \cdot H + \cdot H \longrightarrow \begin{array}{c} H:\ddot{N}:H \\ \underset{\cdot\cdot}{} \\ H \end{array}$$

In ammonia, the nitrogen atom is the more electronegative atom and is assigned an oxidation number of −3; and according to our general rule for writing formulas for binary compounds of two non-metal elements, the formula for ammonia should be written as H_3N. However, chemists always write NH_3 as the formula of ammonia, since this formula was in use long before the rules were formulated and so is still retained.

The atoms of Group IV share four electrons with partner atoms to form covalent compounds. For example, the carbon atom (electron-dot $\cdot\dot{\underset{\cdot}{C}}\cdot$) can share its four valence electrons with four hydrogen atoms (electron-dot formula $\cdot H$) to form the covalent compound methane, CH_4.

$$\cdot\dot{\underset{\cdot}{C}}\cdot + 4\ \cdot H \longrightarrow H:\overset{\displaystyle H}{\underset{\displaystyle H}{\ddot{\underset{..}{C}}}}:H$$

In methane the carbon atom is the more electronegative element and is assigned an oxidation number of −4. Again, the formula of the covalent compound methane, CH_4 (like the formula of ammonia, NH_3), should, according to our rules, be H_4C; but common usage dictates that it be written CH_4. A carbon atom can also share its four valence electrons with four chlorine atoms to form the covalent compound carbon tetrachloride, CCl_4.

$$\cdot\dot{\underset{\cdot}{C}}\cdot + 4\ \cdot\ddot{\underset{..}{Cl}}: \longrightarrow :\ddot{\underset{..}{Cl}}:\overset{\displaystyle :Cl:}{\underset{\displaystyle :\underset{..}{Cl}:}{\ddot{\underset{..}{C}}}}:\ddot{\underset{..}{Cl}}:$$

In this covalent compound the carbon atom is assigned an oxidation number of +4, it being less electronegative than the chlorine atom. Thus, the carbon atom can form some covalent compounds in which its oxidation number is −4 (CH_4) and other covalent compounds in which its oxidation number is +4 (CCl_4), depending on the relative electronegative character of its partner atoms. In fact, we may generalize in regard to the positive oxidation numbers of the elements of Groups I, II, III, IV, V, VI, and VII by saying that an atom can have a maximum positive oxidation number equal to its group number. The upper part of Table 5-14 gives examples of the oxides of one or two elements of each group wherein the maximum positive oxidation number of the element corresponds to its group number. We may also generalize by saying that for the non-metals the Roman numeral group number not only corresponds to the maximum *positive* oxidation number of the element, but also tells us the value of the

TABLE 5-14 ILLUSTRATING THE MAXIMUM POSITIVE AND MAXIMUM NEGATIVE OXIDATION NUMBERS OF SOME ELEMENTS

I	*II*	*III*	*IV*	*V*	*VI*	*VII*
$\overset{+1}{Li_2O}$	$\overset{+2}{BeO}$	$\overset{+3}{B_2O_3}$	$\overset{+4}{CO_2}$	$\overset{+5}{N_2O_5}$	$\overset{+6}{SO_3}$	$\overset{+7}{Cl_2O_7}$
$\overset{+1}{Na_2O}$	$\overset{+2}{MgO}$	$\overset{+3}{Al_2O_3}$	$\overset{+4}{SiO_2}$	$\overset{+5}{P_2O_5}$	$\overset{+6}{SeO_3}$	
			$\overset{-4}{(H_4C)}$	$\overset{-3}{(H_3N)}$	$\overset{-2}{H_2S}$	$\overset{-1}{HF}$
			CH_4	NH_3	$\overset{-2}{Na_2S}$	$\overset{-1}{NaF}$
			$\overset{-4}{Al_4C_3}$	$\overset{-3}{Li_3N}$	$\overset{-2}{Na_2Se}$	
			$\overset{-4}{SiC}$			

maximum *negative* oxidation number, which is the group number minus 8. The lower part of Table 5-14 gives some examples of compounds in which the maximum negative oxidation number of the non-metal corresponds to its group number minus 8.

SUMMARY. Atoms of one element can react with atoms of another element to form ionic compounds or covalent compounds, and can also react with identical atoms to form covalent molecules or crystals of elements. The tendency to form ionic or covalent compounds is related to the number of valence electrons of an atom, and therefore to its position in the Periodic Table. In general:

(1) In the formation of ionic compounds atoms of metals give up one or more electrons, thereby becoming positive ions. This behavior is especially characteristic of the alkali-metal atoms, which give up one electron to form monopositive ions, and for the alkaline-earth metal atoms, which lose two electrons to form dipositive ions. The electron-dot formulas of the resulting monopositive or dipositive ions are similar to those of the preceding noble gas atom in the Periodic Table.

(2) In the formation of ionic compounds, the atoms of some non-metals, particularly the halogen atoms of Group VII and the oxygen and sulfur atoms of Group VI, take on one and two electrons respectively to form negative ions. The electron-dot formulas of these mononegative and dinegative ions are similar to those of the noble-gas atoms that follow them in the Periodic Table. Binary compounds formed by a metal of either Group I (alkali metals) or Group II (alkaline-earth metals) and by a non-metal of either Group VII (halogens) or Group VI (oxygen-sulfur family), are ionic compounds.

(3) The atoms of the non-metals of Groups IV to VII tend to share electrons with one another to form covalent molecules or crystals. In general, when two different non-metals of any of these groups form a binary compound by sharing electrons, a covalent compound results. And two non-metals of the same group form a more truly covalent compound than two non-metals of different groups. The closer the two non-metals are to each other in the same group, the more truly covalent the compound; and where two non-metals of different groups are concerned, the farther apart the groups are, the less covalent is the compound they form.

Exercises

5-1 Explain the meaning of (a) the valence of elements, (b) oxidation number.

5-2 Explain the following terms and give several examples of each: (a) fixed combining capacity of elements, (b) variable combining capacity of elements.

5-3 Explain the following terms on the basis of the sharing of electrons between atoms and the transfer of electrons from one atom to another: (a) an ionic compound, (b) a covalent compound.

5-4 Give the formulas, with appropriate charges, of the particles resulting from the following changes: (a) a sulfur atom takes on two electrons, (b) a sodium atom gives up one electron, (c) a chlorine atom takes on one electron, (d) a copper atom gives up one electron, (e) a copper atom gives up two electrons, (f) the ferrous ion (Fe^{++}) gives up one electron, (g) the cupric ion (Cu^{++}) takes on one electron, (h) the Fe(III) ion takes on one electron, (i) the Cu(II) ion takes on one electron, (j) the Hg(II) ion takes on one electron, (k) the Cu(I) ion gives up one electron.

5-5 Supply the oxidation number of the italicized element in the following formulas: (a) $H\mathrm{Cl}$, (b) $\mathrm{H_2}O$, (c) $\mathrm{H_2}S$, (d) $\mathrm{Zn}O$, (e) $Fe\mathrm{Cl_3}$, (f) $Cu\mathrm{(CrO_4)}$, (g) $Sn_3\mathrm{(PO_4)_2}$, (h) $\mathrm{Ca}(Cr\mathrm{O_4})$, (i) $Cu\mathrm{(OH)_2}$.

5-6 Supply the oxidation number of the italicized element in the following formulas: (a) $\mathrm{S}^{=}$, (b) Cd^{++}, (c) $(\mathrm{SO_4})^{-2}$, (d) $(P\mathrm{O_4})^{-3}$, (e) Ag, (f) $(N\mathrm{H_4})^+$, (g) Cu, (h) $(Cr\mathrm{O_4})^{=}$, (i) $(O\mathrm{H})^{-1}$, (j) $(Cr_2\mathrm{O_7})^{=}$, (k) Cl_2, (l) N_2, (m) $(N\mathrm{O_3})^-$.

5-7 Supply the oxidation number of the italicized element in the following formulas: (a) $\mathrm{Zn_3}(P\mathrm{O_4})_2$, (b) $\mathrm{Na}N\mathrm{O_2}$, (c) $Sn\mathrm{Br_2}$, (d) $\mathrm{H}Sb\mathrm{O_2}$, (e) $\mathrm{Mg}(Mn\mathrm{O_4})_2$, (f) $N\mathrm{H_4}N\mathrm{O_3}$ (note each *N* atom).

5-8 Write formulas for the compounds formed by the combination of the ions shown by the following formulas:

(a) Ca^{++} and $O^{=}$	(f) Sn^{++} and $(C_2H_3O_2)^{-}$
(b) Na^{+} and $(SO_4)^{=}$	(g) Sc^{+++} and $O^{=}$
(c) Cu^{+} and $(SO_3)^{=}$	(h) $(NH_4)^{+}$ and $S^{=}$
(d) Fe^{++} and $(PO_4)^{\equiv}$	(i) La^{+++} and $(CrO_4)^{=}$
(e) Cu^{++} and $(OH)^{-}$	(j) Ti^{+++} and $(Cr_2O_7)^{=}$

5-9 Name the following *ions:*
(a) Ca^{++}, (b) $(SO_4)^{=}$, (c) $(SO_3)^{=}$, (d) $(PO_4)^{\equiv}$, (e) Mg^{++}, (f) Cu^{+}, (g) Cu^{++}, (h) $(MnO_4)^{-}$, (i) $(NO_3)^{-}$, (j) Fe^{++}, (k) Fe^{+++}.

5-10 (a) The formula for chromic chloride is $CrCl_3$. What is the formula for chromic sulfate? (b) The formula for cerium(II) sulfate is $Ce(SO_4)$. What is the formula for cerium(II) carbonate? (c) The formula for calcium oxalate is $Ca(C_2O_4)$. What is the formula for iron(III) oxalate? (d) The formula for sodium hypochlorite is $Na(ClO)$. What is the formula for zinc hypochlorite? (e) The formula for zirconium(IV) chloride is $ZrCl_4$. What is the formula for zirconium(IV) sulfate? (f) The formula for sodium hydrogen carbonate is $NaHCO_3$. What is the formula for magnesium hydrogen carbonate?

.5-11 Write formulas for the following compounds: (a) aluminum acetate, (b) sodium oxide, (c) potassium permanganate, (d) rubidium sulfate, (e) ammonium sulfite, (f) hydrogen sulfide, (g) barium sulfite, (h) hydrogen bromide, (i) hydrogen sulfate, (j) sulfuric acid, (k) sodium hydrogen carbonate, (l) ammonium sulfate, (m) boron trichloride, (n) silicon tetrachloride, (o) hydriodic acid, (p) acetic acid, (q) hydrogen nitrate, (r) nitric acid, (s) magnesium acetate, (t) silver phosphate.

5-12 Supply formulas for the following compounds: (a) ferrous bromide, (b) stannous chloride, (c) ferric bromide, (d) stannic chloride, (e) iron(II) chloride, (f) cupric acetate, (g) iron(III) chloride, (h) copper(II) sulfate, (i) mercury(II) chloride, (j) lead(II) phosphate.

5-13 Name the compounds represented by the following formulas: (a) NO, (b) $KClO_3$, (c) $Ba(ClO_3)_2$, (d) $Cu(SO_3)$, (e) $Cu_2(SO_4)$, (f) P_2S_5, (g) N_2O_5, (h) H_2SO_4 (water solution), (i) HI (gas), (j) HNO_3, (k) HNO_3 (water solution).

5-14 We know that (a water solution of) the compound represented by the formula $HClO_3$ is called chloric acid and (a water solution of) the compound represented by the formula $HClO_2$ is called chlorous acid. (a) Name the following two additional oxyacids of chlorine: water solutions of $HClO$ and $HClO_4$. (b) Write the formulas for (1) sodium chlorite, (2) iron(III) chlorate, (3) calcium hypochlorite, and (4) copper(II) perchlorate. (c) Write the formulas for (1) strontium hypochlorite, (2) titanium(IV) chlorate, and (3) mercury(II) perchlorate.

5-15 The formulas for the two common oxyacids of phosphorus are H_3PO_3 and H_3PO_4. (a) Name the following salts of these oxyacids: (1) $AlPO_4$, (2) $Zn_3(PO_3)_2$, and (3) $Cu_3(PO_4)_2$. (b) Write the formulas for the following salts: (1) iron(II) phosphate, (2) zinc phosphite, and (3) tin(IV) phosphate.

5-16 We have learned that the polyatomic ion represented by the formula $(MnO_4)^{-}$ is called the permanganate ion. Another polyatomic ion of manganese, called the manganate ion, consists of the same atoms but has a double negative charge. Its formula is $(MnO_4)^{=}$. (a) Name the acids $HMnO_4$ and H_2MnO_4. (b) Write the formulas for (1) iron(III) permanganate, and (2) zinc manganate. (c) Write the formulas for (1) iron(II) permanganate, and (2) barium manganate. (d) Chemical analysis of a compound reveals that its composition is represented by the formula $Cu(MnO_4)$. This compound could be either of two compounds. Name these compounds and indicate the oxidation number of copper, manganese, and the ionic charge of the (MnO_4) group in each case.

OXYGEN. OXIDATION–REDUCTION. OZONE

6

So far in our discussion, we have considered the concepts of matter and energy, the atomic structure of matter, and the meaning and use of symbols, formulas, and equations. Now we shall look more closely at the individual chemistry of two of the most important elements: oxygen and hydrogen. We shall consider oxygen in this chapter, and in the next chapter we shall consider hydrogen.

In our discussion of oxygen and hydrogen, and also as we proceed with our study of other individual elements in the chapters ahead, we shall follow a fairly uniform pattern. First, we shall state briefly the occurrence and abundance of the element. Then we shall discuss the methods of obtaining and purifying it, both by laboratory and by industrial methods. Next we shall list the more important physical properties of the element. Then we shall present its chemical properties in terms of its reactions with other elements and compounds. Finally, we shall point out some of the important uses of the element.

6-1 The Discovery of Oxygen

Oxygen was first recognized as an active ingredient of air by Carl Wilhelm Scheele (1742–1786), a Swedish chemist who spent many years investigating the chemical nature of air. The discovery of oxygen, however, is generally attributed to Joseph Priestley (1733–1804), an English philosopher and theologian who prepared the element from air in 1771. It was Lavoisier who first proposed the name oxygen, which means "acid former," for this element, because he thought it was the fundamental constituent of all acids. (Of course, we know now that many acids do not contain oxygen, for example, HCl and H_2S in water solution.)

6-2 The Occurrence and Abundance of Oxygen

Oxygen, the most widely distributed and abundant of the accessible elements, occurs both in the free state as oxygen gas, O_2, and in the combined state in many chemical compounds. In the free state oxygen makes up about 21 per cent by volume of the atmosphere. In the combined state it occurs abundantly in the compound water, which contains 88.9 per cent by weight of oxygen, and in a great number of other naturally occurring compounds that make up the earth. In fact, nearly 50 per cent by weight of the earth's crust consists of oxygen. Oxygen occurs also in all living matter both in the form of water and combined with elements other than hydrogen, and may be regarded as the most important of all the elements because of its vital role in life processes; in fact, the chemistry we are exploring in this book is often referred to as "oxygen-chemistry."

6-3 The Preparation of Oxygen

Some methods of preparing elements or compounds are suitable only for laboratory use; others, only for industrial use; and still others, for either laboratory or industrial use. Laboratory methods are those that can be carried out on a small scale with ordinary laboratory apparatus. Here the convenience and ease of the operation are more important than the cost of the materials used. A commercially suitable industrial method, on the other hand, demands the use of the cheapest possible starting materials—which are usually the most abundant as well.

LABORATORY METHODS

Common laboratory methods for the preparation of oxygen are: (1) the catalyzed thermal decomposition of potassium chlorate, $KClO_3$, (2) the reaction of sodium peroxide, Na_2O_2, with cold water, (3) the catalyzed decomposition of hydrogen peroxide, H_2O_2, and (4) the electrolysis of water.

OXYGEN FROM POTASSIUM CHLORATE. ACTION OF A CATALYST. Potassium chlorate, $K^+ClO_3^-$, is one of many ternary compounds which contain oxygen in a polyatomic ion. The compound $K^+ClO_3^-$, made up of potassium ions, K^+, and chlorate ions, ClO_3^-, is a white crystalline solid with a melting point of 368°C. In the chlorate ion, ClO_3^-, the one chlorine atom and the three oxygen atoms are covalently bonded. At ordinary temperatures, and even at temperatures of 200–250°C, in the absence of certain foreign substances (catalysts), potassium chlorate does not decompose. At somewhat higher temperatures it decomposes slowly. The term "decomposition" refers to a reaction in which a compound is broken down into simpler substances. When potassium chlorate, $K^+ClO_3^-$, is heated to about 400°C, the chlorate ion, ClO_3^-, decomposes rapidly, releasing the oxygen in gaseous form, O_2, and producing chloride ions, Cl^-. Here is the equation that represents this thermal decomposition reaction.*

$$2\ K^+ClO^-_{3(s)} \longrightarrow 2\ K^+Cl^-_{(s)} + 3\ O_{2(g)}$$

When, on the other hand, a mixture of potassium chlorate and a small amount of manganese dioxide, MnO_2, is heated to only 250°C (compare above), the potassium

* If we wish to emphasize that the reactant $KClO_3$ and the product KCl are both solids, whereas O_2 is liberated as a gas, we use the subscripts $_{(s)}$ after the formulas $KClO_3$ and KCl, and the subscript $_{(g)}$ after the formula O_2. To indicate a liquid substance, the subscript used would be $_{(l)}$.

chlorate decomposes rapidly; again oxygen is liberated and potassium chloride forms. Since the small amount of MnO_2 added is essential to obtain this reaction at 250° C, but MnO_2 itself does not appear in the net equation, we indicate its presence by placing its formula above (or below) the arrow of the equation.

$$2\ K^+ClO^-_{3(s)} \xrightarrow{MnO_2} 2\ K^+Cl^-_{(s)} + 3\ O_{2(g)}$$

Thus, the same products are formed as in the thermal decomposition of $K^+ClO_3^-$ alone. Because the thermal decomposition of potassium chlorate in the presence of manganese dioxide will occur at a lower temperature, it provides a more convenient laboratory method for the preparation of oxygen than does the decomposition of potassium chlorate alone.* We simply heat at about 250° C a mixture of five parts by weight of potassium chlorate and one part by weight of maganese dioxide, as shown in Fig. 6-1, and oxygen gas, O_2, is liberated rapidly. Caution must be used in carrying out this experiment since heated $KClO_3$ may react explosively with even small amounts of organic impurities.

The weight of manganese dioxide recovered after the decomposition of the potassium chlorate is exactly the same as its original weight. It has undergone no other observable change, and none of the manganese dioxide appears to have been decomposed. And yet its presence has obviously had a marked effect on the decomposition of the potassium chlorate, for it has caused the action to occur rapidly at a much lower temperature. The action of the manganese dioxide in the decomposition of potassium chlorate is known as *catalysis*, and the manganese dioxide is known as a *catalyst*. In general, *a catalyst is an agent that causes a reaction to occur more rapidly at a given temperature than it ordinarily would*. As we shall see in Chapter 26, a catalyst speeds up a reaction because it affects some intermediate step of the reaction. The action of catalysts is essential to the success of many biological and industrial processes.

OXYGEN FROM SODIUM PEROXIDE AND WATER. In the compound sodium peroxide, Na_2O_2, sodium has its usual fixed oxidation number of +1, but the oxygen, which is present as the peroxide ion, $O_2^=$, has an unusual oxidation number of −1. So long as sodium peroxide, Na_2O_2, is dry, it retains its oxygen; but when it comes in contact with water at *room temperature*, oxygen is rapidly liberated. The reaction of sodium peroxide with water is expressed by the following equation:

$$2\ Na_2O_2 + 2\ H_2O \longrightarrow 4\ NaOH + O_2$$

The sodium hydroxide, NaOH, that is formed dissolves if excess water is present; the oxygen, O_2, comes off as a gas.

Certain other peroxides, such as potassium peroxide, K_2O_2, and barium peroxide, BaO_2, also bring about the release of oxygen gas when they are brought into

* It is possible to heat potassium chlorate alone (without manganese dioxide) to a high enough temperature for it to decompose rapidly simply by using a laboratory burner. However, *heated molten* $K^+ClO_3^-$, alone or mixed with other substances is likely to be explosive.

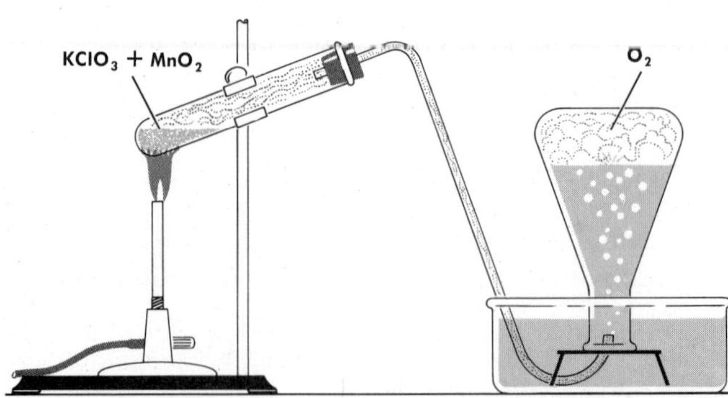

FIGURE 6-1 The preparation and collection of oxygen gas, O_2, over water.

contact with water. Potassium hydroxide, KOH, and barium hydroxide, $Ba(OH)_2$, are respectively the other products.

OXYGEN FROM HYDROGEN PEROXIDE SOLUTION. One of the most convenient methods of preparing oxygen in the laboratory involves the catalyzed decomposition of hydrogen peroxide, H_2O_2, in dilute water solution—commonly a 3 per cent solution. This 3 per cent water solution of pure hydrogen peroxide decomposes very slowly at room temperature, but traces of many substances, for example manganese dioxide, MnO_2, finely divided platinum metal, Pt, or silver metal, Ag, markedly increase the speed of its decomposition. Thus, when an aqueous solution of H_2O_2 at room temperature is brought into contact with manganese dioxide, the hydrogen peroxide decomposes rapidly and smoothly; oxygen gas is evolved, and water is the other product formed. The equation for the reaction is:

$$2\,H_2O_2 \xrightarrow{MnO_2} 2\,H_2O + O_2$$

A suitable laboratory apparatus for this reaction is shown in Fig. 6-2. This method of preparing oxygen is more convenient than the other two we have discussed. There is no danger of explosion, as there is with heated potassium chlorate, and no corrosive by-product, such as sodium hydroxide, is formed, as in the sodium peroxide reaction.

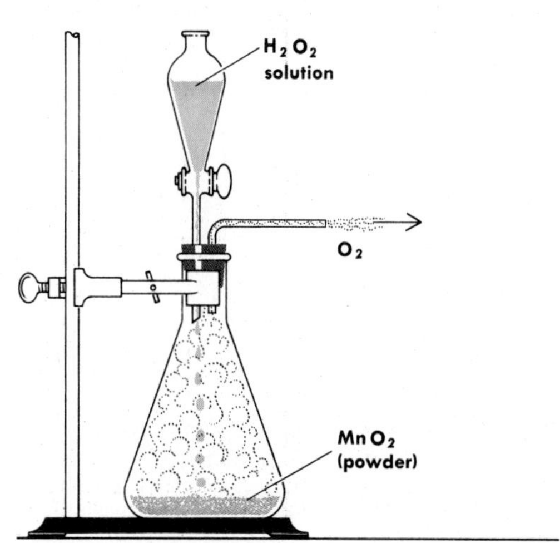

FIGURE 6-2 **The preparation of oxygen from hydrogen peroxide.**

ELECTROLYTIC DECOMPOSITION OF WATER. As we learned in Chapter 3, *pure* water is essentially a covalent compound and is a non-conductor of electricity. However, water that contains a small amount of dissolved H_2SO_4, NaOH, or ionic compounds generally, *is* a conductor of electricity, because it contains in solution the ions of these dissolved substances. When a direct electric current is passed through such as solution, the water is decomposed into hydrogen gas, H_2, and oxygen gas, O_2 (Fig. 6-3). The general process by which a substance is decomposed by means of an electric current is known as *electrolysis*. In the electrolysis of water, hydrogen gas is liberated at the negative electrode, and oxygen gas at the positive electrode. (The "electrodes" are the metal plates between which the electric current passes.) The equation for this reaction is:

$$2\,H_2O_{(l)} \xrightarrow[\text{dil. } H_2SO_4 \text{ or dil. NaOH}]{\text{direct current}} \underset{\text{at negative electrode}}{2\,H_{2(g)}} + \underset{\text{at positive electrode}}{O_{2(g)}}$$

DECOMPOSITION OF METAL OXIDES TO FORM OXYGEN. Most metal oxides do not decompose to form the metal and oxygen unless heated to extremely high temperatures. However, the oxides of a few metals, such as mercury, silver, and gold, can be thermally decomposed at the relatively low temperatures commonly attainable in the laboratory. For example, if mercury(II) oxide, HgO, a bright-red solid, is heated in a test tube over a Bunsen burner, it first turns dark red and then almost black. Soon a lustrous silvery film which can be identified as mercury metal, Hg, appears in the relatively cool upper portion of the test tube. Furthermore, if we slip a glowing wood splint into the tube, it immediately bursts into flame. This indicates the presence of oxygen gas, since we know that oxygen in fairly high concentration causes the glowing wood splint to burn much more rapidly than in air. On the basis of these and other experimental facts, we then know that oxygen gas, O_2, has been released. Since we can detect no other products than mercury metal, Hg, and oxygen gas, O_2, and since the sum of the weights of these two products is found experimentally to be equal to the weight of the single reactant, mercury(II) oxide, HgO, which has decomposed, we can say that the thermal decomposition of mercury(II) oxide yields metallic mercury together with oxygen gas:

$$2\ HgO_{(s)} \xrightarrow{\text{heat}} 2\ Hg_{(l)} + O_{2(g)} \qquad \Delta H = +21.7\ \text{kcal/mole-equation}$$

Silver oxide, Ag_2O, undergoes a similar thermal decomposition, but at a lower temperature, producing solid silver metal, Ag, and oxygen gas, O_2:

$$2\ Ag_2O_{(s)} \xrightarrow{\text{heat}} 4\ Ag_{(s)} + O_{2(g)} \qquad \Delta H = +7.3\ \text{kcal/mole-equation}$$

FIGURE 6-3 The electrolytic decomposition of water.

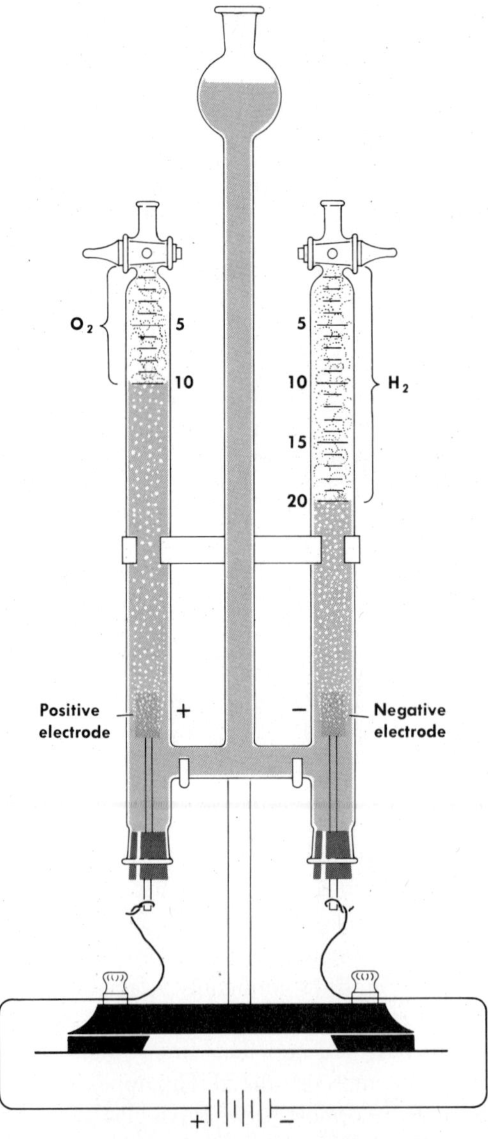

When heated to very high temperatures, the oxides of certain metals liberate only a *part* of their combined oxygen, forming another metal oxide which contains less oxygen than the original metal oxide. Of course, this type of decomposition can occur only with oxides of elements that have variable oxidation numbers. In these examples the metal oxide that contains a higher percentage of oxygen (a higher oxidation number of the metal) is changed into a metal oxide that contains a lower percentage of oxygen (a lower oxidation number of the metal). Examples are:

$$3\ MnO_2 \xrightarrow{\text{heat}} Mn_3O_4 + O_2$$

$$2\ PbO_2 \xrightarrow{\text{heat}} 2\ PbO + O_2$$

$$2\ Pb_3O_4 \xrightarrow{\text{heat}} 6\ PbO + O_2$$

INDUSTRIAL METHODS. Unlimited quantities of oxygen can be separated from the air by the relatively inexpensive process of fractional distillation. Consequently, air is the best commercial source of oxygen. Of course, water is extremely abundant too, but it cannot compete with air as a commercial source of oxygen, because the electrical energy required to decompose water into hydrogen and oxygen is costly.

Air is a complex mixture of several gases, but its chief components are oxygen, O_2, and nitrogen, N_2, with a relatively small amount of the noble gas argon, Ar. These three gases are always present in any sample of air in the proportion of about 21 per cent by volume of oxygen, about 78 per cent by volume of nitrogen, and about 1 per cent by volume of argon and other gases. If the air is free of moisture, these elements constitute about 99.9 per cent of the sample. Water vapor, carbon dioxide, and traces of other gases are present in samples of air in proportions that vary with climatic conditions and geographic location.

SEPARATION OF OXYGEN FROM AIR BY FRACTIONAL DISTILLATION. The most important industrial method for obtaining oxygen is based on the physical separation of oxygen from the other gases present in air. First the air is liquefied—the air is converted from the gaseous state to the liquid state by means of low temperatures and high pressures. Then the nitrogen and oxygen are separated from each other by a process called *fractional distillation*, because successive fractions of liquid air are separated by distillation into the two chief components, oxygen and nitrogen.

This method of fractional distillation is based on the fact that nitrogen is somewhat more volatile—that is, it has a slightly lower boiling point than oxygen. The boiling point of liquid nitrogen is $-196°C$ and that of liquid oxygen is $-183°C$. With the proper apparatus, even this small difference in boiling point is enough to permit the two elements to be separated from each other. When liquid air is partially evaporated, the more volatile nitrogen escapes more rapidly than the less volatile oxygen. Consequently, the vapor that is given off contains a larger percentage of nitrogen than was present in the original liquid air, and the remaining liquid contains a larger percentage of oxygen. Now, if we condense the vapor and then re-evaporate it, the new vapor will contain a still higher percentage of nitrogen, and the remaining liquid will contain a higher percentage of oxygen than the new vapor. If we repeat this re-evaporation and re-condensation process often enough, we can finally separate completely the nitrogen and oxygen.

Oxygen and nitrogen gases are commonly stored and shipped in strong steel cylinders under pressures of about 2,000 pounds per square inch. Liquid oxygen is sometimes shipped in large, specially insulated containers, at atmospheric pressure and at a temperature below its boiling point. Care should be exercised in handling liquid oxygen, because on contact with finely divided oxidizable materials the mixture may explode. A common laboratory type of insulated container for storing low-boiling liquids such as liquid oxygen, liquid nitrogen, and liquid air is the *Dewar flask* (Fig. 6-4). A Dewar flask is a double-walled glass vessel. The inner sides of the walls are silvered and the space between them is evacuated. It is similar to the familiar thermos bottle. A vacuum flask is a convenient way of keeping a hot substance hot or a cold substance cold, because the vacuum between the double glass walls reduces the flow of heat between the air of the atmosphere and the substance inside the Dewar flask. Furthermore, the silvered surfaces reflect the heat which would otherwise escape from the substance or enter the vessel from the outside.

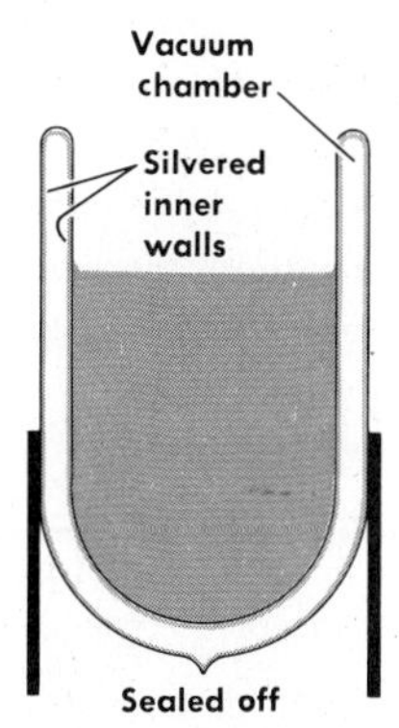

FIGURE 6-4 A Dewar flask.

6-4 The Properties of Oxygen

PHYSICAL PROPERTIES

Oxygen gas, like air, is colorless, tasteless, and odorless. When it is liquefied, it becomes pale blue. If liquid oxygen is further cooled, it solidifies into a blue solid. Liquid oxygen and solid oxygen are paramagnetic—that is, they are attracted by a magnet much like a piece of iron. Gaseous oxygen is also paramagnetic, but the molecules are very much farther apart than in the liquid and solid, so that the effect of the magnet is more difficult to detect.

Oxygen gas, O_2, is only slightly soluble in water. About 3 volumes of oxygen gas, measured at room temperature and at 1 atm pressure, dissolve in 100 volumes of water. It is this small amount of dissolved oxygen that enables fish and plant life to exist underwater.

Oxygen gas is a little heavier than air. It has a density of 1.429 grams per liter (g/l.) measured at 0°C and 1 atm pressure, compared with the average density of air, which is approximately 1.30 g/l. measured under the same conditions. (This figure is only the average density of air, since, as we have seen, air is a mixture of several gases and water vapor which varies in composition with climatic conditions.) Some of the more important physical properties of oxygen are listed in Table 6-1.

In order to separate 1 mole (32.00 g) of diatomic oxygen molecules, O_2, into single gaseous O atoms, 117.3 kcal of energy are required:

$$O_2 \longrightarrow O + O \qquad \Delta H = +117.3 \text{ kcal/mole } O_2$$

Thus, we say that the *dissociation energy*—the energy required to dissociate 1 mole of O_2 molecules into 2 moles of (separate) O atoms—is 117.3 kcal.

TABLE 6-1 SOME PHYSICAL PROPERTIES OF OXYGEN, O_2, AT 1 ATM PRESSURE

Boiling point	−182.97°C
Freezing point	−218.76°C
Density at 0°C	1.429 g/l
Solubility in H_2O at 25°C	3.3 ml/100 ml

Let us compare this value with the dissociation energies of some other gaseous diatomic molecules. For the reaction: $X_{2(g)} \longrightarrow 2\,X_{(g)}$, the ΔH values, in kcal/mole X_2, are: 57.1 for $Cl_{2(g)}$; 45.4 for $Br_{2(g)}$; 16.8 for $Na_{2(g)}$; and 1.6 for $Hg_{2(g)}$. We see that the dissociation energy of O_2 is very much higher—more than twice that of chlorine, for example. This fact indicates that the two atoms of oxygen in the oxygen molecule, O_2, are very firmly bonded, and the value of $\Delta H = +117.3$ kcal/mole O_2 is a measure of the relatively high bond energy of the O_2 molecule.

At ordinary temperatures molecular oxygen, O_2, is only slightly reactive, but at higher temperatures it becomes extremely reactive. Consequently, many elements and compounds which react slowly with oxygen at room temperature react vigorously at higher temperatures. In fact, at appropriate temperatures oxygen is capable of forming compounds by direct reaction with nearly all the other elements. Reaction of the elements with oxygen are examples of what are called *oxidation reactions;* and elements that have combined with oxygen are said to have been *oxidized.*

THE REACTION OF OXYGEN WITH METALS. Oxygen can combine directly with all metals except gold and silver and some of the other noble metals such as platinum and palladium (a metal, such as gold, which is unreactive to oxygen and many other substances, is usually called a *noble metal*). However, the temperature at which the reaction between oxygen and metals begins to take place appreciably varies greatly depending on many factors. One of these is, of course, the nature of the metal; but also very important are the *amount of the surface* of the metal exposed to oxygen (that is, whether the metal is in bulk or finely divided), and the *state of the surface* of the metal, whether untarnished or covered by some protective oxide coating. In all cases, however, when a metal combines with oxygen to form an oxide, heat—and sometimes a very large quantity—is given off. In other words, the reaction of metals with oxygen is always exothermic. In the following examples we will give the values of the heats of reaction, ΔH, together with the reaction equations, so that you may get some idea of the quantity of heat energy involved. Here and in the following chapters, the values of the heats of the reaction, ΔH per mole-equation as written, are all given for reactions at 25°C and 1 atm, to provide a common standard of comparison (see discussion in Chapter 16).

As a typical example, consider the reaction of oxygen with iron. At room temperature, iron combines very slowly with oxygen and moisture in the air to form a reddish-brown solid coating—rust—whose chemical composition approximates $Fe_2O_3 \cdot xH_2O$. But if a clean iron wire is *heated intensely* and then thrust into a container of pure oxygen, the wire burns rapidly throwing off white-hot sparks. In this case, the end-product of the reaction is a black magnetic solid—iron oxide, Fe_3O_4—a mixture of iron(II) oxide (FeO) and iron(III) oxide (Fe_2O_3):

$$3\,Fe + 2\,O_2 \longrightarrow Fe_3O_4 \qquad \Delta H = -267.0 \text{ kcal/mole } Fe_3O_4$$

Some of the more electropositive metals, such as calcium, burn vigorously in pure oxygen when heated only moderately to form the oxide:

$$2\,Ca + O_2 \longrightarrow 2\,CaO \qquad \Delta H = -151.9 \text{ kcal/mole CaO}$$

Some other highly electropositive metals, such as sodium, also burn in air or oxygen when heated only slightly, but they form a metal *peroxide:*

$$2\,Na + O_2 \longrightarrow Na_2O_2 \qquad \Delta H = -123.0 \text{ kcal/mole } Na_2O_2$$

In turn, this peroxide, Na_2O_2, when heated to about 700°C, decomposes, yielding oxygen gas and sodium oxide, Na_2O; and if sodium is burned in air or oxygen at 700°C, only the oxide, Na_2O, is formed:

$$4\,Na + O_2 \longrightarrow 2\,Na_2O \qquad \Delta H = -99.4 \text{ kcal/mole } Na_2O$$

THE REACTION OF OXYGEN WITH NON-METALS. Oxygen combines directly with all the non-metals except the noble gases—helium, He; neon, Ne; argon, Ar; krypton, Kr; xenon, Xe; and radon, Rn—and the halogens—flourine, F_2; chlorine, Cl_2; bromine, Br_2; and iodine, I_2.

Carbon, when heated until it begins to burn with O_2 in the open air, continues to burn *even after the flame has been removed.* Consequently, this chemical change is an exothermic reaction. The gaseous oxide formed may be either carbon dioxide, CO_2, or carbon monoxide, CO, or a mixture of both, depending on the conditions of the reaction:

$$C + O_2 \longrightarrow CO_2 \qquad \Delta H = -94.1 \text{ kcal/mole } CO_2$$

$$2\,C + O_2 \longrightarrow 2\,CO \qquad \Delta H = -26.4 \text{ kcal/mole CO}$$

If a piece of sulfur* is heated in the open air, it combines with the oxygen in the air and begins to burn, forming the oxide of sulfur, SO_2. Sulfur dioxide, SO_2, is a colorless gas with a characteristic choking odor.

$$S + O_2 \longrightarrow SO_2 \qquad \Delta H = -71.0 \text{ kcal/mole } SO_2$$

Under appropriate conditions, hydrogen gas, H_2, combines with oxygen gas, O_2, to form water vapor, H_2O. This experiment was first performed in 1776 by Henry Cavendish (see p. 89) and proved that water was a compound of hydrogen and oxygen. At room temperature the reaction between hydrogen and oxygen takes place so slowly that it is undetectable. As the temperature is raised, however, the speed of reaction increases, and at high temperatures (about 550°C) the gases combine very rapidly. A jet of hydrogen gas, for example, burns in oxygen gas or in air with a very hot and almost colorless flame to produce water vapor:

$$2\,H_2 + O_2 \longrightarrow 2\,H_2O \qquad \Delta H = -57.8 \text{ kcal/mole } H_2O \text{ vapor}$$

* Strictly speaking, because the formula of solid sulfur is S_8 (see Ch. 28), this equation illustrating the combustion of sulfur could also be written as:

$$S_8 + 8\,O_2 \longrightarrow 8\,SO_2$$

Some mixtures of hydrogen with either oxygen or air may explode violently when ignited. On the other hand, in the presence of finely divided platinum, a mixture of hydrogen gas, H_2, and oxygen gas, O_2, will combine quite rapidly and smoothly even at room temperature. In general, platinum has a marked catalytic effect on gas reactions involving hydrogen.

THE REACTIONS OF OXYGEN WITH COMPOUNDS. In addition to its ability to combine directly with elements (metals and non-metals), oxygen can also react with many compounds. For example, oxygen reacts with certain (lower) metal oxides to produce (higher) metal oxides containing a higher percentage of oxygen. For example, iron(II) oxide, FeO, readily combines with oxygen or air to form iron(III) oxide, Fe_2O_3:

$$4\ FeO + O_2 \longrightarrow 2\ Fe_2O_3 \qquad \Delta H = -70.1\ \text{kcal/mole}\ Fe_2O_3$$

In general, metals with *variable* oxidation numbers (for example, iron and copper), can form more than one (lower and higher) metal oxide, and the lower and higher metal oxides are often interconvertible. On the other hand, metals with a fixed oxidation number form only one metal oxide, which undergoes no reaction when heated further in oxygen. For example, oxygen has no effect on the oxide of aluminum, Al_2O_3, or on the oxide of silicon, SiO_2 (sand).

Oxygen also reacts with certain (lower) non-metal oxides to produce (higher) non-metal oxides containing a high percentage of oxygen. For example, carbon monoxide, CO, reacts with oxygen or air to produce carbon dioxide, CO_2:

$$2\ CO + O_2 \longrightarrow 2\ CO_2 \qquad \Delta H = -67.7\ \text{kcal/mole}\ CO_2$$

Compounds which contain carbon and hydrogen only ("hydrocarbons") also react readily with oxygen, producing carbon dioxide, CO_2, and water vapor, H_2O, and releasing large quantities of heat. The hydrocarbon methane, CH_4, for example, which is the chief component of natural gas, burns in air or in oxygen to form carbon dioxide, CO_2, and water vapor, H_2O:

$$CH_4 + 2\ O_2 \longrightarrow CO_2 + 2\ H_2O \qquad \Delta H = -212.8\ \text{kcal/mole}\ CH_4$$

This is the main reaction that occurs when a common fuel such as natural gas is burned in a Bunsen burner in the laboratory or is used in home heating. As another example, heptane, C_7H_{16}, one of the constituents of gasoline, burns in the presence of an excess of oxygen or air:

$$C_7H_{16} + 11\ O_2 \longrightarrow 7\ CO_2 + 8\ H_2O \qquad \Delta H = -1{,}100\ \text{kcal/mole}\ C_7H_{16}$$

The hydrocarbon acetylene, C_2H_2, also burns in oxygen or air to produce carbon dioxide and water; this is the reaction that takes place in the oxy-acetylene torch:

$$2\ C_2H_2 + 5\ O_2 \longrightarrow 4\ CO_2 + 2\ H_2O \qquad \Delta H = -310.6\ \text{kcal/mole}\ C_2H_2$$

Remember that when fuels such as the hydrocarbons are burned, an excess of air should always be available. When an insufficient amount of air is supplied during the combustion process, the poisonous gas carbon monoxide, CO, may be formed instead of carbon dioxide, CO_2. For example, here is the equation for the reaction of methane gas, CH_4, with a *limited* amount of air (oxygen):

$$2\ CH_4 + 3\ O_2 \longrightarrow 2\ CO + 4\ H_2O$$

We see, then, that the product formed in this combustion depends on the amount of oxygen available. The reaction that produces carbon monoxide is called the *incomplete* combustion of the combustible material, and the reaction that produces carbon dioxide is called the *complete* combustion of the combustible material.

Even when the reactant forms only a single oxidation product, an excess of oxygen is generally provided for the combustion of a substance. Theoretically, for example, 1 mole of magnesium, Mg (24.31 g) can be converted completely into magnesium oxide, MgO, by only $\frac{1}{2}$ mole (16.00 g) of oxygen:

$$Mg + \tfrac{1}{2}O_2 \longrightarrow MgO$$

In practice, however, it is very difficult to insure that *exactly* 24.31 g of magnesium will react completely with *exactly* 16.00 g of oxygen. Therefore, to make sure that the magnesium reacts completely, we provide an *excess* of oxygen gas. Under these conditions, *all* the magnesium, Mg, present reacts to form magnesium oxide, MgO, and the excess oxygen gas, O_2, remains unchanged after the reaction has been completed.

6-5 The Rate of Chemical Reactions

Several factors influence the rate at which a specified reaction occurs: (1) the temperature of the reactants, (2) the concentration of the reactants, (3) the amount of contact surface between the reactants, and (4) the presence of foreign substances. Let us illustrate these factors by some familiar examples of oxidation reactions.

TEMPERATURE

You know that milk turns sour more quickly at room temperature than when it is stored in a refrigerator. The milk sours because the chemical reactions involved in the souring process are speeded up at higher temperatures. The speed of chemical reactions increases with an increase in temperature and decreases with a decrease in temperature.

CONCENTRATION OF THE REACTANTS

Substances that burn in air burn much more vigorously in pure oxygen. For example, sulfur burns slowly in air after it has been ignited (or lit), but in a jar containing pure oxygen gas it burns strongly with a bright blue flame. The reason is that more oxygen molecules are present in pure oxygen than in the same volume of air—that is, pure oxygen has a greater *concentration* of oxygen molecules.

Let us look more closely at the effect of an increase in the concentration of oxygen on the speed of oxidation reactions. In a chemical reaction between a given substance and oxygen gas, the O_2 molecules must come into contact, or very nearly so, with the surface of the substance. In an average sample of air, only about 20 per cent of the molecules consist of oxygen, compared with 100 per cent in pure oxygen. Consequently, the atoms in a crystal of sulfur, for example, have a much better chance of coming into contact with oxygen molecules in pure oxygen gas than they have in a sample of ordinary air. As a result, the sulfur burns more brightly—that is, more rapidly—in the oxygen gas. Furthermore, sulfur will burn even more vigorously in oxygen gas under high pressure, for under high pressure the concentration of oxygen molecules is still greater.

AMOUNT OF SURFACE EXPOSED

A pile of wood shavings burns more rapidly than a log of equal weight. Chunks of coal in a furnace burn at controllable speeds; but a mixture of coal dust and air may react explosively. In general, the smaller the particle size of the reacting materials, the greater the total surface area of the reactant exposed to the gaseous O_2 molecules. Consequently, the number of reacting particles in contact at any given time also increases, causing a faster reaction. Thus, specially prepared, finely divided particles of iron burn vigorously even in air at ordinary temperatures, because enough oxygen molecules can come into contact with the tiny metal particles to produce rapid oxidation. But notice that in each case the *same quantity* of heat is liberated in the combustion of the same quantity of iron; in other words the *speed of a reaction has no bearing on the quantity of energy involved.*

PRESENCE OF FOREIGN SUBSTANCES

As we have already mentioned, the speed of many chemical reactions is appreciably increased by the presence of relatively small amounts of certain foreign substances, or catalysts. For example, the presence of manganese dioxide markedly increases the rate of the thermal decomposition of potassium chlorate (p. 73) and of hydrogen peroxide (p. 75). Also, many gaseous reactions involving hydrogen gas, such as the combination of oxygen and hydrogen to form water vapor (p. 80), are catalyzed by platinum metal; and water itself acts as a catalyst in many reactions.

COMBUSTION PROCESSES

As the values of ΔH stated in the previous sections indicate, oxidation reactions are strongly exothermic—that is, they release a great deal of heat. The term "combustion" describes an exothermic oxidation reaction that takes place at a relatively high temperature, and the oxidation, once started, produces enough heat to maintain the reaction at this temperature. Thus a rapid and vigorous oxidation accompanied by the liberation of heat and light energy—the burning of coal or oil, for example—is an example of combustion.

KINDLING TEMPERATURE AND SPONTANEOUS COMBUSTION

A substance that is capable of reacting slowly with oxygen in the air at room temperature reacts more and more rapidly as the temperature increases. The temperature at which the oxidation reaction is rapid enough to become combustion is called the *kindling temperature* of the substance. A piece of wood, for example, oxidizes very slowly in air at room temperature, but as the temperature increases so does the rate of the oxidation. When the kindling temperature is reached even in a small part of the piece of wood, combustion begins and enough heat is liberated as a result of this local combustion to raise the temperature of the adjacent portions of the wood, causing them to burn as well.

If oily rags are piled in a heap so that the heat produced by the slow oxidation (exothermic reaction) of the oil cannot be dissipated, the temperature slowly begins to rise. The rate of oxidation then increases, producing more heat, which is in turn absorbed by the oily rags and further increases the temperature. In time the oxidation proceeds so rapidly, evolving sufficient heat in the process, that the kindling temperature is reached and the rags burst into flame. This kind of phenomenon is called *spontaneous combustion,* and of course is produced only by *exothermic* reactions.

6-6 Reactions of Oxides with Water

Metal oxides and non-metal oxides constitute an important class of compounds. They can best be classified on the basis of their reactions with water.

BASIC OXIDES

The soluble oxides of many metals with an oxidation number of +3 or less react with water to form metal hydroxides. These metal hydroxides, called *bases,* exhibit special characteristics. For example, when sodium oxide, Na_2O, in which the oxidation number of the sodium is +1, is added to water, it dissolves and forms the soluble hydroxide of the metal, sodium hydroxide, NaOH:

$$Na_2O + H_2O \longrightarrow 2\ NaOH$$

Calcium oxide, CaO, in which the oxidation number of the calcium is +2, reacts with water to form the base calcium hydroxide, $Ca(OH)_2$ which is slightly soluble in water:

$$CaO + H_2O \longrightarrow Ca(OH)_2$$

Metal oxides of this kind are called *basic oxides*, because, as just illustrated, they react with water to form *bases*. They are also called *basic anhydrides* (from a Greek word meaning "the absence of water"), because they can be formed by the removal of water from a base.

Among the more important basic oxides are the oxides of the alkali metals—lithium oxide, Li_2O; sodium oxide, Na_2O; potassium oxide, K_2O; and cesium oxide, Cs_2O—and the alkaline-earth metal oxides—calcium oxide, CaO; strontium oxide, SrO; and barium oxide, BaO. Each of these alkali metal and alkaline-earth metal oxides reacts with water to form the corresponding metal hydroxide.

ACIDIC OXIDES

The oxides of certain non-metals react with water to form compounds known as *acids*. Sulfur dioxide gas, SO_2, for example, readily dissolves in water to form sulfurous acid, H_2SO_3:

$$SO_2 + H_2O \longrightarrow H_2SO_3$$

Notice that both in SO_2 and in the acid derived from it, H_2SO_3, the oxidation number of the sulfur is +4. Another oxide of sulfur, sulfur trioxide, SO_3, reacts with water to produce sulfuric acid, H_2SO_4:

$$SO_3 + H_2O \longrightarrow H_2SO_4$$

Notice that in both SO_3 and in the acid derived from it, H_2SO_4, the oxidation number of the sulfur is +6.

Such non-metal oxides as SO_2 and SO_3 belong to a group called *acidic oxides*, because, as we have just seen, they react with water to form *acids*. These non-metal oxides are also called *acid anhydrides*, because they can be formed by the removal of water from an acid.

6-7 The Oxidation Process: Oxidation and Reduction

Here is the equation for the oxidation of magnesium metal by oxygen:

$$2\ Mg^0 + O_2{}^0 \longrightarrow 2\ Mg^{++}O^{=}$$

Notice that the oxidation numbers of both magnesium and oxygen undergo a change. The oxidation number of magnesium, which is zero in the free state, becomes +2 in the combined state. And the oxidation number of oxygen, which is also zero in the free state, becomes −2 in the combined state. The situation is similar when magnesium reacts with chlorine:

$$Mg^0 + Cl_2{}^0 \longrightarrow Mg^{++}(Cl^-)_2$$

Here again the oxidation number of magnesium increases from zero to +2, while the oxidation number of chlorine decreases from zero to −1.

It is apparent, then, that a change in the oxidation number of a metal may occur as the result of its combining with elements other than oxygen. Originally, the term "oxidation" was used to describe the union of an element with oxygen; but now it has been extended to indicate *all reactions* that bring about *an increase in oxidation number.* In other words, in both the reactions above, magnesium metal, Mg^0, is one of the reactants, and the magnesium ion, Mg^{++}, is one of the products, an indication that the magnesium metal undergoes the same fundamental chemical change in each case.

Notice that in both the above reactions—magnesium with oxygen, and magnesium with chlorine—the oxidation number of magnesium is *increased* from zero to +2. An *increase* in *oxidation number* is called *oxidation.* But notice that in the reaction involving the magnesium with the oxygen, the oxidation number of oxygen is *reduced* from zero to −2; and in the reaction involving the magnesium with the chlorine, the oxidation number of chlorine is *reduced* from zero to −1. *A decrease in oxidation number* is called *reduction.*

A substance that causes an *increase* in the oxidation number of another substance is called an *oxidizing agent,* or simply an *oxidant.* A substance that causes a *decrease* in the oxidation number of another substance is called a *reducing agent,* or simply a *reductant.* In general, an oxidant and a reductant (will tend to) react with each other.

When magnesium metal reacts with oxygen to produce magnesium oxide, and when magnesium reacts with chlorine to form magnesium chloride, the magnesium atom, Mg, gives up two electrons, forming the magnesium ion, Mg^{++}. In each of these reactions magnesium metal, Mg^0, with an oxidation number of zero, is oxidized to the magnesium ion, Mg^{++}, with an oxidation number of +2.

$$2\ Mg^0 + O_2 \longrightarrow 2\ Mg^{++}O^{=}$$

$$Mg^0 + Cl_2 \longrightarrow Mg^{++}(Cl^-)_2$$

Now we can present a generalized definition of oxidation. We defined it first as an increase in the oxidation number of an element. But we can also define oxidation as a *loss of electrons* by an element. The number of electrons lost by an element is equal to the increase in the oxidation number of the element. Thus, in the reactions of magnesium metal with oxygen and with chlorine, the magnesium atom loses two electrons (is oxidized) and its oxidation number increases from zero to +2.

In the reaction between oxygen and magnesium, each oxygen atom takes on two electrons, and the oxidation number of oxygen decreases from zero to −2. In the reaction of magnesium with chlorine, each chlorine atom takes on one electron and its oxidation number is decreased from zero to −1. We can then define reduction as a *gain of electrons.* The oxidation number of an element which takes on electrons decreases since an electron is a unit of *negative* charge.

THE RELATIONSHIP OF OXIDATION AND REDUCTION

Each of the reactions we have just discussed involves both a loss and a gain of electrons. In fact, in each reaction the metallic element Mg, gives up electrons to form a positive Mg^{++} ion, while the non-metallic element (oxygen or chlorine) takes on electrons to form a negative ion.

When in a reaction a metal gives up electrons (that is, when it is oxidized), some other substance involved in the reaction must always take on these electrons. By the same token, when a non-metal takes on electrons (that is, when it is reduced), some other substance involved in the reaction must always supply these electrons. Consequently, *oxidation (the loss of electrons) and reduction (the gain of electrons) must always accompany each other in a reaction (oxidation-reduction reaction).* In other words, if a given reaction involves an oxidation, it must also involve a reduction. Oxidation is the reverse of reduction; reduction is the reverse of oxidation.

Now let us consider some other *oxidation-reduction* reactions. Here is the equation for the reaction of sodium metal with chlorine gas:

$$2\ Na^0 + Cl_2{}^0 \longrightarrow 2\ Na^+Cl^-$$

In this reaction each atom of sodium metal, since it gives up one electron, is *oxidized* to the sodium ion, Na^+. Also, each chlorine atom of the Cl_2 molecule is *reduced* to a chloride ion, Cl^-, since each chlorine atom takes on one electron. This reaction, then, is an *oxidation-reduction* reaction. The *reducing* agent is the sodium atom, Na, since it causes each chlorine atom of the Cl_2 molecule to be reduced (to gain one electron). The *oxidizing* agent is the Cl_2 molecule, since each of its chlorine atoms takes on an electron from a sodium atom.

As another example, let us consider the reaction between zinc metal and a solution of copper(II) sulfate. If a strip of metallic zinc is placed in a water solution of copper(II) sulfate, some metallic zinc dissolves, and some metallic copper simultaneously deposits on the surface of the remaining undissolved zinc. Here is what happens: Electrons leave the zinc strip, Zn, resulting in the formation of zinc ions, $Zn^0 - 2e^- \longrightarrow Zn^{++}$. These electrons are taken up by the copper(II) ions, Cu^{++} in solution, which then form metallic copper, $Cu^{++} + 2e^- \longrightarrow Cu^0$. The chemical reaction between Zn metal and a water solution of $Cu^{++}SO_4^{=}$ may be expressed by the following equation:

$$Zn^0 + Cu^{++}SO_4^{=} \longrightarrow Cu^0 + Zn^{++}SO_4^{=}$$

Notice that the sulfate ion, $SO_4^{=}$, does not undergo any change in this oxidation-reduction reaction, and therefore in this reaction may be said to act as a *spectator ion.* Thus, the essential or net chemical reaction that occurs may be expressed as:

$$Zn^0 + Cu^{++} \longrightarrow Cu^0 + Zn^{++}$$

The zinc atom, Zn^0, is oxidized, since it gives up two electrons (its oxidation number increases from zero to +2), and it is transformed into the zinc ion, Zn^{++}. The copper(II) ion, Cu^{++}, is reduced, since it takes on two electrons (its oxidation number decreases from +2 to zero), and it is transformed into the copper atom, Cu^0.

To summarize, in this oxidation-reduction reaction, Zn^0 is *oxidized* and acts as the *reducing agent* (reductant). Cu^{++} is *reduced* and acts as the *oxidizing agent* (oxidant).

OXIDATION-REDUCTION REACTIONS OF COVALENT COMPOUNDS

Many oxidation-reduction reactions involve the formation of covalent compounds rather than ionic compounds. In these reactions there is no clearly distinguishable loss or gain of electrons, but there *is* a change in oxidation numbers. As we saw in Chapter 5 (p. 55), it is customary to assign a positive oxidation number to the *less* electronegative element in a covalent compound, and a negative oxidation number to the *more* electronegative element. Consider, for example, the reaction of hydrogen, H_2, and chlorine, Cl_2, to form hydrogen chloride, HCl:

$$H_2 + Cl_2 \longrightarrow 2\,HCl$$

Each hydrogen atom in the original H_2 molecule, and each chlorine atom in the original Cl_2 molecule, has an oxidation number of zero. In the HCl molecule, the hydrogen atom has an oxidation number of +1, and the chlorine atom has an oxidation number of −1 since the chlorine atom is the more electronegative. Thus in the reaction, $H_2 + Cl_2 \longrightarrow 2\,HCl$, chlorine gas, Cl_2 is the oxidizing agent, for the oxidation number of each Cl atom decreases from zero to −1, whereas hydrogen gas, H_2, acts as the reducing agent, since the oxidation number of each H atom increases from zero to +1.

Hydrogen gas also acts as a reductant in many other reactions; however, in a few cases hydrogen, H_2, may act as an oxidizing agent. An example is the reaction of hydrogen, H_2, with the electropositive metal, sodium, Na, to form the ionic compound Na^+H^-, sodium hydride: $2\,Na + H_2 \longrightarrow 2\,Na^+H^-$. In this reaction H_2 is the oxidizing agent, since each hydrogen atom takes on an electron and is reduced to a hydride ion, H^-. Thus, depending on the substance with which it reacts, H_2 can be either a reducing agent (as in the reaction with chlorine) or an oxidizing agent (as in the reaction with sodium). Although H_2 almost always acts as a reducing agent, it can also be an oxidizing agent when reacting with the most electropositive elements. If we consider the loss and gain of electrons, we can easily tell whether H_2 is acting as a reducing or as an oxidizing agent.

To summarize oxidation-reduction reactions:

Oxidation may be defined either as an increase in oxidation number or as a loss of electrons.

Reduction may be defined either as a decrease in oxidation number, or as a gain of electrons.

In an oxidation-reduction reaction the oxidizing agent (the oxidant) is the substance which causes oxidation. The oxidizing agent takes on electrons and is thereby reduced.

The reducing agent (the reductant) is the substance that causes reduction. The reducing agent gives up electrons and is thereby oxidized.

When an oxidizing agent (an oxidant) and a reducing agent (a reductant) are brought into contact, they react with one another—the reducing agent gives up electrons, and the oxidizing agent takes on electrons.

6-8 Uses of Oxygen

Oxygen in the air plays an important role in the living processes of all animals. In the process of respiration, oxygen is transferred to the blood from the air in the lungs and is carried to all parts of the body. The oxygen is then used in the oxidation of certain compounds to provide the heat and energy that permit the living organism to move and to perform muscular work.

The highly pure, inexpensive oxygen obtained from the fractional distillation of air is widely used in industrial processes involving oxidation reactions, such as steel-making, oxy-acetylene welding (3500°C), the synthesis of nitric acid, HNO_3, from gaseous ammonia, and the setting off of explosives by mixing it with alcohol and other organic materials. Finally, liquid oxygen finds application as a high concentration oxidant used to burn rocket fuel.

6-9 Ozone

Ozone, O_3, consists of molecules containing three atoms of oxygen. The properties of ozone, O_3, and of molecular oxygen, O_2, are different although both contain only oxygen atoms. When an element appears in more than one form—as in the case of diatomic oxygen, O_2, and ozone, O_3—the phenomenon is known as *allotropy.* And the forms themselves are known as *allotropes* of the element.

Even in very small concentrations ozone can be easily recognized by its characteristic odor. In fact, the name "ozone" comes from a Greek word meaning "to smell." The characteristic odor that can often be detected around certain electrical equipment, for example, is caused by ozone. Only traces of ozone occur in the atmosphere at sea level, but in the stratosphere appreciable quantities of ozone are believed to exist.

THE PREPARATION OF OZONE FROM OXYGEN

In order to convert oxygen, O_2, to ozone, O_3, energy must be supplied from some outside source. Since ozone is unstable at high temperatures, however, the energy must in some way be supplied without raising the temperature. This is done by passing oxygen gas through a high-voltage electrical field. Some of the O_2 molecules absorb energy from the electrical field and are converted to O_3 molecules. The quantitative relationships involved in the endothermic conversion of oxygen to ozone are expressed by the equation:

$$3\ O_2 \longrightarrow 2\ O_3 \qquad \Delta H = +68.0 \text{ kcal/mole-equation}$$

In other words, when 3 moles of oxygen (3 O_2) are converted into 2 moles of ozone, (2 O_3), 68.0 kcal of heat energy are converted into chemical energy, stored in the ozone.

THE PROPERTIES OF OZONE

PHYSICAL PROPERTIES. Ozone gas in high concentrations is noticeably blue. The gas has a density of 22.2 g/l. at 0°C and 1 atm pressure. The boiling point of ozone is −112°C at 1 atm pressure. Ozone gas can be liquefied by passing it through a tube cooled by liquid air. Liquid ozone is also blue.

CHEMICAL PROPERTIES. Ozone decomposes slowly at low temperatures, and almost instantaneously at high temperatures. Like hydrogen peroxide, ozone can be catalytically decomposed by the use of finely divided substances such as manganese dioxide, platinum, and silver:

$$2\ O_3 \xrightarrow[\text{Pt, or Ag}]{\text{MnO}_2,} 3\ O_2 \qquad \Delta H = -68.0 \text{ kcal/mole-equation}$$

When 2 moles of O_3 molecules decompose to form 3 moles of O_2 68.0 kcal of heat are evolved and when 3 moles of O_2 form 2 moles of O_3 the same quantity of heat is absorbed.

Ozone, O_3, reacts with other substances more vigorously than oxygen, O_2, because it has greater energy. Consequently, ozone is a powerful oxidizing agent. When ozone acts as an oxidizing agent, only one-third of the oxygen atoms present in the ozone may actually be reduced; the other two-thirds may appear among the products as O_2 molecules. This relationship may be represented as:

$$O_3 \longrightarrow O_2 + (O) + \text{energy}$$

For example, ozone oxidizes lead sulfide, PbS, to lead sulfate, $PbSO_4$, with the evolution of oxygen, O_2:

$$2\ O_3 + PbS \longrightarrow PbSO_4 + O_2$$

But in certain other reactions all the oxygen atoms in the ozone are reduced. For example, when sulfur dioxide, SO_2, reacts with ozone, only one product, sulfur trioxide, SO_3, is formed:

$$3\ SO_2 + O_3 \longrightarrow 3\ SO_3$$

Except in very dilute concentrations, ozone attacks the mucous membranes of the body and therefore is very harmful, if inhaled. Because of its powerful oxidizing ability, ozone is used chiefly as a bleaching agent for starch, oils, and waxes, and as a disinfectant to purify and sterilize water.

Exercises

6-1 What is the most abundant source of (a) free oxygen, (b) combined oxygen?

6-2 Write equations and state the essential conditions for three convenient laboratory methods by which oxygen can be prepared.

6-3 Describe in some detail what you would observe if potassium chlorate were heated by itself in one experiment and then, in a second experiment, a mixture of potassium chlorate and manganese dioxide were heated.

6-4 Show by equations the difference between the reactions of sodium oxide and sodium peroxide with water.

6-5 Discuss the comparative requirements for an ideal laboratory method for the preparation of oxygen and an ideal industrial method for preparing oxygen.

6-6 Describe in detail the industrial method for preparing oxygen.
6-7 Write equations for three less common methods for preparing oxygen.
6-8 Explain fully the meaning of fractional distillation.
6-9 Describe the chemical reactivity of oxygen.
6-10 By means of equations, give examples of several reactions of metals with oxygen. State the essential conditions for the reactions.
6-11 By means of equations, give examples of several reactions of non-metals with oxygen. State the essential conditions for the reactions.
6-12 Give examples of the reactions of oxygen with various compounds.
6-13 List as many elements as you can which will not react with oxygen. List several compounds which you are certain will not react with oxygen.
6-14 (a) Define kindling temperature. (b) Which has the lower kindling temperature, an iron nail or steel wool of the same weight? Explain.
6-15 Give a number of examples from everyday experience illustrating the factors which affect the speed of oxidation reactions.
6-16 Which produces the hotter flame, acetylene burning in air, or acetylene burning in oxygen? Explain.
6-17 Define and give examples of exothermic reactions and spontaneous combustion.
6-18 Write equations for the reactions of four basic oxides with water and the reactions of four acidic oxides with water.
6-19 Define carefully the processes of oxidation and reduction. Illustrate by examples.
6-20 Atom *X* gives up two electrons. The resulting particle formed is ________. *X* is (oxidized, reduced) ________. Atom *X* is called the (oxidizing agent, reducing agent) ________.
Atom *Y* takes on two electrons. The resulting particle formed is ________. Atom *Y* is (oxidized, reduced) ________. Atom *Y* is called the (oxidizing agent, reducing agent) ________.
6-21 In each of the following indicate (a) oxidizing agent, (b) reducing agent, (c) elements which change in oxidation number, (d) the number of electrons given up or taken on by those elements which change in oxidation number: (1) $Mg + Pb^{++}SO_4^{=} \longrightarrow Mg^{++}SO_4^{=} + Pb^0$; (2) $Zn + 2\ HCl \longrightarrow H_2 + Zn^{++} + 2\ Cl^-$; (3) $2\ Al + 3\ Ni^{++} \longrightarrow 2\ Al^{+++} + 3\ Ni^0$; (4) $H_2 + Br_2 \longrightarrow 2\ HBr$; (5) $H_2 + 2\ K \longrightarrow 2\ KH$.
6-22 What general experimental condition is necessary for converting oxygen to ozone?
6-23 How does ozone react in the presence of (a) manganese dioxide, (b) sulfur dioxide, (c) finely divided platinum? Give equations.

Problems

6-1 Oxygen may be prepared by heating mercuric oxide, by heating silver oxide, from the reaction of sodium peroxide with water, or by the decomposition of a 10 per cent solution of hydrogen peroxide. Calculate the relative weights of oxygen obtainable from 1.0 kg of each of the above oxygen-containing compounds.
6-2 Calculate the number of grams of sodium peroxide necessary to react with water to produce 38 g of oxygen.
6-3 What is the volume in liters of 38 g of oxygen gas measured at 0°C and 1 atm pressure? (The density of oxygen gas at 0°C and 1 atm pressure is 1.429 g/l.)
6-4 If 142 g of potassium chlorate are heated in an open crucible above 400°C until no more change occurs, what weight of what substance will be left in the crucible?
6-5 If 75 g of a solution containing 3.0 per cent by weight of hydrogen peroxide are completely decomposed to water and oxygen, how many liters of oxygen at 0°C and 1 atm pressure will be formed? (Note: The volume occupied by 1 mole of any gas at 0°C and 1 atm pressure is 22.4 l.)
6-6 Calculate the energy in calories required for the decomposition of 1.0 kg of molecular oxygen to the atomic form.
6-7 (a) What weight of oxygen is necessary to burn 10 g of sulfur completely to SO_2? (b) What weight of SO_2 is formed?
6-8 How many grams of P_4O_{10} are obtained from the complete burning of 62 g of phosphorus?
6-9 From the information given in the chapter, determine how many calories would be absorbed or liberated in converting 16 g of atomic oxygen to ozone.

HYDROGEN.
THE ELECTROMOTIVE SERIES

Hydrogen is the lightest of all the elements. In its stable form it exists as a diatomic molecule, H_2, the lightest stable molecule known. Hydrogen is essential to life as a component of the compounds that constitute plant and animal tissues.

7-1 The History of Hydrogen

Hydrogen seems to have been known to the alchemists as early as the sixteenth century, but no authentic written reports concerning the gas appeared before 1766. In that year, Henry Cavendish, an English chemist, prepared the gas by several different methods and observed its flammable character. He called the gas "flammable air," but he did not establish that it was an element. Later, it was demonstrated that hydrogen was an element and that it was a component of water. In 1783 Lavoisier named the element (hydrogen, "water-former"), having succeeded in forming water by combining hydrogen with oxygen under certain experimental conditions.

7-2 Occurrence

The atmosphere contains only minute amounts of free hydrogen, H_2, about one part in 1,000,000. Chemically combined with other elements, however, hydrogen appears in a great many compounds in nature. The chief source of hydrogen is water, about $\frac{1}{9}$ of which by weight is made up of chemically combined hydrogen. Hydrogen is also a component of many fuels such as natural gas and petroleum, and it is present in chemical combination in almost all substances that comprise plant and animal tissues. Hydrogen is the most abundant element in the sun and in the major stars.

7-3 The Preparation of Hydrogen

Since only minute quantities of free hydrogen, H_2, occur in nature, it must be prepared by chemical reactions from compounds that contain hydrogen. The compounds that serve as the source of hydrogen are water, H_2O, certain acids (compounds of hydrogen with a non-metallic element or negative polyatomic ion), certain bases (compounds of a metal with the hydroxyl group, OH^-), and hydrocarbons (binary compounds composed of hydrogen and carbon).

THE PREPARATION OF HYDROGEN FROM WATER

At *ordinary temperatures* hydrogen, H_2, may be displaced from water by the action of highly electropositive metals, or by electrolysis. It also can be prepared by the reaction of the hydrides of highly electropositive metals, such as LiH and CaH_2, with water at ordinary and even lower temperatures. At *higher temperatures* hydrogen may be displaced from water by some of the less electropositive metals and some of the non-metals. Although none of these reactions is especially convenient for laboratory use, some are commercially feasible.

REACTION OF METALS WITH WATER AT ORDINARY TEMPERATURES

Only the most electropositive metals, such as potassium, sodium, and calcium, can displace hydrogen from water at ordinary temperatures. In each case the products are molecular hydrogen, H_2, which is evolved as a gas, and the hydroxide of the metal, which may remain in solution. As an example consider the reaction of sodium with water. When a small piece of sodium is placed in water at room temperature, a vigorous reaction follows; the piece of sodium reacts rapidly and hydrogen gas, H_2, is liberated.

$$2\ Na + 2\ H_2O \longrightarrow H_2 + 2\ Na^+ + 2\ OH^-$$

Thus the reaction of liquid water with sodium metal consists essentially of the oxidation of sodium atoms, Na^0, to sodium ions, Na^+, which remain in water solution as hydrated (see Ch. 30) sodium ions. At the same time, one hydrogen atom of each reacting H_2O molecule is reduced from its $+1$ oxidation number in H_2O to zero. The neutral hydrogen atoms then combine to form gaseous H_2 molecules. For each H_2O molecule which has reacted, an OH^- ion is formed which remains in solution as the hydrated hydroxide ion. Thus we often say that sodium metal, Na, reacts with water to form gaseous hydrogen, H_2, and soluble sodium hydroxide, NaOH, and the equation for the reaction is often written as:

$$2\ Na + 2\ H_2O \longrightarrow H_2 + 2\ NaOH$$

So much heat is evolved in this reaction that the sodium (melting point, 98°C) melts into a liquid globule which rushes about over the surface of the water. If the reaction is carried out in the presence of air, the evolved hydrogen may burst into flame as it reacts with the oxygen of air to form H_2O vapor.

The reaction of potassium metal, K, with water is even more rapid than the reaction of sodium with water and the equation may be written as:

$$2\ K + 2\ H_2O \longrightarrow H_2 + 2\ KOH$$

On the other hand, calcium metal, Ca, reacts more slowly with water, again liberating gas, H_2, and forming the hydroxide $Ca(OH)_2$, which may separate from the solution since it is not very soluble in water:

$$Ca + 2\,H_2O \longrightarrow H_2 + Ca(OH)_2$$

Precautions must be taken in carrying out these experiments, because these reactions are very vigorous and may result in an explosion. Therefore, only extremely small amounts of these highly electropositive metals should be used. In fact, because potassium, sodium, and the other highly electropositive metals are so very reactive toward water (moisture), as well as towards many other substances, they are usually stored under an inert solvent such as kerosene.

REACTION OF METAL HYDRIDES WITH COLD WATER. Hydrogen, H_2, can also be prepared by the reaction of the hydride of an electropositive metal with cold water. For example, lithium hydride, LiH, and calcium hydride, CaH_2, react with cold water to form hydrogen, H_2, and the metal hydroxides LiOH and $Ca(OH)_2$.

$$LiH + H_2O \longrightarrow H_2 + LiOH$$

$$CaH_2 + 2\,H_2O \longrightarrow 2\,H_2 + Ca(OH)_2$$

In these reactions a hydride ion, H^-, of the metal hydride reacts with one of the hydrogen atoms (oxidation number $+1$) of H_2O to form hydrogen gas, H_2. In this reaction the hydride ion, H^-, acts as the reducing agent and the $(+1)$ hydrogen atom of water acts as the oxidizing agent.

THE REACTION OF METALS AND NON-METALS WITH WATER AT HIGH TEMPERATURES. Some of the metals less electropositive than calcium—for example, magnesium, Mg; zinc, Zn; and iron, Fe—do not displace hydrogen from water at room temperature but do so if the metals are heated and the water is in the form of steam. The reaction of these metals with steam at high temperatures produces hydrogen gas, H_2, and the *oxide* (rather than the hydroxide) of the metal. For example, when steam is passed over heated magnesium, the magnesium burns brightly, producing solid magnesium oxide, MgO, and hydrogen gas, H_2:

$$\underset{\text{(heated)}}{Mg} + \underset{\text{(steam)}}{H_2O} \longrightarrow H_2 + MgO \qquad \Delta H = -86.0 \text{ kcal/mole-equation}$$

Zinc and iron, at red heat, also react with steam though less readily than magnesium, yielding H_2 gas and zinc oxide, ZnO, and iron(II,III) oxide, $FeO \cdot Fe_2O_3$ (Fe_3O_4), respectively.

$$\underset{\text{(heated)}}{Zn} + \underset{\text{(steam)}}{H_2O} \longrightarrow H_2 + ZnO \qquad \Delta H = -25.4 \text{ kcal/mole-equation}$$

Similarly for iron:

$$\underset{\text{(heated)}}{3\,Fe} + \underset{\text{(steam)}}{4\,H_2O} \longrightarrow 4\,H_2 + FeO \cdot Fe_2O_3 \qquad \Delta H = -35.8 \text{ kcal/mole-equation}$$

Notice that all these reactions are *exothermic,* so that once started they generally give off enough heat to maintain the high temperature required for the reaction to maintain itself at the desired rate. Certain non-metals, such as carbon, can also displace hydrogen from water at high temperatures, producing an oxide of the non-metal and hydrogen gas:

$$\underset{\text{(heated)}}{C} + \underset{\text{(steam)}}{H_2O} \longrightarrow H_2 + CO \qquad \Delta H = +31.4 \text{ kcal/mole-equation}$$

This reaction is *endothermic,* so we must keep supplying heat if we want it to continue.

THE PREPARATION OF HYDROGEN

BY DISPLACEMENT FROM ACIDS. LABORATORY METHODS

Dilute sulfuric acid, H_2SO_4, and both dilute and concentrated hydrochloric acid, HCl, react rapidly and smoothly with many metals and do not oxidize the hydrogen that is formed. These acids, therefore, are the most suitable for preparing hydrogen in the laboratory by displacement with metals. An apparatus for the laboratory preparation of hydrogen by means of the reaction of a metal with an acid is shown in Fig. 7-1.

Zinc metal and a dilute solution of sulfuric acid or hydrochloric acid are usually employed in the laboratory preparation of hydrogen because these materials are readily available.

$$Zn + \underset{\text{(dilute)}}{H_2SO_4} \longrightarrow H_2 + ZnSO_4$$

$$Zn + \underset{\text{(dil. or conc.)}}{2\,HCl} \longrightarrow H_2 + ZnCl_2$$

The hydrogen gas evolved is fairly pure, and the other products of the reaction—zinc sulfate, $ZnSO_4$, or zinc chloride, $ZnCl_2$—remain in solution.

Magnesium metal also reacts with dilute sulfuric acid and dilute or concentrated hydrochloric acid to yield hydrogen gas; the reaction is more vigorous* than that of zinc.

$$Mg + \underset{\text{(dilute)}}{H_2SO_4} \longrightarrow H_2 + MgSO_4$$

$$Mg + \underset{\text{(dil. or conc.)}}{2\,HCl} \longrightarrow H_2 + MgCl_2$$

Tin, a soft white metal, dissolves slowly in cold dilute hydrochloric acid, but readily when the acid is hot and concentrated, to form hydrogen, H_2, and soluble tin(II) chloride, $SnCl_2$:

$$Sn + 2\,HCl \longrightarrow H_2 + SnCl_2$$

IMPURITIES IN HYDROGEN FROM METAL AND ACID. The hydrogen gas produced by these displacement reactions contains water vapor carried along by the gas as it bubbles through the water solution. We can remove the water vapor by passing the gas over a dehydrating agent such as solid calcium chloride, $CaCl_2$; potassium hydroxide, KOH; or phosphorus(V) oxide, P_4O_{10} (Fig. 7-1). These compounds absorb the water vapor present in the gas stream but do not react with the

FIGURE 7-1 The laboratory preparation of hydrogen.

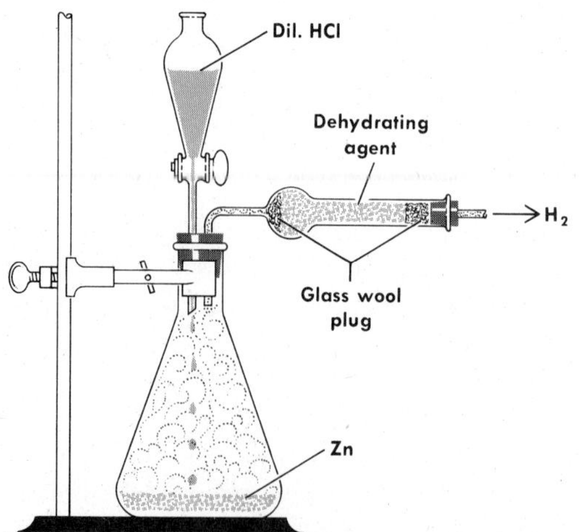

* In either the laboratory or commercial preparation of a substance, the *speed* of the reaction is always important. The rate at which hydrogen gas is evolved in the laboratory, for example, should permit the gas to be produced and handled conveniently in a reasonable time. Although lead, Pb, reacts with hydrochloric acid to produce hydrogen gas, for example, this method is not used in the laboratory because the reaction is too slow. On the other hand metals such as sodium and potassium are not used because they may react explosively with acids.

hydrogen gas. The hydrogen may also contain traces of the hydrides of arsenic, AsH_3, and antimony, SbH_3, if arsenic or antimony is present (as is often the case) as an impurity in the zinc metal. If pure hydrogen is to be produced, pure metal and pure acid must be used, or the impurities from the metal and the acid must be removed. Or some other method of preparation, such as the electrolysis of water, which produces hydrogen gas free from impurities, must be used.

ACIDS USED FOR PRODUCING HYDROGEN FROM METALS. As we have seen, dilute sulfuric acid and dilute hydrochloric acid are suitable for preparing hydrogen from metals. Acetic acid and phosphoric acid may also be used. However some other acids, such as concentrated or dilute nitric acid, HNO_3, or concentrated sulfuric acid, H_2SO_4, are strong oxidizing agents and when they react with metals their negative ions are reduced, the metal is oxidized, and water, H_2O, forms instead of hydrogen, H_2. Nitric acid, HNO_3, reacts with zinc metal to form ammonium nitrate, zinc nitrate, and water. Concentrated sulfuric acid reacts with metals such as copper to produce SO_2, $CuSO_4$, and water. These reactions are considered in more detail in Chapters 28 and 29, but for the present we simply wish to point out that (1) not all acids yield hydrogen when they react with metals, (2) an acid may be either oxidizing or non-oxidizing.

THE PREPARATION OF HYDROGEN BY DISPLACEMENT FROM WATER SOLUTIONS OF STRONG BASES

We have seen that the metals zinc, aluminum, and tin react with non-oxidizing acids to form the salts of the metals and hydrogen gas. These metals also react with concentrated water solutions of strongly basic metal hydroxides, such as sodium hydroxide, NaOH, and potassium hydroxide, KOH, to produce hydrogen gas, H_2, and the hydroxo-complex of the metal. The hydroxo-complexes formed in the reactions of these metals with a water solution of NaOH are: $Na_2[Zn(OH)_4]$, sodium tetrahydroxozincate(II); $Na[Al(OH)_4]$, sodium tetrahydroxoaluminate(III); and $Na_2[Sn(OH)_4]$, sodium tetrahydroxostannate(II).

Here are the equations for these reactions:

$$Zn + 2\,NaOH + 2\,H_2O \longrightarrow H_2 + Na_2[Zn(OH)_4]$$

$$2\,Al + 2\,NaOH + 6\,H_2O \longrightarrow 3\,H_2 + 2\,Na[Al(OH)_4]$$

$$Sn + 2\,NaOH + 2\,H_2O \longrightarrow H_2 + Na_2[Sn(OH)_4]$$

Metals such as zinc, aluminum, and tin, which can replace hydrogen ions from water solutions of both acids and bases, are called *amphoteric metals*, from the Greek *ampho*, meaning *both*.

Certain non-metals also react with concentrated water solutions of strong bases to produce hydrogen gas. For example, Si, a non-metal, reacts with a concentrated water solution of sodium hydroxide to produce H_2 and sodium silicate, Na_2SiO_3:

$$Si + 2\,NaOH + H_2O \longrightarrow 2\,H_2 + Na_2SiO_3$$

7-4 The Electromotive Series of Metals

On the basis of experimental data and exact electrical measurements (discussed in Chapter 22), chemists have listed the common metals (metallic elements) and the element hydrogen in the order of their tendency to lose electrons to form positive ions. At the head of this list, as given in Table 7-1, are the more electropositive elements. As we go down the list, the elements become progressively less electropositive. This listing is known as the *Electromotive Force Series* (abbreviated E.M.F. series) or simply the *Electromotive Series.* An understanding of the Electromotive Series will help you remember the metals that can liberate (displace) hydrogen

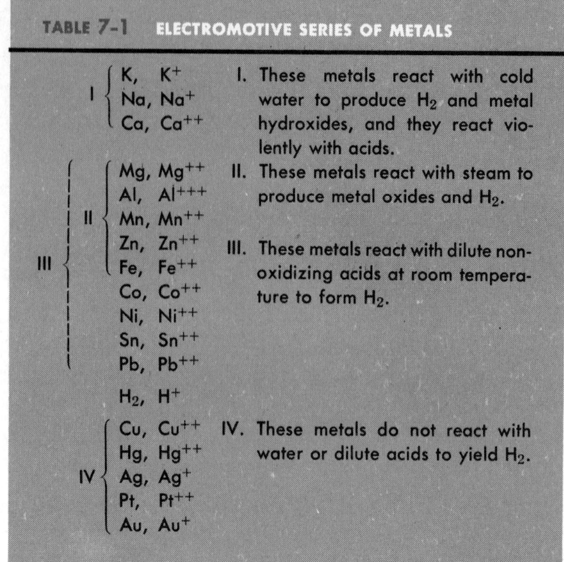

TABLE 7-1 ELECTROMOTIVE SERIES OF METALS

Group	Metal, ion	Behavior
I	K, K^+	I. These metals react with cold water to produce H_2 and metal hydroxides, and they react violently with acids.
I	Na, Na^+	
I	Ca, Ca^{++}	
III, II	Mg, Mg^{++}	II. These metals react with steam to produce metal oxides and H_2.
III, II	Al, Al^{+++}	
III, II	Mn, Mn^{++}	
III, II	Zn, Zn^{++}	III. These metals react with dilute nonoxidizing acids at room temperature to form H_2.
III, II	Fe, Fe^{++}	
III	Co, Co^{++}	
III	Ni, Ni^{++}	
III	Sn, Sn^{++}	
III	Pb, Pb^{++}	
	H_2, H^+	
IV	Cu, Cu^{++}	IV. These metals do not react with water or dilute acids to yield H_2.
IV	Hg, Hg^{++}	
IV	Ag, Ag^+	
IV	Pt, Pt^{++}	
IV	Au, Au^+	

from water, acids, or bases. It will also enable you to predict whether any one metal will displace another metal from its compounds.

Table 7-1 indicates that the most electropositive metals—those highest in the list—can displace H_2 from cold water. Some less electropositive metals can displace hydrogen from acids, or, at high temperatures, from steam. Metals below hydrogen in the Electromotive Series do not displace hydrogen from either water or acids. Thus, if hydrochloric acid is added to copper, mercury, silver, platinum, or gold, no reaction occurs, for these metals are less electropositive than hydrogen.

As we have seen (p. 85), when a strip of zinc metal is placed in a solution of copper(II) sulfate, some of the zinc strip dissolves and a coating of metallic copper forms on the remaining zinc strip. We found that the equation for this reaction was:

$$Zn^0 + Cu^{++}SO_4^{=} \longrightarrow Cu^0 + Zn^{++}SO_4^{=}$$

Notice that the sulfate ion, $SO_4^{=}$, is a spectator ion, so the net equation consists of the transfer of electrons from the zinc atoms to the copper(II) ions:

$$Zn^0 + Cu^{++} \longrightarrow Cu^0 + Zn^{++}$$

Zinc, as indicated by its position in the Electromotive Series, gives up electrons more freely than does copper. Therefore the zinc atoms, Zn^0, pass into solution as zinc ions, Zn^{++}, transferring their electrons to the Cu^{++} ions in solution, which thereby become metallic copper, Cu, and plate out on the surface of the zinc strip. Notice that this reaction depends on the relative positions of the two metals in the Electromotive Series: zinc, Zn, is above copper, Cu, in this list. This reaction of copper(II) ions in solution with zinc metal is characteristic of *any* copper(II) compound that produces Cu^{++} ions in solution. That is, any water-soluble copper(II) salt will react in the same way with zinc metal. We find experimentally, for example, that a strip of metallic zinc placed in a water solution of copper(II) nitrate, $Cu^{++}(NO_3^-)_2$; copper(II) chloride, $Cu^{++}(Cl^-)_2$; or copper(II) acetate, $Cu^{++}(C_2H_3O_2^-)_2$, readily dissolves, and metallic copper is deposited simultaneously on the undissolved zinc metal. Equations for these reactions follow:

$$Zn^0 + Cu^{++}(NO_3^-)_2 \longrightarrow Cu^0 + Zn^{++}(NO_3^-)_2$$
$$Zn^0 + Cu^{++}(Cl^-)_2 \longrightarrow Cu^0 + Zn^{++}(Cl^-)_2$$
$$Zn^0 + Cu^{++}(C_2H_3O_2^-)_2 \longrightarrow Cu^0 + Zn^{++}(C_2H_3O_2^-)_2$$

In these oxidation-reduction reactions, the nitrate ions, NO_3^-, the chloride ions, Cl^-, and the acetate ions, $C_2H_3O_2^-$, like the sulfate ions, $SO_4^{=}$, in the copper(II) sulfate solution considered above, undergo no change (are spectator ions). Thus, the net result of all these changes is the same—namely, two electrons leave the zinc atom, Zn^0, which forms a zinc ion, Zn^{++}; and these two electrons are taken on by the copper(II) ion, Cu^{++}, which becomes metallic copper, Cu^0. The following net oxidation-reduction equation (called in general the *net ionic equation*) holds for each of these reactions.

$$Zn^0 + Cu^{++} \longrightarrow Zn^{++} + Cu^0$$

In each of the above cases, the Zn^0 metal is the reducing agent and the Cu^{++} ion is the oxidizing agent.

In general, Table 7-1 helps us to predict whether any of the metals in the left-hand column will react with any of the ions in the right-hand column. A metal in the left-hand column will react with any ion below it in the right-hand column. The original metal becomes the ion listed beside it in the right-hand column, while the original ion becomes the metal listed beside it in the left-hand column. In other words, a more electropositive metal will displace from a solution the ions of a less electropositive metal. Accordingly, we could predict that Zn metal would displace from solution Cu^{++} ions, forming metallic Cu^0 and Zn^{++} ions (in solution). Similarly, metallic magnesium, Mg, would displace both Fe^{++} ions and Zn^{++} ions from solutions containing these ions, as the following equations indicate:

$$Mg^0 + Fe^{++}SO_4^{=} \longrightarrow Fe^0 + Mg^{++}SO_4^{=} \quad \text{or} \quad Mg^0 + Fe^{++} \longrightarrow Fe^0 + Mg^{++}$$

$$Mg^0 + Zn^{++}SO_4^{=} \longrightarrow Zn^0 + Mg^{++}SO_4^{=} \quad \text{or} \quad Mg^0 + Zn^{++} \longrightarrow Zn^0 + Mg^{++}$$

If, however, a strip of nickel metal, Ni, is placed in a solution of aluminum nitrate ($Al^{+++} + 3\ NO_3^-$) or zinc sulfate ($Zn^{++} + SO_4^{=}$), no displacement reaction will occur, because nickel is lower in the Electromotive Series than both aluminum and zinc.

We can use the E.M.F. Series not only to predict whether a given reaction will take place, but also to work out its balanced equation. Consider, for example, the reaction of zinc metal, Zn^0, with a solution of hydrochloric acid. This solution contains H^+ ions (and Cl^- ions) and since zinc is above hydrogen in the E.M.F. Series we know that Zn^0 metal *does* displace H^+ from solution. Furthermore, we know that Zn^0 becomes Zn^{++} (since this is the ion listed beside Zn), while the H^+ ions become H_2 molecules (as listed alongside).

$$Zn^0 + H^+ \longrightarrow Zn^{++} + H_2$$

By inspection, we balance and obtain the net (ionic) equation:

$$Zn^0 + 2\ H^+ \longrightarrow Zn^{++} + H_2$$

For completeness we may add the spectator Cl^- ions:

$$Zn^0 + 2\ H^+ + 2\ Cl^- \longrightarrow Zn^{++} + 2\ Cl^- + H_2 \quad \text{or} \quad Zn + 2\ HCl \longrightarrow ZnCl_2 + H_2$$

REACTION OF METALS BELOW HYDROGEN IN THE E. M. F. SERIES WITH OXIDIZING ACIDS

Although metals below hydrogen in the Electromotive Series cannot liberate hydrogen from acids, they can react with oxidizing acids to form the reduction products of the oxidizing acid, the salts of the metal, and water. Copper, for example, reacts with dilute nitric acid to produce nitrogen monoxide; copper(II) nitrate, $Cu(NO_3)_2$; and water. An example is the reaction:

$$3\ Cu + \underset{\text{(dilute)}}{8\ HNO_3} \longrightarrow 2\ NO + 3\ Cu(NO_3)_2 + 4\ H_2O$$

Copper also reacts with concentrated H_2SO_4 to produce sulfur dioxide, SO_2; copper(II) sulfate, $CuSO_4$; and water, H_2O:

$$\underset{\text{(concentrated)}}{Cu + 2\,H_2SO_4} \longrightarrow SO_2 + CuSO_4 + 2\,H_2O$$

Copper, which is below hydrogen in the Electromotive Series, does not react with (is not oxidized by) either water or non-oxidizing acids, but it does react with oxidizing acids. The fact that Cu is oxidized to its ion, Cu^{++}, by nitric acid and concentrated sulfuric acid indicates that these acids are good oxidizing agents (good electron-acceptors).

THE RATE OF REACTION BETWEEN METALS AND ACIDS

Whether a given metal will react (spontaneously) with a non-oxidizing acid (H^+) to liberate H, is determined by the position of the metal in the E.M.F. series, and only highly electropositive metals react with non-oxidizing acids under ordinary conditions. On the other hand, the *rate* at which a highly electropositive metal reacts with a non-oxidizing acid depends on many factors, primarily on the temperature, the acid concentration, the state of the metal (whether in bulk or powder), and the nature of both the metal and the acid. Thus, iron filings react quite rapidly with a boiling hydrochloric acid solution, but rather slowly if the acid is ice-cold. At room temperature a solid piece of iron may take days to dissolve in hydrochloric acid, whereas the same amount of finely powdered iron would dissolve in a few hours. Also, the more concentrated the acid solution, the faster the reaction. The effect of the nature of the metal on the rate of the reaction is illustrated by the reaction of a dilute solution of hydrochloric acid with the metals Na, Zn, Fe, and Sn at room temperature.

$$2\,Na + 2\,HCl \longrightarrow H_2 + 2\,NaCl \text{ (explosive!)}$$
$$Zn + 2\,HCl \longrightarrow H_2 + ZnCl_2 \text{ (very rapid)}$$
$$Fe + 2\,HCl \longrightarrow H_2 + FeCl_2 \text{ (fairly rapid)}$$
$$Sn + 2\,HCl \longrightarrow H_2 + SnCl_2 \text{ (quite slow)}$$

Sodium reacts very rapidly. The heat that is evolved in the reaction is sufficient to melt the (remaining) sodium (m.p. 98°C), thereby increasing its contact surface with the acid. On the other hand, Zn, Fe, and Sn have much higher melting points and also are protected by either an original coating of oxide, or by a film of adsorbed H_2 gas, formed in the reaction. Finally, the effect of the nature of the acid is illustrated by the following example. Aluminum metal reacts rather quickly with dilute sulfuric and hydrochloric acids, which are known as strong acids. But it reacts very slowly with acetic acid and with phosphoric acid, which are weak acids. In fact, a general characteristic of all weak acids is their slow reaction with metals. Equations illustrating these reactions follow:

$$2\,Al + \underset{\text{(dil. or conc.)}}{6\,HCl} \longrightarrow 3\,H_2 + 2\,AlCl_3 \quad \text{(rapid)}$$

$$2\,Al + \underset{\text{(dil. or conc.)}}{6\,HC_2H_3O_2} \longrightarrow 3\,H_2 + 2\,Al(C_2H_3O_2)_3 \quad \text{(slow)}$$

$$2\,Al + \underset{\text{(dil. or conc.)}}{2\,H_3PO_4} \longrightarrow 3\,H_2 + 2\,AlPO_4 \quad \text{(slow)}$$

Weak acids react slowly with metals. The anions of weak acids tend to aggregate with the metal ions, and these aggregates are either insoluble and deposit on the surface of the metal, or when soluble are so bulky that they diffuse slowly away from the metal surface into solution. Consequently, the formation of these aggregates (complexes) impedes further contact of the acid with the surface of the metal.

7-5 The Commercial Preparation of Hydrogen

The only starting materials for the industrial preparation of hydrogen that meet the requirements of low cost and abundance are water, coke, and hydrocarbon gases derived from petroleum. Consequently, all commercial methods for preparing hydrogen utilize some combinations of these materials.

THE BOSCH PROCESS

In the Bosch process, named after Carl Bosch (1874–1940), a German mechanical engineer and industrialist who designed the first plant, steam is passed over incandescent coke (at about 1,000°C) to produce a mixture of hydrogen and carbon monoxide called "water gas." The endothermic reaction is:

$$C_{(s)} + H_2O_{(g)} \longrightarrow \underbrace{H_{2(g)} + CO_{(g)}}_{\text{water gas}} \qquad \Delta H = +31.4 \text{ kcal/mole-equation}$$

Notice that the hot carbon "removes the oxygen" from the steam—it acts as a reducing agent. Since heat is absorbed in the reaction, the temperature of the coke drops as the reaction proceeds, and the reaction slows down (and would eventually stop). The coke must then be reheated if the formation of water gas is to proceed at the desired speed. This is done simply by alternating the endothermic "stage"—the production of water gas—with the exothermic "stage" during which preheated air is blown through the coke, causing it to burn partially, according to the following exothermic reaction:

$$C_{(s)} + O_{2(g)} \longrightarrow CO_{2(g)} \qquad \Delta H = -94.1 \text{ kcal/mole-equation}$$

The carbon dioxide thus produced by this combustion is permitted to escape, along with the excess air. Enough heat is evolved to raise the temperature of the coke so that it is again red hot and can react further with the steam to produce hydrogen and carbon monoxide (water gas). Thus the endothermic reaction and the exothermic reaction are alternated in the Bosch process to yield intermittently water gas and carbon dioxide. A variation of the Bosch process uses hydrocarbons in place of coke. Reactions between hydrocarbons and steam in the presence of suitable catalysts at high temperature (1,100°C) produce a mixture of H_2 and CO. The hydrocarbon methane, CH_4, reacts with steam as follows:

$$CH_4 + H_2O_{(steam)} \xrightarrow{\text{catalyst}} 3\,H_2 + CO \qquad \Delta H = +49.3 \text{ kcal/mole-equation}$$

The mixture of the H_2 gas and CO gas formed by these reactions may be used as such —for example as a fuel. If however, this mixture is to be used to prepare hydrogen, then the carbon monoxide gas must be further reacted with additional steam at a lower temperature (500°C) and in the presence of a catalyst (for example, a mixture of ion(III) oxide, Fe_2O_3, and chromium(III) oxide, Cr_2O_3) to produce more hydrogen gas and carbon dioxide gas:

$$CO + H_2O_{(steam)} \xrightarrow{\text{catalyst}} H_2 + CO_2 \qquad \Delta H = -9.9 \text{ kcal/mole-equation}$$

Finally, therefore, a mixture of hydrogen gas and carbon dioxide is obtained, and in order to provide commercially pure hydrogen, the two gases must be separated. Fortunately, carbon dioxide is 100 times more soluble in water than hydrogen gas is. Furthermore, the solubility of carbon dioxide only increases significantly at low temperatures and under high pressures. Consequently, the carbon dioxide gas and the hydrogen gas can be separated very effectively simply by passing a mixture of these gases through cold water and under high pressure. The carbon dioxide gas dissolves, and the hydrogen gas bubbles up through the water and is collected.

LESS COMMON COMMERCIAL METHODS

The reaction of heated iron with steam (p. 91) is also used to a limited extent for the commercial production of hydrogen. Another method employed is the electrolysis of water, which is profitable in those localities where the cost of electricity is relatively low and if very pure hydrogen is required. Where cost of transportation and ease of handling are the primary considerations, solid hydrides of metals such as calcium hydride, CaH_2 (easily transported in air-tight containers), are used to produce hydrogen by reaction with water:

$$CaH_2 + 2\ H_2O \longrightarrow 2\ H_2 + Ca(OH)_2$$

7-6 The Physical Properties of Hydrogen

Pure hydrogen gas, H_2, is colorless, odorless, and tasteless, and is only slightly soluble in water. This insolubility makes it possible for hydrogen gas to be collected over water. Hydrogen gas has a very low boiling point, $-252.7°C$. At a slightly lower temperature, $-259°C$, liquid hydrogen becomes a transparent solid.

Hydrogen gas is the lightest substance known. One liter of hydrogen measured at 0°C and 1 atm pressure weighs only 0.08987 g. The gas is only about $\frac{1}{16}$ as dense as air.

Hydrogen gas is readily absorbed by certain finely divided metals. For example, 1 volume of finely divided palladium metal at room temperature can absorb approximately 850 volumes of hydrogen gas. When the metal is heated, the absorbed hydrogen gas is released.

ISOTOPES OF HYDROGEN, HEAVY WATER

Isotopes, as we saw in Chapter 3, refer to the atoms of an element which have the same number of protons but a different number of neutrons in their nuclei. The isotopes of an element therefore have the same atomic number but different atomic weights. The most abundant isotope of hydrogen has a mass of 1, but a stable isotope of mass 2 and an unstable isotope of mass 3 also exist. In heavy elements a difference of one or more units in atomic weight from one isotope to another causes only a slight difference in their physical properties, because of the slight relative (percentage) difference in atomic weight. In hydrogen, however, one or two additional units in atomic weight actually mean doubling or tripling the mass of the isotopes. In fact, the hydrogen isotope of mass 2 is twice as heavy as the isotope of mass 1, and the hydrogen isotope of mass 3 is three times as heavy. This vast difference causes appreciable variations in the physical properties of the hydrogen isotopes, and for this reason the isotopes of hydrogen are designated by special names and corresponding special symbols.

The hydrogen isotope of mass 2 is called "deuterium" or "heavy hydrogen" and is represented by the symbol D. It constitutes 0.02 per cent, or 1 part in 5,000, of naturally occurring hydrogen. Water that contains heavy hydrogen atoms is known as "heavy water," and is represented by the formula D_2O. The boiling point of heavy water, D_2O, is 101.42°C, and its freezing point is 3.82°C, compared with 100.00°C and 0.00°C for ordinary water, H_2O. Deuterium, D_2; heavy water, D_2O; and various deuterium compounds have proved extremely useful in modern research.

The hydrogen isotope of mass 3 is called "tritium," and its symbol is T. Tritium occurs in natural hydrogen only in very small amounts, but it may be prepared by means of a nuclear reaction between lithium and neutrons. This isotope of hydrogen is unstable and decomposes into an electron and a helium atom.

7-7 The Chemical Properties of Hydrogen

Hydrogen gas consists of very stable, covalently bonded, diatomic molecules, H_2. A great amount of energy must be provided to break these molecules up into their component atoms (H + H). In fact, 104.2 kcal are required to decompose 1 mole of gaseous hydrogen molecules.

$$H_2 \longrightarrow H + H \qquad \Delta H = +104.2 \text{ kcal/mole } H_2$$

This dissociation can be accomplished by passing the H_2 molecules through a source of energy at a very high temperature, such as an electric arc. Conversely, when hydrogen atoms recombine to form hydrogen molecules, this same quantity of energy is liberated (Fig. 7-2). Since 104.2 kcal are needed to dissociate 1 mole of molecular hydrogen into its atoms, the bond dissociation energy or covalent bond strength of the gaseous H_2 molecule is said to be 104.2 kcal/mole. Notice that the reaction of two H atoms to form a hydrogen molecule can be shown schematically by representing each hydrogen atom as $\cdot$H, where the symbol H represents the hydrogen nucleus and the dot represents the one electron that is present in the electron cloud of the hydrogen atom. A molecule of hydrogen gas is depicted as H:H to indicate that each hydrogen atom shares its electron with its partner.

The strong chemical bond that holds the two hydrogen atoms together in a hydrogen molecule consists of the two shared electrons, one from each hydrogen atom. This (electron-pair) bond is a *covalent bond,* which we discussed in Chapter 3.

Gaseous hydrogen atoms, H$\cdot$, can be transformed into mono-positive gaseous ions, H^+, by removing the electron via the following reaction:

$$H\cdot \longrightarrow H^+ + e^- \qquad \Delta H = +313.0 \text{ kcal/mole H atoms}$$

Gaseous hydrogen atoms, H$\cdot$, can also be transformed into mononegative ions H^- (which may exist both in the gaseous state or in ionic crystals), by addition of an electron:

$$H\cdot + e^- \longrightarrow H:^- \qquad \Delta H = -17.8 \text{ kcal/mole H atoms}$$

As the values of ΔH for these reactions indicate, energy is *required* to remove the electron from a gaseous H$\cdot$ atom to form a gaseous H^+ ion, whereas energy is *released* when an electron is added to a gaseous H$\cdot$ atom to form a gaseous hydride ion (H:$^-$).

TYPES OF HYDROGEN COMPOUNDS

Hydrogen gas enters into chemical combination with many non-metals to form covalent compounds, and with the covalent compounds, the hydrogen atom and the atom of the non-metal each contribute a single electron to form the shared electron pair that constitutes the covalent bond. In the ionic compounds, the

FIGURE 7-2 Two hydrogen atoms combine to form a hydrogen molecule.

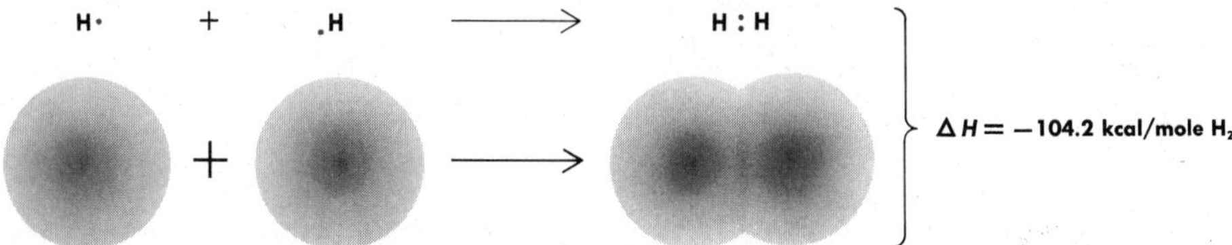

hydrogen atom takes on an electron from the metallic element to form the hydride ion, H^-.

COMPOUNDS OF HYDROGEN WITH NON-METALS. Under the proper conditions, hydrogen gas will enter into chemical combination with all the non-metals except the noble gases. We have already mentioned in Chapter 6 that although pure hydrogen gas does not burn in oxygen or air at room temperature, it reacts rapidly if a catalyst is added, or if the temperature is raised.

Hydrogen gas, H_2, enters into direct chemical combination with fluorine gas, F_2; chlorine gas, Cl_2; bromine vapor, Br_2; and iodine vapor, I_2; to produce volatile binary covalent compounds called hydrogen halides. If X_2 represents a halogen molecule (F_2, Cl_2, Br_2, or I_2), a general equation for this reaction is:

$$H_2 + X_2 \longrightarrow 2\ HX$$

The conditions under which these reactions occur vary widely. Fluorine gas, F_2, for example, reacts rapidly with hydrogen gas, H_2, at temperatures as low as $-250°C$ to produce covalent hydrogen fluoride gas, HF. Hydrogen and fluorine react violently at room temperature, even in the dark. A mixture of hydrogen gas, H_2, and chlorine gas, Cl_2, heated or exposed to a spark or strong light, reacts quite vigorously to produce covalent hydrogen chloride gas, HCl. This reaction between hydrogen and chlorine is an example of the marked effect that light has on the speed of many reactions. In fact, a mixture of hydrogen gas, H_2, and chlorine gas, Cl_2, at room temperature reacts only slightly in the dark; but in the presence of direct sunlight the gases react explosively to form HCl. Thus sunlight initiates and accelerates the reaction. Similarly, the light from a burning magnesium ribbon will cause a mixture of hydrogen and chlorine gases to react explosively.

Bromine, Br_2, which is less reactive than chlorine, reacts with hydrogen at temperatures of about 400°C to produce hydrogen bromide gas, HBr. This reaction is accelerated by the presence of platinum or other catalysts.

Iodine, I_2, the least reactive of these four halogen elements, exhibits the least tendency to react with hydrogen to form hydrogen iodide, HI. At ordinary temperatures a mixture of hydrogen and iodine does not react with measurable speed, but the reaction is rapid at high temperatures (600°C).

At high pressures and at temperatures near 400°C, in the presence of a catalyst, hydrogen gas, H_2, and nitrogen gas, N_2, react to form some ammonia gas, NH_3 (hydrogen and nitrogen do not react at an appreciable rate at ordinary temperatures):

$$3\ H_2 + N_2 \longrightarrow 2\ NH_3 \qquad \Delta H = -22.0\ \text{kcal/mole-equation}$$

At high temperatures hydrogen gas reacts slowly with sulfur vapor to produce hydrogen sulfide gas, H_2S:

$$H_2 + S \longrightarrow H_2S$$

The best way to carry out this reaction is to bubble heated hydrogen gas through molten sulfur.

COMPOUNDS OF HYDROGEN WITH HIGHLY ELECTROPOSITIVE METALS. The more electropositive metals—the alkali and alkaline-earth metals, such as sodium and calcium, for example—react at high temperatures with hydrogen gas to form *hydrides*. Sodium reacts with hydrogen to form sodium hydride, Na^+H^-, and calcium reacts with hydrogen to form calcium hydride, $Ca^{++}(H^-)_2$:

$$2\ Na + H_2 \longrightarrow 2\ Na^+H^-$$

$$Ca + H_2 \longrightarrow Ca^{++}(H^-)_2$$

Notice that in these reactions hydrogen, H_2, takes on electrons and therefore acts as an *oxidizing agent* (an oxidant). These metal hydrides are ionic compounds formed by the transfer of one or two electrons from the strongly electropositive metal to the hydrogen. Each hydrogen atom of the H_2 molecule takes on one electron to become a negative hydride ion, H^-. Each sodium atom, Na, gives up one electron to become the sodium ion, Na^+; and each calcium atom, Ca, gives up two electrons to become the calcium ion, Ca^{++}. In these metal hydrides the electropositive metal ions and the negative hydride ions, H^-, are held together in the stable crystal lattice by ionic attraction.

Ionic hydrides are very unstable in the presence of water because the hydride ion, $H{:}^-$, readily shares its electron pair with a proton from a water molecule, H_2O, to form a covalent H_2 molecule and an OH^- ion, $H{:}^- + H{:}\underset{\displaystyle H}{\overset{}{O}}{:} \longrightarrow H{:}H + ({:}\ddot{O}{:}H^-)$. Thus when an ionic hydride reacts with water, the products are H_2 gas and the hydroxide of the metal. For example, calcium hydride, CaH_2, reacts with water to produce hydrogen gas, H_2, and the slightly soluble calcium hydroxide, $Ca(OH)_2$.

$$Ca^{++}(H^-)_2 + 2\,H_2O \longrightarrow Ca^{++}(OH^-)_2 + 2\,H_2$$

Notice that the hydride ion, H^-, is stable in ionic crystals, such as Na^+H^- and $Ca^{++}(H^-)_2$, but is unstable in water solution. These hydrides of highly electropositive metals are typical examples of ionic compounds in which one of the constituent ions (in this case the H^- ion) is stable in the solid state but not in solution, and they illustrate that the crystal lattice (energy) may be an extremely important factor in determining the stability of compounds.

THE REACTION OF HYDROGEN WITH COMPOUNDS

WITH OXIDES OF METALS. The pronounced tendency of hydrogen to combine with oxygen enables it to remove oxygen from the oxides of many metals, thus forming the free metal and water. Thus, for example, when hydrogen gas, H_2, is passed over mercury(II) oxide HgO, at room temperature, no reaction occurs. But if the oxide is slightly heated (to a temperature lower than that required for its thermal decomposition), it is then readily reduced by hydrogen, producing metallic mercury, Hg, and water vapor, H_2O:

$$HgO + H_2 \longrightarrow Hg + H_2O$$

A similar reduction occurs when certain other metal oxides are heated in the presence of hydrogen. The oxides of chromium and of the metals above chromium in the Electromotive Series cannot be reduced by hydrogen gas. The oxides of iron and the metals below iron in the Electromotive Series can be reduced by hydrogen gas. All the oxides of iron, for example, can be reduced by hydrogen at elevated temperatures to form the free metal and water vapor:

$$FeO + H_2 \longrightarrow Fe + H_2O$$
$$2\,Fe_2O_3 + 6\,H_2 \longrightarrow 4\,Fe + 6\,H_2O$$
$$Fe_3O_4 + 4\,H_2 \longrightarrow 3\,Fe + 4\,H_2O$$

When either copper(II) oxide, CuO, or copper(I) oxide, Cu_2O, is heated in the presence of hydrogen, red metallic copper and water vapor are produced:

$$CuO + H_2 \longrightarrow Cu + H_2O$$
$$Cu_2O + H_2 \longrightarrow 2\,Cu + H_2O$$

These reactions are carried out by heating the finely divided metal oxide and then passing the hydrogen gas over it.

WITH OTHER COMPOUNDS. Important commercial use is made of the reaction of hydrogen with carbon monoxide, at high pressure and under the influence of catalysts, to produce special organic compounds. For example, hydrogen gas reacts with carbon monoxide gas at high temperatures (350–400°C) and high pressures (3,000 lb per sq in.), in the presence of a catalytic mixture of zinc oxide and chromium(III) oxide, to produce methyl alcohol, CH_3OH:

$$CO + 2\,H_2 \xrightarrow[\text{chromium (III) oxide}]{\text{zinc oxide}} CH_3OH$$

This reaction is a good example of how important are the *conditions* under which a reaction is carried out. If these two gases, CO and H_2, were brought together in the *absence* of the appropriate catalyst, no methyl alcohol, CH_3OH, would be formed. And even in the presence of the right catalyst, only a trace reaction would occur if the temperature and pressure were not raised to the proper levels. Again, as in the examples of the rate of reaction of a solid with a gas, we would expect that when a solid such as (ZnO, Cr_2O_3) is used as a catalyst, a finely divided form of the solid catalyst will increase the rate of reaction. And this is the case.

The reaction of hydrogen with certain vegetable oils, in the presence of (finely divided) nickel metal as the catalyst, is also commercially important. Under controlled conditions oils such as cotton seed oil are combined chemically with hydrogen and converted into solid fats. This so-called "hardening of fats" is widely used to produce solid cooking fats. Most varieties of margarine are also produced in this way. The general process by which such oils react with H_2 is called *hydrogenation.*

7-8 The Detection of Hydrogen

Free hydrogen gas, H_2, may be detected by the fact that it burns in air with a nearly colorless flame to produce water vapor (p. 79). If hydrogen gas is present in a mixture of gases, it can be easily separated by absorption on finely divided, spongy palladium. Heating the palladium releases the hydrogen gas, which can then be detected by its reaction with oxygen in the air.

Chemically combined hydrogen can be detected by mixing the compound with copper(II) oxide and heating the mixture. If water vapor forms, we know that chemically combined hydrogen was present in the compound. A quantitative estimate of the amount of hydrogen present in the compound may be made by collecting the water vapor formed on a weighed amount of a suitable drying agent, such as $CaCl_2$ or P_4O_{10}, and then again weighing the drying agent to determine the amount of water absorbed.

7-9 Determining the Percentage of Hydrogen and Carbon in Organic Compounds

The percentage of carbon and hydrogen in an organic compound may be determined simply by burning the organic substance in an atmosphere of oxygen and collecting and weighing the carbon dioxide and water produced by the reaction. The carbon and hydrogen present in the compound are oxidized by the oxygen—the carbon to carbon dioxide, and the hydrogen to water. A schematic drawing of an apparatus suitable for such combustion reactions is shown in Fig. 7-3. A sample of the compound to be analyzed is weighed and placed in a platinum boat, *B.* The boat is then placed in the combustion tube, *T*; a stream of pure, dry oxygen gas, O_2, is passed through the combustion tube and the sample is then heated to about 550°C (dull-red heat). The products of combustion—carbon dioxide, CO_2, and water vapor, H_2O—are carried along through the tube together with the excess oxygen gas. At the end of the combustion tube there is a series of two or more absorption U-tubes. The first of these contains a drying agent, for example calcium chloride, $CaCl_2$, which absorbs water but not carbon dioxide. The next U-tube is filled with a substance which combines with carbon dioxide—for example, sodium and calcium oxides, Na_2O, CaO (soda-lime). The mixture of the gaseous products of combustion—carbon dioxide and water vapor—as well as the excess oxygen, first passes through the U-tube filled with calcium chloride and the water vapor is absorbed. The remaining gas mixture, which now contains only oxygen and carbon dioxide, then passes over the soda-lime absorbant in the second U-tube. Here the carbon dioxide gas is absorbed and the oxygen passes off into the atmosphere.

When the sample in the boat has been completely burned, the U-tubes are detached from the apparatus, stoppered to prevent further absorption of moisture and CO_2 from the air, and weighed. The increase over their original weight (determined just before the experiment) is the weight of the H_2O and of the CO_2 formed in the combustion, and from these we may calculate the weight of hydrogen and carbon originally present in the sample. From these data we can then calculate the percentages by weight of carbon and hydrogen present in the compound, and from these we can determine the empirical formula of the compound (see p. 45).

7-10 Determination of Equivalent Weights

As we discussed briefly in Chapter 3 (p. 20) the equivalent, or combining, weight of an element is the weight in grams of the element that will combine with or displace 8.00 g of oxygen or 1.008 g of hydrogen. Equivalent weights can readily be determined experimentally, since all elements, except the noble gases, either combine with or displace oxygen or hydrogen. Some actual experimental procedures for determining equivalent weights are given in the Appendix.

7-11 Uses of Hydrogen

Hydrogen, H_2, is produced and used on a very large scale in modern industry, for it is an important raw material in many manufacturing processes. Many of the uses of hydrogen are based on its chemical behavior; for example, large quantities of the gas, usually mixed with other gases, are used as fuel. Hydrogen is widely used in the synthesis of ammonia, NH_3, methyl alcohol, CH_3OH, and solidified hydrogenated vegetable oils, and in the manufacture of synthetic liquid hydrocarbons. Large quantities of hydrogen are also required by various hydrogenation processes connected with the manufacture of gasoline.

Other uses of hydrogen are based on its physical properties, particularly on its

FIGURE 7-3 A combustion apparatus for carbon and hydrogen.

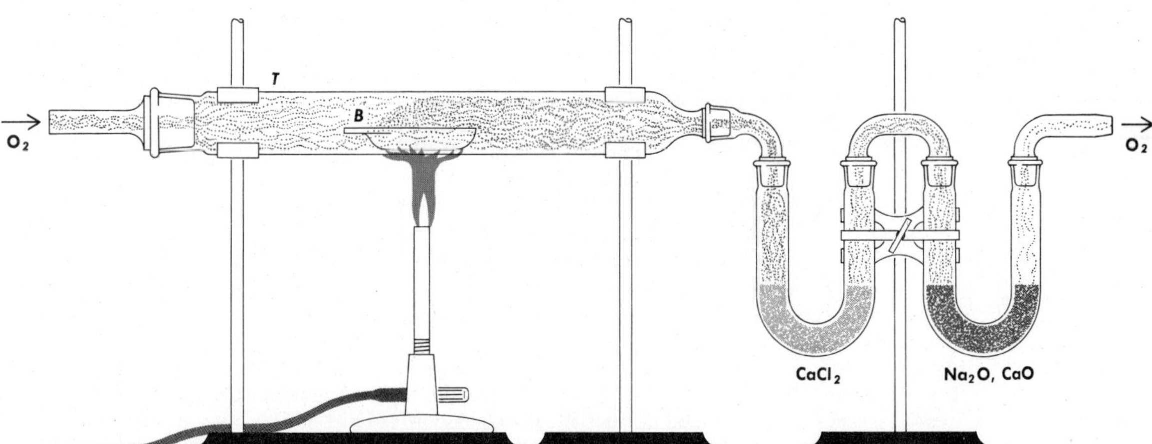

low density and its high heat capacity. Hydrogen is used as a gas for inflating meteorological observation balloons because of its low density, and as a heat-transfer medium in such installations as electrical transformers because of its high heat capacity.

A process involving the decomposition of molecules of hydrogen and the recombination of the atoms of hydrogen is used to produce very high temperatures—from about 4,000° to 5,000°C—in the so-called "atomic hydrogen" torch. Hydrogen molecules, H_2, are first dissociated into their atoms (H + H) by passing the gas through an electric arc. The dissociated atoms are then brought into contact with a metallic surface, where they recombine instantaneously to form hydrogen molecules, thus releasing a great quantity of heat energy (precisely the same quantity of energy which had first to be furnished in the electric arc in order to dissociate the H_2 molecules into atoms).

$$H + H \longrightarrow H_2 \qquad \Delta H = -104.2 \text{ kcal/mole } H_2$$

It is the sudden liberation of this heat which raises the temperature of the metal to 4,000°C or higher. Since hydrogen gas, H_2, is an effective reducing agent especially at very high temperatures, the atomic hydrogen torch (which produces H_2) provides a reducing atmosphere that makes it possible to weld even easily oxidizable metals with high melting points without the possibility of oxidation.

Exercises

7-1 Compare and contrast the abundance and mode of occurrence of hydrogen and oxygen.

7-2 Write equations illustrating how three metals react with cold water to form hydrogen.

7-3 How is the Electromotive Series of metals interpreted?

7-4 Certain metals react with *cold* water to liberate hydrogen. How would these metals react with *hot* water?

7-5 Do elements which react with steam at high temperature to liberate hydrogen also in general react with non-oxidizing acids to liberate hydrogen? Give several examples to illustrate your answer.

7-6 What information may be obtained from the Electromotive Series concerning the reactions of a metal with a salt of another metal in solution?

7-7 Of the three common metals that react with cold water to form hydrogen, which yields the most hydrogen per (a) mole (b) gram, of metal? Explain.

7-8 Sodium at low temperature, or magnesium at higher temperature, may be used to produce hydrogen from water. Which yields more hydrogen per mole of the metal? Explain.

7-9 Write the equations for the reaction of (a) heated zinc, and (b) heated iron, with steam.

7-10 Describe in detail two suitable laboratory methods for preparing hydrogen.

7-11 How can you find out which metals will react with non-oxidizing acids to form hydrogen?

7-12 What does the term "oxidizing acid" mean?

7-13 How may one interpret the fact that a metal such as zinc will react with hydrochloric acid to produce hydrogen but does not yield hydrogen when it reacts with dilute nitric acid?

7-14 Write equations for the reactions of: (a) dilute nitric acid and zinc metal, (b) dilute nitric acid and copper metal, (c) concentrated sulfuric acid and zinc metal, (d) concentrated sulfuric acid and copper metal.

7-15 Why must a non-oxidizing acid be used for preparing hydrogen?

7-16 Write equations illustrating three reactions by which hydrogen is formed from water solutions of bases.

7-17 What happens when we combine the following reactants? If a chemical reaction occurs, write its balanced equation; if no reaction occurs, write N.R.: (a) aluminum metal + iron(II) sulfate solution; (b) $Zn^0 + Cu^{++}$; (c) magnesium metal + zinc sulfate solution; (d) copper metal + zinc sulfate solution; (e) $Ag^0 + Cu^{++}$;

(f) $Fe^0 + H^+ + Cl^-$; (g) copper metal + hydrochloric acid; (h) potassium hydride + water; (i) $Ni^0 + Ag^+ + NO_3^-$.

7-18 Discuss how control of the reaction temperature influences the products formed in the reaction of carbon with steam.

7-19 What does "heavy water" mean?

7-20 From a comparison of the physical properties of ordinary water and heavy water, what conclusions might be drawn about the relation of physical properties to mass?

7-21 Compare briefly the reactions of the halogens (F_2, Cl_2, Br_2, and I_2) with hydrogen gas.

7-22 List five compounds of hydrogen with non-metals in order of increasing thermal stability.

7-23 Which elements combine directly with hydrogen to form ionic compounds?

7-24 Starting with the same reactants, give examples of how different catalysts may cause the formation of different products.

7-25 Write (a) an equation in which H_2 acts as a reducing agent, and (b) an equation in which H_2 acts as an oxidizing agent.

7-26 What substances may be used to absorb (a) water, and (b) carbon dioxide?

7-27 Describe three experimental methods for determining the equivalent weight of an element.

Problems

7-1 (a) Under what conditions can water be electrolyzed? (b) Calculate the number of g of water necessary to produce 250 g of hydrogen by electrolysis.

7-2 Calculate the number of (a) moles (b) grams, of potassium hydroxide that could be obtained from the reaction of 5 g of potassium with water.

7-3 Calculate the heat energy required to separate 1 lb of hydrogen gas into separate atoms (1 lb = 453.6 g).

7-4 Calculate the number of moles of hydrogen obtainable from equal weights of the following metals when they react with the indicated reagent: (a) sodium and water, (b) calcium and water, (c) magnesium and acid, (d) aluminum and base.

7-5 By heating 1.248 g of a metal, M, in a stream of oxygen, 1.392 g of the oxide of the metal was formed. Calculate the simplest formula of the metal oxide.

7-6 Two grams of the oxide of a metal, on reduction with carbon monoxide, yielded 1.40 g of the metal. Calculate the simplest formula of the metal oxide.

7-7 A total of 1.62 g of the metal zinc react with an acid to yield 0.0504 g of hydrogen. Calculate the equivalent weight of zinc.

7-8 Aluminum oxide contains 53.0% by weight of aluminum. Calculate the gram equivalent weight of aluminum.

7-9 The gram equivalent weight of boron is 3.61 g. Boron oxide, when heated in the presence of hydrogen, forms water and boron. How many grams of boron would be produced when 5.79 g of boron oxide are treated in this manner?

7-10 In the laboratory, a chemist found that 5.40 g of zinc reacted with an acid to produce 0.166 g of hydrogen and other products. Calculate the gram equivalent weight of zinc.

THE GASEOUS STATE: I

We have learned that elements combine to produce many different compounds, each with its own characteristic properties. These elements and compounds exist in one of three states: (1) the solid state, (2) the liquid state, or (3) the gaseous state. At a given temperature, a solid is rigid and has a definite shape and volume, a liquid has a definite volume but can assume the shape of any vessel into which it is placed, and a gas has neither shape nor a fixed volume and will spread itself uniformly to occupy completely any space into which it is introduced. For example, when we release a small quantity of a strong-smelling gas such as hydrogen sulfide in a room, we can soon detect its unpleasant odor in all parts of the room. Every gas possesses this property of diffusing itself to occupy all available space, even when the space is already occupied by some other gas, such as air, and even when there seems to be no noticeable movement—no draft, for example—to spread the gas through the space.

Another striking difference between the solid and liquid states and the gaseous state is that the volume occupied by a given weight of the gaseous substance is very much greater than that occupied by the same amount of the same substance in the solid or liquid states. For example, 1 mole (18.01 g) of water molecules, H_2O, at 100°C and 1 atm pressure, occupies 18.8 cm^3 in the liquid state but about 30.2×10^3 cm^3 (that is, a volume more than 1,000 times greater) in the gaseous state. We shall discuss the liquid and solid states of matter later on, in Chapter 10.

The term "gas" usually refers to substances that exist in the gaseous state at *ordinary temperatures and ordinary pressures.* Actually, most liquid and solid materials can be converted to the gaseous state simply by modifying the temperature and pressure. For example, water at high temperatures exists as steam, but at ordinary temperature is a liquid, and at lower temperatures it exists as a solid—ice. There are many reasons for considering in some detail both the experimentally observed behavior of gases and its theoretical interpretation. From the historical viewpoint, the study of gases themselves formed the primary basis of our present-day concept of the molecular constitution of matter. The properties and behavior of gaseous matter are expressed by simple laws and can be interpreted satisfactorily by relatively simple theoretical considerations. Also, because of their relatively uncomplicated behavior, gases are useful in helping us to understand some of the most important concepts of chemistry—the stoichiometry and mechanism of reactions, the energy relationships that are involved in chemical changes, and the criterion of spontaneity for chemical processes.

8-1 Measurable Properties of Gases (*N*, *P*, *V*, and *T*)

Assume that we have a sample of a gas enclosed in a container. By making a few simple measurements, we can determine four properties of the gas: (1) its weight, from which we can calculate the number, N, of molecules of the gas present; (2) its pressure, P; (3) its volume, V; and (4) its temperature, T. We can measure these four properties, N, P, V and T for any sample of any gas, and, as we shall see, if we know any *three* of these quantities, we can calculate the fourth. Let us now consider how these properties can be measured experimentally.

WEIGHT AND NUMBER OF MOLECULES

Gaseous matter, like matter in any other form, possesses weight. Simply because a light gas such as hydrogen or helium can lift a balloon into the air does not mean that the gas is weightless. The gas-filled balloon rises not because it lacks weight, but because the gas it contains weighs less than an equal volume of air. If we tried to suspend a hydrogen-filled balloon in a rarefied atmosphere such as the earth's atmosphere at a very high altitude, it would simply plummet.

MEASURING THE WEIGHT OF A GAS. We can weigh a sample of gas simply by weighing the container full of gas and then reweighing the container after we have pumped out all the gas. Figure 8-1 illustrates the type of apparatus that is used in making measurements of this sort.

RELATION BETWEEN WEIGHT AND NUMBER OF MOLECULES. One mole of any gaseous substance—as of any substance—is equal to 6.02×10^{23} molecules. For example, 32 g of O_2 gas, or 2 g of H_2 gas, are each equivalent to 6.02×10^{23} molecules. Clearly, then, if we know the weight of a given sample of gas, and its molecular weight, we can calculate the number of molecules in the sample. We can also calculate the relative number of molecules in samples of different gases. We have already discussed these relationships in Chapter 3.

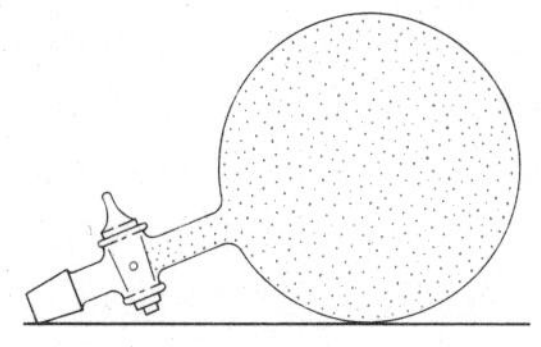

FIGURE 8-1 A gas-weighing apparatus.

PRESSURE EXERTED BY A GAS

Now let us turn to the pressure exerted by a gas, the units in which pressure is expressed, and how pressure can be measured.

Pressure, P, is an expression of force, F, per unit area, A; thus, $P = F/A$. Figure 8-2 shows a gas confined in a cylinder equipped with a movable, leak-proof piston. When the piston is at rest, the upward force and the downward force on it are equal, otherwise the piston would move either up or down in the cylinder until it came to rest at some other position at which the opposing forces were equal. In Fig. 8-2 the upward pressure exerted by the gas in the cylinder is equal to the downward pressure exerted by the weight of the atmosphere plus the weight of the piston. As we shall see later, we can think of the pressure exerted by a confined gas as the force with which the gas molecules are striking the walls of the container. In an automobile tire it is the pressure exerted by the confined molecules of air on the interior of the tire that supports the weight of the automobile.

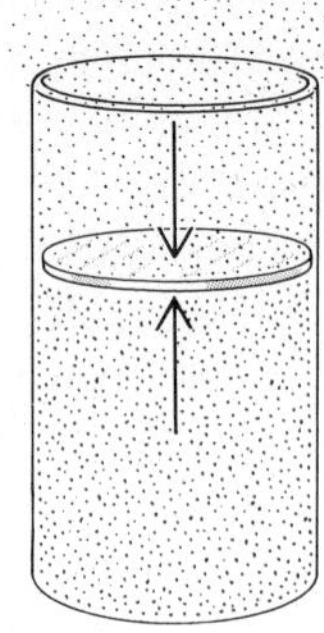

FIGURE 8-2 Gas in cylinder with a movable piston.

MEASURING PRESSURE EXERTED BY A GAS. Since pressure is force per unit area, we may express the magnitude of any pressure by using some unit of force divided by some unit of area—for example, dynes per square centimeter, (dynes/cm^2). For technical purposes, pressure is often expressed in such units as the pound per square inch, lb/in^2, or the gram per square centimeter, g/cm^2. Notice that in order for the pressure to be given in the correct units (force/area), the pound and the gram which appear in these expressions represent units of *weight*, the weight being the force equal to the product of the mass times the acceleration of gravity. In scientific practice, gas pressures are commonly expressed in terms of "pressure" units, such as the atmosphere. One atmosphere is the average pressure exerted by the atmosphere of the earth at sea level, and, as we shall see shortly, is equal to 14.7 lb/in^2, or 1.013×10^6 dynes/cm^2, or 1,034 g/cm^2. When we say that a gas is at a pressure of 2 atm, we mean that it is exerting a force of 29.4 lb/in^2—that is, twice the pressure exerted by the atmosphere at sea level. A convenient device for measuring the pressure exerted by the atmosphere is the mercury barometer. A mercury barometer consists essentially of a length of glass tubing of any convenient diameter and longer than 76 cm, sealed at one end, and completely filled with mercury (Fig. 8-3(a)). When this tube is inverted with its open end immersed in an open vessel of mercury, the level of the mercury in the tube will fall under ordinary conditions to approximately 76 cm above the level of the mercury in the vessel, as illustrated in Fig. 8-3(b).

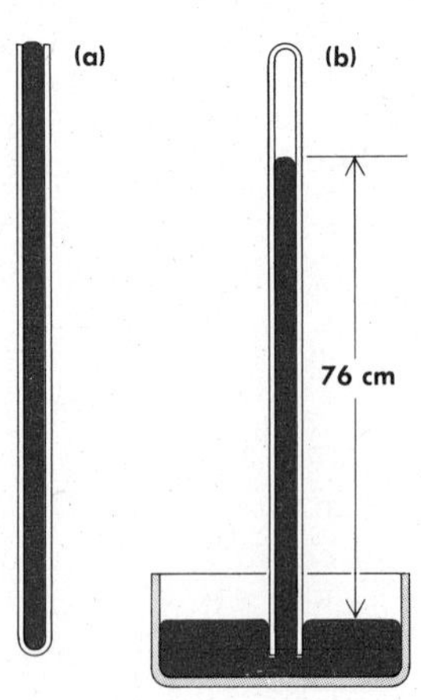

FIGURE 8-3 The measurement of atmospheric pressure.

This experiment indicates that the normal pressure of the atmosphere is capable of supporting a column of mercury 76 cm high (written as 76 cm Hg). The space above the mercury in the sealed end of the vertical tube, almost a perfect vacuum, is known as a Torricellian vacuum, after the Italian physicist, Evangelista Torricelli (1608 1647), who invented the mercury barometer.

What happens when the pressure exerted by the atmosphere increases? The mercury column rises. On the other hand, when the atmospheric pressure decreases, the mercury column falls. The height of the column does not depend on the diameter of the tube, for under the same atmospheric pressure the mercury will assume the same level in a tube of any diameter. Clearly, then, we can *measure* the pressure exerted by the atmosphere (or, as we shall see, the pressure of any gas confined in a container) by determining the height of a mercury column that the pressure will support. The pressure exerted by 1 mm of mercury (by a column of mercury 1 mm high), another unit of pressure in common use, is called a *torr* (again, after Torricelli).

How can we convert a pressure value expressed in atmospheres, or in torr, into units of force per unit area? Let us consider, for example, a pressure value of 760.0 torr —that is, the pressure exerted by a mercury column 76.00 cm high and 1.000 cm^2 in cross section (Fig. 8-3(b)). This column of mercury exerts a downward force equal to the weight of the mercury on 1.000 cm^2 of surface. The volume of mercury in the column is 76.00 cm $\times$ 1.000 cm^2 = 76.00 cm^3. Since the density of mercury is 13.60 g/cm^3, the weight in grams of the mercury in the tube and supported by the atmosphere is: 13.60 g/cm^3 $\times$ 76.00 cm^3 = 1,034 g. We can say, then, that the pressure exerted by this column of mercury is equal to 1,034 g/cm^2. Now since 1.000 g of force equals 980.0 dynes of force, we can also express this pressure in dynes as follows: 1,034 g/cm^2 $\times$ 980.0 dynes/g = 1.013 $\times$ 10^6 dynes/cm^2. Therefore, one atm = 760.0 torr = 1,034 g/cm^2 = 1.013 $\times$ 10^6 dynes/cm^2.

By modifying the design of the mercury barometer shown in Fig. 8-3, we can devise an apparatus to measure the pressure of any gas in a container. This apparatus consists essentially of a U-tube filled with mercury, as shown in Fig. 8-4, and is called a U-tube manometer. In Fig. 8-4(a) both arms of the U-tube manometer are open to the atmosphere. Therefore, the pressure which acts on the left-hand side is equal to the pressure which acts on the right-hand side, and the heights of the mercury levels in the two sides are identical. Now, if one side (the left-hand side, for example) of the U-tube is connected to a vessel containing a gas under a pressure somewhat greater than that of the atmosphere, which still acts on the right-hand side, then the mercury levels in the two sides would *not* be at the same height. In fact, the mercury level in the left-hand side of the U-tube, subjected to the higher pressure would be pushed down, causing the level in the right-hand side to rise (Fig. 8-4(b)). Now the higher pressure in the left-hand side will be equal to the atmospheric pressure plus the pressure corresponding to the difference between the heights of the mercury levels, as shown in Fig. 8-4(b). We can measure the difference between the heights in, say, millimeters, and if we know the pressure of the atmosphere—also in millimeters—as indicated by a barometer (Fig. 8-3(b)), then the sum of these two values will correspond to the pressure of the gas acting on the left-hand side. If, for example, the atmospheric pressure is 750 torr and the difference in heights of the mercury levels in the manometer is 30 mm, then the pressure of the confined gas is 750 + 30 = 780 torr. We use the same apparatus to measure gas pressures lower than that of the atmosphere. In this case the mercury level in the left-hand side would rise and that in the right-hand side would fall.

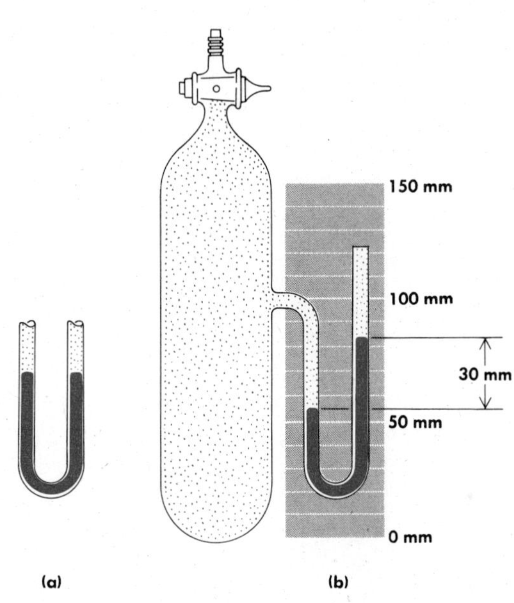

FIGURE 8-4 **The measurement of gas pressure by a U-tube manometer.**

There are a number of other methods that we can use in order to measure the pressure of gas. These make use of mechanical devices, such as the familiar tire gauge, or the pressure gauge on a gas cylinder, which record the pressure of the confined gas directly on a visible scale.

THE VOLUME OCCUPIED BY A GAS

The *volume* occupied by a gas is simply the space in which the molecules of the gas are free to move. When we speak of 1 l. of air, we simply mean that we have a space, with a volume of 1 l., in which air is confined. Since air is a mixture of oxygen, nitrogen, and other gases, the molecules of all these gases are free to move within the 1 l. volume, and we may say that this volume is occupied by each of the gases that constitute the air. The volume occupied by the oxygen is 1 l., and the volume occupied by the nitrogen is also 1 l.; this means that the molecules of both oxygen and nitrogen are free to move throughout a space of 1 l. It is important to keep in mind that a number of gases can occupy the same volume at the same time, in the sense that the molecules of all the gases are free to move in the same space.

MEASURING THE VOLUME OCCUPIED BY A GAS. The volume of a gas is commonly expressed by units of volume based on some unit of length cubed—the cubic centimeter (cm^3), for example. Other common units of volume are the cubic decimeter, dm^3 ($1\ dm^3 = 1{,}000\ cm^3$), the cubic foot (ft^3), and the cubic meter (m^3). As we know, 1 liter (1 l.) is equal to 1,000 cm^3.

We can determine the volume of a given sample of gas simply by measuring the volume of the container in which it is enclosed. A common type of laboratory apparatus for measuring the volume of a gas at atmospheric pressure is the gas burette, illustrated in Fig. 8-5. The gas burette consists essentially of a graduated glass tube *A*, and a reservoir, *B*, filled with mercury. The glass tube has a uniform diameter and is marked from the top downward by regularly spaced horizontal lines, the space between two adjacent lines corresponding to a specified unit of volume. One end of the glass tube is fitted with a stopcock S, and the other is connected through a piece of rubber tubing to the reservoir, *B*. (Notice that this gas collection apparatus is nothing more than a modified U-tube manometer described on p. 109.) The gas whose volume is to be measured is first drawn through the opened stopcock, S, into the glass tube, *A*; the stopcock is closed. Next, reservoir *B* is raised or lowered until the mercury level in both tubes is the same (that is, until the pressure of the sample of the confined gas inside tube *A* is equal to the pressure of the atmosphere). The volume occupied by the confined gas at atmospheric pressure and room temperature may then be read directly from the markings on tube *A*.

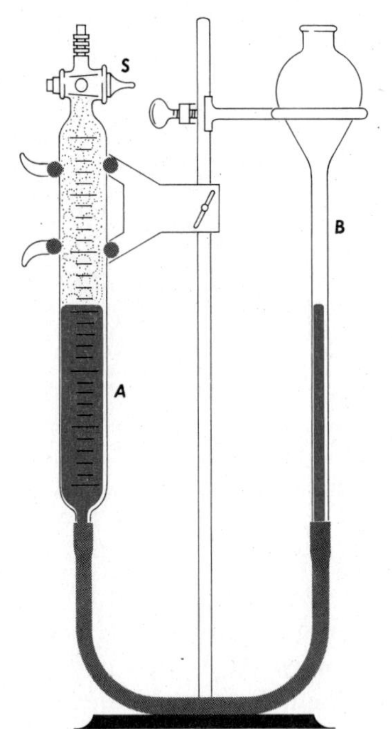

FIGURE 8-5 A gas burette.

THE TEMPERATURE OF A GAS

We can measure the temperature of a gas directly by bringing a thermometer into contact with the gas—as in measuring the temperature of the air, for example. When the vessel that contains the gas is in contact with a relatively large volume of some liquid so that the gas and the surrounding liquid are in thermal equilibrium, we can measure the temperature of the gas *indirectly* by measuring the temperature of the liquid.

THE ABSOLUTE SCALE OF TEMPERATURE. When we are dealing with relationships among the number of molecules (N) present in a gas, and the pressure (P), volume (V), and temperature (T) of the gas, we use a special temperature scale called the absolute scale of temperature. This scale has been derived from the Celsius scale, discussed on p. 13, and from the experimental relationship that exists between the temperature and the volume occupied by a fixed weight of gas that is at constant pressure.

Jacques Charles (1746–1823), a French mathematician and physicist, in 1787 measured systematically the changes that occurred in the volume of a given weight of a gas when he *changed the temperature* while keeping the pressure constant. Charles found that if a given weight of a gas had a volume of 100 cm^3 at 0°C, an increase in temperature of 1°C caused the volume to increase to 100.366 cm^3 (with the pressure constant). A 2°C increase in temperature with pressure constant caused the original 100 cm^3 volume to increase to 100.732 cm^3, a 3°C increase in temperature caused an increase to 101.098 cm^3, and so forth. In other words, for each 1° rise in temperature on the Celsius scale, the volume of the gas (originally 100 cm^3 at 0°C) increased by 0.366 cm^3—that is, by 1/273 (or more exactly 1/273.15) of the volume the gas occupied at 0°C. Charles found that all gases underwent this same *fractional increase* in volume* (expansion) as a result of each 1°C rise in temperature. Thus, in order to double the volume of the original 100 cm^3 of gas at 0°C, the temperature would have to be raised 100/0.366 = 273°C—that is, from 0°C to 273°C.

Similarly, if a given weight (amount) of gas is cooled at a constant pressure, the volume of the gas will decrease (the gas will contract) by 1/273, (or more exactly 1/273.15) of whatever volume the gas occupied at 0°C. Let us now consider what we might expect to happen if we were to lower progressively the temperature of a given weight of gas below 0°C. If for each 1°C decrease in temperature there is a contraction of 1/273 of the volume of the gas at 0°C, by the time we reach a temperature of −273°C we would expect to have no volume left. But this is impossible because matter cannot be destroyed. What actually happens, as we know, is that before we reach −273°C the gas liquefies and then, if cooled further, solidifies. As soon as the gas liquefies, the relationship between volume and temperature for gases no longer applies. Nevertheless, the theoretical deduction that at −273°C, more precisely −273.15°C, the volume of a gas would become zero and that at any temperature lower than −273.15°C the volume of a gas would be negative—a concept which is physically meaningless—suggests a possible lower limit for our temperature scale. A temperature scale which takes this lower limit, −273.15°C, as the zero point is known as the *absolute,* or *Kelvin,* scale, after Lord Kelvin, its originator.

In the absolute, or Kelvin, scale of temperature, each degree (°K) represents an interval of temperature equal to the Celsius degree (°C). However, in the Kelvin scale the zero temperature, 0°K, is −273.15°C, so the zero point on the Celsius scale, 0°C, becomes +273.15°K on the Kelvin scale. The symbol T is used to denote Kelvin temperature. Any Kelvin temperature, T, is equal to the corresponding Celsius temperature, t, expressed in Celsius degrees, °C, plus 273.15 (or, plus 273 rounded off). Thus, $T(°\text{K}) = t(°\text{C}) + 273$. The Kelvin temperature scale reflects the direct relationship between temperature and volume for a given weight of gas. Thus, the volume of a given weight of a gas doubles only when its Kelvin temperature doubles (and *not* when the Celsius temperature doubles).

The relationship between the temperature and the volume of a given weight of gas at a constant pressure is known as *Charles' Law: The volume of a given number*

* For an ideal gas, we now know that this increase in volume is exactly 1/273.15 of the original volume at 0°C for each degree rise in temperature.

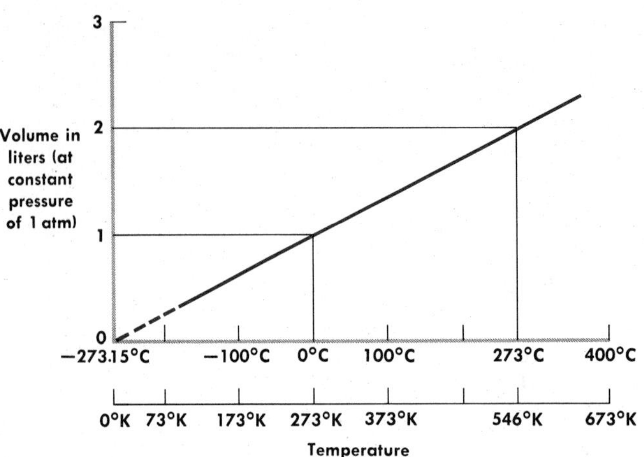

FIGURE 8-6 Relationship of temperature-volume for a gas at constant pressure.

of molecules of a gas is directly proportional to the Kelvin temperature when the pressure, P, is kept constant.* This relationship is represented graphically by the volume versus the temperature plot of Fig. 8-6. The solid line represents the observed behavior of the gas, whereas the dashed line shows that if Charles' Law continued to hold at extremely low temperatures, the lowest temperature possible would be −273.15°C. However, *all* gases liquefy or even solidify before they reach 0°K and no longer then obey the gas temperature-volume relationship. In fact, Charles' Law would hold true in the entire temperature range only for what is called an *ideal*, or *perfect*, gas, and no known gas is ideal.

8-2 The Kinetic Molecular Theory of Gases

Now that we understand the meaning of the weight (or number of molecules), pressure, volume, and temperature of a gas, and the manner in which these properties are measured, we can proceed to the theory that has been developed to explain the behavior of matter in the gaseous state. All through the following discussions, however, remember that the relationships among N, P, V, and T were first arrived at experimentally, before the theory was proposed.

THE KINETIC MOLECULAR THEORY OF AN IDEAL GAS

Many early scientists, among them Robert Boyle, Jacques Charles, Joseph Gay-Lussac, John Dalton, Thomas Graham, and Amedeo Avogadro, devoted years of their lives to studying the behavior of common gases. They devised and constructed pieces of apparatus to learn, through patient experiments, how gases behaved under changing conditions of N, P, V, and T. Then they made their observations available to their contemporaries, and recorded them for the use of further generations.

These men laid the basis for our present understanding of the behavior of gases and for the gradual development of a theory that would describe the behavior of matter in the gaseous state. This theory is now known as the *kinetic molecular theory*. The kinetic molecular theory represents the first successful attempt to relate the macroscopic properties of matter (the properties of matter in bulk) to a microscopic description of matter as a collection of extremely small particles (atoms and molecules). The macroscopic properties of matter in the gaseous state with which we are usually concerned are the volume, the pressure, the weight, the heat capacity, and

* The weight of any sample of a particular gas is determined by the number of molecules of that gas present in the sample. From this point on, we shall usually represent the number of molecules by the letter N.

so forth. In the following discussion we shall try to explain such macroscopic properties, and their interrelationships, in terms of the microscopic properties of gases, such as the mass, velocity, and kinetic energy of the individual molecules making up the gas.

The kinetic molecular theory emerged about the middle of the nineteenth century as a series of postulates on the behavior of gases. A gas that would fit this theory exactly would be called an *ideal gas.* As we shall see later, *real* gases deviate from the behavior of the ideal gas in varying degrees. Here are the essential points of the theory:

1. A gas may be pictured as an assembly of extremely small particles (molecules). For a given gas, the molecules are all alike; in particular, they all have the same mass, m. The molecules of an ideal gas are separated by distances that are very much greater than the size of the molecules themselves. Thus the space actually occupied by the molecules is negligible compared with the volume of the container in which the gas is confined.

2. The molecules of an ideal gas exert no attractive or repulsive force on one another or on the substance composing the walls of the container and exhibit repulsions only when they come in "contact" with one another and with the walls of the container.

3. The molecules of a gas are in constant random motion, and since the molecules are material bodies (in the sense that they possess a mass, m), they obey Newton's laws of motion. Accordingly, each molecule moves in a straight line and with a constant velocity, except at the instant when it collides with another molecule or with the walls of the container. After each collision the molecule is deflected in a new direction, but again it moves in a straight line at a constant velocity until it undergoes another collision. The new directions in which two molecules move after collision depend on the original directions of the molecules before they collided and on the way the collision occurred—that is—whether it was a head-on collision, a grazing collision, and so on. Between two successive collisions, each molecule of mass, m, moves in a constant direction with a constant velocity, v, and has a *kinetic energy,* K.E., expressed as: K.E. $= \frac{1}{2}mv^2$.

The following considerations may help us to understand why the motions of the molecules of a gas are completely random (chaotic). Assume for a moment that all molecules of a gas are moving in the same direction along parallel paths. Such a system would not be stable. If even one single molecule, under the effect of the smallest disturbance, were to deviate slightly from its original path, it would eventually collide with another molecule and both partners in the collision would then move off in different directions at different velocities. These two molecules would then collide with other molecules and the pattern would be repeated. Very soon, therefore, the movement of the gas molecules would become completely chaotic. Therefore, for any gas in equilibrium (in a closed container) the molecular motion is completely random. However, a somewhat directed movement (flow) of gas molecules may occur under appropriate conditions in systems which are *not* in equilibrium—for example, in a gas diffusing into an evacuated space.

4. Collisions of the molecules of an ideal gas with one another and with the walls of the container result in no loss of kinetic energy. We often express this condition by saying that the collisions among the molecules of an ideal gas are *elastic collisions.*

To understand the meaning of this postulate let us consider two molecules of the same mass, which we shall indicate as A and B, each moving along a straight path with its own velocity, v_{1A} and v_{1B}, and its own kinetic energy, $\frac{1}{2}mv_{1A}^2$ and $\frac{1}{2}mv_{1B}^2$, respectively. When these two molecules collide, they not only change their directions but also their velocities and hence their kinetic energies. That is to say, the kinetic energy of each molecule after colliding is different from what it was before colliding.

However, there is no loss of kinetic energy as a result of the collision, so that the sum of the kinetic energies of the two partners is the same after colliding as before. In other words, the collision does not alter the average kinetic energy of the two partners. Where v_{2A} and v_{2B} are the velocities of A and B respectively after collision:

$$\tfrac{1}{2}mv_{1A}^2 + \tfrac{1}{2}mv_{1B}^2 = \tfrac{1}{2}mv_{2A}^2 + \tfrac{1}{2}mv_{2B}^2$$

Total kinetic energy of A and B before colliding = Total kinetic energy of A and B after colliding

If one partner loses energy in the collision, the other partner gains it. The kinetic energy depends on the velocity (the mass, m, of the molecules being constant), so if one molecule travels faster after the collision than it did before the collision, the velocity of the other molecule will be correspondingly less after collision than it was before the collision. When we say that the average kinetic energy of two colliding molecules remains unchanged, we are implicitly assuming that the molecules are hard and undeformable. Nor do gas molecules lose kinetic energy when they collide with the walls of a container. Consequently, since the walls of the container are rigid, a molecule rebounds in a different direction, no doubt, but at the same speed it had before impact (Fig. 8-7).

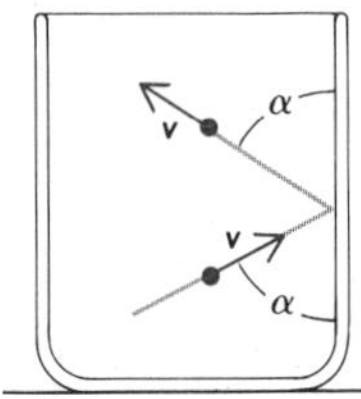

FIGURE 8-7 A gas molecule strikes the wall of the container and rebounds with the same speed, in a new direction which is in the same plane as the original direction, and forms an identical angle α with the wall.

5. The kinetic energy of the gas molecules is directly proportional to the absolute temperature: K.E. = constant $\times$ T. According to this postulate, we assume that all molecular motion ceases at the zero point of absolute temperature. In fact, since the mass, m, of a molecule is constant, a zero kinetic energy (K.E. = $\frac{1}{2}mv^2$) means that the velocity of each molecule must be zero.

KINETIC INTERPRETATION OF GAS PRESSURE

The kinetic molecular theory helps us to visualize the manner in which gas molecules exert pressure on the walls of a container, or on an object immersed in the gas. In a container filled with an ideal gas, countless molecules move along in straight lines in many directions at high speeds. Each fraction of a second, numerous collisions occur between the molecules and the walls of the container, and since the molecules possess both mass and velocity, they exert a continuous *force* on the surfaces with which they collide. Although the force exerted on a given surface by any one molecule is exceedingly small, the collective force of many molecules is quite powerful and creates gas pressure.

PRESSURE EXERTED BY A GAS. On the basis of the kinetic molecular theory we can now derive a quantitative expression for the pressure exerted by a gas. Let us consider N molecules of an ideal gas, contained in a cubic box of edge l. As we have said, we assume these molecules to be points of mass m (negligible volume), moving at random. For simplicity, we may consider that one-third of the molecules are moving in a direction parallel to the length of the cubic box, one-third parallel to the width, and one-third parallel to the height of the box. That is to say, if we take as a reference a set of Cartesian axes x, y, and z, directed at the edges of our cubic box, $\frac{1}{3}$ of the molecules move in the x direction, $\frac{1}{3}$ move in the y direction, and $\frac{1}{3}$ move in the z direction.

Let us consider a single molecule of mass m and velocity v moving in a direction parallel to the y axis toward the right wall of the box (Fig. 8-8). Now let us see how we can express in terms of the mass, m, and the velocity, v, of the molecule the force that the molecule imparts to the right wall when it collides with it. At the instant the molecule strikes the wall, it comes temporarily to rest, so that its velocity decreases from v to zero. The momentum of the moving molecule, which is the product of its mass and its velocity, (mv), therefore decreases from mv to zero when the molecule hits the wall and comes to rest, because the velocity decreases from v to zero. One of the postulates of the kinetic molecular theory is that the collisions of ideal gas molecules are perfectly elastic. So when our molecule frontally strikes the right wall of the container with a kinetic energy $\frac{1}{2}mv^2$, it momentarily comes to rest and then rebounds *in the opposite direction* with the same kinetic energy it had before hitting the wall. Therefore, v^2 is the same before and after hitting the wall, although the velocity, v, itself is opposite in sign (because the direction of travel of the molecule is opposite to what it was). Note that the velocity before and after is the same magnitude, differing only in sign. Hence, the momentum, mv, is positive before the molecule hit the wall and is negative (or, conversely, negative, then positive) after hitting the wall. Consequently, the total *change* in momentum (from $+mv$ to $-mv$) is $2(mv)$.

The change in momentum in unit time (1 sec) represents a force, f. If therefore $\Delta(mv)$ is the change in momentum (where Δ represents "change in") in a time interval Δt, then the change in momentum in unit time equals $\Delta(mv)/\Delta t = f$. Since, however the mass, m, is constant for a given molecule, $\Delta(mv)$ can be expressed as $m\Delta v$ and therefore the force, f, equals $m \times \Delta v/\Delta t$. But $\Delta v/\Delta t$ is the change of velocity, Δv, of the molecule in the time interval, Δt and it is therefore the acceleration, a, of the molecule. It follows that the expression for the force, f, becomes $m \times a$. Newton's second law of motion defines a force, f, as being equal to $m \times a$. Thus we see that a change in momentum in unit time represents a force. The question then arises, how often does a molecule strike the right wall, if we assume that it only moves back and forth in a direction parallel to the y axis? After each instantaneous collision with the right wall, the molecule has to travel a distance l before it strikes the opposite wall, and then again a distance l before it again collides with the right wall. Thus, the total distance a molecule has to travel between two successive collisions with the right wall is $2l$. The number of collisions the molecules makes with the wall per unit time is then given by the velocity of the molecule, v, divided by the distance, $2l$, that the molecule has to travel between two successive collisions, $v/2l$. If we multiply the change of momentum at each collision, $2mv$, by the number of collisions per unit time, $v/2l$, we obtain the change of momentum per unit time: $2mv \times v/2l = mv^2/l$. This is, as we have seen, the average force, f, mutually exerted between the wall and the colliding molecule; $f = mv^2/l$. The total force, F_y exerted on the right wall by the impacts of all the molecules of the gas which travel parallel to the y axis is therefore obtained by multiplying the number of such molecules, $\frac{1}{3}N$, by the force each molecule exerts on the wall; mv^2/l. Thus

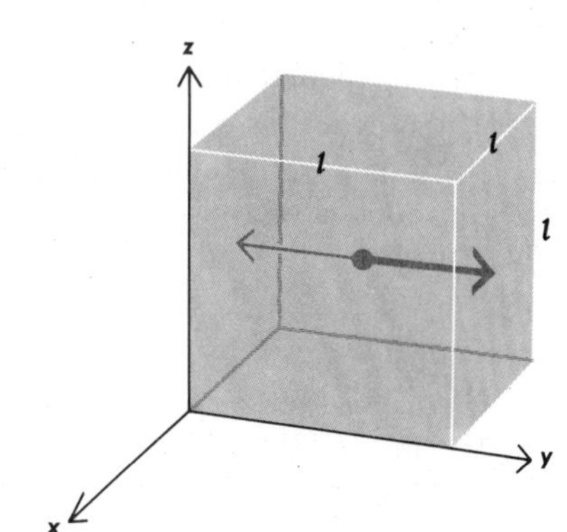

FIGURE 8-8 Diagram for calculating the gas pressure from the mass and velocity of the molecules.

$$F_y = \frac{1}{3} N \times \frac{mv^2}{l} = \frac{1}{3} \frac{Nmv^2}{l}$$

Not all molecules of a gas travel at the same velocity (p. 113). In the above expression of the total force, F_y, v represents the *average velocity* of the gas molecules.

Finally, the pressure, P, on the right wall is obtained by dividing the total average force of impact on the wall, F_y, by the surface area, $A = l^2$, of the wall:

$$P = \frac{F_y}{A} = \frac{1}{3} \times \frac{Nmv^2}{l^2} \times \frac{1}{A} = \frac{1}{3} \times \frac{Nmv^2}{V}$$

where $V = l^3$ is the volume of the cubic box.

This formula, obtained for the pressure exerted on the right face of the cubic box, holds also for all the other faces. Thus we have now an expression which explains a property of gas in bulk—or, as we say, a *macroscopic property* of the gas—namely, the pressure of the gas on the walls of the container in terms of a *microscopic representation* of the gas as a collection of an exceedingly large number of fast moving individual molecules.

It is important to point out here that the assumptions we made at the beginning of our discussion—namely, that the container has a cubic shape and that the molecules of the gas are moving only in three perpendicular directions (one third of the molecules moving along each edge of the cubic container)—do not limit the general validity of our conclusions. In fact we would arrive at the same final formula for any ideal gas enclosed in a container of any shape by assuming that even though the molecules move at random, on the average there is an equal distribution of the components of their velocities along the three Cartesian axes.

KINETIC INTERPRETATION OF TEMPERATURE

In this section we shall consider how the temperature of a gas may be interpreted in terms of the average velocity of the gas molecules. Consider an ideal gas composed of N molecules which are monoatomic and whose only energy is kinetic. This gas is confined in a container of fixed volume, V, at an absolute temperature T_1, and exerts a pressure P_1 on the walls of the container. We know experimentally that if we add a quantity of heat, q, to this system, held at constant volume, both the temperature and the pressure of the gas increase. Thus if the volume, V, and the number of molecules, N, remain constant, the gas system goes from an initial state with P_1 and T_1 to a final state with P_2 and T_2. Let us now see how the kinetic theory explains the significance of both the increase in pressure and the increase in temperature which result from the heat transfer.

For a constant number, N, of gas molecules in a fixed volume, V, an increase in the gas pressure implies that these N molecules strike the walls of the container more often and also with greater momentum than at a lower pressure. This must result from an increase in the average molecular velocity, since the faster the molecules move, the more often they strike the walls and the greater is the change of momentum at each impact. Thus the heat added to the gas at constant volume has increased the average velocity of the gas molecules. And, in fact, for an ideal monoatomic gas which has kinetic energy exclusively, the only change this acquired heat can bring about is an increase in the average velocity of the molecules. At the higher temperature, T_2, the gas molecules strike the bulb of the thermometer immersed in the gas with a greater average velocity (that is, with a greater average kinetic energy), than at the lower temperature, T_1, and the increase in temperature, $\Delta T = (T_2 - T_1)$, registered by the thermometer is related to this increase of the average velocity (kinetic energy) of the gas molecules. This statement, of course, also follows directly from postulate (5) of the kinetic theory (p. 114).

Notice that the temperature change registered by the thermometer is a change of a *macroscopic property* of the gas, which may be regarded as the average measured effect of a very large number of gas molecules, each striking the molecules of the thermometer with its own individual velocity (*microscopic interpretation*). Since the temperature is a macroscopic property which depends on the average molecular velocity, the concept of temperature can be meaningfully ascribed only to sizable samples of matter, consisting of a very large collection of molecules.

THE EFFECT ON PRESSURE OF CHANGES IN QUANTITY OF GAS

Let us now consider how the kinetic molecular theory helps us to explain changes in the pressure of a gas. Assume that we have a cylinder of fixed volume, V, containing a given number N, of gas molecules, at constant temperature, T. What will happen to the pressure exerted by the gas if we change the number of molecules present but keep the volume and temperature of the cylinder constant? If we add molecules, proportionally more molecules will be striking the walls of the container in a given time. Consequently, the pressure exerted by the gas will also increase in direct proportion. If, for example, we double the number of molecules in the container, the pressure will double, if V and T remain constant. In fact, although the molecules are striking the walls of the container with the same force (since T is constant), there are now twice the number of molecules in the same volume and hence twice the number of collisions per unit time between the molecules and any wall of the container. Similarly, if we decrease the number of molecules in the cylinder, while keeping V and T constant, the pressure decreases proportionally, because now there are fewer molecules to strike the walls of the container in a given time.

From the kinetic expression of the pressure of a gas, $P = \frac{1}{3}m(N/V)v^2$, we may derive a simple quantitative expression for the change in the pressure, P, of a gas resulting from a change in the number of molecules, N, when V and T remain constant. In fact for a given gas, m is a constant, and if the volume V is constant and the temperature T (and consequently also the average velocity, v, of the gas molecules) remains constant, then in the above expression $P = \frac{1}{3}m(N/V)v^2$, the term $\frac{1}{3}(mv^2/V)$ is a constant and we may write: $P =$ constant $\times N$; (T and V constant).

If we consider a gas at constant volume, V, and constant temperature, T, passing from an initial state with number of molecules N_i and pressure P_i to a final state with number of molecules N_f and pressure P_f, we have: $P_f = P_i \times N_f/N_i$; (T and V constant). We can use this expression to calculate the change in pressure caused by a given change in the number of molecules composing a gas, at constant V and T.

To help us visualize the relationship between N and P for a gas at constant V and T, consider the apparatus shown in Fig. 8-9, which consists essentially of a vessel equipped with a stopcock and connected to a closed-end U-tube manometer which contains a Torrocellian vacuum (p. 108). The difference in the heights of the mercury levels on the two sides of the manometer gives the pressure of the confined gas, independent of the atmospheric pressure. Figure 8-9(a) shows schematically a given number of gas molecules confined in a container of fixed volume at constant temperature. In Fig. 8-9(b) the number of molecules in the container is doubled and the gas

FIGURE 8-9 Increase in pressure caused by doubling the number of molecules, T and V constant.

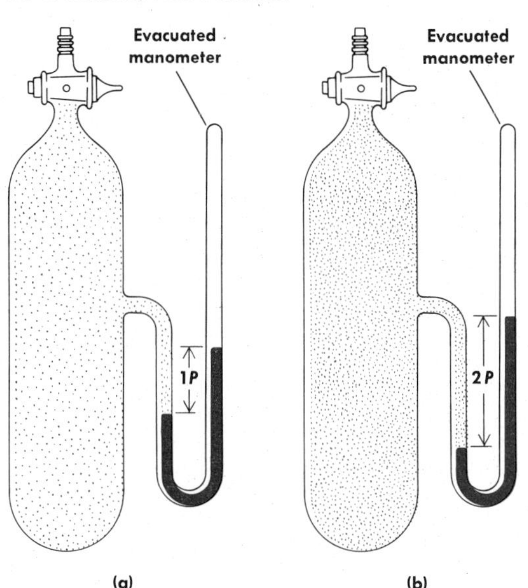

pressure is also doubled, as shown by the doubling of the difference in the mercury levels of the manometer.

Here is a simple problem involving a change in pressure, P, caused by a change in the number of molecules, N, present in a container under conditions of constant volume, V, and constant temperature, T. We shall give the solution of this problem in order to illustrate the general method of solving gas problems.

PROBLEM. At a given temperature, 3×10^{23} molecules (1 g) of H_2 gas in a container exert a pressure of 40 cm of mercury. Now we remove some of the H_2 gas, until the final number of molecules present is 0.3×10^{23} (0.1 g). We keep the volume and temperature constant. Calculate the final pressure, P_f, of the H_2 gas in the container, assuming that the hydrogen acts like an ideal gas.

SOLUTION. In solving gas problems, the first step is to outline the problem, listing the initial and final values for the four factors, P, N, T, and V.

	P	N	T	V
Initial state:	40 cm Hg	3×10^{23} molecules	constant	constant
Final state:	P_f	0.3×10^{23} molecules	constant	constant

Figure 8-9 will help you visualize this problem and its solution. If T and V are constant, the pressure of a gas, P, is directly proportional to the number of molecules present, N. Since the number of molecules present in the container at the final state is less than the number of molecules present at the initial state, the final pressure of the gas, P_f, is *less than* its initial pressure. That is to say, the final pressure must be *less* than 40 cm (the initial pressure). Therefore, the final pressure is equal to the initial pressure multiplied by a fraction "less than 1" (to correct for the change in the number of gas molecules). This fraction is:

$$\frac{0.3 \times 10^{23}}{3 \times 10^{23}}$$

$$P_{\text{final}} = P_{\text{initial}} \times \frac{\text{fraction to correct for change}}{\text{in number of molecules}}$$

Thus, the final pressure is:

$$P_f = 40 \text{ cm Hg} \times \frac{0.3 \times 10^{23} \text{ molecules}}{3 \times 10^{23} \text{ molecules}} = 4 \text{ cm Hg}$$

PROBLEM. If 4.00 g of methane gas exert a pressure of 70.0 cm of mercury, what pressure would be exerted by 10.0 g of this gas, if the volume and temperature are kept constant? Assume that methane acts like an ideal gas.

SOLUTION.	P	N	T	V
Initial state:	70.0 cm Hg	4.00 g	constant	constant
Final state:	P_f	10.0 g	constant	constant

$$P_{\text{final}} = P_{\text{initial}} \times \frac{\text{fraction to correct for change}}{\text{in number of molecules}}$$

$$P_f = 70.0 \text{ cm Hg} \times \frac{N_f}{N_i}$$

Since there are more molecules present in 10.0 g of methane gas than in 4.00 g of methane gas, it follows that the final pressure must be more than 70.0 cm (the initial pressure). And this means that the fraction to correct for the change in the number of methane molecules must be more than 1. Since the numbers of molecules in different weights of the same gas are directly proportional to the weights of the gas, weights can be used in the calculation in place of the numbers of molecules. Since the weight is increased, the number of molecules is correspondingly increased, and the fraction is "greater than 1."

$$P_f = 70.0 \text{ cm Hg} \times \frac{10.0}{4.00} = 175 \text{ cm Hg}$$

THE EFFECT ON VOLUME WHEN THE NUMBER OF GAS MOLECULES IS CHANGED

To help visualize the changes that take place in V as a result of a change in N, we may use a cylinder with a leak-proof, frictionless piston and stopcock as shown in Fig. 8-10. A certain number of gas molecules are initially present in the cylinder Fig. 8-10(a). What change would take place in V if we fed some additional gas into the cylinder through the stopcock while keeping P and T constant? If P is to be kept constant, V must increase because the increased number of molecules now in the container must move within a greater volume, Fig. 8-10(b), otherwise the pressure would increase. In fact, we have seen above that at T and P constant, we can use the following general expression to solve problems dealing with changes V and N:

$V = 1, P = 1, N = 1, T = 1$ (a)

$V = 2, P = 1, N = 2, T = 1$ (b)

FIGURE 8-10 Increase in volume caused by doubling the number of molecules, *T* and *P* constant.

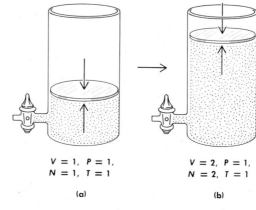

$$V_f = V_i \times \frac{N_f}{N_i} \quad (T \text{ and } P \text{ constant})$$

$$\text{or, } N_f = N_i \times \frac{V_f}{V_i}$$

The fraction N_f/N_i is "greater than 1" or "less than 1," depending on whether the number of gas molecules present is increased or decreased.

PROBLEM. Calculate the weight of nitrogen gas necessary to occupy a volume of 300 l., at a particular P and T, if 200 g of the gas at the same P and T occupy 180 l.

SOLUTION.	N	V	P	T
Initial state:	200 g	180 l.	constant	constant
Final state:	N_f	300 l.	constant	constant

When we are working with different weights of the *same* gas, we need only remember that the number of molecules is directly proportional to the weight:

$$N_{\text{final}} = N_{\text{initial}} \times \frac{\text{fraction to correct for}}{\text{change in number of molecules}}$$

$$N_f = N_i \times \frac{V_f}{V_i} \quad (T \text{ and } P \text{ constant})$$

Since a greater number of molecules is necessary to occupy a volume of 300 l. than 180 l. at constant P and T, a weight of the gas greater than 200 g is needed to increase the volume to 300 l. Consequently, the greater quantity goes in the numerator of the fraction V_f/V_i.

$$N_f = 200\text{ g} \times \frac{300\text{ l.}}{180\text{ l.}} = 333\text{ g}$$

Thus, a *total* weight of 333 g of nitrogen must be provided to produce a volume of 300 l. at the particular pressure and temperature.

CALCULATING THE CHANGE IN *T* NECESSARY TO KEEP *P* AND *V* CONSTANT WHEN *N* CHANGES. In this case, we are changing the number of molecules present, but we are adjusting the temperature so that the change in the number of molecules *does not* change either pressure or volume. In other words, we must adjust the temperature in order to compensate for the change in the number of molecules. If we were to reduce the number of molecules and keep T constant, the volume would decrease if the pressure were held constant, and the pressure would decrease if the volume were held constant. In order to prevent either P or V from decreasing, we must increase the kinetic energy of the molecules by raising T. The *absolute temperature* and the number of molecules necessary to exert a particular P in a particular V are inversely proportional. As an application of this discussion, the student may solve the following problem, the complete solution of which is given in Appendix 8-1.

PROBLEM. If 0.300 g of oxygen gas occupies a particular volume at 30°C and exerts a particular pressure, at what temperature would 0.200 g of oxygen gas exert the same pressure in the same volume?

THE GAS LAWS AND THE KINETIC MOLECULAR THEORY

The kinetic molecular theory of the ideal gas provides a valuable model for understanding the behavior of real matter in the gaseous state, because, as we have seen, the molecules of an ideal gas behave in a relatively uncomplicated manner. In the following sections, therefore, we shall explain the properties of gases in terms of the kinetic molecular theory of the ideal gas and we shall consider the various gas laws as logical results of this theory, rather than as generalizations based on experiments. *But once again, always remember that scientists first found by experiment that the various gas laws were approximately true for real gases, and that it was on the basis of their experimental findings that they developed the kinetic molecular theory of ideal gases.*

THE EFFECT OF PRESSURE ON THE VOLUME OF A GAS. BOYLE'S LAW

To help us visualize the relationship between changes in P and changes in V for a fixed weight of a gas at a constant temperature, T, consider an apparatus such as the one shown in Fig. 8-11, consisting essentially of a cylinder with a leakproof, movable piston. A fixed weight of gas is confined in the cylinder and varying pressures are applied by means of weights on the piston. The temperature of the gas is kept constant by means of a thermostated water bath.

FIGURE 8-11 Effect of change in P on V, with T and N constant.

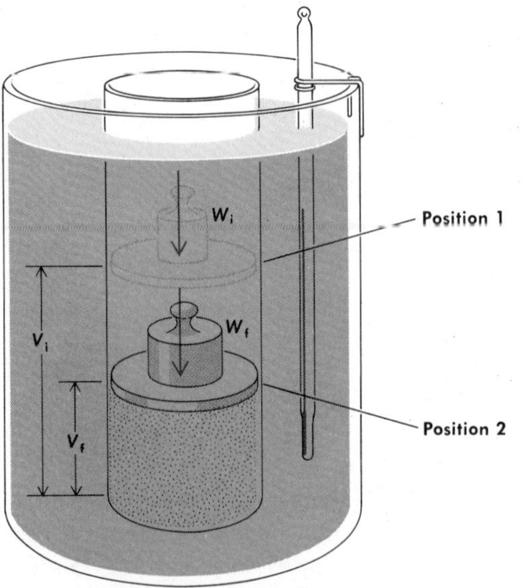

With the piston in position 1, the force exerted on the inner wall of the piston by the bombardment of the gas molecules is equal to the total force exerted by the weight of the piston itself, plus the weight, W_i, and the pressure of the atmosphere. As we have seen, this force of bombardment is the result of the movement of the gas molecules within the volume V_i. Now if a greater weight, W_f, is applied, the piston will move downward and come to rest at a new position (new volume), for which the pressure of the confined gas again equals the total downward pressure. Since the temperature is kept constant, the gas molecules do not move any faster and therefore they can exert a higher pressure only if they bombard the piston more often. This they can do only if the volume in which they are moving is reduced. Thus, since T and N remain unchanged, P can increase only if V is decreased. We can derive a quantitative relationship between P and V (N and T constant) by considering the kinetic expression of the gas pressure which we have previously derived: $P = \frac{1}{3}mv^2(N/V)$.

For a fixed weight of a given gas, both the number of the molecules, N, and the mass, m, of the molecules are constant ($m \times N$ is the weight of the gas). Furthermore, if the temperature, T, is constant, the average velocity, v, is also constant. It follows that in $P = \frac{1}{3}mv^2(N/V)$, the term $\frac{1}{3}mv^2N$ is a constant, and the expression for the pressure becomes:

$$P = \frac{\text{constant}}{V}, \qquad \text{or} \qquad PV = \text{constant}$$

For a given gas (system) which passes from an initial state with volume V_i and pressure P_i to a final state with volume V_f and pressure P_f (the temperature T and the number of molecules N remaining constant) we may write:

$$V_f = V_i \times \frac{P_i}{P_f} \qquad (T \text{ and } N \text{ constant})$$

This expression, as well as the equivalent expression, PV = constant, are the mathematical formulations of the law which Robert Boyle (see p. 18) deduced experimentally and published in 1660 in his book *The Spring of Air.* Boyle's Law states: *The volume, V, occupied by a fixed weight of gas held at constant temperature is inversely proportional to the pressure, P.* Or in other words, *a given weight of a gas at a given temperature has a constant pressure-volume product.*

Boyle's Law can be represented graphically as shown in Fig. 8-12(a) and (b). In Fig. 8-12(a), we plot the volume, V, versus the pressure, P, for a given weight of a gas at a constant temperature, and we obtain a curve which is a *rectangular hyperbola.* Since this curve is obtained at constant temperature, it is called a *Boyle's isotherm,* from the Greek *iso* meaning equal and *therm* meaning heat. The shaded areas in Fig. 8-12(a) show graphically that the product of any value of P by the corresponding value of V is equal to the product of any other value of P by the corresponding value of V—that is, $P_1V_1 = P_2V_2$. Boyle's Law can also be conveniently represented by plotting the value of the product PV against the pressure, P (Fig. 8-12(b)). In this case we obtain a straight line parallel to the P axis and again this line is an isotherm; the solid line represents the PV product at a given temperature, T, and the dashed lines represent the PV product for the same weight of gas at increasing temperatures T_1 and T_2.

CALCULATING THE CHANGES IN P AND V FOR A FIXED WEIGHT OF GAS AT CONSTANT T. We can use Boyle's Law to calculate the change in volume caused by a given change in pressure for a fixed weight of a gas at a constant temperature:

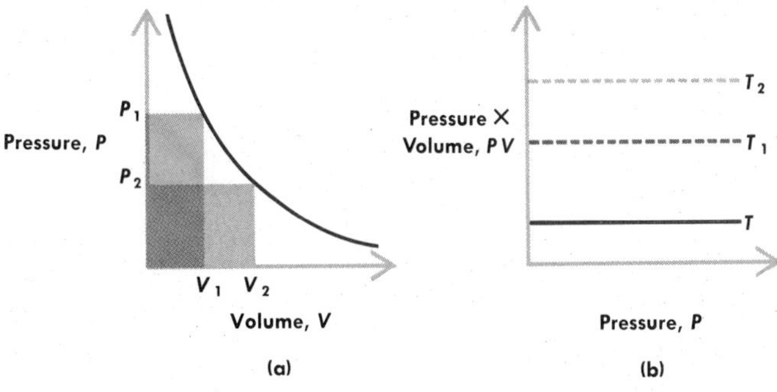

FIGURE 8-12 (a) Boyle's Law hyperbola. (b) PV versus P isotherms at different temperatures.

$$V_{\text{final}} = V_{\text{initial}} \times \frac{\text{fraction to correct for}}{\text{change in pressure}}$$

$$V_f = V_i \times \frac{P_i}{P_f} \qquad (T \text{ and } N \text{ constant})$$

We can tell from the direction of the pressure change whether the final volume will be greater than or less than the initial volume. If the final volume is to be smaller, we place the lower pressure value in the numerator of the fraction. If the final volume is to be greater, we place the larger value in the numerator of the fraction. Vice versa, we can calculate the change in the volume resulting from a given change in the pressure by using the expression:

$$P_{\text{final}} = P_{\text{initial}} \times \frac{\text{fraction to correct for}}{\text{change in volume}}$$

$$P_f = P_i \times \frac{V_i}{V_f} \qquad (T \text{ and } N \text{ constant})$$

The following problem illustrates this procedure.

PROBLEM. If 20 g of gas occupy a volume of 100 l. at 25°C and exert a pressure of 700 torr, what volume will the same weight of gas occupy if the pressure is changed to 600 torr while the temperature remains at 25°C?

SOLUTION.	V	P	N	T
Initial state:	100 l.	700 torr	constant	constant
Final state:	V_f	600 torr	constant	constant

Figure 8-11 helps visualize the initial and final states of the gas in the container. When the external pressure acting on the gas is decreased from 700 to 600 torr (say by substituting a lighter for a heavier weight on top of the piston) the piston is pushed up and finally comes to rest when the pressures below and above the piston again are equal. The pressure outside the container has decreased because some of the weight on the piston has been removed, but the pressure of the gas *inside* the container has decreased because the molecules must now travel farther between successive collisions with the walls of the container, and consequently will strike the walls less often. Consequently, V increases, and the fraction to correct for the change in the pressure P_i/P_f must be "greater than 1."

$$V_f = V_i \times \frac{P_i}{P_f} \qquad (T \text{ and } N \text{ constant})$$

$$V_f = 100 \text{ l.} \times \frac{700 \text{ torr}}{600 \text{ torr}} = 117 \text{ l.}$$

As an additional exercise, solve the following problem, whose complete solution is given in Appendix 8-1.

PROBLEM. To what pressure must 500 ml of gas at a pressure of 700 torr be changed to reduce the volume to 400 ml, with no change in temperature or weight of gas?

THE EFFECT OF TEMPERATURE CHANGES ON PRESSURE AND ON VOLUME. LAW OF GAY-LUSSAC AND LAW OF CHARLES

Let us consider once more the expression for the pressure of a gas derived from the kinetic molecular theory. For a given number, N, of gas molecules each of mass m confined in a container of fixed volume, V, the pressure exerted on the walls of the container is:

$$P = \frac{1}{3} mv^2 \frac{N}{V}$$

Since in this case, m, N, and V are constant, the term $\frac{1}{3}m(N/V)$ is a constant, and therefore P is directly proportional to v^2. Thus, P = constant $\times$ v^2. But we have seen that for the molecules of a gas, v^2 is directly proportional to the absolute temperature, T, of the gas. It follows that P is also directly proportional to the absolute temperature, T:

$$P = \text{constant} \times T$$

If we consider a gas passing from an initial state, P_i and T_i, to a final state, P_f and T_f, we have

$$P_f = P_i \times \frac{T_f}{T_i} \quad (N \text{ and } V \text{ constant})$$

This expression, and the equivalent expression, P = constant $\times$ T, are mathematical formulations of the law which the French scientist, Joseph-Louis Gay-Lussac (1778–1850), professor at the Sorbonne in Paris, deduced from experiments and enunciated in 1802, when he was only 24 years old. Gay-Lussac's Law states: *If the volume remains constant, the pressure exerted by a fixed weight of gas is directly proportional to the absolute temperature.*

In a similar way, if we consider a given number N of gas molecules, each of mass m maintained at a constant pressure P, we can write the expression:

$$P = \frac{1}{3}mv^2\frac{N}{V} \quad \text{as,} \quad V = \left(\frac{1}{3}m\frac{N}{P}\right)v^2 = \text{constant} \times v^2$$

Hence: $$V = \text{constant} \times T$$

Also: $$V_f = V_i \times \frac{T_f}{T_i} \quad (P \text{ and } N \text{ constant})$$

These latter two expressions are mathematical formulations of the law which Charles derived experimentally, as we have discussed previously (p. 111). The proportionality constants of the volume-temperature Law of Charles, V = constant $\times$ T, and of the pressure-temperature Law of Gay-Lussac, P = constant $\times$ T, have the same numerical value if in each case m, P, and V are expressed in the same units. Consequently, Gay-Lussac's Law can be represented by a graph similar to that of Charles' Law, simply by replacing V with P (Fig. 8-13). We can use the two expressions:

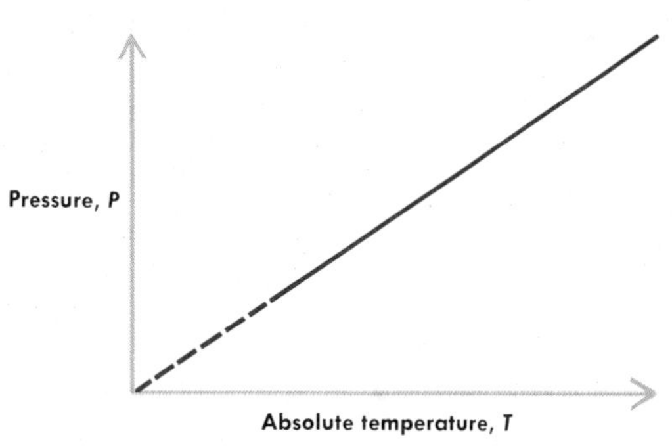

FIGURE 8-13 Temperature-pressure relationship for an ideal gas at constant volume.

$$P_f = P_i \times \frac{T_f}{T_i} \quad (V, N \text{ constant})$$

and $$V_f = V_i \times \frac{T_f}{T_i} \quad (P, N \text{ constant})$$

to calculate the effect of changes in temperature, T, on the pressure, P, or on the volume, V, for a given number, N, of gas molecules. Similarly, for a given number of gas molecules, N, we can use the above two expressions to calculate what change in temperature, T, is necessary to cause a given change in pressure P (at constant volume), or a given change in volume V (at constant pressure). Here are some illustrative examples.

CALCULATING CHANGES IN P RESULTING FROM CHANGES IN T, WITH V AND N CONSTANT. The effect of *temperature changes* on the pressure of a given weight of a gas at constant volume may be followed experimentally by means of an apparatus such as is shown in Fig. 8-14. Here we have a container, C, to which is attached an evacuated, closed-end manometer, M, for measuring the inside pressure. This container is immersed in a water bath, B, which makes it possible to change the temperature of the gas simply by changing the temperature of the water bath. The stopcock of the container is gas-tight to prevent the gas from leaking and thus to keep the number of gas molecules constant.

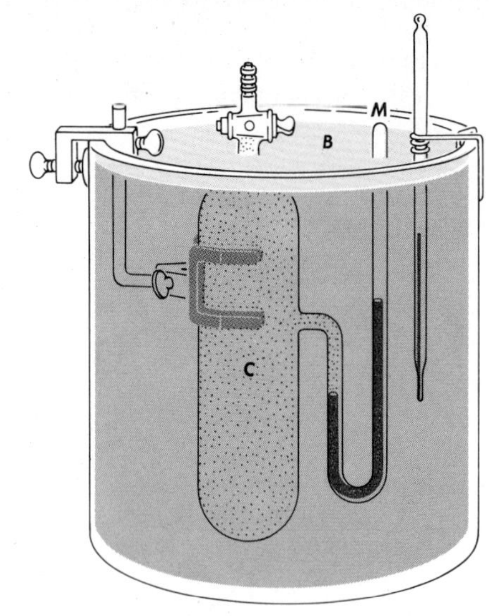

FIGURE 8-14 Effect of change in T on P, with V and N constant.

PROBLEM. When the temperature of the water bath is 30°C the initial pressure reading is 600 torr. Suppose we raise the temperature to 60°C. What will be the final pressure?

SOLUTION.	P	T	N	V
Initial state:	600 torr	303°K	constant	constant
Final state:	P_f	333°K	constant	constant

The direct effect of the rise in temperature is to increase the kinetic energy, and therefore the velocity, of the molecules. As a result, the frequency with which the molecules bombard the container walls will increase, and each molecule will strike the container with greater force. Consequently, P will increase, as Gay-Lussac's Law predicts. Conversely, a lowering of temperature will cause a decrease in pressure. Since kinetic energy is directly proportional to absolute temperature, the final pressure can be calculated by multiplying the original pressure by the ratio of the absolute temperatures:

$$P_{\text{final}} = P_{\text{initial}} \times \frac{\text{fraction to correct for}}{\text{change in absolute temperature}}$$

$$P_f = P_i \times \frac{T_f}{T_i} \qquad (N \text{ and } V \text{ constant})$$

Once again we select the absolute temperature ratio by deciding whether, on the basis of the direction of the temperature change, the pressure should increase or decrease. In this case the pressure increases, so we use $\frac{333°\text{K}}{303°\text{K}}$.

$$P_f = 600 \text{ torr} \times \frac{333°\text{K}}{303°\text{K}} = 659 \text{ torr}$$

An additional problem of a similar type follows; its complete solution is given in Appendix 8-1.

PROBLEM. If a fixed weight of gas in a fixed volume exerts a pressure of 2.0 atm at 20°C, at what temperature will the weight of gas in the same volume exert a pressure of 0.50 atm?

CALCULATING CHANGES IN V RESULTING FROM CHANGES IN T, WITH P AND N CONSTANT. To visualize the relationship between T and V at constant pressure we may refer to an apparatus similar to that shown in Fig. 8-10. *Since the weight of the movable piston is fixed and the atmospheric pressure is constant, the pressure is constant on the weight of gas which is also fixed.* The temperature of the gas can be varied by varying the temperature of a water bath surrounding the cylinder.

PROBLEM. If the volume of gas in a cylinder is 4.0 l. when the temperature is 25°C, what will the volume be when the temperature is lowered to 10°C when P and N remain constant?

SOLUTION.	V	T	P	N
Initial state:	4.0 l.	$(273 + 25)^\circ K$	constant	constant
Final state:	V_f	$(273 + 10)^\circ K$	constant	constant

What happens when we lower the temperature of the water bath? The temperature of the gas decreases until it is the same as that of the bath. The direct effect of lowering the gas's temperature is that the average kinetic energy (K.E. $= \frac{1}{2}mv^2$) of a gas molecule decreases. Since the mass of the molecules is constant, the kinetic energy will decrease only if v, the *average* velocity of the molecules, is reduced. The molecules therefore have a lower velocity and will bombard the piston *less frequently and with less force* after the temperature is lowered. As the gas molecules slow down and strike the piston less often and with less force, the force holding the piston up is decreased, whereas the force pushing the piston down remains the same. Therefore, the piston moves downward in the cylinder until the internal pressure becomes equal to the external pressure. This will happen when the molecules, which are now moving more slowly, are crowded together into a smaller volume so that they bombard the piston often enough to exert a pressure equal to the external pressure. As a result, the volume has decreased. Since volume is directly proportional to absolute temperature, the new volume can be calculated by multiplying the initial volume by the ratio of the absolute temperatures. This relationship may be expressed as follows: The final volume equals the initial volume multiplied by T_f/T_i when the temperatures are expressed on the Kelvin scale. In symbols,

$$V_{\text{final}} = V_{\text{initial}} \times \frac{\text{fraction to correct for change}}{\text{in Kelvin temperature}}$$

$$V_f = V_i \times \frac{T_f}{T_i} \qquad (P \text{ and } N \text{ constant})$$

Obviously, since V_f has to be less than V_i, the term T_f/T_i must be less than 1.

$$V_f = 4.0 \text{ l.} \times \frac{(273 + 10)}{(273 + 25)} = 4.0 \text{ l.} \times \frac{283}{298} = 3.8 \text{ l.}$$

Here is an additional problem of a similar kind. Its solution is given in Appendix 8-1.

PROBLEM. If a given weight of a gas in a volume of 5.000 l. exerts a pressure of 1 atm at 30°C, at what temperature will the same weight of gas occupy a volume of 400 ml and exert the same pressure?

AVOGADRO'S LAW

We have already found that the pressure of an ideal gas is directly proportional to the number of molecules present for any specified values of the volume and temperature:

$$P = \frac{1}{3}mv^2 \frac{N}{V} \qquad (V \text{ and } T \text{ constant})$$

We can rewrite this expression in a somewhat different manner. Let us multiply the right-hand side by 1 (i.e., $\frac{2}{2}$):

$$P = \frac{1}{3}mv^2 \frac{N}{V} \times \frac{2}{2}$$

$$P = \frac{2}{3} \times \left(\frac{1}{2}mv^2\right) \times \frac{N}{V}$$

Since $(\frac{1}{2}mv^2)$ is the average kinetic energy, K.E., of one molecule of the gas, we can write:

$$P = \frac{2}{3}(\text{K.E.}) \times \frac{N}{V}$$

Let us now consider two different ideal gases, A and B, at the same temperature, T. As we have seen, if they have the same temperature, they also have the same average kinetic energy: $K.E._A = K.E._B$. For gas A we may write: $P_A = \frac{2}{3}(K.E.) \times N_A/V_A$. For gas B we may write: $P_B = \frac{2}{3}(K.E.) \times N_B/V_B$. If the two gases A and B also exert the same pressure, P, (that is, if $P_A = P_B$), and occupy the same volume, V (that is, if $V_A = V_B$), then they must also have the same number of molecules, N. In fact, for gas A, $P = \frac{2}{3}(K.E.)N_A/V$, and for gas B, $P = \frac{2}{3}(K.E.)N_B/V$. Hence, $N_A = N_B$.

The kinetic molecular theory thus brings us to the same conclusion that Avogadro reached on the basis of the experimentally observed behavior of gases. *Avogadro's Law states that equal volumes of all gases, if they are at the same temperature and pressure, contain the same number of molecules.* Avogadro's Law emphasizes that equal numbers of molecules of different gases exert the same pressure at constant T and V because different gases at the same temperature, regardless of the weights of their individual molecules, have the same average kinetic energy. For example, 6.02×10^{23} molecules of O_2, in a fixed volume and at a fixed temperature, exert the same pressure as 6.02×10^{23} molecules of H_2 because, even though each molecule of O_2 is 16 times heavier than each molecule of H_2, when these gases are at the same temperature they have the same average kinetic energy, $\frac{1}{2}mv^2N$. In fact, the lighter H_2 molecules, which have the smaller value of m (mass), have the larger value of v (velocity). The greater velocity of the lighter H_2 molecules together with their more frequent collisions with the walls of the container exactly compensate for the greater mass of the heavier but slower-moving O_2 molecules. Thus, at the same temperature, $\frac{1}{2}mv^2$ for $H_2 = \frac{1}{2}mv^2$ for O_2, assuming, of course, that hydrogen and oxygen both behave like an ideal gas.

On the basis of these considerations we can now calculate the relationship between the volume and the pressure of equal weights of *different* gases at the same temperature. Regardless of the nature of the gas involved, it is only the *number* of gas molecules that is significant, and not the total weight. Since, on the average, all ideal gas molecules behave the same at the same temperature, all we need do in order to obtain the pressure or volume, or both, of given weights of different gases at the same temperature is to calculate the relative numbers of molecules (moles). Here are two illustrative problems.

PROBLEM. If 11 g of ethane gas, C_2H_6 (mol wt 30), occupy a volume of 1.5 l. at some definite temperature and pressure, what volume will be occupied by 11 g of carbon dioxide gas, CO_2 (mol wt 44), at the same temperature and pressure?

SOLUTION. If these different weights of different gases contain the same number of molecules at the same T and P, then their volumes are the same. If these different weights of different gases contain an unequal number of molecules, then that gas which contains more molecules will occupy the greater volume and the other gas with fewer molecules will occupy a smaller volume. Since the same weight of each gas (11 g) is involved, the gas with the higher molecular weight will have fewer molecules. Consequently, the carbon dioxide gas will occupy a volume *less* than 1.5 l. It is more convenient, however, to actually calculate the number of moles, n, rather than the number of molecules, N, in the weight of a gas. Since 1 mole of any gas contains the same number of molecules (6.02×10^{23}) as 1 mole of any other gas, the relative numbers of molecules are the same as the relative numbers of moles. In this and the following problems, we shall calculate the number of moles.

First, we calculate the number of moles present in the samples of ethane and carbon dioxide. The number of moles of C_2H_6 is:

$$\frac{11 \text{ g}}{30 \text{ g/1 mole}} = \frac{11}{30} \text{ mole}$$

The number of moles of CO_2 is:

$$\frac{11 \text{ g}}{44 \text{ g/1 mole}} = \frac{11}{44} \text{ mole}$$

	V	n	P	T
Initial state:	1.5 l.	$\frac{11}{30}$ mole	constant	constant
Final state:	V_f	$\frac{11}{44}$ mole	constant	constant

$$V_{final} = V_{initial} \times \frac{\text{fraction to correct for change}}{\text{in number of moles}}$$

$$V_f = V_i \times \frac{n_f}{n_i} \quad (P \text{ and } T \text{ constant})$$

The volume occupied by the carbon dioxide will be less than the volume occupied by an equal weight of the ethane because the number of moles of carbon dioxide is less than the number of moles of ethane. So we put the smaller number in the numerator of the fraction n_f/n_i:

$$V_f = 1.5 \text{ l.} \times \frac{\frac{11}{44} \text{ mole}}{\frac{11}{30} \text{ mole}}$$

$$V_f = 1.5 \text{ l.} \times \frac{30}{44} = 1.0 \text{ l.}$$

PROBLEM. Suppose 10 g of gas *A* (mol wt 40) in a container of fixed volume exert a pressure of 20 cm Hg at a given temperature. Then, 5.0 additional grams of gas *A* and 5.0 g of gas *B* (mol wt 20) are introduced into the container at a constant given temperature. Calculate the final pressure in the container.

SOLUTION. The initial number of moles of gas *A* is:

$$\frac{10 \text{ g}}{40 \text{ g/1 mole}} = \frac{1}{4} \text{ mole}$$

The final number of moles (gas *A* + gas *B*) is: Number of moles of gas *A* originally present, $\frac{1}{4}$ mole, plus number of moles of gas *A* added, $\frac{5.0 \text{ g}}{40 \text{ g/1 mole}} = \frac{1}{8}$ mole, plus number of moles of gas *B* added, $\frac{5.0 \text{ g}}{20 \text{ g/1 mole}} = \frac{1}{4}$ mole. Thus the total number of moles of the two gases $= \frac{5}{8}$ mole.

	n	P	V	T
Initial state:	$\frac{1}{4}$ mole	20 cm Hg	constant	constant
Final state:	$\frac{5}{8}$ mole	P_f	constant	constant

Since the number of moles of gas in the container increases, there is an increase in pressure:

$$P_{final} = P_{initial} \times \frac{\text{fraction to correct for}}{\text{change in number of moles}}$$

$$P_f = P_i \times \frac{n_f}{n_i} \quad (V \text{ and } T \text{ constant})$$

$$P_f = 20 \text{ cm} \times \frac{\frac{5}{8} \text{ mole}}{\frac{1}{4} \text{ mole}} = 50 \text{ cm Hg}$$

Here is another problem illustrating the use of Avogadro's Law. The complete solution is given in Appendix 8-1.

PROBLEM. If 5.00 g of gas *A* (mol wt 150) occupy a certain volume and exert a certain pressure at 40°C, at what temperature will 6.00 g of gas *B* (mol wt 90.0) occupy the same volume and exert the same pressure?

MOLAR VOLUME AT STANDARD CONDITIONS. It follows from Avogadro's Law that 1 mole of any gas will occupy the same volume as 1 mole of any other gas, if *T* and *P* are the same and if the gases behave ideally. Let us consider what volume is actually occupied by 1 mole of an ideal gas at a particular chosen temperature—say 0°C and at a particular pressure, say, of 1 atm, 760 torr. *The volume occupied by 1 mole of (ideal) gas at 0°C and 760 torr is 22.4 l.* The selected temperature of 0°C is commonly referred to as the *standard temperature*, and the selected pressure of 760 torr is commonly referred to as the *standard pressure*. The volume 22.4 l. is referred to as the *molar volume* (or the gram molecular volume) of a gas at standard conditions (S.T.P.).

GAY-LUSSAC'S LAW OF COMBINING VOLUMES

We now wish to consider two different gases which react with each other—for example, hydrogen gas, H_2, and chlorine gas, Cl_2, which react to form hydrogen chloride gas, HCl:

$$H_2 + Cl_2 \longrightarrow 2\ HCl$$

From this equation we see that *one* molecule of H_2 reacts with *one* molecule of Cl_2 to form two molecules of HCl. It follows that N molecules of H_2 react with N molecules of Cl_2 to form 2 N molecules of HCl. Since equal numbers of gas molecules at the same temperature and pressure occupy equal volumes (Avogadro's Law), any volume, V, of hydrogen gas at a given (constant) T and P reacts with an equal volume, V, of chlorine gas at the same T and P to form twice this volume—that is, a volume 2 V of hydrogen chloride gas—if it is also at the same T and P.

In reactions between gases, generally one molecule of one gas reacts with one, two, or three molecules of another gas—or perhaps two molecules of one gas will react with three molecules of another. In other words, the numbers of reacting molecules (of different gases) are in the ratio of simple whole numbers, such as 1:1, or 1:2, or 1:3, or perhaps 2:3. Since at constant T and P the volume of gas is directly proportional to the number of molecules present, the ratio of the volumes of gases reacting equals the ratio of the number of molecules reacting. In fact, in his studies on the behavior of gases, Gay-Lussac observed that the volumes of gases at constant T and P which react chemically with one another are in the ratio of simple whole numbers, and this experimental observation is now known as *Gay-Lussac's Law of Combining Volumes.*

As another illustration of Gay-Lussac's Law of Combining Volumes, consider the reaction:

N_2	$+$	$3\ H_2$	$\longrightarrow$	$2\ NH_3$
1 molecule		3 molecules		2 molecules
1 mole		3 moles		2 moles
1 volume		3 volumes		2 volumes

Here the reaction between 1 volume of nitrogen gas, N_2, and 3 volumes of hydrogen gas, H_2, produces 2 volumes of ammonia gas, NH_3, all volumes being measured at the same T and P. Conversely, if a given volume of ammonia—for example, 200 l.—were decomposed completely into nitrogen, N_2, and hydrogen, H_2, and if all these gases were kept at the same temperature and pressure, the total volume of gas produced would be 400 l.

DALTON'S LAW OF PARTIAL PRESSURES

We have seen that the pressure exerted by any sample of gas depends on the force exerted by each molecular collision with the walls of the container, and on the number of such collisions per unit area and per unit time. In a mixture of various ideal gases, each molecule of each gas contributes to the *total pressure.* Therefore, the fraction of the *total pressure* exerted by each gas of the mixture is directly proportional to its fraction of the total number of molecules. As an example, let us consider air, which contains approximately 80 molecules of N_2 for every 20 molecules of O_2. On the assumption that air acts like an ideal gas, the total pressure exerted by air is the sum of the pressures exerted by the N_2 molecules and the O_2 molecules. The fraction of the *total pressure* caused by the N_2 molecules is 80/100, and the fraction of the total pressure caused by the O_2 molecules is 20/100.

The pressure produced by the molecules of any one gas in a mixture of gases is called the *partial pressure* of that gas. The relationship between total pressure and partial pressure in a mixture of gases is *Dalton's Law of Partial Pressures: In any mixture of gases, the total pressure is equal to the sum of the partial pressures exerted by the individual gases. The partial pressure of any one gas is proportional to the percentage of its molecules in the total mixture.* We can express this law mathematically as follows:

$$P_{total} = p_1 + p_2 + p_3 + \cdots$$

where p_1, p_2, p_3, . . . represent the partial pressures of the individual gases in the mixture.

COLLECTING GAS OVER WATER. One of the most common applications of Dalton's Law of Partial Pressures is the calculation of the actual pressure exerted by a (dry) gas when this gas is collected by the displacement of a liquid using the apparatus shown in Fig. 6-1.

Any confined space above the surface of liquid water contains molecules of water vapor exerting a fixed pressure, which depends only on the temperature of the liquid water. This (equilibrium) pressure exerted by water vapor in contact with liquid water in a confined space is the same regardless of the presence or absence of any other gas, and is known as the *vapor pressure* of water; again, its value depends only on the temperature of the liquid water. Values for the vapor pressure of water at various temperatures are listed in Table 8-1.

When a gas (oxygen, for example), is collected over water, the confined space above the liquid water contains oxygen molecules *and* water vapor molecules. The total pressure of the gas mixture is the sum of the pressure exerted by the O_2 molecules plus the pressure exerted by the H_2O vapor molecules (Dalton's Law of Partial Pressures). The pressure exerted by the O_2 molecules alone is the total pressure *minus* the pressure exerted by the water vapor molecules. If we measure the total pressure of the oxygen-water vapor mixture with a manometer, and from it subtract the (appropriate) value of the vapor pressure of water (Table 8-1), we can determine the pressure of the O_2 gas alone. For example, a sample of O_2 gas is collected over water exposed to an atmospheric pressure of 740.0 torr. The temperature of the water is 22°C. From Table 8-1 we find that at 22°C the vapor pressure of water is 19.8 torr. The partial pressure of the O_2 gas alone in the oxygen-water vapor mixture is then the atmospheric pressure minus the partial pressure of water vapor at 22°C. Pressure of O_2 alone = 740.0 − 19.8 = 720.2 torr. Here are two other problems illustrating the above discussion.

TABLE 8-1 VAPOR PRESSURE OF WATER IN TORR AT VARIOUS TEMPERATURES

°C	P	°C	P
0	4.58	25	23.76
10	9.21	26	25.21
11	9.84	27	26.74
12	10.52	28	28.35
13	11.23	29	30.04
14	11.99	30	31.82
15	12.79	31	33.70
16	13.63	32	35.66
17	14.53	33	37.73
18	15.48	34	39.90
19	16.48	35	42.18
20	17.54	36	44.56
21	18.65	37	47.07
22	19.83	38	49.70
23	21.07	39	52.44
24	22.38	40	55.32

PROBLEM. The volume occupied by O_2 gas collected over water at 22°C, and at an atmospheric pressure of 740.0 torr is 155 ml. What would the volume be if the O_2 gas were separated from the water vapor and then placed in a cylinder at a pressure of 740.0 torr?

SOLUTION. As we saw above, the pressure of the oxygen molecules when collected over water as 22°C and at a total pressure of 740.0 torr is: 740.0 torr − 19.8 torr = 720.2 torr.

	V	P
Initial state:	155 ml	720.2 torr
Final state:	V_f	740.0 torr

$$V_{\text{final}} = V_{\text{initial}} \times \frac{\text{fraction to correct for}}{\text{change in pressure}}$$

$$V_f = 155 \text{ ml} \times \frac{720.2 \text{ torr}}{740.0 \text{ torr}} = 151 \text{ ml}$$

PROBLEM. Calculate the pressure of the O_2 gas if the dry gas is then placed in a container with a fixed volume of 200 ml.

SOLUTION.

	P	V
Initial state:	740 torr	151 ml
Final state:	P_f	200 ml

$$P_{\text{final}} = P_{\text{initial}} \times \frac{\text{fraction to correct for}}{\text{change in volume}}$$

$$P_f = 740 \text{ torr} \times \frac{151 \text{ ml}}{200 \text{ ml}} = 559 \text{ torr}$$

EFFECT ON ONE OF THE FOUR PROPERTIES, *N*, *P*, *V*, AND *T*, OF SUCCESSIVE CHANGES IN THE OTHER THREE PROPERTIES

In the preceding sections we considered all the possible cases in which a change in any *one* property of a gas causes a change in another property, the other two properties remaining constant. Now we wish to consider a more general case—namely, how the change of any three of the four properties, N, P, V, and T, affects the fourth property. One way to solve this type of problem is to consider the change as though it occurred by successive steps, each step involving a change in only two properties. For example, if we wish to calculate the final volume, V_f, from the initial volume, V_i, of a gas, when the number of molecules, the pressure, and the temperature of the gas all change from a given initial state, N_i, P_i, V_i, to a given final state, N_f, P_f, V_f, we can assume that the process takes place in three successive steps. First, the number of molecules changes from N_i to N_f, while the pressure and temperature remain constant. We can then calculate the change in volume as follows:

1st step:
$$V_{\text{inter(1)}} = V_i \times \frac{\text{fraction to correct for change}}{\text{in number of molecules}} = V_i \times \frac{N_f}{N_i}$$

Next, we can calculate the change that this first intermediate volume undergoes when the pressure changes from P_i to P_f, while the number of molecules and the temperature remain constant. The volume change is then given by Boyle's Law:

2nd step:
$$V_{\text{inter(2)}} = V_{\text{inter(1)}} \times \frac{\text{fraction to correct for}}{\text{change in pressure}} = V_{\text{inter(1)}} \times \frac{P_i}{P_f}$$

Finally, consider a third step involving a change in the absolute temperature from T_i to T_f, both the number of molecules and the pressure remaining constant. We then apply Charles' Law:

3rd step:
$$V_f = V_{\text{inter(2)}} \times \frac{\text{fraction to correct for}}{\text{change in abs temp}} = V_{\text{inter(2)}} \times \frac{T_f}{T_i}$$

From these three expressions, we finally obtain:

$$V_f = V_i \times \frac{\text{fraction to correct for change}}{\text{in number of molecules}} \times \frac{\text{fraction to correct for}}{\text{change in pressure}} \times \frac{\text{fraction to correct for}}{\text{change in abs temp}}$$

That is: $$V_f = V_i \times \frac{N_f}{N_i} \times \frac{P_i}{P_f} \times \frac{T_f}{T_i}$$

This expression may be rewritten in a more general form,

$$\frac{P_iV_i}{N_iT_i} = \frac{P_fV_f}{N_fT_f}$$

which permits us to calculate the change of any one of the four properties, P, V, N, and T, when the other three undergo a change. The student can verify as an exercise that this same final expression is obtained if steps (1), (2), and (3) considered above are assumed to occur in a different order. In fact, regardless of the path by which the change from the initial state—N_i, P_i, V_i, T_i—to the final state—N_f, P_f, V_f, T_f—may actually occur, the relationship between N_i, P_i, V_i, T_i and N_f, P_f, V_f, T_f is always the same. Here is a similar problem in which we change N, P and V, and wish to calculate the resulting change in the temperature, T.

PROBLEM. If 1.50 g of a gas at 20°C and under a pressure of 800 torr occupy 200 ml, at what temperature will 3.00 g of the same gas occupy 650 ml and exert a pressure of 700 torr?

SOLUTION.	*T*	*P*	*V*	*N*
Initial state:	293°K	800 torr	200 ml	1.50 g
Final state:	T_f	700 torr	650 ml	3.00 g

Since we want to calculate temperature, we use relationship:

$$T_f = T_i \times \frac{P_f}{P_i} \times \frac{V_f}{V_i} \times \frac{N_i}{N_f}$$

As before, we must consider each step separately. In the first step, we calculate the T necessary to produce a P of 700 torr, while the volume is held constant at 200 ml and the weight is held constant at 1.50 g. Clearly, T must be lowered to decrease the pressure from 800 torr to 700 torr when N and V are kept constant:

$$T_{\text{inter(1)}} = 293°\text{K} \times \frac{700 \text{ torr}}{800 \text{ torr}}$$

In the second step, we calculate the T necessary to yield a V of 650 ml, while P is held constant at 700 torr and N at 1.50 g. To obtain an increase in volume from 200 ml to 650 ml, the temperature must be higher. Thus,

$$T_{\text{inter(2)}} = 293°\text{K} \times \frac{700 \text{ torr}}{800 \text{ torr}} \times \frac{650 \text{ ml}}{200 \text{ ml}}$$

In the third step, we calculate the T necessary to compensate for increasing N from 1.50 g to 3.00 g while keeping V at 650 ml and P at 700 torr. If N is to be increased and P and V are to be kept constant, T must be lowered:

$$T_f = 293°\text{K} \times \frac{700 \text{ torr}}{800 \text{ torr}} \times \frac{650 \text{ ml}}{200 \text{ ml}} \times \frac{1.50 \text{ g}}{3.00 \text{ g}} = 417°\text{K, or } 144°\text{C}$$

A more general way of approaching problems which involve a change in three of the four properties of a gas is to derive from the kinetic molecular theory an expression relating in a simple mathematical form N, P, V, and T. Such an expression can then be applied to the solution of any problem, as discussed in the following section.

THE IDEAL GAS LAW EQUATION

Let us consider again the general expression:

$$\frac{P_iV_i}{N_iT_i} = \frac{P_fV_f}{N_fT_f}$$

which we obtained in the previous section from Boyle's Law, Charles' Law (or Gay-

Lussac's Law), and the fact that volume is an extensive property, and hence proportional to the number of molecules (or moles) of the gas. Since the above expression holds for any two chosen states of the gas, and the number of moles of gas, n, is proportional to the number of gas molecules, N (for $n = 1$, $N =$ Avogadro's number, 6.02×10^{23}), we can write in general:

$$\frac{PV}{nT} = \text{constant} = R$$

This expression tells us that, for any ideal gas, the ratio PV/nT has a constant value, indicated by the symbol R. Usually rewritten in the form:

$$PV = nRT$$

this expression, called the *Ideal Gas Law* or the *General Gas Law,* correlates simply the four macroscopic properties of a gas—P, V, T and the number of moles (or the weight)—and permits us to calculate rapidly any one of these four quantities if we know the other three. (Notice that if we consider a fixed amount of a gas at constant T, the expression $PV = nRT$ becomes $PV =$ const—that is Boyle's Law. If we consider a fixed amount of gas at constant V, the Ideal Gas Law expression becomes $P = \text{const} \times T$—that is, Gay-Lussac's Law. Finally if we consider a fixed amount of a gas at a constant P, we have Charles' Law, $V = \text{const} \times T$.)

THE NUMERICAL VALUE OF THE CONSTANT R. The value of the constant R in the Ideal Gas Law expression, $PV = nRT$, can be estimated, for example, by measuring the volume, V, occupied by 1 mole of a gas, $n = 1.00$, assumed to behave ideally, at standard conditions of temperature, $T = 273°$K, and pressure, $P = 1.00$ atm. The volume occupied by 1.00 mole of an ideal gas under these (standard) conditions is, as we have seen, 22.4 liters. Thus substituting the appropriate values in the expression $R = PV/nT$, we obtain:

$$R = \frac{PV}{nT} = \frac{1.00 \text{ atm} \times 22.4 \text{ l.}}{1.00 \text{ mole} \times 273°\text{K}} = 0.0820 \frac{\text{atm} \times \text{l.}}{\text{mole} \times \text{degree}}$$

Of course, the numerical value of R depends on the units in which the pressure, volume, and temperature are expressed. As an illustration, let us also calculate the value of R for another set of useful units, expressing P in dynes/cm^2, V in cm^3, and T, as usual, in degrees Kelvin:

$$R = \frac{PV}{nT} = \frac{1.013 \times 10^6 \text{ dynes/cm}^2 \times 2.24 \times 10^4 \text{ cm}^3}{1.00 \text{ mole} \times 273°\text{K}}$$

$$= 8.314 \times 10^7 \text{ dynes} \times \text{cm/mole} \times \text{degree}$$

Conversion Factors

$P = 1.000$ atm $= 1.013 \times 10^6$ dynes/cm^2 (see p. 108)
$V = 22.4$ l. $= 2.24 \times 10^4$ cm^3
4.184 cal $= 1.000 \times 10^7$ erg
4.184 cal $= 1.000$ joule

The *erg* is a unit of work (dyne $\times$ cm) and is equivalent to 2.39×10^{-8} calories. Thus $R = 8.31 \times 10^7 \times 2.39 \times 10^{-8}$ cal/mole $\times$ degree $= 1.98$ cal/mole $\times$ degree.

If we compare the value $R = 1.98$ cal/mole $\times$ degree, in which R is expressed in units of heat energy per mole per degree, with the value $R = 0.0820$ l. $\times$ atm/mole $\times$ degree, the l. $\times$ atm must also be a unit of energy. In fact 1 l. $\times$ atm represents the work energy involved when a gas undergoes a volume change of 1 l. against a constant pressure of 1 atm at a constant temperature.

Since heat energy and mechanical work—as well as other forms of energy—are interconvertible, it is useful to be able to convert a quantity of energy expressed in liter $\times$ atmosphere units into the same quantity of energy expressed in calories. Knowing the value of R expressed in both units, we can calculate the conversion factor of one unit to the other:

$$\frac{1.98 \text{ cal/mole} \times \text{degree}}{0.0820 \text{ l.} \times \text{atm/mole} \times \text{degree}} = 24.2 \text{ cal/l.} \times \text{atm}$$

Thus, to convert into calories a quantity of energy expressed in liter × atmospheres, we must multiply the number of liter × atmospheres by 24.2 cal/l. × atm.

THE IDEAL GAS LAW EQUATION FROM THE KINETIC THEORY

We also could have derived the Ideal Gas Law, $PV = nRT$, from the kinetic expression of the pressure of a gas $P = \frac{1}{3}mv^2(N/V)$. Let us rewrite this expression as $PV = \frac{1}{3}mv^2N$, and then multiply the right-hand side by $\frac{2}{2}$ (that is, by 1):

$$PV = \tfrac{2}{2} \times \tfrac{1}{3}mv^2N \text{ and thus } PV = \tfrac{2}{3} \times (\tfrac{1}{2}mv^2)N$$

Now $(\frac{1}{2}mv^2)$ is the average kinetic energy, K.E., of a gas molecule, and this, according to one of the fundamental postulates of kinetic theory (p. 114), is directly proportional to the absolute temperature, T, of the gas. We may then write

$$\text{K.E.} = (\tfrac{1}{2}mv^2) = (\text{constant}) \times T$$

It follows that:

$$PV = \tfrac{2}{3} \times (\text{constant}) \times T \times N$$

The number of gas molecules, N, can be expressed as the product of the number of moles of the gas, n, multiplied by the number of molecules in each mole of gas—Avogadro's number, N_A. Thus, $N = N_A \times n$, and for the expression

$$PV = \tfrac{2}{3} \times (\text{constant}) \times N \times T$$

we may write:

$$PV = \tfrac{2}{3} \times (\text{constant}) \times N_A \times n \times T$$

Each factor in the term $\{\frac{2}{3} \times (\text{constant}) \times N_A\}$ is a constant, so this term is itself a constant, which we indicate as R. Thus the equation:

$$PV = nRT.$$

Here are two problems illustrating the application of the Ideal Gas Law.

PROBLEM. Calculate the pressure exerted by 10 g of carbon monoxide, CO (mol wt = 28), at a temperature of 40°C in a volume of 3.0 l.

SOLUTION. We use the Ideal Gas Law equation, $PV = nRT$, and solve for P:

$$P = nRT/V \qquad n = \frac{10 \text{ g}}{28 \text{ g/1 mole CO}} = \frac{10}{28} \text{ mole CO}$$

$$T = 273° + 40 = 313°\text{K}$$

$$V = 3.0 \text{ l.}$$

$$R = 0.0820 \frac{\text{atm} \times \text{l.}}{\text{mole} \times \text{degree}}$$

Then,

$$P = \frac{10}{28} \text{ mole} \times \frac{0.0820 \text{ atm} \times \text{l.}}{\text{mole} \times \text{degree}} \times \frac{313°\text{K}}{3.0 \text{ l.}} = 3.1 \text{ atm}$$

PROBLEM. What is the volume occupied by 5.6 g of nitrogen gas, N_2, at 100°C and 20.0 atm, if we assume that the gas behaves ideally?

SOLUTION. From the expression $PV = nRT$, by solving for V we obtain:

$$V = n\frac{RT}{P} \qquad \text{Mol wt } N_2 = 28.0$$

$$n = \frac{5.6 \text{ g}}{28.0 \text{ g/mole}} = 0.20 \text{ mole}$$

$$T = 100° + 273° = 373°\text{K}$$

$$P = 20.0 \text{ atm}$$

$$R = 0.0820 \text{ l.} \times \text{atm/mole} \times \text{degree}$$

Introducing our values in this expression we have:

$$V = \frac{0.20 \text{ mole} \times 0.0820 \text{ l.} \times \text{atm/mole} \times \text{degree} \times 373^\circ\text{K}}{20.0 \text{ atm}} = 0.31 \text{ l.}$$

Thus the volume occupied by 5.6 g of N_2 at 100°C and 20.0 atm, assuming it to obey the ideal gas equation, is 0.31 l.

CALCULATING MOLECULAR WEIGHTS FROM THE WEIGHT OF A KNOWN VOLUME OF GAS AT KNOWN *T* AND *P*. If we measure the weight, volume, temperature, and pressure of a sample of a gas, we can calculate the theoretical molecular weight of the gas, assuming that the gas behaves like an ideal gas. Most real gases follow the ideal gas laws closely enough so that the calculated molecular weight is near enough to the true molecular weight to be useful.

The following problem illustrates the method of calculating the molecular weight of a gas from the weight of a known volume of the gas at known temperature and pressure.

PROBLEM. If 0.250 g of a gas at 150°C and 720 torr occupy a volume of 85.0 ml, what is the approximate molecular weight of the gas?

SOLUTION. Remember that the number of moles, n, of a substance is equal to the weight (wt) of the substance, divided by its molecular weight (mol wt). That is, n = wt/mol wt. Hence the ideal gas law equation can be written as:

$$PV = nRT = PV = \frac{\text{wt}}{\text{mol wt}} \times RT$$

$$\begin{aligned} \text{wt} &= 0.250 \text{ g} \\ T &= 150^\circ + 273^\circ = 423^\circ\text{K} \\ P &= \tfrac{720}{760} = 0.947 \text{ atm} \\ V &= 0.085 \text{ l.} \\ R &= 0.0820 \text{ l.} \times \text{atm/mole} \times \text{degree} \end{aligned}$$

And solving for mol wt, we obtain:

$$\text{mol wt} = \text{wt} \times \frac{RT}{PV}$$

For our specific example, therefore,

$$\text{mol wt} = 0.250 \text{ g} \times 423^\circ\text{K} \times \frac{0.0820 \text{ l.} \times \text{atm/mole} \times \text{degree}}{0.947 \text{ atm} \times 0.085 \text{ l.}} = 107 \text{ g/mole}$$

In solving gas problems, it is often helpful to express the relationship of weight and volume in terms of *density*, for the density of a gas at any given temperature and pressure is the weight of any sample of the gas divided by its volume. If we know the density (weight of 1 l.) of a gas under given condition of temperature and pressure, we can again calculate the approximate molecular weight of the gas by applying the equation $PV = nRT$.

PROBLEM. The measured density of a gas is 3.33 g/l. at 30°C and 780 torr. Calculate the approximate molecular weight of the gas.

SOLUTION. We saw above that the approximate molecular weight of a gas is given by the expression:

$$\text{mol wt} = \frac{\text{wt} \times RT}{PV}$$

Now the density, d, of a gas is the ratio of its weight (wt) to its volume, V. That is, d = wt/V, and the above expression becomes:

$$\text{mol wt} = \frac{\text{wt}}{V} \times \frac{RT}{P} = \text{mol wt} = d \times \frac{RT}{P}$$

$d = 3.33$ g/l.
$T = 30° + 273° = 303°K$
$P = \frac{780}{760} = 1.02$ atm
$R = 0.0820$ l. × atm/mole × degree

For our example we then have:

$$\text{mol wt} = 3.33 \text{ g/l.} \times \frac{0.0820 \text{ l.} \times \text{atm/mole} \times \text{degree} \times 303°\text{K}}{1.02 \text{ atm}} = 80.5 \text{ g/mole}$$

Thus the approximate molecular weight of the gas is 80.5.

DIFFUSION OF GASES

Experiments show that gases spread themselves almost instantaneously to occupy an evacuated space, and also diffuse rapidly, though not instantaneously, through one another. Assume that we have a colored gas (bromine, for example) confined in a container *A* and separated by a closed stopcock from an evacuated container *B* (Fig. 8-15(a)). When we open the stopcock we observe that the orange-colored bromine vapor immediately begins to spread into container *B*, and that soon after the color in the two containers, *A* and *B*, is uniformly light-orange (Fig. 8-15(b)).

We can readily understand these experimental observations on the basis of the kinetic theory. At the start of the experiment, when the stopcock is closed, the bromine molecules, Br_2, move very rapidly and randomly within the entire volume of container *A* until they are uniformly distributed. Each Br_2 molecule, from pure chance, is just as likely to move in one direction as in any other. As soon as the stop-

FIGURE 8-15 (a) ⟶ (b) Spontaneous flow of a gas into an evacuated space. (c) ⟶ (d) Spontaneous diffusion of two gases through each other.

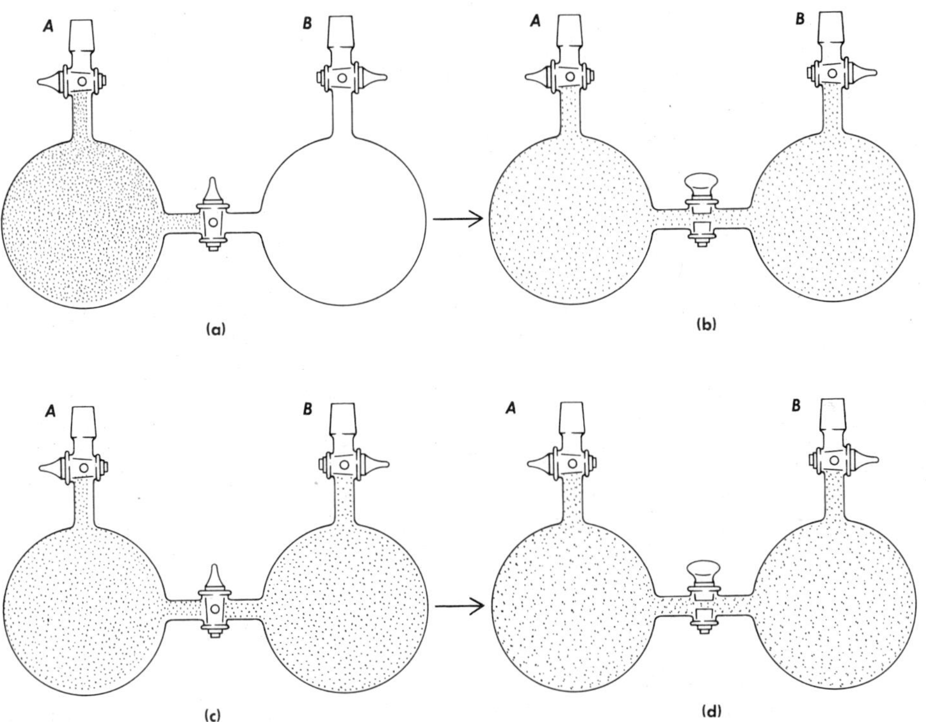

cock is opened, some of the Br_2 molecules which are in the vicinity of the stopcock and traveling toward container B will pass through the opening into B. Once they are inside container B, these molecules will rebound in different directions after colliding with the walls of the container and with one another, and will thus distribute themselves throughout the entire volume of B. Now there are a few Br_2 molecules in the vicinity of the stopcock in container B, and some of these molecules will, of course, move back through the opening into container A. However, there are still many, many more Br_2 molecules in A than in B (and hence many more in the vicinity of the stopcock in A), so the probability is that more molecules will move from A into B than from B into A. Consequently, the *net* effect is a further flow of Br_2 molecules from A to B. As time passes, this *net flow* of Br_2 molecules from A to B decreases, since the difference in concentration of Br_2 molecules in A and B (and therefore also in the vicinity of the stopcock openings in A and B) gradually diminishes as a result of the flow. Finally, when the concentration of Br_2 molecules in A and B (and likewise the gas pressure in A and B) has become equalized, the same number of molecules will pass in each moment from A to B as from B to A, and the concentration of the gas in the two containers will remain constant. An *equilibrium* has been established. Thus, simply on the basis of the random motion of the individual gas molecules (microscopic behavior) we can explain the flow of a gas to occupy uniformly an evacuated space (macroscopic behavior).

We may repeat the experiment with container A again filled with orange-colored bromine gas and container B now filled with a colorless gas, say nitrogen, N_2 (Fig. 8-15(c)). Again, after equilibrium is established we will observe a uniform orange color and the same pressure in both containers. This shows that—as a consequence of the random molecular motion—not only has bromine diffused from A to B, but also nitrogen has diffused from B into A. At equilibrium the gas in both containers is a homogeneous mixture of Br_2 molecules and N_2 molecules (Fig. 8-15(d)), and consequently during each instant equal numbers of Br_2 molecules and equal numbers of N_2 molecules are diffusing from A to B as from B to A.

THE RATE OF DIFFUSION OF GASES. GRAHAM'S LAW

The *rate* at which a gas diffuses through a given volume of space depends on the average velocity at which the molecules of the gas are moving, and in fact is directly proportional to it. All ideal gases at the same temperature have the same average kinetic energy. Thus, for example, the average kinetic energy of a molecule of gas A is equal to the average kinetic energy of a molecule of gas B at the same temperature. In symbols: $\text{K.E.}_A = \text{K.E.}_B$; or, $\frac{1}{2}m_A v_A^2 = \frac{1}{2}m_B v_B^2$. We can rearrange this latter expression to obtain the ratio of the squares of the average velocities of the two gases:

$$\frac{v_A^2}{v_B^2} = \frac{m_B}{m_A}$$

If we take the square root of each side of this equation, we get:

$$\frac{v_A}{v_B} = \frac{\sqrt{m_B}}{\sqrt{m_A}}$$

The final equation states that at the same temperature the average velocities of two different gases are in the inverse ratio of the square roots of their masses. It follows that, since the rate of diffusion of a gas is directly proportional to its average velocity, the rates of diffusion of two different gases at the same temperature are inversely proportional to the square roots of their masses. We can calculate the relative rates of diffusion of any two gases if we know their molecular weights, because the molecular weights express the relative masses of molecules. For example, we can calculate the relative rates of diffusion of hydrogen gas, H_2, and oxygen gas, O_2, at the same temperature, assuming that H_2 and O_2 each behave like an ideal gas:

$$\frac{v_{H_2}}{v_{O_2}} = \frac{\sqrt{32}}{\sqrt{2}} = \sqrt{16} = 4$$

This means that at any given temperature the H_2 molecules move on the average four times as rapidly as the O_2 molecules and therefore hydrogen, H_2, also diffuses four times as rapidly as does oxygen, O_2. Before the kinetic molecular theory had been developed and these conclusions established, the experimental observation that lighter gases diffuse more rapidly than heavier gases led the Scottish chemist Thomas Graham (1805–1869), Professor of Chemistry at University College, London, to formulate his law for gaseous diffusion: *Under the same conditions of temperature and pressure, the rates of diffusion of gases are inversely proportional to the square roots of the molecular weights of the gases.**

This knowledge of the diffusion rates of various gases has been put to valuable use in the separation of isotopes. A successful process was developed for example, for separating two isotopes of uranium, U_{235} and U_{238}. In this process gaseous uranium hexafluoride, UF_6, in which about 0.7 per cent of the uranium exists as U_{235} and the rest as U_{238}, is permitted to diffuse repeatedly through a porous wall. Each time, the UF_6 that contains U_{235} tends to pass through the porous wall a little more rapidly than the UF_6 that contains U_{238}. By means of extremely elaborate and carefully controlled operations, the two isotopes of uranium can eventually be separated.

Exercises

8-1 Describe how to determine experimentally the weight of a known volume of gas.

8-2 What information is needed to determine the number of molecules in any volume of gas?

8-3 What is the relationship between the numbers of molecules in equal weights of different gases?

8-4 Describe the construction and use of a barometer.

8-5 What does a pressure of 1 atm mean?

8-6 Explain the meaning of the following statement: "Several different gases can occupy the same volume at the same time."

8-7 What is the Kelvin scale of temperature? How is this scale related to the Celsius scale?

8-8 Summarize in your own words the kinetic molecular theory of an ideal gas.

8-9 On the basis of the kinetic molecular theory, explain the following facts: (1) Gases exert pressure. (2) Gases diffuse through one another. (3) Gases fully occupy any available volume.

8-10 State in your own words Dalton's Law of Partial Pressures.

8-11 What is the most direct effect of a change in temperature on the behavior of a gas molecule?

8-12 Compare the relative speeds of SO_2, CO_2, and O_2 molecules at the same temperature.

8-13 Explain on the basis of the ideal gas theory why the pressure of a gas changes if the temperature is changed while the volume and the number of molecules are held constant.

8-14 If the temperature and pressure of a fixed weight of gas are increased, what can be predicted about the change in pressure? Why?

8-15 How is the pressure of a gas collected over water calculated from the total pressure?

* Graham's Law holds rigorously only for gases diffusing under very low pressures where intermolecular interactions are unimportant.

Problems

In the following problems, assume that each of the gases act like an ideal gas.

8-1 Calculate the number of molecules (a) in 5 g of CO, (b) in 10 g of CO_2.

8-2 Calculate the weight in grams (a) of 7×10^{30} molecules of helium, He, (b) of 7×10^{30} molecules of hydrogen chloride, HCl.

8-3 If the volume and temperature of a gas are held constant, and 3 g of the gas exert a pressure of 15 torr, what pressure would be exerted by 8 g of the gas?

8-4 If 4 g of a gas at 50°C exert a certain pressure in a certain volume, how many grams of the same gas would exert the same pressure in the same volume if the temperature was changed to 30°C?

8-5 If 5 g of a gas at 25°C exert a certain pressure in a certain volume, at what temperature would 3 g of the same gas exert the same pressure in the same volume?

8-6 If 300 ml of a gas at 20°C weigh 0.1 g and exert a pressure of 400 torr, (a) What would be the volume of 0.05 g of the same gas at 30°C and a pressure of 900 torr? (b) At what temperature would 0.2 g of the same gas exert a pressure of 500 torr in a volume of 250 ml? (c) What weight of the same gas in a volume of 250 ml would be required to exert a pressure of 2 atm at a temperature of 25°C?

8-7 Gas *A* and gas *B* each occupy a volume of 2 l. at the same conditions of temperature and pressure. If the weight of gas *A* is one-half that of gas *B*, determine the molecular weight of gas *A* (molecular weight of gas *B* is 16).

8-8 The molecular weight of a gaseous compound is 16, and 1.2 moles (gram molecular weights) of this gas in a rigid vessel exert a pressure of 746 torr at 20°C. If the volume and temperature of the vessel are kept constant, what will be the new pressure if 4 more g of the compound are added?

8-9 If a fixed weight of gas at a fixed pressure occupies 300 ml at 25°C, what volume will it occupy at 47°C? At what temperature would the same weight of gas at the same pressure occupy 250 ml?

8-10 If a fixed weight of gas at a fixed volume exerts a pressure of 3 atm at 0°C, at what temperature will it exert a pressure of 4 atm? What pressure at 200°C?

8-11 A cylinder is provided with an adjustable piston and with a valve that automatically permits gas molecules to enter or leave the cylinder to maintain constant pressure. Six moles of a gas present in the vessel exert a pressure of 72 torr. The piston is pulled up until the volume is doubled, and the temperature is kept constant. (a) Do gas molecules enter or leave the vessel? (b) Calculate the number of moles of gas present in the vessel after the volume has been doubled.

8-12 Calculate the grams of carbon monoxide required to occupy 10 l. at 100°C and a presure of 2 atm.

8-13 If 500 ml of a gas measured at 800 mm Hg and a temperature of 25°C weigh 0.2 g, what is the molecular weight of the gas?

8-14 If 2 g of oxygen at a certain temperature and pressure occupy 2 l., what volume would be occupied by 2 g of hydrogen at the same temperature and pressure?

8-15 What is the approximate molecular weight of a gas if 0.231 g at 40°C and 720 mm pressure occupies a volume of 150 ml?

8-16 A sample of a gas collected over water at 21°C occupies a volume of 265 ml when the external pressure is 720 mm Hg. Calculate the volume occupied by the dry gas at 25°C and an external pressure of 700 mm.

8-17 If 10.8 l. of a gas collected over water have a total pressure of 780 mm Hg at 24°C, what will be the volume of the dry gas at standard conditions?

8-18 A 1,000 ml flask is completely filled with oxygen collected over water at 20°C and 750 mm Hg. Calculate the volume of dry oxygen at 15°C and 765 mm Hg.

8-19 Calculate the approximate molecular weight of a gas if 0.3 g occupies a volume of 250 ml at standard conditions.

8-20 Hydrogen gas formed by the reaction of excess hydrochloric acid on zinc is collected over water at 29°C, the atmospheric pressure being 720 mm of mercury. Under these conditions the mixture of hydrogen gas and water vapor occupies a volume of 500 ml. (a) What is the volume occupied by the mixture of gases at 10°C and 700 mm of mercury? (b) What is the volume occupied by the mixture of gases under conditions of standard temperature and pressure? (c) If the water vapor is condensed and removed what would be the volume at 29°C and an atmospheric pressure of 720 mm Hg of the dry hydrogen gas?

THE GASEOUS STATE: II

In the preceding chapter we considered the relationships between N, P, V, and T for an ideal gas—a theoretical gas in which the molecules behave as though they were moving points exerting no attraction for one another and occupying no space. For real gases, however, these relationships do not apply exactly. Thus, when we calculate N, P, V, and T for a real gas on the assumption that it acts like an ideal gas, the calculated values and the observed values do not agree exactly. In general, a real gas deviates more and more markedly from the behavior of the ideal gas as the temperature is lowered and the pressure is raised. The deviation becomes greatest near the condensation point of the gas, and of course when the gas liquefies the gas laws cease to apply altogether.

In this chapter we shall consider to what extent the behavior of real gases deviates from the behavior of an ideal gas. We shall also discuss how such deviations may be logically explained on the basis of the attractive forces between the gas molecules and of the space occupied by the molecules themselves.

9-1 Deviation in Behavior of Real Gases from Ideal Gas

If we determine experimentally how the value of the pressure-volume product, PV, varies with the pressure, P, for a real gas at constant temperature—methane, CH_4, for example—we obtain the kind of plot shown in Fig. 9-1. We know that for an ideal gas, PV is a constant at constant temperature (Boyle's Law), so that for each value of the temperature the plot of PV versus P is a straight horizontal line, a Boyle's isotherm (broken lines in Fig. 9-1). For methane, on the other hand, the experimentally determined values of PV vary with P (solid curves in Fig. 9-1) in a manner which depends on the temperature. For each value of the temperature *above* a certain value typical of the particular gas considered, the experimental value of PV is always greater than the ideal value, and deviates more and more from the ideal value as the pressure increases. Below this particular temperature, however, the experimental value of PV varies with increasing pressure in a more complicated manner: It first becomes less than the ideal value, reaches a minimum, then increases again to the ideal value (for a specified pressure and temperature), and finally increases regularly with the pressure above the ideal PV value.

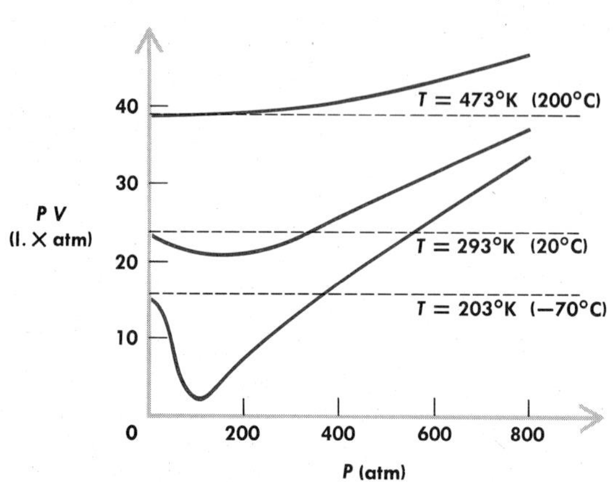

FIGURE 9-1 ***PV* versus *P* isotherms for methane, CH_4, at different temperatures.**

How can we explain that a real gas deviates from the behavior of the ideal gas, and that this deviation becomes increasingly greater as the pressure increases and the temperature decreases? Furthermore, how can we explain that under a given set of conditions some real gases depart more than others (Fig. 9-2) from the ideal behavior? A simple but very rewarding explanation of the observed deviations of real gases from the calculated behavior of the ideal gas was advanced in 1873 by the Dutch scientist Johannes Diderik van der Waals (1837–1923), Professor of Physics at Amsterdam University. Van der Waals examined critically the postulates of the kinetic molecular theory and recognized that some of these postulates had to be modified if the kinetic theory was to account more accurately for the behavior of real gases. As we have seen, the simple kinetic molecular theory postulates that in an ideal gas the molecules behave as randomly moving points having a given mass but no volume, and exert no interactions on one another. In real gases, however, the molecules *do* have a volume, and *do* interact with one another through space, and these two factors—as

FIGURE 9-2 **(a) Deviation of *PV* with pressure for N_2, H_2, and CO_2. (b) Enlarged lower pressure portion (bracketed) of diagram (a) for N_2 and H_2.**

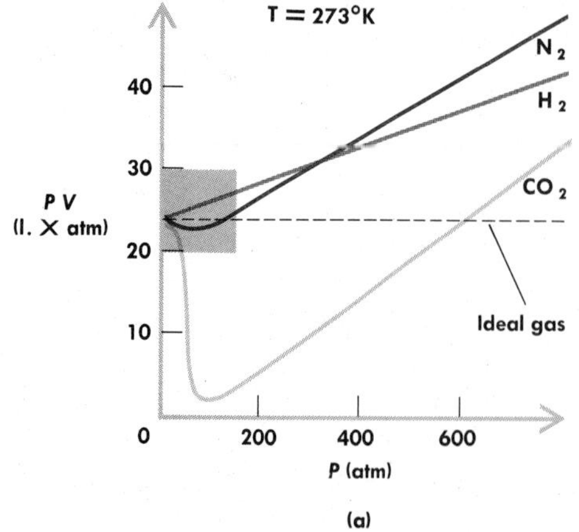

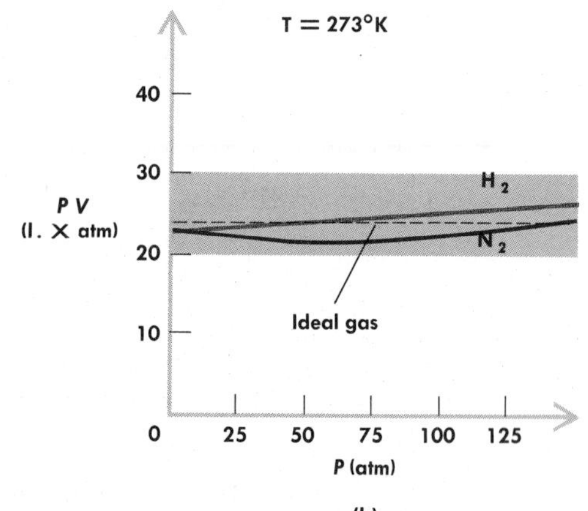

van der Waals pointed out—cannot be entirely ignored except under very special conditions. In the following pages we shall consider how both these factors—the volume occupied by the molecules themselves, and the intermolecular interactions—cause real gases to deviate from the ideal behavior.

THE EFFECT OF THE SPACE OCCUPIED BY THE MOLECULES

According to the simple kinetic theory for an ideal gas, each molecule is assumed to move about in a space equal to the volume occupied by the gas. That is to say, each molecule is assumed to have an *available free space* equal to the volume of the enclosing container. This assumption obviously cannot apply to a real gas, whose molecules possess a finite size, because the available free volume in which the molecules can actually move about is *less* than the total volume of the container. Since the space already occupied by one molecule is not at the same instant available to another, each molecule "excludes" a certain volume from all other molecules. Consequently, for a real gas the available free volume is smaller than the total volume by a factor *related*, although not equal, to the volume proper of the molecules themselves. If we consider 1 mole of a real gas, the total volume that the molecules mutually exclude from one another is a constant, b, characteristic of the gas considered. Then if 1 mole of the gas is confined in a container of volume V, the free available volume is $(V - b)$. By substituting this free available volume (per mole) for the total volume, V, in the ideal gas law equation *for 1 mole of gas*, $PV = RT$, we obtain a new equation,

$$P(V - b) = RT$$

which accounts more accurately for the behavior of a real gas whenever the excluded volume, b, is appreciable as compared with the total volume, V (see also p. 149). This new expression tells us that the excluded volume, b, tends to increase the pressure exerted by the real gas above the ideal value. In fact, if the molecules occupy a fraction of the total volume of the container, they will collide with the walls of the container more frequently (at any fixed temperature) than they would if the entire container were available. From another viewpoint, if the molecules have a finite diameter, the intermolecular collisions will shorten the path each molecule has to travel between successive collisions with the walls, and thereby increase the rate of impact with the walls (Fig. 9-3), and consequently the pressure.

How is the van der Waals correction factor, b, related to the actual size of the individual molecules themselves? If we assume that the molecules are rigid, impenetrable spheres (hard-sphere model) of radius r, then the centers of any two molecules A and B will come no closer than a distance of $2r$, equal to the diameter, d, of the molecules (Fig. 9-4). Thus molecule A will exclude the center of molecule B from occupying a space equal to the volume of a sphere of radius d, having its center at the center of A; this volume is $V = \frac{4}{3}\pi d^3$. Similarly, molecule B excludes the center of molecule A from a space again equal to $\frac{4}{3}\pi d^3$. In general, half of the molecules of the gas exclude the other half from a volume equal to $\frac{4}{3}\pi d^3$. The *total excluded volume*—that is, the volume that all N molecules in 1 mole of gas (N = Avogadro's number, 6.02×10^{23}) mutually exclude from the space actually available for their

FIGURE 9-3 Relative distance traveled by molecules upon head-on collision. (a) Each point molecule travels a distance 2 l between successive collisions with the same wall. (b) Real molecules of diameter d. Each real molecule travels a distance, $2(l - d)$, between successive collisions with the same wall.

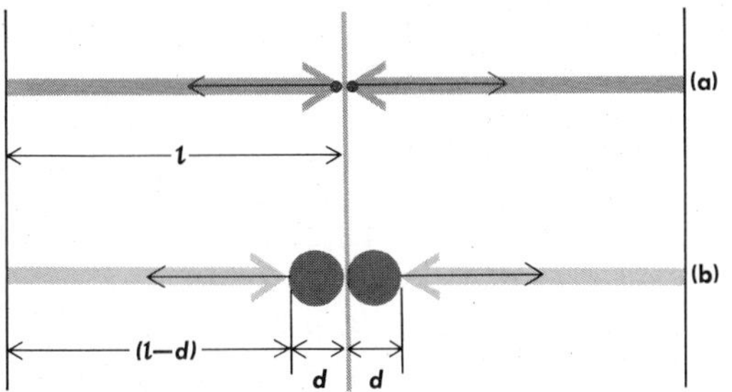

movement—is indicated by the symbol b and is $b = N/2 \times \frac{4}{3}\pi d^3 = \frac{2}{3}\pi d^3 N$. Therefore, the experimental determination of b (from measurements of the volume occupied by a gas under a given pressure at different temperatures, for example) gives us an estimate of the actual size of the molecules of gas.

THE SIZE OF MOLECULES

The actual size of the molecules has been determined for a number of substances. One way of estimating indirectly the size of the molecules of a given substance is based on the experimental determination of its density in the liquid or solid state. For example, 1 mole (16.06 g, 6.02×10^{23} molecules) of the hydrocarbon methane, CH_4, in the liquid state at $-183°C$ (its melting point), occupies a volume of 33.6 cm^3. Hence each individual CH_4 molecule may be assumed to occupy on the average a volume of about: $\frac{33.6\ cm^3}{\text{mole}} \times \frac{1\ \text{mole}}{6.02 \times 10^{23}\ \text{molecules}} = 5.6 \times 10^{-23}\ cm^3/\text{molecule}$. Hence the radius of each methane molecule, considered as a rigid sphere, is 1.9×10^{-8} cm = 1.9 angstroms (A) (1 A = 10^{-8} cm). More appropriately, 1.9 A is half the average distance between the centers of two adjacent CH_4 molecules in liquid methane. We would have obtained an almost identical result if we had considered solid, crystalline methane, which at its melting point, $-183°C$, occupies a volume of 30.9 cm^3 per mole. In fact, from this value for solid methane, we calculate the radius of each CH_4 molecule to be 1.85 A. As this example illustrates, the sizes of atoms and molecules are often expressed in terms of their atomic or molecular radii, and these are usually of the order of a few angstroms. This means that if a gas molecule has a radius of 2 A, or 2×10^{-8} cm, 50 million of these molecules placed side by side would extend the length of only 1 cm! Table 9-1 lists the molecular radii of some common substances which are gaseous at ordinary temperature and pressures together with the values of their van der Waals correction factor, b.

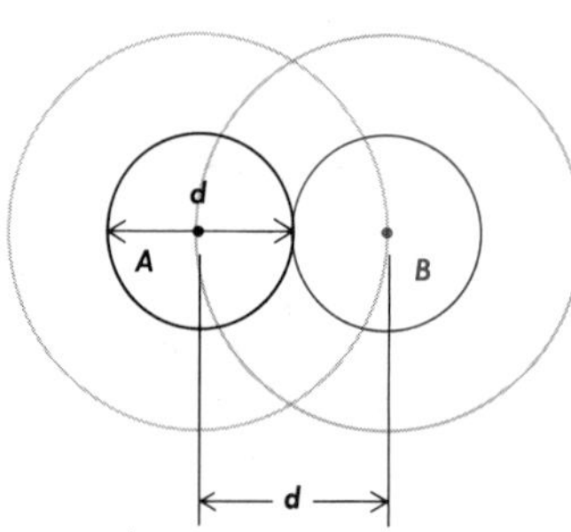

FIGURE 9-4 Volume mutually excluded by two identical molecules.

TABLE 9-1 MOLECULAR RADIUS AND VAN DER WAALS CORRECTION FACTOR, b, FOR SOME COMMON GASES

Gas	Radius, A	b, cm^3/mole
He	1.3	23.6
H_2	1.4	26.5
Ar	1.7	32.2
O_2	1.7	32.2
N_2	1.8	38.3
CO_2	1.9	42.5
CH_4	1.9	42.6
Xe	2.0	50.8
Cl_2	2.1	56.0

9-2 Interaction between Molecules of a Gas

The kinetic molecular theory of the ideal gas assumes that no interactions exist among the gas molecules. But for real gases, the attraction between the molecules of the gas is indicated by a number of experimental observations, the most common of which is that all gases liquefy when the temperature is sufficiently low (and the pressure sufficiently high). The fact that a gas can be converted into a liquid implies that the molecules of the gas attract one another strongly enough to overcome their kinetic energy, resulting in cohesion and liquefaction. Also, many real gases become cooler when they effuse into an evacuated space. This decrease in the temperature of the gas indicates that some of the kinetic energy of the gas molecules themselves has been expended to overcome the *inter*-molecular attractions.

The forces existing between the molecules of a real gas are considered to arise chiefly from the nuclei-electrons and electrons-electrons interactions *among neighboring molecules.* The gravitational forces due to the masses of the molecules are negligible. Let us now consider how the interaction between any two molecules of a gas varies with their intermolecular distance. When two molecules are separated by an infinite distance, $r = \infty$, their interaction is zero—that is, the molecules exert no force on each other. Under these conditions, we also assign a zero value to the potential energy of interaction: $\text{P.E.}_{\text{interaction}} = 0$ when $r = \infty$. As the two molecules approach, they begin to attract each other; this attraction increases rapidly and becomes relatively strong when the two molecules are about a few molecular diameters apart. The potential energy of attraction, $\text{P.E.}_{\text{attraction}}$, varies with the intermolecular distance, r, as shown in Fig. 9-5. Mathematically, this potential energy of attraction is expressed by the formula:

$$\text{P.E.}_{\text{attraction}} = -\frac{b}{r^6}$$

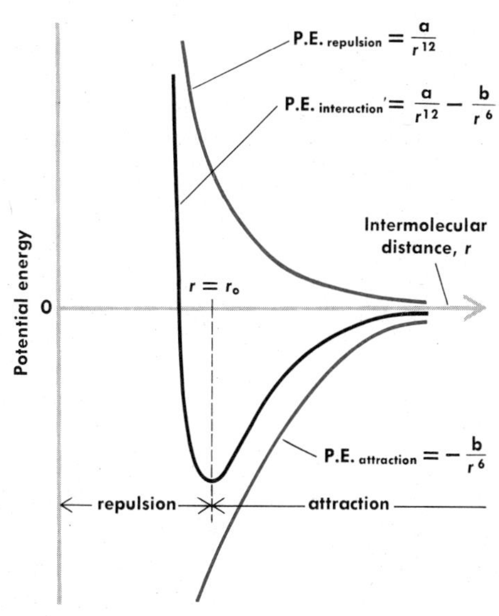

FIGURE 9-5 Energy of van der Waals interactions versus intermolecular distance.

where b is a proportionality constant* which depends on the particular molecules considered. This formula tells that the magnitude of the attractive energy is inversely proportional to the sixth power of the intermolecular distance. Notice that a potential energy of attraction is conventionally given a negative sign. As the molecules approach even closer, so that their outer electron clouds begin to overlap, a strong repulsion sets in, and the potential energy of this repulsion increases very steeply (Fig. 9-5) as the overlap of their electron clouds increases. This potential energy of repulsion is expressed quite faithfully by the formula:

$$\text{P.E.}_{\text{repulsion}} = \frac{a}{r^{12}}$$

where a is a proportionality constant† which depends on the particular molecules considered. Notice that a potential energy of repulsion is conventionally given a positive sign. The net potential energy of the attractive-repulsive interaction between the two

* Even though they are commonly indicated by the same symbol, the proportionality constant in the expression $\text{P.E.}_{\text{attraction}} = -b/r^6$ and van der Waals excluded volume, b, bear no relationship to each other.

† Even though they are commonly indicated by the same symbol, the proportionality constant in the formula $\text{P.E.}_{\text{repulsion}} = a/r^{12}$ and the van der Waals correction factor, a, bear no relationship to each other.

molecules may then be expressed as the sum of two terms, the potential energy of repulsion and the potential energy of attraction:

$$\text{P.E.}_{\text{interaction}} = \text{P.E.}_{\text{repulsion}} + \text{P.E.}_{\text{attraction}}$$

$$\text{P.E.}_{\text{interaction}} = \frac{a}{r^{12}} - \frac{b}{r^6}$$

Now if we consider how the net interaction between two molecules varies as the molecules move farther and farther apart, we see that at very close range, when there is an appreciable overlap of their outer electron clouds, the two molecules repel each other very strongly. (A somewhat equivalent way of interpreting this intermolecular repulsive behavior is to assume that each molecule has its own volume, as would a slightly compressible sphere, and that obviously one molecule cannot occupy a space already occupied by another molecule.) As the two molecules move apart, this repulsion diminishes very rapidly, and the attraction between the molecules begins to predominate. The attraction again decreases as the molecules move farther and farther apart, but more slowly than does the repulsion—in fact, the repulsive energy decreases with the 12th power, and the attractive energy decreases only with the 6th power, of the intermolecular distance, *r*. Thus the van der Waals intermolecular attractions are still effective when the repulsion between the electron clouds has already fallen practically to zero, even though they too become negligible when the intermolecular distance exceeds a few molecular diameters.

VAN DER WAALS INTERMOLECULAR ATTRACTIONS

What is the nature of these van der Waals attractive forces? First, let us take into consideration a gas in which the nature of such forces can be explained fairly simply—for example, hydrogen iodide gas, which consists of diatomic molecules, HI. In a diatomic molecule composed of two unlike atoms, such as HI, the electron cloud is not distributed symmetrically about the center of gravity of the molecule. Even though the molecule as a whole is neutral, there is a relative accumulation of negative charge (electrons) about the I atom and a relative deficiency of negative charge about the H atom, so that from the electrostatic viewpoint the HI molecule behaves as if it contained fractional twin charges, one negative and one positive, separated by a fixed distance. Such a molecule, which has two charge centers, one positive and the other negative, may be regarded as a permanent *dipole*, with the I atom at the negative end of the dipole and the H atom at the positive end. We commonly say in such cases that the molecule is *dipolar*. In gaseous hydrogen iodide the dipolar HI molecules are in ceaseless translational motion, while also rotating about their center of gravity (we shall discuss molecular rotation in a later section, (p. 156). Whenever two HI molecules approach each other closely enough, the electrostatic interaction between their respective dipoles becomes appreciable. This interaction will result in an attraction when the two dipolar molecules approach each other by their oppositely charged ends (head-to-tail collision, Fig. 9-6(a)), and in a repulsion when the two dipolar molecules approach each other by their similarly charged ends (head-to-head, or tail-to-tail collision, Fig. 9-6(b)). Since dipolar molecules have a tendency to orient one another head-to-tail in order to achieve maximum attraction (minimum energy), the molecular motions are to some extent correlated so that on the whole there is a slightly greater probability of an attractive (head-to-tail) collision than for a repulsive (head-to-head or tail-to-tail) collision. Thus the net result of the innumerable attractive and repulsive collisions among the HI molecules is a weak attraction. This attraction is generally called *orientation attraction*, or *dipole-dipole attraction*. In gaseous hydrogen iodide these dipole-dipole attractions

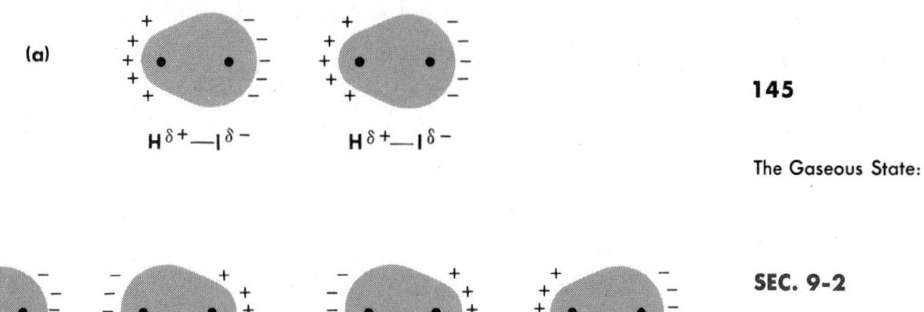

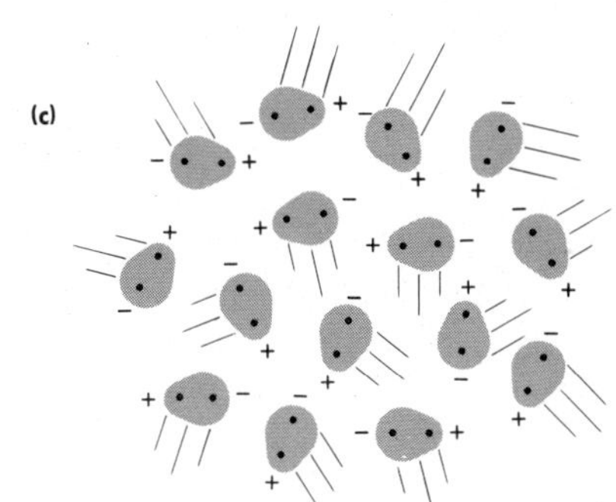

FIGURE 9-6 Orientation interaction of dipolar molecules. (a) Attractive collisions (head-to-tail). (b) Repulsive collisions (head-to-head and tail-to-tail). (c) Molecular motions correlated to give slightly greater probability for attractive collisions.

are rather strong and cause a marked deviation from the ideal gas behavior. Similar *inter*molecular attractions exist in all gases whose molecules contain unlike atoms and whose electron clouds therefore are unsymmetrically distributed, resulting in a permanent dipole.

Another factor which must be considered in order to understand the nature of van der Waals *inter*molecular attraction is that, in general, the electron clouds of all atoms and molecules may be deformed to some extent by an electrical charge (an ion or a dipole). Whenever an atom or a symmetrical molecule—a molecule whose electron cloud is distributed symmetrically about its center of gravity—is exposed to the influence of an electrical charge, the originally symmetrical electron cloud becomes deformed and the molecule acquires a dipolar character. This deformation is not permanent, however, and the molecule returns to its original, symmetrical electron distribution as soon as the perturbing charge is no longer present. We generally express this process by saying that the electrical charge gives rise to an *induced dipole* in the (originally symmetrical) molecule, and that the (originally symmetrical) molecule is *polarized.* This phenomenon is called *polarization* of a symmetrical molecule by an electrical charge. The tendency of atoms and molecules—more appropriately, of their electron clouds—to be deformed by an electrical charge is called *polarizability,* and a deformable atom or molecule is said to be *polarizable.* The concept of polarizability helps us to understand the nature of the *inter*molecular attractions which exist between dipolar molecules and non-dipolar, or symmetrical, molecules.

Let us consider as an example a gas consisting of a mixture of dipolar hydrogen iodide, HI, molecules and non-dipolar argon, Ar (or nitrogen, N_2) molecules. How do we account for the attraction between the dipolar and the non-dipolar molecules? Let us assume that a non-dipolar molecule approaches a dipolar molecule, toward its positively charged end. The positive end of the dipolar molecule attracts the electron cloud of the non-dipolar molecule and polarizes it, giving rise to an induced dipole (Fig. 9-7(a)). Similarly, if we assume that the non-dipolar molecule approaches the dipolar molecule toward its negatively charged end, this negative end will repel the electron cloud of the (originally) non-dipolar molecule, again forming an induced dipole (Fig. 9-7(b)). In either case, the permanent dipole of the dipolar molecule and the induced dipole of the (originally) non-dipolar molecule attract each other, this attraction persisting only as long as the two molecules remain close enough to each other in their translational motions to give rise to polarization. Of course, the permanent dipoles of the dipolar molecules also interact with one another, as we discussed before, and the net effect of all the interactions among permanent and induced dipoles is again an attractive force among the gas molecules.

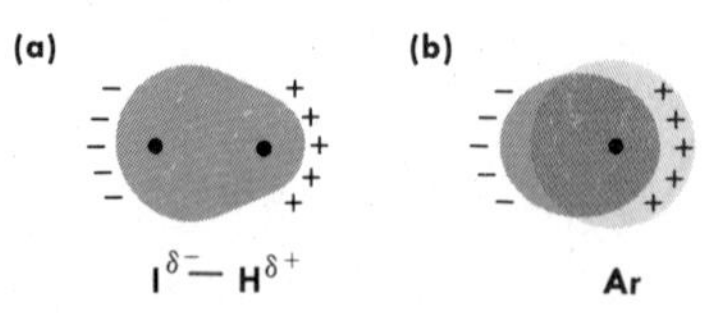

FIGURE 9-7 Mutual attraction between a permanent dipole and an induced dipole. (Gray circle shows contour of originally symmetrical electron cloud of argon.)

Let us finally consider a gas in which none of the molecules has a permanent dipole. Examples are the noble gases, which have monoatomic symmetrical molecules (for example, argon, Ar); the elements H_2, O_2, and N_2; and compounds such as methane, CH_4 and carbon dioxide, CO_2. Even when no permanent molecular dipoles exist to attract one another, *inter*molecular attractions still occur among the molecules and may be explained as follows.

We know that our electron cloud representation of the electrons in atoms and molecules arises from the fact that electrons do not occupy fixed positions, but rather move about the nucleus in what is called their *orbital motion*. Whenever two molecules approach each other, their electron clouds, because of their like electrical charges, tend to avoid each other as much as possible and thus become mutually distorted. Consequently, two approaching molecules become two mutually induced dipoles, which attract each other (Fig. 9-8(a)). Since in this case there is no perturbing electrical charge which determines the preferred orientation of the induced dipole (as in the example above), the mutual distortion of the two electron clouds fluctuates in all possible directions, but in every instant the distortion of the two electron clouds is so correlated as to set up an attraction between the instantaneously induced dipoles. In other words, even though the distribution of the electron cloud of each molecule is still symmetrical about the nucleus—as it must be in the absence of a perturbing electrical charge or permanent dipole—the electrons of the two molecules correlate their orbital motions in such a way that at every instant they are as far apart as possible (Fig. 9-8(b)). Notice that this kind of interaction between atoms and molecules—called *dispersion interaction*—always results in an attraction. Furthermore, this dispersion interaction is common to all atoms and molecules, both dipolar and non-dipolar, and hence is always superposed on the interactions among dipolar molecules (permanent dipole-permanent dipole interactions) as well as on the interactions between dipolar and non-dipolar molecules (permanent dipole-induced dipole interactions).

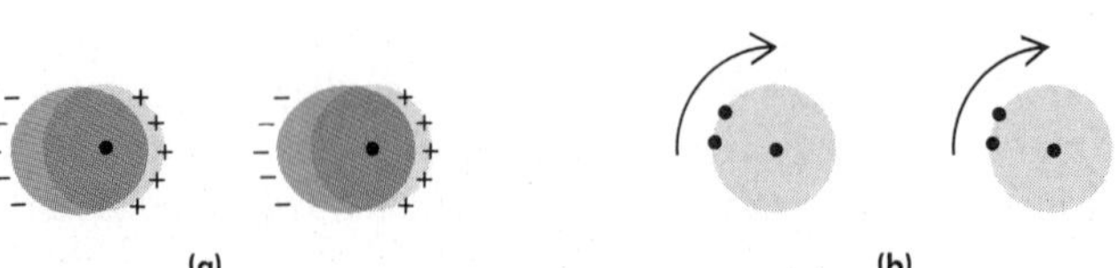

FIGURE 9-8 (a) Mutually induced instantaneous distortion of the electron clouds of two non-dipolar molecules. (b) Correlation of electron motion between two non-dipolar molecules.

In general, the term *van der Waals attractions* pertains to all the *intermolecular* attractive forces whose nature we have just discussed. As you might expect, the intensity of van der Waals attractions varies depending on the structure of the molecules of the gas. For highly symmetrical molecules such as the monoatomic noble gases, the energy associated with van der Waals intermolecular attractions is of the order of only a few tenths of a kilocalorie per mole. However, the attraction gradually increases with increasing dipolar character, and in general with increasing complexity of the gas molecules, and reaches values as high as 6 kcal/mole when hydrogen bonding is possible, as, for example, in water vapor (Ch. 11).

EFFECT OF VAN DER WAALS ATTRACTIONS ON THE BEHAVIOR OF A REAL GAS

How do van der Waals attractive forces affect the behavior of real gases? These forces tend to draw together the molecules of the real gas, and thus the pressure *exerted by the gas* is lowered below the value corresponding to ideal behavior. The van der Waals *inter*molecular attractions may therefore be likened to an *internal pressure* of the gas.

To help us visualize the significance of the internal pressure, let us focus our attention on a gas molecule as shown in Fig. 9-9. If the molecule is in the interior of the gas, on a time average it is surrounded uniformly on all sides by other gas molecules. The attractions that these surrounding molecules exert on it mutually cancel, so that there is no net force acting on it. If, however, the molecule draws close to the container's wall, it will become surrounded by other gas molecules on all sides *except* toward the wall of the container. The attractions exerted on this molecule by the surrounding molecules no longer will be balanced, and a net force will result which will tend to pull this molecule from the wall and into the interior of the gas. Thus, if the molecule is moving toward and about to strike the wall, it will collide with the wall with less momentum than if it were completely free from *inter*-molecular attractions. It follows that for a real gas the actual pressure, resulting from the impact of all molecular collisions on the walls of the container, is smaller than the pressure calculated on the assumption that the gas is ideal. The actual pressure of the real gas, P, is equal to the ideal pressure, P_{ideal}, minus the so-called internal pressure, P_{internal}, of the gas:

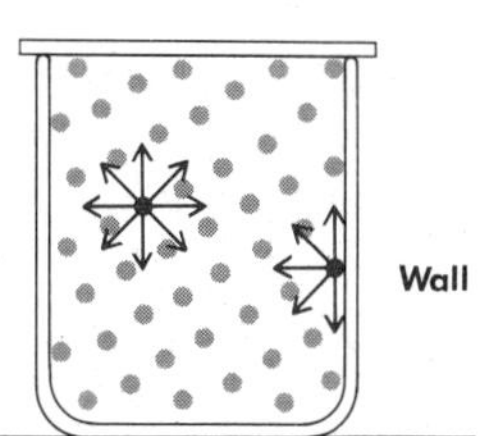

FIGURE 9-9 **Intermolecular attractions on a gas molecule in the interior of the gas and near the wall of the container.**

$$P = P_{\text{ideal}} - P_{\text{internal}}; \qquad \text{and} \qquad P_{\text{ideal}} = P + P_{\text{internal}}$$

How can we express the internal pressure in terms of a measurable macroscopic property of the gas? Since van der Waals attractive forces are appreciable only when the intermolecular distances do not exceed a few molecular diameters, only close neighbors interact. Consequently, the net effect of the intermolecular attractions on a given molecule increases as the concentration of the molecules, N/V (i.e., the density of the gas), increases. Further, the number of molecules on which such an effect operates also increases as the molecular concentration increases. So for a given gas, the internal pressure is directly proportional to $(N/V)^2$, and if N is fixed, is inversely proportional to V^2. Hence the ideal pressure may be expressed as:

$$P_{\text{ideal}} = P + \frac{a}{V^2}$$

where a is a constant (per 1 mole of gas) characteristic of the gas considered. If we substitute this expression of the ideal pressure for the P which appears in the ideal gas law, $PV = RT$ (for 1 mole of gas), we obtain:

$$(P + P_{\text{internal}})\, V = RT$$

and:

$$\left(P + \frac{a}{V^2}\right)V = RT \text{ (for 1 mole of gas)}$$

Whenever the internal pressure of the gas has an appreciable value, this new equation represents more accurately the behavior of a real gas than does the ideal gas law, $PV = RT$.

9-3 Van der Waals Equation for a Real Gas

Let us now consider both the effect of the total excluded volume per mole, b, and of the internal pressure, a/V^2, on the behavior of a real gas as compared with the ideal gas. If in the ideal gas law for *1 mole* of gas, $PV = RT$, we substitute for the ideal pressure and the ideal volume the corrected values we obtained in the preceding sections, we arrive at the expression:

$$\left(P + \frac{a}{V^2}\right)(V - b) = RT \text{ (for 1 mole of gas)}$$

This expression is called the *van der Waals equation.* The van der Waals equation is still concerned with an idealized gas, since many simplifying assumptions have been made in deriving the corrected expressions of the pressure and volume; but it does represent fairly closely the pressure-volume relationship of a real gas for all ranges of temperature and pressure.

The van der Waals equation is no longer a general gas law, as is the $PV = RT$ equation from which it derives, but is specific for (1 mole of) each real gas, because the values of the correction factors a and b are specific for 1 mole of each gas.

Table 9-2 gives the values of van der Waals correction factors a and b for some common gases. Let us see how important these correction factors are for a gas such as nitrogen at 0°C and 1 atm. For nitrogen the excluded volume for 1 mole of gas, b, is about 38 cm^3/mole and represents therefore about 0.2% of the volume (22.4×10^3 cm^3) occupied by 1 mole of nitrogen gas at 0°C and 1 atm. Under the same conditions, since a for 1 mole of nitrogen is 1.35×10^6 atm $\times$ $(cm^3)^2$, the internal pressure for nitrogen gas is:

$$P_{\text{internal}} = \frac{a}{V^2} = \frac{1.35 \times 10^6 \text{ atm} \times (\text{cm}^3)^2}{(22.4 \times 10^3)^2(\text{cm}^3)^2} = \frac{1.35 \times 10^6 \text{ atm}}{502 \times 10^6} = 0.0027 \text{ atm}$$

That is, the internal pressure is 0.27% of the observed pressure, 1 atm. So for a gas

TABLE 9-2 VAN DER WAALS CORRECTION FACTORS, *a* AND *b*, FOR SOME COMMON GASES

Gas	a atm × $(cm^3/mole)^2$	b cm^3/mole
He	0.0354×10^6	23.6
H_2	0.245×10^6	26.5
Ar	1.35×10^6	32.2
O_2	1.32×10^6	32.2
N_2	1.35×10^6	38.3
CO_2	3.68×10^6	42.5
CH_4	2.27×10^6	42.6
Xe	4.20×10^6	50.8
Cl_2	6.65×10^6	56.0

such as nitrogen at standard conditions the van der Waals correction factors are small but meaningful. However, at the same temperature, 0°C, but at a much lower pressure than 1 atm, say 1×10^{-3} atm, the volume occupied by 1 mole of nitrogen would become 1,000 times larger, 22.4×10^6 cm^3. The excluded volume, b, would now be only about 0.0002% of the total volume, and the internal pressure (calculated as above) would be very small indeed, only 0.027×10^{-6} atm. Notice that although the actual pressure P has decreased by a factor of a thousand, the internal pressure has decreased by a factor of a million, since the internal pressure is inversely proportional to the square of the volume. In general, as the pressure of a gas decreases, the van der Waals correction factors become less and less significant. In fact, when the pressure is extremely low, the volume, V, occupied by 1 mole of the gas is comparatively very large, so that the molecules are, on the average, very far apart and their mutual interactions are very weak. Under these conditions the potential energy of the intermolecular attractions is so much smaller than the kinetic energy of the molecules that the real gas behaves practically as if it were ideal. In other words, the internal pressure, a/V^2, which is a measure of the intermolecular attractions, becomes negligible as compared to P. Furthermore, if the volume, V, occupied by 1 mole of gas is very large, then the excluded volume, b, attributable to the molecules themselves, is only a minute fraction of the total volume. Thus, at very low pressure, both van der Waals correction factors become negligible and the van der Waals equation becomes again the ideal gas law, $PV = RT$. Thus we can consider that the ideal gas law represents the limiting behavior of any real gas at an extremely low pressure.

EFFECT OF TEMPERATURE ON THE DEVIATION OF REAL GASES FROM THE IDEAL BEHAVIOR. Now let us see how we can explain the fact that at any fixed pressure, real gases depart markedly from the ideal behavior at extremely low temperatures, and begin to follow the ideal gas laws more and more closely as the temperature is raised. As we know, an increase in the temperature of a gas corresponds to an increase in its average kinetic energy.

When in their random translational motion two molecules approach one another so closely that the intermolecular attractions become operative, it is the ratio of their kinetic energy to their potential energy of attraction which determines the extent of their departure from ideal behavior. If the kinetic energy is much greater than the potential energy of attraction, then the two real gas molecules behave essentially as if they did not interact—that is, they behave as ideal gas molecules. Conversely, if the kinetic energy of the colliding molecules is not very much greater than their potential energy of attraction, then the two molecules will be appreciably influenced by each other and some deviation from ideal behavior will result. In the unlikely event that the potential energy of attraction is comparable, or actually exceeds, the kinetic energy, the colliding molecules will tend to stick together until a successive collision involving other higher-energy (faster) molecules separates them again. (And if the average kinetic energy of the gas molecule is very low, a large proportion of the molecular collisions will result in cohesion, and the gas will liquefy). Thus, in general, fast-moving (hot) molecules will be influenced by the intermolecular attractions much less than will slow-moving (cold) molecules. This explains why real gases depart less from the ideal behavior as their temperatures increase.

We could arrive at these same conclusions simply by considering the van der Waals equation $(P + a/V^2)(V - b) = RT$ (for 1 mole of gas). First, notice that the correction constants a and b are assumed to be independent of the temperature. Then we see that if we increase T and keep V constant, the effect of the correction term, which remains constant, becomes less and less significant as P increases with increasing temperature. Thus, as the temperature is raised, the term $(P + a/V^2)$ in the van der Waals equation gradually approaches the value expected for the pressure of an ideal gas. Similarly, if T is raised while P is kept constant, the expressions $(P + a/V^2)$ and $(V - b)$ approach the ideal values of the pressure and volume, respectively, because the corrective term a/V^2 becomes negligible with respect to P, and the corrective term b becomes negligible with respect to V.

EFFECT OF THE SIZE AND MASS OF THE MOLECULES ON DEVIATION FROM IDEAL GAS BEHAVIOR. Various real gases deviate to different extents from the behavior of the ideal gas (Fig. 9-2). We can understand these differences in behavior among the various real gases if we keep in mind that the extent of deviation from the ideal depends on the ratio of the molecular kinetic energy to the potential energy of intermolecular attraction (see p. 143). At the same temperature, the average kinetic energy of all gases is the same. Thus, the stronger their intermolecular attractions, the more will various real gases depart from the ideal under the same conditions of temperature and pressure. We have seen in a preceding section that van der Waals *inter*-molecular forces result from the attraction between the neighboring distorted (polarized) gas molecules. Large molecules (molecules with large electron clouds) are more polarizable than small molecules (with small electron clouds) because generally the larger the electron cloud of an atom or molecule, the smaller the attraction exerted by its nucleus on its outer electrons. It follows that van der Waals attractions are stronger among large molecules than among small molecules. Thus, under the same conditions of pressure and temperature, a gas composed of larger molecules deviates more from the behavior of an ideal gas than does a similar gas composed of smaller molecules.

INTERMOLECULAR COLLISIONS AND BROWNIAN MOVEMENT

In their random translational motion, the molecules of a gas ceaselessly collide with one another and with the walls of the container. As we know, collisions of the gas molecules with the walls of the container manifest themselves as the pressure exerted by the gas. On the other hand, collisions among gas molecules do not give rise to a directly observable macroscopic property of the gas, although we can still observe the collisions indirectly. For example, a beam of light passing through a dark space, would be invisible from any transverse direction if the air were perfectly pure and clear. Air, however, usually contains a myriad of suspended dust particles which are not heavy enough to settle (rapidly) under the influence of gravity, and these suspended dust particles scatter the radiations of the beam in all directions, thus making the light beam itself visible. This phenomenon is called the *Tyndall effect*, after the English scientist, J. Tyndall, who in 1860 studied the scattering of light by minute particles. The explanation of the Tyndall effect is that the molecules of air (as of any gas) are too small to scatter the light, so that a beam of light passing through pure air is invisible from a transverse direction. Dust particles, however, are large enough to scatter the light, so each particle in the light path appears as an extremely minute speck of light, a multitude of such specks showing up as a "beam of light." If we now focus a powerful microscope transversely on the light beam, the light scattered by each dust particle appears as a tiny halo. We can thus follow the movement of the dust particles even though the particles themselves may be too small to be seen directly. We find that the particles undergo a ceaseless and random motion, following a somewhat "zig-zag" course. This motion never stops, even if the air in the room is perfectly still. In a draft or convection current, the particles still show this "zig-zag," superposed on the collective directed motion.

In general all kinds of suspensions in both gases and liquids exhibit this erratic motion, provided the particles are small enough to escape settling under the force of gravity. This erratic motion of suspended particles (Fig. 9-10) is called *Brownian motion*, after the English botanist Robert Brown (1773–1858), who in 1827 first noted this phenomenon while observing pollen grains suspended in water. The Brownian motion is quite independent of the *nature* of both the suspended substance and the suspending medium (gaseous or liquid), but the erratic motions slow down as the size of the suspended particles and the viscosity of the suspending medium increase.

The Brownian motion is simply explained by the kinetic molecular theory and actually represents strong experimental evidence for the molecular kinetic picture we developed in Chapter 8. Each suspended particle, which may consist of hundreds and even thousands of aggregated molecules and which is therefore considerably larger than the molecules of the surrounding medium (a gas, for example), is bombarded continuously by the randomly moving gas molecules. At any given instant, a suspended particle may be struck by more gas molecules from one direction than from another direction. As a result, a net impulse may be imparted to the particle, causing it to move (an extremely short distance) in one direction. In the next instant, more gas molecules may bombard the particle from another direction, thus causing it to shift its course. And so, the incessant random movement of the gas molecules causes the suspended particle to shift ceaselessly. As we would expect, then, for any given kind of suspended particle, the higher the temperature, the more rapid the Brownian motion, since an increase in temperature increases both the kinetic energy of the bombarding gas molecules and the frequency of their collisions with the suspended particle.

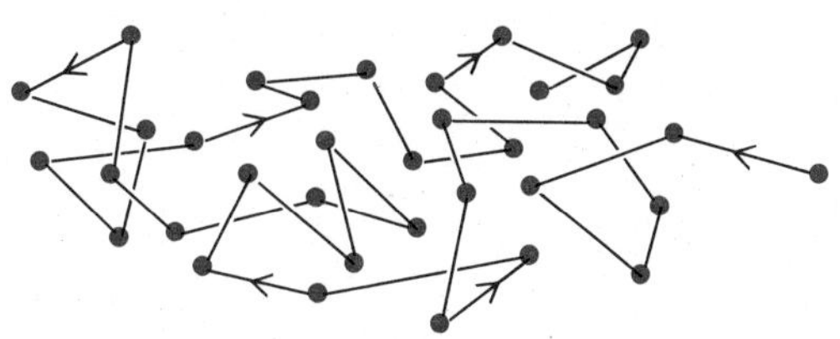

FIGURE 9-10 Idealized representation of the Brownian movement. The dots represent the position of a given particle, determined at successive time intervals. The actual path followed by the particle is not a series of straight-line paths, but rather a smoothly changing curving path.

9-4 Velocity Distribution of Gas Molecules

The random motion of gas molecules has a two-fold aspect. First, as we know, the molecules are traveling at random in all directions. Second, the molecules are moving at different velocities, some very fast, some very slowly, and some at intermediate velocities.* Both the random directions of the molecules and the distribution of their velocities result from the molecular collisions. Assume that we have two molecules, A and B, of equal mass, m, and moving toward each other from opposite directions with the same velocity, v. When these two molecules strike head-on in an elastic collision, each molecule rebounds with the same velocity it possessed before colliding, but in the opposite direction (Fig. 9-11(a)). However, if before colliding the velocity, v_A, of molecule A was higher than the velocity, v_B, of molecule B, then

* At this point it may be useful to recall that the velocity is a property which is properly defined only when both the magnitude (speed) and the direction of the motion are specified. Keeping this in mind, however, we shall often use the term velocity simply to indicate the magnitude of the velocity.

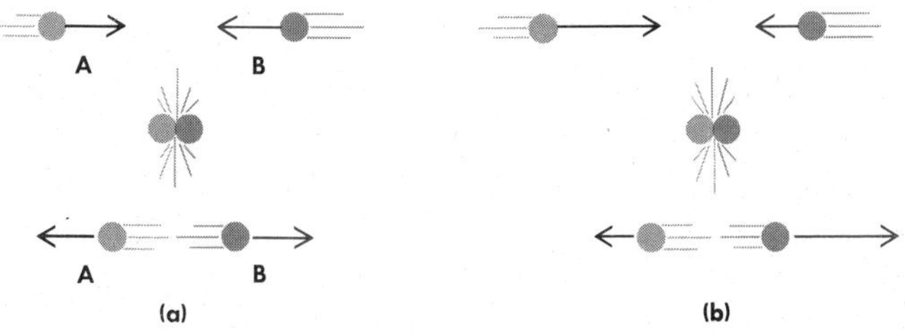

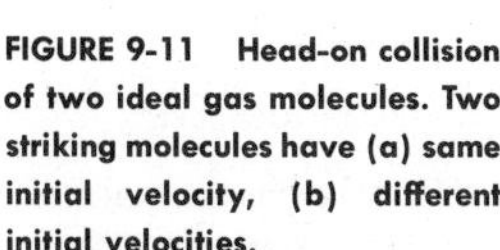

FIGURE 9-11 Head-on collision of two ideal gas molecules. Two striking molecules have (a) same initial velocity, (b) different initial velocities.

molecule A will rebound with the lower velocity, v_B, and molecule B will rebound with the higher velocity, v_A. In other words, the two molecules have exchanged the magnitude of their velocities, and of course each molecule now travels in the direction opposite from whence it came (Fig. 9-11(b)).

Now let us consider two molecules A and B of equal mass, m, moving with the same velocity, v_1, at right angles to each other (Fig. 9-12(a)). When these molecules collide (Fig. 9-12(b)), molecule A hits molecule B frontally and is abruptly stopped. Since the collision is elastic (that is, the total kinetic energy is conserved) all the kinetic energy which A possessed before the collision will now be transferred to B. Therefore, B bounces off in a new direction (at an angle of 45° from its original direction) and with twice its original kinetic energy. The kinetic energy of molecule B after collision is $2 \times (\frac{1}{2}mv_1^2) = mv_1^2$. Since the mass, m, of the molecule is unchanged, a doubling of the kinetic energy means that B's new velocity must be greater than it was originally. In fact, if we call the new velocity v_2, the kinetic energy of B after collision may be written as: K.E. $= \frac{1}{2}mv_2^2 = mv_1^2$. From this expression we have $v_2 = \sqrt{2} \times v_1 = 1.41 \times v_1$. Thus, the velocity of B has increased by the factor 1.41 as a result of the collision with A, whereas the velocity of A has fallen to zero (Fig. 9-12(c)). Molecule A, however, does not remain stationary for any length of time (if it did, it would begin to fall to the bottom) since it will soon be struck by another moving molecule and thus begin to move again at a new velocity, different from its original one in both direction and magnitude. In turn, molecule B will very soon collide with another molecule, again changing both the magnitude of its velocity and its direction.

Between these two extremes of head-on collision from opposite directions, and frontal collisions from perpendicular directions, any other type of collision is possible and would change both the velocities and the directions of both colliding molecules. Therefore, if we consider a large collection of gas molecules, the result of their collisions is not only a random motion in all directions (p. 150), but also a distribution of their velocities over a very wide range.

What is the distribution of velocities among the molecules of a gas under a given set of conditions? In order to obtain a significant answer, we must consider this distribution of velocities over a period of time long enough to obtain a statistical or probability distribution. In fact, if we asked how many molecules of a gas have a particular velocity, v, at a given instant, the answer could be none of the molecules at one instant but a finite number at another instant. However, if we consider a sufficiently long period of time, we can calculate what percentage of the total number of molecules possesses this particular velocity. In other words, we can calculate the probability of a molecule having a particular velocity at a given instant.

VELOCITY DISTRIBUTION CURVE. If we plot the probability that any given molecule of a gas has precisely the velocity, v, (at absolute temperature, T), we get a curve such as is shown in Fig. 9-13. Any point on the curve represents the probability that a molecule will have exactly the velocity represented by the abscissa of that point. Point X, for example, represents the probability that a molecule will possess exactly

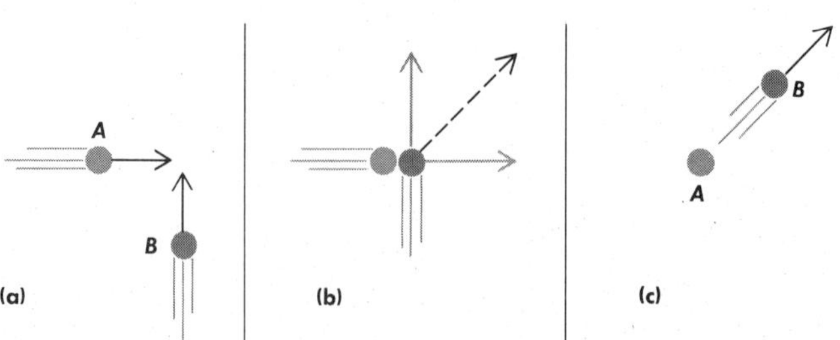

FIGURE 9-12 Perpendicular collision of two ideal gas molecules.

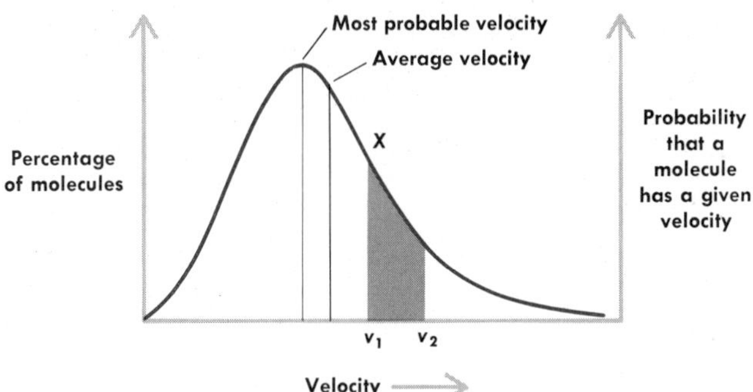

FIGURE 9-13 Distribution of the velocities of the molecules in an ideal gas.

the velocity v_1. This curve also indicates the percentage of molecules with velocities within a given range of velocities. For example, the percentage of molecules with velocities between v_1 and v_2 is represented by the shaded area under the curve. The *entire area* under the entire curve represents all the molecules of the gas moving at all possible velocities. To help us visualize the meaning of a distribution curve of this type, Table 9-3 lists the calculated numbers of O_2 molecules with velocities within the indicated intervals, in every 1,000 molecules of oxygen at 0°C (oxygen is considered to behave as an ideal gas).

As Fig. 9-13 shows, the curve of the probability distribution of the molecular velocities reaches a maximum at a certain value called the *most probable velocity.* Most probable velocity means that, on a time average, more molecules have this velocity rather than any other single velocity value. The shape of the distribution curve reveals that a majority of the molecules have velocities confined within a relatively small range, more or less centered around the highest point of the curve—the most probable velocity. Also, the percentage of molecules with velocities higher than the most probable velocity is greater than the percentage of molecules with velocities lower than the most probable velocity.

A change in temperature does not alter the general trend of the distribution curve, but produces the two general effects shown in Fig. 9-14. First, for a given gas the value of the most probable velocity increases as the temperature rises. Second, as the temperature rises the curve becomes more flattened. This means that a rise in temperature increases the proportion of high-velocity molecules and also brings about a more even distribution of the velocities about the most probable value. Thus, the higher the temperature, the higher the most probable velocity, but the percentage of molecules moving at this most probable velocity decreases because the molecular

TABLE 9-3 DISTRIBUTION OF MOLECULAR VELOCITIES FOR OXYGEN GAS, O_2, AT 0°C, ASSUMED TO BEHAVE IDEALLY

Approx. No. of molecules per 1,000 mol.	*Range of velocity cm/sec*
14	less than 100×10^2
82	between 100×10^2 and 200×10^2
167	between 200×10^2 and 300×10^2
215	between 300×10^2 and 400×10^2
203	between 400×10^2 and 500×10^2
152	between 500×10^2 and 600×10^2
92	between 600×10^2 and 700×10^2
77	above 700×10^2
1,002	

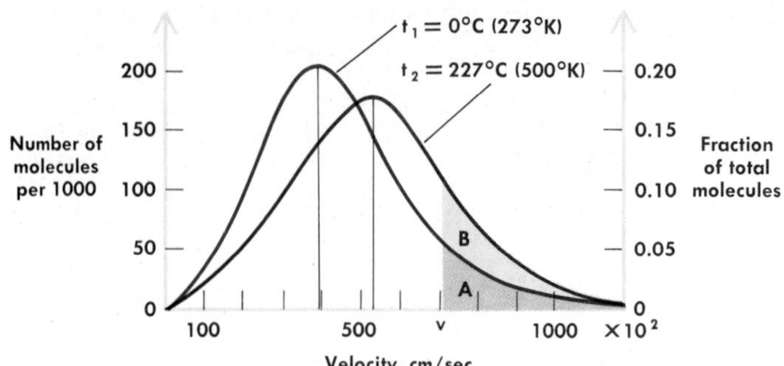

FIGURE 9-14 The distribution of velocities for the molecules of oxygen gas, O_2, at two different temperatures.

velocities are now more widely distributed. In studying chemical reactions, it is often important to determine the percentage of molecules that have a velocity, and hence a kinetic energy, higher than a certain specified value. By comparing the shaded areas under the curves for $t_1 = 0°C$ (273°K) and $t_2 = 227°C$ (500°K) in Fig. 9-14, we see that the number of molecules with velocities above the value, v, increases as the temperature rises. At 0°C, the percentage of molecules with velocities exceeding the value, v, is represented by the area A, but at 227°C, the percentage of molecules with velocities exceeding v is represented by area A plus area B.

THE AVERAGE VELOCITY

We have seen that many of the macroscopic properties of a gas are related to the velocity of its molecules. Since within any sizeable sample of gas the individual molecular velocities are distributed as shown in Fig. 9-13, it is generally convenient to consider the *average velocity* of the molecules of a gas. The average velocity is the sum of all the individual velocities, divided by the total number of the molecules. For an ideal gas its value is:

$$v_{\text{average}} = 1.45 \times 10^4 \times \frac{\sqrt{T}}{\sqrt{M}} \text{ cm/sec} \qquad (T = \text{absolute temperature, } M = \text{mol wt})$$

This formula shows that the average velocity of the molecules of a gas is directly proportional to the square root of the absolute temperature, $\sqrt{T}$, and inversely proportional to the square root of the molecular weight, $\sqrt{M}$. It is interesting to compare the value of the average velocity with that of the most probable velocity, which from the equation of the curve of Fig. 9-13 is calculated to be:

$$v_{\text{most probable}} = 1.29 \times 10^4 \times \frac{\sqrt{T}}{\sqrt{M}} \text{ cm/sec} \qquad (T = \text{absolute temperature, } M = \text{mol wt})$$

For each gas at the same temperature the average velocity is somewhat higher than the most probable velocity:

$$v_{\text{average}} = \frac{1.45 \times 10^4}{1.29 \times 10^4} \times v_{\text{most probable}} = 1.128 \times v_{\text{most probable}}$$

This relationship follows from the shape of the distribution curve, which is not symmetrical about its maximum but slopes less rapidly on the right-hand side of the maximum (the area under the curve at the right of the maximum represents more than half the total number of molecules). The above formula also shows that the average velocities of different gases at the same temperature are in the inverse ratio of the square roots of their molecular weights. This, as we have seen, is nothing else but Graham's Law of diffusion (p. 136).

The velocity of gas molecules is an important factor in explaining the composition of the atmosphere of the planets. For example, to escape the earth's gravitational attraction, a moving body must have a velocity of approximately 25,000 miles/hour. Now from the above formula we can calculate that at a temperature of 0°C the average velocities are, approximately, for hydrogen, H_2, 3,785 miles/hour; for oxygen, O_2, 952 miles/hour; and for nitrogen, N_2, 981 miles/hour. Thus, at 0°C only a very small percentage of the molecules of oxygen or nitrogen gases have enough velocity to escape from the earth's atmosphere, but an appreciable percentage of hydrogen molecules could escape. On the other hand, the moon has a lower gravitational field and a molecule needs a velocity of only about 5,400 miles/hour to escape the moon's attraction. Since the moon is quite warm on the side illuminated by the sun's rays, the gases produced on the moon's surface have enough speed to escape from it.

THERMAL EQUILIBRIUM BETWEEN TWO GASES

If two bodies initially at different temperatures are brought into contact, eventually they both attain a common temperature, intermediate between their original temperatures. If this system formed by the two bodies is thermally isolated, the two bodies thereafter remain at constant temperature, and we say that they are in a state of *thermal equilibrium.* Thus, two bodies in thermal equilibrium have at least one property in common, their temperature. Of course, these general considerations apply also to gases. When two ideal gases, A and B, initially enclosed in separate containers at different temperatures are diffused through each other, the resulting homogeneous gaseous mixture attains a temperature, T, intermediate between the original temperatures of A and B. If the two ideal gases are then separated again by diffusing them through a porous wall, each separate gas will have the same temperature as the mixture. We conclude that, upon mixing, the originally warmer gas cools down and the originally colder gas warms up, to a common intermediate temperature. This equilibration of the temperature—and of the average kinetic energy—of the two gases is attained through the continuous collisions among the molecules and the resulting exchange of kinetic energy. Notice that mixing a warmer gas with a colder gas results in a transfer of heat from the warmer to the colder gas.

This same transfer of heat from the warmer to the colder gas, and the same final state of common intermediate temperature, are also obtained if the two gases A and B, instead of being allowed to mix, are brought into contact through a heat-conducting wall—for example, a metal wall. In this case the *net* transfer of heat as kinetic energy from the molecules of the warmer gas to the molecules of the colder gas occurs through collisions of the gas molecules with the opposite sides of the conducting wall. In our previous simple picture of the collisions of gas molecules with the walls of their container (p. 115), we assumed that each molecule rebounds from the wall with exactly the same kinetic energy it possessed before striking the wall. Actually, a more accurate representation of the collisions of gas molecules with the walls of the container would be that each striking molecule can also rebound from the wall faster (with more energy) or more slowly (with less energy) than before striking the wall, depending on whether the molecule receives energy from the wall, or imparts energy to it. If the walls of the container are insulating (i.e., non-conducting), the average kinetic energy of the gas molecules inside the container still remains constant, because over a period of time all the energy imparted to the wall by striking gas molecules is returned to other gas molecules when they rebound. However, if two gases, A and B, are in contact with the opposite sides of a heat-conducting wall, then the energy which at a given instant is imparted to the wall by a given striking molecule—say a molecule of gas A—may be returned to the same or to other molecules of gas A, or it may be transferred through the wall to molecules of gas B. Thus heat (as kinetic energy) is exchanged continuously through the wall between the two gases. If the two gases have different initial temperatures (if, for example, A is warmer than B), on the average more energy will be imparted to the wall on the side struck by the faster moving A molecules than on the side struck by the slower moving B molecules. The continuous exchange of kinetic energy between the opposite sides of the wall (via vibrations of the molecules of the wall) therefore results in a net transfer of heat from the warmer to the colder gas. As time passes and this net energy transfer continues, the temperature of the warmer gas gradually decreases while the temperature of the colder gas gradually increases. Finally, a state is reached in which the two gases, A and B, attain the same average kinetic energy—the same temperature—and from then on the quantity of energy which at each instant is transferred from A to B through collisions with the interposed wall is equal to the quantity of energy transferred in the same way from B to A. We say that A and B have reached a state of thermal equilibrium, and thereafter their temperature remains constant (if heat is neither given up nor added to the system). Thus the molecules of two gases in contact through a heat-conducting wall tend to equilibrate their temperature, just as do the molecules of the two gases diffusing through each other.

Heat always flows spontaneously from a warmer to a colder body. In other words, it is always the more energetic molecules of a warmer gas, for example, which give up energy to the less energetic molecules of a colder gas. The reverse process—namely, the transfer of heat from a colder to a warmer body—has never been observed to occur spontaneously. This point, which we shall discuss again in Chapter 16, is very important both from a theoretical and a practical viewpoint.

HEAT CAPACITIES OF GASES

MONOATOMIC MOLECULES. We have seen that we can increase the temperature of a gas by transferring heat to the gas from its surroundings and that we can lower the temperature of a gas by transferring heat from the gas to its surroundings. We have also seen that in the case of an ideal monoatomic gas, whose only energy is kinetic, all the heat transferred to the gas from its surroundings is stored in the gas itself as internal energy—the translational kinetic energy of the random molecular motions. It is calculated that the total kinetic energy of translation for 1 mole of an ideal monoatomic gas is $\frac{3}{2}RT$. If we take as a reference system a set of Cartesian axes, x, y, and z, we may again consider for the sake of simplicity that $\frac{1}{3}$ of the monoatomic gas molecules are moving parallel to the x axis, $\frac{1}{3}$ are moving parallel to the y axis, and $\frac{1}{3}$ are moving parallel to the z axis. We may also consider the total kinetic translational energy, $\frac{3}{2}RT$ per mole, to be similarly distributed: $\frac{1}{3} \times \frac{3}{2}RT = \frac{1}{2}RT$, along the x axis; $\frac{1}{2}RT$ along the y axis; and $\frac{1}{2}RT$ along the z axis. Because the gas molecules can move in three possible directions (x, y, z), we say that there are three *degrees of freedom* for the translational motion of the system; the total kinetic translational energy of the system is equally distributed among these three degrees of freedom.

DIATOMIC MOLECULES. Consider how heat energy may be stored by an ideal gas made up of homonuclear *diatomic* molecules. We may represent these diatomic molecules as two spheres joined by a massless spring (Fig. 9-15). Such a gaseous molecule can (1) travel in space in any direction (translational motion), (2) rotate about its center of mass—the midpoint of the spring connecting the two spheres, and (3) vibrate along its axis. Figure 9-15 illustrates these three kinds of motion, using as the reference the Cartesian axes x, y, and z. Since the two atoms of the diatomic molecule move about in space as a unit, we may simply describe the translational motion of the molecule as the motion of its center of mass (Fig. 9-15(a)). Consequently, there are still three degrees of freedom for the translational motion of a diatomic gas molecule, just as for a monoatomic gas molecule. Now let us focus our attention on the rotational motions of the molecule; if we place the molecule along the x axis with its center of mass at the origin, any possible rotation about the center of mass may be considered to result from the combination of two rotations in perpendicular planes, say one in the

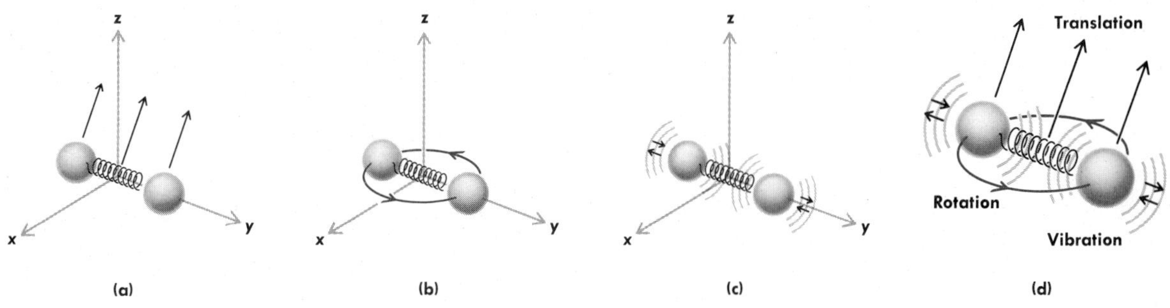

FIGURE 9-15 Motions of a diatomic molecule: (a) translational, (b) rotational, (c) vibrational. (d) Schematic representation of a gaseous diatomic molecule that moves about in space while rotating and vibrating.

xz plane and one in the xy plane (Fig. 9-15(b)). Notice that we are not considering the rotation of the molecule about its own axis as a possible degree of freedom because such a rotation simply constitutes the spins of the nuclei and their respective electrons about the molecular axis, and the corresponding rotational energy is negligible. So there are two rotational degrees of freedom for a diatomic molecule. It is interesting that all possible orientations of the molecular axis are energetically equivalent. (That is to say, there is no preferred direction and therefore there is no potential energy of rotation, only kinetic energy.) Finally, the vibrational motion of the diatomic molecule (Fig. 9-15(c)) is essentially a stretch-pull motion; the two bonded atoms oscillate about their equilibrium positions, alternately lengthening and shortening their internuclear distance. The vibrational motion has only one degree of freedom, since the internuclear distance is sufficient to describe the vibration at any given instant. The bonding force between the two atoms of a diatomic molecule is in some respects similar to a spring tending to hold the atoms at their equilibrium distance, so the energy associated with the vibrational motion is both kinetic and potential.

Since the molecules of a diatomic gas not only have a random translational motion, but also rotational and vibrational motions (Fig. 9-15(d)), we can expect any heat energy taken on by a diatomic gas at a constant volume to be stored in the gas as *internal energy* consisting of: (1) kinetic translational energy, (2) kinetic rotational energy, and (3) vibrational energy (both kinetic and potential) of the gas molecules. In general, the internal energy of a gas tends to be distributed equally among all the various kinds of potential and kinetic energy of the system. More specifically, each translational and rotational degree of freedom has a (kinetic) energy equal to $\frac{1}{2}RT$ per mole, and each vibrational degree of freedom also has an energy (kinetic + potential) equal to $\frac{2}{2}RT = RT$ per mole. (Notice that only vibrational motions have both kinetic and potential energy.)

The situation for a monoatomic and a diatomic gas is summarized as follows:

TABLE 9-4 MOLECULAR DEGREES OF FREEDOM

Molecule	*Degrees of Freedom*			*Total Energy*
	trans.	rot.	vibr.	
Monoatomic	3	0	0	$3 \times (\frac{1}{2}RT) = \frac{3}{2}RT$ (K.E. trans.)
Diatomic	3	2	1	$3 \times (\frac{1}{2}RT)$ (K.E.) trans. $+ 2 \times (\frac{1}{2}RT)$ (K.E.) rot. $+ 1 \times (RT)$ (K.E. + P.E.) vibr. $= \frac{7}{2}RT$

We see that the average value for the total internal energy (translational, rotational, vibrational) increases from $\frac{3}{2}RT$ for 1 mole of an ideal monoatomic gas to $\frac{7}{2}RT$ for 1 mole of an ideal diatomic gas.

At this point we should consider one important difference between the translational motion and the rotational and vibrational motions of molecules. As we have seen, in a large collection of molecules the values of the individual translational velocities range from almost zero to very high, and so do the values of the translational kinetic energies. Therefore, any quantity of heat transferred from the surroundings to the gas at any temperature can be transformed into kinetic translational energy. On the other hand, a given molecule rotates and vibrates only with well-defined, specified frequencies, and therefore with specified kinetic and potential energies. We express this by saying that the rotational and vibrational motions of the molecule are *quantized* and so also are the corresponding energies.* At relatively low temperatures, a high percentage of the gas molecules will tend to be in the lowest-energy rotational and vibrational states—that is, in states having no rotational and vibrational energy. This means that the heat energy taken on by a diatomic gas can be stored in the gas as rotational and vibrational energies—that is, it can serve to activate the rotational and vibrational motions—only if the temperature of the gas is sufficiently high. Therefore, a given quantity of heat taken on by an ideal diatomic gas always increases its translational kinetic energy (that is, the temperature of the gas), although it may not be sufficient to excite as well either the rotation or the vibration of the molecules, or both. In general, the absorbed heat can activate the rotational motions of molecules at a temperature much lower than that required for the activation of the vibrational motions.

HEAT CAPACITY OF GASES AT CONSTANT VOLUME. On the basis of the preceding considerations, we can now explain the relationship between the quantity of heat absorbed by a gas and the resulting increase in the temperature of the gas. It is convenient to consider here the quantity of heat required to increase by 1 degree the temperature of 1 mole of a gas maintained at constant volume. This quantity of heat is called the *heat capacity at constant volume* of that particular gas and is indicated by the symbol C_v. If a gas enclosed in a container *at a fixed volume* absorbs a certain quantity of heat from its surroundings, both the temperature and the pressure of the gas increase. Since the volume remains constant, the gas does not expand and consequently does not perform any work in pushing back the atmosphere (Ch. 17). All the heat absorbed by the gas goes to increase the internal energy of the gas, which, as we have seen, is equally distributed among all the degrees of freedom of the motions excited. Then if we look back at the number of degrees of freedom of monoatomic and diatomic gases, we can calculate the theoretical heat capacity, C_v, of a gas at constant volume. For an ideal monoatomic gas:

$$C_v = \frac{3}{2}R = \frac{3}{2} \times 2 \text{ cal/mole} \times \text{degree} = 3 \text{ cal/mole} \times \text{degree}$$

where R is taken as 2 cal/mole/deg. And for an ideal diatomic gas:

$$C_v = \frac{7}{2}R = \frac{7}{2} \times 2 \text{ cal/mole} \times \text{degree} = 7 \text{ cal/mole degree}$$

Notice that for a monoatomic gas the heat capacity, $C_v = \frac{3}{2}R$, is smaller than for a diatomic gas, $C_v = \frac{7}{2}R$. This is so because for an ideal monoatomic gas we need supply only the heat necessary to increase the kinetic translational motion of the molecules in order to increase by 1 degree the temperature of 1 mole of gas at constant volume. On the other hand, to increase by 1 degree the temperature of 1 mole of an ideal diatomic gas, we need supply not only this same quantity of heat per mole to increase equally the kinetic translational energy, but must also supply an additional quantity

* At an extremely low temperature, near absolute zero, the translational motion is also quantized.

of heat to increase the rotational and vibrational energies of the diatomic molecules. For monoatomic gases, such as the noble gases, the observed value of the heat capacity at constant volume is indeed $C_v = 3.0$ cal/mole × degree as theoretically expected. For diatomic gases the observed value of C_v depends on the temperature. For example, at the extremely low temperature of 50°K (−223°C), the diatomic gas H_2 has a C_v value of about 3.0 cal/mole × degree. At room temperature, however, the heat capacity of H_2 at constant volume is $C_v = 5.0$ cal/mole × degree. This indicates that heat absorbed by hydrogen gas, H_2, at room temperature increases not only the kinetic translation energy but also the kinetic rotational energy of the H_2 molecules. Finally, the theoretical value $C_v = \frac{7}{2}R = 7.0$ cal/mole × degree is approached for hydrogen, H_2, only at the extremely high temperature of 2,000°K, indicating that at this temperature the absorbed heat is transformed into translational, rotational, and vibrational energy. As another example, the C_v value of the diatomic gas N_2, just above its boiling point of 77°K (−196°C), is 5 cal/mole × degree—that is, the N_2 molecules have rotational as well as translational motion at this temperature. The heat capacity of nitrogen remains almost constant at 5 cal/mole × degree up to about 1,000°K, then very slowly begins to increase as the N_2 molecules also begin to vibrate. In general, at ordinary temperatures, the heat capacity experimentally observed for the common diatomic gases indicates that the heat absorbed is converted into kinetic translational energy and kinetic rotational energy, but not into vibrational energy.

Exercises

9-1 What are the chief factors that determine the departure of a real gas from the ideal gas behavior?

9-2 The van der Waals correction factor, b, is called the *"total excluded volume."* Explain what b represents. Does b depend on the temperature of the gas? Explain your answer.

9-3 Discuss the relationship between the van der Waals correction factor, b, for a given real gas and the radius of the molecules of the gas.

9-4 List the diameter in centimeters of several gas molecules. How many molecules having a diameter of 2 A would be required to extend a distance of 2 cm?

9-5 Under normal conditions what fraction of a total gas volume is occupied by the molecules themselves?

9-6 Discuss the nature of van der Waals intermolecular interactions for: (a) neon gas, Ne, (b) air, (c) air mixed with hydrogen chloride gas, HCl, (d) pure anhydrous hydrogen chloride gas, HCl.

9-7 Define the terms "polarization" and "polarizability." In general, which is more polarizable, a small or a large molecule?

9-8 Give examples of simple molecules which are (a) non-dipolar; (b) dipolar.

9-9 Describe the phenomenon of induced polarization. Give examples of two different substances whose molecules, if mixed together, would give rise to induced polarization.

9-10 What do we mean by the term "internal pressure" of a gas? How does the effect of the internal pressure on the observed behavior of a real gas vary (a) with increasing temperature, (b) with increasing pressure?

9-11 Under what conditions do real gases approximate ideal gas behavior?

9-12 Is the van der Waals equation a general gas law? Explain your answer.

9-13 Describe the Brownian motion. How can the Brownian motion be observed for a suspension of dust particles in air?

9-14 At a fixed temperature, do all molecules of an ideal gas have (a) the same velocity, (b) the same kinetic energy? Explain your answers.

9-15 Give a qualitative description of the probability distribution of the molecular velocities for an ideal gas (use a graph to illustrate).

9-16 The *average* velocity of the molecules of an ideal gas is slightly higher than the *most probable* velocity. Explain.

9-17 Two ideal gases originally at different temperatures attain thermal equilibrium when they are brought into contact through a heat-conducting wall. (a) Describe the process by which equilibrium is attained. (b) What do you need to know in order to be able to calculate the equilibrium temperature that the two gases will eventually attain?

9-18 Complete the following statements:
(a) For a monoatomic ideal gas the internal energy consists of ______ alone.
(b) For a monoatomic real gas the internal energy consists of ______ and ______.

9-19 How many degrees of freedom have the molecules of (a) a monoatomic ideal gas (b) a diatomic real gas?

9-20 Describe the kinds of molecular motions possible for the molecules of diatomic gas.

9-21 Why is the heat capacity at constant volume, C_v, greater for a diatomic ideal gas than for a monoatomic ideal gas?

9-22 A certain diatomic real gas at extremely low temperature has the same heat capacity (at constant volume) as a monoatomic real gas. Explain.

Problems

9-1 Calculate the average velocity of (a) hydrogen molecules, (b) oxygen molecules, at 0°C. Would the pressure have any effect on the velocity?

9-2 Calculate the average velocity in cm/sec and miles/hr and the average kinetic energy of the molecules of nitrogen gas, N_2, at 25°C and 1 atm.

9-3 How much energy (in calories) is required to heat 2 moles of an ideal (a) monoatomic gas, and (b) diatomic gas, from -100°C to $+100$°C?

9-4 Two moles of an ideal monoatomic gas absorb 10 cal from the surroundings. Calculate the increase in the temperature of the gas.

9-5 One mole of an ideal monoatomic gas at 100°C and 1 mole of an ideal diatomic gas at 0°C are allowed to mix. Calculate the temperature of the resulting mixture.

THE LIQUID STATE AND THE SOLID STATE. TRANSITIONS BETWEEN STATES

10

In the two preceding chapters we discussed matter in the gaseous state. In this chapter we shall consider the liquid and solid states of matter, and the transitions from any one of the three states to another.

As we know, molecules of matter in the gaseous state move about freely, because their mutual attractions are very weak and the distances separating them are relatively great. In liquids the molecules still move about rather freely, but their freedom of motion is much more restricted than in the gaseous state, because the individual molecules are in close contact and the attractions between them are much stronger. In the solid state each particle (molecule, atom, or ion) is closely surrounded by other particles in a fixed arrangement; the particles oscillate about their fixed positions but are very limited in their translational motion, because their mutual attractions overcome the effect of thermal agitation.

CONDENSED STATE OF MATTER. At ordinary temperature and pressure, the volume occupied by a given quantity of any substance in the liquid and solid states is always very much smaller than the volume occupied by the same quantity of that substance in the gaseous state, because the particles of a substance are much more widely separated in the gaseous state than they are in the liquid and solid states. The volume occupied by a certain quantity of substance in the liquid state is generally slightly larger than it is in the solid state —although there are some exceptions, the most notable being water. But in any case, the difference in density between the solid and the liquid forms of the same substance is rather slight.

The liquid and solid states of matter are often called "condensed states" because their constituent particles are so close—actually they are often as close as possible. Consequently, an increase in external pressure has no appreciable effect on the volume of liquids and solids. Also, since the particles of liquids and solids are so close, they interact vigorously and give rise to the property of cohesion which characterizes the condensed states.

The fundamental difference between solids and liquids is that the forces of attraction among particles of a solid are strong enough to hold them in fixed relative positions, whereas in liquids the intermolecular forces are strong enough to hold the particles in close contact but not to prevent their moving about freely. Thus in liquids the particles move about, but at all times are closely surrounded by other particles; each particle interacts with its immediate neighbors, but as the particle moves its neighbors change and are replaced by others.

As a result of the difference in the energy of interaction among their particles, liquids and solids differ in structure. There is a high degree of order in the distribution of particles in solids, whereas in liquids the particles wander about and are distributed at random. And this difference in structure leads, as we shall see, to the observed differences in the properties of liquids and solids.

10-1 The Liquid State

Before we consider in detail the physical properties of liquids, let us summarize briefly some fundamental features of the liquid state of matter. In discussing the liquid state it is at times advantageous to compare it with the gaseous state and, at other times, with the solid state of matter.

The molecules of a liquid, like the molecules of a gas, move about in a random translational motion with an average velocity, and hence with an average kinetic energy, which increases with an increase in temperature. But the molecules of a liquid are restricted in their movement by strong forces of attraction that bind them closely and make it difficult for any molecule to escape from the vicinity of others. Because the molecules of liquids can move about, while retaining a cluster of continuously changing close neighbors at the same average distance, liquids are able to flow, they are *fluids*. Thus a liquid can flow to assume the shape of its container, but its volume remains constant as long as the temperature is constant. In fact, one of the most readily observable properties of liquids is that at constant temperature their volume is almost independent of the pressure exerted on it. Unlike gases, liquids are not compressible to any appreciable degree, even under very high pressures.

Generally, a liquid particle is surrounded by its closest neighbors in some spatial arrangement which permits the strongest possible interaction among the particles, thus giving rise to a somewhat ordered cluster. The individual particles which compose a given cluster are continually changing and shifting, but on the average, the most stable ordered configuration of the clusters prevails so we say that liquids have a short-range ordered arrangement. This situation is somewhat similar to that occurring in amorphous solids like glass, but differs from the repeating crystalline solids pattern.

FIGURE 10-1 Distribution of translational velocity among the molecules of a liquid at a given (constant) temperature.

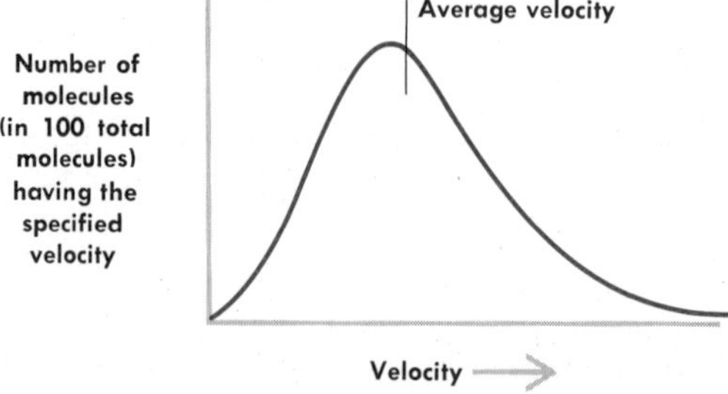

In liquids, as in gases, the *average* kinetic energy of the molecules depends only on the temperature and has a constant fixed value for every temperature value. However, not all molecules actually have the same kinetic energy, since some move faster and some move slower than the average. The distribution of the molecular velocity, v, and hence of the molecular kinetic energy, $\frac{1}{2}mv^2$, follows for liquids the same pattern we discussed in detail for gases, as shown by the same energy-distribution diagram repeated in Fig. 10-1. As we shall see, this energy-distribution curve for the molecules of a liquid permits us to explain why liquids evaporate (have some vapor pressure) even at relatively low temperatures.

For every liquid substance there is a certain temperature above which the kinetic energy of the molecules is so high that the forces of attraction among the mole-

TABLE 10-1 MAIN TYPES OF CRYSTALLINE SOLIDS

Type of Crystals	*Fundamental Particles*	*Examples*	*Nature and Energy of Bonding*	*Some Characteristic Features*
Ionic Crystals	Positive and negative ions arranged in an orderly three-dimensional array.	$NH_4^+Cl^-$ Na^+Cl^- $Mg^{+2}O^{-2}$ $Ca^{+2}(F^-)_2$ $Sc^{+3}(Cl^-)_3$	Strong Electrostatic Attraction. Lattice Energy (kcal/mole): $NH_4^+Cl^-$ = 112 Na^+Cl^- = 184 $Mg^{+2}O^{-2}$ = 918 $Ca^{+2}(F^-)_2$ = 624 $Sc^{+3}(Cl^-)_3$ = 1,165	Relatively hard and brittle. High melting point. Usually soluble (at least to some extent) in water and other highly polar ionizing solvents. The solids do not conduct an electric current, but melts and solutions do.
Covalent Lattice	1. Atoms bonded covalently in an orderly three-dimensional array.	Diamond, C_{diam}; Carborundum, SiC; Quartz, SiO_2	Covalent bonds. Heat of atomization (kcal/mole): C_{diam} = 171 SiC = 291 SiO_2 = 432	High melting point. Do not conduct an electric current either as solids or as melts. Generally very hard. Insoluble in both polar and non-polar solvents.
	2. Atoms covalently bonded in orderly two-dimensional layers.	Graphite, C_{gr}; Talc, $\{Mg_3(OH)_2Si_4O_{10}\}$ (talcum powder)	Covalent bonds within each layer. Van der Waals attractions between separate layers. Heat of atomization of C_{gr} = 171.5 kcal/mole.	High melting point. Some conduct an electric current (graphite, for example). Generally soft in regard to breaking the bonds between layers (flake easily) but each layer is very tough. Insoluble in solvents.
Molecular	Individual molecules (mono-, di- or polyatomic) arranged in orderly three-dimensional array.	Solid Argon, Ar; Solid CO_2; Iodine, I_2; ice, H_2O	Van der Waals intermolecular forces ranging from very weak (for example, crystalline argon, below 2 kcal/mole) to relatively strong (5 to 7 kcal/mole) for hydrogen-bonding substances.	Relatively soft; low melting point; high vapor pressure. Usually very soluble in appropriate solvents. Do not conduct an electric current.
Metallic	Cores of atoms arranged in a regular three-dimensional array; "metallic electrons" in multicenter bonds.	Sodium Zinc Copper Silver Iron	Metallic bonding. The heat of atomization of metals ranges from a low of 19 kcal/mole for cesium, Cs; to 100 kcal/mole for iron, Fe, to a high of 188 kcal/mole for osmium, Os	All metals are characterized by an electrical conductivity which decreases as the temperature increases; by a high thermal conductivity, a typical surface luster, and a very high boiling point. Their hardness and melting points vary widely: for example, sodium is so soft that it can be cut with a knife and melts at 98°C, whereas titanium is very hard and melts at 1,725°C.

cules can no longer bind them together in a *true liquid state.* Above this temperature, which is called the *critical temperature* of the substance, increasing the pressure does not cause a continuous transition from a gas to a liquid phase.

THE PHYSICAL PROPERTIES OF LIQUIDS

DENSITY. The densities of liquids are much greater than are the densities of gases under the same conditions. The density of a liquid is directly proportional to its molecular weight and inversely proportional to its molecular volume, and also depends on the spatial arrangement in the liquid. For example, the substitution of heavier chlorine atoms for hydrogen atoms in the molecules of two liquid substances of similar formulas increases the density of the liquid. Thus, carbon tetrachloride, CCl_4, is a denser liquid than chloroform, $CHCl_3$, and chloroform is denser than dichloromethane, CH_2Cl_2.

The general effect of *increasing temperature* on a liquid, as on a gas, is to increase the kinetic energy of its molecules, so that the intermolecular attractions become less important. Consequently, an increase in temperature usually increases the volume of a liquid, although the relative increase in volume is much less than it is for a gas.

SURFACE TENSION. A characteristic property of a liquid is its *surface tension.* Surface tension is defined as the force that prevents the surface of a liquid from expanding. It is commonly expressed as the work which has to be done to increase by 1 cm^2 the surface of a liquid.

Why do liquids exhibit surface tension? Molecules in the interior of the liquid are completely surrounded by other molecules, and are consequently attracted equally in all directions, as illustrated in Fig. 10-2. On the other hand, the molecules at the surface of a liquid are subjected only to the forces of attraction exerted by the molecules alongside and below them. On the average, the net force acting on the molecules located in the interior of the liquid is zero, whereas the molecules at the surface are subjected to a net force attracting them toward the interior of the liquid. This force will tend to pull as many molecules as possible from the surface to the interior of the liquid, thus reducing as much as possible the surface area of the liquid. This explains why a drop of liquid tends to assume a spherical shape, a sphere having the minimum surface area for a given volume. Since surface tension is caused by the *inter*molecular attractions, any factor that weakens these attractions or makes them relatively less important will lower the surface tension. For example, an increase in temperature will decrease the surface tension.

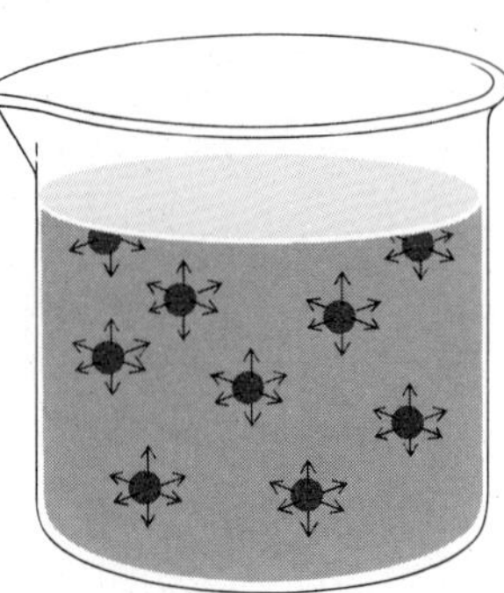

FIGURE 10-2 Schematic representation of intermolecular forces causing surface tension.

Surface tension is responsible for the rise and fall of liquids in capillary (very small diameter) tubes. Water is an example of a liquid that rises in a glass capillary tube, and mercury is an example of a liquid that falls. This difference in behavior arises from the fact that water molecules are attracted by a glass surface more strongly than they are by one another. The molecules of mercury, on the other hand, are more strongly attracted to one another than they are to glass. Thus mer-

FIGURE 10-3 Capillary fall (mercury) and rise (water).

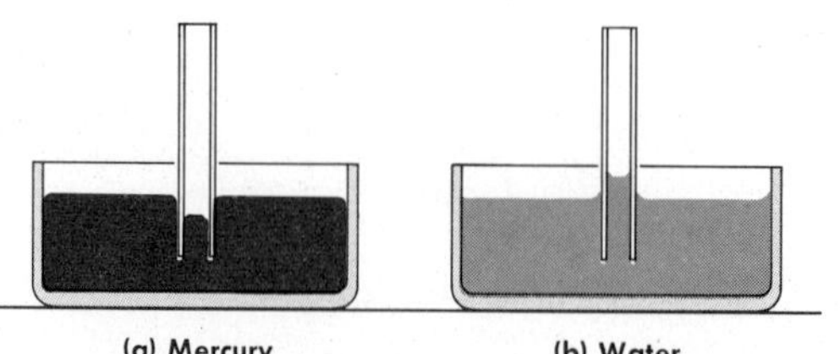

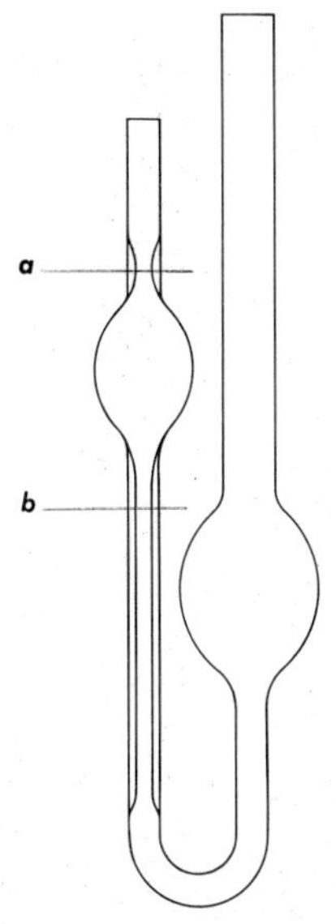

FIGURE 10-4 A simple viscosimeter.

cury molecules are drawn together and away from the glass, and a convex surface (capillary depression) results (Fig. 10-3(a)), whereas water molecules are drawn to the glass. Water spreads to produce a concave surface (capillary rise, Fig. 10-3(b)). The greater the surface tension of liquids whose molecules are attracted by a glass surface, the higher they rise in glass capillary tubes. Consequently, we can use capillary rise as a measure of the surface tension of such liquids.

VISCOSITY. The slow flowing of such liquids as heavy lubricating oil and molasses, as well as the rapid but not instantaneous flowing of other liquids, such as water, are familiar effects of a property common to all liquids and known as viscosity. Viscosity is the resistance of a liquid to flowing, and, like most other properties of liquids, is caused by *inter*molecular forces of attraction. Accordingly, as the temperature of a liquid increases, its viscosity decreases.

The viscosity of a liquid can be determined by measuring the time required for the volume of liquid (contained between *a* and *b*) to empty through a capillary. A simple laboratory apparatus for this purpose, called a *viscosimeter,* is pictured in Fig. 10-4. The viscosity of liquids varies within rather wide limits. Water is moderately viscous; liquids such as ether and benzene are less viscous; lubricating oils are highly viscous.

10-2 Liquid-Gas Transformations

THE EVAPORATION OF LIQUIDS

We all know that when a liquid, such as water, is placed in an open vessel exposed to the atmosphere it gradually disappears. Although at a given temperature the *average* kinetic energy of the molecules of the liquid is constant, some molecules have higher energies than the average (Fig. 10-1). A molecule moving upward with sufficiently high kinetic energy may break through the surface of the liquid and pass into the gaseous state, diffusing through the molecules that make up the air. Occasionally, some of these escaped molecules, after colliding with air molecules or with other vaporized molecules, return to the surface of the liquid and become again part of the liquid. But most of the vaporized molecules escape completely, and the liquid eventually disappears. Figure 10-5(a) represents schematically the evaporation of a liquid into the atmosphere. The long vertical arrow (with the head pointing upward, alongside the vessel) indicates the escape of the molecules from the liquid to the vapor. The short vertical arrow (with the head pointing downward) indicates the return of some molecules from the vapor to the liquid. Since more molecules *escape* than *return,* the liquid eventually is transformed completely into vapor. The transformation of a liquid to its vapor

FIGURE 10-5 Schematic representation of evaporation of a liquid. (a) Evaporation in an open vessel. (b) Evaporation in a closed vessel.

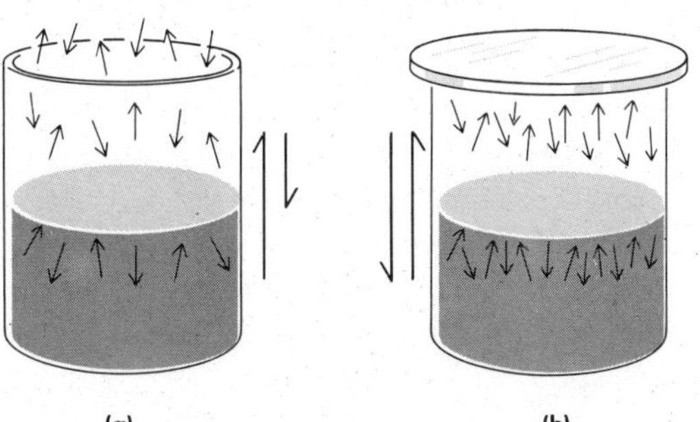

or gas is known as *vaporization*. The reverse process, the transformation of a gas into its liquid, is called *liquefaction*, or *condensation*.

We know that only those molecules that possess a kinetic energy above a certain minimum value, dependent on the particular liquid, are able to break away from the liquid and pass into the gaseous state. Thus when a liquid evaporates, the more energetic molecules escape and the less energetic ones remain, so that the *average* kinetic energy of the remaining liquid gradually decreases and the temperature of the liquid drops unless heat is added to the system from an external source. Hence, heat is required to maintain constant the temperature of a liquid which is evaporating.

HEAT OF VAPORIZATION. As we have just seen, if we insulate the container from which a liquid is evaporating in order thereby to prevent the transfer of heat from the surroundings (for example, if the liquid is placed in a Dewar flask), we find that the temperature of the liquid decreases as vaporization proceeds. Thus, in order to keep a liquid that is evaporating at a constant temperature, heat must be supplied from some external source. The quantity of heat which must be supplied to vaporize a specific quantity of a certain liquid at constant temperature depends first of all on the liquid itself, and also, to a lesser extent, on the temperature and pressure at which the evaporation occurs. When we state the quantity of heat required to vaporize a given quantity of a liquid, we must always specify the temperature and pressure. The molar *heat of vaporization* of a substance, usually expressed in kcal, is the quantity of heat required to vaporize 1 mole of a liquid at its normal boiling temperature under 1 atm pressure. The specific heat of vaporization is similarly defined for 1 g of the liquid. For example, at 100°C and 1 atm, the molar heat of vaporization of water is 9.72 kcal/mole, and the specific heat of vaporization of water is (9.72/18.0) = 0.540 kcal/g, or 540 cal/g.

The heat of vaporization may also be viewed in part as the energy necessary to overcome the forces that bind molecules together in the liquid state.* The conversion of a liquid to its gas involves the separation of the molecules, so energy must be supplied to overcome the forces of attraction among them. A fairly large amount of energy must always be supplied to make a liquid evaporate at constant temperature.

The heat of vaporization for a particular liquid varies with the temperature at which the vaporization occurs. As the temperature rises, the energy of the intermolecular attractions becomes less and less important relative to the average kinetic energy of the molecules, and the heat of vaporization consequently decreases. The specific heat of vaporization of water, for example, decreases from 590 cal/g at 10°C to 540 cal/g at 100°C.

VAPOR PRESSURE

The molecules of a liquid that have passed into the gaseous state constitute the *vapor* of the liquid. When a sufficient quantity of a liquid is placed in a vessel with a tightly fitting lid (Fig. 10-5(b)), the liquid does not evaporate completely, because the molecules which pass into the gaseous state cannot escape from the closed container, and many of them eventually return to the liquid state. Soon the number of molecules returning to the liquid in a given period of time, represented by the arrow pointing upward alongside the vessel in Fig. 10-5(b), equals the number of molecules leaving the liquid in a given period of time, represented by the arrow pointing downward, alongside the vessel. A state of equilibrium is reached, and the number of vapor molecules in the fixed volume above the liquid remains constant thereafter, as long as the temperature is maintained constant. At a fixed temperature, this constant number of vapor molecules exerts a constant pressure, called the *vapor pressure* of the liquid. Notice that the vapor pressure does not depend on the relative amounts

* Energy is also required to push the surrounding atmosphere out of the way—to make room for the gas from the evaporating liquid. For water, of the 540 cal/g, less than 55 cal is used in this manner; about 9 kcal is used to overcome the molecular binding forces.

of liquid and vapor present. As long as the rate at which the molecules leave the liquid surface is equal to the rate at which they return to it—that is, as long as the liquid and its vapor are in equilibrium—the pressure exerted by the vapor is constant.

THE MEASUREMENT OF VAPOR PRESSURE. Let us consider that a sufficient quantity of a liquid, *L*, has been placed in flask *V* (Fig. 10-6) and that all the air and other foreign molecules have been pumped out. Then the stopcock, *S*, is closed, and the system is brought to, and maintained at, a fixed temperature. Under these conditions part of the liquid evaporates, and when sufficient time has elapsed for equilibrium to be established, a definite pressure registers on the manometer, *M*. Since all the air and other gases have been pumped away, the molecules exerting the pressure must have come only from the liquid. The observed pressure, therefore, is the vapor pressure of the liquid at that particular temperature. As long as the temperature of the bath, *B*, in which the apparatus is placed is held constant, the pressure exerted by the vapor remains unchanged. But if the temperature is raised, a higher vapor pressure registers on the manometer. And if the temperature is lowered, the vapor pressure falls.

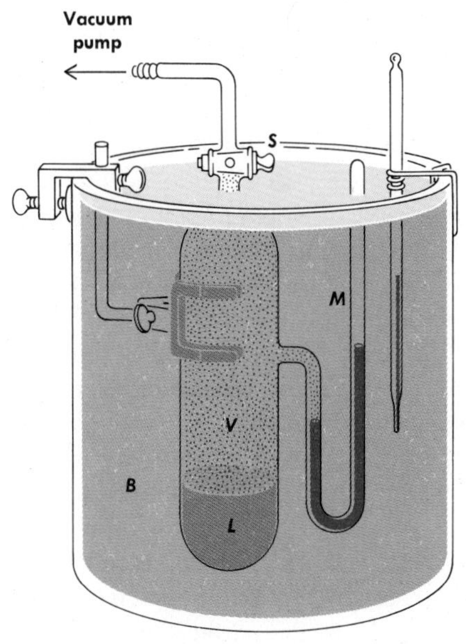

FIGURE 10-6 Apparatus for measuring vapor pressure.

TEMPERATURE AND VAPOR PRESSURE. Two factors explain why an increase in temperature causes an increase in vapor pressure. First, as the temperature of a liquid is increased, more molecules acquire enough kinetic energy to escape into the gaseous state. And even though at equilibrium the increased rate of escape is balanced by an increased rate of return, the higher the temperature the greater the number of molecules present in the vapor. Second, the molecules of the vapor possess a higher kinetic energy at higher temperatures, and hence exert a greater pressure. Therefore, the vapor pressure of a liquid is greater at a higher temperature than at a lower temperature owing to both the greater number of gaseous molecules present in the fixed available volume and their greater average kinetic energy. Figure 10-7 illus-

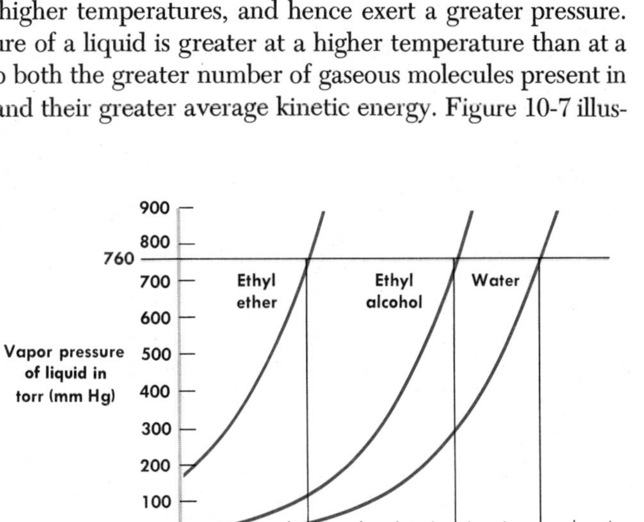

FIGURE 10-7 Vapor pressure of three liquids.

trates a simple way of showing how the vapor pressure of liquids varies with temperature; vapor pressure is indicated in torr (mm Hg) and temperature in °C. Notice that the vapor pressure rises faster at higher than at lower temperatures.

EFFECT OF OTHER GASES ON THE VAPOR PRESSURE OF A LIQUID. So far, we have been considering vapor pressure as measured in a laboratory apparatus free of foreign gases. What effect would other gases, such as air, have on the vapor pressure of a liquid? Measurements show that the presence of other gases has a very small effect on the vapor pressure. For our purposes, we can say that the total pressure of the gas mixture in contact with a liquid is simply the pressure of the foreign gas *plus* the vapor pressure of the liquid.

THE BOILING POINT

Boiling and evaporation are similar processes, but they differ in important respects. Evaporation occurs spontaneously and continuously when any liquid is exposed to the atmosphere. The process consists essentially of the diffusion of vapor molecules from the liquid into the atmosphere. *Boiling differs from evaporation in that the vapor from a boiling liquid escapes with sufficient pressure to push back and displace any other gas present, rather than diffusing through it.* In order for a liquid to boil, its vapor pressure must be equal to the *total* pressure of the gas above the liquid, and heat must be supplied rapidly enough to cause vapor molecules to form and to displace the gas above.

When a liquid, exposed to the atmosphere, is heated gradually, its temperature rises and its vapor pressure increases gradually (Fig. 10-6). Although the number of molecules escaping from the liquid increases as the temperature rises, evaporation still occurs largely through diffusion. Finally, at a certain temperature (the boiling point), the vapor pressure becomes equal to the total external pressure above the liquid, and the molecules escape from the liquid so quickly and massively that they displace completely the molecules of air which were originally above the liquid.

Another point of difference between evaporation and boiling is that evaporation occurs only at the surface of a liquid, whereas boiling involves the formation of bubbles of vapor below the surface of the liquid. The rate at which boiling takes place depends on how rapidly the necessary heat of vaporization is supplied to the liquid.

VARIATION OF BOILING POINT WITH PRESSURE. *The boiling point of a liquid is the temperature at which the vapor pressure of the liquid equals the total external (opposing) pressure.* Consequently, the boiling point varies with the external (opposing) pressure. The values cited for the boiling points of liquids are usually those that prevail at the normal atmospheric pressure of 760 torr. At a lower pressure, the boiling point will be lower, and vice versa.

Under certain conditions a liquid may be heated to a temperature slightly above its boiling point without actually "coming to a boil." A liquid in such a state is said to be *superheated.* Very often, in the laboratory, liquids become superheated and then suddenly begin to boil violently.

THE LIQUEFACTION OF GASES. We have seen that in order to convert a liquid to its gas, we must raise its temperature or decrease the pressure above it, or do both. Conversely, to convert a gas to its liquid, we can either lower its temperature, or if the temperature is below the critical temperature, increase the pressure acting upon it, or do both. It is possible to liquefy any vapor or gas by lowering the temperature alone. It is not possible, however, to liquefy a vapor or gas solely by increasing the pressure if the temperature is above the critical temperature, because the average kinetic energy of the gas molecules must be reduced below a critical value before the intermolecular attractions can give rise to cohesion and the liquid state. The greater the energy of attraction among the molecules, the higher will be the maximum temperature at which liquefaction is still possible.

DISTILLATION. The process of distillation consists of converting a liquid to its vapor by heating, then condensing the vapor to its liquid by cooling. This process is often used for purifying liquids. Simple distillation is very effective in separating a liquid from impurities that do not vaporize at the boiling point of the liquid, and hence remain behind in the flask. If the impurities are volatile and vaporize appreciably at the boiling point of the liquid, a more elaborate procedure (fractional distillation) is necessary to effect complete separation.

CRITICAL TEMPERATURE, CRITICAL PRESSURE, AND CRITICAL VOLUME. Let us now consider the behavior of a liquid as it is heated in a closed container to successively higher temperatures. The experimental set-up consists of a sealed, evacuated tube, strong enough to withstand the pressure to be developed and containing a suitable quantity of liquid (Fig. 10-8). The tube contains no gas other than the vapor of the liquid. As the temperature increases, the density of the liquid decreases. At the same time, more and more liquid is converted to vapor and the pressure of the vapor and its density increase. Finally, a temperature is reached at which the density of the vapor and the density of the liquid are equal—that is, the two phases become identical, and the visible line of separation between them disappears. This point is the *critical temperature* of the substance. The volume occupied by 1 mole of a substance at the critical temperature is called the molar *critical volume,* and the pressure exerted by a substance at the critical temperature is called the *critical pressure.* At any temperature above the critical temperature, the clear-cut distinction between gaseous and liquid states no longer holds. At ordinary pressures and above their critical temperature, substances exist in a gas-like state.

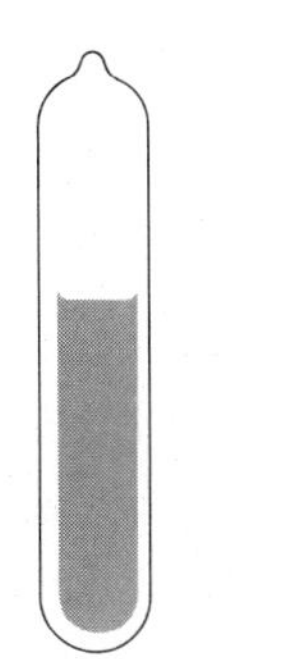

FIGURE 10-8 An apparatus for the observation of critical temperature.

10-3 The Solid State

Unlike liquids and gases, the most readily observable characteristics of matter in the solid state are its relative hardness, its rigidity, and the fact that it possesses characteristic shape. Actually, any individual particle of a solid possesses a characteristic shape. In fact, a collection of very small particles of a solid such as sand or sugar, for example, may take on the shape of the container in which it is placed, just as a liquid does. Some solids can be so finely divided that it is possible to move them through pipe lines, just as though they were liquids. Each individual, small, solid particle, however, retains its own characteristic shape.

The basic reason for the hardness and characteristic shape of solids lies in the manner in which the forces of attraction between the particles (molecules, atoms, or ions) are exercised. In a liquid the strong forces acting between particles hold them close together but leave them free to move in any direction with respect to one another. In a solid, however, the forces of attraction hold the particles in definite spatial relationships to one another. The freedom of translational motion characteristic of the particles of a liquid is almost entirely absent in a solid, although in the latter the particles can still undergo limited oscillations (and also rotations) about their equilibrium positions.

The fact that the particles of a solid do not completely lose their kinetic energy is evidenced by the high vapor pressure of some solids, such as iodine and camphor. The oscillatory motions of the individual particles of these solids develop sufficient kinetic energy to enable some of the particles to overcome the intermolecular forces that tend to hold them together in the solid.

CRYSTALLINE SOLIDS AND AMORPHOUS SOLIDS

Solids can be divided into two groups, crystalline and amorphous. Familiar examples of crystalline solids are sodium chloride, sugar, and sand; the most common and by far the more important amorphous solids are glass and many of the synthetic polymeric materials (resins and fibers).

Crystalline and amorphous solids differ in structure. A crystalline solid consists of an array of particles arranged with regular periodicity in a well-defined, continuous, three-dimensional network called the *crystal lattice*. Visualize a crystal lattice as resulting from the continuous repetition, in three directions, of a structural building unit, *the unit cell*. The unit cell is the smallest portion of a crystal necessary to represent the fashioning of the crystal structure. The unit cell repeats itself regularly and indefinitely in the crystal, so that *the crystal structure exhibits periodic regularity*. Different crystalline solids may have different crystal structures, but all exhibit this property of periodic regularity in the arrangement of their particles.

In an amorphous solid (amorphous, from a Greek word meaning *"without shape"*), the particles are distributed at random, much as the particles are in a liquid. In amorphous solids, as in liquids, there may be some small regions with a relatively ordered arrangement, but there is no continuous periodically repeated array of particles.

The outward shape and appearance of a solid may occasionally indicate whether it is crystalline or amorphous. For example, under appropriate conditions, in nature or artifically, crystalline solids may be produced as easily recognizable large single crystals. On the other hand, a perfectly formed crystal may be modified by abrasive action into a smooth pebble-like specimen. Diamond, for example, a most typical crystalline substance, often occurs in nature as rough pebbles. And an amorphous solid such as glass can be cut and polished into the shape of a perfect crystal. Thus we can confidently differentiate between a crystalline and an amorphous solid only by physical experiments. One such simple experiment is the determination of the melting point (see p. 186); a more accurate but more complicated one involves investigating the X-ray diffraction of the specimen.

TYPES OF CRYSTALLINE SOLIDS

Depending on the nature of the particles (molecules, atoms, ions) present, and the type of forces which hold them together in the lattice, crystalline solids may be divided into four main groups: *ionic* crystals, *covalent* crystals, *molecular* crystals, and *metallic* crystals.

10-4 Ionic Crystals

We know that ionic compounds are made up of an assemblage of positive ions and negative ions held together by forces which are primarily electrostatic in character. In the solid state, the oppositely charged ions are held together in some definite arrangement that results in a specific crystal structure. Ionic forces are fundamentally non-directed—i.e., in an ionic compound the ions behave similar to electrically charged spheres, and the ionic forces between spherical ions, like the electrostatic forces between charged spheres, extend equally in all directions. Because ionic forces attract ions of opposite charge and repel ions of the same charge, each positive ion will tend to surround itself with the maximum possible number of negative ions, and each negative ion will tend to surround itself with the maximum possible number of positive ions. You must keep in mind that ions of the same sign repel one another and hence normally tend to stay as far apart from one another as possible. Thus the number of negative ions which can be grouped around a given positive ion is limited to some extent by the repulsive interactions among the negative ions themselves. The same situation, of course, holds for the number of positive ions which can be grouped around a given negative ion. We see, then, that for a specific ionic compound only a certain number of negative ions can be arranged around a given positive ion, and vice versa. The resulting arrangement is a regular three-dimensional network of alternately positive and negative ions which is called an *ionic crystal lattice.*

CLOSEST PACKING OF SPHERES. The compounds which are most ionic in character, such as Na^+Cl^-, K^+Cl^-, Cs^+Cl^-, and K^+Br^-, are those in which both the positive and the negative ions possess a noble gas-like electron configuration. These symmetrical ions, if not distorted by other forces, act as charged spheres that exert their electrostatic forces uniformly in all directions. Consequently, each symmetrical ion, as we have already mentioned, will tend to surround itself as closely as possible with the greatest possible number of ions of the opposite charge. It is not surprising, therefore, that the crystal structures of ionic compounds are frequently identical to a closely packed three-dimensional arrangement of positively and negatively charged spheres.

As an illustration, we shall consider two typical examples of ionic compounds in which each negative ion present is matched by a positive ion. For simplicity we shall take compounds made up of monopositive ions (monovalent cations), M^+, and mononegative ions (monovalent anions) X^-. Ionic compounds of this type, formulated as M^+X^-, are called mono-monovalent salts. In considering the crystal structure of a mono-monovalent salt such as M^+X^-, keep in mind the following three points: (1) The ionic compound is electrically neutral, so the number of positive ions must be equal to the number of negative ions. (2) The crystal consists of oppositely charged spherical ions which generally differ in size. (3) Because the positive and negative ions are held together by electrostatic forces, each ion will be surrounded closely by ions of opposite charge.

CRYSTAL STRUCTURE OF K^+Cl^-

The ionic compound potassium chloride, K^+Cl^-, is an example of a mono-monovalent salt. A crystal of K^+Cl^- contains K^+ ions with an ionic radius of 1.33 A, and Cl^- ions with an ionic radius of 1.81 A. Now, as we have said, each positive ion and negative ion in the crystal lattice will attract as many oppositely charged ions as can pack themselves around or actually contact it. If we prepared spheres that were the same sizes as the K^+ ions and the Cl^- ions, we would find that the smaller K^+ ion (1.33 A) could physically accommodate six of the larger Cl^- ions, and the larger Cl^- ion (1.81 A) could accommodate eight of the smaller K^+ ions. However, the ionic crystal of formula K^+Cl^- will be electrically neutral only if the number of Cl^- ions grouped around the K^+ ion is the same as the number of K^+ ions grouped around the Cl^- ion. Consequently, the size of the smaller ion, in this case the cation, K^+, determines the maximum number of oppositely charged neighbors that can be arranged around each central ion. Around each K^+ ion, then, are six Cl^- ions, and the K^+ ion is said to have a *crystal* coordination number of 6. Each Cl^- ion also has a crystal coordination number of 6, because it too is surrounded by six K^+ ions. *The crystal coordination number of an ion in a crystal lattice is defined as the number of its nearest oppositely charged neighboring ions.*

THE GEOMETRICAL ARRANGEMENT OF OPPOSITELY CHARGED IONS IN A CRYSTAL LATTICE

Now that we know that in a crystal of potassium chloride, K^+Cl^-, the crystal coordination number of each K^+ ion and of each Cl^- ion is 6, what can we conclude concerning the arrangement in space of the six Cl^- ions around each K^+ ion, and of the six K^+ ions around each Cl^- ion? If the positive and negative ions act as charged spheres and obey the simple law of electrostatics, then we would expect that the six Cl^- ions surrounding each K^+ ion will arrange themselves to be as close as possible to the (central) positive K^+ ion, and as far away from one another as possible. Such a situation is realized when the K^+ ion is surrounded symmetrically by six Cl^- ions arranged at the corners of an octahedron.* (Four Cl^- ions are arranged at the corners of a square and the fifth and sixth Cl^- ions are directly above and below the central K^+ ion, Fig. 10-9(a).) Similarly, six positive K^+ ions are arranged octahedrally about each negative Cl^- ion (Fig. 10-9(c)). The arrangement of the K^+ ions and the Cl^- ions in the three-dimensional crystal lattice of K^+Cl^- is generally portrayed as in Fig. 10-9(b). Notice that if we look at the ionic lattice of K^+Cl^- from another angle, as shown in Fig. 10-9(d), we see that the K^+ ions and also the Cl^- ions are arranged in planes. Thus, this ionic lattice could also be described as being made up of alternating planes of K^+ ions and Cl^- ions.

The K^+Cl^- crystal is similar to the ionic sodium chloride crystal, Na^+Cl^-, except that a K^+ ion replaces a Na^+ ion in the crystal lattice. Hence, such a crystal structure is often called the *sodium chloride,* or *rock salt structure.* The sodium chloride structure has a *face-centered cubic* lattice, because the unit cell is a cube having a certain ion—either the positive K^+ ion or the negative Cl^- ion—at each of the corners as well as at the center of each face (Fig. 10-9(b)). The diagrams in Fig. 10-9 show that we can consider an ionic crystal from various standpoints—the crystal coordination number of each ion, the geometrical arrangement of the ions around one another, the repeated alternating planes of cations and anions, and the unit cell of the crystal lattice. Each of these approaches emphasizes one aspect of the ionic crystalline structure, and together they afford a better understanding of the structure being considered.

UNIT CELL OF K^+Cl^-. X-ray diffraction measurements show that the internuclear distance between a K^+ ion and an adjacent Cl^- ion is 3.1464 A, meaning that the length (width and height) of the cubic unit cell of potassium chloride is 6.2928 A (6.2928×10^{-8} cm) (Fig. 10-10). The Cl^- ion in the center of the unit cell (not shown) in Fig. 10-10, "belongs" only to this unit cell, whereas each Cl^- ion situated on an edge is shared by four adjacent cells, and therefore only $\frac{1}{4}$ of each such Cl^- ion can be counted as belonging to the unit cell considered. Similarly, each K^+ ion in the center of the face of the unit cell is shared with an adjacent cell, and each K^+ ion at the corner of the unit cell is shared by eight adjacent cells. Thus the unit cell of potassium chloride contains: $(1) + (12 \times \frac{1}{4}) = 4\ Cl^-$, and $(6 \times \frac{1}{2}) +$

* An octahedron is a solid having eight equal regular triangular faces (as outlined in Fig. 10-9(a)) and derives its name from the Greek words *octa* = eight, and *hedron* = base.

FIGURE 10-9 The crystal structure of potassium chloride, K^+Cl^-. (a) Octahedral arrangement of six negative Cl^- ions around a central positive K^+ ion. (b) Portion of the crystal lattice, showing the unit cell (shaded). (c) Octahedral arrangement of six positive K^+ ions around a central negative Cl^- ion. (d) View of KCl lattice, showing the alternating planes of the K^+ ions and Cl^- ions.

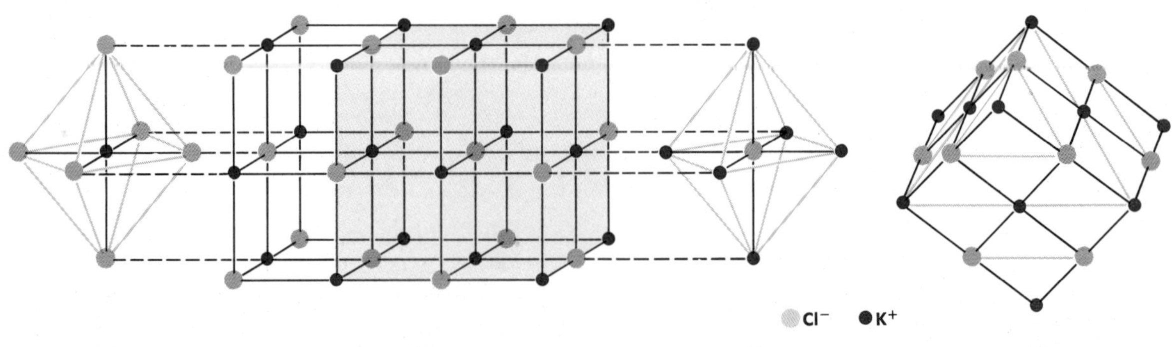

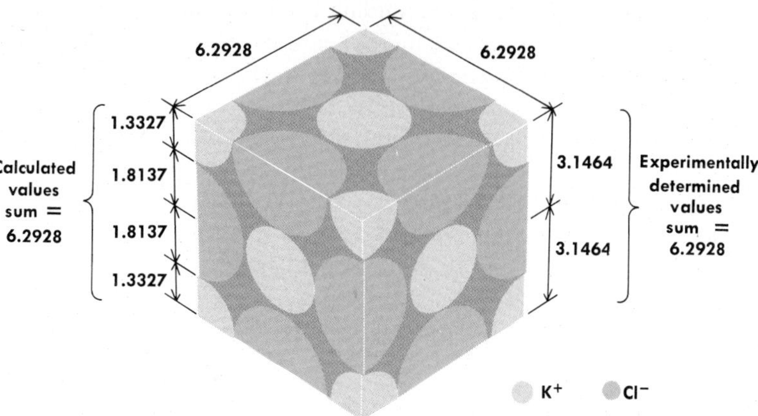

FIGURE 10-10 Unit cell of potassium chloride. All values given are in Angstrom units (A).

$(8 \times \frac{1}{8}) = 4\ K^+$, or $4\ K^+Cl^-$. Since the formula weight of potassium chloride is 74.55 g/mole and the density of potassium chloride is 1.988 g/cm³, the volume occupied by 1 mole of K^+Cl^- is:

$$\frac{74.55\ \text{g}}{\text{mole}} \times \frac{1\ \text{cm}^3}{1.988\ \text{g}} = \frac{38.003\ \text{cm}^3}{\text{mole}}$$

Also, since the volume of the unit cell is $(6.2928 \times 10^{-8})^3$ cm³ and has four K^+Cl^-, the volume occupied by one K^+Cl^- is $\left(\frac{6.2928 \times 10^{-8}}{4}\right)$ cm³. Consequently, N, the number of ion pairs of K^+Cl^- is:

$$\frac{38.003\ \text{cm}^3}{\text{mole}} \times \frac{4}{(6.2928 \times 10^{-8})^3\ \text{cm}^3} = \frac{6.023 \times 10^{23}}{\text{mole}}$$

This number you will recognize as Avogadro's number, and the X-ray diffraction method we have just described supplies a very accurate determination of this value—within ±0.01%. Actually, the internuclear (K^+ to Cl^-) distance can be measured very accurately by X-ray diffraction, but the density of solid potassium chloride is experimentally difficult to obtain as accurately and this is the limiting factor in determining Avogadro's number most precisely by this method.

Many ionic compounds containing one anion per each cation (general formula, $A^{+n}B^{-n}$) have the sodium chloride structure. An example is magnesium oxide, $Mg^{++}O^{=}$, composed of dipositive magnesium ions, Mg^{++}, and dinegative oxide ions, $O^{=}$. Another example is ammonium chloride, $(NH_4)^+Cl^-$, in which the polyatomic $(NH_4)^+$ ions take the positions occupied by the Na^+ ions in the crystal of sodium chloride. Similarly, in potassium perchlorate, $K^+(ClO_4)^-$, the polyatomic perchlorate ions $(ClO_4)^-$ occupy the same positions as the Cl^- ions. Finally, ammonium perchlorate, $(NH_4)^+\ (ClO_4)^-$, is an example of an ionic compound with a rock salt structure in which both the cations and the anions are polyatomic.

CRYSTAL STRUCTURE OF Cs^+Cl^-

Let us consider the ionic crystal of cesium chloride, Cs^+Cl^-, again composed of monopositive and mononegative ions. The radius of the Cs^+ ion (1.69 A) is greater than the radius of the K^+ ions (1.33 A), so now eight Cl^- ions (1.81 A) can be accomodated around the larger Cs^+ ion. In turn, each Cl^- ion, being larger than the Cs^+ ion, also can accomodate eight Cs^+ ions. Again, the geometrical arrangement of eight similarly charged ions around an oppositely charged central ion will be determined by the simple laws of electrostatics. The eight similarly charged ions will tend to arrange themselves around the oppositely charged central ion so that they are as far away from one another, and as close to the central ion, as possible. Thus, in the crystal of ionic cesium chloride, Cs^+Cl^-, each Cs^+ ion is symmetrically surrounded by eight Cl^- ions, each occupying the corner of a (imaginary) cube (Fig. 10-11(a)), and each Cl^- ion is symmetrically surrounded by eight cations, each also occupying a corner of a (imaginary) cube with the Cl^- ion at its center (Fig. 10-11(b)). The resulting structure is called a *body-centered cubic* lattice, and the crystal coordination number of each Cs^+ ion and each Cl^- ion is 8.

The body-centered cubic lattice, also called the *cesium chloride structure* (8:8 crystal coordination), is fairly common among ionic compounds. Of the alkali metal halides, cesium bromide, Cs^+Br^-, and cesium iodide, Cs^+I^-, exhibit the cesium chloride structure; all other alkali metal halides have the sodium chloride structure (6:6 crystal coordination).

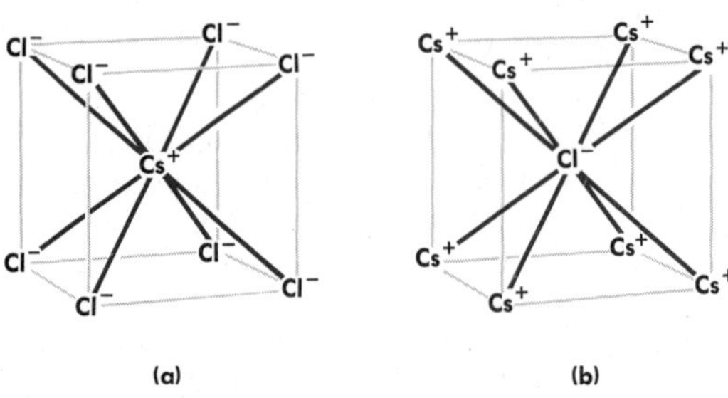

FIGURE 10-11 Body-centered cubic arrangement of eight similar ions around a central ion of opposite charge.

In general, ionic compounds of the general formula $A^{+n}B^{-n}$ have either a face-centered cubic lattice (Fig. 10-9) and a 6:6 crystal coordination, or a body-centered cubic lattice (Fig. 10-10) and an 8:8 crystal coordination, the particular type of lattice depending on the relative sizes of the ions involved. In fact, if the size of the smaller ion (A^{+n} or B^{-n}) is such that eight of the oppositely charged ions can arrange themselves around it, the compound will generally have an 8:8 crystal coordination, similar to cesium chloride. If the size of the smaller ion is such that only six oppositely charged ions can be accommodated around it, the compound will have a 6:6 crystal coordination.

By a simple geometrical calculation, we can show that if the (radius of cation)/(radius of anion) ratio ranges from 1 to 0.73, eight of the larger ions (anions) can be accomodated at the corners of a cube around the central smaller ion (cation), resulting in an 8:8 coordination. On the other hand, if the (radius of cation)/(radius of anion) ratio is smaller than 0.73, the 6:6 coordination results. This generalization, called the *Radius Ratio rule,* enables us to predict the crystal coordination number of the cation (A^{+n}) and the anion (B^{-n}) in a crystalline compound, $A^{+n}B^{-n}$, if we know the radii of the ions. Calculated Crystal Coordination Numbers (C.C.N.) may differ from those found experimentally, especially if the crystal consists of extremely large negative ions and extremely small positive ions. In such a case, the interionic repulsions of the large negative ions will slightly modify the crystal structure even if the ions of the crystal behave as rigid spheres. Furthermore, the larger the anion the more it can be deformed by the small cation, (see p. 146) and the deformation of the anions will influence the modification of the expected crystal structure.

OTHER CRYSTAL STRUCTURES

For ionic compounds whose cations and anions carry different ionic charges, and hence do not contain equal numbers of oppositely charged ions, the C.C.N. of each ion is determined by the relative numbers as well as by the relative sizes of the cations and anions. Therefore, many different kinds of crystal structures are possible and indeed exist. As an illustration, let us consider the structure of some ionic compounds containing (a) one cation and two anions, and (b) two cations and one anion.

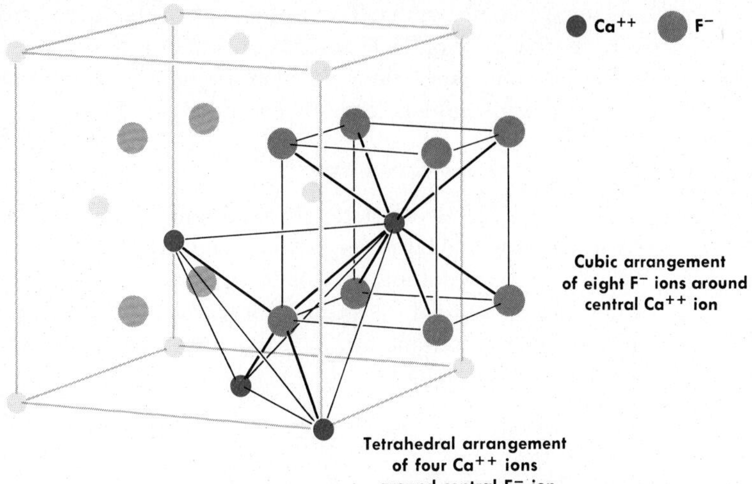

FIGURE 10-12 The fluorite structure (CaF_2) showing the cubic coordination of the Ca^{++} ion and the tetrahedral coordination of the F^- ion.

FLUORITE STRUCTURE. An example of (a) is the compound calcium fluoride, CaF_2 (a di-monovalent salt), which occurs as the mineral fluorite. The crystal structure of CaF_2 consists of a three-dimensional network of Ca^{++} ions and F^- ions, in which each Ca^{++} ion is surrounded by eight F^- ions, and each F^- ion is surrounded by four Ca^{++} ions (Fig. 10-12). The Ca^{++} ion is at the center of a (imaginary) tetrahedron,* with each of the four surrounding Ca^{++} ions at a corner of the tetrahedron. Since there are eight F^- ions cubically arranged around each (central) Ca^{++} ion and four Ca^{++} ions tetrahedrally arranged around each (central) F^- ion, calcium fluoride, CaF_2, has an 8:4 crystal coordination number. This kind of crystal lattice is called the *fluorite structure.* Very closely related is another common crystal arrangement composed of two cations for each anion, and called the *anti-fluorite* structure. In the anti-fluorite structure the geometrical arrangement of the ions is the same as in the fluorite structure, but the positions of the positive and negative ions are interchanged. An example is sodium sulfide, Na_2S. In a crystal of Na_2S, each negative ion, $S^=$, is at the center of a (imaginary) cube surrounded by eight Na^+ ions located at the corners. In turn, each positive Na^+ ion is at the center of a (imaginary) tetrahedron, surrounded by four $S^=$ ions located at the corners. Notice that in both the fluorite (CaF_2) and the antifluorite (Na_2S) structures it is the divalent (positive or negative) ion which is at the center of the cube, while each monovalent ion is at the center of a tetrahedron. The crystal coordination number of fluorite (CaF_2) is 8:4, whereas in the anti-fluorite structure (Na_2S) it is 4:8.

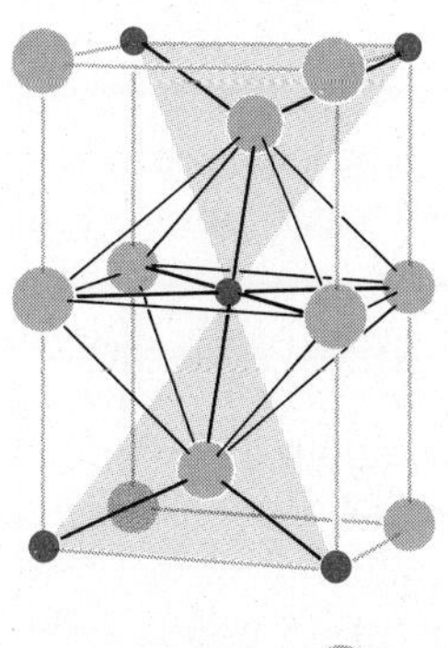

FIGURE 10-13 Rutile structure (TiO_2) showing the octahedral coordination of the Ti^{+4} and the planar trigonal coordination of the $O^=$.

RUTILE STRUCTURE. Another kind of ionic lattice common for compounds that have the general formula AB_2 is that of crystalline titanium dioxide, TiO_2, which occurs naturally as the mineral rutile. Its structure, called the *rutile structure,* is very different from that of fluorite. The crystal structure of TiO_2 (Fig. 10-13) is a three-dimensional network in which each Ti^{+4} ion is surrounded by six $O^=$ ions, and each $O^=$ ion is surrounded by three Ti^{+4} ions. The Ti^{+4} ion is located at the center of an octahedron and is surrounded by six $O^=$ ions located at the corners. Each $O^=$ ion is located at the center of an

* By tetrahedron here we mean a regular tetrahedron, which is a body with four faces, each face being an equilateral triangle.

equilateral triangle, with a Ti^{+4} ion at each of the three corners of the triangle. Thus, since the structure of TiO_2 consists of six $O^{=}$ ions octahedrally arranged about each central Ti^{+4} ion, and of three Ti^{+4} ions trigonally arranged about each central $O^{=}$ ion, titanium dioxide has a 6:3 crystal coordination number.

CRYSTAL LATTICE ENERGY

The electrostatic attraction that holds together the oppositely charged ions in an ionic crystal is very strong, and the energy required to completely break down an ionic crystal into its isolated gaseous positive and negative ions may be regarded as a measure of the strength of such an attraction. For a solid ionic compound with the general formula $M^{+n}X^{-n}$, this dissociation process may be expressed by the equation:

$$M^{+n}X_{(s)}^{-n} + \text{heat} \longrightarrow M_{(g)}^{+n} + X_{(g)}^{-n} \qquad (\Delta H = \text{high positive values})$$

Heat has to be supplied to the ionic solid from an external source in order to break it down into its gaseous ions; hence, the enthalpy change, ΔH, of the above reaction has a positive sign. The quantity of heat energy evolved in the reverse process, the formation of 1 mole of an ionic solid from its gaseous ions, is called the *crystal lattice energy* of the ionic compound and is commonly expressed in kcal/mole of compound. The lattice energy of an ionic compound can be determined experimentally or it may be calculated, as we shall see in later chapters. The value of the lattice energy depends on the ionic charges and the sizes of the ions, the number of neighbors of opposite charge surrounding each ion, and the type of crystal structure. For similar crystal structures the smaller the ions the higher the crystal lattice energy.

To take two examples, the crystal lattice energy of the face-centered cubic compounds LiF and KF are 238 kcal/mole and 190 kcal/mole, respectively, the ionic radius of the lithium ion, Li^{+} (0.68 A), being smaller than that of the K^{+} ion (1.33 A). Also for similar structures, the higher the ionic charge (of either or both ions), the higher the crystal lattice energy. Thus the face-centered magnesium oxide, in which both the cation and the anion are divalent, $Mg^{++}O^{=}$, has a high crystal lattice energy, 918 kcal/mole MgO, although the radius of the Mg^{++} ion (0.65 A) is about equal to that of the Li^{+} ion (0.68 A), and the radius of the $O^{=}$ ion (1.32 A) is about equal to that of the F^{-} ion (1.33 A). In general, then, the compounds with the highest lattice energies are those composed of small divalent and trivalent cations—for example, Mg^{++} and Al^{+++}— and of relatively small divalent anions, such as the oxide ion, $O^{=}$.

SOME PROPERTIES OF IONIC SOLIDS. We know that in ionic crystals the ionic bonding is very strong. Any change, therefore, which would disrupt the ordered crystalline aggregate and reduce it to the more disordered liquid state or the even more disordered gaseous state would require an extremely large quantity of external energy, and could occur only at extremely high temperatures. Thus, ionic solids have negligible vapor pressures at room temperature and in general have high melting points.

Ionic compounds in the solid state, although composed of electrically charged particles, are very poor conductors of electricity, because each ion virtually occupies a fixed position in the crystal lattice. However, once an ionic compound has melted, its liquid is a very good conductor of an electric current because now the ions are free to move relative to one another under the influence of an applied electrical field.

Ionic solids are generally soluble (to a greater or lesser extent) in water, and in some other highly polar solvents such as alcohol, C_2H_5OH, but are insoluble in nonpolar solvents such as the hydrocarbon benzene, C_6H_6, and carbon tetrachloride, CCl_4. The solubility of ionic compounds in polar solvents can be explained in part on the basis of their ionic structures and will be discussed in Chapter 18.

10-5 Continuous Covalent Crystal Lattices

In a crystalline covalent solid, the atoms are held together by covalent bonds to form a continuous, three-dimensional lattice. We have already mentioned in Chapter 5 that covalent bonds (shared electron pairs) are formed by the valence electrons of atoms, and that each atom usually forms with its partner atoms as many covalent bonds as the number of its valence electrons. Later, we shall see that the covalent bonds formed by an atom have well-defined orientations in space relative to one another or, as we may say, have a "directional character." These two factors: (1) the tendency of certain atoms to use all their valence electrons for covalent bonding, and (2) the directional character of covalent bonds, permit us to explain the typical features of covalent crystals.

To illustrate these two factors, let us first consider a compound with which we are already familiar—the gaseous hydrocarbon, methane, CH_4. We can visualize the CH_4 molecule as being formed from the combination of a carbon atom, with four valence electrons, $\cdot\overset{\cdot}{\underset{\cdot}{\mathrm{C}}}\cdot$, and four hydrogen atoms, each with one valence electron, $\cdot\mathrm{H}$. Therefore, in the CH_4 molecule the carbon atom shares an electron pair (covalent bond) with each of its four partner hydrogen atoms, which are arranged at the corners (vertices) of a regular tetrahedron with the carbon atom at the center. Thus we say that the four carbon-to-hydrogen covalent bonds of methane are directed from the center toward the corners of a regular tetrahedron, or simply that the carbon atom forms four tetrahedral covalent bonds. This tetrahedral arrangement of the covalent bonds formed by carbon is typical of substances containing carbon—some gaseous, such as CH_4; some liquid, such as CCl_4; and some solid, such as diamond, which we will now consider.

$$\begin{matrix} & \mathrm{H} & \\ & \cdot\cdot & \\ \mathrm{H}: & \mathrm{C} & :\mathrm{H} \\ & \cdot\cdot & \\ & \mathrm{H} & \end{matrix}$$

In diamond, each carbon atom is surrounded tetrahedrally by four other equivalent and equidistant carbon atoms. In turn, each of the four carbon atoms located at the corners of this tetrahedron acts as the center of another tetrahedron, in which it is surrounded by four equivalent carbon atoms, and so on throughout the crystal. This arrangement produces the characteristic three-dimensional structure of diamond, a small part of which is shown in Fig. 10-14(a). Thus, every individual crystal of diamond can be regarded as a giant molecule in which each carbon atom (except the relatively few on the surface of the crystal) is joined tetrahedrally by single covalent bonds to four other equivalent and equidistant carbon atoms.

Just as we explained the structure of the single gaseous molecule of methane on the basis of the tendency of the carbon atom to form four tetrahedrally directed covalent bonds, so we can explain the observed arrangement of an assemblage of carbon atoms in a crystal of diamond. A carbon atom with its four valence electrons, $\cdot\overset{\cdot}{\underset{\cdot}{\mathrm{C}}}\cdot$, can share an electron pair with each of four other carbon atoms located at the vertices of a regular tetrahedron. In the resulting group of five carbon atoms (Fig. 10-14(b)), only the

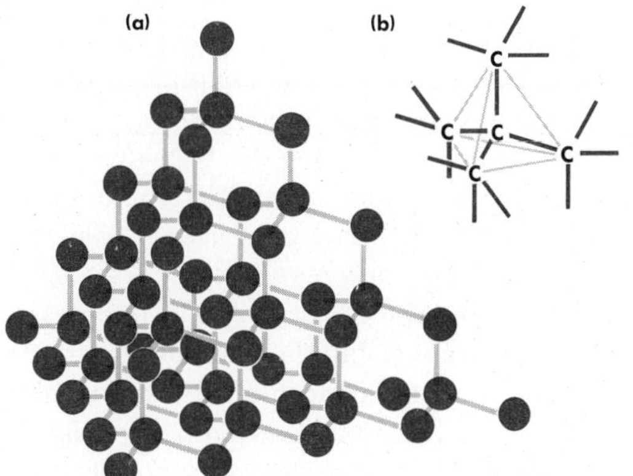

FIGURE 10-14 The arrangement of carbon atoms in a small part of diamond crystal.

central carbon atom has used all its (four) valence electrons in covalent bonding, whereas each of the four C atoms located at the vertices of the tetrahedron still has three valence electrons remaining. Consequently, each of these carbon atoms can form three other covalent bonds with three other C atoms, thus becoming itself the "central" atom of another tetrahedral group. This process can be continued indefinitely throughout the crystal, and results in the characteristic three-dimensional arrangement of carbon atoms (Fig. 10-14(a)).

A three-dimensional continuous covalent lattice such as we have just described for diamond can be formed not only when the atoms are all identical (that is, for an element), but also for binary compounds in which the two partner elements do not differ significantly in electronegativity and have the required number of valence electrons. For example, silicon carbide, or carborundum, SiC, has the same type of covalent lattice as diamond, except that each carbon atom is tetrahedrally surrounded by and covalently bonded to four equivalent and equidistant silicon atoms, and each silicon atom is tetrahedrally surrounded by and covalently bonded to four equivalent and equidistant carbon atoms.

In general, a great deal of energy is necessary to break even partially the covalent bonds which hold together the atoms of a continuous, covalent, three-dimensional, crystal lattice such as diamond and carborundum. Consequently, these crystalline solids are extremely hard and are among the substances with the highest melting points. (Diamond is the hardest of all known natural substances and synthetic carborundum is even harder.) Also, diamond and carborundum do not conduct an electric current, because all valence electrons of the constituent atoms are used to form strong covalent bonds. Actually, both diamond and carborundum are very good insulators. Covalent crystals are also generally insoluble in all solvents (both polar and non-polar), because the relatively weak attraction of the solvent molecules for the atoms of the solid cannot successfully compete with the strong covalent bonding existing between the atoms in the crystal.

The quantity of heat energy required to break apart 1 mole of a crystalline substance to yield the isolated gaseous atoms is called the *heat of atomization* of the substance, and is taken as a measure of the strength of the bonding which holds together the atoms in the solid. For substances which exist as continuous covalent lattices, the heat of atomization is usually very high. The heat of atomization of diamond, for example, is 171.4 kcal/mole of C atoms, as represented by the equation:

$$C_{(diam)} \longrightarrow C_{(g)} \qquad \Delta H = +171.4 \text{ kcal/mole C atoms}$$

10-6 Crystals Composed of Discrete Covalent Molecules

This group includes those solids in which the individual molecules exist as discrete units held together in a regular three-dimensional array by van der Waals forces. As we discussed in Chapter 9, van der Waals attractions result from electron correlation and dipole-dipole interactions, and are strongest for those highly polar molecules which can give rise to hydrogen bonding. For example, the van der Waals *inter*molecular forces among the non-polar monoatomic (spherical) molecules of the noble gas argon, Ar (formula wt, 39.95) are much weaker than those present in water, H_2O (formula wt, 18), because the H_2O molecules can hydrogen bond. In fact, solid argon melts at $-189°C$, whereas ice melts at $0°C$. Another factor which influences appreciably the van der Waals attractions in molecular crystals is the distance between the molecules. You will recall that the potential energy of the van der Waals attractions decreases proportionally to the sixth power of the intermolecular distance (p. 143). Hence, other factors being equal, the intermolecular forces of attraction are greater for a substance whose molecules have a shape suitable to compact packing, than for a similar substance whose molecules are irregularly shaped.

We know that the van der Waals attractions are very much weaker than either the electrostatic (coulombic) attraction among oppositely charged ions in an ionic crystal, or the covalent bonding present in covalent crystals. Accordingly, molecular solids are usually rather soft, have relatively low melting points, low heats of atomization, and a relatively high vapor pressure. Familiar examples are iodine, whose violet vapor is plainly visible in any flask containing iodine crystals at ordinary temperatures, and such organic compounds as napthalene and camphor, which in the form of pellets constitute the so-called moth-balls. Figure 10-15 shows the arrangement of the diatomic iodine molecules, I_2, in crystalline iodine.

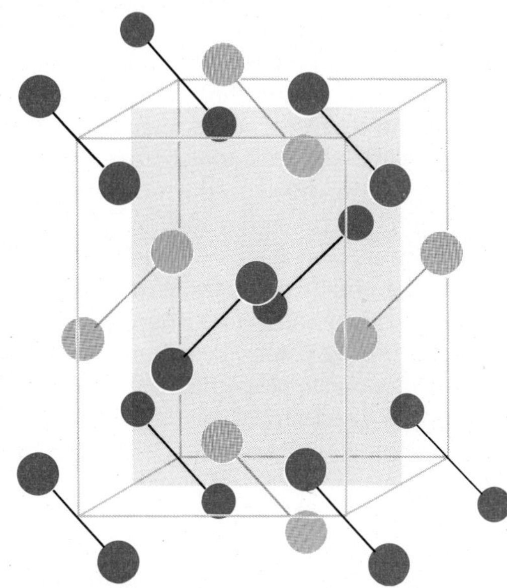

FIGURE 10-15 Molecular crystal lattice of iodine, I_2.

Most molecular solids are highly soluble in an appropriate solvent. Here the criterion which decides solubility is "like dissolves like," in the sense that a solid substance whose molecules contain polar groups will dissolve more readily in a liquid containing similar polar groups and may be virtually insoluble in a non-polar substance, and vice versa. This is so because the attraction of the solvent molecules for the molecules of the solid can best compete with the attractions between the molecules of the solid itself when the chemical nature of the solid and of the liquid solvent are somewhat alike. In this case it is the increase in "disorder" resulting when the ordered array of the molecular crystal changes to the less-ordered arrangement of the liquid solution that contributes significantly to making the solid dissolve (see Chapter 18).

AMORPHOUS SOLIDS—THE GLASSY STATE

In general, we know that as the temperature of a liquid is lowered, the thermal agitation of its particles gradually decreases, until the cohesive forces among the particles prevail and the liquid solidifies. In most cases, the liquid solidifies to a crystalline solid in which the particles are arranged orderly in the three-dimensional lattice which establishes maximum attraction among the particles. There are cases, however, when a liquid is cooled too abruptly for the particles to arrange themselves in the appropriate positions in the crystal lattice, and the liquid then changes to an amorphous solid, or *glass.* A glass is a solid in which the particles have the same disordered (or short-range ordered) distribution as in the liquid state, but the translational motions of the particles have virtually ceased. Hence glasses do not crystallize at ordinary temperatures because their particles are not sufficiently mobile to rearrange themselves into the appropriate positions required of a crysal lattice. Glass may also be considered as a liquid which has been cooled so much that its viscosity has increased to the point where it has lost the typical liquid property of fluidity. Accordingly, when a glassy solid is heated, instead of melting suddenly at a fixed temperature as crystalline substances do, it slowly softens and gradually becomes more free-flowing. This is exactly the way in which a highly viscous liquid behaves when it is heated. Keep in mind, however, that although ordinary glass is a familiar substance and is extremely important commercially and industrially, the glassy state is rather an exception in nature, since most liquids when cooled solidify to the crystalline state.

10-7 Metals

A large majority of the elements are classified as *metals.* Actually, some 65 of the known elements, not including the transuranium ones, are metallic in character (see Table 12-3 in Chapter 12). The term "metal" designates *an element which is a good conductor of electricity and whose electrical resistance is directly proportional to the absolute temperature.* Thus, the electrical resistance of a metal decreases as temperature decreases. For some metals, when temperature falls enough—close to absolute zero—the resistance becomes negligible and the metal behaves as a *superconductor.* In addition to this distinctive characteristic, metals share several other typical physical properties such as: (1) high thermal conductivity; (2) high density; (3) opacity accompanied by a typical surface luster; (4) malleability and ductility—that is, the ability to be drawn into sheets and wires, respectively; (5) favorable mechanical properties—for example, resistance to traction, flexion, torsion; and (6) a very high boiling point. Several non-metallic elements, however, also exhibit one or more of these same properties, so that the only feature that identifies a metal unambiguously is the electrical conductivity which decreases with increasing temperature. The question now arises, which is the structural characteristic, common to all metals, that accounts for this set of physical properties, the so called *metallic character*?

THE STRUCTURE OF SOLID METALS

X-ray diffraction experiments show that solid metals are crystalline. Actually, for the majority of metals the atoms are arranged in the simple structures which correspond to the two possible closest-packed arrangements of spheres of equal size.

CLOSEST PACKED STRUCTURES OF EQUAL SPHERES. If a number of rigid spheres of equal size are gathered together as closely as possible on a plane surface, they will arrange themselves in the regular array shown in Fig. 10-16(a), each sphere being

FIGURE 10-16 Closest-packed arrangements of equal spheres. (a) One layer. (b) Two superimposed layers. (c) Three superimposed layers in hexagonal close-packed arrangement. (d) Three superimposed layers in cubic close-packed arrangement.

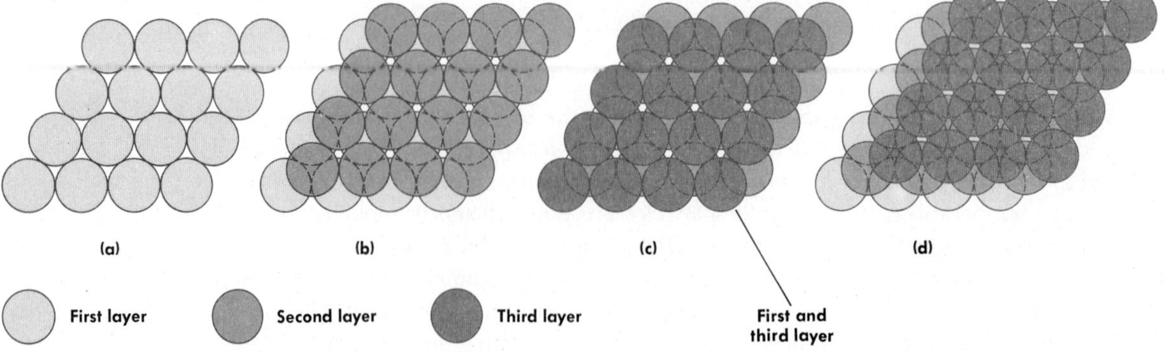

surrounded by six equivalent spheres situated at the corners of a regular hexagon. When two such identical layers of equal spheres are placed one on the top of the other, the most compact (most space-filling) arrangement is that in which each sphere of the second layer is vertically above the "hole" between three spheres of the first layer (Fig. 10-16(b)). Now a third identical layer of equal spheres can be placed on top of the other two layers in two different ways, both resulting in a maximum space-filling arrangement. In one of these two possible arrangements the spheres of the third layer are vertically on top of the spheres of the first layer (Fig. 10-16(c)); this arrangement is called *hexagonal close-packed,* and its unit cell is shown in Fig. 10-17(b). In the other possible arrangement each sphere of the third layer is vertically above a hole in the second layer, which in turn is above a hole in the first layer (Fig. 10-16(d)). This arrangement is called *cubic close-packed* or *face-centered cubic,* and its unit cell is shown in Fig. 10-17(a). The hexagonal closed-packed and the cubic closed-packed structures are the only two possible ways of packing three identical layers of equal spheres most compactly. Notice that it takes at least three superimposed layers to identify a structure as either hexagonal or cubic close-packed. In both these arrangements, each sphere is surrounded by its twelve nearest neighbors at equal distance (Fig. 10-17(a) and (b)), but the relative positions of the neighbors differ, as the diagrams show.

BODY-CENTERED CUBIC STRUCTURE. Another common kind of metallic lattice, only slightly less compact, is the body-centered cubic lattice, whose unit cell is shown in Fig. 10-17(c). In the body-centered lattice each sphere has eight equivalent and equidistant neighbors situated at the corners of a cube.

METALLIC COORDINATION NUMBER. Several other types of metallic lattices exist, but the three types just mentioned (hexagonal close-packed, face-centered cubic, body-centered cubic) are by far the most common. Because each metal atom has 12 nearest neighbors in both the hexagonal closed-packed and in the face-centered cubic lattice, we often say that for these lattices the *metallic coordination number is 12.* Similarly, because in the body-centered cubic lattice each atom has 8 nearest neighbors, we say that its *metallic coordination number is 8.* For example, crystalline magnesium, $Mg_{(s)}$, has a hexagonal close-packed lattice (metallic coordination number = 12); crystalline silver, $Ag_{(s)}$, has a face-centered cubic lattice (metallic coordination number = 12); and crystalline potassium, $K_{(s)}$ has a body-centered lattice (metallic coordination number = 8). It is important to recall, here, that the atoms of solid

FIGURE 10-17 Unit cells of the three most common metallic lattices. The nearest neighbors of an arbitrarily chosen atom in each cell are also shown. (a) Face-centered cubic lattice (cubic close-packed), 12 nearest neighbors. (b) Hexagonal close-packed lattice, 12 nearest neighbors. (c) Body-centered cubic lattice, 8 nearest neighbors.

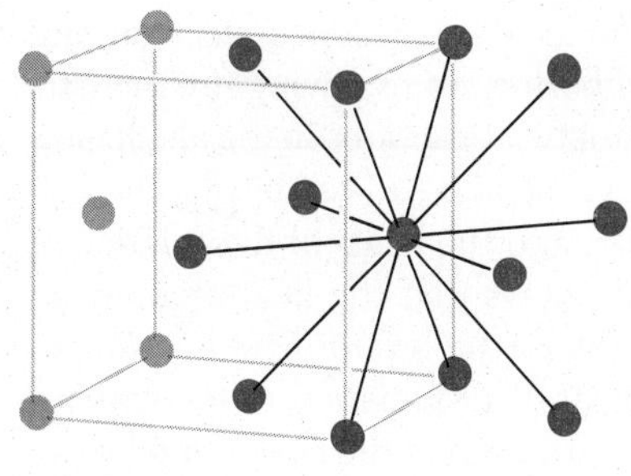

(a)

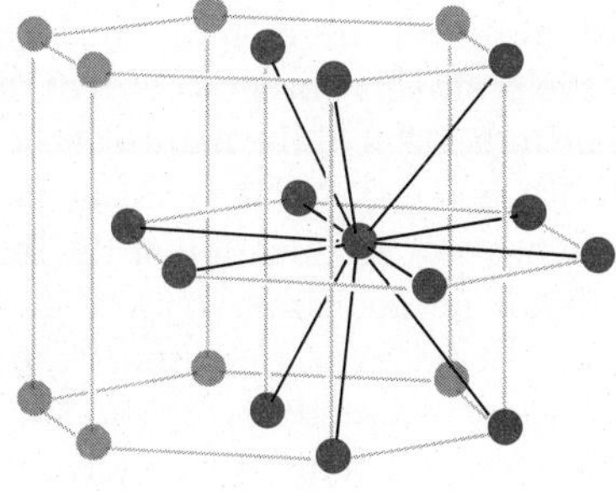

(b)

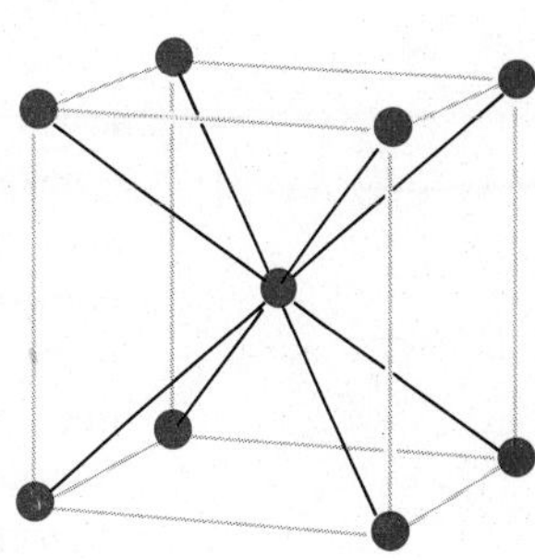

(c)

metals, even though arranged in fixed relative positions in the crystal lattice, are not completely motionless. Rather, the atoms of solid metals, just as the particles of any solid, oscillate about their equilibrium positions in the lattice, the amplitude of the oscillation increasing with increasing temperature.

METAL BONDING. The fact that the relative arrangement of the atoms in metallic lattices has been accurately determined for most metals does not, in itself, give us any direct indication of the kind of bonding which holds the atoms together in the lattice. However, the general observation that metal structures are very compact is significant, as we shall soon see.

In discussing the nature of metal bonding, the following considerations are of interest. First of all, metals retain many of their typical properties (electrical and thermal conductivity, high density, opacity, and luster) even in the molten state, so we may infer that the bonding is very much the same in liquid as in crystalline metals. Furthermore, the heats of atomization of metals are generally high, and so are their boiling points—even for those few metals which have low melting points. For example, the metal gallium, Ga (atomic wt = 70), which is a liquid on a hot day (melting point = 30°C), boils at 2,240°C and has a heat of atomization of 65.4 kcal/mole Ga atoms. Compare these values with those of the molecular solid, white phosphorus (atomic wt = 31), which is composed of P_4 molecules (melting point = 44°C; boiling point = 280°C; $\Delta H_{\text{atomization}} = +79.8$ kcal/mole P atoms). Finally, the metals have relatively high densities. Compare, for example, the molecular non-metallic solid iodine, I_2 (formula wt = 254, density 4.94 g/cm^3 at 20°C, melting point 114°C, boiling point 183°C), with metallic solid uranium (atomic wt = 238, density 19.1 g/cm^3 at 20°C, melting point 1130°C, and boiling point 3820°C).

Thus we may conclude that the atoms of metals are held together in a very compact arrangement by strong forces of attraction whose nature is essentially the same in the solid and liquid states.

The high metal coordination number rules out the possibility that the bonding between the atoms of metals may be of the normal covalent type (shared electron pairs), because the atoms of the metals do not have sufficient valence electrons to form so many covalent bonds. The sodium atom, for example, has only one valence electron, and thus can form only one covalent bond; in fact, in the gaseous state sodium can exist as diatomic $Na_{2(g)}$ (Na—Na) molecules, but not as molecular aggregates of more than two atoms. In the solid, body-centered sodium metal, each Na atom, with its single valence electron, somehow manages to bond with its eight neighboring atoms. We can then assume that the single electron of each Na atom is *not* confined to a single covalent bond, but is shared equally with all the equidistant nearest neighboring Na atoms and also to some extent with the next nearest neighbors.

A simple way of viewing metallic bonding is to consider the positively charged cores* of the metal atoms as being arranged in a continuous three-dimensional lattice and embedded in a "sea of electrons" or "metallic electron cloud" made up of the valence electrons of all the metal atoms. These non-localized valence electrons are attracted by the positively charged cores of the neighboring atoms, giving rise to metal bonding. Some indication of the nature of the interatomic attractions in the alkali metals (Li, Na, K, Rb, and Cs), and the coinage metals (Cu, Ag, and Au) can be obtained by comparing the heats of atomization of the solids, $M_{(s)}$, and the heats of dissociation of the gaseous diatomic molecules, $M_{2(g)}$. Figure 10-18 shows that the heat of atomization, which may be taken as a measure of the strength of the *interatomic bonding in the metallic lattice,* is directly proportional to the heat of dissociation of the gaseous diatomic molecules, which in turn is a measure of the strength of the *covalent bonding*

* The nuclei plus all the electrons except the valence electrons.

between two M atoms in an isolated molecule. Furthermore, even though the values of $\Delta H_{\text{atomization}}$ and $\Delta H_{\text{dissociation}}$ vary widely, for the metals under consideration (Fig. 10-18), the ratio $\Delta H_{\text{atomization}}/\Delta H_{\text{dissociation}}$ is almost constant, the $\Delta H_{\text{atomization}}$ being about 3 to $3\frac{1}{2}$ times greater than the $\Delta H_{\text{dissociation}}$. This relationship suggests that the same fundamental factors must determine the bond strength in solid (and molten) metals, as well as in their gaseous diatomic covalent molecules. In other words, the kind of bonding in metals bears some relationship to covalent bonding.

Another way to picture metals, therefore, is to consider them as an assemblage of atoms held together by the covalent sharing of their valence electrons. However, as we have mentioned the covalent bonding of metals differs essentially from that of giant covalent crystals such as diamond, or of discrete covalent molecules such as iodine, in that each atom does not have enough valence electrons to form a normal covalent bond (a shared electron pair) with each of its equivalent neighbors (usually 8 or 12). Thus, we may visualize the metal bonding as resulting from shared electrons which can occupy different but almost equivalent positions and hence belong simultaneously to more than two neighboring cores of atoms (also called multicenter bonds). Furthermore, the energy that is required to shift these bonding electrons from one position to an adjacent one in the lattice is very small.

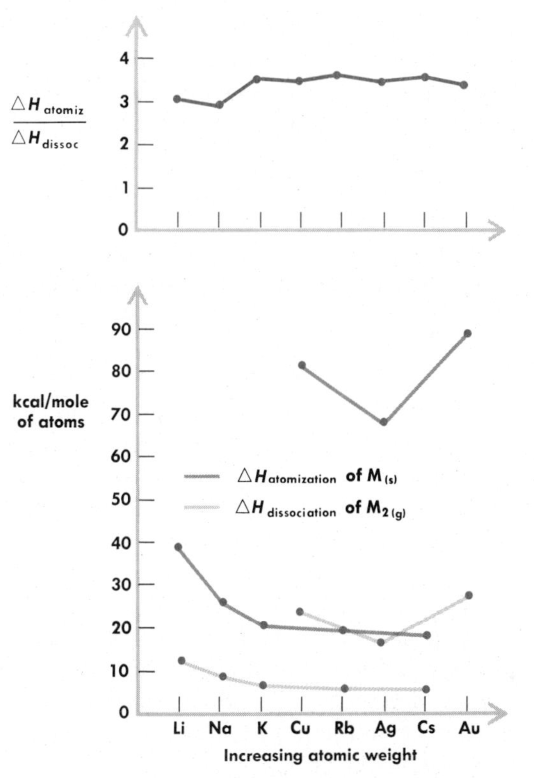

FIGURE 10-18 Relationship between heat of atomization and heat of dissociation of diatomic molecules for some metals.

Both these pictures of the metallic state serve to explain the typical properties of metals. For example, the fact that even low-melting metals have high boiling points can be attributed to the fact that a fairly low thermal agitation may be sufficient to disrupt the ordered packing of the cores of the atoms in the metallic lattice to form a molten metal, but considerably more energy is required to break completely the metal bonding to form individual gaseous atoms or molecules. Also, when a metal is under the influence of an external electrical field, the mobile electrons which constitute the metal bonding migrate toward the positively charged pole, and the metal is a conductor of electricity. The electrical conductivity of metals decreases with increasing temperature because at higher temperatures the increased vibrational motions of the cores of the atoms hinder more effectively this flow of electrons through the crystal lattice. Also, since the bonding electrons are not localized in fixed positions but move easily from one position to a neighboring one, the atoms of a metal can be made to shift with respect to one another, while maintaining their characteristic crystalline environment and bonding. Thus, metallic crystals are fairly easily deformed (are ductile and malleable).

The above discussion of the nature of metal bonding finally explains why the characteristic *metallic properties are evident only for a relatively large assemblage of atoms in a condensed state* (solid or liquid), but not for individual atoms, pairs of atoms, or very small clusters of atoms, such as may be present in the gaseous state.

10-8 Transition Between States

SOLID-SOLID TRANSITIONS. ALLOTROPY

Many solid substances exist in two or more crystalline forms, differing in the spatial arrangement of the molecules, atoms, or ions which make up the substance. The existence of a substance in more than one crystal form is known as *allotropy,* from the Greek word, *allotropia,* meaning variety. Different crystalline forms of the same substance sometimes are called *allotropes.* For any substance which exists in allotropic forms, one of the allotropes is more stable than the others, under specified conditions of temperature and pressure. In the crystalline state, however, the particles have practically no mobility, so if two or more allotropic forms of a substance can be obtained at room temperature, the transformation of the less stable form into the more stable one may not occur at a detectable rate. When one allotropic form of a substance is stable at low temperatures and another is stable at higher temperatures, heating or cooling the substance slowly to a certain temperature will cause the structural change from one to the other allotropic form. The temperature at which this change occurs is known as the *transition temperature,* and has a fixed value for each pair of allotropes.

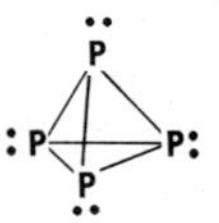

Phosphorus is an example of a substance which exists in several allotropic forms. The two most common forms are red phosphorus, which is stable under ordinary conditions of temperature and pressure, and white phosphorus, which is less stable. White phosphorus is a molecular crystal, composed of individual P_4 molecules held together by van der Waals forces. In each P_4 molecule four P atoms are linked together by covalent bonds in a tetrahedral arrangement, as shown in the marginal figure. Red phosphorus, on the other hand, is a covalent crystal in which each P atom is covalently bonded to its neighbors in a continuous three-dimensional lattice. Accordingly, the white allotrope is softer, lower melting, readily volatile, and more soluble in non-polar solvents than the red allotrope. In fact, white phosphorus is a waxy material (density 1.83 g/cm^3 at 20°C) which melts at 44°C and boils at 280° (at 1 atm pressure), whereas red phosphorus (density 2.35 g/cm^3) is fairly hard and brittle and does not melt until it reaches a temperature of 590°C. Although under ordinary conditions the white allotrope of phosphorus is less stable than the red allotrope, white phosphorus can exist for a long time at room temperature because its transformation into red phosphorus occurs very slowly. If, however, white phosphorus is heated in the presence of a catalyst—for example, a small quantity of iodine, I_2,—then the transformation of the white to the red allotrope proceeds fairly rapidly, and heat is liberated.

$$P_{4(white)} \longrightarrow 4\ P_{(red)} \qquad \Delta H = -17.2 \text{ kcal/mole-equation}$$

White and red phosphorus generally undergo similar chemical reactions, but the white form is far more reactive at lower temperatures, and the exothermic reactions involving the white form liberate more heat. For example, both white and red phosphorus react with oxygen gas; white phosphorus is spontaneously flammable in air at room temperature, whereas red phosphorus must be ignited, and when they react, more heat is liberated by the combustion of white phosphorus:

$$\begin{array}{llr} P_{4(white)} + 5\ O_2 \longrightarrow P_4O_{10} & \Delta H = & -732.2 \text{ kcal/mole-equation} \\ 4\ P_{(red)} + 5\ O_2 \longrightarrow P_4O_{10} & \Delta H = & -715.0 \text{ kcal/mole-equation} \\ \hline & \text{(difference)} = & -\ 17.2 \text{ kcal/mole-equation} \end{array}$$

Notice that the difference between the heat liberated in the above two reactions is exactly the quantity of heat evolved in the allotropic transformation from white to red phosphorus.

As we know, carbon is another element which exists in two allotropic forms, diamond and graphite. Pure diamond is colorless, transparent and, as we said, is extremely hard and has no electrical conductivity. Graphite, on the other hand, is dark gray, opaque, very soft, and is a very good conductor of electricity. In fact, graphite rods are used as electrodes in many electrochemical processes. Diamond is denser than graphite, 3.5 g/cm^3 compared with 2.3 g/cm^3 for graphite. These different properties arise from the way in which the carbon atoms are linked to one another in the two allotropic forms. As we have just discussed, the structure of diamond is a continuous covalent three-dimensional lattice in which each C atom is covalently bonded to four tetrahedrally arranged C atoms. In graphite, too, carbon atoms are arranged according to a regular pattern. Unlike the structure of diamond, however, the carbon atoms in graphite are bonded firmly to one another in a planar, rather than in a three-dimensional, pattern. Each carbon atom in graphite is covalently bonded to only three other carbon atoms, located at the corners of an (imaginary) equilateral triangle. The resulting structure is a two-dimensional network made up of innumerable regular hexagons of carbon atoms (Fig. 10-19(a)). Look for a moment at any one of the hexagons in this layer (for example, the purple one) and notice that it shares each of its six sides with an adjacent hexagon. In other words, each hexagon is surrounded by six other hexagons in the same plane. This process can be continued indefinitely to produce giant layers of covalently bonded C atoms. In a later chapter we shall discuss the type of bonding between the C atoms of each layer of graphite; here we will merely say that the adjacent layers of carbon atoms are held together in a crystal of graphite by only relatively weak van der Waals forces. In fact, the distance between the nearest carbon atoms in adjacent layers (3.35 A) is about 2.3 times the distance between carbon atoms within the hexagonal layers (1.42 A). Notice in Fig. 10-19(b) that the carbon atoms of alternate layers fall vertically above one another, the distance between them being 6.70 A. Because adjacent layers are held together only by weak van der Waals forces the

FIGURE 10-19 The arrangement of carbon atoms in a portion of the crystal structure of graphite. (a) Top view of a portion of a single layer of graphite. (b) Alternating layers of graphite.

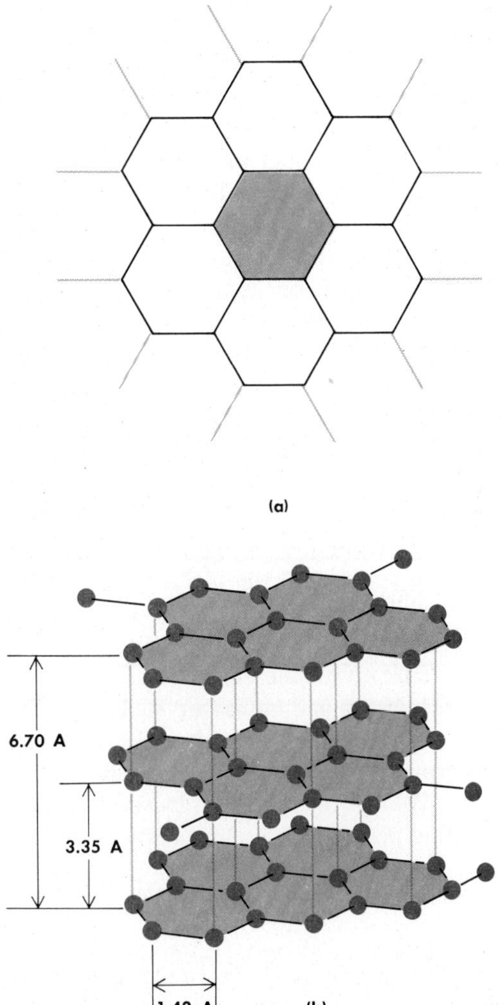

layers slide over one another easily, thus making graphite an extremely useful solid lubricant. The marks made by an ordinary "lead" pencil are really layers of hexagonal sheets of carbon atoms, hence the name "graphite," from the Greek word to write.

Under ordinary conditions, the more stable allotropic form of carbon is graphite, and the energy relationship between these allotropes is supplied by the following equation:

$$C_{(diam)} \longrightarrow C_{(gr)} \qquad \Delta H = -0.5 \text{ kcal/mole C atoms}$$

However, at room temperature diamond (fortunately!) does not transform to graphite, because the C atoms do not possess enough thermal agitation to effect the necessary rearrangement.

SOLID-LIQUID TRANSITIONS. FUSION AND CRYSTALLIZATION

When we supply heat to a solid its temperature increases and so does the vibrational and rotational kinetic energy of the molecules, atoms, or ions that make up the solid. Eventually, the kinetic energy becomes great enough to overcome the potential energy of the forces (covalent, ionic, van der Waals, or metallic) that hold the particles together in the ordered array of the crystal. At this temperature, then, this ordered array is disrupted and the solid melts. For each pure crystalline solid there is a fixed temperature at which the transition from solid to liquid occurs. This temperature is called the *melting point* (or *freezing point*) of the solid, and is generally indicated as m.p. (or f.p.).

Let us now consider what happens when a liquid is cooled. As the temperature falls, the kinetic energy of the particles of the liquid gradually decreases. Finally, when the temperature becomes low enough, the intermolecular interactions, which even in the liquid state tend to arrange the particles in a somewhat orderly arrangement, finally prevail and crystallization begins. If a liquid is a pure substance, crystallization begins and is completed at a fixed constant temperature—the freezing point of the liquid. For a pure substance, the melting point and the freezing point are of course identical. We know that the intermolecular attractions among the particles of a substance in the liquid state are weaker than in the crystalline state of the same temperature and pressure. Hence, heat energy must always be supplied from an external source in order to transform a solid into its liquid, at the same temperature. Conversely, heat is always released when a liquid crystallizes to its solid at the same temperature. Consider 1 mole of a solid substance at its melting point and at 1 atm pressure. If we begin to supply some heat to the substance, some of the solid begins to melt, while the temperature remains constant. As more and more heat is supplied, more and more of the solid passes to the liquid state, but the temperature remains constant at the melting point as long as some solid is present together with its liquid. Only after all the solid has melted, if additional heat is supplied, does the temperature of the *liquid* begin to rise.

Pure crystalline solids melt completely at one temperature, whereas *amorphous* solids (glasses) and *impure* crystalline solids begin to melt at one temperature but become completely liquid only at a higher temperature. This simple test can be used to determine whether a given crystalline solid is pure or impure.

We can represent the transformation of 1 mole of any solid to its liquid, at its melting point, by the schematic equation:

$$\text{Crystalline solid (1 mole, } P = 1 \text{ atm, } T = \text{m.p.)} \longrightarrow \text{Liquid (1 mole, } P = 1 \text{ atm, } T = \text{m.p.)}$$
$$\Delta H = +q \text{ kcal/mole}$$

The energy required to convert 1 mole of a substance from the solid to the liquid state, at a constant temperature, is called the *molar heat of fusion* of that substance, and is commonly expressed in kcal/mole. Sometimes it is convenient to use the specific heat of fusion, which is the quantity of heat needed to convert 1 g of a solid at a given temperature into its liquid at the same temperature. The specific heat of fusion is commonly expressed in calories per gram. For example, at 0°C the molar heat of fusion of ice is 1.44 kcal/mole, and the specific heat of fusion of ice is 80 cal/g.

Although both fusion and vaporization require energy, essentially to separate molecules, there is a fundamental difference between these two processes. In order to melt a solid, only enough energy need be supplied to overcome the forces that hold the molecules in fixed relative positions in the crystal lattice. In order to vaporize a liquid, however, enough energy must be supplied to overcome completely the intermolecular attractions (cohesive forces) which hold together the particles in the condensed states. Consequently, heats of vaporization are much higher than heats of fusion. For example, the molar heat of vaporization of water is 9.72 kcal/mole at 100°C, but the molar heat of fusion of ice is only 1.44 kcal/mole at 0°C.

SOLID-LIQUID EQUILIBRIUM. Let us assume that we bring together, inside a Dewar flask, a certain quantity of a solid substance at its melting point and a certain quantity of the same substance in the liquid state, at a temperature higher than the melting point. The solid does not become warmer, but some or all of it will melt, while the liquid becomes cooler. If there is enough of the solid present, the temperature of the resulting solid-liquid mixture finally attains the melting point of the substance being used. Heat can neither enter nor leave the Dewar flask, so both the temperature and the quantities of the solid and liquid remain constant thereafter, and we then say that *equilibrium* is established between the solid and the liquid. For example, by adding enough ice cubes at 0°C to water at room temperature, we can lower the temperature of the water to its freezing point so that equilibrium is established between the remaining ice and the liquid water, both at 0°C.

A state of solid-liquid equilibrium can also be attained by bringing together a solid, having a temperature below the melting point, and the corresponding liquid at the melting point. In this case the solid gradually warms up, while some or all of the liquid crystallizes. Finally, if enough liquid is present, a solid-liquid mixture in equilibrium at the melting point is obtained. More generally, whenever we bring the pure solid and the pure liquid of the same substance into contact, the temperature of the solid-liquid mixture tends toward the melting point. The liquid becomes cooler and the solid becomes warmer. If appropriate relative quantities of the solid and liquid are present, the solid-liquid mixture will finally attain a state of equilibrium when the temperature reaches the melting point.

UNDERCOOLING OF LIQUIDS. When the temperature of a liquid falls to the freezing point, the slowly moving molecules usually assume the fixed relative positions characteristic of the crystalline state, and the liquid crystallizes. But sometimes a liquid continues to cool below the freezing point without changing into its solid. A liquid that has been cooled below its melting point while still remaining in the liquid state is said to be *undercooled* (or supercooled).

Under carefully controlled conditions, water, for example, may be undercooled to as low as −35°C! For most liquids there is a definite limit below which they cannot be undercooled without being converted into solids. Undercooled liquids are usually in a very unstable condition and any disturbance, such as shaking or adding solid particles, may cause the system to solidify suddenly.

The liquids that are easiest to undercool are those with a high viscosity. The reason may be that the strong flow-resistant quality of these molecules inhibits their moving into the relative positions characteristic of the solid state. Many viscous solutions may be undercooled indefinitely without solidifying. Glass, as we have said, may be regarded as an undercooled liquid of extremely high viscosity.

It is interesting to note that although it is possible to undercool certain liquids, apparently it is not possible to "superheat" a solid beyond its melting point without transforming it into a liquid.

THE EFFECT OF PRESSURE ON BOILING POINT AND MELTING POINT. Pressure has a marked effect on the boiling point of liquids, but it has only a slight effect on the melting point of solids. By reducing the pressure from 760.0 torr to 4.6 torr, we can lower the boiling point of water from 100°C to 0°C. Yet the same change in pressure alters the melting point of ice by less than 0.01°C.

VAPOR PRESSURE OF SOLIDS. SUBLIMATION

Each solid, like each liquid, has a definite vapor pressure at a given temperature, which means that it is possible for the molecules of a solid to pass directly from the solid state to the gaseous state. Such a process is called *sublimation.* Snow, for example, can "disappear"—that is, it can sublime directly to the gaseous state—even if the temperature remains below 0°C. Another familiar example is the slow vaporization of "dry ice" (solid CO_2) and of moth balls (naphthalene) when exposed to the air. The vapor pressure of solids, like that of liquids, increases with increasing temperature, and the rate of increase is greater at higher temperatures.

Over a range of very low temperatures, then, a solid substance may sublime at a temperature below its normal melting point, and a liquid may boil at a temperature below its normal boiling point provided that the pressure is low enough. Any solid will sublime if the pressure of the gaseous form of the substance is less than the vapor pressure of the solid. Any liquid will boil, as we know, if the total pressure of the gas above the liquid is equal to (or less than) the vapor pressure of the liquid. For example, the vapor pressure of ice at 0°C is 4.58 torr. If the pressure of water vapor in the air is less than 4.58 torr, ice will change directly into water vapor. The vapor pressure of solid carbon dioxide is more than 1 atm at temperatures near −60°C (the approximate temperature of dry ice); the pressure of gaseous carbon dioxide in the atmosphere is rarely even a few torr. Hence, solid carbon dioxide sublimes. Or, at its melting point, −56°C, the vapor pressure of carbon dioxide is 5.25 atm; it follows that if a pressure of 5.25 atm or more of carbon dioxide gas is imposed on solid carbon dioxide, it will melt as it is warmed up to −56°C. And if the pressure upon it is slightly greater than 5.25 atm, the liquid carbon dioxide will boil as it is warmed a bit more. Carbon dioxide is ordinarily stored in steel cylinders under pressures greater than 7.5 atm. (The critical pressure of CO_2 is 7.3 atm.)

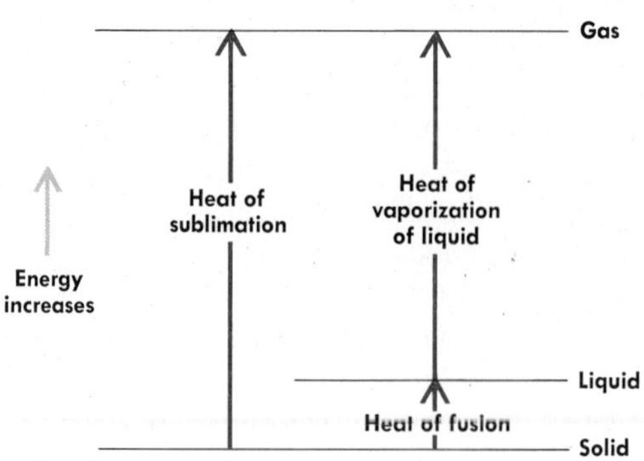

The *molar heat of sublimation* is the quantity of heat required to convert 1 mole of a solid substance into its vapor, at the same temperature and pressure. The specific heat of sublimation is defined similarly for 1 g of a solid. The heat of sublimation of a solid is equal to the sum of the heat of fusion and the heat of vaporization, assuming that all processes occur at the same temperature, as shown in the diagram.

THE COEXISTENCE OF THE SOLID, LIQUID, AND VAPOR STATES OF A SUBSTANCE. PHASE DIAGRAMS

The solid, liquid, and gaseous forms of a substance can coexist indefinitely without change (that is, i.e., they are in equilibrium with one another) when the solid and the liquid have the same vapor pressure. This situation can be realized only at a specified temperature, characteristic of the substance considered, and only when the total pressure under which the solid-liquid mixture is maintained is equal to their common vapor pressure. Therefore, for each pure substance, there is only one specified set of conditions, a specified temperature and a specified pressure, at which the three phases can coexist in equilibrium. For water, the temperature at which solid, liquid, and vapor are in equilibrium with one another is 0.01°C, under a pressure of 4.60 torr.

The pressure-temperature relations that exist for water—solid, liquid, and vapor—are shown in Fig. 10-20. Here the *AL* curve represents the vapor pressure of liquid water from 0.01°C to higher temperatures. The *AS* curve is the vapor pressure of ice from 0.01°C to lower temperatures. The broken curve shows the vapor pressure of undercooled liquid water at various temperatures. The line *AV* represents the melting point of ice at various pressures.

Any point on the curves in Fig. 10-20 represents a particular temperature and a particular pressure. All points in the region below *SAL*, marked vapor, correspond to pressures that are too low for a liquid or solid to exist at the corresponding temperatures. In this area water can exist only as a vapor. Similarly, any point in the region limited by *VAL* corresponds to pressures that are too high for the vapor to exist at the corresponding temperatures. In this area water can exist only as a liquid. The region *SAV* corresponds to temperatures so low, and pressures so high, that water can exist only as a solid.

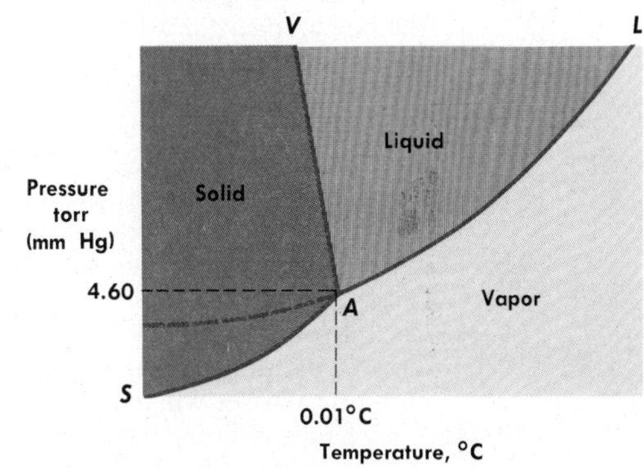

FIGURE 10-20 Vapor pressure of water and ice. A is the triple point.

Liquid and vapor can coexist only at points on the *AL* curve; liquid and solid can coexist only at points on the line *AV*; and solid and vapor can coexist only at points on the *AS* curve. Only at the single point, *A*, can all three phases coexist at equilibrium. This point, for any substance, is called the *triple point*, and as we have said, for water occurs at $T = 0.01°C$ and $P = 4.60$ torr.

Exercises

10-1 What is the fundamental difference in the arrangement of the molecules of a given substance in the solid, liquid and gaseous state?

10-2 Why are the liquid and solid states of matter often referred to as "condensed states?"

10-3 Compare and explain the relative effects of an increase of pressure on the volume of a liquid and on the volume of a gas.

10-4 Can an ideal gas be liquefied? Discuss the reasons for your answer.

10-5 What single difference in the nature of gases and liquids makes gases easily compressible whereas liquids are only slightly compressible?

10-6 Explain the effect that an increase in temperature has on the density of a liquid.

10-7 Name several liquids whose densities are greater than that of water; several whose densities are less than that of water.

10-8 What is considered to be the cause of surface tension in a liquid?

10-9 How is the phenomenon of capillary action related to surface tension?

10-10 What effect does an increase in temperature have on the surface tension of water?

10-11 (a) Explain in your own words the meaning of the term "viscosity." (b) Why should different grades of lubricating oil be used in an automobile engine in different seasons or in different climates?

10-12 (a) Discuss the process of evaporation. Explain why a liquid becomes cooler as it evaporates from an insulated vessel. (b) What condition(s) must be changed to increase the rate of evaporation of a liquid?

10-13 Describe a procedure for experimentally determining the vapor pressure of a liquid at several temperatures.

10-14 State what effect, if any, variations in the following have on the vapor pressure of a liquid: (a) volume of liquid, (b) surface area of liquid, (c) volume of vapor, (d) temperature of liquid, (e) presence of non-reacting gases in the vapor.

10-15 What effect does a change in temperature have on the vapor pressure of a liquid? Explain and illustrate with a graph.

10-16 Explain the meaning of "heat of vaporization." How do the forces of attraction between molecules help to explain the heat of vaporization?

10-17 Compare the values of the heat of fusion of water and the heat of vaporization. Are the relative values what you would expect in light of our ideas about the nature of the solid, liquid, and gaseous states?

10-18 (a) How does heat of vaporization, in general, change with temperature? (b) What is the principal difference between evaporation and boiling? (c) Does the boiling point of a liquid vary if the external pressure is lowered? Explain your answer.

10-19 What general procedures are used to liquefy a gas?

10-20 Which is the more fundamental requirement for the liquefaction of a gas, low temperature or high pressure? Explain.

10-21 What is meant by the critical temperature of a substance?

10-22 The surface tension of liquids generally decreases with increasing temperature. What happens if the temperature is raised until the surface tension becomes zero?

10-23 The rate of evaporation of a liquid in an open container is increased by blowing air over its surface. Can the rate of boiling also be increased by means of air currents? Why or why not?

10-24 What happens during the process of simple distillation? What kind of impurities may be removed by distillation?

10-25 Define a crystalline solid.

10-26 Do the particles of a crystalline solid at room temperature have any kinetic energy? If so, what kind of kinetic energy do they have?

10-27 What is the structural difference between crystalline and amorphous solids?

10-28 Discuss the structure of ionic crystals and explain the meaning of the following terms giving an example of each: (a) crystal coordination number (C.C.N.), (b) mono-monovalent salt, (c) 6:6 and 6:3 crystal coordination, (d) octahedral and tetrahedral environment of a given ion in the crystal lattice, (e) face-centered cubic lattice, (f) body-centered cubic lattice.

10-29 For any salt that carries the general formula $M^{+n}X^{-n}$, which is the most important factor in determining the type of crystal lattice?

10-30 What is meant by the lattice energy of an ionic compound? How can the lattice energy explain some of the fundamental properties of ionic solids?

10-31 Describe the characteristic features of (a) covalent crystals and (b) molecular crystals, giving two examples of each. Discuss the nature of the bonding which holds together the particles in each kind of crystal.

10-32 Which are the characteristic features of metals?

10-33 Discuss how each of the following properties of a metal is explained in terms of the metallic structure: (a) thermal conductivity, (b) electrical conductivity, (c) malleability and ductility, (d) high boiling point, (e) high heat of vaporization.

10-34 When the temperature is lowered, does the electrical conductivity of metals (a) always decrease, (b) always increase, (c) vary irregularly, or (e) decrease for some metals and increase for others? Explain your answer.

10-35 Briefly describe the structural characteristics of glass.

10-36 Define the term "allotropy." Give two examples of substances which exist as allotropes and discuss the difference in their structures.

10-37 Define molar and specific heat of fusion of a substance. Why is heat required to melt a solid to its liquid at constant temperature?

10-38 How does the vapor pressure of a solid and a liquid at, above, and below the freezing point compare?

10-39 When heated, some substances sublime readily at atmospheric pressure. Most substances melt before they boil. Can any substance be made to sublime under controlled experimental conditions? Why?

10-40 Under what conditions do the solid, liquid and gaseous state of a substance co-exist in equilibrium?

WATER AND HYDROGEN PEROXIDE

11

In Chapter 10 we considered water and ice as examples of the liquid and solid states of matter, and we also mentioned some of the physical properties of this common substance. In Chapters 6 and 7, on the chemistry of oxygen and hydrogen, we discussed the synthesis and decomposition of water. In this chapter we shall turn our attention to the physical and chemical properties of water, and to some of the many interesting facts about this remarkable compound.

It is interesting, and in a way paradoxical, that water, the most familiar and important of all liquids, and the first liquid we are going to discuss in detail, is—as far as liquids go—an exception rather than the norm. In fact, water is, in many respects, a most unusual compound—and as we shall see, it is because of this very characteristic that water plays a unique, vitally important role in our lives. Although we often refer to the properties of water as being "abnormal" with respect to those of other liquids, we should realize that such properties are logically explainable—as we shall later see—on the basis of the same theories of structure and bonding which we apply to all substances.

11-1 Water

OCCURRENCE

Water is the only natural substance present on earth abundantly and simultaneously as a gas (vapor), a liquid, and a solid. As a liquid it fills the oceans, lakes and streams of the world, covering about five-sevenths of the earth's surface. The volume of water in the oceans alone is about 10^{20} ft^3. In the solid state, as ice, it occurs in enormous quantities in the polar regions and mountainous areas of the earth. Tremendous quantities of water vapor are present in the atmosphere. In addition, water is present in all living plants and animals; it is also a constituent of many minerals.

PURIFICATION OF NATURAL WATER

Liquid water occurs in nature as sea water, surface water, spring and well water, and rain water. Water is an extremely effective solvent, so that not only sea water, but also water from other sources, always contains appreciable amounts of dissolved substances, the nature and quantity of which depend of course on the origin of the water and the materials with which it has come into contact. The only readily available natural water that is relatively pure is rain water, but this too contains some dissolved carbon dioxide, oxygen, and nitrogen, and may carry dust and other impurities, taken from the atmosphere.

Surface and well water usually contain certain dissolved ionic compounds of calcium, magnesium, and iron which impart to the water the property known as hardness. Hard water does not form effective lathers with soaps and detergents, and when used in water heaters and steam boilers soon forms an undesirable deposit of dissolved salts on their metal walls. Before hard water can be used for some industrial and even for some household purposes, the substances responsible for the hardness must be removed, at least to some extent. This can be done by various methods, the most economical being the process called "water softening," which can be accomplished by adding appropriate reagents to remove most of the objectionable ions as insoluble compounds. Water can also be purified by the ion-exchange process. The water to be purified is passed through columns filled with a finely granulated solid—the ion-exchanger—which is generally a synthetic resin (polymer) which binds chemically both the metal cations and their partner anions present in the water. For each monovalent cation which the resin binds (for example, a Na^+ ion), one hydrogen ion, H^+, is released; for each divalent cation (for example, Ca^{++}), two H^+ ions are released, and so forth. Similarly, for each monovalent anion (for example, Cl^-) which the resin binds, one hydroxide ion, OH^-, is released; for each dinegative ion retained (for example, $SO_4^=$), the resin releases two OH^- ions, and so forth. The H^+ and OH^- ions thus released immediately combine to form water molecules, H_2O, and the water that emerges from the ion-exchange apparatus is substantially free of all ionic impurities.

Distillation is another common process for purifying water, especially if the original water contains a large quantity of dissolved ionic and non-ionic impurities. In this process, water is heated to boiling, and the water vapor which passes off is then condensed to liquid. In the first stages of the distillation process (as the water is gradually heated), some of the more volatile gases dissolved in water, such as oxygen and nitrogen, are expelled. The less volatile dissolved gases, such as ammonia and carbon dioxide, are released at higher temperatures, though even at the boiling point some may remain and pass off with the water vapor and reappear as impurities in the first portions of the condensed water. Consequently, the first portions of the condensate are discarded. The process of boiling and condensation is continued until almost all the water has been distilled. Since the mineral salts dissolved in water are non-volatile, they do not pass off with the water vapor. To insure that not even a small quantity of these salts can pass into the distillate, the process is interrupted before all the water has been distilled, and the salts are left behind in solution. The distilled water thus obtained is almost completely free of any dissolved gaseous or solid impurities. The distillation of sea water is being used more and more extensively to produce the enormous quantities of pure water required for domestic and industrial uses by large coastal cities throughout the world.

Water that is to be used for drinking must be carefully treated to insure that it is free from harmful bacteria. It may be sufficient to filter the water through beds of sand, but many municipalities treat water for drinking with chlorine to insure that almost all bacteria are destroyed.

THE PHYSICAL PROPERTIES OF WATER

COLOR, TASTE, AND SMELL. At ordinary temperatures pure water is a transparent, colorless liquid. Pure water is also tasteless and odorless. Having no taste of its own, water cannot mask the taste or smell of even small amounts of impurities, and in fact it readily "picks up" the flavors of any substances dissolved in it. Because water is a stable compound and can readily be obtained in the pure state, many of its properties are used as standard references.

TEMPERATURE STANDARD. The *triple point* of water, 0.01°C (Fig. 10-12), which is the temperature at which solid, liquid, and gaseous water are in equilibrium with one another, is used as a reference, or temperature standard. The melting point of pure ice at 1 atm pressure is 0°C. A mixture of ice and water is easy to prepare, and if sufficient ice is present the temperature of this mixture will spontaneously attain 0°C, almost exactly, and can then be maintained at this temperature as long as ice is present in the mixture. The boiling point of pure water at 1 atm pressure—exactly 100°C—is the other reference standard for the Celsius scale.

DENSITY STANDARD. At a temperature of 4.0°C, 1,000 g of pure water occupies a volume of exactly 1 cubic decimeter = 1,000 cm^3 (1 l.). Hence the density of water at 4.0°C is exactly 1.000 g/cm^3, and this value is often taken as a reference in measuring the density of other substances.

HEAT QUANTITY STANDARD. We have already seen that the unit of heat quantity, the calorie (cal), is the quantity of heat necessary to raise the temperature of 1 g of water from 14.5°C to 15.5°C. The temperature range, 14.5°C to 15.5°C, is specified because the amount of heat necessary to raise the temperature of 1 gram of water by 1 degree varies slightly with the temperature. For example, 1.0000 cal is needed to raise the temperature of exactly 1 g of water from 14.5°C to 15.5°C; 1.0049 cal are needed to raise the temperature of exactly 1 g of water from 4.0°C to 5.0°C; and only 0.9971 cal are needed to raise the temperature of exactly 1 g of water from 30.0°C to 31.0°C. Except for the most precise work, however, 1 cal is regarded as the amount of heat necessary to raise by 1°C the temperature of 1 g of liquid water at any temperature from 0°C to 100°C.

Some of the physical properties of water are given in Table 11-1, and they illustrate effectively our earlier statement that water is an "abnormal" compound and that if it were not, life on earth would be quite different. We see from the table that the density of liquid water is greater than that of ice by about 10%—that is, liquid water expands about 10% on freezing to ice. Hence ice floats on water. Most other solids, however, are denser than the respective liquids at the same temperature, so they sink in their liquid. We also see from the table that the density of water does not regularly decrease with increas-

TABLE 11-1 SOME PHYSICAL PROPERTIES OF WATER

Melting point at 1 atm	0.00°C
Triple point	0.01°C, 4.60 torr
Boiling point at 1 atm	100.00°C
Critical point	374.0°C, 218 atm
Density of solid at 0°C	0.917 g/cm^3
Density of liquid at 0°C	0.999 g/cm^3
Density of liquid at 4°C	1.000 g/cm^3
Density of liquid at 10°C	0.999 g/cm^3
Density of liquid at 25°C	0.997 g/cm^3
Density of liquid at 100°C	0.958 g/cm^3
Heat capacity of liquid (from 14.5° to 15.5°C)	1.00 cal/g × deg 18.00 cal/mole × deg
Heat of fusion at 0°C	1.44 kcal/mole
Heat of vaporization at 100°C	9.71 kcal/mole
Dielectric constant at 25°C	78.5

ing temperature, as it does for ordinary liquids. When water is gradually heated from 0.0°C to 4.0°C, it contracts and its density increases accordingly; but as the temperature rises above 4.0°C, water begins to expand and its density gradually decreases, as is the case with a normal liquid. Thus water has a maximum density (1.000 g/cm^3) at 4.0°C, and above or below this temperature it is less dense. These peculiar properties of water have tremendous consequences. For example, if ice did not float on water, lakes and rivers would freeze throughout during a cold winter, and all underwater fish and plant life would perish. Furthermore, if ice did not float on water, climatic conditions would be quite different. When water freezes, the ice crust that forms over it considerably reduces additional freezing by providing a sort of insulating layer through which the heat of the water below is only slowly dispersed to the colder air above. And if ice formed during the cold seasons were to sink to the bottom of seas and lakes and rivers instead of remaining at the surface, it might not melt completely during the warm seasons, so that progressively larger amounts of ice would form through the years. Also, the fact that water has a maximum density at 4.0°C insures that deep water seldom cools below this temperature, because water colder than 4.0°C remains close to the surface in contact with the ice crust. If it were not for these two properties of water, a polar climate would exist over vast areas of the earth.

Another abnormal property of water of tremendous consequence is its boiling point. If we compare the boiling point of water (100°C at 1 atm) with those of other substances of similar formula and almost identical formula weight (Table 11-2), we see that water (formula wt, H_2O = 18) has an abnormally high boiling point. In fact at 1 atm, methane (formula wt, CH_4 = 16) and ammonia (formula wt, NH_3 = 17) have boiling points of −161.5°C and −33.4°C, respectively. If water behaved likewise, no liquid water could exist within our ordinary range of temperatures—just a large cloud of water vapor would be present! And, of course, because liquid water is the main constituent of plant and animal cells, there would be no life on earth as we know it. These, and many other properties of water—a full discussion of which would fill volumes—can be explained on the basis of the structure of water, which we shall now consider.

THE POLAR CHARACTER OF WATER

In Chapter 3 (p. 27), we stated that water is composed of essentially covalent molecules in which an oxygen atom shares a pair of electrons with each of two hydrogen atoms (Fig. 11-1(a)). It is characteristic of covalent molecules that the atoms are held at definite angles to one another. In the gaseous water molecule, experiments show that the oxygen atom is covalently bonded to two hydrogen atoms, with

IV	V	VI	VII
C	N	O	F
Si	P	S	Cl

TABLE 11-2 BOILING AND MELTING POINTS OF SOME COVALENT NONMETAL HYDRIDES AT 1 ATM PRESSURE

Compound	Formula Weight	Boiling Point, °C	Heat Vapor. kcal/mole	m.p., °C
Hydrogen fluoride (HF)	20	19.5	—	−83.0
Water (H_2O)	18	100.0	9.7	0.0
Ammonia (NH_3)	17	−33.4	5.6	−77.0
Methane (CH_4)	16	−161.5	2.2	−184.0
Hydrogen chloride (HCl)	37	−85.0	3.9	−114.0
Hydrogen sulfide (H_2S)	34	−62.0	4.5	−85.5
Phosphine (PH_3)	34	−87.7	3.5	−133.0
Silane (SiH_4)	32	−14.0	—	−133.0

a O—H distance of 0.96 A and a HOH bond angle of 105°. (When an atom is (covalently) bonded to two other atoms, the angle formed by the two lines passing through the nuclei of the bonded atoms is called the *bond angle*). Schematic representations of a covalent water molecule are given in Fig. 11-1(a), (b), and (c). Now let us look more closely at the two pairs of electrons shared by the oxygen atom and the hydrogen atoms in a molecule of water. We know that a covalent bond results when two atoms share a pair of electrons. We also know that when the two bonded atoms are not identical (not of the same element), one atom generally exerts a greater attraction on the electron pair than does the other atom, and consequently the bond electron cloud is not equally shared between the bonded atoms. In the water molecule, for example, the electron cloud of each covalent bond is attracted more strongly by the more electronegative oxygen atom than by the less electronegative hydrogen atom. As a result of this unequal sharing of the electron pair, the oxygen acquires a partial negative charge and each of the hydrogen atoms acquires a partial positive charge—or, in other words, the molecule of water is *polar* (see also p. 199). Figure 11-1(d) is a schematic representation of a water molecule, showing the partial positive charge, δ^+, on each of the two hydrogen atoms, and the partial negative charge, $\delta^=$, on the oxygen atom. *The double partial negative sign is used to indicate that the atom concerned acquires partial negative charge from each of two covalent bonds.*

There is an essential difference between the *partial charges* assigned to the atoms of a polar molecule and the *full charges* on the ions of an ionic compound. In a polar molecule the electron cloud shared by the atoms is more concentrated about one atom than about the other. The atom that commands the greater concentration of the electron cloud is assigned a partial negative charge, and its partner atom, which draws the lesser concentration of the electron cloud, is assigned a partial positive charge; but the electron pair still is shared by the two atoms. In an ionic compound, however, each negative ion possesses almost completely the one or more electrons that originally belonged to what is now the positive ion.

HYDROGEN BONDING

In general, whenever polar molecules draw near to one another, they interact because of the electrostatic attraction between the positive end (δ^+) of one molecule and the negative end (δ^-) of another. For water, therefore, the partially positive hydrogen atom, $H^{\delta+}$, of one water molecule interacts with the partially negative oxygen atom, $O^{\delta=}$, of another water molecule. The resulting linkage is called a *hydrogen bond.* In general, to differentiate a hydrogen bond from a covalent bond, which we know is schematically represented in formulas as a full straight line (—), a hydrogen bond is generally represented schematically by a broken line (– – – –), as in Fig. 11-2.

FIGURE 11-1 The water molecule. (a) Electron-dot formula. (b) Shape of molecule. (c) Electron-cloud representation. (d) Partial charges of the O and H atoms of the polar H_2O molecule.

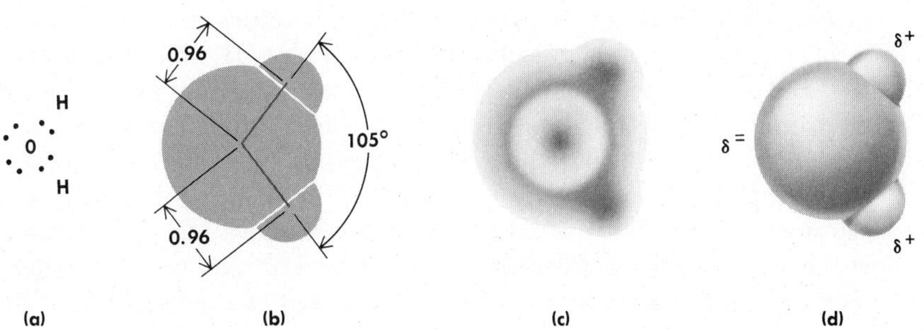

The hydrogen bond between H_2O molecules is much weaker than the hydrogen-to-oxygen covalent bonds within each H_2O molecule. The total energy required to break all the hydrogen bonds in 1 mole of liquid water is about 7 kcal, whereas the energy required to break one of the covalent bonds (H—OH) within a water molecule is about 110 kcal per mole of covalent bonds. Also, the *inter*molecular distance between the H and O atoms of two water molecules joined by a hydrogen bond, (1.77 A), is appreciably greater than the *intra*molecular distance between an H and O atom joined by a covalent bond.

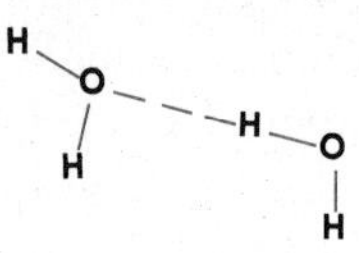

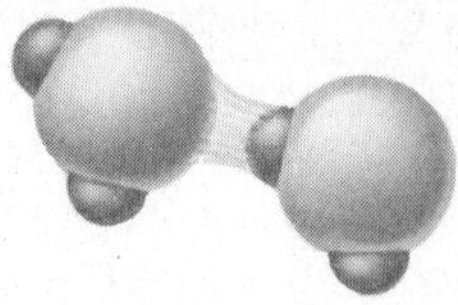

FIGURE 11-2 Electrostatic attraction between adjacent water molecules (hydrogen bonding).

The existence of this rather strong electrostatic interaction between the positively charged poles (the H atoms) and the negatively charged pole (the O atom) of adjacent H_2O molecules in liquid water gives rise to the formation of molecular aggregates, $(H_2O)_n$. In these aggregates or clusters of water molecules held together by hydrogen bonding, each O atom tends to surround itself with H atoms and each H atom tends to surround itself with O atoms. On the average each O atom is hydrogen bonded to two H atoms. The structure of these aggregates is closely knit but extremely flexible, because the molecules of a given cluster continually shift their relative positions and also move from one cluster to another in the chaotic manner characteristic of thermal agitation. Figure 11-3 represents a possible aggregate of five H_2O molecules, $(H_2O)_5$, held together by hydrogen bonding. In liquid water, hydrogen bonds are continually being formed and broken in a dynamic equilibrium, but their average number remains constant.

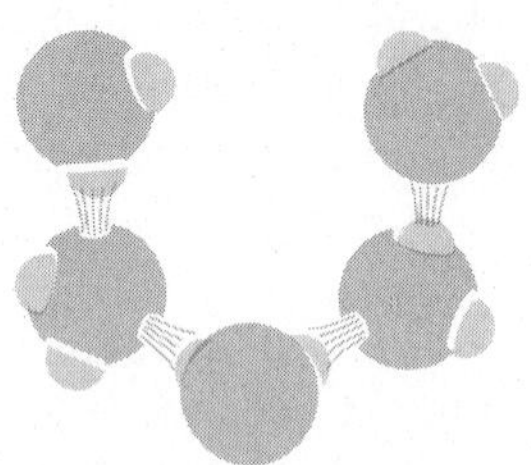

FIGURE 11-3 A possible aggregate of five hydrogen-bonded H_2O molecules in liquid water.

As the temperature of liquid water gradually falls below room temperature, and as the thermal agitation of the H_2O molecules decreases accordingly, the hydrogen bonding that holds the molecules in a closely knit structure gradually becomes more and more effective. The average distance between the molecules decreases, and so, as we know, does the density of water. When the temperature reaches 4.0°C, the clusters of water molecules begin to assume a more fixed and symmetrical structure, each O atom being tetrahedrally surrounded by 4 H atoms, and each H atom by two O atoms only. This type of arrangement leads to a less dense arrangement of molecules in the clusters, with relatively large empty spaces now separating the H_2O molecules. Finally, at 0.0°C, the forces tending to hold the H_2O molecules in fixed relative positions completely overcome the decreased kinetic translational energy of the molecules of the liquid, and water freezes to ice.

Ice has a molecular crystal lattice in which each H_2O molecule has four nearest neighbors. The O atom of each H_2O molecule is tetrahedrally surrounded by two different pairs of H atoms; with the two closest H atoms it forms covalent bonds (O—H); with the other two H atoms, which are farther away, it forms electrostatic (hydrogen) bonds (O———H). In turn, each H atom is joined to two O atoms; with one it forms a covalent bond and with the other it forms a hydrogen bond. The resulting structure is a network of hexagonal "tunnels" (Fig. 11-4) in which the hexagons are not flat but puckered. As the figure shows, the structure of ice is an "open" network, with considerable empty space between the molecules,* thus explaining the lower density of ice compared with that of liquid water.

* However, this effect has been greatly exaggerated in the diagram.

THE EFFECT OF HYDROGEN BONDING ON THE BOILING POINT OF WATER. We have just discussed how the "abnormal" densities of liquid water and ice result from hydrogen bonds that operate among separate water molecules in both the liquid and solid states but not in the gaseous state. The other "abnormal" physical properties of water may similarly be explained on the basis of hydrogen bonding. For example, the boiling point of water is remarkably high in comparison with the boiling points of similar covalent hydrides, such as ammonia, NH_3; methane, CH_4; hydrogen sulfide, H_2S; phosphine, PH_3, and silane, SiH_4.

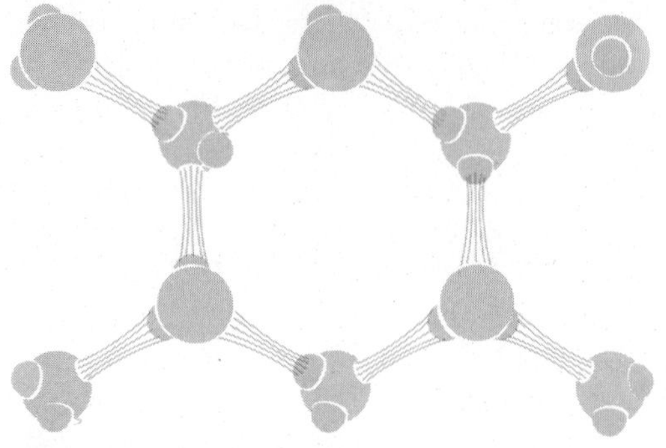

FIGURE 11-4 The crystal structure of ice. View showing network of hexagonal tunnels.

We know from Chapter 10 that the boiling point of a liquid is largely determined by the energy required to overcome the intermolecular forces that hold the molecules together in the liquid state. For a series of compounds with similar molecular structures and therefore similar intermolecular attractions, the boiling points should be about the same except for the variation due to the differences in molecular weights (the substance with the higher molecular weight boiling at the higher temperature). If we compare the *formula weights* of the compounds listed in Table 11-2, we see that the *formula* weight of H_2O, 18, is about the same as or less than the formula weights of the other substances. Consequently, it is not the weight that accounts for the extreme difference between the boiling point of water and those of the other listed compounds, but rather the difference in intermolecular interactions in the liquid state.

Figure 11-5 shows how the boiling points of the hydrides of the elements of Groups IV to VII vary with their formula weights (in the two short periods of the Periodic Table). We see that silane, SiH_4, has a higher boiling point than methane, CH_4, the lighter compound. We might expect this of two substances that are similar in structure and which are both held together in the liquid state only by van der Waals forces. On the other hand, the boiling point of phosphine, PH_3, is lower than that of the lighter similar compound ammonia, NH_3. An even more pronounced decrease in the boiling point is observed for the pairs of analogous compounds HF and HCl, and H_2O and H_2S. We can rationalize this behavior in terms of the formula of the hydride concerned and the nature of the element bonded to hydrogen in the hydride compounds. There is no hydrogen bonding between CH_4 or SiH_4 molecules because the C and Si atoms of these compounds do not have a lone pair of

FIGURE 11-5 Boiling points of non-metal covalent hydrides at 1 atmosphere.

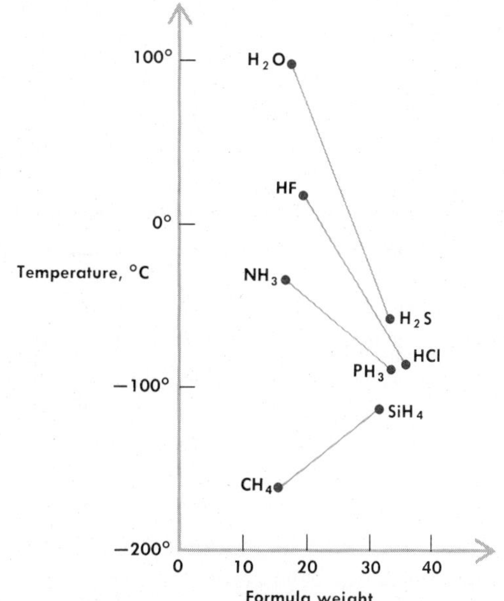

electrons; moreover, these two elements are not highly electronegative, and the C—H and Si—H bonds are only slightly polar.

Turning to the other hydride compounds of the second period, PH_3, H_2S, and HCl, we see that the phosphorus, sulfur, and chlorine atoms have one, two, and three lone pairs of electrons, respectively, and also become progressively more electronegative as we proceed from Group V to Group VII. But in these compounds the polarity of the P—H, H—S, and H—Cl bond is not sufficient to induce effective hydrogen bonding. In ammonia, hydrogen bonding exists to some extent, otherwise ammonia, NH_3, would boil at a lower temperature than the heavier phosphine, PH_3. But it is less pronounced than in water—as shown by the fact that water (formula 18 against 17 for ammonia) boils at a temperature 133 degrees higher!

The weaker hydrogen bonding in ammonia results from the fact that the electronegativity of the N atom is somewhat lower than that of the oxygen atom. Moreover, in NH_3 each N atom is bonded to three H atoms, whereas in H_2O each O atom is bonded only to two H atoms. Consequently, the N—H bond in ammonia is less polar that the O—H bond in water—that is, the H atom is less suitable for hydrogen bonding. Another factor contributing to the weaker hydrogen bonding in ammonia is that the N atom of NH_3 has only *one* lone pair of electrons for every *three* H atoms, whereas the O atom of H_2O has *two* lone pairs of electrons for every *two* hydrogen atoms. In principle, then, all O atoms and all H atoms of water could be fully engaged in hydrogen bonding (and in fact they are in ice).

We should point out, however, that the N atom in ammonia still has the ability to attract and bind firmly a "lone" proton, H^+, to form the ammonium ion, NH_4^+. Hydrogen fluoride, which boils 80.5°C lower than water, even though it is slightly heavier, requires some additional discussion. Here we have an atom, F, which is the most electronegative of all atoms and has three lone pairs. The H—F bond is extremely polar, and thus the hydrogen bonding in hydrogen fluoride is very strong. Even in the vapor state hydrogen fluoride exists in the form of clusters of molecules, linked together to form short zig-zag chains, $(HF)_2$ and $(HF)_3$, as well as higher aggregates up to the ring species $(HF)_6$. In the liquid state hydrogen fluoride is extensively associated, $(HF)_n$, and the solid consists of zig-zag chains containing an extremely large number of HF molecules linked together by hydrogen bonding. If we compare the evaporation of liquid hydrogen fluoride with that of liquid water, we see that there is one marked difference. First of all, each HF molecule can, on the average, form only one hydrogen bond (however stronger), whereas each H_2O molecule can form two. Furthermore, to vaporize hydrogen fluoride, we must break the zig-zag polymeric chains into small fragments, not necessarily into isolated molecules. To vaporize water, however, we must break completely the three dimensional aggregates present in the liquid state, because, as we mentioned before, water vapor is not associated and actually consists of single molecules (monomers).

A liquid such as water, in which the molecules associate to form small aggregates, is called an *associated liquid.* Any liquid in which the molecules do not associate to form aggregates is called a *normal liquid.* Clearly, more heat (energy) is required to vaporize an associated liquid than a normal liquid, so the boiling points of associated liquids are "abnormally" high as compared with those of normal liquids. This is why water is a liquid at room temperature, whereas the similar hydrides listed in Table 11-1 are gases. To summarize, the variation in the boiling points and other physical properties of the covalent non-metallic hydrides listed in Table 11-2 can be traced to the fact that only some of these hydrides form effective hydrogen bonding.

WATER AS A SOLVENT

One of the most important properties of liquid water is its ability to dissolve other substances—gases, liquids, and solids—to form solutions. In fact, there are so many substances at least partly soluble in water that water is known as the "universal solvent." Solutions are extremely important in chemistry, because they provide a suitable medium through which substances can effectively come into contact and hence interact. Many substances which would react only slowly and to an inappreciable extent when mixed as solids react rapidly and completely in solutions. For example, when solid sodium chloride and solid silver nitrate are mixed, they react very slowly and only to an inappreciable extent. But when these two substances are dissolved in water and mixed, they react instantaneously and completely. Similarly, plants do not absorb solid mineral salts, but when the salts are present in water solution they are absorbed fairly rapidly.

A reaction between solid substances occurs only at the contact surfaces between the solids, and the thin layer of products which forms coats the surfaces of the reactants and tends to prevent further reaction. In solution, the particles (molecules, ions) of the reagents are relatively free to move about and come easily into contact with one another, thereby reacting.

SOLUBILITY OF IONIC SOLIDS. We have learned in the preceding chapter that in ionic solids the oppositely charged ions are held together in a rigid three-dimensional crystal lattice by strong electrostatic forces. Consequently, a very large quantity of energy is required to break apart this lattice to form the isolated (gaseous) ions. In order to dissolve an ionic solid, the oppositely charged ions present in the crystal lattice must be separated and dispersed throughout the solvent. Why, we may ask ourselves, does this process occur spontaneously and generally without the application of any appreciable quantity of energy?

We shall discuss at length the phenomenon of solubility in Chapter 18; here we shall only consider two factors which favor greatly the dissolution of an ionic solid, such as Na^+Cl^-, in a polar liquid such as water. A first important factor which favors the dissolution of $Na^+Cl^-_{(s)}$ in water is the electrostatic attraction of the partially negatively charged oxygen atoms of the polar water molecules for the positive ions, Na^+, present in the crystal, and of the partially positively charged hydrogen atoms of the water molecules for the negative ions, Cl^-, of the crystal. When solid sodium chloride is added to water, the small polar molecules are attracted to, and tend to surround, the Na^+ and Cl^- ions, starting with those ions at the surface of a crystal. The electrostatic attraction between the surface Na^+ ions of the $Na^+Cl^-_{(s)}$ and the negatively charged end of the polar water molecules, together with the electrostatic attraction between the surface Cl^- ions and the positively charged ends of the polar water molecules, then tends to counteract the electrostatic attractions that link the positive Na^+ ions and negative Cl^- ions in the Na^+Cl^- crystal. Another important factor is the high dielectric constant of water—almost 80. The dielectric constant of a substance represents its tendency to reduce the electrostatic attraction between opposite charges relative to the attraction in a vacuum (or roughly, the attraction in the crystal). It follows that once some water molecules have interposed themselves between the Na^+ and Cl^- ions, the electrostatic attraction between these ions decreases very markedly. Consequently, the crystal lattice of sodium chloride is disrupted and the solid dissolves.

HYDRATION ENERGY OF IONIC COMPOUNDS. Let us now consider in a more quantitative manner the energy changes involved in the dissolution of Na^+Cl^- in water. We know from our discussion of ionic lattice energies (p. 176) that when 1 mole of gaseous Na^+ ions and 1 mole of gaseous Cl^- react to form crystalline Na^+Cl^-, a large quantity of heat, 183.8 kcal/mole—the lattice energy of NaCl—is evolved.

$$Na^+_{(g)} + Cl^-_{(g)} \longrightarrow Na^+Cl^-_{(s)} \qquad \Delta H = -183.8 \text{ kcal/mole}$$

Energy is also evolved when 1 mole of gaseous sodium ions, $Na^+_{(g)}$, is surrounded by the partially negative O atoms of water molecules to form hydrated Na^+ ions, $Na^+(OH_2)_x$. Of the x H_2O molecules surrounding the Na^+ ion, six are generally in direct contact with the Na^+ ion, and surround it octahedrally, as shown in Fig. 11-6(a).

Similarly, energy is evolved when 1 mole of gaseous chloride ions, $Cl^-_{(g)}$, is surrounded by the partially positive H atoms of the water molecules to form hydrated Cl^- ions, $Cl^-(H_2O)_y$. Of the y H_2O molecules surrounding each Cl^- ion, four are generally in close contact with the Cl^- ion and surround it tetrahedrally, as shown in Fig. 11-6(b). It should be mentioned here that we do not actually know whether the two H atoms of each H_2O molecule are equidistant from the negative ion, as shown in the diagram, or whether one of the H atoms is closer than the other to the negative ion.

In the hydration of 1 mole each of gaseous Na^+ and Cl^- ions, 183.0 kcal/mole are evolved:

$$Na^+_{(g)} + Cl^-_{(g)} + (x + y)H_2O_{(l)} \longrightarrow Na^+(OH_2)_{x(soln)} + Cl^-(H_2O)_{y(soln)} \qquad \Delta H = -183.0 \text{ kcal/mole}$$

Notice that the hydration energy of Na^+Cl^- (-183.0) and its lattice energy (-183.8) are about the same. Thus the hydration energy provides the energy necessary to counterbalance the lattice energy, which tends to hold together the ions in the crystal, and dissolution can occur without requiring that energy be supplied by some external source. As we shall discuss in more detail in Chapters 15 and 16, the difference between the hydration energy and the lattice energy is the heat involved in the dissolution of 1 mole of crystalline Na^+Cl^- in water:

$$Na^+Cl^-_{(s)} + (x + y)H_2O_{(l)} \longrightarrow Na^+(OH_2)_{x(soln)} + Cl^-(H_2O)_{y(soln)} \qquad \Delta H = +0.8 \text{ kcal/mole}$$

The energy relationships involved in the dissolution of 1 mole of crystalline Na^+Cl^- in water may be summarized by the following scheme:

$$\underbrace{Na^+(OH_2)_{x(soln)} + Cl^-(H_2O)_{y(soln)}}_{\uparrow} \xleftarrow[(x+y)H_2O]{\Delta H = -183.0 \text{ kcal/mole}} \{Na_{(g)}^+ + Cl_{(g)}^-\} \xrightarrow{\Delta H = -183.8 \text{ kcal/mole}} Na^+Cl_{(s)}^-$$

$$\Delta H = +0.8 \text{ kcal/mole} \quad (Na^+Cl^-_{(s)} \to \text{solution})$$

The hydration energy of an ionic compound represents quantitatively the interaction of the (polar) solvent water molecules with the gaseous (positive and negative) ions $M^{+n}_{(g)} + X^{-n}_{(g)}$ of the ionic compound. Similar to the lattice energy, the hydration energy increases as the charge on the ions increases and their size decreases. For example, here is an approximate but very useful generalization: the heat of hydration of a monopositive ion, M^+, is about 100 kcal/mole of ions; that of a dipositive ion, M^{+2}, is about 400 kcal/mole of ions; and that of a tripositive ion, M^{+3}, is about 1,000 kcal/mole of ions. Hydrated ions in solution are often designated by placing the symbol (aq) after the formula of the ion. For example, for a positive ion such as the sodium ion, Na^+, we may write $Na^+(aq)$ instead of $Na^+(OH_2)_x$, and both formulas stand for a sodium ion surrounded by the oxygen atoms of a number of H_2O molecules in aqueous solution—a hydrated sodium ion. Similarly, for a negative ion such as the chloride ion,

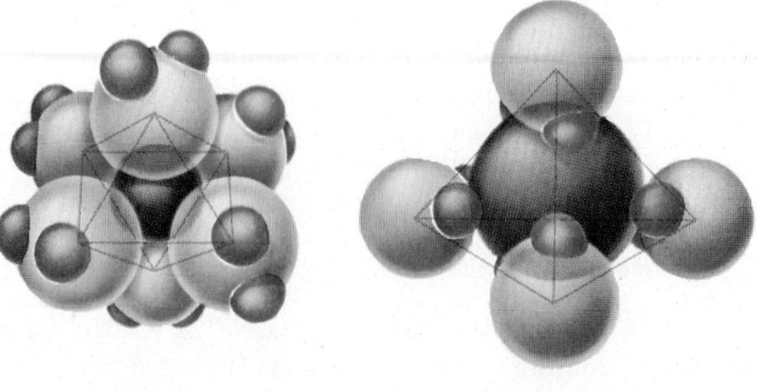

FIGURE 11-6 (a) Hydrated sodium ion, $Na^+(OH_2)_6$. (b) Hydrated chloride ion, $Cl^-(H_2O)_4$.

Cl^-, we may write $Cl^-(aq)$ instead of $Cl^-(H_2O)_y$, and both formulas represent a chloride ion surrounded by the hydrogen atoms of a number of H_2O molecules in aqueous solution—a hydrated chloride ion.

THE IONIZING PROPERTY OF WATER. Another important property of water is its tendency to bring about the *ionization* of acids—that is, to break down the *molecules* of an acid into *ions*. Pure acids, liquid or gaseous, are essentially covalent compounds, even though the electron-pair bonds generally are unequally shared by the partner atoms and consequently are highly polar. Thus a pure, perfectly anhydrous, liquid acid such as HCl generally is a very poor conductor of electricity and does not attack some metals which would react readily with H^+ ions. However, when gaseous or liquid HCl is dissolved in water, a fundamental change occurs in its properties. A water solution of hydrogen chloride is a good electrical conductor and dissolves electropositive metals with the evolution of hydrogen gas, H_2. Hence, the solution contains ions, specifically hydrogen ions and chloride ions, and is commonly called a solution of *hydrochloric acid.* This change of properties indicates that the polar covalent molecules of liquid or gaseous HCl have reacted with the polar covalent water molecules. The covalent bond that had been holding the hydrogen and chlorine atoms together within the HCl molecule is broken, forming a hydrogen ion which combines with water molecules to produce a hydrated hydrogen ion, $H^+(aq)$, and a chloride ion, which combines with water molecules to form a hydrated chloride ion, $Cl^-(aq)$.

The changes that occur when hydrogen chloride is dissolved in water result from the polar character of both the HCl and the H_2O molecules. When a hydrogen chloride molecule comes into contact with water molecules, the partially negative oxygen atoms of the water molecules exert a strong attraction on the partially positive hydrogen atom of the hydrogen chloride molecule, while the partially positive hydrogen atoms of water are attracted by the partially negative chlorine atom of the hydrogen chloride molecule. The effect of these combined attractions is so great that the hydrogen atom surrenders its hold on the electron pair that it had been sharing with the chlorine atom in H:Cl and becomes a hydrated positively charged hydrogen ion, $H^+(aq)$, while the partner chlorine atom takes sole possession of the electron pair and becomes a hydrated negatively charged chloride ion, $Cl^-(aq)$.

Another way of visualizing the separation of the HCl molecule into a H^+ ion and a Cl^- ion is in terms of the high dielectric constant of water; once water molecules have interposed themselves between the H^+ ion and the Cl^- ion, their mutual attraction decreases very sharply (actually becomes $\frac{1}{80}$ of what it would be if the ions were in a vacuum). The H^+ ion formed by the dissociation of HCl is surrounded by (associated with) water molecules. The resulting particle is often represented by the simplest formula, H_3O^+ (hydronium ion), but of course the hydronium ion itself is surrounded by other water molecules, resulting in a hydrated hydronium ion, $H^+(OH_2)_x$ or simply $H^+(aq)$. In turn, the negatively charged Cl^- ion attracts to itself the positively charged ends of several water molecules to form the hydrated Cl^- ion, represented as $Cl^-(H_2O)_y$, or simply $Cl^-(aq)$. A considerable amount of heat is evolved in the hydration of hydrogen chloride; precisely 17.56 kcal are evolved whenever 1 mole (36.5 g) of gaseous HCl is dissolved in about 1 l. of water at room temperature.

The reaction of hydrogen chloride with water to form a solution of hydrochloric acid may then be represented as;

$$HCl + (x + y)H_2O \longrightarrow H^+(OH_2)_x + Cl^-(H_2O)_y \qquad \Delta H = -17.56 \text{ kcal/mole HCl}$$

or simply

$$HCl \xrightarrow{\text{water}} H^+(aq) + Cl^-(aq) \qquad \Delta H = -17.56 \text{ kcal/mole HCl}$$

Thus the ionization of any acid in water always gives rise to hydrated hydrogen ions, $H^+(aq)$, and hydrated anions $X^-(aq)$. Bare hydrogen ions, H^+ (protons), are not present in aqueous solutions of acids, nor are bare anions, whether monatomic, such as Cl^-, or polyatomic, such as $SO_4^{=}$. If we keep this in mind, we may for simplicity omit the symbol (aq) which indicates that in water solutions ions are hydrated, so the ionic dissociation of HCl in water may be simply represented as $HCl \longrightarrow H^+ + Cl^-$. The reaction of a pure anhydrous acid with water to form hydrated H^+ ions and hydrated anions always releases a great deal of heat energy—that is, the reaction is strongly exothermic. Once the pure acid has been ionized to form the hydrated ions in solution, it is generally quite difficult to remove completely all the water and restore the original acid to its anhydrous form.

SOLID HYDRATES

We have seen that when an ionic solid dissolves in water, its ions become hydrated. When a water solution of an ionic solid is evaporated until it recrystallizes, the resulting crystalline solid often still contains water. A crystalline salt that contains a definite and constant quantity of water is called a *hydrate,* and the water present in a hydrate is called *water of hydration* or *water of crystallization.* Hydrates have a constant composition, as represented by their formulas, and hence are chemical compounds. For example, if a water solution of calcium chloride is evaporated to dryness, the resulting crystals that form contain six molecules of water for each $CaCl_2$, and are represented as $CaCl_2 \cdot 6\,H_2O$. When the water of crystallization is removed from a hydrate, the resulting solid is called an *anhydrous* salt. Hydrates may also be formed when an anhydrous salt is simply exposed to moist air. For example, white anhydrous $CuSO_4$ gradually absorbs water from the atmosphere to form the blue hydrate, $CuSO_4 \cdot 5\,H_2O$. We shall discuss in Chapter 34 this change of color resulting from the formation of the hydrated Cu(II) salt.

DELIQUESCENCE. Some anhydrous salts not only absorb enough of the water vapor present in the air to form a hydrate, but continue to absorb water until the hydrate dissolves to a liquid solution. A substance that takes up water vapor until it actually forms an aqueous solution is called *deliquescent* (Latin: to become liquid). The process is known as *deliquescence.* For example, when the anhydrous salt $CaCl_2$ is exposed to moist air, it first absorbs enough water from the air to form the hydrate $CaCl_2 \cdot 6\,H_2O$, and then this hydrate absorbs additional water until droplets of its solution are formed. Because of this property, calcium chloride is sometimes used to keep down the dust on dirt roads.

A substance that absorbs moisture from the atmosphere is called *hygroscopic.* All deliquescent substances are hygroscopic, but not all hygroscopic substances are deliquescent. For example, finely divided substances, such as salt and flour, are slightly hygroscopic, but they do not deliquesce because they do not absorb enough water to form a solution.

Many hydrates lose water when they are exposed to dry air or when they are heated. For example, when copper(II) sulfate pentahydrate, $CuSO_4 \cdot 5\,H_2O$, is heated to 250°C, it loses its water of crystallization, $5\,H_2O$, and forms the anhydrous salt $CuSO_4$. When this anhydrous salt is again exposed to moist air at room temperature, it re-forms the original hydrate. Other hydrates, however, do not lose their water of hydration when exposed to dry air, and if heated, decompose rather than re-form the anhydrous salt. For example, anhydrous $AlCl_3$ absorbs moisture from the atmosphere to form aluminum chloride hexahydrate, $AlCl_3 \cdot 6\,H_2O$. But this hydrate, if heated, instead of re-forming the anhydrous salt $AlCl_3$ decomposes into Al_2O_3 and HCl.

A substance that spontaneously loses its water of hydration when exposed to the atmosphere is called *efflorescent* (Latin: to blossom), because sometimes the crystals of the hydrate break apart in a flower-like shape. Notice that the terms "deliquescence," "efflorescence," and "hygroscopic" refer to *relative* properties. A hydrate may effloresce if the air is very dry, but if the air is quite moist the same hydrate may deliquesce. In fact, hydrates have a definite vapor pressure at any given temperature. If the vapor pressure of a hydrate is *greater than* the partial pressure of water vapor in the surrounding air, in time some or all of the water of hydration will leave the hydrate and pass into the air as water vapor (the hydrate effloresces). If the vapor pressure of the hydrate is *less than* the partial pressure of the water vapor in the air, efflorescence does not occur. For example, $SrCl_2 \cdot 6\,H_2O$ has a vapor pressure of 8.4 torr at 25°C. Consequently it loses its water of crystallization when it is placed in air at 25°C if the partial pressure of water vapor is less than 8.4 torr. On the other hand, the anhydrous salt $SrCl_2$, placed in air at 25°C containing a partial pressure of water vapor greater than 8.4 torr, takes on water to form the hydrate $SrCl_2 \cdot 6\,H_2O$. A deliquescent substance begins to take on water from the atmosphere and continues to do so as long as its vapor pressure is lower than the partial pressure of water vapor in the surrounding atmosphere. The process continues until at last a solution is produced whose vapor pressure is equal to the partial pressure of the water vapor in the air.

Some of the substances that deliquesce, such as $CaCl_2$, form definite solid hydrates, whereas others do not. For example, pellets of sodium hydroxide, NaOH, when exposed to the atmosphere, take up so much water vapor that they form a solution; but NaOH does not form any solid hydrates. Obviously any substance that deliquesces is extremely soluble in water.

MOISTURE IN THE AIR

Water in the gaseous form—what we call water vapor or steam—is always present in the atmosphere. When at a given temperature the water vapor in the air exerts a partial pressure equal to the vapor pressure of water at that temperature, the air contains the maximum amount of water vapor for that particular temperature. The air is then said to be saturated, or to have a relative humidity of 100%. The amount of water vapor required to produce 100% relative humidity increases with increasing temperature because, as we know, the vapor pressure of water increases with increasing temperature. Both the relative humidity of air and the absolute percentage of moisture in the air vary widely from place to place and from time to time. Surprisingly enough, even after a rainstorm, or near a large body of water, the moisture content of the air may be far from saturation conditions, and actually may be relatively low.

RELATIVE HUMIDITY. At any temperature, the *relative humidity* of air (as of any gas) is defined as the ratio of the partial pressure of water vapor present in the air to the vapor pressure of water at the temperature considered. For example, if the partial pressure of the water vapor in the air at 22°C is 9.9 torr (the vapor pressure of water at 22°C is 19.8 torr), then the relative humidity of the air is $(9.9/19.8) \times 100 = 50\%$. And if the partial pressure of the water vapor at 22°C is 4.95 torr, the relative humidity is only $(4.95/19.8) \times 100 = 25\%$.

As we know, the higher the temperature, the greater the vapor pressure of water, as shown in Table 8-1 of Chapter 8. Thus air that is saturated with water vapor at a given temperature will no longer be saturated if the temperature is increased. Conversely, if unsaturated air is suddenly cooled, it may become saturated. For example, if the partial pressure of the water vapor present in a sample of air at 25°C is 19.8 torr (the vapor pressure of water at 25°C is 25.2 torr), the air is not saturated. If this air is cooled to 22°C, however, it becomes saturated, because now the partial pressure of the water vapor in the air (which is still 19.8 torr) is equal to the vapor pressure of water, which is 19.8 torr at 22°C.

Suppose the temperature falls enough for the air to become saturated; then, water vapor will condense in the form of mist or dew, if the temperature falls still more. The *dew point* is the temperature to which a particular sample of air must be lowered to become saturated with water vapor.

THERMAL DECOMPOSITION OF WATER. Although water is a very stable compound, at very high temperatures it decomposes into its elements, hydrogen and oxygen, with the absorption of a large quantity of heat:

$$2\ H_2O_{(steam)} \rightleftharpoons 2\ H_{2(g)} + O_{2(g)} \qquad \Delta H = +116.2\ \text{kcal/mole-equation}$$

At 1,000°C and 1 atm pressure, only about 0.000026% of a given quantity of water is decomposed. But the percentage increases with increasing temperature, until at 3,500°C about 30% of a given quantity of water is decomposed. Unless the hydrogen and oxygen gases are removed, however, they recombine instantaneously to form steam as the mixture cools.

ELECTROLYSIS OF WATER. In our discussion of the methods of preparing hydrogen gas (p. 75), we saw that water containing a small amount of an acid, alkali, or salt can be easily decomposed by means of a direct electric current to form gaseous hydrogen and gaseous oxygen:

$$2\ H_2O \xrightarrow[\text{(acid or alkali or salt)}]{\text{electric current}} 2\ H_2 + O_2$$

REACTIONS OF WATER. Water is involved in an extremely large number of reactions—which, however, can be divided into a few main types, some of which are already familiar and which we shall now recall briefly.

DECOMPOSITION OF WATER TO LIBERATE HYDROGEN GAS. As we have seen in Chapter 7 (p. 90), water reacts with the more electropositive metals such as sodium and calcium to form hydrogen gas and the metal hydroxide:

$$2\ Na + 2\ H_2O \longrightarrow H_2 + 2\ NaOH$$
$$Ca + 2\ H_2O \longrightarrow H_2 + Ca(OH)_2$$

Water also reacts with ionic hydrides of electropositive metals such as calcium hydride, CaH_2, forming H_2 gas and the hydroxide of the metal.

$$CaH_2 + 2\ H_2O \longrightarrow 2\ H_2 + Ca(OH)_2$$

A number of elements, metals as well as non-metals, which have almost no effect on water at room temperature are very effective in decomposing water vapor (steam) at high temperature (p. 91). For example, red-hot iron reacts with steam to form hydrogen and iron(III) oxide:

$$2\ Fe + 3\ H_2O_{(steam)} \longrightarrow 3\ H_2 + Fe_2O_3$$

Similarly, red-hot coke (carbon) reacts with steam to form "water gas" ($H_2 + CO$, p. 91). Many compounds also react with steam at high temperatures. Examples are the reaction of steam with methane, CH_4, which produces hydrogen, H_2, and carbon dioxide, CO_2, and the reaction of steam with carbon monoxide, CO, to form H_2 and CO_2 (p. 97).

11-2 Heavy Water

In Chapter 7 we mentioned that hydrogen occurs in nature as a mixture of three isotopes: ordinary hydrogen of atomic weight 1, deuterium of atomic weight 2, and tritium of atomic weight 3. Hydrogen gas, water, and all hydrogen compounds in nature contain 1 atom of deuterium, D, to about 6,000 atoms of "ordinary" hydrogen, H, whatever the source and nature of the compound considered. Tritium, on the other hand, is present only in extremely minute amounts (believed to be less than 1 atom of tritium to 10^{17} atoms of ordinary hydrogen), and moreover, since it is radioactive and decays rather rapidly, its content may vary depending on the age and origin of the substance considered.

Water containing two deuterium atoms in place of two ordinary hydrogen atoms is called "heavy" water, or deuterium oxide, and its formula is D_2O. Molecules of water may also contain one light hydrogen atom and one heavy hydrogen atom. In this case, the formula is HDO. Since "ordinary" hydrogen atoms and deuterium atoms always appear in nature in the relative proportions of about 6,000 to 1, and since the deuterium in water is almost all HDO, a sample of natural water contains about 1 molecule of HDO to every 3,000 molecules of H_2O.

THE PREPARATION OF HEAVY WATER

Heavy water, D_2O, may be obtained from the residues of the electrolysis of large quantities of ordinary water. During the electrolysis of water, "light" hydrogen gas, H_2, is formed more rapidly than "heavy" hydrogen gas (deuterium), D_2. As a result, the residues of the electrolysis contain a higher percentage of deuterium than does ordinary water. From these deuterium-rich residues pure D_2O can be obtained by fractional distillation, taking advantage of the fact that its boiling point, 101.42°C, is somewhat higher than that of "ordinary" water, 100.00°C. Pure D_2O may also be prepared by the reaction of deuterium gas, D_2, with oxygen gas, O_2, in the presence of an electric spark: $2\ D_2 + O_2 \longrightarrow 2\ D_2O$.

THE PROPERTIES OF HEAVY WATER

As we might expect, heavy water resembles ordinary water very closely in its chemical reactions. It also resembles ordinary water in its physical properties, except for some differences arising from the higher formula weight (20.0 instead of 18.0). Thus, for example, both ordinary and heavy water are transparent, colorless, and odorless, but the freezing point of ordinary water is 0.00°C whereas the freezing point of heavy water is 3.82°C; and as we have stated, at 1 atm pressure the boiling point of ordinary water is 100.00°C, whereas heavy water boils at 101.42°C. Heavy water reaches its maximum density, 1.1073 g/cm^3, at 11.6°C; ordinary water reaches its maximum density, 1.0000 g/cm^3, at 4.0°C. Also, heavy water is somewhat more viscous than ordinary water.

Like ordinary water, heavy water exists in the liquid state as molecular aggregates, $(D_2O)_n$, held together by strong electrostatic interactions between the partially positive deuterium atoms and the partially negative oxygen atoms of separate D_2O molecules—or, as we may say, by "deuterium bonds."

Although it closely resembles ordinary water in its chemical reactions, deuterium oxide exhibits very different physiological properties. In fact, deuterium oxide appears to be "non-utilizable" for reactions that occur in living plants and animals. Seeds moistened with D_2O do not sprout, and mice that are fed only D_2O die of thirst.

USES OF HEAVY WATER

Deuterium oxide is important in chemical research, because compounds that contain reactive hydrogen atoms exchange them with deuterium atoms if treated with D_2O. The new compounds thus obtained differ from the original compounds in some of their properties owing to the presence of the heavier and more slowly vibrating deuterium atoms, and the differences often help in the structural study of these compounds. Heavy water is also used widely in nuclear reactors as a moderator of neutrons.

11-3 Hydrogen Peroxide

Normally, hydrogen and oxygen combine to form ordinary water, H_2O (hydrogen oxide). Under special conditions, however, they may combine to form a less stable compound of formula H_2O_2, called *hydrogen peroxide.* Notice that hydrogen peroxide contains twice the weight of oxygen that is present in water. In fact, the prefix "per" in its name simply means "more," to indicate that hydrogen peroxide contains more oxygen than does hydrogen oxide. The hydrogen peroxide molecule contains two hydrogen atoms to two oxygen atoms, and because oxygen is a more electronegative element than hydrogen each H atom of H_2O_2 is assigned an oxidation number of $+1$, and each O atom is assigned an oxidation number of -1. Notice, therefore, that in H_2O_2, oxygen has an oxidation number of -1, intermediate between it oxidation number in elementary oxygen, O_2 (Ox. No. = 0) and in water, H_2O (Ox. No. = -2). Only slight traces of hydrogen peroxide occur in nature—in the atmosphere and in rain and snow, for example. These traces are probably formed by the action of ultraviolet light on oxygen in the presence of water vapor.

STRUCTURE AND BONDING IN THE HYDROGEN PEROXIDE MOLECULE

Like water, H_2O, hydrogen peroxide, H_2O_2, is an essentially covalent compound. In the H_2O_2 molecule, the two oxygen atoms are equivalent, and so are the two hydrogen atoms. Each oxygen atom shares one electron pair with a hydrogen atom and one electron pair with its partner oxygen atom. In addition, each oxygen atom has two lone electron pairs, as shown by the electron dot formula, $H:\ddot{\underset{..}{O}}:\ddot{\underset{..}{O}}:H$. The spatial arrangement of the atoms in the H_2O_2 molecule and the shape of the molecule are illustrated in Fig. 11-7. We see from these diagrams that the H_2O_2 molecule is non-planar, the two O—H covalent bonds being almost at right angles to each other and the molecule having what is sometimes called a skew-chain or gauche structure.

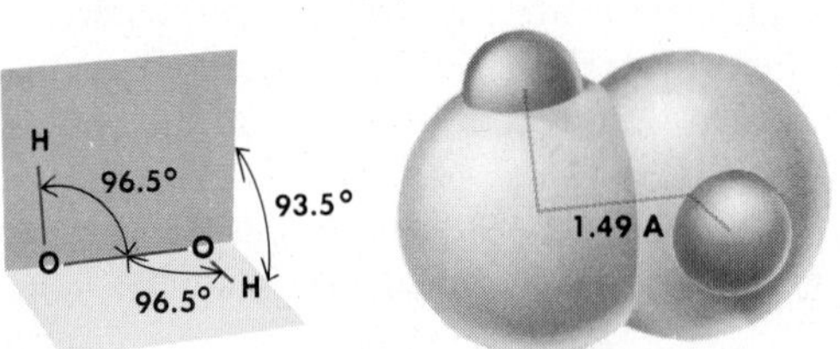

FIGURE 11-7 The structure of H_2O_2.

As in water, the electron cloud of each O—H bond of H_2O_2 is attracted more strongly by the more electronegative oxygen atom, which thereby acquires a partial negative charge (δ^-), whereas the partner H atom acquires an equal partial positive charge (δ^+). The electron pair which constitutes the O—O bond, on the other hand, is equally shared between the two equally electronegative O atoms. It follows that the molecule of hydrogen peroxide, like the molecule of water, has a polar character (H_2O_2 differs from H_2O in that it has two "negative" poles—two O atoms—whereas H_2O has only one). Thus, H_2O_2 molecules may form hydrogen bonding as a result of the electrostatic attraction between the partially positive H atoms of one H_2O_2 molecule and the partially negative O atoms of other H_2O_2 molecules, and the extent of hydrogen bonding in liquid H_2O_2 is actually slightly more than in liquid H_2O.

THE PHYSICAL PROPERTIES OF HYDROGEN PEROXIDE

Some of the physical properties of hydrogen peroxide are listed in Table 11-3. Hydrogen peroxide is soluble in water in all proportions and except for very special purposes is always prepared and used as a more or less concentrated water solution. The dilute solutions commonly used contain 3% by weight of H_2O_2; the most concentrated commercial solutions contain about 30% H_2O_2 by weight. The dissolution of hydrogen peroxide in water is slightly exothermic; about 0.8 kcal are evolved when 1 mole of H_2O_2 (34.0 g) is diluted in about 2 l. of water. Like water, 100% pure (anhydrous) hydrogen peroxide is a colorless liquid, although a large quantity of the liquid may have a faint blue color. It is almost odorless, but a faint smell somewhat akin to ozone and the halogens can be detected by inhaling the vapor of its solutions. Water solutions of hydrogen peroxide lack a well-defined taste, but produce an astringent, prickling sensation on the skin. Anhydrous hydrogen peroxide is denser than water and has a lower melting point (−0.42°C) and a higher boiling point (150.2°C at 1 atm) than water. The triple point of hydrogen peroxide, −0.42°C, also occurs at a lower temperature than that of water, +0.01°C. Hydrogen peroxide has a higher heat of fusion than water does; that is, more energy is required to melt 1 mole of crystalline hydrogen peroxide to its liquid at −0.42°C than to melt 1 mole of ice to liquid water at 0.00°C. Similarly, hydrogen peroxide has a higher heat of vaporization, again indicating that comparatively more energy is required to break completely the intermolecular bonding of liquid H_2O_2 than of liquid H_2O. To avoid decomposition, hydrogen peroxide usually is distilled at a pressure lower than 1 atm. At 68 torr, for example, the boiling point of hydrogen peroxide is 84.0°C, a temperature at which it can be safely distilled without decomposition.

In the vapor state, hydrogen peroxide, like water, is composed of single non-associated molecules; in the liquid state, it is associated by hydrogen bonding much in the same way as water. Actually, estimates indicate that hydrogen bonding is even more extensive in H_2O_2 than it is in H_2O; thus liquid hydrogen peroxide consists of molecular aggregates $(H_2O_2)_n$—of course, the molecules of each aggregate are continuously shifting partners. The structure of solid H_2O_2 is also heavily hydrogen bonded. Each O atom is tetrahedrally surrounded by four atoms—one O and one H atom of the same molecule and two H atoms of neighboring molecules. That is, each O atom forms two covalent bonds (a O—O bond and a O—H bond) and two hydrogen bonds. The resulting structure is quite compact; in fact, H_2O_2, unlike H_2O, expands on melting, like a normal liquid.

TABLE 11-3 SOME PHYSICAL PROPERTIES OF HYDROGEN PEROXIDE

Melting point at 1 atm	−0.43°C
Triple point	−0.42°C, 0.26 torr
Boiling point at 1 atm	150.2°C
Critical point	457.0°C, (214 atm)
Density of solid at −20°C	1.71 g/cm^3
Density of liquid at 0°C	1.471 g/cm^3
Density of liquid at 20°C	1.442 g/cm^3
Heat of fusion at m.p.	2.7 kcal/mole
Heat of vaporization at 25°C	362.0 kcal/mole
Heat capacity of liquid	0.62 cal/g × deg 21.36 cal/mole × deg
Heat of dilution to form a 3% water solution at 25°C	0.8 kcal/mole H_2O_2
Dielectric constant at 20°C	73

Because of the polar character of the H_2O_2 molecule—and of the consequent association through hydrogen bonding—liquid hydrogen peroxide has a high dielectric constant (about 73 as compared to 80 for water), and hence is almost as effective a solvent. Since both liquid water and liquid hydrogen peroxide are strongly hydrogen bonded, so is a mixture of the two liquids. The hydrogen peroxide solutions in water consist of molecular aggregates of the general formula $(H_2O_2)_x \cdot (H_2O)_y$, held together by hydrogen bonding.

LABORATORY PREPARATION OF HYDROGEN PEROXIDE

We can prepare a dilute solution of hydrogen peroxide in the laboratory by adding solid sodium peroxide to ice-cold water. Hydrogen peroxide and sodium hydroxide are formed, as shown by the following equation:

$$Na_2O_2 + 2\,H_2O \longrightarrow H_2O_2 + 2\,NaOH$$

The product is an alkaline solution of hydrogen peroxide, because both hydrogen peroxide and the base sodium hydroxide are soluble in water. In an earlier chapter we mentioned that oxygen gas is released by the reaction between excess water and sodium peroxide at room temperature. The oxygen is produced by the decomposition of the H_2O_2 that is first formed. We shall refer to this reaction again in our discussion of the decomposition of hydrogen peroxide.

If we want to prepare a *neutral* solution of H_2O_2, we simply substitute the required amount of an ice-cold acid solution for the water. Here is the equation for the reaction with cold hydrochloric acid:

$$Na_2O_2 + 2\ HCl \longrightarrow H_2O_2 + 2\ NaCl$$

The reaction of either water or a water solution of hydrogen chloride (hydrochloric acid) with sodium peroxide at low temperatures, then, produces a solution containing H_2O_2 and either soluble sodium hydroxide or soluble sodium chloride. But it is difficult to separate the hydrogen peroxide from either of these dissolved compounds except by distillation. Consequently, if we are to obtain a solution containing only hydrogen peroxide by the reaction of a metal peroxide with an acid, we must start with reactants that will produce hydrogen peroxide and an *insoluble* salt. For example, if we mix a solution of barium peroxide, BaO_2, with the calculated amount of ice-cold dilute sulfuric acid, we obtain a solution of relatively pure hydrogen peroxide and a precipitate of white, insoluble barium sulfate:

$$BaO_{2(aq)} + H_2SO_{4(aq)} \longrightarrow H_2O_{2(aq)} + BaSO_{4(s)}$$

In this equation the subscript (aq) indicates that the substance is present in aqueous solution, and the subscript (s) indicates, as we know, that the product, $BaSO_4$, is precipitated as an insoluble substance. Simply by filtering the mixture that results from this reaction we can remove the precipitate and obtain a solution of hydrogen peroxide free of dissolved salts. In place of H_2SO_4, we could use H_3PO_4, phosphoric acid, because barium phosphate, $Ba_3(PO_4)_2$, is also insoluble:

$$3\ BaO_{2(aq)} + 2\ H_3PO_{4(aq)} \longrightarrow 3\ H_2O_{2(aq)} + Ba_3(PO_4)_{2(s)}$$

INDUSTRIAL PREPARATION OF HYDROGEN PEROXIDE

The most important industrial method of preparing hydrogen peroxide involves the electrolysis of a water solution of sulfuric acid or ammonium hydrogen sulfate, NH_4HSO_4. This method produces hydrogen peroxide with a concentration of about 30 per cent. Although we cannot go into a detailed discussion of the reactions that occur in this process, the following equations provide an adequate summary:

$$1.\quad 2\ HSO_4^- \xrightarrow[\text{current}]{\text{electric}} S_2O_8^{=} + 2\ H^+ + 2\ e^-$$

$$2.\quad S_2O_8^{=} + 2\ H_2O \longrightarrow 2\ HSO_4^- + H_2O_2$$

Notice that the hydrogen sulfate ions, HSO_4^-, with which this process starts in reaction (1), are re-formed in reaction (2). Consequently, the preparation of hydrogen peroxide by this method can be carried on as a continuous, cyclic operation.

11-4 The Chemical Properties of Hydrogen Peroxide

TENDENCY TO SPONTANEOUS DECOMPOSITION

Unlike water, H_2O, which is an extremely stable compound and decomposes endothermally only at extremely high temperatures, hydrogen peroxide, H_2O_2, tends to break down spontaneously into water and oxygen. A large quantity of heat is evolved in the process:

$$H_2O_2 \longrightarrow H_2O + \tfrac{1}{2}\ O_2 \qquad \Delta H = -23.6\ \text{kcal/mole}\ H_2O_2$$

Notice in this reaction that for each oxygen atom of $H_2\overset{(-1)}{O}_2$ which is oxidized to molecular oxygen, $\overset{(0)}{O}_2$, another oxygen atom of $H_2\overset{(-1)}{O}_2$ is reduced to form water $H_2\overset{(-2)}{O}$. Hence for each oxygen atom of hydrogen peroxide which acts as an oxidant, there is one oxygen atom which acts as a reductant. We express this by saying that H_2O_2 undergoes a self oxidation-reduction reaction, or a *disproportionation* reaction. This disproportionation reaction is common to hydrogen peroxide either in the gaseous or in the liquid form, and even to hydrogen peroxide in dilute water solutions. The rate at which disproportionation occurs, however, varies greatly depending on the conditions, particularly temperature, concentration, and the presence of foreign substances which may either speed up or retard the reaction.

EFFECT OF TEMPERATURE. The rate at which hydrogen peroxide decomposes increases as the temperature rises, other conditions being equal. Very pure solutions of hydrogen peroxide kept in small aluminum containers in a cool place decompose less than 1 per cent in a year's time, but at 100°C they decompose fairly rapidly unless a stabilizer is added.

The effect of temperature explains why the reaction of sodium peroxide with water produces H_2O_2 at low temperatures and O_2 at higher temperatures. In both cases, hydrogen peroxide is first formed according to the following reaction:

$$Na_2O_2 + 2\,H_2O \longrightarrow H_2O_2 + 2\,NaOH$$

But unless the temperature is kept low, H_2O_2 decomposes immediately:

$$2\,H_2O_2 \longrightarrow O_2 + 2\,H_2O$$

Now you can see why we specified that *ice-cold* water and *ice-cold* acid solutions must be used in preparing hydrogen peroxide.

EFFECT OF CONCENTRATION. Other factors being equal, the rate of decomposition of hydrogen peroxide solutions generally increases with the concentration. However, very pure anhydrous hydrogen peroxide can be kept without appreciable decomposition for a relatively long time at low temperatures and in the absence of light and impurities which may act as catalysts.

EFFECT OF CATALYSTS. Many finely divided substances will sharply increase the rate of decomposition of hydrogen peroxide, either anhydrous or in aqueous solution, even at low temperatures. In fact, some of these catalysts are so effective that under certain conditions the decomposition may occur explosively. A great variety of substances, such as finely divided platinum, silver and gold, manganese dioxide, MnO_2, charcoal, and even dirt and dust particles are effective catalysts in this connection. As we described in Chapter 6, the catalytic decomposition of an ordinary 3% solution of hydrogen peroxide in the presence of some powdered MnO_2 is a safe and convenient method for preparing oxygen gas in the laboratory.

The catalytic decomposition of H_2O_2 at times occurs explosively, because the decomposition reaction, as we know, is highly exothermic. If the decomposition is fast enough at the outset, the heat released further increases the rate of decomposition; more heat is then released, and so on, the decomposition proceeding at a rapidly increasing rate. In concentrated solutions the heat energy evolved by the decomposition may be great enough to vaporize all the water present. The steam thus produced, together with the oxygen gas released by the reaction, constitutes such a great volume of gas that an explosion occurs.

Hydrogen peroxide is so sensitive to decomposition that even the container in which it is stored may act as a catalytic agent. Since high-purity aluminum seems to have no appreciable catalytic effect, commercial concentrated hydrogen peroxide solutions are shipped in aluminum drums and tank trucks.

STABILIZERS. Some substances have on hydrogen peroxide an effect opposite to that of catalysts—that is, they *slow down* the rate of decomposition. These substances are known as *stabilizers* or *inhibitors*. The stabilizer most commonly used to decrease the decomposition rate of ordinary "drugstore" hydrogen peroxide is a trace amount of sodium pyrophosphate, $Na_4P_2O_7$.

OXIDIZING POWER OF HYDROGEN PEROXIDE

The most important chemical property of hydrogen peroxide is its strong oxidizing power. When hydrogen peroxide acts as an oxidizing agent, H_2O is formed and the other oxygen atom, (O), is made available for oxidation, according to the following schematic equation:

$$H_2O_2 \longrightarrow H_2O + (O)$$

For every mole of hydrogen peroxide that reacts, 1 mole of water is produced and 1 mole of (O) enters into some further chemical combination. Thus, the reaction between hydrogen peroxide and any reducing substance, R, may be schematically written as follows:

$$H_2O_2 + R \longrightarrow H_2O + RO$$

For example, hydrogen peroxide reacts with lead sulfide, PbS, to form water and insoluble lead sulfate, $PbSO_4$:

$$PbS_{(s)} + 4\ H_2O_{2(soln)} \longrightarrow 4\ H_2O_{(l)} + PbSO_{4(s)}$$

This reaction is often used to restore the colors of old paintings. Over the years, traces of hydrogen sulfide in the air react with the lead pigments in the paint to form a coating of black lead sulfide, PbS. But when the darkened surface of the painting is treated with a solution of hydrogen peroxide, the lead sulfide is oxidized and white lead sulfate, $PbSO_4$, is formed.

Similarly, a solution of sodium sulfite, Na_2SO_3, is easily oxidized by hydrogen peroxide to sodium sulfate, Na_2SO_4:

$$Na_2SO_3 + H_2O_2 \longrightarrow Na_2SO_4 + H_2O$$

HYDROGEN PEROXIDE AS A REDUCING AGENT

When hydrogen peroxide comes into contact with an oxidizing agent even stronger than itself, a reaction occurs in which both oxygen atoms of H_2O_2 are *oxidized* to gaseous molecular oxygen, O_2. An example is the reaction of an aqueous solution of hydrogen peroxide with chlorine gas:

$$H_2O_{2(soln)} + Cl_{2(g)} \longrightarrow O_{2(g)} + 2\ HCl_{(soln)}$$

In this reaction chlorine is the oxidizing agent, as its oxidation number is reduced from zero in Cl_2 to -1 in HCl, whereas the oxygen atoms of H_2O_2 are oxidized from the oxidation number -1 to zero in O_2.

THE DETECTION OF HYDROGEN PEROXIDE. Most of the tests used to determine the presence of hydrogen peroxide are based on its oxidizing action. For example, if a solution of hydrogen peroxide is added to a dilute solution of potassium iodide containing a small amount of acid, the hydrogen peroxide oxidizes the iodide ion, I^-, to iodine, I_2, according to the following equation:

$$H_2O_2 + 2\ KI + 2\ HCl \longrightarrow I_2 + 2\ KCl + 2\ H_2O$$

The presence of the iodine may be easily detected by immersing a strip of starch paper in the resulting solution, for the iodine reacts with the starch to form a characteristic dark bluish compound. But before we can accept the formation of iodine as a reliable indication of the presence of hydrogen peroxide, we must make sure, by other chemical tests, that no other oxidizing agent (such as, for example, chlorine) was present in the original solution and could have been responsible for the formation of free iodine.

USES OF HYDROGEN PEROXIDE

Most of the uses of hydrogen peroxide are based on its oxidizing action. Hydrogen peroxide is one of the most widely used bleaching agents because it is effective yet mild and can act as an oxidizer in neutral solutions. In fact, hydrogen peroxide is used extensively in bleaching organic materials, such as wood, straw, vegetable fibers for textiles, and hair, all of which could be damaged by the more vigorous bleaching action of other oxidizing agents, such as chlorine. Concentrated hydrogen peroxide is also widely employed for the propulsion of rockets and rocket-propelled aircraft. The ordinary solution of hydrogen peroxide which is sold in drugstores and contains 3 per cent hydrogen peroxide by weight finds some minor use as an antiseptic in cleansing wounds, for it oxidizes the coagulated blood and pus and thereby eliminates the breeding ground of bacteria. A very dilute hydrogen peroxide solution is also sometimes used as a mouth wash.

Exercises

11-1 State several different natural sources of water and mention the impurities that are most likely to be present in each.

11-2 Define the term "hard water."

11-3 Describe briefly the purification of sea water by distillation.

11-4 Explain briefly what steps must be taken to prepare (a) drinking water, (b) chemically pure water from well water.

11-5 Summarize the most important physical properties of water and discuss those in which water is "abnormal" with respect to most liquids.

11-6 Mention some important consequences of the "abnormal" properties of water.

11-7 In describing water as a polar molecule, what do we mean? Cite examples of some non-polar molecules.

11-8 Draw a diagram of a water molecule showing (a) the bonding of the atoms and the angle between them, and (b) the polar character of the molecule by means of the partial charges assigned to each atom.

11-9 Explain the type of bonding present between adjacent molecules in liquid water.

11-10 The experimentally determined molecular weight of water in the vapor state is approximately 18. What does this fact indicate about hydrogen bonding between water molecules in the *vapor* state?

11-11 Give the approximate relative value of the strength of the O———H hydrogen bond of water compared with a O—H covalent bond. Of what nature is the hydrogen bond?

11-12 Discuss the melting and boiling points of the hydrides of the elements of Groups IV to VII, for the two Short Periods of the Periodic Table, in terms of the *inter*-molecular interactions of the hydride molecules.

11-13 Define a normal and an associated liquid and discuss the differences in intermolecular interactions involved in each type.

11-14 The experimentally determined molecular weight of acetic acid, $HC_2H_3O_2$, in the vapor state is approximately 120. What does this indicate about hydrogen bonding in acetic acid vapor?

11-15 Comment on the general properties of water as a solvent.

11-16 Ionic potassium bromide is soluble in water. What changes take place when a crystal of this salt is brought into contact with water? Briefly discuss the energy factors involved in the dissolution process.

11-17 Using covalent hydrogen bromide, $HBr_{(g)}$, as an example, discuss the ionizing property of water.

11-18 A certain material may be deliquescent under certain atmospheric conditions and efflorescent under other atmospheric conditions. Explain.

11-19 What is the relationship between relative humidity and the vapor pressure of water?

11-20 If the pressure on a sample of moist air is reduced, while the temperature remains constant, does the relative humidity change? Explain your answer.

11-21 Under which conditions can water be decomposed into gaseous oxygen and gaseous hydrogen?

11-22 State the approximate extent of decomposition of H_2O into O_2 and H_2 at room temperature and at 1,000°C.

11-23 Discuss briefly the reactions of water (liquid or steam) at room temperature with the following: (a) potassium metal, (b) magnesium metal, (c) red-hot carbon, (d) solid calcium hydride, CaH_2, (e) gaseous methane, CH_4, at high temperature.

11-24 What is "heavy water"? What is the approximate ratio of "heavy" to "normal" water in naturally occurring spring water?

11-25 Briefly describe two methods for obtaining deuterium oxide. How does deuterium oxide differ in its physical, chemical, and biological properties from hydrogen oxide?

11-26 Sketch the structure of the H_2O_2 molecule, indicating the approximate values of the bond angles. What is the oxidation state of (a) oxygen, and (b) hydrogen in hydrogen peroxide?

11-27 Is H_2O_2 a polar molecule? Is liquid hydrogen peroxide an associated liquid? Compare the extent of hydrogen bonding in liquid water and liquid hydrogen peroxide.

11-28 Is hydrogen peroxide a good solvent for ionic compounds? Why is the use of hydrogen peroxide as a solvent so much more limited than that of water?

11-29 Give an example of a reaction by which a water solution of hydrogen peroxide can be obtained in the laboratory.

11-30 If 1 g of pure H_2O_2 is decomposed to water and O_2, how much heat is liberated?

11-31 Give two examples of reactions in which hydrogen peroxide acts (a) as an oxidant, and (b) as a reductant.

11-32 Discuss the decomposition of hydrogen peroxide into water and oxygen gas and the factors which influence the rate of decomposition.

THE PERIODIC SYSTEM AND THE ELECTRONIC STRUCTURE OF THE ELEMENTS

12

In Chapter 3 we outlined the fundamental features of the structure of the atom. We saw that an atom consists of a positively charged nucleus surrounded by a diffuse cloud of electrons, and that the number of electrons in this cloud is equal to the number of positive charges (protons) in the nucleus. In this chapter we shall consider the electronic structure of the atoms—that is, the arrangement of the electrons in the electron clouds of the atoms. We shall also discuss in detail the classification of the elements, called the *periodic system,* which we have already briefly described in Chapter 5, and which, as we shall see, is based on the electronic structure of the elements.

12-1 Classification of the Elements

In a science such as chemistry we have to deal with an extremely vast number of experimental facts. It is one of the main concerns of chemists to classify such facts and observations—which often may appear to be isolated and unrelated—in such a way that the underlying similarities and differences not only become apparent, but also can be logically correlated and explained. During the first decades of the nineteenth century, as soon as it was realized that elements are the "building blocks" of all chemical compounds and as more and more elements were discovered, chemists started to search for and to propose various systems for classifying the elements into related groups. Although incomplete and inadequate, these early classifications of the elements proved very useful in developing the presently adopted system. It is therefore interesting to consider some of them briefly.

EARLY ATTEMPTS AT CLASSIFICATION

METALS AND NON-METALS. In the first attempts at classification the elements were simply divided into two classes: metals and non-metals. Even this was an important step forward, for it revealed significant similarities among certain elements and enabled chemists to anticipate the properties of metals and non-metals that were still undiscovered.

PROPERTIES AND ATOMIC WEIGHTS. Once the atomic weights of the elements had been established fairly accurately, chemists began to search for relationships between the properties of the elements and their atomic weights. Among the first researchers to point out relationships of this sort was a German chemist, Johann W. Döbereiner, who in 1829 found that several of the elements fell together naturally into groups of three, which he called *triads*. He noticed that the physical and chemical characteristics of the three elements of each triad were similar, and that when the three elements were arranged in order of increasing atomic weight, the atomic weight of the second element was approximately equal to the average of the atomic weights of the first and third elements. One of the triads he considered was composed of the chemically analogous non-metals, chlorine (Cl = 35.5), bromine (Br = 79.9), and iodine (I = 126.9). The atomic weight of the middle element, bromine (Br = 79.9) is very close to the average of the atomic weights of chlorine and iodine (35.5 + 126.9)/2 = 81.2. Another of Döbereiner's triads consisted of the three related metals, calcium (Ca = 40.1), strontium (Sr = 87.6), and barium (Ba = 137.3). Again, the atomic weight of strontium (87.6) is almost equal to the average of the atomic weights of calcium and barium (40.1 + 137.3)/2 = 88.7.

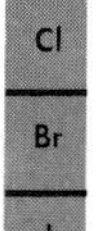

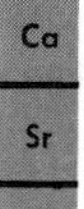

THE LAW OF OCTAVES. Döbereiner's discovery of triads encouraged other chemists to search for additional relationships. In 1864, John Newlands, an English industrial chemist, discovered another type of relationship between the atomic weights and properties of elements and suggested the existence of a natural law, which he proposed to call the *Law of Octaves*. Newlands pointed out that if elements were arranged according to increasing atomic weight, a particular element had chemical and physical properties closely similar to those of the element eight places before it and also to those of the element eight places after it on the list (the noble gases were not then known). Unfortunately, this basically sound idea was not well received by the chemists of Newlands' time, and its further development was delayed.

ATOMIC WEIGHTS AND PERIODIC VARIATIONS. Other speculative minds were wondering whether it was possible to establish a more general relationship between the properties of elements and their atomic weights. In 1862 a French scientist, A. E. Beguyer de Chancourtois, constructed a cylinder on which he arranged the elements spirally at heights proportional to their atomic weights. He discovered that similar elements appeared above one another on the cylinder. This spiral arrangement was probably the first expression of a complete periodic arrangement of the elements.

THE PERIODIC SYSTEM

In 1869 a German, Julius Lothar Meyer, and a Russian, Dimitri Mendeleef, working independently and from different approaches, succeeded in establishing a more detailed relationship between the properties of the elements and their atomic weights. These scientists, too, observed that some sort of periodic repetition of chemical and physical properties became apparent when the elements were arranged in order of increasing atomic weight. Meyer selected several physical properties of about fifty of the then-known elements and plotted them in graphs against the atomic weights of the elements. He observed, for example, that by plotting the atomic volume (the volume occupied by 1 mole of an element in the solid state) against the atomic weight, the graph obtained (Fig. 12-1) revealed a *periodic* variation of atomic volume with atomic weight—that is, the variation repeated itself at more or less regular intervals.

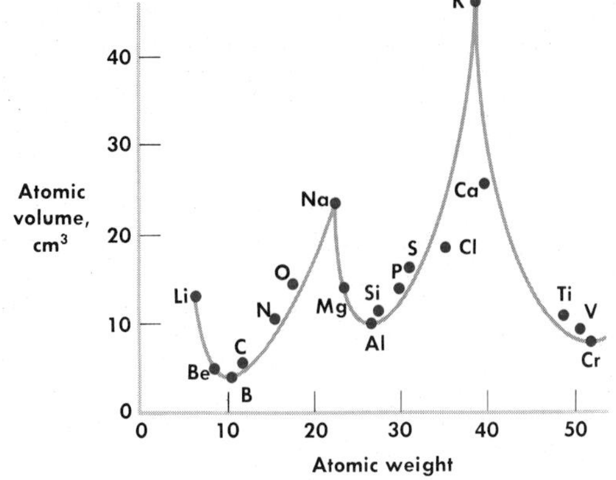

FIGURE 12-1 Periodic change of atomic volume with atomic weight.

Mendeleef, on the other hand, took into consideration not only the physical but also the chemical characteristics of the then known elements and set up a periodic system in which the elements were arranged in horizontal rows and vertical columns according to increasing atomic weight. Mendeleef felt confident that if all the existing elements were arranged according to increasing atomic weight, regular and periodic similarities and differences in their properties would become apparent. In 1869 he arranged all the sixty-five elements known at that time in a table, leaving gaps for as yet undiscovered elements, whose properties, nevertheless, he predicted. In order to keep similar elements together, Mendeleef reversed the order of two pairs of elements, putting cobalt, Co (58.9), before nickel, Ni (58.7), and tellurium, Te (127.6), before iodine, I (126.9). These exceptions proved to be justified years later, when the concept of atomic numbers of the elements became established.

Mendeleef is generally given credit for establishing the periodic system of the elements, because he felt so sure of his classification that he not only boldly left gaps in his table for six then unknown elements, but proceeded one step further. Using the properties of the known neighboring elements as a basis, he predicted the properties of the unknown ones to an amazing degree of accuracy. Compare, for example, some properties predicted by Mendeleef in 1871 for the element below silicon (called ekasilicon = below silicon) in the same column of the periodic table with those actually found for this element after it was isolated in 1886 by the German chemist, Winkler, and named germanium, Ge.

C
Si
Ge
Sn
Pb

"Ek" *Ekasilicon (predicted 1871)*	*Ge* *Germanium (observed 1886)*
1. At Wt of "Ek" = mean of at wts of its two neighbors, Ga and As: (69.7 + 74.9)/2 = 72.3.	1. At Wt = 72.6
2. Density = 5.5 g/cm^3; gray metal.	2. Density = 5.47 g/cm^3; grayish, white metal.
3. M.p. = higher than that of tin, perhaps 800°C.	3. M.p. = 958°C.
4. White powder formed on calcination (heating in air), EkO_2; density 4.7 g/cm^3; lower oxide EkO may also exist.	4. Ge reacts with O_2 forming GeO_2; density 4.70 g/cm^3; GeO is also known.
5. The metal oxides dissolve in both acids and bases.	5. Ge metal is amphoteric; the oxides dissolve in both acids and bases.
6. The higher oxide, EkO_2, will be more acidic than the lower one, EkO.	6. The higher oxide, GeO_2, is soluble in water forming a weak acid.
7. Zinc will displace Ek from solution. Ek will react slowly with HCl.	7. Zinc displaces Ge from solution. The element does *not* react with HCl.
8. Like tin, it will form a chloride, $EkCl_4$, a heavy fuming liquid.	8. $GeCl_4$ is very much like $SnCl_4$, a colorless fuming liquid, density 1.88 g/cm^3.
9. Like tin, it will form a yellow sulfide, EkS_2, insoluble in dilute acids.	9. GeS_2 is a *white* (not yellow) sulfide, insoluble in dilute acids.

In the years that followed, as the elements for which Mendeleef had left gaps in his table were discovered and their properties fitted in neatly with those predicted, the concept of a "periodic law" became accepted as valid and the Periodic Table entered into general use. The discovery of the noble gases—helium, He; neon, Ne; argon, Ar; krypton, Kr; xenon, Xe; and radon, Rn—during the years 1890–1900 by William Ramsay, Professor of Chemistry at University College, London, demanded no serious modification in Mendeleef's Periodic Table; nor did subsequent discoveries concerning atomic numbers and isotopes. In fact, it was found that if elements were arranged in order of increasing atomic number, rather than atomic weight, then Mendeleef's reversal of the two pairs of elements, Co—Ni and Te—I, became justified. As knowledge of atomic structure advanced and new elements were discovered, the original statement of the periodic law was slightly modified as follows: *The physical and chemical properties of the elements are periodic functions of their atomic numbers.* Also, Mendeleef's original Periodic Table was modified to the so-called "long-form" (Fig. 12-2), originally proposed in 1895 by a Danish chemist, Julius Thomsen.

THE LONG FORM OF THE PERIODIC TABLE

In this long form of the Periodic Table the elements are arranged in order of increasing atomic number and are divided into seven horizontal rows called *series*, or *periods*, and into sixteen vertical columns called *groups* (or *families*).

H																	He
Li	Be											B	C	N	O	F	Ne
Na	Mg											Al	Si	P	S	Cl	Ar
K	Ca	Sc	Ti	V	Cr	Mn	Fe	Co	Ni	Cu	Zn	Ga	Ge	As	Se	Br	Kr
Rb	Sr	Y	Zr	Nb	Mo	Tc	Ru	Rh	Pd	Ag	Cd	In	Sn	Sb	Te	I	Xe
Cs	Ba	La–Lu	Hf	Ta	W	Re	Os	Ir	Pt	Au	Hg	Tl	Pb	Bi	Po	At	Rn
Fr	Ra	Ac–															

A periodic group is a vertical column of elements in the Periodic Table. In general, elements within the same periodic group resemble one another closely. *A periodic series is a horizontal row of elements in* the Periodic Table. In general, the properties of elements within a series vary gradually and regularly from a highly electropositive (metallic) character at the beginning (left-hand side) of the series to a highly electronegative (non-metallic character) at the end of the series.

Series 1, the first series of the Periodic Table, contains the elements hydrogen, H, and helium, He, a noble gas. This series is often called the *hydrogen-helium series* or the *very short series.*

Series 2 contains eight elements, lithium, Li, to neon, Ne; it is often called the *first short series.*

Series 3 comprises the elements sodium, Na, to argon, Ar, a total again of eight

Series 2	Li	Be											B	C	N	O	F	Ne
Series 3	Na	Mg											Al	Si	P	S	Cl	Ar
Series 4	K	Ca	Sc	Ti	V	Cr	Mn	Fe	Co	Ni	Cu	Zn	Ga	Ge	As	Se	Br	Kr

elements. Series 3 is often referred to as the *second short series.* Series 2 and 3 are the only series that contain eight elements, and the elements in these series frequently are referred to as the *typical elements.*

Series 4 contains eighteen elements, potassium, K, to krypton, Kr, ten more than the preceding series, and is often called the *first long series.* The first two elements of Series 4, potassium, K, and calcium, Ca, closely resemble the elements directly above them in Series 2 and 3, and so do the last six elements of the series, gallium, Ga, through krypton, Kr. For example, bromine shares many properties with chlorine and fluorine, and the noble gas krypton is very similar in physical and chemical properties to argon and helium. The ten elements from scandium, Sc, to zinc, Zn, however, have no counterparts in the preceding series and constitute the *first transition series,* they are all metallic, and exhibit somewhat similar chemical properties. They are generally called *transition metals.*

The first seven elements of Series 4 and the first seven elements of each of the following series are called *A Group elements.* The next three elements of Series 4—iron, Fe; cobalt, Co; and nickel, Ni—are labeled Group VIII, the only group that contains more than one element within the same series. (These three elements were placed in the same group because they were at first believed to resemble one another

FIGURE 12-2 The long form of the Periodic Table.

Series or Period	GROUPS IA	IIA	IIIA	IVA	VA	VIA	VIIA	VIII			IB	IIB	IIIB	IVB	VB	VIB	VIIB	O
1	H 1																	He 2
2	Li 3	Be 4											B 5	C 6	N 7	O 8	F 9	Ne 10
3	Na 11	Mg 12											Al 13	Si 14	P 15	S 16	Cl 17	Ar 18
4	K 19	Ca 20	Sc 21	Ti 22	V 23	Cr 24	Mn 25	Fe 26	Co 27	Ni 28	Cu 29	Zn 30	Ga 31	Ge 32	As 33	Se 34	Br 35	Kr 36
5	Rb 37	Sr 38	Y 39	Zr 40	Cb 41	Mo 42	Tc 43	Ru 44	Rh 45	Pd 46	Ag 47	Cd 48	In 49	Sn 50	Sb 51	Te 52	I 53	Xe 54
6	Cs 55	Ba 56	57–71	Hf 72	Ta 73	W 74	Re 75	Os 76	Ir 77	Pt 78	Au 79	Hg 80	Tl 81	Pb 82	Bi 83	Po 84	At 85	Rn 86
7	Fr 87	Ra 88	89–103															
Lanthanides (Rare Earths)			La 57	Ce 58	Pr 59	Nd 60	Pm 61	Sm 62	Eu 63	Gd 64	Tb 65	Dy 66	Ho 67	Er 68	Tm 69	Yb 70	Lu 71	
Actinides			Ac 89	Th 90	Pa 91	U 92	Np 93	Pu 94	Am 95	Cm 96	Bk 97	Cf 98	Es 99	Fm 100	Md 101	No 102	Lw 103	

very closely.) The terms *Group VIII triads* or *transition triads* are used to designate the set of three elements in Group VIII of Series 4, 5, and 6. The next seven elements are labeled Group IB to VIIB. These elements are called *B Group elements.* A Groups and B Groups are frequently referred to as subgroups—for example, Group I comprises an A subgroup and a B subgroup.

The terms A Group and B Group will be used in this sense throughout the rest of the book. This is an important point to remember, since usage is not uniform in all textbooks.

Series 5, like Series 4, contains eighteen elements—rubidium, Rb, to xenon, Xe, and is called the *second long series.* The eighteen elements of Series 5 parallel the eighteen elements of Series 4, and the arrangement of the elements in the two series is identical.

Series 4	K	Ca	Sc	Ti	V	Cr	Mn	Fe	Co	Ni	Cu	Zn	Ga	Ge	As	Se	Br	Kr
Series 5	Rb	Sr	Y	Zr	Nb	Mo	Tc	Ru	Rh	Pd	Ag	Cd	In	Sn	Sb	Te	I	Xe
Series 6	Cs	Ba	La–Lu	Hf	Ta	W	Re	Os	Ir	Pt	Au	Hg	Tl	Pb	Bi	Po	At	Rn
Series 7	Fr	Ra																

Lanthanides	La	Ce	Pr	Nd	Pm	Sm	Eu	Gd	Tb	Dy	Ho	Er	Tm	Yb	Lu
Actinides	Ac	Th	Pa	U	Np	Pu	Am	Cm	Bk	Cf	Es	Fm	Md	No	Lw

Series 6. This series contains thirty-two elements—cesium, Cs, to radon, Rn—and is called the *first very long series.* It contains fourteen additional elements which have no counterpart in the preceding Series 5. The first three elements of Series 6—cesium, Cs; barium, Ba; and lanthanum, La—resemble the corresponding first three elements in Series 5. The next fourteen elements, however, are very much alike in physical and chemical properties, and because they closely resemble lanthanum they are generally called the *lanthanide elements (lanthanides).* They are also known as the *rare-earth elements.* For the sake of convenience, these fourteen elements are grouped together with lanthanum in the common long form of the Periodic Table and are generally listed separately below the Periodic Table proper. The last fifteen elements of Series 6 are placed in the Periodic Table in the same way as the last fifteen elements of Series 5 and 4, to which they correspond in properties and behavior.

Series 7, the last and incomplete series of the Periodic Table, contains elements 87 (francium, Fr) to 103 (lawrencium, Lw); the last elements of the series do not occur in nature. The elements from 89 to 103, actinium (Ac) through lawrencium (Lw), are called the *actinide elements (actinides)* after actinium.

The physical and chemical properties of the elements of each series vary gradually along the series, whereas the elements in each vertical column are closely related. As we shall now see, the long form of the Periodic Table is very helpful in correlating the physical and chemical properties of the elements with their electronic structure, and we shall therefore adopt it throughout this book. As we have seen, the periodic classification of the elements was based solely on the observed properties and behavior of the elements and their compounds, and preceded by several decades the discoveries and theories of atomic structure. However, it is on the basis of the electron structure of the atoms that the periodic classification of the elements can be logically explained, and hence becomes much more meaningful and also easier to remember. For this reason, we shall now digress to discuss some fundamental concepts of atomic structure; then, in the last part of this chapter we shall return to the periodic classification of the elements and consider it in the light of these structural concepts and principles.

12-2 The Theory of Atomic Structure

GENERAL STRUCTURE OF THE ATOM

We learned in Chapter 3 that the three elementary particles of matter are the electron, the proton, and the neutron. The proton has an electrical charge of +1 and a mass of 1. The neutron has no electrical charge and has a mass approximately equal to the mass of the proton. The electron has an electrical charge of −1 and a mass equal to approximately 1/1,850 the mass of the proton. We also learned that an atom consists of a small nucleus of protons and neutrons which is surrounded by a diffuse electron cloud. Since the proton is positively charged and the neutron is, as the name itself implies, neutral, the nucleus has a net positive charge which is the same for all atoms of a given element. The numerical value of the nuclear charge is the *atomic number* of the element. For example, the element helium, which has two protons in its nucleus, has an atomic number of 2. And sodium, which has eleven protons in its nucleus, has an atomic number of 11. The nucleus of each of the known 103 elements has a characteristic, unique charge which means that each element can be identified by its atomic number.

An atom is an electrically neutral entity; hence, the positive nuclear charge must be neutralized by an equal negative charge of the electron cloud. In other words, the number of electrons in the electron cloud of an atom is equal to the number of protons in the nucleus of the atom; hence, the atomic number of an element also immediately tells us how many electrons compose the electron cloud of its atom. As we know, chemical interactions between atoms actually involve interactions between their outermost electrons. Clearly, then, it is desirable to know as much as possible about the way in which the electrons in the electron cloud are arranged about the nucleus.

Our present concept of the electron structure of the atom, originally suggested in 1899 by Ernest Rutherford, was extended in 1913 by Niels Bohr, and was then further modified in succeeding years by several other physicists. It is important to realize that our knowledge of the structure of the atom has been acquired indirectly from many different bits of experimental evidence. On the basis of experimental observations and inductive reasoning, scientists built various *models* to represent the structure of the atom and through a long process of successive modifications and refinements finally arrived at what we may consider a satisfactory model—that is, a model which accounts for all experimental facts so far known about atoms. Unfortunately, this model of the electron structure of atoms can be described only in complex mathematical terms. Because such terms are far too difficult for beginning students, we shall use here a much simplified atomic model, which, however, is very useful in interpreting chemical phenomena. We shall begin by considering the electron configuration of the simplest of all atoms, the hydrogen atom.

THE ELECTRON CONFIGURATION OF THE HYDROGEN ATOM

As we have seen in Chapter 6, the hydrogen atom, H, consists of a nucleus with a positive charge of +1 (relative unit) and an electron with a negative charge of −1 (relative unit) held together by a very strong mutual electrostatic attraction. The electrostatic attraction between the electron and the nucleus is greatest when the distance between these oppositely charged particles is a certain small value. The electron-nucleus system is then in its most stable state or, as we commonly say, is in its lowest possible *energy level.* This lowest energy state, of the electron-nucleus system is known as the *ground state* of the hydrogen atom, and any other state having an energy higher than the ground state is called an *excited* or *promoted state.* In each excited state of the H atom, the average electron-nucleus distance is greater than that in the ground state; in fact, the greater the electron-nucleus distance, the smaller the electron-nucleus attraction, and the higher the energy of the electron-nucleus system.

Experimental observations indicate, and quantum theory explains, that the electrostatic attraction between the nucleus and the electron can only assume certain well-defined values, or, in other words, the electron-nucleus system can occupy only certain well-defined energy levels. Theoretically, the system can occupy an infinite number of such discrete energy levels, each corresponding to a certain average distance of the electron from the nucleus. However, the H atom has been observed to exist only in a relatively small number of such energy levels. A schematic representation of the allowed energy levels of the H atom is given in Fig. 12-3.

As Fig. 12-3 shows, each energy level of the hydrogen atom is associated with a value of an integer, n, ($n = 1, 2, 3, \ldots$ up to but not including $n = \infty$) called the *principal quantum number.* The lowest energy level corresponds to $n = 1$, the next lowest energy level corresponds to $n = 2$, and so on, n increasing by integers from 1 to infinity as the electrostatic attraction between nucleus and electron gradually approaches zero. Thus for the hydrogen atom, H, the $n = 1$ state is the ground state, and states corresponding to $n = 2, 3, \ldots$ are excited states. If the hydrogen atom is supplied with an appropriate quantity of energy (for example, if it is irradiated with a light wave of appropriate frequency), it can pass from a lower to a higher energy level —or, as we usually say, it can undergo a transition from a lower energy level to a higher energy level. Figure 12-3 shows some of the infinite number of possible transitions of the hydrogen atom. We see that energy must always be supplied to the hydro-

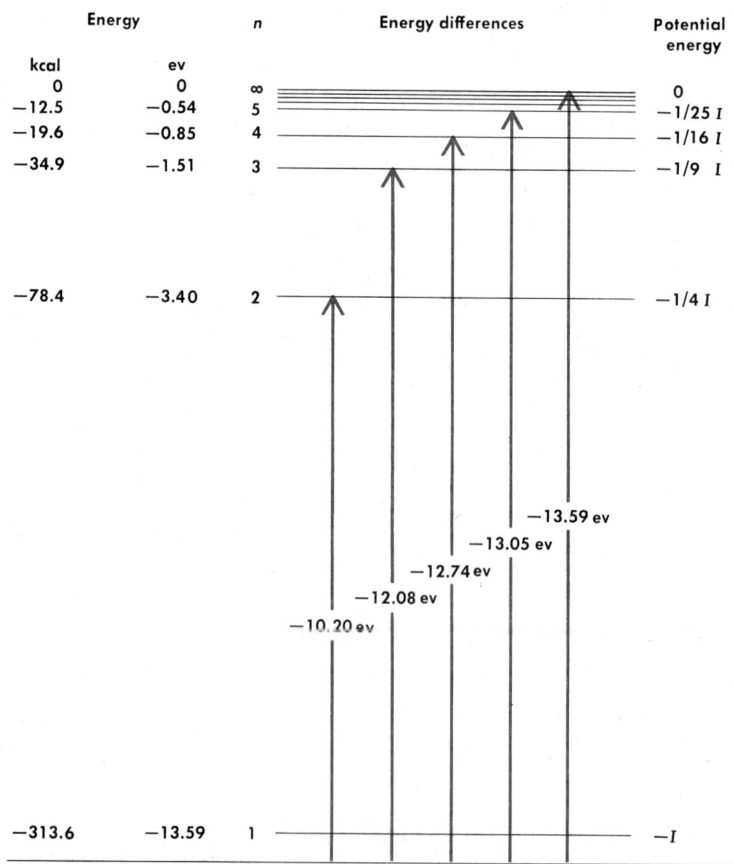

FIGURE 12-3 Energy levels of the H atom, ground ($n = 1$) and excited ($n = 2, 3, \ldots$) states.

gen atom to raise it from the ground state to a higher excited state (or from a "lower" excited state to a "higher" excited state). In other words, energy is always required to promote the electron of the hydrogen atom from the ground state ($n = 1$) to any higher energy (excited) state ($n = 2, 3, \ldots$). As the hydrogen atom passes from any higher excited state to any lower excited state, or from any excited state to the ground state, energy is liberated—for example, as light emission.

The energy level at which the distance between the nucleus and the electron is so great that no electrostatic attraction exists between them (the Coulombic potential energy is zero) is taken by convention as the zero value of the potential energy of the system. At this zero potential energy level the system consists of a hydrogen ion (a proton), H^+, and an electron, e^-, completely independent of each other, and so does *not* represent a hydrogen atom, H. In fact, as we know, what we call a hydrogen atom is a system made up of a proton and an electron held together by a strong mutual attraction.

Figure 12-3 also gives the relative energy values for the ground state ($n = 1$) and for the next four excited states ($n = 2$, $n = 3$, $n = 4$, and $n = 5$) of the hydrogen atom. These relative energy values (per mole of hydrogen atoms) are given on the left-hand side of the diagram in the familiar energy unit, the kilocalorie (kcal), as well as in electron volts (ev), an energy unit frequently used in dealing with ionization processes (p. 256). Figure 12-3 shows schematically that there are countless discrete energy levels between $n = 5$ and $n = \infty$, the $n = \infty$ energy level corresponding to the ionized state of hydrogen—a proton, H^+, and an electron, e^-, free of their mutual electrostatic attraction and having, as we just said, a potential energy of zero. The energy required to excite 1 mole of hydrogen atoms from the ground state ($n = 1$) to the ionized (highest excited) state ($n = \infty$) is 313.6 kcal = 13.59 ev. This quantity of energy, called the *ionization energy* (*I.E.*) of the hydrogen atom, represents the energy which must be supplied to transform 1 mole of (gaseous) hydrogen atoms, H, in the ground state, into 1 mole of (gaseous) hydrogen ions, H^+, and 1 mole of electrons, e^-, completely free of their mutual electrostatic attraction.

$$H_{(g)} \longrightarrow H^+_{(g)} + e^- \qquad \Delta H = +313.6 \text{ kcal/mole H atoms}$$

We also see from Fig. 12-3 that the energy required to ionize a gaseous H atom in an n energy level decreases very steeply as n increases from $n = 1$, to $n = 2$, to $n = 3, \ldots$, and is given by a simple expression. In fact, to ionize a H atom in the $n = 1$ ground state requires 313.6 kcal/mole; to ionize a H atom in the $n = 2$ first excited state requires 78.4 kcal/mole (that is, 313.6/4 kcal/mole); for the $n = 3$ state, the energy required is 34.8 kcal/mole (that is, 313.6/9 kcal/mole); and so forth. Thus the energy required to ionize the H atom in any given n energy state is inversely proportional to the square of the principal quantum number: $(1/n^2) \times 313.6$ kcal/mole = $1/n^2 \times I.E.$ As this formula indicates, the energy difference between any two successive states, n and $n + 1$, decreases very sharply as the value of n successively increases. For example, the energy required to promote the electron of the H atom from the $n = 1$ ground state to the $n = 2$ first excited state is 3/4 of the total ionization energy: $1/(1)^2\ I.E. - 1/(2)^2\ I.E. = 3/4\ I.E. = 3/4 \times 313.6 = 235.2$ kcal/mole, but the energy required to promote the electron from the $n = 2$ to the $n = 3$ state is only $5/36\ I.E. = 43.5$ kcal/mole. Notice that while it takes 3/4 of the total ionization energy to raise the electron from the $n = 1$ to the $n = 2$ state, only 1/4 of the total ionization energy is required to raise the electron of the H atom from the $n = 2$ to the $n = \infty$ state—that is, to ionize the H atom which is in the $n = 2$ state. Thus the ionization energy of hydrogen has a finite value, $I.E. = 313.6$ kcal/mole of H atoms, even though there exists an infinite number of excited energy levels between $n = 1$ and $n = \infty$. When a collection of hydrogen atoms *in the ground state* absorbs energy —from a light beam, for example—the smallest quantity of energy that such H atoms can absorb is exactly equal to the energy required to promote the electron from the $n = 1$ state to the $n = 2$ state. Similarly, if we supply energy to hydrogen atoms originally in the $n = 2$ state, each mole of hydrogen atoms can be excited to the $n = 3$ state by taking on an amount of energy (43.5 kcal) exactly equal to the energy difference between the $n = 2$ and $n = 3$ states, and so on. In general, whenever energy is absorbed by a collection of H atoms, the energy or energies absorbed correspond exactly to the energy difference between the ground state and an excited state, or between any two excited states. The same energy relationships hold, of course, for the energies emitted by a collection of hydrogen atoms during the reverse processes, namely the transitions from a higher to a lower excited state or to the ground state.

HYDROGEN-LIKE SYSTEMS. The only neutral system composed of a nucleus and a single electron is the hydrogen atom. All other systems consisting of a nucleus and a single electron are ionic systems (positive ions), such as He^+, Li^{+2}, and Be^{+3}. These positive ions are called hydrogen-like systems or hydrogen-like ions, and their energy level diagrams are very similar to that of the hydrogen atom. The energies of the various levels, however, differ from those of the corresponding levels of hydrogen owing to the greater attraction exerted on the single electron by the higher nuclear charge.

For any hydrogen-like ion of nuclear charge Z, the energy required to ionize 1 mole of ions in the n energy level is related to the ionization energy of the hydrogen atom by the expression: *I.E.* of hydrogen-like ion $= 1/n^2 \times Z^2 \times$ (*I.E.* of hydrogen atom). For instance, the energy required to ionize a hydrogen-like He^+ ion in the $n = 2$ energy level $= 1/4 \times 4 \times 313.6 = 313.6$ kcal/mole—i.e., four times greater than the energy required to ionize 1 mole of gaseous H atoms in the same $n = 2$ energy level.

12-3 The Periodic System and the Electron Configurations of Atoms

The chemical elements, as we have seen, exhibit regular and periodic trends in their chemical and physical properties when arranged in order of increasing atomic numbers. In general, the periodic properties of the elements depend on the arrangement of the electrons in the ground state and in the lower excited states of their atoms, on the energies required to completely remove one or more electrons from their atoms (forming positive ions) or promote one or more electrons from the ground state to one of the lower excited states. For atoms and ions containing two or more electrons (polyelectron atoms and ions) two major opposing factors determine the total energy of the nucleus-electron system—total electrostatic attraction between the nucleus and all the electrons, and the forces of repulsion between the electrons themselves. The nuclear attraction tends to draw the electrons as close as possible to the nucleus, but as a result the electrons also draw closer to one another and their mutual repulsion thus increases. Thus, the ground state of a polyelectron atom or ion actually represents a balance between these two opposing effects, the electrons being as close to the nucleus (maximum possible electrostatic attraction) as is compatible with their mutual repulsion (minimum possible electron-electron repulsion).

The electrons composing the electron cloud of an atom interact with one another and this reveals some properties of electrons which are not evident in an isolated atom containing a single electron, such as the hydrogen atom. These properties of the electrons, which we must take into consideration in describing the electron configuration of polyelectron atoms and ions, may be summarized as follows: (1) Electrons may be distributed differently in the space around the nucleus, and their mutual electrostatic repulsion depends to a large extent upon such distribution (called spatial distribution, see Section 12-6). (2) Each electron, like an electrical charge in motion, corresponds to a very small orbital *magnetic dipole.* The orbital magnetic dipoles of different electrons interact with one another, and with an applied external magnetic field, in a manner which is again dependent on the spatial distribution of the electrons.

(3) Electrons rotate about their own axes. This rotation—the so-called *spin* of the electron—can occur in two opposite directions, clockwise and counterclockwise. Therefore an electron, like a spinning electrical charge, corresponds to a *spin* magnetic dipole. In an atom the spin magnetic dipoles of different electrons interact with one another, and also with an applied external magnetic field, in a manner which depends upon their relative spinning directions. If we wish to describe unambiguously the state of each electron in a polyelectron atom or ion, we must take into consideration all these factors. A convenient way of doing so is to introduce, in addition to the principal quantum number, *n*, three other quantum numbers which we shall now discuss.

QUANTUM NUMBERS

In general, the state (energy level) of each electron in a polyelectron system is defined by four quantum numbers.

1. *The principal quantum number, n,* indicates, as we have already discussed, the average distance of the electron from the nucleus. The quantum number n is therefore the main factor in determining the value of both the nucleus-electron attraction and the electron-electron repulsion, and hence the potential energy of the electron. This is why n is called the *principal* quantum number.

The principal quantum number may assume the values $n = 1, 2, 3, \ldots$, increasing by integral numbers to infinity. As the value of the principal quantum number of an electron increases, the potential energy of the electron becomes progressively greater. We often express this relationship by saying that in a polyelectron atom or ion the electrons which have the higher principal quantum numbers are at the higher energy levels; whereas those electrons with the lower principal quantum numbers are at the lower energy levels. An electron with $n = 1$ is in the lowest possible energy level in an atom, and any electron with a value of n higher than 1 is in a higher energy level—that is to say, it is bound less firmly to the nucleus.

Although the quantum number n may theoretically assume any integer from 1 to ∞, only values from 1 to 7 have thus far been established for the atoms of the known elements *in their ground states*. The letters *K, L, M, N, O, P,* and *Q** are sometimes used to designate energy levels or shells of electrons with an n value of 1, 2, 3, 4, 5, 6, 7, respectively. The shell closest to the nucleus, with $n = 1$, is called the *K* shell, and succeeding shells are indicated by successive letters of the alphabet. The symbolism used to indicate the principal energy levels of the electrons around the nucleus of an atom or ion is summarized in Table 12-1.

Each energy level of principal quantum number n is further divided into sublevels whose relative energies are determined by the values of another quantum number—the *orbital quantum number.*

2. The *orbital,* also called the *angular* or *azimuthal quantum number, l,* defines the spatial distribution of the electron about the nucleus. In other words, the quantum number l defines the shape of the *orital* occupied by the electron, the term "orbital" referring to the region where we may expect to find the electron. In Section 12-6 we shall consider in detail the concept of the spatial distribution of electrons.

TABLE 12-1 ARRANGEMENT OF ELECTRONS IN PRINCIPAL LEVELS AROUND NUCLEUS

Energy Level	Principal Quantum Number	Letter
1st	$n = 1$	K
2nd	$n = 2$	L
3rd	$n = 3$	M
4th	$n = 4$	N
5th	$n = 5$	O
6th	$n = 6$	P
7th	$n = 7$	Q

* The *K, L, M* . . . terminology is taken from X-ray spectroscopy, where these letters are used to label certain groups of spectral lines in the X-ray spectra of the various elements.

For any given value of the principal quantum number, n, the orbital quantum number l may assume all integral values from 0 to $n - 1$. Hence the total number of possible sub-levels in each principal level is numerically equal to the principal quantum number of the level considered. When $l = 0$, the orbital is designated by the letter s, and is called an s orbital; when $l = 1$, the orbital is called a p orbital; when $l = 2$, a d orbital; and when $l = 3$, an f orbital.* Thus for the principal quantum number $n = 1$, the only possible value of the orbital quantum number l is 0—that is, there is only one possible orbital, an s orbital ($n = 1$, $l = 0$). For $n = 2$, the two possible values of l are $l = 0$ and 1 (that is $2 - 1$). Again, $l = 0$ indicates an s orbital, and $l = 1$ indicates a p orbital. For $n = 4$, the values of the angular quantum number are 0 (s orbital), 1 (p orbital), 2 (d orbital), and 3 (f orbital). For values of $n = 5$ and higher, the number of possible values of the orbital quantum number increases. However, the orbital quantum number never has values higher than 4 (f orbitals) for atoms in their ground states.

3. The application of an external magnetic field to atoms and ions reveals that electrons having the same values of the principal quantum number, n, and of the orbital quantum number, l, may still differ in their behavior and hence must be differentiated by introducing a new quantum number, the *magnetic quantum number, m.* For each value of the orbital quantum number l, the magnetic quantum number, m, can have all the integral values between $+l$ and $-l$: that is, $+l\ (+l - 1) \ldots 0 \ldots (-l + 1), -l$. Thus, for each value of the orbital quantum number, l, the magnetic quantum number, m, can have a total of $(2l + 1)$ values. Thus if $l = 0$, $m = 0$, and no other value. This means that *for each value of the principal quantum number, n, there is only one s orbital.* For $l = 1$, the magnetic quantum number assumes three values: $+1$, 0, and -1; so for each value of the principal quantum number $n = 2$ and higher, there are three p orbitals, differing only in the value of the magnetic quantum number. In the absence of a magnetic field, these three p orbitals are equivalent in energy and are said to be *three-fold degenerate*, or *triply degenerate.* (If an external magnetic field is applied, the relative energies of the three p orbitals vary depending on the value of the magnetic quantum number.) For $l = 2$, the magnetic quantum number assumes five $(2 \times 2 + 1)$ values: $+2$, $+1$, 0, -1, -2. Thus there are five d orbitals for each value of the principal quantum number $n = 3$ and higher. These five d orbitals are equivalent in energy as long as the atom is not subjected to a magnetic field, and are said to be *five-fold degenerate.* Sometimes we refer to them as "a set of five-fold degenerate d orbitals." For $l = 3$, there are seven values of the magnetic quantum number: $+3$, $+2$, $+1$, 0, -1, -2, -3. Hence for each value of the principal quantum number $n = 4$ and higher, there are seven f orbitals, which again have equal energies (in the absence of a magnetic field) and constitute a set of *seven-fold degenerate* orbitals.

4. The *spin quantum number, s,* is related to the direction of the rotation of the electron about its own axis. Since the electron can rotate in two opposite directions, the spin quantum number of an electron can have either of two equal and opposite values: $s = +\frac{1}{2}$ or $s = -\frac{1}{2}$. In our future discussion of the electron configuration of the elements, we shall not need to concern ourselves with the numerical value of the spin quantum number, which follows from mathematical considerations. It is sufficient to remember that for any electron the spin quantum number may have either of two identical but opposite (in sign) values. Electrons with the same sign of the spin quantum number are said to have *parallel spins;* electrons with opposite signs of the spin quantum number are said to have *opposite* (or paired up) *spins.*

* The s, p, d, f terminology came originally from visible and ultraviolet spectroscopy, where these letters were originally used to label various series of spectral lines emitted by the elements (s = sharp, p = principal, d = diffuse, f = fundamental).

THE ENERGY OF AN ELECTRON IN A POLYELECTRON ATOM OR ION

We have seen that the energy of an electron is determined mainly by the value of its principal quantum number, n. Within each principal level, however, the various sub-levels exhibit slightly different energies, which increase in the same order as the value of the orbital quantum number, l. Thus, for a given principal level, $n = 4$ and higher, which has an s orbital ($l = 0$), p orbitals ($l = 1$), d orbitals ($l = 2$) and f orbitals ($l = 3$), the energy increases in the order $s < p < d < f$. The energy of an electron with a principal quantum number n and orbital quantum number l is always less than that of an electron with principal quantum number $n + 1$ and the same orbital quantum number l. For example, the energy of a $3s$ orbital is less than that of a $4s$ orbital; the energy of a $3p$ orbital is less than the energy of a $4p$ orbital; and so on.

We have seen in Fig. 12-3 that the energy interval between successive principal energy levels of the H atom decreases sharply as the value of the principal quantum number increases. A similar situation holds for polyelectron atoms and ions. Therefore, we might expect that the orbitals with principal quantum number, $n = 2$ (one s orbital and three p orbitals), even though somewhat spread, will still be lower in energy than any orbital of the $n = 3$ quantum number. But as the value of n increases and the energy difference between successive n levels decreases, the lowest energy orbital, s, of a given principal quantum number ($n + 1$) may fall below the highest energy orbitals (d, for example) of the n quantum number. In potassium, K, for example, the $4s$ orbital is lower in energy than the $3d$ orbitals.

THE GROUND STATE ELECTRON CONFIGURATIONS OF THE ELEMENTS

GENERAL RULES. In the ground state electron configuration of the H atom, as we know, the single electron occupies the lowest-lying energy level whose principal quantum number is 1 and orbital quantum number is 0 (s orbital). For more complicated atoms and ions which contain many electrons and have available many energy levels, or orbitals, we can determine the arrangement of the electrons in the orbitals by following these three general rules:

1. In the ground state of an atom or ion the electrons tend to occupy the available orbitals in order of increasing energy, starting with the lowest-energy orbital. This rule, which is called the "building-up principle," reflects the fact that electrons tend to occupy first those orbitals which are closest to the nucleus and hence afford the greatest electrostatic attraction with the nucleus—that is, the greatest stability of the nucleus-electrons system. In general, each successive electron is added to the available orbital which has the lowest value of the principal quantum number, n, and the lowest value of the orbital quantum number, l. This rule is followed regularly for the first eighteen elements, $_{1}H$ to $_{18}Ar$. For the following elements, this rule still holds in general, but there are some variations in the order of the energy levels, as we shall see in a later section.

2. Each orbital can contain a maximum of two electrons (Pauli Exclusion Principle), and the two electrons present in the same orbital must spin in opposite directions. We often express this condition by saying that the spins of the two electrons in the same orbital are "paired." This rule means that no two electrons within an atom can have the same values of all four quantum numbers. And since each orbital has its own characteristic set of values for the quantum numbers n, l, and m, two electrons in the same orbital must differ in the sign of their spin quantum numbers, s.

3. When several orbitals of equal energy (degenerate orbitals) are available—for example, the *p* orbitals—the electrons tend to occupy as many of the degenerate orbitals as possible and exhibit the maximum possible number of parallel spins (Hund's Rule). The electrons tend to occupy as many of the equal-energy orbitals as possible because their mutual repulsion tends to keep them as far apart from one another as possible. Also, when single electrons occupy degenerate orbitals, their spins are parallel because this configuration results in the greatest stability (an explanation of this property of electrons is given by quantum theory).

Whenever two electrons pair up in the same orbital, their greater mutual repulsion tends to decrease the stability of the system. However, the increase in energy due to this electron-electron repulsion of the two paired-up electrons is still lower than the increase in energy which would result from the promotion of one electron to the next available higher energy orbital. That is to say, it is still more favorable from an energy standpoint for two electrons with opposite spins to pair up in the same orbital rather than for one electron to seek a higher energy orbital. In helium, $_2He$, for example, the two electrons in the ground state both occupy the $1s$ orbital ($1s^2$), *rather than* one in the $1s$ and one in the $2s$ orbital ($1s^1,2s^1$). Thus we see that the order in which electrons occupy successive orbitals of atoms results from a balance of two effects: the mutual attraction between the nucleus and the electron, and the mutual repulsion between electrons (interelectron repulsion).

MAXIMUM NUMBER OF ELECTRONS IN EACH SHELL. Each individual orbital of any type (s, p, d, or f) can contain a maximum of two electrons. Consequently, if we know the number of orbitals in a given principal energy level, we can calculate the maximum number of electrons that level can contain. For example, the $n = 1$ principal shell contains only one sublevel, $1s$, which can have only a $1s$ orbital; consequently, the $n = 1$ principal shell can contain a maximum of two electrons. Similarly, in the $n = 2$ shell, the $2s$ sub-level can have only one $2s$ orbital and thus a maximum of two electrons. The $2p$ sub-level, on the other hand, has three p orbitals, each of which can contain a maximum of two electrons. Thus, in the $n = 2$ shell there is a total of four orbitals ($2s$ $2p$ $2p$ $2p$) and a maximum of eight electrons.

In the $n = 3$ shell, the d sub-level, which has five d orbitals, can hold a maximum of ten electrons. Consequently, the $n = 3$ shell has a total of nine orbitals (one s, three p, and five d) and can contain a maximum of eighteen electrons.

In the $n = 4$ shell, in addition to one $4s$ orbital, three $4p$ orbitals, and five $4d$ orbitals, there are seven $4f$ orbitals. These seven $4f$ orbitals can contain a maximum of fourteen electrons. Thus, the $n=4$ shell can have a maximum of $(1+3+5+7)=16$ orbitals and thirty-two electrons.

To summarize:

1. The s sub-level, no matter which principal shell it belongs to, has only one s orbital. This s orbital can contain a maximum of two electrons.

2. The p sub-level, no matter which principal shell it belongs to (however, n must be 2 or higher), has three p orbitals. Each p orbital, like each s orbital, can have no more than two electrons; and thus the p sub-level (the three p orbitals) can contain any number of electrons up to six.

3. The d sub-shell, no matter which principal shell it belongs to (for $n = 3$ or higher), has five d orbitals. Each d orbital, like each s or p orbital, can have no more than two electrons; and thus the d sub-level (the five d orbitals) can have any number of electrons up to ten.

4. The f sub-shell, no matter which principal shell it belongs to (for $n = 4$ or higher), has seven f orbitals. Each f orbital, like each s, p, and d orbital, can have no more than two electrons; and thus the f sub-level (the seven f orbitals) can have any number of electrons up to fourteen. Thus, the s, p, d, and f sub-shells can hold a maximum of two, six, ten, and fourteen electrons, respectively.

SCHEMATIC REPRESENTATION OF THE ELECTRON CONFIGURATION OF AN ATOM OR ION

To define completely the state of an atom or ion, we must include the values of the 4 quantum numbers (n, l, m, s) for every electron of the atom or ion. For example, the electron configuration of the ground state of the hydrogen atom, H, which has only one electron, is identified by the values of its four quantum numbers: $n = 1$, $l = 0$, $m = 0$, and $s = +\frac{1}{2}$ or $-\frac{1}{2}$. (Remember that l can have only $n - 1$ values and that the values of m vary by integers from $+l$ to 0 to $-l$.) Thus a complete representation of the electronic state of an atom is somewhat cumbersome even for the simplest of all atoms, and becomes more and more so for polyelectron atoms and ions. For this reason it is customary to represent the electron configuration of atoms in a simplified way, specifying only the value of the n and l quantum numbers of each electron. For example, the electron configuration of the H atom is indicated simply as $1s^1$ or as $\underset{(\uparrow)}{1s}$. In the $1s^1$ notation the coefficient 1 represents the principal quantum number, n; the letter s represents the value of the orbital quantum number, $l = 0$; and the superscript ^{1} indicates that there is only one electron in the $1s$ orbital. In the notation $\underset{(\uparrow)}{1s}$, the arrow, $\uparrow$, represents the spin of the electron in the $1s$ orbital.

ELECTRON CONFIGURATIONS OF THE ATOMS OF THE FIRST TEN ELEMENTS. Now we can write down rapidly the electron configurations of at least the simplest atoms on the basis of the three rules we have just covered. We begin with helium, $_2$He, atomic number 2 (two protons in the nucleus, two electrons in the electron cloud). Notice that the subscript preceding the symbol of the element indicates the atomic number of the element.

The $1s$ orbital is the lowest-lying energy level for all atoms, so the two electrons of the helium atom in the ground state will both, with opposite spins, occupy the $1s$ orbital. The electron configuration of the He atom can therefore be represented as $1s^2$. Or, we may use the notation $\underset{(\uparrow\downarrow)}{1s}$, where the opposite directions of the two arrows shows graphically the opposite spins of the two paired electrons. Notice that the $n = 1$ principal level contains its maximum possible number of electrons—two; or, as we often briefly say, it is completely filled. For the $_2$He atom, the possible electron configuration $1s^1,2s^1$, in which one electron occupies the higher-energy $2s$ orbital, is less stable than the $1s^2$ electron configuration, because the energy difference between the $1s$ and $2s$ orbitals is much greater than the inter-electron repulsion of the two electrons in the same $1s$ orbital. In other words, the electrostatic attraction of the nuclear charge for the two electrons in the $1s$ orbital is much greater than the electrostatic attraction of the nuclear charge for one electron in the $1s$ orbital and one electron in a $2s$ orbital. This offsets the unfavorable inter-electron repulsion, which is greater for the two paired electrons occupying the same $1s$ orbital than for the two electrons occupying separate ($1s$ and $2s$) orbitals. Thus, the $1s^2$ configuration corresponds to the *ground* state, and the $1s^1,2s^1$ configuration to an *excited* (or *promoted*) state of the He atom.

On the basis of the building-up principle, the ground state electron configuration of the third element of the Periodic Table, lithium, $_3$Li, is $1s^2,2s^1$, or $\underset{(\uparrow\downarrow)}{1s}$, $\underset{(\uparrow)}{2s}$, two electrons with opposite spins occupying the $1s$ orbital and the third electron occupying the higher-energy $2s$ orbital. Since two electrons occupy the $1s$ orbital, as in the preceding noble gas, He, we sometimes represent the electron configuration of $_3$Li as [He]$2s^1$. The next element is beryllium, $_4$Be, and its ground state electron configuration is $1s^2,2s^2$, or $\underset{(\uparrow\downarrow)}{1s}$, $\underset{(\uparrow\downarrow)}{2s}$, rather than $1s^2,2s^1\,2p^1$, because again the stronger nuclear attraction for the two paired electrons in the $2s$ orbital more than compensates for the increased inter-electron repulsion.

The electron configuration of boron, $_5B$, is $1s^2,2s^2\,2p^1$, or 1s 2s 2p, or 1s 2s 2p 2p 2p, with one electron (the 5th) present in one of the three 2p orbitals (*triply degenerate orbitals*). The electron configuration of the carbon atom, $_6C$, is an example of the application of Hund's Rule. As we would expect from the building-up principle, the first five electrons of the carbon atom occupy the same orbitals as the five electrons of boron. The sixth electron of the C atom will then occupy one of the two still vacant *equivalent p* orbitals, because electrons repel one another. Moreover, the two electrons in the two *p* orbitals have parallel spins, because this electron configuration corresponds to the minimum energy (maximum stability) of the system. Thus the ground state electron configuration of $_6C$ is $1s^2,2s^2\,2p^2,(1s^1,2s^2\,2p^1\,2p^1)$ or 1s 2s 2p 2p 2p. On the basis of Hund's Rule and of the building-up principle, we can write the ground state electron configuration of the nitrogen atom, $_7N$, as $1s^2,2s^2\,2p^3$, or more explicitly, $1s^2,2s^2\,2p^1\,2p^1\,2p^1$, or also as 1s 2s 2p 2p 2p. Notice that this configuration has the maximum number of electrons with parallel spins in the degenerate *p* orbitals. We may label the three *p* orbitals as p_x,p_y,p_z (see p. 243) and the electron configuration of the N atom can then be written in more detail as $1s^2,2s^2\,2p_x^1 2p_y^1 2p_z^1$. For the oxygen atom, $_8O$, the ground state electron configuration is $1s^2,2s^2\,2p_x^2 2p_y^1 2p_z^1$, or 1s 2s $2p_x$ $2p_y$ $2p_z$. The configuration of the last two elements of the second period of the periodic system, fluorine $_9F$, and neon, $_{10}Ne$, are built up regularly in a similar manner (Table 12-2). Notice that in neon, $_{10}Ne$ $(1s^2,2s^2\,2p^6)$, the $n = 2$ principal level is completely filled. If we keep in mind that the filled $1s^2$ principal level, which represents the electron configuration of the noble gas $_2He$, is common to all eight elements from $_3Li$ to $_{10}Ne$, we can schematically represent their electron configurations as shown in the third column of Table 12-2. This representation shows the relationship between the position of an element in the Periodic Table and the distribution of electrons in the principal level which is being filled.

If we now consider the eight elements which follow neon in order of increasing atomic number, ($_{11}Na$, $_{12}Mg$, $_{13}Al$, $_{14}Si$, $_{15}P$, $_{16}S$, $_{17}Cl$, and $_{18}Ar$) we see that the ten lowest-energy electrons (next to the nucleus) are arranged like those of neon: $1s^2,2s^2\,2p^6$. The additional electrons occupy the $n = 3$ level, and the *s* and *p* orbitals of the $n = 3$ level are filled in exactly as are those of the $n = 2$ level. For example, the first element in the series, sodium, $_{11}Na$, has one electron in the 3s orbital, and its

TABLE 12-2 ELECTRON CONFIGURATION OF SERIES 2 ELEMENTS

Element with At. No.	Electron Arrangement $n = 1$	$n = 2$	Abbreviated Electron Configuration	Schematic Representation of Orbitals† 1s	2s	2p
$_3Li$	$1s^2$	$2s^1$	[He] $2s^1$	(↑↓)	(↑)	( )( )( )
$_4Be$	$1s^2$	$2s^2$	[He] $2s^2$	(↑↓)	(↑↓)	( )( )( )
$_5B$	$1s^2$	$2s^2\,2p^1$	[He] $2s^2\,2p^1$	(↑↓)	(↑↓)	(↑)( )( )
$_6C$*	$1s^2$	$2s^2\,2p^2$	[He] $2s^2\,2p^2$	(↑↓)	(↑↓)	(↑)(↑)( )
$_7N$	$1s^2$	$2s^2\,2p^3$	[He] $2s^2\,2p^3$	(↑↓)	(↑↓)	(↑)(↑)(↑)
$_8O$	$1s^2$	$2s^2\,2p^4$	[He] $2s^2\,2p^4$	(↑↓)	(↑↓)	(↑↓)(↑)(↑)
$_9F$	$1s^2$	$2s^2\,2p^5$	[He] $2s^2\,2p^5$	(↑↓)	(↑↓)	(↑↓)(↑↓)(↑)
$_{10}Ne$	$1s^2$	$2s^2\,2p^6$	[He] $2s^2\,2p^6$	(↑↓)	(↑↓)	(↑↓)(↑↓)(↑↓)

* Notice that starting with $_6C$, each *p* orbital is first occupied by a single electron with parallel spins and only after each of the three *p* orbitals has one electron does a second electron enter a *p* orbital, with opposite spin (Hund's Rule).

† With electrons present.

TABLE 12-3 ELECTRON CONFIGURATION OF SERIES 3 ELEMENTS

Element with At. No.	Electron Arrangement $n = 1$	$n = 2$	$n = 3$	Schematic Representation of Orbitals with Electrons Present 1s	2s	2p	3s	3p
$_{11}$Na	$1s^2$	$2s^2\ 2p^6$	$3s^1$	(↑↓)	(↑↓)	(↑↓)(↑↓)(↑↓)	(↑)	( )( )( )
$_{12}$Mg	$1s^2$	$2s^2\ 2p^6$	$3s^2$	(↑↓)	(↑↓)	(↑↓)(↑↓)(↑↓)	(↑↓)	( )( )( )
$_{13}$Al	$1s^2$	$2s^2\ 2p^6$	$3s^2\ 3p^1$	(↑↓)	(↑↓)	(↑↓)(↑↓)(↑↓)	(↑↓)	(↑)( )( )
$_{14}$Si	$1s^2$	$2s^2\ 2p^6$	$3s^2\ 3p^2$	(↑↓)	(↑↓)	(↑↓)(↑↓)(↑↓)	(↑↓)	(↑)(↑)( )
$_{15}$P	$1s^2$	$2s^2\ 2p^6$	$3s^2\ 3p^3$	(↑↓)	(↑↓)	(↑↓)(↑↓)(↑↓)	(↑↓)	(↑)(↑)(↑)
$_{16}$S	$1s^2$	$2s^2\ 2p^6$	$3s^2\ 3p^4$	(↑↓)	(↑↓)	(↑↓)(↑↓)(↑↓)	(↑↓)	(↑↓)(↑)(↑)
$_{17}$Cl	$1s^2$	$2s^2\ 2p^6$	$3s^2\ 3p^5$	(↑↓)	(↑↓)	(↑↓)(↑↓)(↑↓)	(↑↓)	(↑↓)(↑↓)(↑)
$_{18}$Ar	$1s^2$	$2s^2\ 2p^6$	$3s^2\ 3p^6$	(↑↓)	(↑↓)	(↑↓)(↑↓)(↑↓)	(↑↓)	(↑↓)(↑↓)(↑↓)

complete electron configuration is $1s^2,2s^2\ 2p^6,3s^1$, or simply [Ne],$3s^1$. The electron configuration of magnesium, $_{12}$Mg, is $1s^2,2s^2\ 2p^6,3s^2$. In aluminum, $_{13}$Al, the additional electron appears in the p orbital of the $n = 3$ principal level: $1s^2,2s^2\ 2p^6,3s^2\ 3p^1$. The electron configuration of $_{14}$Si is $1s^2,2s^2\ 2p^6,3s^2\ 3p_x^1\ 3p_y^1$. With each successive member of the third series, the additional electron is added to the $3p$ orbitals according to Hund's Rule. When we reach argon, $_{18}$Ar, last member of Series 3, all the $n = 3$ orbitals are not yet completely occupied (the $3d$ orbitals are vacant), but the electron configuration of $_{18}$Ar, $1s^2,2s^2\ 2p^6,3s^2\ 3p^6$, is closely analogous to that of the preceding noble gas, neon, $_{10}$Ne. The electron configurations of the eight elements in Series 3 are listed in Table 12-3, together with schematic representations of their orbitals and electrons. The accompanying scheme shows the relationships between electron configuration and position in the Periodic Table.

Li	Be	B	C	N	O	F	Ne
Na	Mg	Al	Si	P	S	Cl	Ar

This scheme shows that for elements of the same periodic group, the electrons in the outermost energy level, are arranged in the same way. The electrons underlying the outermost level, the so-called *inner electrons*, have the electron configuration of He, for the elements from $_3$Li to $_{10}$Ne (first short series), and the electron configuration of Ne for the elements from $_{11}$Na to $_{18}$Ar (second short series).

Let us now consider the electron configurations of the elements following $_{18}$Ar. The electron configuration of the first element, potassium, $_{19}$K, is $1s^2,2s^2\ 2p^6\ 3p^6,4s^1$, or simply [Ar],$4s^1$. In the ground state the K atom has one electron in the $4s$ orbital and no electrons in the $3d$ orbitals (Table 12-4). Similarly, calcium, $_{20}$Ca, has two electrons in the $4s$ orbital and no electrons in the $3d$ orbital. In these atoms the $4s$ orbital has a lower energy than the five degenerate $3d$ orbitals and therefore, according to the "building-up principle," is filled first. With the next element, scandium, $_{21}$Sc, the $3d$ orbitals begin to be filled, because they are now the lowest-energy orbitals available after the $4s$ orbital, which has just been filled in calcium. In the nine following elements—titanium, $_{22}$Ti, to zinc, $_{30}$Zn—the five $3d$ orbitals are progressively filled. The electron configurations of these elements, which constitute the first transition series, are given in Table 12-4 and illustrate the operation of Hund's Rule in regard to the five-fold degenerate d orbitals. From this table we see that the electron configurations of two elements, $_{24}$Cr and $_{29}$Cu, differ slightly from what we might expect solely on the basis of the building-up principle and Hund's Rule. The explanation for this apparent irregularity will be given in a later section (p. 232). The following diagram shows the relationship between the electron configuration of the atoms of these elements and their positions in the Periodic Table.

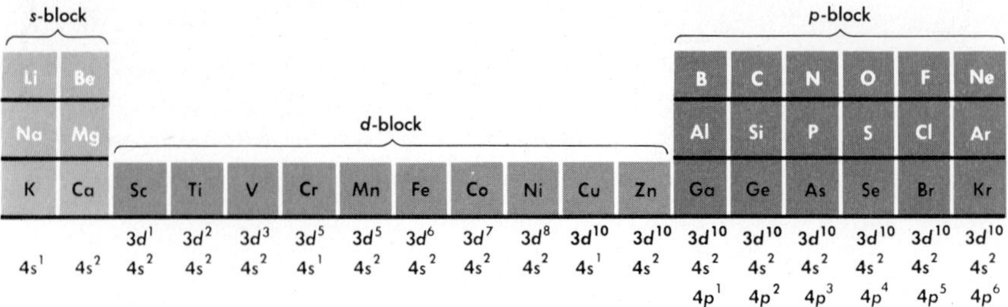

We see from the above diagram that the first two elements of this first long period, K and Ca, have electron configurations similar to those of the elements directly above them—Li and Na to K, and Be and Mg to Ca. On the other hand, the ten elements from scandium, $_{21}$Sc, through zinc, $_{30}$Zn, have no counterparts in the three preceding short series, because their highest-energy electrons occupy the 3*d* orbitals, and there are no *d* electrons in the elements of Series 1, 2, and 3.

In the element following zinc, gallium, $_{31}$Ga, the additional electron now enters the next higher available sub-level, the 4*p*. The electron configuration of $_{31}$Ga is $1s^2,2s^2\,2p^6,3s^2\,3p^6\,3d^{10},4s^2\,4p^1$, or simply $[Ar]3d^{10},4s^2\,4p^1$. In each of the next five elements, $_{32}$Ge through $_{36}$Kr, an additional electron is added to the 4*p* orbitals until these three degenerate orbitals become completely filled (with six electrons) in the noble gas krypton, $_{36}$Kr (see Table 12-4 and the above diagram). Notice that for elements Ga to Kr, the outermost electron configurations again correspond to that of the elements directly above them in the Periodic Table. There is, however, one difference. The next to the outermost electrons are now the ten *d* electrons of the completely filled 3*d* sub-level, whereas in the elements of the first two short periods the next to the outermost electrons are in the filled $1s^2$ level for Series 2 and in the filled $2p^6$ sub-level for Series 3.

TABLE 12-4 ELECTRON CONFIGURATIONS OF THE ELEMENTS $_{18}$Ar TO $_{31}$Ga

Element with At. No.	Electron Arrangement (Number of Electrons in Successive Orbitals)				Schematic Representation of Outer Orbitals with Electrons Present				
	n = 1	n = 2	n = 3	n = 4	3s	3p	3d	4s	4p
$_{18}$Ar	$1s^2$	$2s^2\,2p^6$	$3s^2\,3p^6$		(II)	(II)(II)(II)	( )( )( )( )( )	( )	( )( )( )
$_{19}$K	$1s^2$	$2s^2\,2p^6$	$3s^2\,3p^6$	$4s^1$	(II)	(II)(II)(II)	( )( )( )( )( )	(I)	( )( )( )
$_{20}$Ca	$1s^2$	$2s^2\,2p^6$	$3s^2\,3p^6$	$4s^2$	(II)	(II)(II)(II)	( )( )( )( )( )	(II)	( )( )( )
$_{21}$Sc	$1s^2$	$2s^2\,2p^6$	$3s^2\,3p^6\,3d^1$	$4s^2$	(II)	(II)(II)(II)	(I)( )( )( )( )	(II)	( )( )( )
$_{22}$Ti	$1s^2$	$2s^2\,2p^6$	$3s^2\,3p^6\,3d^2$*	$4s^2$	(II)	(II)(II)(II)	(I)(I)( )( )( )	(II)	( )( )( )
$_{23}$V	$1s^2$	$2s^2\,2p^6$	$3s^2\,3p^6\,3d^3$	$4s^2$	(II)	(II)(II)(II)	(I)(I)(I)( )( )	(II)	( )( )( )
$_{24}$Cr	$1s^2$	$2s^2\,2p^6$	$3s^2\,3p^6\,3d^5$†	$4s^1$†	(II)	(II)(II)(II)	(I)(I)(I)(I)(I)	(I)	( )( )( )
$_{25}$Mn	$1s^2$	$2s^2\,2p^6$	$3s^2\,3p^6\,3d^5$	$4s^2$	(II)	(II)(II)(II)	(I)(I)(I)(I)(I)	(II)	( )( )( )
$_{26}$Fe	$1s^2$	$2s^2\,2p^6$	$3s^2\,3p^6\,3d^6$	$4s^2$	(II)	(II)(II)(II)	(II)(I)(I)(I)(I)	(II)	( )( )( )
$_{27}$Co	$1s^2$	$2s^2\,2p^6$	$3s^2\,3p^6\,3d^7$	$4s^2$	(II)	(II)(II)(II)	(II)(II)(I)(I)(I)	(II)	( )( )( )
$_{28}$Ni	$1s^2$	$2s^2\,2p^6$	$3s^2\,3p^6\,3d^8$	$4s^2$	(II)	(II)(II)(II)	(II)(II)(II)(I)(I)	(II)	( )( )( )
$_{29}$Cu	$1s^2$	$2s^2\,2p^6$	$3s^2\,3p^6\,3d^{10}$†	$4s^1$†	(II)	(II)(II)(II)	(II)(II)(II)(II)(II)	(I)	( )( )( )
$_{30}$Zn	$1s^2$	$2s^2\,2p^6$	$3s^2\,3p^6\,3d^{10}$	$4s^2$	(II)	(II)(II)(II)	(II)(II)(II)(II)(II)	(II)	( )( )( )
$_{31}$Ga	$1s^2$	$2s^2\,2p^6$	$3s^2\,3p^6\,3d^{10}$	$4s^2\,4p^1$	(II)	(II)(II)(II)	(II)(II)(II)(II)(II)	(II)	(I)( )( )

* Notice that starting with $_{22}$Ti each *d* orbital is first occupied by a single electron with parallel spins and only after each of the five *d* orbitals has one electron does a second electron enter an orbital with opposite spin (Hund's Rule).

† $_{24}$Cr has only one electron in the 4*s* orbital, and 5 electrons in the 3*d* orbital: $3d^5,4s^1$, (rather than $3d^4,4s^2$). The $3d^5,4s^1$ electron arrangement gives to the Cr atom a *half-filled* 3*d* sub-shell which has a greater stability than $3d^4,4s^2$. Similarly, $_{29}$Cu has a $3d^{10},4s^1$ electron arrangement, giving the Cu atom a *filled* 3*d* shell and also resulting in a greater stability than $3d^9,4s^2$.

For the eighteen elements which follow the noble gas krypton and constitute Periodic Series 5—rubidium, $_{37}$Rb, to the noble gas xenon, $_{54}$Xe—the outermost energy levels are filled with electrons very much as those of the elements of Series 4 (Table 12-5). Each element of Series 5 has an outermost electron configuration analogous to that of the element of Series 4 directly above it in the Periodic Table. Notice

TABLE 12-5 ELECTRON CONFIGURATIONS OF THE GASEOUS ATOMS OF THE ELEMENTS

At. No.	Symbol	Electron Configuration	At. No.	Symbol	Electron Configuration
1	H	$1s^1$	52	Te	[Kr] $4d^{10}$ $5s^2\,5p^4$
2	He	$1s^2$	53	I	[Kr] $4d^{10}$ $5s^2\,5p^5$
			54	Xe	[Kr] $4d^{10}$ $5s^2\,5p^6$
3	Li	[He] $2s^1$	55	Cs	[Xe] $6s^1$
4	Be	[He] $2s^2$	56	Ba	[Xe] $6s^2$
5	B	[He] $2s^2\,2p^1$	57	La	[Xe] $5d^1$ $6s^2$
6	C	[He] $2s^2\,2p^2$			
7	N	[He] $2s^2\,2p^3$	58	Ce	[Xe] $4f^2$ $6s^2$
8	O	[He] $2s^2\,2p^4$	59	Pr	[Xe] $4f^3$ $6s^2$
9	F	[He] $2s^2\,2p^5$	60	Nd	[Xe] $4f^4$ $6s^2$
10	Ne	[He] $2s^2\,2p^6$	61	Pm	[Xe] $4f^5$ $6s^2$
			62	Sm	[Xe] $4f^6$ $6s^2$
11	Na	[Ne] $3s^1$	63	Eu	[Xe] $4f^7$ $6s^2$
12	Mg	[Ne] $3s^2$	64	Gd	[Xe] $4f^7$ $5d^1$ $6s^2$
13	Al	[Ne] $3s^2\,3p^1$	65	Tb	[Xe] $4f^9$ $6s^2$
14	Si	[Ne] $3s^2\,3p^2$	66	Dy	[Xe] $4f^{10}$ $6s^2$
15	P	[Ne] $3s^2\,3p^3$	67	Ho	[Xe] $4f^{11}$ $6s^2$
16	S	[Ne] $3s^2\,3p^4$	68	Er	[Xe] $4f^{12}$ $6s^2$
17	Cl	[Ne] $3s^2\,3p^5$	69	Tm	[Xe] $4f^{13}$ $6s^2$
18	Ar	[Ne] $3s^2\,3p^6$	70	Yb	[Xe] $4f^{14}$ $6s^2$
			71	Lu	[Xe] $4f^{14}$ $5d^1$ $6s^2$
19	K	[Ar] $4s^1$			
20	Ca	[Ar] $4s^2$	72	Hf	[Xe] $4f^{14}$ $5d^2$ $6s^2$
21	Sc	[Ar] $3d^1$ $4s^2$	73	Ta	[Xe] $4f^{14}$ $5d^3$ $6s^2$
22	Ti	[Ar] $3d^2$ $4s^2$	74	W	[Xe] $4f^{14}$ $5d^4$ $6s^2$
23	V	[Ar] $3d^3$ $4s^2$	75	Re	[Xe] $4f^{14}$ $5d^5$ $6s^2$
24	Cr	[Ar] $3d^5$ $4s^1$	76	Os	[Xe] $4f^{14}$ $5d^6$ $6s^2$
25	Mn	[Ar] $3d^5$ $4s^2$	77	Ir	[Xe] $4f^{14}$ $5d^7$ $6s^2$
26	Fe	[Ar] $3d^6$ $4s^2$	78	Pt	[Xe] $4f^{14}$ $5d^9$ $6s^1$
27	Co	[Ar] $3d^7$ $4s^2$			
28	Ni	[Ar] $3d^8$ $4s^2$	79	Au	[Xe] $4f^{14}$ $5d^{10}$ $6s^1$
			80	Hg	[Xe] $4f^{14}$ $5d^{10}$ $6s^2$
29	Cu	[Ar] $3d^{10}$ $4s^1$	81	Tl	[Xe] $4f^{14}$ $5d^{10}$ $6s^2\,6p^1$
30	Zn	[Ar] $3d^{10}$ $4s^2$	82	Pb	[Xe] $4f^{14}$ $5d^{10}$ $6s^2\,6p^2$
31	Ga	[Ar] $3d^{10}$ $4s^2\,4p^1$	83	Bi	[Xe] $4f^{14}$ $5d^{10}$ $6s^2\,6p^3$
32	Ge	[Ar] $3d^{10}$ $4s^2\,4p^2$	84	Po	[Xe] $4f^{14}$ $5d^{10}$ $6s^2\,6p^4$
33	As	[Ar] $3d^{10}$ $4s^2\,4p^3$	85	At	[Xe] $4f^{14}$ $5d^{10}$ $6s^2\,6p^5$
34	Se	[Ar] $3d^{10}$ $4s^2\,4p^4$	86	Rn	[Xe] $4f^{14}$ $5d^{10}$ $6s^2\,6p^6$
35	Br	[Ar] $3d^{10}$ $4s^2\,4p^5$			
36	Kr	[Ar] $3d^{10}$ $4s^2\,4p^6$	87	Fr	[Rn] $7s^1$
			88	Ra	[Rn] $7s^2$
37	Rb	[Kr] $5s^1$	89	Ac	[Rn] $6d^1$ $7s^2$
38	Sr	[Kr] $5s^2$	90	Th	[Rn] $6d^2$ $7s^2$
39	Y	[Kr] $4d^1$ $5s^2$	91	Pa	[Rn] $5f^2$ $6d^1$ $7s^2$
40	Zr	[Kr] $4d^2$ $5s^2$	92	U	[Rn] $5f^3$ $6d^1$ $7s^2$
41	Nb	[Kr] $4d^4$ $5s^1$	93	Np	[Rn] $5f^4$ $6d^1$ $7s^2$
42	Mo	[Kr] $4d^5$ $5s^1$	94	Pu	[Rn] $5f^6$ $7s^2$
43	Te	[Kr] $4d^6$ $5s^1$	95	Am	[Rn] $5f^7$ $7s^2$
44	Ru	[Kr] $4d^7$ $5s^1$	96	Cm	[Rn] $5f^7$ $6d^1$ $7s^2$
45	Rh	[Kr] $4d^8$ $5s^1$	97	Bk	[Rn] $5f^9$ $7s^2$
46	Pd	[Kr] $4d^{10}$	98	Cf	[Rn] $5f^{10}$ $7s^2$
			99	Es*	[Rn] $5f^{11}$ $7s^2$
47	Ag	[Kr] $4d^{10}$ $5s^1$	100	Fm	[Rn] $5f^{12}$ $7s^2$
48	Cd	[Kr] $4d^{10}$ $5s^2$	101	Md	[Rn] $5f^{13}$ $7s^2$
49	In	[Kr] $4d^{10}$ $5s^2\,5p^1$	102	No	[Rn] $5f^{14}$ $7s^2$
50	Sn	[Kr] $4d^{10}$ $5s^2\,5p^2$	103	Lw	[Rn] $5f^{14}$ $6d^1$ $7s^2$
51	Sb	[Kr] $4d^{10}$ $5s^2\,5p^3$			

* Element 99 is called einsteinium in honor of Albert Einstein; element 100, fermium, in honor of Enrico Fermi; element 101, mendelevium, in honor of Dmitri Mendeleef; element 102, nobelium, after the Nobel Institute in Stockholm; and element 103, lawrencium, in honor of Ernest O. Lawrence.

that for the elements of Series 5 ($n = 5$) the $4f$ orbitals are still vacant although they have a lower principal quantum number ($n = 4$), because their energy is higher than that of the $5s$, $4d$, and $5p$ orbitals.

In cesium, $_{55}$Cs, and barium, $_{56}$Ba, the first two elements of the next Periodic Series ($n = 6$), the additional electrons appear in the $6s$ sub-shell, following the pattern of all the preceding series.

In the next element, $_{57}$La, the additional electron occupies one of the $5d$ orbitals (sub-shell), just as in the corresponding element of Series 5, ytterbium, $_{39}$Yb, the additional electron occupies a $4d$ orbital. Beginning with cerium, $_{58}$Ce, however, the occupancy of the $4f$ sub-shell begins and continues regularly for the next thirteen elements, until the seven degenerate $4f$ orbitals contain their maximum number of electrons—fourteen. In lutetium, $_{71}$Lu, the $4f$ sub-shell becomes complete, ($4f^{14}$). In the next nine elements, hafnium, $_{72}$Hf, through mercury, $_{80}$Hg, the additional electrons occupy the $5d$ orbitals until these are filled ($5d^{10}$) in $_{80}$Hg, following a pattern similar to that of the first and second transition series. After the filling of the $5d$ and the $6s$ orbitals in $_{80}$Hg, the additional electrons of the following six elements, thallium, $_{81}$Tl, through radon, $_{86}$Rn, fill the $6p$ orbitals. The electron configurations of the elements of Series 6 are listed in Table 12-5. Notice that for each of the elements which follow $_{71}$Lu, the electron configuration is similar to those of the elements directly above them in the Periodic Table. There is, however, one difference—namely, the presence of the underlying filled sub-shell of seven $4f$ orbitals.

In the first two elements of series 7, $_{87}$Fr and $_{88}$Ra, the additional electrons occupy the $7s$ orbital, resulting in $7s^1$ and $7s^2$ outermost electron configurations, respectively. Insofar as the remainder of the elements in this series are concerned, the $6d$ and the $5f$ sub-shells are filled in a way that resembles the process by which the $5d$ and $4f$ sub-shells are filled in Series 6. Table 12-5 summarizes all our previous discussion and lists the electron distribution of the atoms of all the elements.

The general statements that we have made about the order in which the shells and sub-shells are filled apply to almost all the atoms. There are however, a few minor exceptions, for the electron arrangement based on the building-up principle and Hund's Rule does not actually apply for a few elements. In $_{24}$Cr, for example, we would expect the outermost electron distribution to be $3d^4,4s^2$, but as we have pointed out, it actually is $3d^5,4s^1$. This electron configuration arises from the fact that a half-filled d sub-shell, d^5 (one electron in each of the five d orbitals, all with parallel spins) is very stable. In the atoms of copper, $_{29}$Cu, silver, $_{47}$Ag, and gold, $_{79}$Au, the electron distribution is d^{10},s^1, rather than the expected d^9,s^2. Here the special stability of a completely filled d sub-shell (d^{10}) is responsible for the actual electron configurations. The difference in energy between a d electron of a particular principal quantum number, n, and an s electron of the next higher principal quantum number, $(n + 1)$, is relatively small, and the shift of an electron from one orbital to the other is effected quite easily. A similar exception to the expected arrangement occurs in $_{46}$Pd, where we find $4d^{10}$ ($5s^0$) instead of $4d^8,5s^2$. Thus there is a delicate balance in the relative energy values of lower-quantum-number orbitals $n(d)$ and the next higher quantum-number orbitals $(n + 1)s$.

12-4 Electron Configuration of the Elements and the Periodic Law

We have seen in the previous sections that all elements in the same group of the Periodic Table have analogous outer electron configurations. We also know that all elements in the same periodic group resemble one another closely in their physical and chemical properties, which is why they were first assigned to the same group by Mendeleef. Obviously, there must be a relationship between the similar physical and chemical properties and the analogous electron structure of the elements of the same group, and later we shall illustrate such a relationship with several examples.

In general, the electron configuration of the elements varies gradually and regularly along each periodic series, each additional electron entering the lowest-energy orbital available, in accordance with the building-up principle, Hund's Rule, and the Pauli Exclusion Principle. This gradual change in electron configuration must be responsible for the observed gradual change in the physical and chemical properties of the elements of a periodic series. As an illustration let us now discuss in more detail the elements of Series 1 to 4, their electron configurations, and some of their physical and chemical properties.

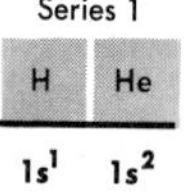

Series 1 consists of two elements, hydrogen and helium, which are gases under ordinary conditions. Hydrogen exists in the form of diatomic molecules, H_2, in which each H atom shares its 1*s* electron with its partner H atom to form a covalent H—H bond. With most of the elements with which it combines, hydrogen forms compounds that are essentially covalent, such as HCl, H_2SO_4, HNO_3, H_2O, and H_2S. In these compounds hydrogen is assigned an oxidation number of +1 (for review of oxidation numbers, see p. 52). When hydrogen combines with the most electropositive metals, however, it forms ionic hydrides (p. 67) in which it appears as the monovalent negative hydride ion, H^-, with an oxidation number of −1 and an electron configuration of $1s^2$, similar to that of the next element, helium. The formulas of the ionic compounds formed by the reaction of hydrogen with the highly electropositive metals sodium, potassium, and calcium, for example, are Na^+H^-, K^+H^-, and $Ca^{++}(H^-)_2$.

Helium molecules are monoatomic, He; unlike hydrogen atoms, helium atoms are unable to combine with one another to form diatomic molecules. Helium does not ordinarily enter into chemical combination with the atoms of other elements to form either covalent or ionic compounds.

Series 2. The first element of this series, lithium, Li, is a highly electropositive element (a metal) and the seventh element, fluorine, F, is a highly electronegative element (a non-metal). As the series progresses, the successive elements lose electropositive (metallic) characteristics and gain electronegative (non-metallic) characteristics. The last element of Series 2, the noble gas neon, Ne, exhibits chemical and physical properties that are similar to those of the noble gas helium, He, which appears eight places before it in the Periodic Table. Like helium, neon exists as monoatomic molecules and does not ordinarily enter into chemical combination with other elements.

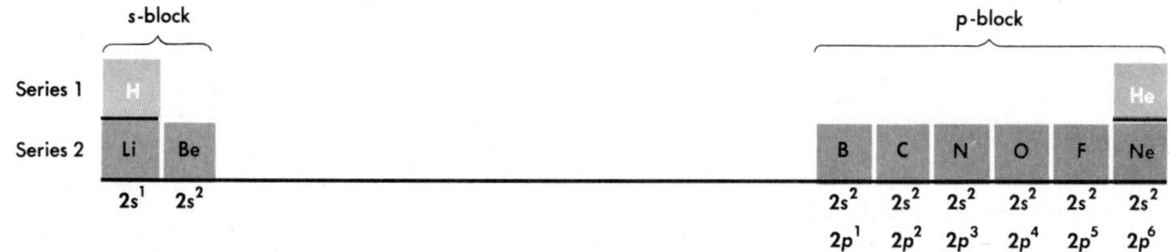

Lithium, a very soft metal, can be cut with a knife. In its compounds it exists as a univalent positive lithium ion, Li^+. Beryllium, Be, the next member of the series, has definite metallic characteristics, but it is less electropositive than lithium. Beryllium is a hard, white metal that reacts rapidly with acids to liberate hydrogen, and is present in some compounds as the dipositive beryllium ion, Be^{++}. The electron configuration of both the Li^+ and the Be^{++} ions is $1s^2$, the same as that of the preceding noble gas, He. The third element of Series 2, boron, B, is essentially non-metallic, even though some of its properties resemble those of metals. In its compounds, boron is almost always assigned an oxidation number of +3. The next two elements, carbon, C, and nitrogen, N, are non-metallic in character and form only covalent compounds.

Oxygen is a very electronegative non-metal and combines directly with almost all the other elements. In combination with electropositive metals such as sodium, potassium, and calcium, oxygen forms ionic compounds that contain the dinegative oxide ion, $O^{=}$, with the same electron configuration ($1s^2,2s^2,2p^6$) as the next noble gas, neon. Examples are sodium oxide, $(Na^+)_2O^{=}$; potassium oxide, $(K^+)_2O^{=}$; and calcium oxide, $Ca^{++}O^{=}$. In combination with other non-metals, however, oxygen forms covalently bonded compounds. Examples are water, H_2O; carbon dioxide, CO_2; and sulfur dioxide, SO_2.

Fluorine, the seventh member of the series, is the most highly electronegative of all the elements. Fluorine combines with almost all the elements to form either covalent compounds containing fluorine with an oxidation number of -1, or ionic compounds containing the mononegative fluoride ion, F^-. Examples are HF and Na^+F^-. As the diagram shows, the elements in which the outermost electron occupies an *s* orbital are called in general "*s*-block" elements, and those in which the outermost electron occupies a *p* orbital are called generally "*p*-block" elements.

Series 3. The first element in Series 3, sodium, Na, is a highly electropositive metal and exhibits chemical and physical properties very similar to those of the element directly above it in Group I, lithium. In fact, each element in Series 3 has physical and chemical properties similar to those of the element directly above it in Series 2, and directly below it in Series 4. For example, some of the physical and chemical properties of magnesium are similar to those of beryllium; sulfur is similar in some respects to oxygen; and chlorine resembles fluorine. Argon, Ar, has characteristics similar to those of both the noble gases above it, neon, Ne, and helium, He. As in Series 2, the elements of Series 3 show a progressive decrease in metallic properties and a progressive increase in non-metallic properties from left to right along the series.

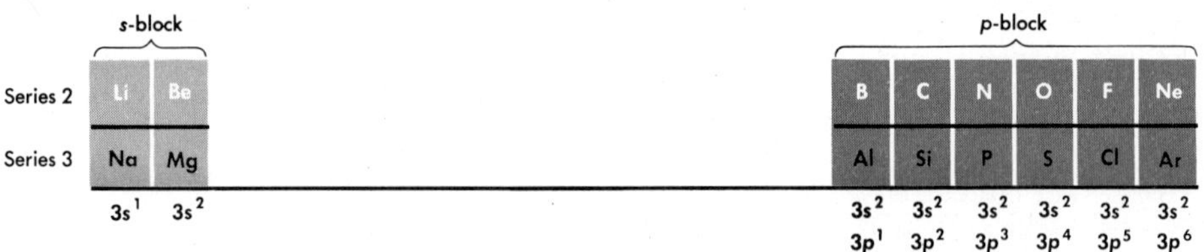

Series 4. Starting with the highly electropositive metal potassium, K, there are eighteen elements in Series 4 before the next highly electropositive element, rubidium, Rb, appears in Series 5. The first two elements—potassium, K, and calcium, Ca—closely resemble the two elements directly above them in their respective groups—sodium, Na, and magnesium, Mg. The next eight elements of the series, scandium, $_{21}Sc$, through nickel, $_{28}Ni$, are called the first series of *transition* elements. They are less electropositive than calcium but still have a definitely metallic character. Although the properties of these eight transition elements change regularly from Sc to Ni, the differences between them are less marked than those between successive elements of a regular series. As the diagram shows, the elements in which the outermost electron enters a *d* orbital are called in general "*d*-block" elements.

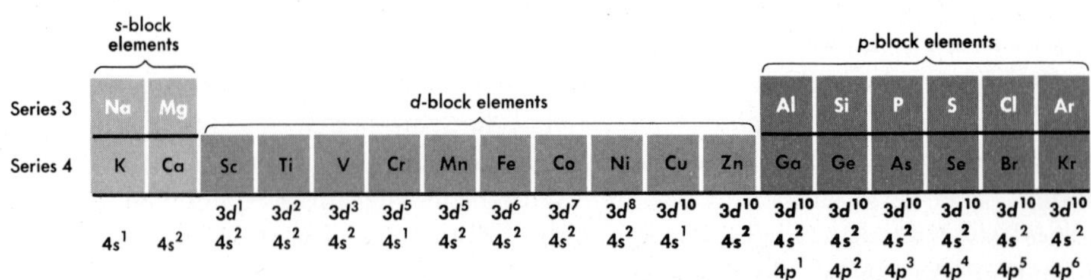

In our discussion so far we have emphasized the *differences* among elements within each *series*. Now let us turn to the *similarities* that exist among elements within each *group*. As we know, elements within the same periodic group generally resemble one another fairly closely, and as an illustration we shall now consider the elements of Group I.

ALKALI METALS

Group IA of the Periodic Table contains the *alkali metals*—lithium, Li; sodium, Na; potassium, K; rubidium, Rb; cesium, Cs; and francium, Fr. Elements of a group that exhibit very similar physical and chemical properties are said to belong to the same *family;* thus the elements of Group IA constitute the *alkali-metal family.* Hydrogen, H, is sometimes included in Group IA, because, like the alkali metals, it can give up its one *s* electron to form a monopositive ion, H^+. However, the physical and chemical properties of hydrogen differ very markedly from those of the alkali metals, and it is better to consider hydrogen by itself.

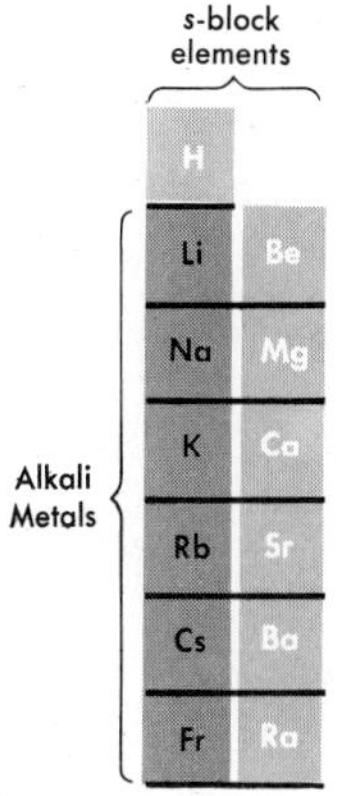

All the elements of the alkali-metal family have a metallic character (they are good conductors of heat and electricity, are soft enough to be cut with a knife, have rather low densities, and are highly electropositive). Their melting points are relatively low for metals and decrease with increasing atomic number as we go down the family. Thus the highest-melting element of the family is lithium (m.p. 180°C) and the lowest-melting is cesium (m.p. 29°C). Actually, cesium is a liquid on a hot day. All the alkali metals react with cold water to liberate hydrogen gas, H_2, and to form a metal hydroxide with the general formula, $M^+(OH^-)$, where M^+ stands for the monopositive alkali-metal ion.

The similarity of the elements that make up the alkali-metal family is further indicated by the formulas of their chlorides, M^+Cl^-; oxides $(M^+)_2O^=$; and sulfates $(M^+)_2(SO_4^=)$, in which the alkali metals always have an oxidation number of +1. The electropositive character of the alkali metals increases with increasing atomic number, so that cesium is the most electropositive of the naturally occurring alkali metals. (The heaviest of all alkali metals, francium, Fr, is a radioactive element not present in nature.)

THE COINAGE METALS

The elements of Group IB, often called the *coinage metals* because they are part of the alloys used to make coins, are copper, Cu; silver, Ag; and gold, Au. These three metals resemble one another closely; they are relatively hard, extremely malleable and ductile, and have melting points close to 1,000°C. The coinage metals do not react with water or with non-oxidizing acids, and silver and gold are among the very few metals which do not combine directly with oxygen to form stable oxides. Thus the coinage metals do not bear any resemblance to the alkali metals (Group IA) except that they are good conductors of heat and electricity, as are all metals. However, both the coinage metals and the alkali metals can form compounds in which they have an oxidation number of +1.

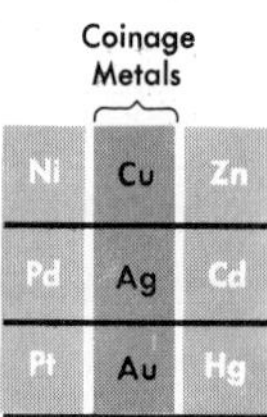

We have considered the alkali metals (Group IA) and the coinage metals (Group IB) in order to illustrate some of the similarities between metallic elements of the same group, and some of the differences between metallic elements of different groups. Now we shall turn to the non-metals of Group VIIB and the metals of Group VIIA to illustrate further the similarities and differences that exist among the elements in a particular group of the Periodic Table.

GROUP VIIB. THE HALOGENS

The similarities that exist between the non-metallic members of the same Group are exemplified by the elements of Group VIIB: fluorine, F; chlorine, Cl; bromine, Br; iodine, I; and astatine, At. These five elements constitute a family known as the *halogens.*

The halogens are all highly electronegative and are very similar in many of their physical and chemical properties. For example, all the halogens exist as diatomic covalent molecules, X_2, in which two halogen atoms share their unpaired $n\ p$ electron with one another in a covalent bond. All halogens are non-conductors of electricity and have relatively low boiling points, ranging from $-188°C$ for the lowest-boiling, fluorine, F_2, to $+183°C$ for the highest-boiling, iodine, I_2.

Halogens

The halogens form similar compounds with many elements. For example, the compounds they form with hydrogen, called hydrogen halides, are all covalent gaseous substances of the same general formula HX (in which X represents either F, Cl, Br, or I). Similarly, the compounds formed by the halogens with the alkali metals have the general formula M^+X^-, and all are colorless, high-melting, water-soluble solids with an ionic structure.

Although the halogens resemble one another closely, certain differences do appear as we move down the family—that is, as the atomic weight of the element increases. For example, fluorine, F_2, is a pale-yellowish gas; chlorine, Cl_2, is a yellowish-green gas; bromine, Br_2, is a dark-red liquid; and iodine, I_2, is a steel-gray solid (iodine *vapor* is violet). Furthermore, the halogens differ in their tendency to react with hydrogen to form the hydrogen halides. Fluorine reacts explosively with hydrogen in the dark at room temperature; chlorine reacts explosively in the presence of light at room temperature, but only very slowly in the dark; bromine must be heated before it will react; and iodine, even when heated, reacts slowly and then only partially. Also, in passing from the lighter to the heavier elements, the electronegative character of the halogens gradually decreases. Thus, fluorine is the most electronegative element and iodine is the least electronegative element of the family.

GROUP VIIA METALS

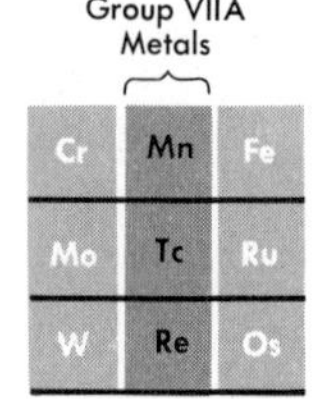

Unlike the non-metallic elements of Group VIIB, the halogens, the elements of Group VIIA—manganese, Mn; technetium, Tc; and rhenium, Re—are all metals. These metals have very high melting points, form many similar compounds, and generally resemble one another closely. The Group VIIA metals and the Group VIIB halogens have very little in common except their ability to form complex negative oxoanions with the same oxidation number—such as, for example, MnO_4^- and ClO_4^-.

GROUP O ELEMENTS

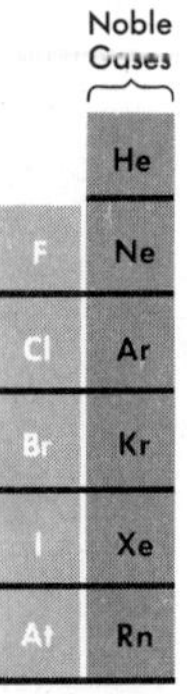

So far, we have considered the alkali metals (Group IA), the coinage metals (Group IB), the halogens (Group VIIB), and the metals of Group VIIA to illustrate the resemblances and differences within periodic groups. Now, to complete our illustrations of periodic groups, we shall discuss briefly the unique Group O, which comprises the family of elements called the *noble gases.* The elements of Group O—helium, He; neon, Ne; argon, Ar; krypton, Kr; xenon, Xe; and radon, Rn—are monoatomic gases with extremely low boiling points. The atoms of these elements have no tendency to combine with one another to form molecules, and their low boiling points indicate that only weak van der Waals forces exist between the monoatomic molecules. Clearly, then, the atoms of the noble gases are very unreactive toward one another. They are also generally unreactive toward other elements, and in fact until 1960 it was generally believed that the noble gases did not enter into chemical combination at all. Now we know that under appropriate conditions xenon, Xe, and krypton, Kr, form a variety of stable compounds, but so far none of the lighter elements of the family—He, Ne and Ar—has been observed to form compounds. Thus, we may say that as the atomic number of the elements increases down Group O, so does their capacity to enter into chemical combination.

It is a general characteristic of families of elements that the similarity between successive members increases in passing from the top to the bottom. For example, in the halogen family (Group VIIB) fluorine is less like chlorine than chlorine is like bromine, or than bromine is like iodine. Similarly, in the alkali-metal family (Group IA) lithium is less like sodium than sodium is like potassium, and so on.

OXIDATION NUMBERS OF ELEMENTS AND POSITION IN PERIODIC TABLE

By means of a few general rules, we can correlate the oxidation number of the common elements with their position in the Periodic Table and hence with their electron configuration.

Rule I. The alkali metals (Group IA) and the alkaline-earth metals (Group IIA), which constitute the s block elements, and the metals of Group IIIA (with the exception of some rare-earth elements) have *only one* oxidation number. This oxidation number is positive and is equal to the number of the outermost electrons in the atoms of these elements, which is also the periodic group number. For example, the oxidation number of lithium, Li, sodium, Na, and of the other alkali elements in Group IA is +1; the oxidation number of beryllium, Be; magnesium, Mg; and of the other alkaline-earth metals of Group IIA is +2; and the oxidation number of scandium, Sc, of Group IIIA is +3. The elements zinc, Zn, and cadmium, Cd, of Group IIB; boron, B, and aluminum, Al, of Group IIIB; and silicon, Si, of Group IVB also have *only one* (positive) oxidation number equal to their periodic group number.

Rule II. When an element forms a monoatomic negative ion, its negative oxidation number is always equal to its periodic group number minus 8. For example, the halogens of Group VIIB have a negative oxidation number of −1 (7 − 8), in the ionic compounds K^+Br^-, Cs^+I^-, and $Ca^{++}(Cl^-)_2$. Oxygen, sulfur, and selenium, which appear in Group VIB, have a negative oxidation number of −2 (6 − 8), in the ionic compounds $Ca^{++}O^=$, $Zn^{++}S^=$, H_2S^{-2} and H_2Se^{-2}. However, oxygen in peroxides and sulfur in disulfides are present as diatomic ions, $O_2^=$ and $S_2^=$, with an oxidation number of −1.

Rule III. a. All other elements except fluorine and those mentioned in Rule I have variable oxidation numbers. Except for the coinage metals, copper, Cu; silver, Ag; and gold, Au; and the noble gases krypton, Kr; and xenon, Xe; the oxidation numbers are never greater than the group number.

b. The A Group elements may have oxidation numbers that differ from one another by single units. For example, manganese, Mn, in Group VIIA, has a maximum positive oxidation number of +7, which is equal to its periodic group number, and exhibits also lower oxidation numbers of +6, +5, +4, +3, +2 and +1, 0, −1 and −2.

c. The B Group elements usually have, in addition to the maximum positive oxidation number equal to their group number, lower oxidation numbers that differ from one another by two units. For example, in the halogen family (Group VIIB) chlorine, Cl, has a maximum positive oxidation number of +7, and also lower oxidation numbers of +5, +3, +1 and −1. Similarly, arsenic, As, in Group VB, has +5 as its highest oxidation number, but it also exhibits an oxidation number of +3.

12-6 Electron Distribution of the Atomic Orbitals

We have mentioned earlier that electrons in the atomic orbitals *s*, *p*, *d* and *f* differ in their distribution in space. Let us now discuss what such a statement means, and let us begin by considering again the simplest atomic system—the hydrogen atom.

s ORBITALS. THE HYDROGEN ATOM

In the hydrogen atom, the probability of finding the electron at any given point in the space around the nucleus depends only on the *distance* of the point from the nucleus, and can be pictorially represented as in Fig. 12-4(a), where the intensity of the shading corresponds to the increasing possibility of finding the electron.

FIGURE 12-4 (a) Electron-cloud density of the H atom. (b) Point electron density of the H atom as a function of *r*. (c) Probability of finding the electron of the H atom inside a sphere of radius *r* (also fraction of the total electron cloud enclosed by the sphere of radius *r*). (d) Boundary surface of the 1s orbital enclosing 90 per cent of the total electron cloud of the H atom. (e) Shell electron density of the H atom as a function of *r*.

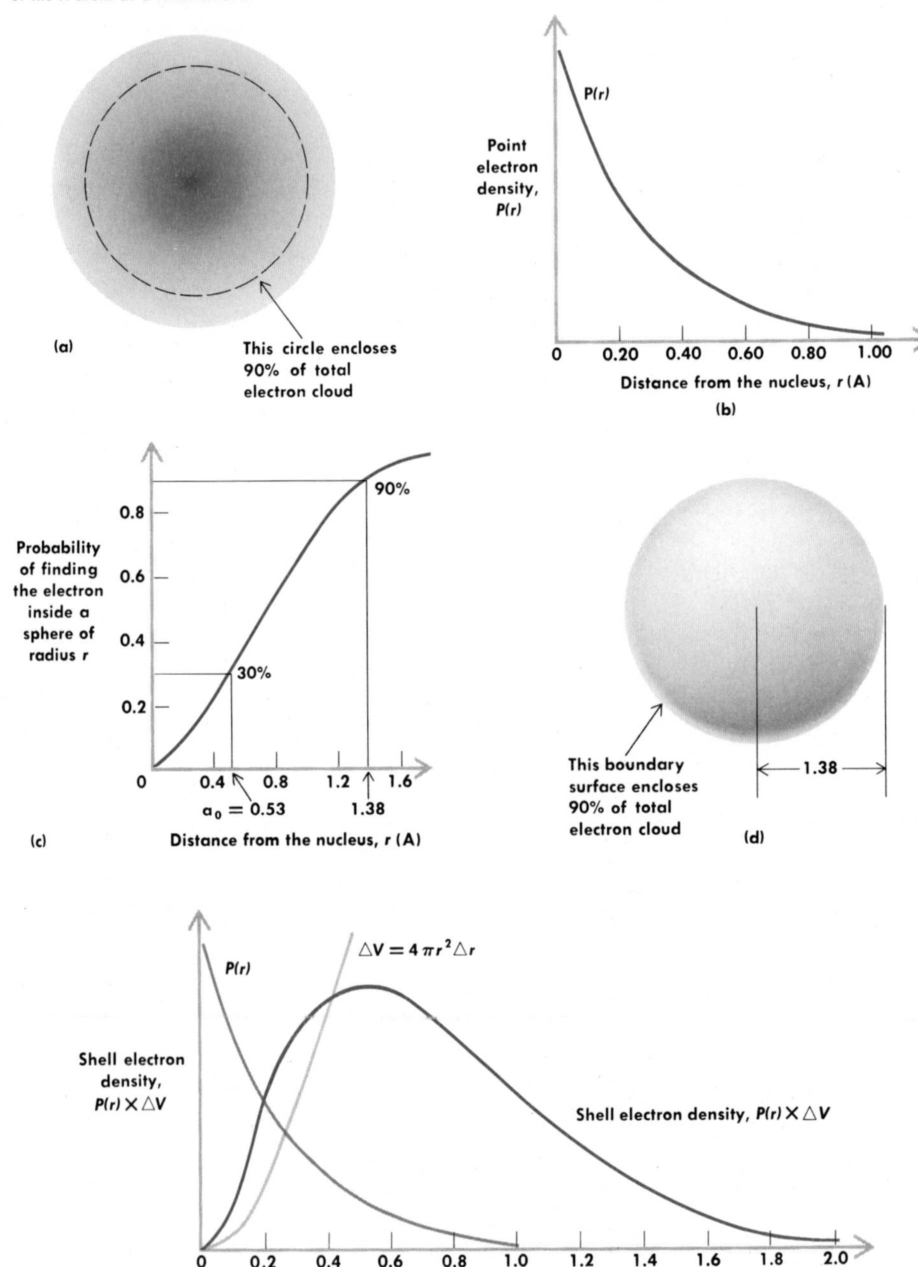

The diagram shows that the probability of finding the electron at a given point is greatest very close to the nucleus, then it gradually and steadily decreases as the distance from the nucleus increases, finally becoming extremely small. Figure 12-4(a) also represents the distribution of the negative charge of the electron in the space about the nucleus, as we have already mentioned in Chapter 3, and is therefore a pictorial representation of the *electron cloud density* or *point electron density*, or simply of the *electron density*, of the H atom. To help us visualize how such a diagram is obtained, let us *assume* that we are able to determine by some experiment the exact position occupied by the electron at a given moment; this position we represent as a small dot. We repeat this experiment many times and represent by a small dot the position where each time we find the electron. After an extremely large number of such determinations, the single dots blend with one another and are no longer individually distinguishable. The resulting effect is that of a "cloud," darker and therefore "denser" in regions where there are more dots. This electron cloud, or charge cloud, represents the electron distribution about the nucleus, not at a particular moment, but over a relatively long period of time. In other words, it represents the statistical distribution of the electron, or the statistical electron density. Because the density of the electron cloud is greatest in the regions of space where we are most likely to find the electron, the (point) electron density and the probability distribution are proportional to one another, and these two concepts are used interchangeably. It is important to point out here that the electron cloud representation of an atom cannot actually be obtained in the manner we have just described, because the electron is not a particle which can be pin-pointed exactly at a given instant. However, the resulting representation of the electron distribution is correct, because by assuming that we can determine the position of the electron an infinite number of times, we are actually considering the statistical, or probability, distribution of the electron around the nucleus, which can be calculated accurately by mathematics.

For the ground state of the H atom, 1*s*, the probability of finding the electron at a given point at a distance r from the nucleus is the same regardless of the direction, so that every point on a surface of a sphere of radius r (having the nucleus as the center) has the same point electron density. Similarly, all points on the surface of any given sphere (having the nucleus at the center) have the same particular point electron density. As the distance from the nucleus—the radius of the sphere—increases, the point electron density on the surface of the sphere progressively decreases and finally becomes zero. Since the point electron density for the electron of the H atom in the ground state (a 1*s* electron) depends only on the distance, r, from the nucleus, we may represent it as $P(r)$. For the ground state of the H atom, the point electron density, $P(r)$, which is also the probability of finding the (1*s*) electron at a given distance r from the nucleus, varies with r as shown by the plot of Fig. 12-4(b). This diagram shows that the probability of finding the electron at a given point is greatest very close to the nucleus (when r approaches zero), and then decreases exponentially, becoming very small when r is about 1.00A (1A $= 10^{-8}$ cm), and approaching zero when r approaches infinity. Since all points which are at the same distance, r, from the nucleus, (that is, which are on the surface of a sphere of radius r) have the same electron density, we say that the spatial distribution, or electron density, of the 1*s* electron in the H atom is *spherically symmetrical* about the nucleus.

The term *orbital* is used to indicate briefly the spatial distribution around the nucleus of an electron in a given energy level. It follows from the above considerations that the 1*s* orbital of the H atom is spherically symmetrical about the nucleus.

Although, as we have seen, the electron cloud of the H atom does not end sharply at a certain distance from the nucleus, but merely becomes less and less dense as the distance from the nucleus increases, it is of practical interest to have some idea of how far from the nucleus we must go before the electron cloud density becomes negligible. Figure 12-4(c) shows how the probability of finding the 1*s* electron of the H atom inside a sphere of radius *r* (having the nucleus at the center) varies with *r*. This diagram also represents the fraction of the total electron cloud to be found inside a sphere of radius *r*. For example, the fraction of the electron cloud of the H atom found inside the sphere of radius $r = a_0{}^*$ = 0.53 A is about 30%, and the fraction of the electron cloud contained inside a sphere of radius $2.6a_0$ = 1.38 A is about 90%. Consequently, for many purposes this latter value, 1.38 A, might be considered to be the "radius" of the H atom. (In taking 1.40 A as the radius of the H atom we neglect about 10% of its total electron cloud.) From Fig. 12-4(c) we can construct *boundary surfaces* (spherical surfaces in a three-dimensional representation, circles in a two-dimensional representation), each enclosing a given fraction of the total electron cloud, as shown in Fig. 12-4(d). The 1*s* orbital of hydrogen—that is, the hydrogen atom in its ground state—is generally represented as the spherical boundary surface enclosing 90% of the total electron cloud.

We have seen that for the H atom in its ground state the point electron density, *P*(r), is the same for all points which lie on the surface of a sphere of radius *r*, with the nucleus at the center. The surface area of this sphere of radius *r* is $4\pi r^2$. The total electron density on the surface of such a sphere is therefore obtained by multiplying the surface area, $4\pi r^2$, by the point electron density, $P(r)$, and is $4\pi r^2 P(r)$. We can repeat these considerations for a slightly larger sphere, of radius $(r + \Delta r)$, where Δr is extremely small. By simple geometry we can calculate the total electron density within the spherical shell of thickness Δr, limited by the inner sphere of radius *r* and the outer sphere of radius $(r + \Delta r)$. This total electron density within the spherical shell of thickness Δr, called *radial shell electron density,* is $4\pi r^2 P(r) \times \Delta r$. Figure 12-4(e) shows the plot of the radial shell electron density, also called the *radial shell distribution,* versus *r*. This diagram shows also how this curve of the radial shell distribution is derived from those of the point electron density $P(r)$, and of the radial shell volume, $\Delta V = 4\pi r^2 \, \Delta r$. As *r* increases, the point electron density, $P(r)$, decreases, but the shell volume, ΔV, increases. The value of the radial shell density depends both on $P(r)$ and on ΔV—in fact, it is their product. For large values of the radius, *r*, the point electron density $P(r)$ becomes so extremely small that even though the volume of the shell is relatively large, the radial shell density becomes very small. On the other hand, for very small values of *r* the volume of the ΔV becomes so very small that, even though the point electron density is large, again the radial shell density becomes small. For intermediate values of *r*, the two opposing factors $P(r)$ and ΔV, equal each other and we have a maximum of the radial shell electron density for the 1*s* electron of the H atom at r = 0.529 A (Bohr radius).

The electron distribution we have so far considered is that of the hydrogen atom in its lowest energy state—the ground state, corresponding to the 1*s* energy level. In an excited state of the hydrogen atom the distribution of the electron may also be spherically symmetrical, or it may have a more complicated spatial distribution.

Let us consider now the electron distribution of the first few elements which follow hydrogen in the Periodic Table.

HELIUM ATOM. The helium atom, $_2$He, has a nuclear charge of +2 and two electrons. The electron cloud of He in the ground state is very similar in spatial distribution to that of H in the ground state, but it is pulled in closer to the nucleus because of the greater effective nuclear charge of helium. If the two electrons of He were at each moment equidistant from the nucleus, they would completely shield one another from the nuclear charge, and each electron would experience an effective nuclear charge of +1. However, although on a time average each 1*s* electron has the same

* This value of *r*, symbolized as a_0, is the so-called Bohr radius of the H atom, first proposed by the Danish physicist Niels Bohr.

distribution (Fig. 12-4(b)), at times one electron will be closer to the nucleus than the other, and consequently will experience an effective nuclear charge greater than +1. On the other hand, the electron which at that moment is farther from the nucleus experiences an effective nuclear charge of +1, because the other closer electron completely screens one unit of positive nuclear charge. Each of the two 1*s* electrons of He, therefore, is attracted more strongly to the nucleus than the one 1*s* electron of H, which always is exposed to an effective nuclear charge of +1. Consequently, the two 1*s* electrons of He are, on the average, closer to the nucleus than the 1*s* electron of H, and we express this by saying that the 1*s* orbital of He is smaller, or more contracted toward the nucleus, than the 1*s* orbital of H. It follows that the He atom is smaller than the H atom, although it weighs four times as much and it contains two electrons instead of one.

LITHIUM ION, Li^+, AND LITHIUM ATOM, Li. The lithium ion, Li^+, has two 1*s* electrons, like the He atom, but has a nuclear charge of +3. The electron cloud of the Li^+ ion is similar to that of the He atom in that it is spherically symmetrical about the nucleus but is attracted toward the nucleus much more strongly, because in the Li^+ ion the two electrons are exposed to a +3 nuclear charge. Similarly, in the dipositive beryllium ion, Be^{+2}, which has a +4 nuclear charge and only two electrons in the 1*s* orbital, the electron cloud is pulled in even more strongly toward the nucleus (or we may say the 1*s* orbital is even smaller) than in the lithium ion, Li^+.

Consider now the neutral lithium atom, Li, having a nuclear charge of +3 and 3 extranuclear electrons. The electron configuration of $_3Li$ is $1s^2,2s^1$, and the electron cloud density of the Li atom is represented in Fig. 12-5(a). The darkest region around the nucleus represents the electron density of the two electrons occupying the 1*s* orbital, $1s^2$. Their distribution is spherically symmetrical about the nucleus and thus is qualitatively the same as that of the H and He atoms, though more contracted toward the nucleus. The outer dark region represents the region of maximum probability for the third electron, occupying the 2*s* orbital, $2s^1$. The radial shell distribution of the 2*s* electron is shown in Fig. 12-5(b). From these diagrams we see that the 2*s* orbital—similar to the 1*s* orbital—is spherically symmetrical about the nucleus and has the same kind of electron distribution. However, the region of maximum probability, or maximum point density, of the 2*s* orbital is farther away from the nucleus than that of the 1*s* orbital. Such an electron distribution for the 2*s* orbital results from the balance of two opposite forces acting on the 2*s* electron, the attraction by the effective nuclear charge, and the repulsion by the (negative) charges of the two inner 1*s* electrons. Because of this interelectron repulsion, the probability of finding the 2*s* electron of Li close to the region of maximum density of the 1*s* electrons is extremely small. On the other hand, the nucleus still attracts the 2*s* electron, which then tends to occupy a position in space as close as possible to the nucleus, compatible with the repulsion by the two 1*s* electrons.

For a 3*s*, a 4*s*, or in general for any *n s* orbital, the radial shell distribution is again spherically symmetrical about the nucleus, but the region of maximum probability moves farther and farther away from the nucleus as the principal quantum number increases from $n = 2$ to $n = 3$ to $n = 4$, and so on.

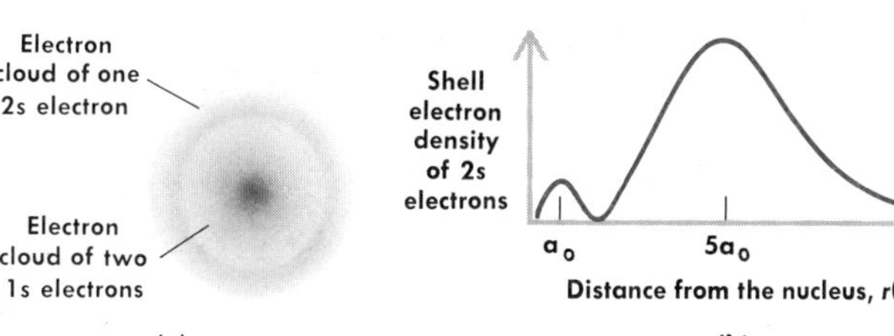

FIGURE 12-5 (a) Electron-cloud density of the Li atom. (b) Shell electron density of the 2s electron.

Figure 12-5(b) shows that for a $2s$ electron there are two regions of maximum shell electron density separated by a region, at some certain distance, r, from the nucleus, where the shell electron density is zero. At this certain distance from the nucleus the shell electron density, $P(r) \times 4\pi r^2 \Delta r$, is zero because the point electron density, $P(r)$, is zero (the shell volume obviously has a finite value, $\Delta V = 4\pi r^2 \Delta r$). Such a region of space, where the point electron density is zero (but r is not infinite) is generally called a *node* of the electron distribution diagram. If there is a node in the $2s$ orbital at some distance from the nucleus, then there is a spherical surface around the nucleus where there is no probability of finding the electron. If the electron were a charged particle, localizable at a given point in space at a given instant, a problem would arise: how can the electron be at one instant in the inner region of (smaller) probability and then at some other instant in the outer region of (greater) probability, without also being at an intermediate instant in the interposed region of zero probability? The problem, however, is only apparent, because, as we said before (p. 239) it is not correct to visualize the electron as an exactly localizable point charge, although we may use such a picture to help us understand how we may obtain the electron cloud representation. We should always keep in mind that it is only the probability distribution of the electron density which is truly correct.

For the second element of the $n = 2$ periodic series, $_4Be$, the electron configuration is $1s^2,2s^2$, and the distribution of the electron cloud density is very similar to that we have just described for Li, $1s^2,2s^1$. However, the $2s$ orbital of Be has a greater electron density than that of Li, because it contains two electrons instead of one. Also, the electron cloud of Be is pulled in closer to the nucleus, because it is exposed to a greater effective nuclear charge.

THE BORON ATOM, B. p ORBITALS

The electron configuration of boron, $_5B$, is $1s^2,2s^2\ 2p^1$. The previous discussion permits us to visualize the electron density of the four electrons occupying the $1s$ and $2s$ orbitals, $1s^2,2s^2$, but not that of the fifth electron occupying a different type of orbital not as yet discussed, the $2p$ orbital. Therefore, for a complete picture of the electron distribution in the boron atom, we need to know also the electron distribution of the p orbitals. For a p orbital, the point electron density depends on two factors: (1) *the radial distribution*, which determines how the point electron density for any given orientation in space varies with the distance, r, from the nucleus, and (2) the *angular distribution*, which determines how the point electron density, for any given distance, r, from the nucleus, varies with the orientation in space. These two factors are discussed individually in the Appendix, Section 12-1.

The electron distribution in a $2p$ orbital, resulting from both the radial distribution and the angular distribution, is usually represented as an electron cloud (Fig. 12-6(a)), or as a boundary surface in which each point has the same electron density (Fig. 12-6(b)). The boundary surface is usually considered to enclose about 90% of the total electron cloud. These diagrams show that an electron in a p orbital has two

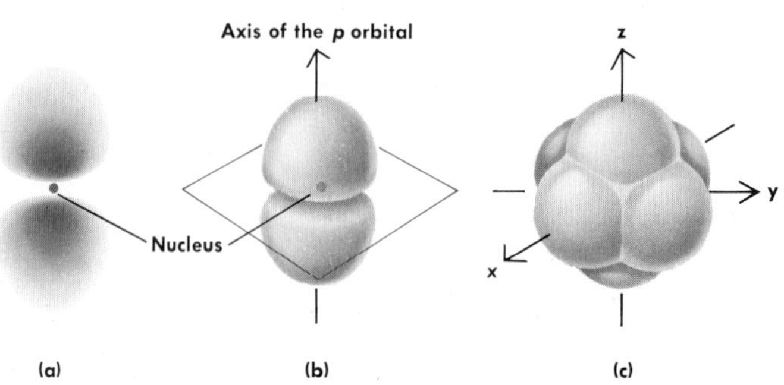

FIGURE 12-6 Electron distribution of p orbital (s). (a) Electron-cloud representation of a p orbital. (b) Boundary surface of a p orbital. (c) Ensemble of the boundary surfaces of three p orbitals.

regions of equal probability symmetrically situated along the axis of the orbital on opposite sides of the nucleus. These two regions are often called the two *lobes* of the p orbital. The diagram also shows that as we proceed from the nucleus along the axis of the orbital or in any other direction within the boundary of the orbital, the electron density is zero at the nucleus, rapidly increases to a maximum, and then gradually decreases until it becomes negligible. In the direction of the axis of the orbital the electron density varies with r as the radial distribution; in all other directions (except those perpendicular to the axis of the orbital), it follows a similar pattern but with a lower maximum density. Finally, in all directions perpendicular to the axis of the orbital, the electron density is zero.

As we know, all atoms or ions with principal quantum number $n = 2$ and higher (but not $n = 1$) have three p orbitals of equal energy, called *three-fold degenerate orbitals*. Each of these three p orbitals has the type of electron distribution we have just discussed, and the three p orbitals differ only in their orientation in space, being directed at right angles to one another. If we take as a reference a system of Cartesian axes with the origin at the nucleus, then the three p orbitals may be directed along the x, y, z axes and are designated as p_x, p_y, and p_z, respectively. Of course, for an isolated atom all directions are equivalent and indistinguishable, so that any three given directions at right angles to one another may be chosen as the Cartesian axes x, y, and z, and any one of the three p orbitals may be labeled as p_x (or p_y or p_z). But when an atom becomes part of a molecule or compound, the positions of the other atoms with respect to it immediately differentiate the various directions. In this case, once a given set of Cartesian axes has been chosen to describe the relative positions of the atoms in the compound, the p_x, p_y, and p_z orbitals become "individualized" in their orientations in space.

Figure 12-6(c) shows the boundary surfaces, enclosing about 90% of the electron cloud, for the ensemble of the three p orbitals. We see from this diagram that if we consider the three p orbitals together, rather than individually, their electron clouds occupy nearly all the space about the nucleus except for a small region *at* the nucleus. If we had not limited ourselves to considering only 90% of the electron cloud, but had considered 100% of it for each p orbital, then we would see that the overall electron density resulting from the ensemble of the three p orbitals has a perfectly spherical distribution about the nucleus. Hence, when we consider an isolated atom, for which all directions are fully equivalent and the three p orbitals are three-fold degenerate, we can represent the electron distribution of its p electrons as being spherical. As the value of the principal quantum number increases (from $n = 2$, to $n = 3$, to $n = 4, \ldots$) the angular distribution of the p orbitals remains the same, while the radial distribution varies in that the region of the maximum electron density moves farther and farther from the nucleus, as for the s orbitals.

If we know the electron distribution of the s and p orbitals, we can visualize the electron structure of the first 20 elements of the Periodic Table, $_1$H to $_{20}$Ca, whose electrons occupy only s and p orbitals. When we reach element 21, scandium, $_{21}$Sc, the electrons begin to occupy the 3d energy level (3d orbitals), and therefore we need to consider now the electron distribution of d orbitals.

d ORBITALS

For the d orbitals, as for the p orbitals, the point electron density depends on two factors. These are (1) the distance r of the point from the nucleus and (2) its orientation in space relative to a reference system (for example, a set of three Cartesian axes, x, y and z, originating at the nucleus). These two factors are considered in some detail in the Appendix, Section 12-2. Here it suffices to say that the dependence of the electron density on the distance from the nucleus (*radial distribution*) resembles closely that of the s and p orbitals. The *angular distribution* is, on the other hand, rather more complicated than for the p orbitals, and is shown as three-dimensional boundary surfaces in Fig. 12-7(a). (These boundary surfaces have the same meaning as those of the p orbitals, discussed in detail in the Appendix, Section 12-1.)

The angular distributions of three of the five d orbitals, d_{xy}, d_{xz}, and d_{yz}, have the same shape and equivalent orientations in space, each orbital consisting of four identical lobes directed along the lines bisecting the xy, xz, yz, planes, respectively. These three d orbitals constitute a set generally designated as t_{2g} (read, t-two-g) or as $d\varepsilon$ (read d-epsilon) orbitals. The angular distribution of another d orbital, the $d_{x^2-y^2}$ orbital, is similar in shape to that of the d_{xy}, d_{xz}, and d_{yz} orbitals, but its four identical lobes are directed along the x and y Cartesian axes. The angular distribution of the remaining d oribital, the d_{z^2} orbital, consists of two larger, identical, lobes lying along the z axis, and of a less extended "doughnut" shaped portion with maximum extension in the xy plane. The $d_{x^2-y^2}$ and the d_{z^2} orbitals have one feature in common—their lobes extend chiefly along the Cartesian axes (along the x and y axes for the $d_{x^2-y^2}$ orbital, and along the z axis for the d_{z^2} orbital). The $d_{x^2-y^2}$ and d_{z^2} orbitals constitute a set of orbitals generally designated as e_g (read, e-g) or $d\gamma$ (read, d-gamma). In general, we can say that the $d\varepsilon$ orbitals have their maximum electron density in the regions of space between the Cartesian planes xy, xz, and yz, whereas the $d\gamma$ orbitals have their maximum electron density along the Cartesian axes.

The actual electron density in a d orbital depends, as we said before, on the distance from the nucleus as well as on the orientation in space. Figures 12-7(b) and (c) give a pictorial representation of the electron density for the d_{xy} orbital; (b) is the electron cloud and (c) is the boundary surface. If we consider all five d orbitals together, the overall electron distribution is spherically symmetrical about the nucleus (see similar considerations for the three p orbitals on p. 243).

We know that for an isolated gaseous atom, the five d orbitals are equivalent in energy (five-fold degenerate orbitals). Also, for the same reasons discussed for the p orbitals (p. 243), the five d orbitals of an isolated gaseous atom are not distinguishable. When, however, an atom is bonded to other atoms (for example, in a molecule) then its d orbitals may become distinguishable from one other, as we shall later discuss in the chapter on transition elements.

FIGURE 12-7 Electron distribution of d orbitals. (a) Angular distributions of the five d orbitals. (b) Electron-cloud representation of the d_{xy} orbital. (c) Boundary surface of the d_{xy} orbital.

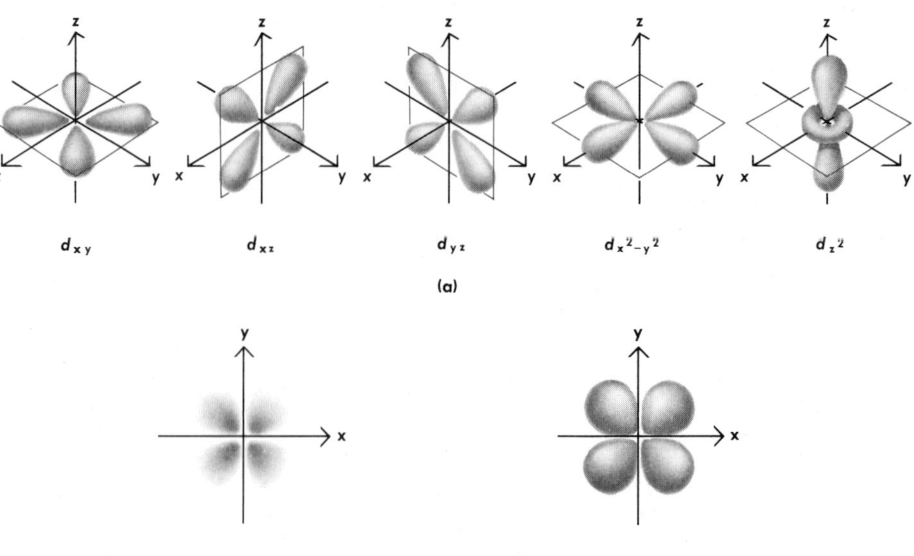

EXERCISES

12-1 Explain the following statement: "The physical and chemical properties of the elements are periodic functions of their atomic numbers."

12-2 What is the basis for the arrangement of the elements in the Periodic Table?

12-3 Complete the following: The number of elements in Series 1 is ______; in Series 2, ______; in Series 3, ______; in Series 4, ______; in Series 5, ______; in Series 6, ______.

12-4 Explain the following terms and illustrate by reference to specific examples: (a) series (or period), (b) group, (c) subgroup, (d) transition element, (e) typical elements, (f) first transition series, (g) second transition series, (h) first very long series, (i) rare-earth elements, (j) incomplete series, (k) triads, (l) A and B subgroups, (m) family.

12-5 Discuss the electronic structure of the H atom, considering specifically the following: (a) the nature of the interaction holding together the nucleus and the electron; (b) the energy of the nucleus-electron interaction and how such energy depends on the distance of the electron from the nucleus; (c) the meaning of the terms "energy level," "ground state," and "excited state"; (d) the "allowed" energy levels as characterized by the values of the principal quantum number, n, (e) the ionization energy, *I.E.*; and (f) the relationship between the values of the ionization energy of the H atom and the values of the principal quantum number, n.

12-6 Sketch the energy level diagram for the electron of the H atom and explain its meaning. How many energy levels should you theoretically put down in the diagram?

12-7 Briefly discuss the possible kinds of interactions involving the electrons composing the electron cloud of an atom.

12-8 Each electron in a polyelectron atom or ion is identified by a unique set of four quantum numbers. (a) Give names and symbols used to indicate these four quantum numbers. (b) Discuss the significance of the principal quantum number, n. What values can n assume? (c) What values of n have been established for the electrons of the elements in their ground states? (d) Discuss the significance of the orbital quantum number, l. What values can l assume? List the symbols used to indicate briefly the value of l for an electron. (e) Discuss the significance of the magnetic quantum number, m, and specify the values it can assume. (f) Discuss the significance of the spin quantum number, s, and specify the values it can assume.

12-9 (a) Explain the meaning of the term "degenerate orbitals." (b) What do degenerate orbitals have in common? (c) What differentiates degenerate orbitals from one another? (d) How can you tell whether a given sub-shell consists of one single orbital or of a number of degenerate orbitals? List the sub-shells that are known to consist of degenerate orbitals, and the number of degenerate orbitals in each sub-shell.

12-10 List the s, p, d, and f orbitals (of a given principal quantum number, n) in order of increasing energy. Compare the energy difference between the s, p, d, and f orbitals of the same principal shell, n, with the energy difference between the ns and the $(n + 1)s$ orbitals, or between the np and the $(n + 1)p$ orbitals.

12-11 State the maximum number of electrons in (a) the sub-shells with $l = 0$, 1, 2, and 3; (b) the principal shells with $n = 1$, 2, 3, 4, and 5.

12-12 On the basis of the building-up principle, the Pauli Exclusion Principle, and Hund's Rule, write the electron configurations of the following elements: (a) $_{3}Li$, $_{4}Be$, $_{5}B$, $_{6}C$, $_{7}N$, $_{8}O$, $_{9}F$, (b) $_{11}Na$, $_{12}Mg$, $_{13}Al$, $_{14}Si$, $_{15}P$, $_{16}S$, $_{17}Cl$, (c) $_{9}F$, $_{17}Cl$, $_{35}Br$, $_{53}I$, (d) $_{3}Li$, $_{11}Na$, $_{19}K$, $_{37}Rb$, $_{55}Cs$, (e) $_{29}Cu$, $_{47}Ag$, $_{79}Au$.

12-13 Compare the distribution of electrons in the following pairs of atoms: (a) $_{19}K$ and $_{29}Cu$, (b) $_{25}Mn$ and $_{35}Br$.

12-14 Assume that the specified number of protons (but no electrons) are added to the nucleus of each of the following elements. Give the name, atomic number and electron configuration of the resulting positive ion in its ground state.

1. Ca^0 + 1 proton
2. Ca^0 + 2 protons
3. Ca^0 + 3 protons
4. Mn^0 + 3 protons
5. Mn^0 + 2 protons
6. Cu^0 + 2 protons
7. Ti + 2 protons
8. Cr^0 + 1 proton
9. Cr^0 + 2 protons
10. V^0 + 1 proton
11. V^0 + 2 protons
12. Fe^0 + 3 protons
13. Co^0 + 3 protons

12-15 If the specified number of protons is added to the nucleus of each of the following positive ions, an ion of higher positive charge results, give its name, atomic number and ground state electron configuration.

1. K^+ + 2 protons
2. Mn^{++} + 1 proton
3. Cr^{++} + 1 proton
4. Cu^+ + 1 proton
5. Ni^{++} + 2 protons

12-16 Explain why the ground state electron configuration of $_5B$ is $1s^2,2s^2\,2p^1$, rather than, for example, $1s^2,2s^1\,2p_x^1\,2p_y^1$.

12-17 The outer electron configurations of the elements $_{24}Cr$ and $_{29}Cu$ differ slightly from those expected on the basis of the building-up principle (see Table 12-4). What can we conclude regarding the stability of half-filled and completely filled *d* sub-shells?

12-18 (a) List the metals of the alkali-metal family (Group IA). (b) List the coinage metals (Group IB). (c) List the elements of the halogen family (Group VIIB). (d) List the elements of the noble-gas family (Group O).

12-19 (a) What type of compounds do the alkali metals form? Give examples. (b) What type of compounds do the halogens form? Give examples.

12-20 On the basis of position in the Periodic Table, name: (a) the most electropositive metal of the alkali-metal family, (b) the most electronegative non-metal of the halogens, (c) the most stable hydrogen halide.

12-21 Write formulas for the oxides of the members of: (a) Series 3, (b) Group IVB, (c) Series 5, (d) Group IIA.

12-22 Write the formulas for the oxides and hydrides of the elements of Groups IB, IVA, VIB, and VIIB.

12-23 On the basis of the relationship between the positive oxidation number of an element and its position in the Periodic Table, write formulas for the following: (a) the oxides of calcium and aluminum, (b) the oxides and hydrides of sulfur, chlorine, and oxygen.

12-24 Where are the following found in the Periodic Table: (a) metals, (b) non-metals, (c) most electropositive elements, (d) most electronegative elements?

12-25 Which element of each of the following pairs is the more electropositive? (a) $_{56}Ba$ or $_{20}Ca$ (b) $_{37}Rb$ or $_{11}Na$ (c) $_{55}Cs$ or $_{56}Ba$

12-26 Which element of each of the following pairs is the more electronegative? (a) $_{16}S$ or $_{17}Cl$ (b) $_{16}S$ or $_{34}Se$ (c) $_7N$ or $_{15}P$

12-27 Which of the elements in the parentheses most closely resembles the preceding element? Explain your answers.

(a) Zn (Ca, Sr, Ba, Cd)
(b) Rb (Li, Cu, Cs, Ag, Au)
(c) Cl (Mn, Tc, Br, Re)
(d) Ge (Ti, Zr, Sn, Hf, Pb)

12-28 Complete the following statements: (a) The formula of a compound containing silicon and hydrogen is ________. (b) The formula of a compound containing silicon and fluorine is ________. (c) The formula of a compound containing aluminum and oxygen is ________. (d) The formula of a compound containing antimony and oxygen is ________.

12-29 Fill in the blanks with the atomic number (14, 15, 16, 17, or 18) that corresponds to the element described in the statement. (a) An inert gas is ________. (b) An element that forms an oxide of the type RO_2 is ________. (c) The element most similar to the element nitrogen (at. no. 7) is ________. (d) An element that forms a hydride of the type RH_2 is ________.

12-30 Explain the following terms for a 1*s* electron; illustrating your answer with diagrams: (a) point electron density, (b) radial shell density, (c) boundary surface. (d) Compare the spatial electron distribution in a 1*s* orbital with that in 2*s* and 3*s* orbitals.

12-31 What factor(s) determine the point electron density in: (a) *s* orbitals, (b) *p* orbitals, (c) *d* orbitals?

12-32 Sketch the electron distribution (as boundary surface) of: (a) an *s* orbital, (b) a *p* orbital, (c) the five degenerate *d* orbitals.

THE ELECTRONIC THEORY OF CHEMICAL BONDING: I. THE FORMATION OF IONS

13

In Chapter 3 we mentioned that chemical bonds between atoms are formed by the interaction of their electron clouds. In the preceding chapter we have become familiar with the make-up of the electron cloud of atoms. We have learned that the electrons forming the electron cloud of an atom are arranged according to a well-defined and fixed pattern in atomic orbitals which differ from one another in both energy and spatial distribution. Now, in this and in the following two chapters, we shall consider chemical bonding in more detail—specifically, ionic bonds, covalent bonds, and bonds that are intermediate between ionic and covalent; and we shall correlate the type of chemical bonding formed by an atom with its electronic structure and hence with its position in the Periodic Table.

We shall also consider the general relationships between the type of chemical bonding and the physical and chemical properties of a substance. Finally, we shall begin to analyze chemical reactions in more detail, pointing out the "make-up" of the substances involved in the reaction (type of bonding, electronic structure, and shape), as well as the electronic interactions by which the reaction occurs. In this chapter we shall concern ourselves especially with the formation of ions from their parent atoms and we shall see how we can correlate the sizes of ions and the energies involved in their formation with the electronic structure of the ions themselves and with that of the atoms from which they are formed.

13-1 Representations of the Structure of Atoms and Ions

As we have seen in the preceding chapter, we can represent the electronic structure of an atom in several schematic ways. The most common and explicit representation consists simply of the symbol of the element followed, usually in parentheses, by the number of electrons occupying the atomic orbitals listed in order of increasing energy. Thus, the sodium atom, $_{11}Na$, may be represented as $_{11}Na(1s^2, 2s^2\, 2p^6, 3s^1)$, where the symbol $_{11}Na$ stands for the nucleus of the atom. Similarly, $_{11}Na^+(1s^2, 2s^2\, 2p^6)$ represents the sodium ion. The single plus sign indicates that in the sodium ion, Na^+, the number of protons exceeds by one unit the number of electrons.

A less detailed but more pictorial description of the electronic structure of an atom is the electron cloud representation, which may be shown as a section (in a plane passing through the nucleus, Fig. 13-1(a), or as a boundary surface, Fig. 13-1(b). You will recall that the electron cloud density falls off gradually as we move away from the nucleus, and therefore the boundary surface of the electron cloud is not sharp and clear. However, for purposes of representation, the electron clouds in the diagrams of this and of the following chapters terminate more or less sharply at a boundary surface enclosing the largest part (let us say 90 per cent) of the total electron cloud.

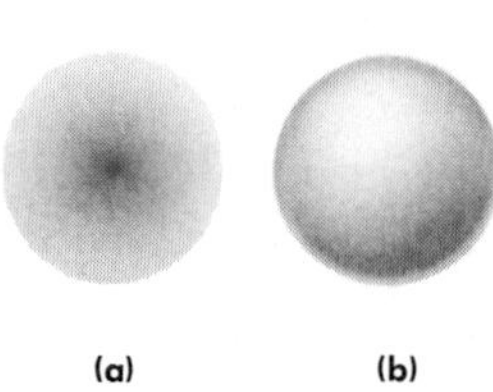

FIGURE 13-1 The hydrogen atom, H. (a) Electron-cloud representation. (b) Boundary surface.

To call attention to the outermost electrons of an atom—those which are involved in chemical reactions and hence often called *valence electrons*—we may simply represent the structure of the atom by the symbol of the element, together with a dot (·) for each electron in the outermost (valence) shell. For example, we can represent the sodium atom at Na· and the chlorine atom as $:\ddot{\underset{..}{Cl}}\cdot$. In these notations, which are called *Lewis electron-dot formulas*, or simply *electron-dot formulas*, the symbol represents the core of the atom—the nucleus plus all the electrons *except* those in the outermost shell. Electron-dot formulas are useful especially in representing simply the chemical union of various atoms.

In the following discussion, we shall make use of one or another of these three schematic representations of the electron configuration of atoms and ions, depending on the particular aspect of the electronic structure that we wish to emphasize.

13-2 Size of Atoms and Ions

Atomic sizes are generally expressed in Angstrom units, A (1 A = 10^{-8} cm). We can get some idea of the range of atomic sizes from the fact that one of the smallest atoms, F, has a radius of 0.72 A, whereas one of the largest, Cs, has a radius of 2.35 A. We know that an atom is made up of a compact nucleus surrounded by a diffuse electron cloud, whose density gradually decreases with the distance from the nucleus, but does not have a sharply defined boundary. It follows that the size of an atom, which is the space occupied by its electron cloud, is not really a clearly defined concept. We can, however, get a fairly good idea of the sizes of the atoms of the various elements by measuring accurately the volume occupied by 1 mole of the element considered in its most compact form—generally the solid—and then dividing this volume by the number of atoms in 1 mole—Avogadro's number, 6.02×10^{23}. For example, the volume occupied by 1 mole of atoms of solid gold metal is 10.20 cm^3 at 20°C. Hence, each gold atom in solid gold occupies a volume of about $10.20 \text{ cm}^3/6.02 \times 10^{23} = 1.69 \times 10^{-23} \text{ cm}^3 = 16.9 \text{ A}^3$. If we consider the gold atom to be perfectly spherical, then $V = \frac{4}{3}\pi r^3 = 16.9 \text{ A}^3$, and we can calculate $r^3 = \frac{3}{4} \times \frac{V}{\pi} = \frac{3}{4} \times \frac{16.9}{3.14} = 4.04 \text{ A}^3$, and $r = 1.59$ A. More accurately we could measure, by X-ray diffraction, the shortest distance between the nuclei of two adjacent atoms in gold metal, then divide such distance by 2 and call it the radius of the gold atom. The value thus obtained is $r = 1.44$ A. Obviously, by both methods we have determined the radius of the gold atom in solid gold metal, or what we call the *metallic radius* of the gold atom. This need not be exactly the same as the radius of an isolated gold atom in the gaseous state—a value which we cannot determine experimentally—but we may expect the difference to be relatively small.

In general, we can determine the radii of the atoms of all elements existing as crystalline solids from either the measured molar volume or the shortest internuclear distance in the crystal. For elements which exist as discreet covalent molecules, such as the halogens, X_2, or white phosphorus, P_4, we can estimate the atomic radius by determining the shortest distance between the nuclei of two neighboring atoms belonging to different molecules, and dividing such distance by 2. The atomic radius thus determined is called *van der Waals radius*. The internuclear distance for two atoms bonded together in the same molecule is smaller than the sum of their van der Waals radii, because covalently bonded atoms are held closer together than are atoms or molecules held together only by the weak van der Waals forces. If we divide by two the internuclear distance of the covalently bonded atoms of an element, we obtain what is generally called the *covalent radius* (for that form of the element considered), but this is not quite the atomic radius that would apply to the isolated gaseous atom (Fig. 13-2). Thus, there are inherent difficulties in determining the sizes of atoms. The electron cloud of an atom does not end sharply, and we cannot as yet measure directly the size of the electron clouds of isolated atoms—such as would exist at an extremely high temperature in the gas phase. Our measurements usually deal with elements present as solids, liquids, or di- and poly-atomic gases, where we may expect the size of the electron cloud of each individual atom to be influenced by the mutual interactions with other atoms. In spite of these limitations, however, we have now an approximate but sufficiently reliable estimate of the sizes of the atoms of the various elements, which are of interest because they are clearly related to the atomic number and electron configuration of the elements.

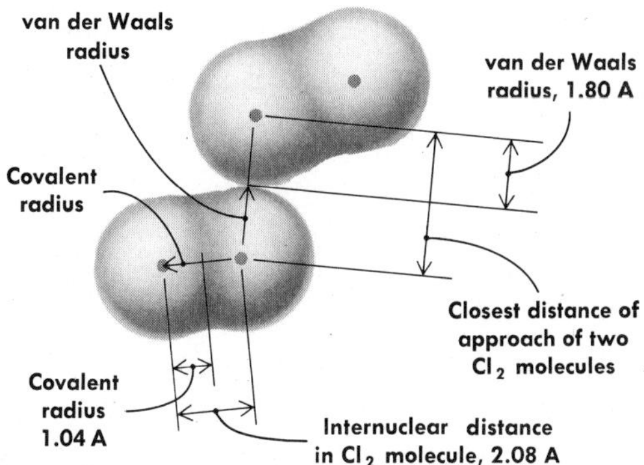

FIGURE 13-2 The covalent and van der Waals radii of chlorine, Cl_2.

RELATIVE SIZES OF NUCLEI AND ELECTRON CLOUDS IN ATOMS

As an indication of how the size of the nucleus compares with the size of the atom as a whole, let us consider the lightest of all atoms, hydrogen, and one of the heaviest atoms, gold. An ordinary hydrogen atom, H, consists of a nucleus made up of a single proton and surrounded by an electron cloud made up of a single electron. Although, as we know, the nucleus contains almost all the mass of the H atom (the mass of an electron is about 1/1,850 the mass of the proton), the electron cloud of the hydrogen atom has a radius over 10,000 times the radius of the nucleus. In fact, the radius of a hydrogen atom is about 0.5×10^{-8} cm (0.5 A) and the radius of its nucleus is about 10^{-13} cm (10^{-5} A). Here is another way of putting it: If we magnified the radius of the nucleus of a hydrogen atom to 1 in., the radius of the electron cloud would be about 850 ft. Similarly, for the atom of a common isotope of gold, $_{79}$Au, which has 79 protons and 118 neutrons in its nucleus and 79 electrons in its electron cloud, measurements reveal that the radius of the nucleus is 1.5×10^{-5} A, while the radius of the entire atom (which is essentially the radius of the electron cloud) is 1.5 A. This means that the radius of the gold atom is 10^5 (or 100,000) times greater than the radius of its nucleus.

We can see from these examples that the radius of the electron cloud of an atom may range from 10,000 to 100,000 times the radius of the nucleus. Clearly, then, it is impossible to give a graphic representation of an atom that would show even approximately the relative sizes of the nucleus and of the electron cloud.

SIZE OF THE ELECTRON CLOUDS IN ATOMS

Now let us consider how the sizes of atoms—that is, the sizes of their electron clouds—change throughout the Periodic Table.

The size of an atom varies with (1) the positive charge on the nucleus (the atomic number of the element), and (2) the number of occupied electron shells surrounding the nucleus—that is, the value of the principal quantum number, n, of the outermost occupied shell. Generally speaking, for atoms of the same family, which have the same number of electrons in the outermost shell, the *greater* the value of n of the outermost shell, the *larger* the atom, because, as we know, successive principal energy levels are at successively greater distances from the nucleus; e.g., the radii (in A) of the alkali metal atoms (outer electron configuration, ns^1) appear in Table 13-1. Notice that the radius of Cs in series $n = 6$ is almost twice that of Li in series $n = 2$. For atoms in the same series—that is, atoms whose outermost electrons have the same principal quantum number—the size decreases as the nuclear charge increases, because electrons in the same shell do not shield one another completely from the attraction of the nucleus. As the effective nuclear charge increases, a stronger inward pull is exerted on the surrounding electron cloud, causing it to shrink. As we have seen in Chapter 12, this reciprocal screening effect of electrons within the same shell results from their diffuse radial distribution (p. 240). The magnitude of this effect is illustrated, for example, by the radii of the elements of the $n = 3$ periodic series, $_{11}$Na to $_{17}$Cl; the radii decrease steadily as we proceed along the series, from 1.57 for the Na atom to 0.99 for

TABLE 13-1 RADII (A) OF ALKALI METAL ATOMS

Series	Alkali Metal	Size (A)
$n = 2$	Li	1.22
$n = 3$	Na	1.57
$n = 4$	K	2.02
$n = 5$	Rb	2.16
$n = 6$	Cs	2.35
$n = 7$	Fr	—

the Cl atom—a decrease of approximately 30 per cent. The increased number of electrons and the decreased size of the electron cloud as we move along the series from Na to Cl causes a considerable increase in the electron density. The schematic electron cloud diagrams in Fig. 13-3 suggest the *relative* sizes of these atoms.

Series n=3	Na	Mg	Al	Si	P	S	Cl
Radius A	1.57	1.36	1.25	1.17	1.10	1.04	0.99

THE SIZES OF MONOATOMIC IONS

As we have said, there is an intrinsic difficulty in defining the size of an ion, because its electron cloud does not end sharply and abruptly at a well-defined distance from the nucleus. Moreover, there is *no experimental way of determining directly the size of an ion.* In fact, ions occur only in (ionic) compounds in which they are associated with other ions of opposite sign, and although we can measure by X-ray diffraction the distance between the nuclei of two adjacent ions of opposite sign (closest neighbors), there is no experimental way of determining how much of this internuclear distance actually represents the radius of each of the two oppositely charged ions. For example, in crystalline potassium chloride, KCl, the internuclear K^+ to Cl^- distance determined experimentally by X-ray diffraction technique is 3.14 A. But how can we divide such a distance to obtain the radius of the K^+ ion and the radius of the Cl^- ion? Since the ${}_{19}K^+$ ion ($1s^2$, $2s^2\ 2p^6$, $3s^2\ 3p^6$) has the same number of electrons and also the same electron configuration as the ${}_{17}Cl^-$ ion ($1s^2$, $2s^2\ 2p^6$, $3s^2\ 3p^6$), but has a greater nuclear charge—19 as compared to 17—we may logically assume that the potassium ion, K^+, is smaller than the isoelectronic* Cl^- ion, because its greater nuclear charge will exert a greater attraction on an electron cloud composed of the same number of electrons. Actually, if we consider the *effective* nuclear charges (p. 241) of the two oppositely charged ions, we find that their relative difference is even greater than the difference between the two (formal) nuclear charges—+19 for K^+ and +17 for Cl^-—because the inner shells ($1s^2$, $2s^2\ 2p^6$) have approximately the same screening effect in both K^+ and Cl^-. By assigning the same value to this screening effect of the inner shells, we can calculate the radius of the potassium ion, K^+, to be 1.33 A, and the radius of the Cl^- ion, 1.81 A. By this procedure we can estimate the ionic radii of the various ions which occur in ionic compounds, and it is interesting that we do obtain a consistent set of values for the radius of a given ion in different compounds. Thus, on the basis of the above considerations, we can define the radius of an ion. Values for a number of the more common ions are listed in Table 13-2.

In general, the size of monoatomic ions differs markedly from the size of their parent atoms. A positive ion is always smaller than its (neutral) parent atom, and a negative ion is always larger than its parent atom.

POSITIVE IONS. Whenever an atom gives up one, two, or three electrons to form a mono-, di-, or tripositive ion, the ions always are markedly smaller than the

* Isoelectronic means "same number of electrons."

FIGURE 13-3 Relative sizes of atoms of Series n = 3.

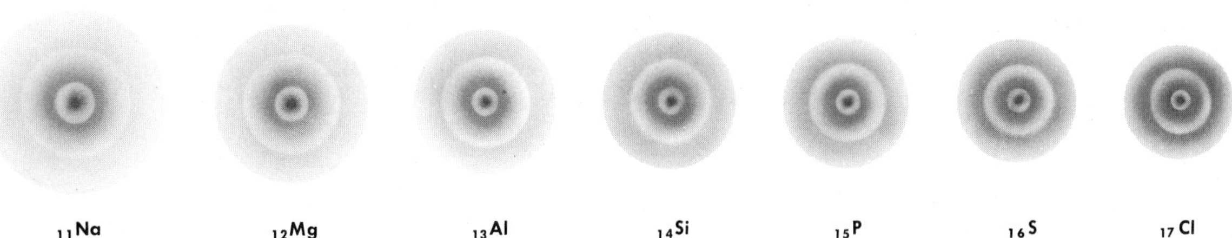

TABLE 13-2 IONIC RADII (A) OF COMMON IONS

1	2	3	4	5	6	7	8	9	10	11	12	13	14	15	16	17	18
H^+ ~10^{-5}	H^- 2.08																He —
Li^+ 0.60	Be^{++} 0.31											B —	C —	N^{-3} 1.71	$O^{=}$ 1.40	F^- 1.36	Ne —
Na^+ 0.95	Mg^{++} 0.65									Cu^+ 0.96		Al^{+3} 0.50	Si —	P^{-3} 2.12	$S^{=}$ 1.84	Cl 1.81	Ar —
K^+ 1.33	Ca^{++} 0.99	Sc^{+3} 0.81	Ti^{++} 0.90 Ti^{+3} 0.76	V^{++} 0.88 V^{+3} 0.74	Cr^{++} 0.84 Cr^{+3} 0.69	Mn^{++} 0.80 Mn^{+3} 0.66	Fe^{++} 0.76 Fe^{+3} 0.64	Co^{++} 0.74 Co^{+3} 0.63	Ni^{++} 0.72	Cu^{++} 0.72	Zn^{++} 0.74	Ga^{+3} 0.62	Ge —	As^{-3} 2.22	Se 1.98	Br 1.95	Kr —
Rb^+ 1.48	Sr^{++} 1.13									Ag^+ 1.26	Cd^{++} 0.97	In^{+3} 0.81	Sn —	Sb 2.45	Te 2.21	I 2.16	Xe —
Cs^+ 1.69	Ba^{++} 1.35									Au 1.37	Hg^{++} 1.10	Tl^{+3} 0.95	Pb —	Bi —	Po —	At —	Rn —
Fr —	Ra —																

parent atom, because the electron cloud of a positive ion consists of fewer electrons than that of the parent neutral atom and the (unchanged) positive nuclear charge exerts a greater attraction on the remaining electrons, drawing them closer to the nucleus. For the same reasons, of the ions of the same element, the dipositive ion is smaller than the monopositive ion, and the tripositive ion is smaller than the dipositive ion.

When an atom gives up all the electrons in its outermost shell to form an ion, the decrease in size is relatively very large. This shrinkage results chiefly from the loss of the outermost electrons—since they are farthest from the nucleus, their cloud is the most diffuse; the positive charge of the nucleus now exceeds the negative charge of the remaining electron cloud, and so attracts it more strongly, and also contributes, as we said, to this decrease in size. As an example, consider the sodium atom and the sodium ion. The sodium atom, Na^0, ($1s^2$, $2s^2\ 2p^6$, $3s^1$) has a radius of 1.57 A, compared with a radius of 0.95 A for the sodium ion, Na^+, ($1s^2$, $2s^2\ 2p^6$), so loss of the single $3s$ electron from the sodium atom in forming the sodium ion results in a shrinkage of approximately 40 per cent, as shown schematically in Fig. 13-4. In a similar way, the monopositive ions of the other alkali metals are appreciably smaller than their parent atoms, as shown in Table 13-3. Notice also that the smaller the atom, the greater the percentage of shrinkage which accompanies the reaction: $M^0(ns^2np^6, (n+1)s) \longrightarrow M^+(ns^2np^6) + e^-$. For example, from the Li^0 atom to the Li^+ ion, the decrease is 51 per cent, but only a 28 per cent decrease occurs from the Cs^0 atom to the Cs^+ ion.

Let us now consider the relative decrease in size involved when two and three electrons are given up by atoms to form di- and tripositive ions respectively, using the atoms of magnesium, Mg, and aluminum, Al, as specific examples. The sizes of these atoms and their ions—together with those of sodium, Na, for comparison—are listed in Table 13-4 on the following page. As we might expect, the percentage of size decrease rises as more electrons are lost in the formation of the positive ion. Notice that we may compare the atoms $_{11}Na$, $_{12}Mg$, and $_{13}Al$, because their three ions, Na^+, Mg^{++}, and Al^{+++}, have the same number of electrons in the same number of shells, $1s^2$, $2s^2\ 2p^6$—that is, these ions are iso-electronic.

FIGURE 13-4 Relative sizes of the sodium atom, Na, and sodium ion, Na^+.

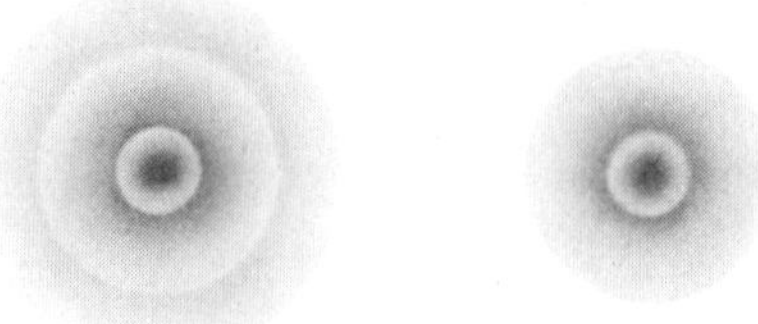

Na (1.57A) Na^+ (0.95A)

TABLE 13-3 SIZES (A) OF ALKALI ATOMS AND IONS

Atom	Electron Configuration	Radius	Ion	Electron Configuration	Radius	% Decrease
Li	Li ([He] $2s^1$)	1.22	Li^+	Li^+ ([He])	0.60	51
Na	Na ([Ne] $3s^1$)	1.57	Na^+	Na^+ ([Ne])	0.95	40
K	K ([Ar] $4s^1$)	2.02	K^+	K^+ ([Ar])	1.33	34
Rb	Rb ([Kr] $5s^1$)	2.16	Rb^+	Rb^+ ([Kr])	1.48	31
Cs	Cs ([Xe] $6s^1$)	2.35	Cs^+	Cs^+ ([Xe])	1.69	28
Fr	Fr ([Rn] $7s^1$)	—	Fr^+	Fr^+ ([Rn])	—	—

The difference in size of differently charged ions of the same element is illustrated by the Fe^{++} and Fe^{+++} ions. The Fe^{+++} ion (0.60 A) is much smaller than the Fe^{++} ion (0.83 A), as shown in Fig. 13-5, and both ions are smaller than the neutral parent Fe atom.

Generally, the relative sizes of ions with the same charge and with similar electron configurations vary in the same manner as the relative sizes of their parent atoms. For example, if atom A is larger than atom B and has a similar electron configuration, the positive A^{+n} ion will be larger than the positive B^{+n} ion.

THE SIZES OF NEGATIVE IONS. As we have learned, a negative ion has more electrons in its electron cloud than the neutral parent atom. Consequently, the interelectron repulsion in the negative ion is stronger than it is in the parent neutral atom, the electrons tend to get farther apart from one another, and the electron cloud expands. For this reason, *negative ions are larger than the neutral atoms from which they are formed.* Table 13-5 lists the covalent and van der Waals radii of several neutral atoms and the ionic radii of their negative ions.

FIGURE 13-5 The relative sizes of the Fe atom, Fe^{++} ion, and Fe^{+++} ion.

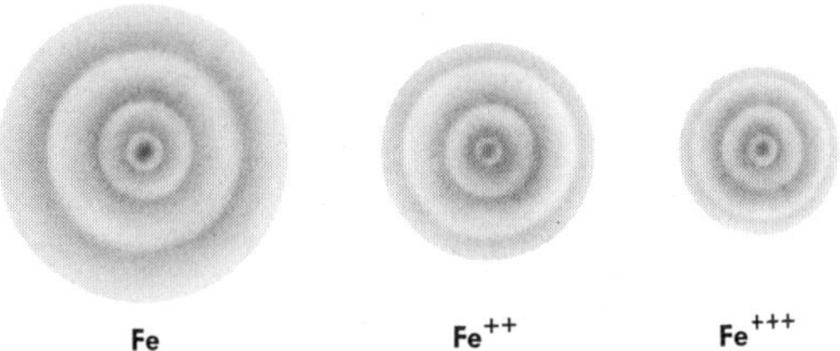

TABLE 13-4 SIZES (A) OF Na, Mg, AND Al ATOMS AND THEIR ISO-ELECTRONIC IONS

	Atom or Ion	Electron Configuration	Radius	Atom or Ion	Electron Configuration	Radius	Atom or Ion	Electron Configuration	Radius
Atom	Na°	Na ([Ne] $3s^1$)	1.57	Mg°	Mg ([Ne] $3s^2$)	1.57	Al	Al ([Ne] $3s^2$ $3p^1$)	1.25
Ion	Na^+	Na^+([Ne])	0.95	Mg^{++}	Mg^{++}([Ne])	0.65	Al^{+++}	Al^{+++}([Ne])	0.50
% Size Decrease	40			52			60		

TABLE 13-5 SIZES (A) OF NEUTRAL ATOMS AND IONIC RADII OF THEIR CORRESPONDING NEGATIVE IONS

Atom	Covalent Radius of Atom	Van der Waals Radius of Atom	Negative Ion	Ionic Radius of Negative Ion
F	0.68	1.35	F^-	1.36
Cl	0.99	1.80	Cl^-	1.81
Br	1.13	1.95	Br^-	1.95
I	1.35	2.15	I^-	2.16
O	0.60	1.40	$O^=$	1.40
S	1.06	1.85	$S^=$	1.84
Se	1.16	1.97	$Se^=$	1.98
Te	1.44	2.20	$Te^=$	2.21

To show how the nuclear charge affects the sizes of electron clouds having the same number of electrons and the same electron configuration, let us compare the size of the atoms of the noble gases with the size of iso-electronic positive and negative ions. As the nuclear charge increases, the electron clouds are drawn in more tightly, as shown in Table 13-6. Notice that the negative ions are appreciably larger than the iso-electronic positive ions. Moreover, the greater the negative charge on the ion, the larger the ion; and the greater the positive charge on the ion, the smaller the ion. Thus, in the $O^=$, F^-, Na^+, and Mg^{++} ions, which have the same number of electrons and the same electron configuration, the electron shells are drawn inward more and more tightly as the positive charge of the nucleus increases. Consequently, the largest particle in this iso-electronic series is the $O^=$ ion, and the smallest is the Mg^{++} ion.

TABLE 13-6 SIZES OF ATOMS AND IONS WITH SAME NUMBER AND ARRANGEMENT OF ELECTRONS (ISO-ELECTRONIC)

Atom or Ion ($1s^2$, $2s^2\ 2p^6$)	$O^=$	F^-	Ne^0	Na^+	Mg^{++}
Radius (A)	1.40	1.36	1.12	0.95	0.65
Atom or Ion ($1s^2$, $2s^2\ 2p^6$, $3s^2\ 3p^6$)	$S^=$	Cl^-	Ar^0	K^+	Ca^{++}
Radius (A)	1.84	1.81	1.5	1.33	0.99

Another good example of the effect of the nuclear charge on the size of the electron cloud is this series: the hydrogen ion, H^+ 10^{-5} A; the hydrogen atom, H^0 (van der Waals radius, 1.2 A); and the hydride ion H^- 2.1 A. (Notice that the hydride ion, H^-, is slightly larger than the chloride ion, Cl^- 1.81 A, even though its electron cloud consists of two electrons and the chloride ion of eight.) In all these species of hydrogen, the nuclear charge is +1. The strikingly great relative decrease in size which the H atom experiences when it gives up its one electron in forming a "naked" proton is understandable because the one electron constitutes its entire electron cloud. On the other hand, when the H atom takes on an electron to form the hydride ion, H^-, the great relative increase in size can be explained by the fact that now the electron cloud contains two electrons, twice as many electrons, that is, than the neutral H atom. These two electrons, as we know, not only try to avoid each other as much as possible (interelectron repulsion), but also screen one another from the +1 nuclear charge so that the H^- ion has a much lower effective nuclear charge than does the neutral H^0 atom.

In this section, we shall consider the energy relationships involved in the formation of positive and negative ions from neutral atoms. We shall also discuss the relationship of the energy of ion formation to the electron configuration and size of the atom, and the charge on the ion formed.

ENERGY RELATIONSHIPS IN THE FORMATIONS OF POSITIVE IONS

In order for a positive ion to be formed, one or more electrons must be detached from the electron cloud of a neutral atom, and this process always requires energy. The amount of energy required to form a positive ion varies from atom to atom, and depends chiefly on (1) the size and the electron configuration of the parent atom from which the positive ion is formed, and (2) the number of electrons that must be removed to form the positive ion.

ENERGY AND THE SIZE FACTOR IN POSITIVE ION FORMATION. As we know, the closer an electron is to the nucleus, the more strongly it is attracted, all other factors being equal. Accordingly, the larger an atom, the farther from the positively charged nucleus the electrons in the outer shell are, and the weaker the mutual attraction is between the nucleus and these electrons. This means that for atoms of the same family (same outer electron configuration, but different principal quantum number, n) less energy is required to detach electrons from the outer shell of a large atom than from that of a small atom. In other words, it requires less energy to form positive ions from large atoms than from small atoms of the same family.

Let us see how these relationships apply to a specific family of elements. Of the alkali-metal atoms (Li, Na, K, Rb, Cs), cesium is the largest, and, as we would expect, less energy is needed to remove the outermost s electron from the cesium atom than from any other alkali-metal atom. The amount of energy required decreases as the size of the atoms increases.

The (first) *ionization energy* of an element is the energy needed to remove 1 electron from the electron cloud of an isolated gaseous atom, $M_{(g)}$, of the element to form an isolated gaseous monopositive ion, $M^+{}_{(g)}$, as shown by the equation:

$$M_{(g)} \longrightarrow M^+{}_{(g)} + e^- \qquad \Delta H = +x \text{ kcal/mole } M_{(g)} \text{ atoms}$$

Thus the (first) ionization energy of an element is the ΔH value of the above ionization reaction. The values of the (first) ionization energy have been determined for almost all elements from spectroscopic data. The ionization energies of the alkali metals, expressed in kcal per mole of atoms (6.02×10^{23} atoms), are given in Table 13-7. These values show, as we discussed above qualitatively, that the energy needed to detach one electron—the outermost s electron—from the electron cloud of an alkali metal atom decreases as the size of the atom increases. The smallest of the alkali metals, the Li atom, has the highest ionization energy, and the largest alkali atom, the Cs atom, has the lowest ionization energy. For comparison the table includes the ionization energy of the H atom. Notice that the ionization energy of a hydrogen atom is about three times greater than that of an alkali-metal atom, because the single s electron of hydrogen is of course not shielded from the nuclear charge by a noble-gas-like core.

The graph in Fig. 13-6 plots the (first) ionization energies of the elements H to Mg against their atomic numbers. We see from this graph that the hydrogen atom ${}_1H(1s^1)$, which has only one extranuclear electron, has a fairly high ionization energy (313 kcal or 13.6 ev) and that the ionization energy of the next element, the noble gas helium, ${}_2He(1s^2)$, has the highest ionization energy (567 kcal) of all the atoms listed.

The extremely high ionization energies for hydrogen and helium atoms are associated with their small sizes and their electron configurations, as discussed above.

TABLE 13-7 IONIZATION ENERGIES OF THE ALKALI METALS

	Element	Electron Configuration	Ionization Reaction	Ionization Energy (kcal/mole atoms)	
	H	$(1s^1)$	$(H_{(g)} \longrightarrow H^+_{(g)} + e^-)$	(313)	
Increasing size of atoms ↓	Li	[He] $2s^1$	$Li_{(g)} \longrightarrow Li^+_{(g)} + e^-$	124	Increasing energy required to detach one electron from outermost shell ↑
	Na	[Ne] $3s^1$	$Na_{(g)} \longrightarrow Na^+_{(g)} + e^-$	118	
	K	[Ar] $4s^1$	$K_{(g)} \longrightarrow K^+_{(g)} + e^-$	100	
	Rb	[Kr] $5s^1$	$Rb_{(g)} \longrightarrow Rb^+_{(g)} + e^-$	96	
	Cs	[Xe] $6s^1$	$Cs_{(g)} \longrightarrow Cs^+_{(g)} + e^-$	90	
	Fr		$Fr_{(g)} \longrightarrow Fr^+_{(g)} + e^-$	—	

The smallest atom, helium, He, has the highest ionization energy. Then continuing with the Li atom, whose electronic configuration is $_3$Li: $1s^2$, $2s^1$, we find a marked decrease in the first ionization energy, that is, a much smaller quantity of energy is required to remove the single $2s$ electron from this larger atom. The next seven successive elements from $_3$Li($1s^2$, $2s^1$) through $_{10}$Ne($1s^2$, $2s^2\ 2p^6$) have an additional proton in the nucleus and an additional electron in the same main (second) shell. In each case the more highly charged nucleus of the atom exerts a stronger attraction for the electrons surrounding it, and we would expect to find, and in fact do find, that each atom is smaller than Li, and that the first ionization energy of each atom is greater than the first ionization energy of Li. Furthermore, we would expect to find a gradual in-

FIGURE 13-6 The first ionization energies of atoms of elements of Series 1 ($_1$H, $_2$He), Series 2 ($_3$Li to $_{10}$Ne), and the first two elements ($_{11}$Na, $_{12}$Mg) of Series 3.

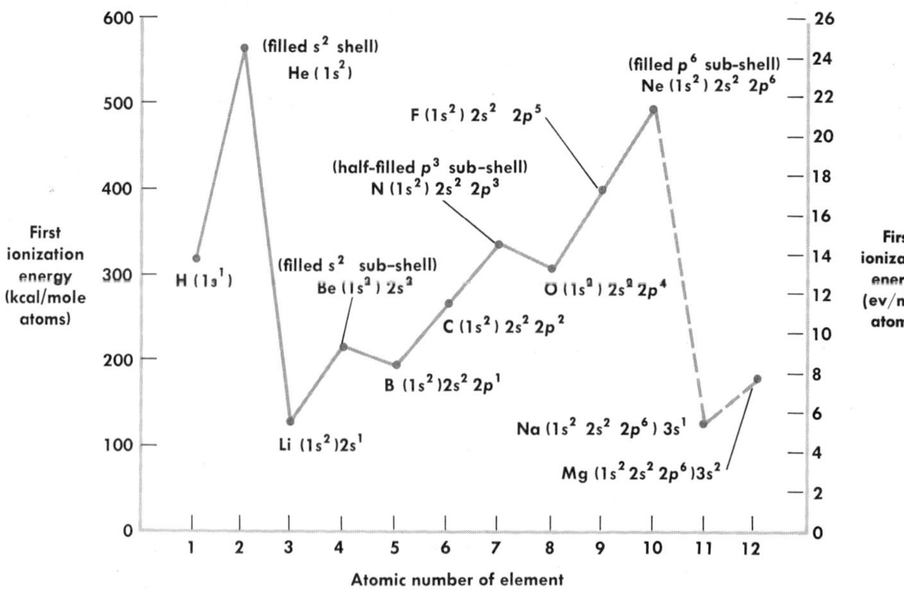

crease in the first ionization energy from Li to Ne as the atomic numbers of the elements increase. And such is the case, although there are irregularities—one between beryllium, Be, and boron, B, and the other between nitrogen, N, and oxygen, O. The irregularity involving boron stems from the fact that the boron atom is the first atom with a p electron ($_5$B: $1s^2$, $2s^2\ 2p^1$), and this single p electron is less difficult to remove than one of the s electrons in the filled $2s^2$ orbital of beryllium, $_4$Be: $1s^2$, $2s^2$. In fact the $2p$ electron is removed with less difficulty than is a $2s$ electron because it is less penetrating, its average distance from the nucleus being larger. In the case of oxygen, O, the irregularity very likely arises from the fact that this atom has four $2p$ electrons, $_8$O: $1s^2$, $2s^2\ 2p^4$ ($1s^2$, $2s^2\ 2p^2\ 2p^1\ 2p^1$). That is, it has one electron more than is needed to half fill its p orbitals, and this electron is more easily removed than one of the three $2p$ electrons in an atom of nitrogen, $_7$N: $1s^2$, $2s^2\ 2p^3$($1s^2$, $2s^2\ 2p^1\ 2p^1\ 2p^1$). In an atom which has a s^2p^4 outermost electronic configuration, the fourth p electron, which is the one to be removed in forming the monopositive ion, is paired in an orbital with one of the other three p electrons and thereby experiences greater interelectron repulsion (and hence is held less tightly) than an electron which is not paired in a p orbital.

In passing on to the first element of the $n = 3$ periodic series, the alkali metal sodium, $_{11}$Na: $1s^2$, $2s^2\ 2p^6$, $3s^1$, we find that it has an ionization energy lower than that of the alkali metal, $_3$Li, in the $n = 2$ periodic series. Since sodium is larger than lithium, we would expect this to be the case. We also see that, just as the ionization energy of boron, B, is smaller than that of beryllium, Be, so less energy is required to remove an electron from the aluminum atom, $_{13}$Al: $1s^2$, $2s^2\ 2p^6$, $3s^2\ 3p^1$ (138 kcal) than from the magnesium atom, $_{12}$Mg: $1s^2$, $2s^2\ 2p^6$, $3s^2$ (176 kcal). Again, the fact that the (single) $3p^1$ electron of the Al atom is relatively less difficult to remove than 1 electron from the filled $3s^2$ orbital of the Mg atom, indicates that a ns^2 orbital has a particularly high stability. Finally, the ionization energy of the (larger) phosphorus atom, $_{15}$P, is greater than that of the (smaller) sulfur atom, $_{16}$S, just as was the case for the corresponding pair of atoms in the $n = 2$ series nitrogen, $_7$N, and oxygen, $_8$O. A similar trend characterizes the corresponding elements of the other periodic series.

IONIZATION ENERGY AND THE NUMBER OF ELECTRONS REMOVED. As we know, the (first) ionization energy is the energy needed to remove one electron—precisely, the least-tightly held electron—from the electron cloud of an isolated gaseous atom, M^0, to form an isolated gaseous monopositive ion, M^+. Now if we want to go further and remove the next-least-tightly held electron from the resulting monopositive ion, M^+, to form the dipositive ion, M^{++}, we must supply additional energy. This additional energy is called the *second ionization energy* and is always greater than the first ionization energy. The total energy required to remove *two* electrons from the electron cloud of an atom is then the *sum* of the first ionization energy and the second ionization energy.

Consider, for example, the removal of one electron from a Cu atom to form the Cu^+ ion, and the additional removal of one electron from the Cu^+ ion to form the Cu^{++} ion. The first and second ionization energies are:

$$Cu^0_{(g)} \longrightarrow Cu^+_{(g)} + 1\ e^- \qquad \Delta H = +178 \text{ kcal/mole Cu atoms}$$
$$Cu^+_{(g)} \longrightarrow Cu^{++}_{(g)} + 1\ e^- \qquad \Delta H = +468 \text{ kcal/mole } Cu^+ \text{ ions}$$

The total ionization energy needed to remove two electrons from an isolated Cu atom to form the Cu^{++} ion is the sum of the first and second ionization energies.

$$Cu_{(g)} \longrightarrow Cu^{++}_{(g)} + 2\ e^- \qquad \Delta H = +646 \text{ kcal/mole Cu atoms}$$

The fact that an increasingly larger quantity of energy is required to remove successive electrons from a positively charged ion is readily understandable if we keep in mind that (1) the higher the charge of a positive ion, the smaller its size (and hence

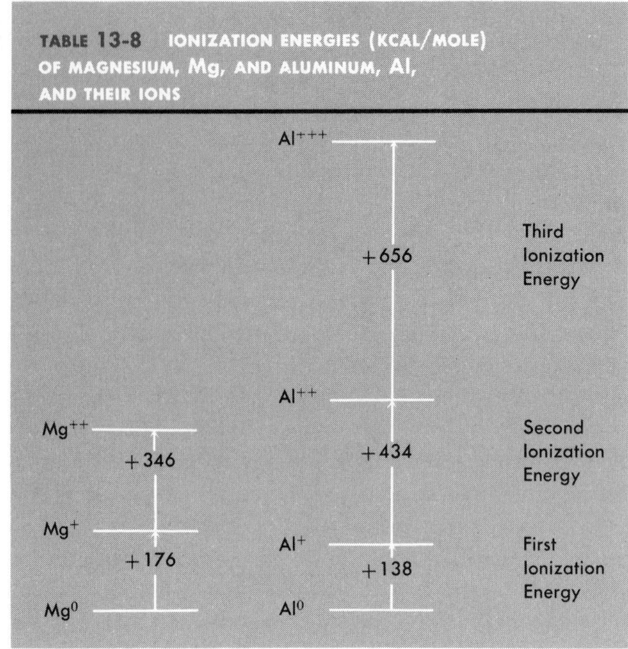

TABLE 13-8 IONIZATION ENERGIES (KCAL/MOLE) OF MAGNESIUM, Mg, AND ALUMINUM, Al, AND THEIR IONS

the more tightly held are its outer electron(s), and (2) the effective nuclear charge acting on the electron cloud progressively increases. As another example, the ionization energies of magnesium, Mg, and aluminum, Al, are given in Table 13-8. We see that their second ionization energies are each larger than the first, and the third ionization energy of Al is larger than its second. We also see, as we already said, that more energy is required to ionize the Mg atom to the monopositive Mg^+ ion ($Mg \longrightarrow Mg^+ + e^-$) than to ionize the Al atom to the monopositive Al^+ ion ($Al \longrightarrow Al^+ + e^-$). The Mg atom has a higher first ionization energy because $_{12}Mg$: $1s^2, 2s^2\,2p^6, 3s^2$, has a filled $3s^2$ orbital, whereas for the $_{13}Al$ atom: $1s^2, 2s^2\,2p^6, 3s^2\,3p^1$, the outer electron configuration is $3s^2\,3p^1$, and less energy is required to detach the one $3p^1$ electron from the Al atom than to detach one electron from the filled $3s^2$ orbital of Mg. Notice also that the ionization of the Al^+ ion ($Al^+ \longrightarrow Al^{++} + e^-$) requires more energy than the corresponding ionization of the Mg^+ ion ($Mg^+ \longrightarrow Mg^{++} + e^-$). That is, more energy is required to remove one electron from the filled $3s^2$ orbital of the Al^+ ion ($1s^2, 2s^2\,2p^6, 3s^2$) than to remove the one $3s^1$ electron from the Mg^+ ion ($1s^2, 2s^2\,2p^6, 3s^1$).

Table 13-9 lists some successive ionization energies of the neutral gaseous atoms of the first four elements of the first short series in the Periodic Table—namely, $_3Li$, $_4Be$, $_5B$, $_6C$; and the graph in Fig. 13-7 plots these successive ionization energies of these four elements. We see from these values that the energy needed to remove the second electron from Li—that is, the energy needed to remove one electron from the Li^+ ion ($1s^2$)—is approximately 15 times the energy required to remove the first electron from the Li atom ($1s^2, 2s^1$). The removal of the third electron from Be requires almost ten times the energy required to remove the second, and the removal of the fourth electron from B and the fifth electron from C require even more substantial increases in energy. The graph shows strikingly that the energy required to remove the first electron from Li is much less than that required to remove the second electron, and that each of the first two electrons of Be can be removed by supplying much less energy than is required for the third. In fact, the sum of the first two ionization energies of Be (215 + 420 = 635 kcal/mole) is markedly less than the third ionization energy (3,546 kcal/mole). Similarly, each of the first three electrons can be re-

TABLE 13-9 SUCCESSIVE IONIZATION ENERGIES (KCAL/MOLE) FOR $_3Li$, $_4Be$, $_5B$, AND $_6C$

Element		Li	Be	B	C
Electron Configuration		$1s^2, 2s^1$	$1s^2, 2s^2$	$1s^2, 2s^2\ 2p^1$	$1s^2, 2s^2\ 2p^2$
Ionization Energy (kcal/mole)	1st	124	215	191	260
	2nd	1,743	420	580	562
	3rd		3,546	874	1,103
	4th			5,977	1,486
	5th				9,035

moved from the B atom with less difficulty than the fourth (the sum of the first three ionization energies is less than the fourth), and the first four electrons of C together can be removed with less difficulty than the fifth. Here we have experimental evidence that one electron in the electron cloud of Li (Group I) is very different from the other two, which can be grouped together, and that two electrons in Be (Group II) are quite different from the other pair and can also be grouped together. Similarly, the values of the successive ionization energies show that three electrons in the electron cloud of B (Group III) are very different from the other pair and can be grouped together. Finally, four electrons in the electron cloud of the C atom (Group IV) are quite different from the other pair and can be grouped together.

Similar considerations apply to the other elements. In general, for any element each successive ionization energy is much greater than the preceding one, but a particularly large increase in the ionization energy occurs at the ionization stage corresponding to the removal of one electron from the positive ion having a noble-gas-type electron configuration. In fact, the energy required to remove an electron from a positive ion with a noble-gas-type electron configuration is greater than the sum of all the ionization energies involved in the preceding ionization steps.

FIGURE 13-7 Successive ionization energies of elements: E = $_3Li$, $_4Be$, $_5Be$, $_6C$.

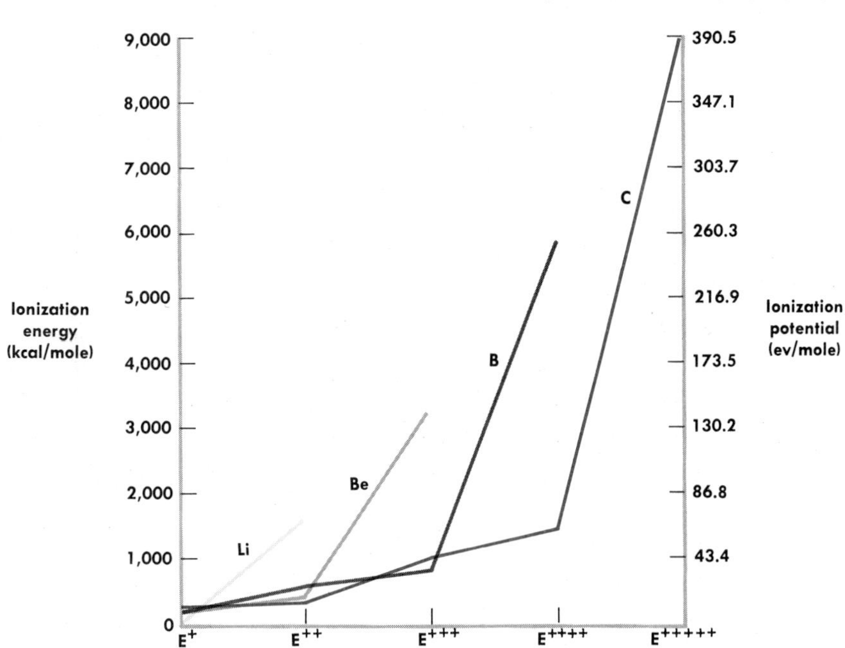

To remove an electron from a positive ion having a noble gas electron configuration requires an extremely large amount of energy, because the electron has to be pulled away from a filled shell. This explains why some elements—in particular the alkali metals, the alkaline-earth metals, and the metals of Group IIIB, such as aluminum—exist in their compounds as ions with a fixed oxidation number. Let us take as a specific example the sodium atom, Na. We have seen that the loss of one electron from the sodium atom Na($1s^2$, $2s^2\ 2p^6$, $3s^1$) causes the remaining electron cloud of the sodium ion, Na^+($1s^2$, $2s^2\ 2p^6$) to be held more firmly than the electron cloud of the original atom, so that the energy required to form a Na^+ ion from a Na atom is 118 kcal, but that the energy required to form a Na^{++} ion from a Na^+ ion is 1,090 kcal. The total energy required to form a Na^{++} ion from a Na atom, then, is 118 + 1,090 = 1,208 kcal. Consequently the formation of a dipositive sodium ion, Na^{++}($1s^2$, $2s^2\ 2p^5$) is energetically very unfavorable, and in fact, the divalent sodium ion, Na^{++}, does *not* exist in stable chemical compounds. The first ionization energies and the second ionization energies for the atoms of the alkali metals are given in Table 13-10 and are represented graphically in Fig. 13-8.

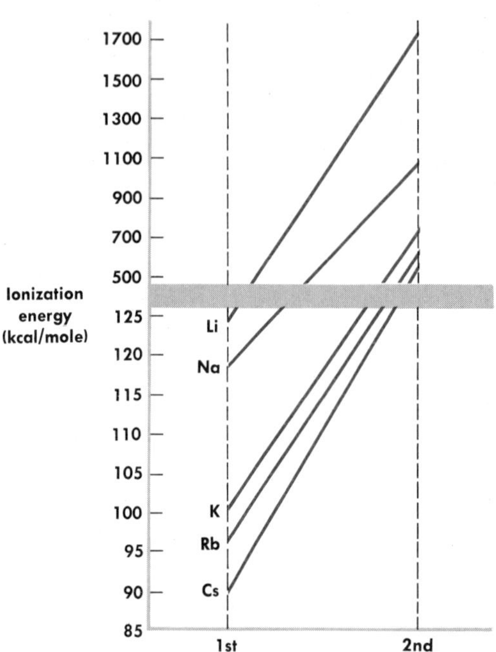

FIGURE 13-8 The first and second ionization energies of alkali metals, Li, Na, K, Rb, Cs.

TABLE 13-10 IONIZATION ENERGIES OF THE ALKALI-METAL ELEMENTS (KCAL/MOLE)

Element		*First Ionization Energy*		*Ion*		*Second Ionization Energy*		*Ion*
M	+	**kcal**	⟶	M^+	+	**kcal**	⟶	M^{++}
H	+	313	⟶	(H^+)		–		–
Li	+	124	⟶	Li^+	+	1743	⟶	Li^{++}
Na	+	118	⟶	Na^+	+	1090	⟶	Na^{++}
K	+	100	⟶	K^+	+	733	⟶	K^{++}
Rb	+	96	⟶	Rb^+	+	634	⟶	Rb^{++}
Cs	+	90	⟶	Cs^+	+	578	⟶	Cs^{++}
Fr		–	⟶	Fr^+		–		–

The above data show that the greater the number of electrons that a neutral atom of a given periodic series must give up in order to form a positive ion with a noble-gas structure, the greater the energy required for the formation of that ion. Let us look, as an illustration, at the elements of Series 3 (Na, Mg, Al, Si, P, S, Cl). Experiments show that the first element of this series, sodium, Na($1s^2$, $2s^2\,2p^6$, $3s^1$), is always present in its *stable* compounds in the form of the monopositive ion, Na^+($1s^2$, $2s^2\,2p^6$), formed from the neutral Na^0 atom by the removal of the $3s^1$ outer electron. Similarly, magnesium is present in its stable compounds as the dipositive ion Mg^{++}($1s^2$, $2s^2\,2p^6$), formed from the neutral atom Mg^0($1s^2$, $2s^2\,2p^6$, $3s^2$), by the removal of the two outer $3s$ electrons. Finally, the third element of the $n = 3$ series, aluminum, is present in its stable ionic compounds as the tripositive ion Al^{+3}($1s^2$, $2s^2$ $2p^6$), formed from the neutral atom, Al($1s^2$, $2s^2\,2p^6$, $3s^2\,3p^1$) by the removal of the three outer electrons, one $3p$ and two $3s$ electrons. Notice that even though far more energy is required to form the dipositive magnesium ion, Mg^{++}, than the monopositive Mg^+ ion, only the dipositive Mg^{++} ion exists in stable compounds of the element. Similarly, only the tripositive aluminum ion, Al^{+3}, exists in stable ionic compounds of aluminum, even though less energy is required to form the mono- and dipositive ions. The reasons for this behavior will be explained in a following section (the Born-Haber cycle, p. 264). Here we wish to point out that the first three elements of each periodic series (the two s-block elements and the first of the p-block elements) exist in their stable compounds as ions with the same electron configuration as the preceding noble gas. This condition is sometimes expressed by saying that the atoms of the elements have a tendency to form stable ions with a noble-gas-like electron configuration. This statement, however, is not correct in itself, because if we must always supply energy to transform 1 mole of (gaseous) neutral aluminum atoms, Al, into a mole of trivalent (gaseous) aluminum ions, Al^{+3}, obviously we cannot say that an aluminum atom, for example, *tends* to form a trivalent ion. It is true, on the other hand, that when all energy factors are taken into account, the formation of positive ions with the noble-gas-like electron configuration is the most favorable procedure for the first three elements of each periodic series.

As the number of electrons that must be given up by an atom to form a positive ion with a noble-gas-like electron configuration increases across each periodic series, the formation of these positive ions becomes progressively more difficult. Hypothetically, the next four elements of Series 3, Si, P, S, and Cl could form the positive ions Si^{+4}, P^{+5}, S^{+6}, and Cl^{+7}, each with a neon-like electron configuration, $1s^2$, $2s^2\,2p^6$. But the formation of these ions requires tremendous amounts of ionization energy, and consequently these positive ions are not present in stable compounds. In fact, these elements form either covalent compounds or ionic compounds in which they gain electrons to become negative ions.

If we consider all the successive ionization energies of a given element, for example, $_{19}K$, we find that the quantity of energy required to remove successively each of the 19 electrons of the potassium atom follows the trend shown in Fig. 13-9. These ionization energy values provide us with an experimental basis for the statement that a particularly high stability is related to atoms or ions having a noble-gas-like electron configuration.

ENERGY RELATIONSHIPS IN THE FORMATION OF NEGATIVE IONS

In order for a *negative* ion to be formed, one or more electrons must be added to the electron cloud of the parent atom. As we have just discussed, the removal of one electron from a (gaseous) atom to form a monopositive (gaseous) ion always requires the absorption of energy. On the other hand, when an isolated gaseous atom acquires an electron to form an isolated gaseous mononegative ion, *energy may*

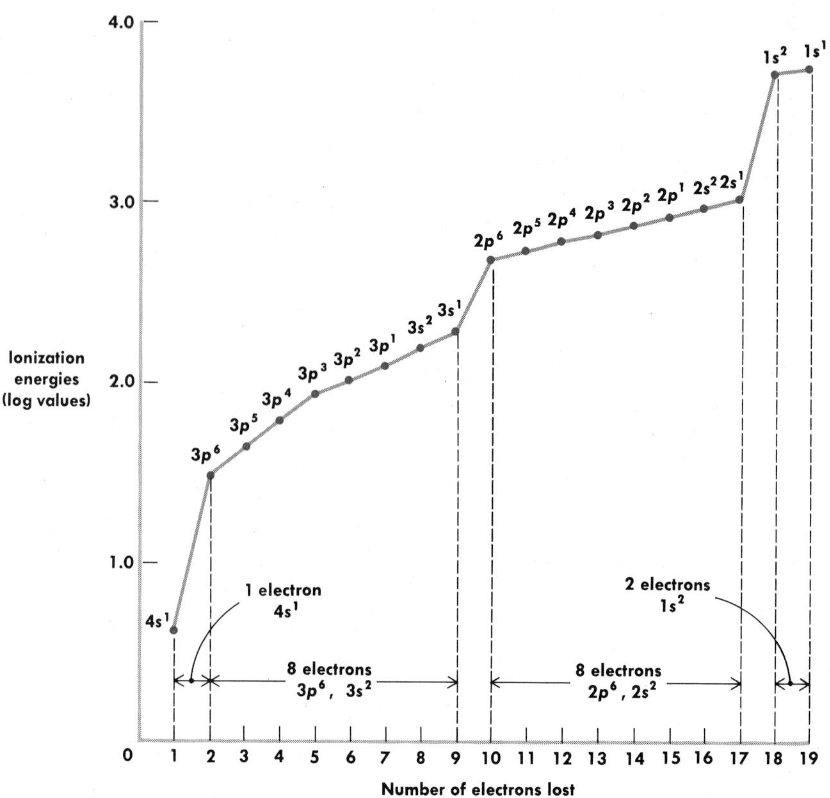

FIGURE 13-9 The nineteen successive ionization energies (kcal/mole) for potassium, $_{19}K$, expressed as logarithm values.

be either absorbed or released. The energy involved in this reaction, $X_{(g)} + e^- \longrightarrow X^-_{(g)}$, is called the *electron affinity* of the element and is usually expressed in kcal/mole of atoms. If heat is *evolved* in the reaction (ΔH is negative), we say that the element has a *positive* electron affinity; if heat is *absorbed* in the reaction (ΔH is positive), we say that the element has a *negative* electron affinity. With only a few exceptions, the gaseous atoms of the elements take on one electron with the evolution of heat, (ΔH is negative), hence their electron affinities are positive. For example, when a hydrogen atom, H, takes on one electron to form the gaseous hydride ion, H^-, 16.1 kcal per mole of H atoms are evolved: $H_{(g)} + e^- \longrightarrow H^-_{(g)}$, $\Delta H = -16.1$ kcal/mole of H atoms. The electron affinity of hydrogen is therefore 16.1 kcal/mole (of H atoms). Like the formation of positive ions, the quantity of energy involved in the formation of mononegative gaseous ions from their parent neutral gaseous atoms depends chiefly on two factors: the outer electron configuration and the size of the parent atom.

THE SIZE FACTOR IN THE FORMATION OF NEGATIVE IONS. The effect that the size of the parent atom has on the energy involved in the formation of negative ions is opposite to its effect in the formation of positive ions. We have seen that less energy is needed to remove an electron from a large atom than from a small atom of the same outer electron configuration (same family). On the other hand, a small atom generally *takes on* an electron more readily than a large *atom*, because, as we have seen, when other factors are equal the attraction of the nucleus on the electron cloud is greater for smaller than for the larger atom.

As an example, let us consider three elements of the halogen family, chlorine bromine, and iodine, whose atoms increase regularly in size (p. 254). The reaction in which a (gaseous) halogen atom, X^0, (with an outer electron configuration of ns^2, np^5) takes on an electron to become a mononegative (gaseous) halide ion, X^-, (with an outer electron configuration of ns^2, np^6 similar to that of the next noble gas), may be represented by the following general equation:

$$X_{(g)} + e^- \longrightarrow X^-_{(g)} \qquad \Delta H = -q \text{ kcal/mole } X_{(g)} \text{ atoms}$$

In this process energy is liberated (ΔH is negative) and the electron affinity of the halogen atom is positive. Table 13-11 lists the electron affinities of the halogen atoms. We would expect more energy to be released when an electron is taken on by a small halogen atom than when an electron is taken on by a larger atom. Such is the case for the chlorine, bromine, iodine trio. But fluorine, F, the smallest halogen atom does not conform to the pattern—in fact, its electron affinity is smaller than that of chlorine, Cl, the next larger halogen, because the seven outer valence electrons ($:\ddot{\underset{..}{F}}\cdot$) of the extremely small fluorine atom exert a relatively greater inter-electron repulsion on the additional electron.

TABLE 13-11 ELECTRON AFFINITIES OF HALOGEN ATOMS

Element	Reaction	Electron Affinity of Atom (kcal/mole)
F	$F + 1e^- \longrightarrow F^-$	83.5
Cl	$Cl + 1e^- \longrightarrow Cl^-$	85.1
Br	$Br + 1e^- \longrightarrow Br^-$	79.6
I	$I + 1e^- \longrightarrow I^-$	72.7
At	$At + 1e^- \longrightarrow At^-$	—

The electron affinities of the first ten elements, $_1$H to $_{10}$Ne, are shown in the diagram. All but two of these elements (Be, −4.4, and Ne, −13.1) release energy when they take on one electron to form a mononegative ion; even the atom of the noble gas He ($1s^2$) forms the He$^-$ ion ($1s^2$, $2s^1$) with the evolution of heat. However, of all these mononegative ions, only the hydride ion, H^-, and the fluoride ion, F^-, are present in stable chemical compounds—for example, Li^+H^- and K^+F^-. Here again we see that the energy (favorable or unfavorable) involved in the formation of a given (gaseous) ion from its (gaseous) atom does not, in itself, constitute the only criterion by which we can decide whether the ion exists in stable compounds. (See discussion on Born-Haber cycle, p. 264.)

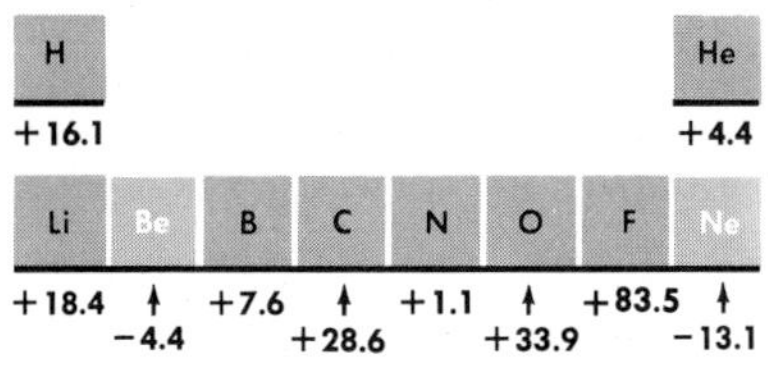

THE FORMATION OF POLYNEGATIVE IONS. When a neutral atom takes on two or more electrons to form a dinegative or polynegative ion, the effect of the number of electrons is much the same as in the formation of positive ions. For example, we found that it is more difficult to remove two electrons from a neutral atom than it is to remove one electron, although in both cases energy is *required* in the ionization process. For the formation of negative ions, we have seen that the addition of a first electron to a neutral atom is almost always accompanied by release of energy—or, as we may say, is energetically favorable. However, once an atom has taken on one electron and has become a mononegative ion, its negative charge makes the addition of a second electron very difficult. In fact, *energy is always required to add an electron to a mononegative ion,* and even more is necessary to add a third electron to a dinegative ion. For example, 33.9 kcal/mole of atoms are *evolved* when the oxygen atom, O, takes on one electron to form the mononegative ion, O^-, but when the O^- ion adds another electron to form the dinegative oxide ion, $O^=$, 119.0 kcal/mole of O^- ions are *ab-*

sorbed. Since the addition of successive electrons to negative ions requires increasingly larger amounts of energy, the formation of any trinegative ion is energetically less favorable than the formation of any dinegative ion, which in turn is less favorable than the formation of any mononegative ion. For example, in the formation of Cl^- ions from Cl atoms, 85.1 kcal/mole of Cl atoms are *evolved,* in the formation of $O^=$ ions from O atoms, $(119.0 - 33.9) = 85.1$ kcal/mole of O atoms are *absorbed.* If the occurrence of monoatomic negative ions in stable chemical compounds were determined solely by the energy involved forming the gaseous isolated ions, then only mononegative ions might be expected to result. On the contrary, we know of only a few mononegative ions in stable compounds—namely, the halides, F^-, Cl^-, Br^-, and I^-, the hydride, H^-, and the auride, Au^-; whereas the dinegative oxide, $O^=$, and sulfide, $S^=$, ions exist in many stable compounds. Notice that these stable anions all have the electron configuration of a noble gas. Generally an element which appears in a periodic series one or two places before a noble gas can attain an electron configuration like that of the noble gas by taking on one or two electrons. This is still possible, though far more difficult, for an atom having three electrons less than the next noble gas—for example, $P^0(3s^2\ 3p^3) + 3\ e^- \longrightarrow P^{-3}(3s^2\ 3p^6)$. When an atom, X^0, needs more than three electrons to attain a noble-gas-like configuration, however, the energy required to add the fourth electron is so exceedingly large that simple monoatomic tetranegative ions, X^{-4}, are very seldom found in stable compounds.

Thus, of the elements of Series 3 which we have been considering as examples (Na, Mg, Al, Si, P, S, Cl), only the last two, sulfur and chlorine, form negative ions readily. The sulfur atom, $_{16}S(1s^2,\ 2s^2\ 2p^6,\ 3s^2\ 3p^4)$ forms the sulfide ion, $S^=$, by taking on two electrons in its $3p$ orbitals, to produce an electron configuration $(1s^2,\ 2s^2\ 2p^6,\ 3s^2\ 3p^6)$ similar to that of the next noble gas, argon, Ar. The chlorine atom, which has the electron arrangement, $Cl(1s^2,\ 2s^2\ 2p^6,\ 3s^2\ 3p^5)$, needs to add but a single electron into its $3p$ orbitals to achieve the argon-like configuration.

As we have already discussed, a negative ion is always larger than the neutral atom from which it is formed. As is the case with positive ions, so the relative size of negative ions is influenced by the relative size of the original atoms. Consider, for example, two atoms A and B, having similar electron configurations. If atom A is larger than atom B, and if each atom takes on the same number of electrons, the negative ion formed from atom A will be larger than the negative ion formed from atom B. That is, the A^- ion is larger than the B^- ion, and the $A^=$ ion is larger than the $B^=$ ion.

ENERGY INVOLVED IN THE FORMATION OF IONIC COMPOUNDS

THE BORN-HABER CYCLE. The formation of ionic compounds composed of monoatomic positive and negative ions is easily represented on the basis of the electron configuration of their atoms. As an illustration, let us consider the ionic compound sodium fluoride, Na^+F^-, composed of Na^+ ions and F^- ions arranged in a three-dimensional face-centered cubic lattice. Assuming that solid sodium fluoride is formed by the reaction of gaseous sodium atoms with gaseous fluorine atoms: $Na_{(g)} + F_{(g)} \longrightarrow Na^+F^-_{(s)}$, we shall now consider in some detail the electronic changes which occur in this reaction.

We know that the sodium atom, $_{11}Na$, follows the noble gas neon, $_{10}Ne$, in the Periodic Table, and has an electron configuration similar to that of neon, *plus one electron* in the next higher shell, $Na(1s^2,\ 2s^2\ 2p^6,\ 3s^1)$ or $Na([Ne]\ 3s^1)$. If the sodium atom loses this extra $(3s^1)$ electron, it acquires an electron configuration similar to that of neon, and the resulting particle (the monopositive ion, Na^+) has a positive charge of +1. Notice that the sodium atom, $_{11}Na$, is neutral, because it has 11 protons in its nucleus and 11 electrons in its electron cloud, whereas the sodium ion, Na^+, has a single positive charge, because it has 11 protons in its nucleus but only ten electrons in its electron cloud. The loss of one electron by a sodium atom, Na, to form a sodium ion, Na^+, may also be represented as follows:

$$_{11}Na^0(\text{nucleus: } 11p, 12n)\ 1s^2, 2s^2\ 2p^6, 3s^1 \longrightarrow {}_{11}Na^+(\text{nucleus: } 11p, 12n)\ 1s^2, 2s^2\ 2p^6 + 1\ e^-$$

Or more simply: $_{11}Na^0(1s^2, 2s^2\ 2p^6, 3s^1) \longrightarrow {}_{11}Na^+(1s^2, 2s^2\ 2p^6) + 1\ e^-$

Since the Na^+ ion ($1s^2, 2s^2\ 2p^6$) is isoelectronic with the Ne atom ($1s^2, 2s^2\ 2p^6$), this change may also be represented as:

$$_{11}Na^0([Ne]\ 3s^1) \longrightarrow {}_{11}Na^+([Ne]) + 1\ e^-$$

If we make use of the electron-dot formulas, then the sodium atom is represented as Na·, in which the dot represents the $3s^1$ electron and the symbol Na represents the core of the atom, the nucleus surrounded by all the inner electrons ($1s^2, 2s^2\ 2p^6$). Since only the highest-energy electron ($3s^1$) in the outermost shell of the sodium atom is lost, the ionization reaction may be represented simply as, Na· $\longrightarrow$ $Na^+ + 1\ e^-$.

Now let us consider the fluorine atom, $_9F$, or $_9F(1s^2, 2s^2\ 2p^5)$, which in the Periodic Table comes just before neon, $_{10}Ne(1s^2, 2s^2\ 2p^6)$. When a fluorine atom acquires one electron, the resulting particle has an electron configuration similar to that of neon; in the process, the neutral fluorine atom, $_9F$ (which has nine protons and ten neutrons in the nucleus and a total of nine electrons in its electron cloud: ($1s^2, 2s^2\ 2p^5$)) becomes a negatively charged fluoride ion, F^-, (with nine protons and ten neutrons in the nucleus and a total of ten electrons in the electron cloud, F^- ($1s^2, 2s^2\ 2p^6$))). Notice that the fluorine atom, F, is neutral, because it has nine protons and nine electrons, whereas the fluoride ion, F^-, has a net single negative charge because it has nine protons but ten electrons. The reaction by which the fluorine atom takes on an electron to form the fluoride ion may be represented schematically by one of the following equations:

$$_9F^0(\text{nucleus: } 9p, 10n)\ 1s^2, 2s^2\ 2p^5 + 1\ e^- \longrightarrow {}_9F^-(\text{nucleus: } 9p, 10n)\ 1s^2, 2s^2\ 2p^6$$

$$_9F(1s^2, 2s^2\ 2p^5) + 1\ e^- \longrightarrow {}_9F^-(1s^2, 2s^2\ 2p^6)$$

$$:\ddot{\underset{..}{F}}\cdot + 1\ e^- \longrightarrow :\ddot{\underset{..}{F}}:^-$$

Notice that in the last equation the fluorine atom, F, is represented by the symbol F surrounded by seven electrons (the number of electrons in its outmost shell, $2s^2\ 2p^5$) and likewise the fluoride ion, F^-, is represented by the symbol F surrounded by eight electrons ($2s^2\ 2p^6$) and a negative superscript. In both electron-dot formulas, the symbol F represents, as usual, the core of the fluorine atom or fluoride ion—namely, the nucleus surrounded by the inner electrons, $1s^2$.

Now when a gaseous sodium atom, $Na_{(g)}$, and a gaseous fluorine atom, $F_{(g)}$, come together, the sodium atom gives up one electron to form a positive ion, Na^+, and the fluorine atom takes on this electron to form a negative ion, F^-. This electronic interaction may be represented schematically as follows:

$$Na_{(g)}(1s^2, 2s^2\ 2p^6, 3s^1) + F_{(g)}(1s^2, 2s^2\ 2p^5) \longrightarrow Na^+_{(g)}(1s^2, 2s^2\ 2p^6) + F^-_{(g)}(1s^2, 2s^2\ 2p^6)$$

The chemical reaction between gaseous sodium atoms, $Na_{(g)}$, and gaseous fluorine atoms, $F_{(g)}$, involves the transfer of a single electron from the electron cloud of a sodium atom to the electron cloud of a fluorine atom. The transfer of this single electron converts the sodium atom, Na, and the fluorine atom, F, into a gaseous sodium ion, Na^+, and a gaseous fluoride ion, F^-, respectively.

Let us now consider the energy involved in the above reaction. The equation of the reaction may be obtained by summing up the two equations representing the formation of the $Na^+_{(g)}$ and the $F^-_{(g)}$ ions from their respective gaseous atoms. Hence, the ΔH value of the reaction is also given by the sum of the ΔH values of these two reactions:

$$Na\cdot_{(g)} \longrightarrow Na^+_{(g)} + e^- \qquad \Delta H = +118.0 \text{ kcal/mole } Na^+_{(g)}$$

$$:\ddot{F}\cdot_{(g)} + e^- \longrightarrow :\ddot{F}:^-_{(g)} \qquad \Delta H = -83.5 \text{ kcal/mole } F^-_{(g)}$$

$$Na\cdot_{(g)} + :\ddot{F}\cdot_{(g)} \longrightarrow \{Na^+_{(g)} + :\ddot{F}:^-_{(g)}\} \qquad \Delta H = +34.5 \text{ kcal/mole } Na^+_{(g)} + F^-_{(g)}$$

Thus, if we wish 1 mole of gaseous $Na_{(g)}$ atoms to react with 1 mole of gaseous $F_{(g)}$ atoms to produce 1 mole of gaseous sodium ions, $Na^+_{(g)}$ and 1 mole of gaseous fluoride ions, $F^-_{(g)}$, we must supply to the reaction mixture a relatively large quantity of energy, precisely 34.5 kcal/mole of rectant atoms.

On the other hand, if 1 mole of *crystalline sodium metal,* $Na_{(s)}$, and $\frac{1}{2}$ mole of *gaseous fluorine molecules,* $F_{2(g)}$, are brought into contact, a lively, almost violent, reaction occurs, which produces 1 mole of crystalline ionic sodium fluoride, $Na^+F^-_{(s)}$, with the evolution of a large quantity of heat—precisely $\Delta H = -136$ kcal/mole $Na^+F^-_{(s)}$ formed.

$$Na_{(s)} + \tfrac{1}{2} F_{2(g)} \longrightarrow Na^+F^-_{(s)} \qquad \Delta H = -136 \text{ kcal/mole } Na^+F^-_{(s)}$$

To explain the difference between the energy involved in the reaction between gaseous sodium atoms, $Na_{(g)}$, and gaseous fluorine atoms, $F_{(g)}$, to form the corresponding gaseous mono-charged ion pair, $\{Na^+_{(g)} + F^-_{(g)}\}$ and the energy involved in the reaction of solid sodium metal, $Na_{(s)}$, with gaseous fluorine molecules, $F_{2(g)}$, to form solid sodium fluoride, $Na^+F^-_{(s)}$, consider the series of steps illustrated:

$$\begin{array}{ccccc} Na^+F^-_{(s)} & \xleftarrow{-L} & Na^+_{(g)} & + & F^-_{(g)} \\ \uparrow {\scriptstyle -\Delta H_f} & & \uparrow {\scriptstyle +I} & & \uparrow {\scriptstyle -E} \\ Na_{(s)} + \frac{1}{2} F_{2(g)} & \xrightarrow{+A + \frac{1}{2}D} & Na_{(g)} & + & F_{(g)} \end{array}$$

A = atomization (sublimation) energy of Na = +26 kcal/mole $Na_{(s)}$
D = dissociation energy of F_2 = +38 kcal/mole $F_{2(g)}$ molecules
I = ionization energy of Na = +118 kcal/mole $Na_{(g)}$ atoms
E = electron affinity of F = −83 kcal/mole $F_{(g)}$ atoms
L = lattice energy of Na^+F^- = −235 kcal/mole $Na^+F^-_{(s)}$
ΔH_f = heat of formation of crystalline Na^+F^- = −155 kcal/mole $Na^+F^-_{(s)}$

This scheme, which is called the *Born-Haber cycle* for the formation of crystalline sodium fluoride, $Na^+F^-_{(s)}$, shows the magnitude and the significance of the energy involved in each step of the reaction (the energy values are all expressed in kcal/mole). The total energy involved in the reaction is the sum of the energies liberated or absorbed in the various steps. If we consider separately the energy involved in each of the single steps, we see that the formation of gaseous sodium atoms, $Na_{(g)}$, and gaseous fluorine atoms, $F_{(g)}$, from solid sodium metal, $Na_{(s)}$, and gaseous fluorine molecules, $F_{2(g)}$, requires energy, and so does the transformation of gaseous atoms, $Na_{(g)}$, into their gaseous ions, $Na^+_{(g)}$. We also see that some of this required energy is supplied by the formation of the gaseous ions, $F^-_{(g)}$, from their gaseous atoms, $F_{(g)}$. However, the combination of the isolated gaseous positive and negative ions, $Na^+_{(g)}$ and $F^-_{(g)}$, to form crystalline sodium fluoride, $Na^+F^-_{(s)}$, liberates a large amount of energy, which more than compensates for the energy absorbed in the other energetically unfavorable steps. As we have already discussed (p. 176), this *crystalline* or *lattice energy* has a relatively large value, because of the strong electrostatic attraction between the oppositely charged Na^+ and F^- ions in the crystal of sodium fluoride.

In general, an ionic crystalline compound can be formed by the direct reaction of its elements if its lattice energy is sufficiently high. Since the lattice energy is proportional to the square of the charges of the ions, its value is higher for ionic compounds containing di-charged ions than for those containing mono-charged ions, and even higher for compounds containing tri-charged ions. Thus an ionic compound such as MgO (Mg^{++} and $O^{=}$) is formed by the direct combustion of magnesium metal, $Mg_{(s)}$, and oxygen gas, $O_{2(g)}$, with the evolution of considerable heat.

$$Mg_{(s)} + \tfrac{1}{2}\,O_{2(g)} \longrightarrow Mg^{++}O^{=}_{(s)} \qquad \Delta H = -152 \text{ kcal/mole } Mg^{++}O^{=}_{(s)}$$

The reason is that the energetically favorable and very high lattice energy of $Mg^{++}O^{=}_{(s)}$ ($\Delta H = -940$ kcal/mole $MgO_{(s)}$) more than compensates for the sum of all the energetically unfavorable energy terms: the energies required to form the gaseous magnesium atoms, $Mg_{(g)}$, from magnesium metal, $Mg_{(s)}$ ($\Delta H = +36$ kcal/mole $Mg_{(g)}$ atoms); the gaseous oxygen atoms, $O_{(g)}$, from gaseous oxygen molecules, $O_{2(g)}$ ($\Delta H = +59$ kcal/mole O atoms); the gaseous magnesium ions, $Mg^{++}{}_{(g)}$, from the gaseous magnesium atoms, $Mg_{(g)}$ ($\Delta H = +523$ kcal/mole Mg^{++} ions); and the gaseous oxide ions, $O^{=}{}_{(g)}$, from gaseous oxygen atoms, $O_{(g)}$ ($\Delta H = +170$ kcal/mole $O^{=}$ ions).

As another illustration, let us consider the reaction between the atoms of the two elements that are two positions removed in the Periodic Table from the noble gas argon, ${}_{18}Ar$. These elements are calcium, ${}_{20}Ca$, (which appears two positions after argon) and sulfur, ${}_{16}S$ (which appears two positions before argon). The electron configurations of these atoms follows:

$${}_{16}S(1s^2, 2s^2\,2p^6, 3s^2\,3p^4) \quad {}_{18}Ar(1s^2, 2s^2\,2p^6, 3s^2\,3p^6) \quad {}_{20}Ca(1s^2, 2s^2\,2p^6, 3s^2\,3p^6, 4s^2)$$

When a calcium atom, Ca, and a sulfur atom, S, react, two electrons are transferred from the calcium atom to the sulfur atom to form Ca^{++} ions and $S^{=}$ ions, respectively. The schematic representation of this reaction is:

$$\begin{array}{ccccccc} {}_{20}Ca & + & {}_{16}S & \longrightarrow & {}_{20}Ca^{++} & + & {}_{16}S^{=} \\ (1s^2, 2s^2\,2p^6, & & (1s^2, 2s^2\,2p^6, & & (1s^2, 2s^2\,2p^6, & & (1s^2, 2s^2\,2p^6, \\ 3s^2\,3p^6, 4s^2) & & 3s^2\,3p^4) & & 3s^2\,3p^6) & & 3s^2\,3p^6) \\ \dot{Ca}\cdot & + & \cdot\ddot{S}: & \longrightarrow & Ca^{++} & + & :\ddot{\underset{..}{S}}:^{=} \end{array}$$

Notice that the positive ${}_{20}Ca^{++}$ ion, the neutral noble-gas atom, ${}_{18}Ar^0$, and the negative ${}_{16}S^{=}$ ion are isoelectronic. When large numbers of these oppositely charged Ca^{++} and $S^{=}$ ions combine together, the crystalline lattice of calcium sulfide, $Ca^{++}S^{=}{}_{(s)}$ results, which has a rock-salt structure. The Born-Haber cycle for the reaction of calcium metal, $Ca_{(s)}$, with solid sulfur, $S_{(s)}$, to form crystalline calcium sulfide, $Ca^{++}S^{=}{}_{(s)}$, is shown below.

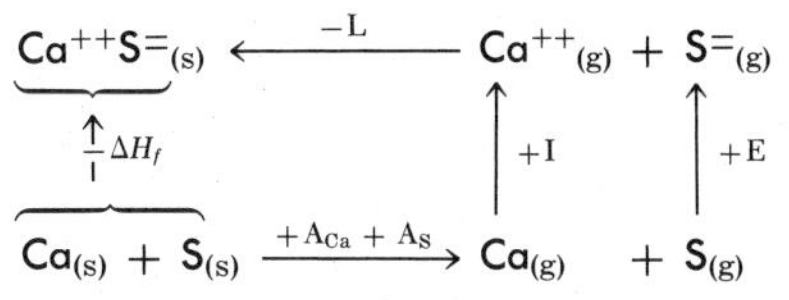

$$\begin{array}{ccccc} Ca^{++}S^{=}{}_{(s)} & \xleftarrow{-L} & Ca^{++}{}_{(g)} & + & S^{=}{}_{(g)} \\ \uparrow \Delta H_f & & \uparrow +I & & \uparrow +E \\ Ca_{(s)} + S_{(s)} & \xrightarrow{+A_{Ca} + A_S} & Ca_{(g)} & + & S_{(g)} \end{array}$$

A_{Ca} = Atomization (sublimation) energy of solid calcium = $+47.8$ kcal/mole $Ca_{(s)}$.
A_S = Atomization (sublimation) energy of solid sulfur = $+66.3$ kcal/mole $S_{(s)}$.
I = Ionization energy required to remove two electrons from a gaseous Ca atom = $+415.8$ kcal/mole $Ca^{++}{}_{(g)}$.
E = Electron affinity, the energy required to attach two electrons to a gaseous sulfur atom = $+79.7$ kcal/mole $S^{=}{}_{(g)}$.
L = Lattice energy of $Ca^{++}S^{=}{}_{(s)} = -723.0$ kcal/mole $Ca^{++}S^{=}{}_{(s)}$.
ΔH_f = Heat of formation of crystalline $Ca^{++}S^{=} = -113.4$ kcal/mole $Ca^{++}S^{=}{}_{(s)}$.

STABLE IONS WITH ELECTRON CONFIGURATIONS UNLIKE THE NOBLE GASES

Many stable ionic compounds contain positive ions having an electron arrangement that does not resemble that of a noble gas. Examples are the copper(I); copper(II); iron(II); and iron(III) ions.

THE COPPER(I) AND COPPER(II) IONS. First, let us list the electron configurations of the copper atom, together with those of the noble gases, which precede and follow copper in the Periodic Table, argon, and krypton, respectively:

$${}_{18}Ar(1s^2, 2s^2\ 2p^6, 3s^2\ 3p^6) \qquad {}_{29}Cu(1s^2, 2s^2\ 2p^6, 3s^2\ 3p^6\ 3d^{10}, 4s^1)$$
$${}_{36}Kr(1s^2, 2s^2\ 2p^6, 3s^2\ 3p^6\ 3d^{10}, 4s^2\ 4p^6)$$

In order to attain the stable electron configuration of either ${}_{18}Ar$ or ${}_{36}Kr$, the copper atom, ${}_{29}Cu$, would have to lose eleven electrons (to attain the electron arrangement of argon, ${}_{18}Ar$), or gain or share seven electrons (to attain the electron arrangement of krypton, ${}_{36}Kr$). Actually, the copper atom $Cu(1s^2, 2s^2\ 2p^6, 3s^2\ 3p^6\ 3d^{10}, 4s^1)$ undergoes neither of these changes. But it may give up one electron to form the copper(I) ion, with the electron configuration: $Cu^+(1s^2, 2s^2\ 2p^6, 3s^2\ 3p^6\ 3d^{10})$ or $Cu^+([Ar]\ 3d^{10})$:

$$Cu^0([Ar]\ 3d^{10}, 4s^1) \longrightarrow Cu^+([Ar]\ 3d^{10}) + 1\ e^-$$

or simply:

$$Cu\cdot \longrightarrow Cu^+ + 1\ e^-$$

The copper atom thus resembles the atoms of the alkali metals in its ability to give up its outermost *s* electron and form a monopositive ion, stable in such compounds as CuCl, CuBr, and CuCN. But notice that the resulting electron configuration of the copper(I) ion, is not that of a noble gas but rather of the noble gas argon *plus* a complete $3d^{10}$ sub-shell, $Cu^+([Ar]\ 3d^{10})$.

The copper atom may also give up two electrons forming the copper(II) ion, with the electron configuration Cu^{++}: $1s^2, 2s^2\ 2p^6, 3s^2\ 3p^6\ 3d^9$, or $Cu^{++}([Ar]\ 3d^9)$. The copper(II) ion is stable in such compounds as CuO, $CuCl_2$ and $CuSO_4 \cdot 5\ H_2O$. Notice that the Cu(II) ion has an *incomplete* 3*d* electron shell ($3d^9$):

$$Cu^0([Ar]\ 3d^{10}, 4s^1) \longrightarrow Cu^{++}([Ar]\ 3d^9) + 2\ e^-$$
$$\dot{Cu}\cdot \longrightarrow Cu^{++} + 2\ e^-$$

THE IRON(II) AND IRON(III) IONS, Fe^{++} AND Fe^{+++}. Other examples of ions that have an incomplete *d* sub-shell are the iron(II) and iron(III) ions, Fe^{++} and Fe^{+++}. The dipositive Fe^{++} ion is formed when the Fe^0 atom loses its two $4s^2$ electrons, and the tripositive Fe^{+++} ion is formed when the Fe^0 atom loses its two $4s^2$ and *one* of its $3d^6$ electrons, or when the Fe^{++} ion loses *one* of its $3d^6$ electrons. The electron configurations of Fe^0, Fe^{++}, and Fe^{+++} follow:

Fe^0,	$1s^2, 2s^2\ 2p^6, 3s^2\ 3p^6\ 3d^6, 4s^2$	or	Fe^0	$([Ar]\ 3d^6, 4s^2)$
Fe^{++},	$1s^2, 2s^2\ 2p^6, 3s^2\ 3p^6\ 3d^6$	or	Fe^{++}	$([Ar]\ 3d^6)$
Fe^{+++},	$1s^2, 2s^2\ 2p^6, 3s^2\ 3p^6\ 3d^5$	or	Fe^{+++}	$([Ar]\ 3d^5)$

The Fe^{++} and Fe^{+++} ions are stable in such compounds as $Fe^{II}O$, $Fe_2{}^{III}O_3$, $Fe^{II}SO_4 \cdot 6\ H_2O$, and $Fe^{III}PO_4$. Similarly, the atoms of the other transition elements usually form several ions with an incomplete *d* sub-shell. Notice that the atoms of the transition elements exhibit variable oxidation numbers because one or more electrons may be lost from the 3*d* sub-shell.

POLARIZING POWER AND POLARIZABILITY. As we have already discussed in Chapter 9 (p. 145), the electron cloud of an atom is not rigid and undeformable. Rather, the electron clouds of all atoms, molecules, and ions are susceptible to being deformed or *polarized* under the influence of an electrical field, such as is provided by the nuclei of other atoms, molecules, or ions. As a result, the atoms, molecules, or ions generally acquire an electric dipole moment—that is, they become *polar* even if originally they had a perfectly spherical charge distribution. Because of their electrical charge, positive ions are particularly effective in causing the polarization (deformation) of the electron clouds of atoms, molecules, and especially of negative ions. In turn, the electron clouds of negative ions are relatively more polarizable than are those of the corresponding neutral atoms, because, as we know, the electron clouds of negative ions are larger and less tightly bound to the nucleus than those of the corresponding neutral atoms. The ability of a positive ion to distort the electron clouds of atoms, molecules, and negative ions is called its *polarizing power.* The tendency of the electron cloud of an atom (or of a negative ion) to be distorted by a given positive ion or by a positive charge is called the *polarizability* of the atom (or of the negative ion).

Now that we have discussed the basis for the polarization of ions, let us consider in some detail the rules which summarize this phenomenon (*Fajan's Rules*):

1. (a) The smaller the size of a cation (a positive ion), the greater is its polarizing power (other factors being as equal as possible). For example, of the alkali-metal ions, Li^+, Na^+, K^+, Rb^+, Cs^+, all of which have the same charge and the same general type of noble-gas electron configuration, the smallest, the Li^+ ion, is the most effective in distorting the electron cloud of a given anion (a negative ion) X^{-n} because its positive charge is concentrated over the smallest volume.

The smallest of all the monopositive cations, the proton, H^+, would be expected to have the greatest polarizing power and hence to form the most covalent compounds. In fact, we know that the hydrogen halides, HX, in the anhydrous state have a covalent structure. The halides LiX, of the next smallest stable monopositive ion, Li^+, have a very pronounced ionic character compared with HX, because the radius of Li^+ (0.60 A) is considerably greater than that of the proton (estimated to be about 10^{-5} A).

(b) The higher the charge of the cation, the greater its polarizing power (other factors being as equal as possible). For example, of Ba^{++} and K^+, the dipositive Ba^{++} (radius = 1.33 A), with the same general electron configuration (Xe noble-gas core) and the same size as the monopositive K^+ (radius = 1.33 A, Ar noble-gas core), has the greater polarizing power. Also the dipositive and very small Be^{++} (radius = 0.31 A) and Mg^{++} (radius = 0.65 A) ions polarize negative ions so strongly that their ionic compounds all exhibit an appreciable covalent character. In general, *small cations which have a high charge have a high polarizing power.*

By considering together the two factors discussed in (a) and (b), we may state that *the polarizing power of a cation is directly proportional to the ratio of its charge to its radius.* We shall often use this concept of charge/radius ratio in discussing the properties of elements in later chapters.

2. (a) and (b). The same factors of size and charge that influence the ability of positive ions to polarize negative ions also influence the readiness of negative ions to be polarized. The *larger* the size of an anion and the greater its negative charge, the greater is its tendency to be polarized by a given cation. Of the halide ions, F^-, Cl^-, Br^-, and I^-, the largest one, the I^- ion, has the greatest polarizability, because its outermost orbitals, which are less tightly held at its nuclear charge, can be more easily deformed by a given positive ion. If the polarizability of the fluoride ion is conventionally taken to be 1.0, then that of each of the other halide ions is: (F^- = 1.0), Cl^- = 3.5; Br^- = 5.0; I^- = 7.5. Thus in the series of the silver halides, AgF, AgCl, AgBr, and AgI, the polarization of the halide ion, X^-, by the Ag^+ cation and hence the covalent character of the Ag-X interaction (bonding) is expected to increase in the order: $F < Cl < Br < I$. Actually, the observed difference in the

color of the AgF (colorless), AgCl (also colorless), AgBr (pale yellow), and AgI (intense yellow) is explained on the basis of the increasing covalent character of the Ag-X bond. Similarly, the dinegative $S^{=}$ ion (radius = 1.84 A), owing to its greater charge, is more polarizable than the mononegative Cl^- (radius = 1.81 A), which is almost identical in size, and has the same argon-like electron structure—and indeed the black AgS has a far more covalent character than AgCl.

3. The polarizing power of a cation (of a given size and charge) increases as the electron configuration departs from that of a noble-gas type. A noble-gas-like electron configuration is most effective in shielding the nuclear charge from any negative charges at its surface, and consequently the positive ions with such electron configurations have the smallest polarizing power (other factors being equal). Consider as an example KI and AgI. The K^+ ion (1.33 A) and the Ag^+ ion (1.26 A) are about the same size, but the K^+ ion has an argon-like electron configuration, whereas the Ag^+ ion has a filled outer d^{10} shell ([Kr] $4d^{10}$). Again, the difference in color between KI (colorless) and AgI (intense yellow) is explained on the basis of the greater covalent character of the bonding in AgI as compared with that in KI.

Exercises

13-1 Explain how the relative sizes of the atoms of Series 3 of the Periodic Table change with increasing atomic number.

13-2 What two factors are most important in determining the size of an atom? Illustrate your answer with specific examples.

13-3 Explain the relative sizes of the atoms within a given group of the Periodic Table. Illustrate your answer with specific examples.

13-4 Compounds formed from the loss of one or more electrons by one atom and the gain of one or more electrons by another atom are called ________.

13-5 Compare the relative sizes of neutral atoms and their positive ions.

13-6 List the following particles in order of decreasing size: Kr, Sr^{++}, Rb^+.

13-7 Compare and explain the differences in size between the following groups of particles: (a) Fe^{++} and Fe^{+++}; (b) Cu^0, Cu^+, and Cu^{++}.

13-8 Compare the sizes of a negative ion and its neutral atom. Illustrate with specific examples.

13-9 Explain the extraordinary difference in size between the hydrogen atom, H, and the hydrogen ion, H^+.

13-10 List the following particles in order of decreasing size: K^+, Ar, $S^=$, Cl^-, Ca^{++}.

13-11 Explain the formation of positive ions from neutral atoms in terms of energy relationships. Illustrate with specific examples.

13-12 Explain the differences in the ionization energies of the alkali metals.

13-13 Explain the very high ionization energy required for reaction (2) as compared with the energy required for reaction (1):

$$(1)\ Na^0 \longrightarrow Na^+ + e^- \qquad (2)\ Na^+ \longrightarrow Na^{++} + e^-$$

13-14 The first ionization energy of Cu is 178 kcal/mole and the second, as expected, is larger, 468 kcal/mole. On the basis of the electron configurations of Cu^0, Cu^+, and Cu^{++}, explain why the second ionization energy is so very much higher ($2\frac{1}{2}$ times) than the first.

13-15 Explain the relative tendencies of the halogen atoms to take on electrons to form negative ions. Illustrate with specific examples.

13-16 Explain in terms of their electron configuration the tendency of some atoms to lose electrons and the tendency of other atoms to gain electrons. Illustrate your answer by use of schematic equations, showing the loss or gain of electrons.

13-17 By means of simple electronic representations showing the number of electrons in each shell, explain the following reactions: (a) Potassium atoms with chlorine atoms to form ionic potassium chloride. What constitutes the real chemical change in this reaction? (b) Calcium atoms with fluorine atoms to form ionic calcium fluoride. What constitutes the real chemical change in this reaction? (c) Magnesium atoms and sulfur atoms to form ionic magnesium sulfide. What constitutes the real chemical change in this reaction?

13-18 In general, the atoms of what elements tend to react to form ionic compounds? Give specific examples.

13-19 Using electron-dot formulas, write equations to represent the following reactions: (a) The loss of one electron by a sodium atom to form a sodium ion. (b) The loss of one electron by a copper atom to form a copper(I) ion. (c) Explain any differences in (1) the tendency of each of these reactions to take place, and (2) the electronic configurations of the resulting ions.

13-20 Using electron-dot formulas, write equations to represent the following reactions: (a) An iron atom loses two electrons. (b) An iron atom loses three electrons.

13-21 Sodium chloride, Na^+Cl^-; potassium chloride, K^+Cl^-; sodium fluoride, Na^+F^-; and magnesium oxide, $Mg^{++}O^=$, all have the same crystalline structure. (a) Assume that the distances between the ions in the crystal lattice of these ionic compounds are the same. List these compounds in order of increasing density. (b) Explain the difference in the melting points of the following pairs of these compounds: NaCl (800°C) and NaF (992°C); NaCl (800°C) and KCl (790°C); NaCl (800°C) and MgO (2800°C).

13-22 Both ionic compounds Na^+F^- and $Mg^{++}O^=$ have a crystal structure like that of the compound Na^+Cl^-. Sketch the crystal structure of these ionic compounds. (a) The ions Na^+ and Mg^{++} have the same number of electrons. Compare the relative sizes of these ions. (b) The ions F^- and $O^=$ have the same number of electrons. Compare the relative sizes of these ions. (c) On the basis of your answers to (a) and (b), and on the basis of the charges of the ions involved, which compound would you expect to have the highest melting point? Explain your answer.

13-23 From the following data, calculate the lattice energy, L, of ionic potassium hydride, $K^+H^-_{(s)}$ (that is, calculate the ΔH for the reaction $K^+_{(g)} + H^-_{(g)} \longrightarrow K^+H^-_{(s)}$).

(a) $K_{(s)} + \frac{1}{2} H_{2(g)} \longrightarrow K^+H^-_{(s)}$ $\Delta H_f = 14.5$ kcal/mole $K^+H^-_{(s)}$
(b) Heat of atomization, A, of $K_{(s)} = 21.3$ kcal/mole $K_{(s)}$
(c) Dissociation energy, D, of $H_{2(g)} = 104.2$ kcal/mole $H_{2(g)}$
(d) Electron affinity, E, of $H_{(g)} = 16.1$ kcal/mole $H_{(g)}$
(e) Ionization energy, I, of $K_{(g)} = 100$ kcal/mole $K_{(g)}$

13-24 List the following in order of increasing polarizing power.

(a) Rb^+(1.48 A), Cu^+(0.96 A), Au^+(1.37 A), K^+(1.33 A)
(b) Li^+(0.60 A), Mg^{++}(0.65 A), Al^{+++}(0.50 A)
(c) Zn^{++}(0.74 A), Hg^{++}(1.10 A), Ba^{++}(1.35 A)

13-25 List the following in order of increasing polarizability.

(a) H^-(2.08 A), I^-(2.16 A), Br^-(1.95 A), $Te^=$(2.21 A), P^{-3}(2.12 A)
(b) N^{-3}(1.71 A), $O^=$(1.40 A), F^-(1.36 A).

THE ELECTRONIC THEORY OF CHEMICAL BONDING: II. COVALENT BONDING IN POLYATOMIC MOLECULES AND IONS

14

In Chapter 13 we considered the formation of isolated ions from their isolated parent atoms and the assemblage of oppositely charged ions, through electrostatic attraction, into crystalline ionic compounds. In this and in the following chapter we shall discuss how two or more atoms may link to one another (and to monoatomic ions) by sharing electron pairs in covalent bonds and how we can represent schematically, but clearly, the electronic structures of the resulting polyatomic molecules and ions. In this chapter we shall concern ourselves mainly with the simple rules which govern the relative positions of the atoms in molecules and in polyatomic ions—their stereochemistry—and we shall relate these rules to the electron-dot formulas of the molecules and ions. In Chapter 15 we shall proceed to consider in more detail the atomic orbitals involved in the formation of covalent bonds in polyatomic molecules and ions, and again we shall correlate the kind and number of the orbitals involved to the stereochemistry of the molecules.

14-1 Covalent Bonds between Atoms of the Same Elements

Let us consider the change in electronic arrangement that occurs when atoms of the same element combine covalently to form homonuclear molecules, such as, for example, H_2, F_2, and Cl_2.

THE HYDROGEN MOLECULE, H_2. We will discuss first the simplest diatomic homonuclear molecule, the hydrogen molecule, H_2. The electron configuration of the hydrogen atom, H, is $1s^1$, or $\underset{(\uparrow)}{1s}$ and, as we have seen, may be represented schematically by the electron-dot formula $H\cdot$, or by a modification of the electron-dot formula, $H\uparrow$, in which the electron is shown as an arrow to indicate its spin. When two H atoms join to form a H_2 molecule, each atom contributes its electron to form a pair of electrons with opposite spins. In general, the H_2 molecule may be represented by the electron-dot formula $H{:}H$, or by the modified formula, $H\uparrow\downarrow H$. The pair of electrons with opposite spins ($:$ or $\uparrow\downarrow$), which is shared by the nuclei of the two bonded hydrogen atoms of the H_2 molecule, constitutes the covalent electron pair—generally called the bond pair—that links the two atoms together. The reaction of two H atoms to form the H_2 molecule may be represented by the following schematic equation:

$$\mathrm{H}(1s^1) + \mathrm{H}(1s^1) \longrightarrow \mathrm{H}\underbrace{(1s^1 1s^1)}_{\text{covalent bond}}\mathrm{H}$$

This equation tells us that the electron in the $1s$ orbital of one hydrogen atom joins with the electron in the $1s$ orbital of the other hydrogen atom to form a pair of electrons (with opposite spins) which binds together the two hydrogen atoms in the hydrogen molecule, H_2. Because the two H atoms of a H_2 molecule are identical, the bond pair of electrons is shared equally by both H atoms so that each hydrogen atom now has attained a $1s^2$ helium-like electron configuration.

In the H_2 molecule the bonding electron pair may be considered to occupy a *bonding orbital* belonging to the entire H_2 molecule rather than to the individual H atoms. The bonding orbital of the H_2 molecule may be thought to derive from the combination of the $1s$ orbital of one H atom with the $1s$ orbital of the other H atom. We first consider two isolated H atoms and represent their electron clouds and the boundary lines of their $1s$ orbitals as in Fig. 14-1(a). Next we consider a hypothetical system of two non-bonded H atoms brought together to a distance equal to the internuclear distance in the H_2 molecule, and we represent in Fig. 14-1(b) the overlap of their individual electron clouds. Finally, we consider the H_2 molecule. In H_2 the bonding electron pair is shared equally by the two bonded identical nuclei, so the electron cloud will be symmetrically distributed between them, and the region of maximum electron probability will be found to lie along the H—H internuclear axis and midway between the two nuclei. Actually, the electron density between the two nuclei of the H_2 molecule is greater than it would be if the electron clouds of the two H atoms were simply overlapped as in Fig. 14-1(b), while it is smaller in the other regions of space. The boundary line of the bonding orbital of H_2 is shown in Fig. 14-1(c). This bonding orbital may be considered to result from the combination of the two $1s$ atomic orbitals along the H—H internuclear axis. As we said above, this bonding orbital has more electron density along the internuclear axis between the two bonded nuclei, and less in the other regions, than would result from the simple overlap of the atomic orbitals. Keeping this difference in mind, it is convenient to consider that the bonding pair occupies an orbital formed simply by the overlap of the atomic orbitals of the isolated atoms.

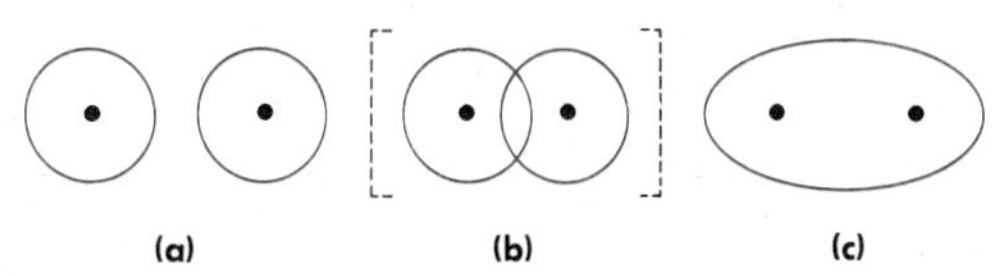

FIGURE 14-1 Orbital boundary lines in (a) two separate H atoms, (b) hypothetical system of two non-bonded H atoms at internuclear distance, (c) bonding orbital in H_2 molecule.

The H_2 molecule may also be formed by the reaction of a hydride ion, $H{:}^-$, with a proton, H^+, as represented schematically by the electron-dot equation,

$H:^- + H^+ \longrightarrow H:H$, and pictorially in Fig. 14-2. A comparison between this diagram and Fig. 14-1 shows that in a H_2 molecule the electron distribution is always the same, regardless of how the H_2 molecule is formed. At times it may be helpful to think of a polyatomic molecule or ion as being formed by different reactions, *even by a reaction which does not take place experimentally.* The important point to keep in mind is that a molecule or ion, once formed, is always the same regardless of how it was actually formed, or thought to be formed. Later we shall often use this concept in discussing the structural and energetic aspects of the formation of compounds.

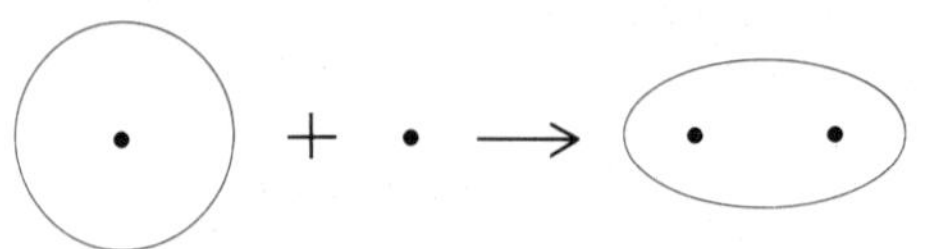

Hydride ion, $H:^-$ Proton, H^+ Hydrogen molecule, $H:H$

FIGURE 14-2 Boundary lines of the electron clouds for the hydride ion, H^-, and the hydrogen molecule, H_2.

THE FLUORINE MOLECULE, F_2. Now let us see how two fluorine atoms can combine to form a fluorine molecule. As we know, the fluorine atom, $_9F$, consists of a nucleus with nine protons and ten neutrons and an electron cloud that contains nine electrons, $F(1s^2, 2s^2\ 2p^5)$. In the formation of the F_2 molecule, each of the two F atoms contributes one of its $2p$ electrons to form a pair of electrons that is shared by both atoms. That is to say, the lone (unpaired) electron in one of the $2p$ orbitals of one F atom, conventionally assumed to be the $2p_z$ orbital $(1s^2, 2s^2\ 2p_x^2\ 2p_y^2\ 2p_z^1)$, pairs up with the lone electron in a $2p_z$ orbital of another F atom to form the bond pair of the F_2 molecule. We can represent the chemical union of two fluorine atoms to form a fluorine molecule as follows:

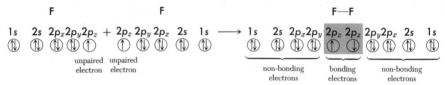

F						F						F—F									
1s	2s	$2p_x$	$2p_y$	$2p_z$	+	$2p_z$	$2p_y$	$2p_x$	2s	1s	→	1s	2s	$2p_x$	$2p_y$	$2p_z$	$2p_z$	$2p_y$	$2p_x$	2s	1s
⇅	⇅	⇅	⇅	↑		↑	⇅	⇅	⇅	⇅		⇅	⇅	⇅	⇅	↑	↓	⇅	⇅	⇅	⇅
				unpaired electron		unpaired electron						non-bonding electrons				bonding electrons		non-bonding electrons			

Or more simply as:

$$:\ddot{\underset{..}{F}}\cdot + \cdot\ddot{\underset{..}{F}}: \longrightarrow :\ddot{\underset{..}{F}}:\ddot{\underset{..}{F}}:$$

The bond pair in the F_2 molecule belongs equally to the two bonded fluorine atoms; by sharing this pair of electrons, each fluorine atom in the molecule attains the stable ten-electron arrangement of the following noble gas, neon $(1s^2, 2s^2\ 2p^6)$. When the two isolated $F_{(g)}$ atoms combine to form the $F_{2(g)}$ molecule, their electron clouds are modified so that the region of highest electron density of the bond pair lies in between the nuclei of the two bonded atoms. As we discussed for the hydrogen molecule, H_2, we may consider here that the bond electron pair of the fluorine molecule, F_2, occupies a bonding orbital derived from the combination or overlap of the two $2p$ atomic orbitals which in the isolated F atoms contain the unpaired electron. Since the p_x, p_y, and p_z orbitals of any isolated atom are equivalent, in the above representation we have arbitrarily placed the one lone p electron of each F atom in the p_z orbital. Consequently, the bonding orbital of

FIGURE 14-3 Schematic representation of the orbitals involved in the formation of the F_2 molecule.

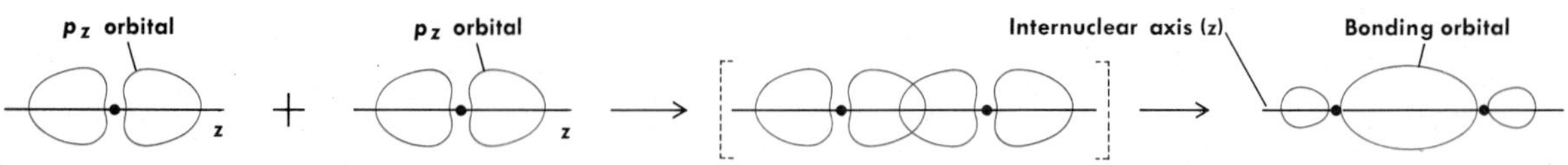

the F_2 molecule, occupied by the bonding electron pair, is formed by the combination, or overlap, of the two $2p_z$ orbitals of the two isolated atoms (Fig. 14-3).

Like fluorine, all other halogens form covalent diatomic homonuclear molecules: Cl_2, Br_2, and I_2, in which each of the two halogen atoms contributes its unpaired outer p_z electron to the commonly shared electron pair. In the resulting molecule, each halogen atom attains an electron arrangement similar to that of the following noble gas.

The formation of homonuclear covalent molecules by covalent bonding between atoms of the same elements is not limited to the non-metals. The atoms of the metals also combine covalently to form molecules. For example, at temperatures above its boiling point, 1,326° C, the alkali metal lithium exists in the gaseous state as diatomic molecules, Li_2, which derive from the combination of one lithium atom, Li, with another lithium atom, Li, as shown by the following schematic equations:

$$Li\cdot + \cdot Li \longrightarrow Li:Li$$

Li			Li			Li₂			
1s	2s	+	2s	1s	⟶	1s	2s	2s	1s
(↑↓)	(↑)		(↑)	(↑↓)		(↑↓)	(↑)	(↓)	(↑↓)
						non-bonding electrons	bond electron pair		non-bonding electrons

Again, we may consider the bond electron pair of the Li_2 molecule occupies a *bonding orbital* derived from the overlap of the two atomic $2s$ orbitals of the two isolated Li atoms. At high temperature, all the alkali metals (Group IA) form gaseous diatomic molecules, $Li_{2(g)}$, $Na_{2(g)}$, $K_{2(g)}$, $Rb_{2(g)}$, $Cs_{2(g)}$, in which each atom shares with the other its lone s electron to form a bond pair. At high temperatures in the vapor state, the atoms of the coinage metals (Group IB) behave similarly, forming the gaseous diatomic molecules, $Cu_{2(g)}$, $Ag_{2(g)}$, $Au_{2(g)}$; again, the lone s electron from each atom pairs up to form a covalent electron-pair bond, Cu:Cu; Ag:Ag; Au:Au. In the diatomic molecules of the alkali metals and coinage metals, the electron cloud consisting of the two shared electrons (the bond pair of electrons) is drawn in between the nuclei of the two bonded atoms, just as in the diatomic molecules of fluorine and hydrogen.

COVALENT σ (SIGMA) BOND

In all the diatomic molecules we have just considered—H_2; F_2 and the other halogens; gaseous Li_2 and the other gaseous alkali metals; gaseous Cu_2 and the other gaseous coinage metals—the distribution of the electron cloud of the bond pair has one common characteristic. If we rotate the diatomic molecule about its internuclear axis (Fig. 14-4(a)), the electron distribution of the bond pair always looks the same. We express this by saying that the electron distribution of the bond pair of the H—H molecule (and also, of course, of the F—F, Li—Li, Cu—Cu, and other similar molecules) is *cylindrically symmetrical* about the internuclear axis. A bond in which the

FIGURE 14-4 (a) Boundary surface of the electron cloud of the bond pair in the H_2 molecule. (b) Section of the boundary surface in a plane perpendicular to the H—H internuclear axis.

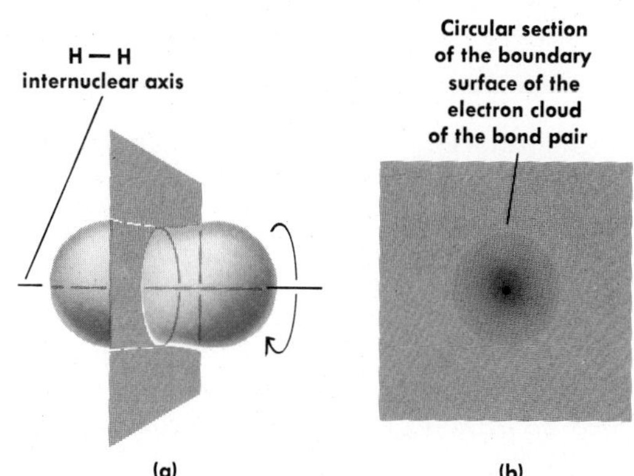

electron density distribution is concentrated mainly along the internuclear axis, and is cylindrically symmetrical about this axis, is called a σ (read: *sigma*) bond. If we were to cut through the electron cloud of a σ bond with a plane perpendicular to the internuclear axis, the boundary of the electron cloud would appear as a circle, having the trace of the internuclear axis as a point at the center, as shown in Fig. 14-4(b).

14-2 Covalent Bonds between Atoms of Different Elements

Atoms of different elements may also link themselves together by a covalent bond to form a molecule of a compound. Take, for example, the union of a gaseous hydrogen atom, H, with a gaseous fluorine atom, F, to form a gaseous (heteronuclear) molecule of hydrogen fluoride, HF, held together by a covalent bond:

$$\mathrm{H}\cdot + \cdot\overset{\cdot\cdot}{\underset{\cdot\cdot}{\mathrm{F}}}: \longrightarrow \mathrm{H}:\overset{\cdot\cdot}{\underset{\cdot\cdot}{\mathrm{F}}}:$$

If we wish to show explicitly which electrons take part in the formation of the covalent bond of HF, we may represent the reaction as:

H		F					H—F					
1s +	2p	2p	2p	2s	1s	⟶	1s	2p	2p	2p	2s	1s
↑	↓	↑↓	↑↓	↑↓	↑↓		↑	↓	↑↓	↑↓	↑↓	↑↓
							bond electron pair of HF molecule		non-bonding electrons of fluorine			

Thus we see that the covalent bond of the HF molecule consists of an electron cloud made up of one 1*s* electron ($1s^1$) of the hydrogen atom and one 2*p* electron ($2p^1$) of the fluorine atom. *It is this sharing of the electron pair by the hydrogen atom and the fluorine atom that constitutes the chemical change from an (isolated) gaseous H atom and an (isolated) gaseous F atom to a gaseous HF molecule.* Notice that as a result of this sharing of an electron pair, the hydrogen nucleus is now surrounded by two electrons (an electron cloud like that of helium atom) and the fluorine nucleus is now surrounded by eight electrons (an electron cloud like that of the neon atom). As the above schematic reaction indicates, the bond pair of the HF molecule may be considered to occupy a bonding orbital formed by the combination, along the internuclear H—F axis, of the 1*s* orbital of H and of the 2*p* orbital of F. This is shown pictorially in Fig. 14-5. The molecule of HF may also be thought to be formed by the union of a fluoride ion, F^-, with a proton, H^+; in this reaction the fluoride ion shares a lone electron pair with the proton (the nucleus of the H atom) to form a bond pair:

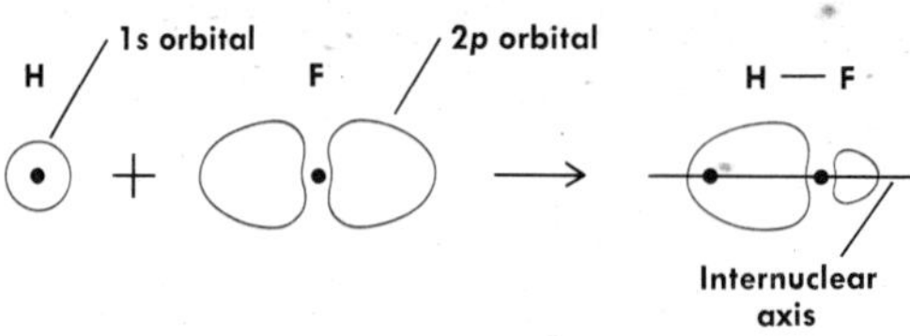

FIGURE 14-5 Bonding orbital of the HF molecule.

$$\mathrm{H}^+ + :\overset{\cdot\cdot}{\underset{\cdot\cdot}{\mathrm{F}}}:^- \longrightarrow \mathrm{H}:\overset{\cdot\cdot}{\underset{\cdot\cdot}{\mathrm{F}}}:$$

Again, the bond pair of the resulting HF molecule occupies a bonding orbital formed by the overlap of the originally empty 1*s* orbital of H^+ with a completely filled 2*p* orbital of F^-. The electron cloud of the bond pair of HF is cylindrically symmetrical about the H—F internuclear axis, just as the bond pairs of the H_2 and F_2 molecules are. Thus, the HF covalent bond is a σ (sigma) bond.

A similar type of bond is also present in the gaseous hydrogen chloride molecule, HCl, which may be thought to result from the union of a hydrogen atom, $\mathrm{H}\cdot$, with a chlorine atom, $\cdot\ddot{\underset{\cdot\cdot}{\mathrm{Cl}}}:$, or of a proton, H^+, with a chloride ion, $:\ddot{\underset{\cdot\cdot}{\mathrm{Cl}}}:^-$, as represented by the equations:

$$\mathrm{H}\cdot + \cdot\ddot{\underset{\cdot\cdot}{\mathrm{Cl}}}: \longrightarrow \mathrm{H}:\ddot{\underset{\cdot\cdot}{\mathrm{Cl}}}:$$

$$\mathrm{H}^+ + :\ddot{\underset{\cdot\cdot}{\mathrm{Cl}}}:^- \longrightarrow \mathrm{H}:\ddot{\underset{\cdot\cdot}{\mathrm{Cl}}}:$$

If we wish to show specifically the electrons involved in the bonding, the first of these reactions may be written as

$$\overset{\mathrm{H}}{1s^1} + \overset{\mathrm{Cl}}{3p^1\,3p^2\,3p^2\,3s^2,2p^6\,2s^2,1s^2} \longrightarrow \overset{\mathrm{H{-}Cl}}{\underbrace{1s^1\,3p^1}_{\text{bond electron pair of HCl}}\;\underbrace{3p^2\,3p^2\,3s^2,2p^6\,2s^2,1s^2}_{\text{non-bonding electrons of Cl}}}$$

Notice that as a result of this sharing of an electron pair, the hydrogen atom attains the stable electron configuration of helium, He($1s^2$), and the chlorine atom attains the stable electron configuration of argon, Ar($1s^2$, $2s^2\ 2p^6$, $3s^2\ 3p^6$). In a similar manner we can represent the bonding in the molecules of the other hydrogen halides, HBr and HI.

POLAR CHARACTER OF COVALENT BONDS BETWEEN UNLIKE ATOMS

In the HF molecule the bonding electron pair is not shared equally by the H and F atoms, because these unlike atoms exert unequal attractions on the electron cloud of the bond pair. The F atom exerts a stronger attraction for the bond pair than does the H atom, and consequently the bond pair is pulled closer to the F atom.

Actually, the smaller H atom is almost embedded in the electron cloud of the larger and electronegative fluorine atom. In general, for all molecules in which two unlike atoms share a bond pair, the electron cloud of the bond pair is pulled closer to that atom which attracts it more; and, as we have already mentioned (p. 195), the attracting power of an atom for a bonding electron pair is called the *electronegativity* of that atom. The greater the difference in electronegativity between two bonded atoms, the more the bonding electron cloud is pulled toward the atom with the greater electronegativity. Thus in a bond between unlike atoms, the more electronegative atom has a fraction of negative charge ($\delta-$) in excess of electrical neutrality, and the less electronegative atom, an equal fraction of positive charge ($\delta+$). Thus, an electric dipole is associated with such a bond, and the bond is said to have a *dipolar character.* Even though it may not be explicitly indicated, we must keep in mind that all covalent bonds between unlike atoms have a certain dipolar character. The greater the difference in electronegativity between the two bonded atoms, the greater the dipolar character of the bond. The most electronegative of all elements is F, followed (in order of decreasing electronegativity) by O, Cl $\cong$ N, Br, C $\cong$ S $\cong$ I, P $\cong$ H, B, Si. The least electronegative element is the alkali metal Cs; the other alkali metals and the alkaline-earth metals, all have very low electronegativity. Later in this chapter we shall discuss the concepts on which the above order of electronegativities is based, and we shall see how the electronegativity of an element may be expressed quantitatively.

COVALENT MOLECULES CONTAINING MORE THAN TWO ATOMS

So far, our examples of covalent bonds have involved diatomic, homo- or heteronuclear molecules formed by the sharing of only one pair of electrons between two identical or different atoms. Let us now proceed to the covalent polyatomic molecules that are formed when one atom enters into chemical combination with two or more other identical or different atoms by sharing a pair of electrons with each of them.

VALENCY STATE OF ATOMS AND IONS. In the examples of diatomic molecules we have just considered, the electron configuration of the ground state of the atom is the same as that of the *combining,* or *valency,* state. For these atoms, therefore, the electron dot formula, which shows the valency electrons, also represents the ground state outer electron configuration. However, for most of the atoms which form polyatomic covalent molecules, the valency state and the ground state have different electron configurations, so the electron-dot formula does *not* represent the ground state. For example, the ground state electron configuration of the beryllium atom, $_4Be$, is: $1s^2, 2s^2$ or $\underset{(\uparrow\downarrow)}{1s}, \underset{(\uparrow\downarrow)}{2s}$, but the electron configuration of the beryllium atom when it enters into chemical combinations with other atoms—for example with two chlorine atoms to form the gaseous beryllium chloride molecule, $BeCl_2$—is: $1s^2, 2s^1\ 2p^1$, or $\underset{(\uparrow\downarrow)}{1s}, \underset{(\uparrow\downarrow)}{2s}\ \underset{(\uparrow)}{2p}\,\underset{(\ )}{2p}\,\underset{(\ )}{2p}$. The electron-dot formula of beryllium is $\cdot Be \cdot$, where the two outer electrons of the ground state ($2s^2$) are written separately to indicate that the combining power of beryllium in some compounds (for example, in $BeCl_2$) is two. Similarly, the electron configuration of the boron atom, B, in the ground state is $1s^2, 2s^2\ 2p^1$ or $\underset{(\uparrow\downarrow)}{1s}, \underset{(\uparrow\downarrow)}{2s}\ \underset{(\uparrow)}{2p}\,\underset{(\ )}{2p}\,\underset{(\ )}{2p}$; but in the valency state the configuration is $1s^2, 2s^1\ 2p^2$ or $\underset{(\uparrow\downarrow)}{1s}, \underset{(\uparrow)}{2s}\ \underset{(\uparrow)}{2p}\,\underset{(\uparrow)}{2p}\,\underset{(\ )}{2p}$. Therefore, the electron-dot formula of boron is $\cdot \dot{B} \cdot$, with the three valency electrons written separately to indicate that boron has a combining power (valency) of three in many of its compounds—for example, in BF_3 and $B(CH_3)_3$. For the carbon atom, the ground state electron configuration is $1s^2, 2s^2\ 2p^2$ or $\underset{(\uparrow\downarrow)}{1s}, \underset{(\uparrow\downarrow)}{2s}\ \underset{(\uparrow)}{2p}\,\underset{(\uparrow)}{2p}\,\underset{(\ )}{2p}$; but in the electron-dot formula the four valency electrons, $2s^2\ 2p^2$, are written separately, $\cdot \dot{\underset{\cdot}{C}} \cdot$, because carbon has a valence of four, $\underset{(\uparrow\downarrow)}{1s}, \underset{(\uparrow)}{2s}\ \underset{(\uparrow)}{2p}\,\underset{(\uparrow)}{2p}\,\underset{(\uparrow)}{2p}$, in most of its compounds (for example, in CH_4 and CCl_4).

Even though in some cases (for example, hydrogen, the alkali metals, and the halogens) the ground and valency states are identical, in general the outer electron configuration of the valency state of an atom is different from the outer electron configuration of the ground state. The difference may be of two kinds: (a) In the valency state two or more electrons, which in the ground state are paired up in the same orbital, are unpaired and occupy, with parallel spins, the lowest available (empty) orbitals. To pass from the ground state to the valency state we must promote (excite) one or more electrons from a lower to a higher energy orbital. (b) In the valency state two or four electrons, which in the ground state occupy singly, with parallel spins, energetically equivalent atomic orbitals (Hund's Rule), become paired, thus leaving vacant one or two, respectively, of the previously occupied orbitals. In this case, energy is required to overcome the interelectron repulsion and pair up two electrons, with parallel spins, in a single orbital. Hence the valency state of an atom is one of its excited states, generally the lowest of the many possible excited states. Actually, the valency state is that excited state in which there is the necessary number of unpaired electrons in the proper low-energy orbitals required to form the covalent bonds in the resulting compound.

14-3 The Stereochemistry of Polyatomic Molecules

MOLECULES CONTAINING A CENTRAL ATOM WITH A SYMMETRICAL CORE AND HAVING BOND PAIRS ONLY

Let us begin by considering the relationships between electron-dot formula and stereochemistry for some polyatomic molecules containing Be, B, and C as the central atoms—for example, the gaseous molecules $BeCl_2$, BCl_3, and CH_4.

THE $BeCl_2$ MOLECULE. Experiments show that the gaseous $BeCl_2$ molecule is linear—that is, the nuclei of the (central) Be atom and of the two Cl atoms lie on a straight line. We may think of the $BeCl_2$ molecule as being formed by the union of a beryllium atom in its valency state, ·Be·, with two chlorine atoms, also in their valency state (which coincides with their ground state), ·C̤̈l:, as schematically represented by the equation:

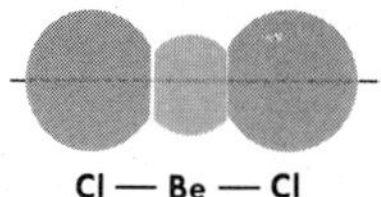

$$:\ddot{\underset{..}{Cl}}\cdot + .Be\cdot + .\ddot{\underset{..}{Cl}}: \longrightarrow :\ddot{\underset{..}{Cl}}:Be:\ddot{\underset{..}{Cl}}:$$

The electron-dot formula, $:\ddot{\underset{..}{Cl}}:Be:\ddot{\underset{..}{Cl}}:$, shows that the central Be atom has two *bond pairs,* each shared with one of the Cl atoms, and that no other electrons are present in the valency shell of the Be atom. Also, the beryllium atom has a helium-like filled inner shell of electrons, $1s^2$, which constitutes a *spherically symmetrical core.* (As we know, for a completely filled shell of electrons, distribution of the electron density about the nucleus is spherical, p. 243.) We may express all this briefly by saying that in the $BeCl_2$ molecule the central Be atom has a symmetrical core and two bond pairs (but no lone pairs). In the $BeCl_2$ molecule the central Be atom is linked to *two* atoms—the Cl atoms—and hence is said to have an *atom coordination number* or simply *coordination number* (C.N.) equal to 2.

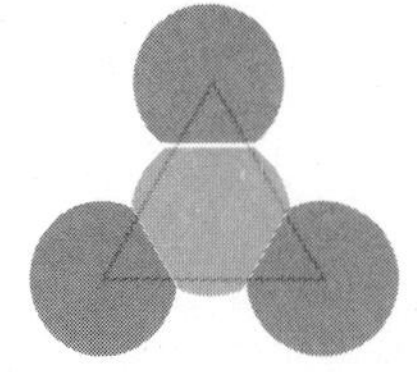

THE BF_3 MOLECULE. The gaseous BF_3 molecule is trigonal, as shown in the margin. The B atom and the three F atoms all lie in the same plane; the three F atoms are situated at the corners of an equilateral triangle, with the B atom at the center. The three F atoms are equidistant from the B atom and each of the three F—B—F angles is 120°. We can picture the BF_3 molecule as being formed by the union of a boron atom in its valency state, $.\dot{B}.$, with three fluorine atoms (each in its valency-ground state), $.\ddot{\underset{..}{F}}:$, as shown by the equation:

$$.\dot{B}. + 3\ .\ddot{\underset{..}{F}}: \longrightarrow \begin{matrix} & :\ddot{\underset{..}{F}}: & \\ & B & \\ :\ddot{\underset{..}{F}}: & & :\ddot{\underset{..}{F}}: \end{matrix}$$

As the electron-dot formula of BF_3 indicates, the central B atom has a symmetrical helium-like core ($1s^2$); three bond pairs, each shared with one of the three F atoms; and no lone pairs. In the BF_3 molecule the central B atom is linked to *three* atoms (the F atoms) and hence is said to have a coordination number equal to 3.

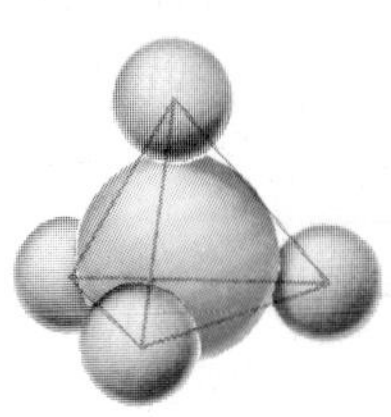

THE CH_4 MOLECULE. The methane molecule, CH_4, is tetrahedral, as shown in the margin. The four H atoms are arranged at the four vertices of a regular tetrahedron with the C atom at the center; all H atoms are equidistant from the C atom and all four H—C—H bond angles are equal, each measuring 109°28′.

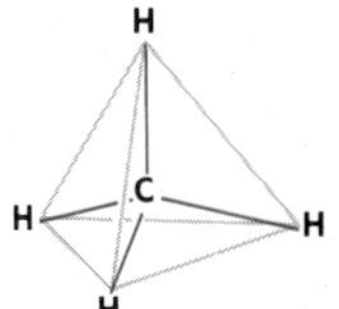

In the methane molecule, CH_4, the central carbon atom in its valency state has four unpaired electrons, $\cdot\dot{\underset{\cdot}{C}}\cdot$, and the hydrogen atom has, of course, one electron, (· H). The carbon atom shares each of its four electrons with a hydrogen atom, and, in turn, each of the four hydrogen atoms shares its electron with the carbon atom. The reaction of a carbon atom with four hydrogen atoms to form one molecule of methane may then be represented as follows:

$$\cdot\dot{\underset{\cdot}{C}}\cdot + 4\,\cdot H \longrightarrow H:\overset{H}{\underset{H}{\ddot{\underset{\cdot\cdot}{C}}}}:H$$

In CH_4, the central C atom has a symmetrical core, $1s^2$; four bond pairs, one to each of the four H atoms; and no lone pairs. Notice that in methane the carbon atom attains a neon-like electron configuration ($1s^2$, $2s^2$ $2p^6$) and the hydrogen atoms attain a helium-like electron configuration, $1s^2$. In the CH_4 molecule, the central C atom is linked to *four* atoms (the H atoms) and hence is said to have a coordination number equal to 4.

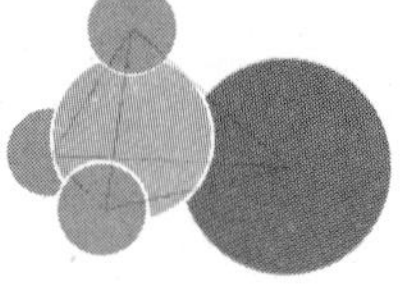

H
H C Cl
H

THE METHYL CHLORIDE MOLECULE, CH_3Cl. This molecule is again tetrahedral, with the carbon atom at the center, a hydrogen atom at each of three corners, and the chlorine atom at the fourth corner. Thus the stereochemistry of the CH_3Cl molecule is essentially the same as that of the CH_4 molecule, except that a Cl atom replaces a H atom at one corner of the tetrahedron. And because a Cl atom is much larger than a H atom, and the C—Cl distance (1.77 A) is much greater than the C—H distance (1.08 A), the tetrahedral symmetry of the central C atom is appreciably distorted. The formation of the CH_3Cl molecule from a carbon atom with four valency electrons; three hydrogen atoms, each with one electron; and a chlorine atom with one unpaired electron and three lone pairs in its outer shell, may be schematically represented as follows:

$$\cdot\dot{\underset{\cdot}{C}}\cdot + 3\,\cdot H + \cdot\ddot{\underset{\cdot\cdot}{Cl}}: \longrightarrow H:\overset{H}{\underset{H}{\ddot{\underset{\cdot\cdot}{C}}}}:\ddot{\underset{\cdot\cdot}{Cl}}:$$

Again we see that in the CH_3Cl molecule the central C atom has a symmetrical core ($1s^2$); four bond pairs, three in common with the three H atoms and one with the Cl atom; and no lone pairs.

MOLECULES WITH BOND PAIRS ASSOCIATED WITH A CENTRAL ATOM HAVING A SYMMETRICAL CORE

We could consider many other molecules and we would find, as for $BeCl_2$, BCl_3, CH_4, and CH_3Cl, that there is a general relationship between the stereochemistry of molecules and the electron configuration of their central atom. For molecules in which the central atom has completely filled inner electron shells (a symmetrical core) and only bond pairs in the valency shell, this relationship is expressed by the following three simple rules:

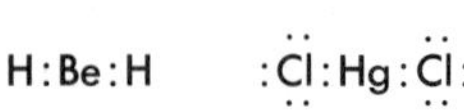

H:Be:H $:\ddot{\underset{\cdot\cdot}{Cl}}:Hg:\ddot{\underset{\cdot\cdot}{Cl}}:$

Rule 1. If the central atom has a symmetrical core, two bond pairs, and no lone pairs, the molecule is linear. Examples are, in addition to $BeCl_2$, the gaseous molecules BeH_2 and $HgCl_2$.

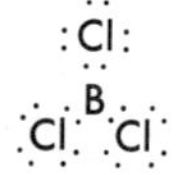

Rule 2. If the central atom has a symmetrical core, three bond pairs, and no lone pairs, the molecule is trigonal. In addition to BF_3, another example is gaseous BCl_3.

$$\begin{matrix} & :\ddot{F}: & \\ :\ddot{F}: & Si & :\ddot{F}: \\ & :\ddot{F}: & \end{matrix} \qquad \begin{matrix} & :\ddot{Cl}: & \\ :\ddot{Cl}: & Sn & :\ddot{Cl}: \\ & :\ddot{Cl}: & \end{matrix}$$

Rule 3. If the central atom has a symmetrical core, four bond pairs, and no lone pairs, the molecule is tetrahedral. There are many molecules of this type. Examples are SiF_4 and $SnCl_4$.

These rules are easily explained on the basis of simple electrostatics. If a spherically symmetrical positively charged core is surrounded by two, three, or four pairs of electrons, these negatively charged electron pairs are attracted by the positively charged core but repel one another. Simple geometry shows that these bond pairs are most widely separated and hence give rise to the least mutual repulsion when two bond pairs are arranged in a linear arrangement, three bond pairs in a planar trigonal arrangement, and four bond pairs in a tetrahedral arrangement.

MOLECULES IN WHICH THE CENTRAL ATOM HAS ONE OR TWO LONE PAIRS

Let us now go on to those molecules in which a central atom has a symmetrical inner electron core and one or two lone pairs of electrons in its valency shell, in addition to the bond pairs. Recall that a *lone pair of electrons,* or simply a *lone pair,* is a pair of electrons in the valence shell of an atom which is not shared with any other atom. As a first example, consider ammonia, NH_3. From experimental data we find that the NH_3 molecule has a regular trigonal pyramidal shape, as shown in the margin. The N atom is situated at the apex, and each of the three H atoms is at one of the corners of the base. The three H atoms are equidistant from the N atom, and the three H—N—H bond angles are identical, each measuring 107°.

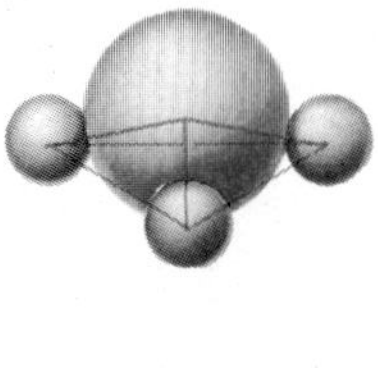

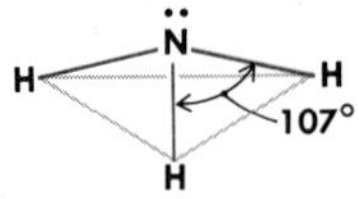

Envision the NH_3 molecule as resulting from the union of an isolated nitrogen atom in its valence state (which is the same as its ground state), $\cdot\ddot{N}\cdot$, with three isolated hydrogen atoms, H·,

$$\cdot\ddot{\underset{\cdot}{N}}\cdot + 3\,\cdot H \longrightarrow H:\ddot{\underset{\cdot\cdot}{N}}:H \quad (\text{with H below N})$$

Notice that each of the atoms in the NH_3 molecule attains a stable electron configuration similar to that of a noble gas. The electron-dot formula of NH_3 shows that the symmetrical central N atom has in its valence shell three bond pairs, each shared with one of the three H atoms, and also a lone pair of electrons. In other words, the core of the nitrogen atom of ammonia is surrounded by three bond pairs and one lone pair.

In the NH_3 molecule the central N atom is linked to three atoms (the H atoms) and hence its atom coordination number is 3. However, since the N atom is associated with a total of four outer electron pairs (three bond pairs and one lone pair), its *electron-pair coordination number (E.P.C.N.) is 4.*

The molecule of nitrogen trichloride, NCl_3, is structurally similar to the NH_3 molecule; it is pyramidal, with the N atom at the apex and each of the Cl atoms at one of the corners of the equilateral triangular base. The central nitrogen atom of the NCl_3 molecule again has a symmetrical core, three bond pairs, and one lone pair. The corresponding covalent compounds of phosphorus—phosphine, PH_3; and phosphorus trichloride, PCl_3—have similar electron configurations and trigonal pyramidal molecules:

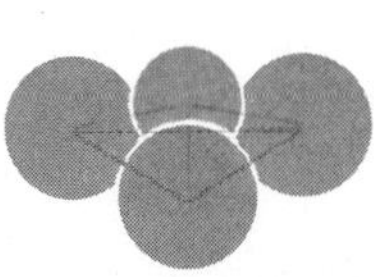

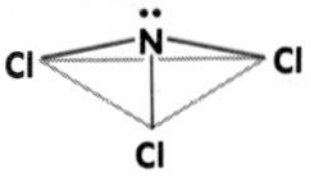

$$H:\ddot{\underset{\cdot\cdot}{P}}:H \quad (\text{with H below P})$$

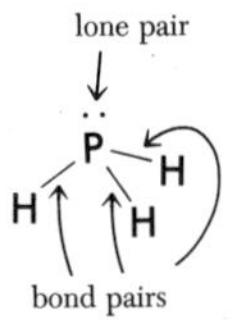

$$:\ddot{Cl}:\ddot{\underset{\cdot\cdot}{P}}:\ddot{Cl}: \quad (\text{with }:\ddot{Cl}:\text{ below P})$$

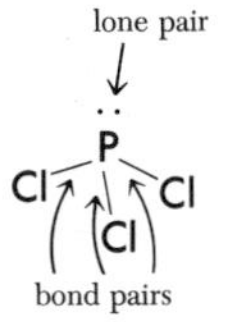

In the PH_3 and PCl_3 molecules, as in NH_3 and NCl_3, the coordination number of the central P is 3, but the electron-pair coordination number is 4.

We can explain the stereochemistry of the NH_3 molecule and of the other trigonal pyramidal molecules we have just considered on the basis of simple electrostatics, just as we did for the linear, trigonal planar, and tetrahedral molecules. First, if the spherically symmetrical core of the central atom is surrounded by a total of four electron pairs—three bond pairs and one lone pair—we would expect these four electron pairs to arrange themselves tetrahedrally about the symmetrical core in order to minimize their mutual electrostatic repulsion. And of course if the three bond pairs and the lone pair are arranged tetrahedrally about the central atom, the molecule—NH_3, for example—will have a trigonal pyramidal stereochemistry, as schematically illustrated in the margin. But why is the H—N—H bond angle of ammonia 107°0′, and not 109°28′, as is the regular tetrahedral angle? To explain this fact, we must consider the difference between the mutual repulsion of two bond pairs and the repulsion of a lone pair and a bond pair. Each of the three bond pairs of NH_3 is shared by the central N atom and an H atom, and consequently the electron cloud of each bond pair is spread out between the bonded N and H atoms. On the other hand, the lone pair belongs only to the N atom and hence its electron cloud is more concentrated in the vicinity of the N atom. We would therefore expect the repulsion between the lone pair and a bond pair to be greater than that between two bond pairs. Consequently, we would expect the lone pair in NH_3 to push the three bond pairs somewhat closer together than does a bond pair in CH_4.

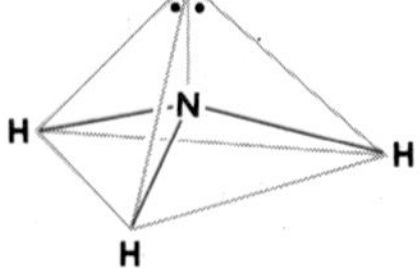

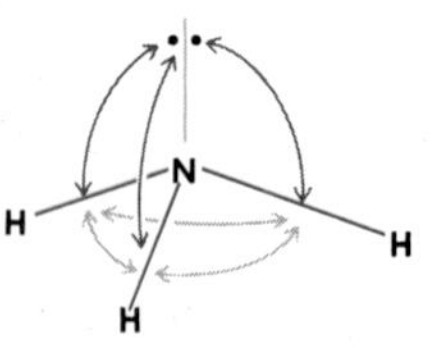

Lone pair — bond pair, stronger repulsion, larger angle

Bond pair — bond pair, weaker repulsion, smaller bond angle

Similar considerations explain the stereochemistry of H_2O, which—as we know—is bent, with the central O atom bound to each of the two H atoms. The two H atoms are equivalent and equidistant from the O atom, and the H—O—H bond angle is 104°30′. Notice that the three atomic nuclei of the water molecule all lie in one plane (three points define a plane), but the electron cloud projects out from this plane in all directions, so that the molecule actually has a distorted tetrahedral shape. The electron-dot formula, $\mathrm{H{:}\ddot{O}{:}}$ (with H below O), shows two bond pairs and two lone pairs around the central O atom, which has a symmetrical core ($1s^2$). Here we would expect the two lone pairs to repel each other more strongly than do a lone pair and a bond pair, and of course even more strongly than two bond pairs. Consequently, we would expect the two lone pairs of H_2O to force the two (O—H) bond pairs closer together than the one lone pair of NH_3 forces together the three (N—H) bond pairs. And in fact this is so, the H—O—H bond angle being only 104°30′ as compared with the H—N—H bond angle of 107°0′ and with the H—C—H bond angle of 109°28′. The hydrogen sulfide molecule, H_2S, is structurally similar to the water molecule, H_2O. The Group VI sulfur atom, S, has six electrons in its outermost shell and the hydrogen atom, H, has one electron. The formation of the H_2S molecule from its atoms may be represented schematically as:

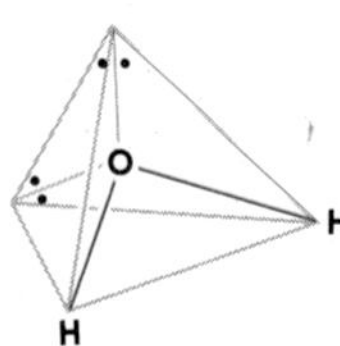

$$:\ddot{\underset{\cdot}{S}}\cdot + 2\,\cdot H \longrightarrow \underset{\textstyle H}{H{:}\ddot{\underset{\cdot\cdot}{S}}{:}}$$

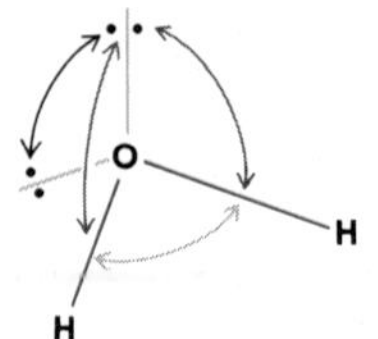

Lone pair — lone pair repulsion (strongest)

Lone pair — bond pair repulsion (intermediate)

Bond pair — bond pair repulsion (weakest)

The H_2S molecule, like the H_2O molecule, is bent, but the H—S—H angle is smaller (92°) than the H—O—H angle (104°30′). This is because the S atom is less electronegative and larger than the O atom. Both these factors tend to decrease the H—S—H angle relative to the H—O—H angle. In fact, the smaller and more electronegative the central atom, the closer to the central atom are the electron pairs shared in covalent bonds. Consequently, the repulsion between the bond electron pairs increases more than does the repulsion of the lone pairs, and the H—S—H bond angle decreases proportionally.

On the basis of the considerations developed in this section we can state two additional rules concerning the shapes of molecules:

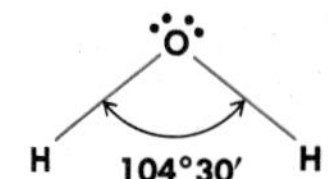

Rule 4. If the central atom has a symmetrical core, three bond pairs, and one lone pair, the molecule or ion is trigonal pyramidal. Examples are NH_3, PF_3, $AsCl_3$, $SO_3^{=}$, and H_3O^+.

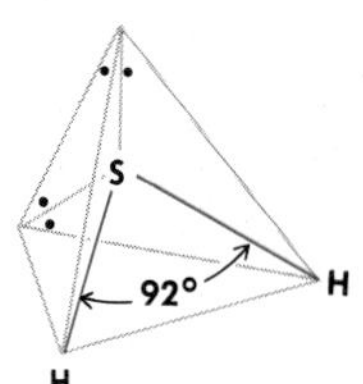

Rule 5. If the central atom has a symmetrical core, two bond pairs, and two lone pairs, the molecule or ion is bent. Examples are H_2O, H_2S, H_2Se, and NH_2^-.

For both cases we may roughly predict the relative magnitude of bond angles on the basis that, *in general, the repulsion between electron pairs decreases in the order: lone pair–lone pair > lone pair–bond pair > bond pair–bond pair.*

MOLECULES IN WHICH THE CENTRAL ATOM HAS MORE THAN FOUR ELECTRON PAIRS IN ITS VALENCE SHELL

Up to now, we have considered molecules in which a central atom has a filled symmetrical core and a total of four electron pairs (bond pairs or lone pairs) that can be accommodated into the outer $(n)s$ and $(n)p$ orbitals of the central atom. Many molecules also exist in which a central atom with a symmetrical core has more than four (five or six) electron pairs in its valence shell, so that some of the outer $(n)d$ orbitals of the central atom also become occupied. Let us now consider some examples.

MOLECULES IN WHICH THE CENTRAL ATOM HAS A SYMMETRICAL CORE AND FIVE ELECTRON PAIRS. The gaseous phosphorus pentachloride molecule, PCl_5: Imagine the gaseous PCl_5 molecule as resulting from the union of a (gaseous) phosphorus atom, in its valency state having five unpaired electrons with five (gaseous) Cl atoms, each with one unpaired electron:

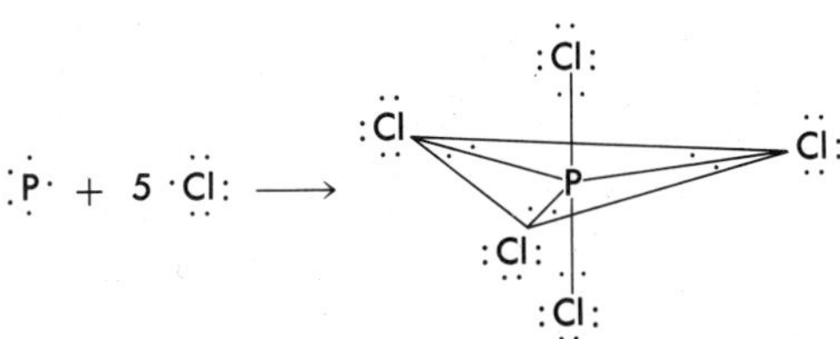

As the electron-dot formula of PCl_5 shows, the central P atom has *five* electron pairs—a total of 10 electrons—in its outer shell. In the gaseous PCl_5 molecule the phosphorus atom, P, and three of the chlorine atoms (equatorial Cl atoms) lie in a plane, with the P atom at the center and the Cl atoms at the corners of an equilateral triangle, as shown in the margin. The other two Cl atoms (axial Cl atoms) are at opposite sides of the equatorial plane, equidistant from the P atom but farther from it than are the three equatorial Cl atoms. Thus in the gaseous PCl_5 molecule the five Cl atoms are not all equivalent, because their distances from the central P atom, and also from their adjacent Cl atoms, are not all equal. This fact, again, may be explained on the basis of the attraction of the (positive) symmetrical core of the central P atom for the five electron bond pairs, P:Cl, and of the mutual repulsion among the five bond pairs themselves. Because of the attraction of the positively charged symmetrical core of the P atom, the five P—Cl bond pairs would tend to arrange themselves as close as possible to the P atom and equidistant from it. At the same time, because of their mutual repulsion, the five P—Cl bond pairs would tend to arrange themselves so as to be equidistant and as far apart from one another as possible. Now, geometric considerations show that the only one way in which five points (the chlorine atoms) can be grouped about a center

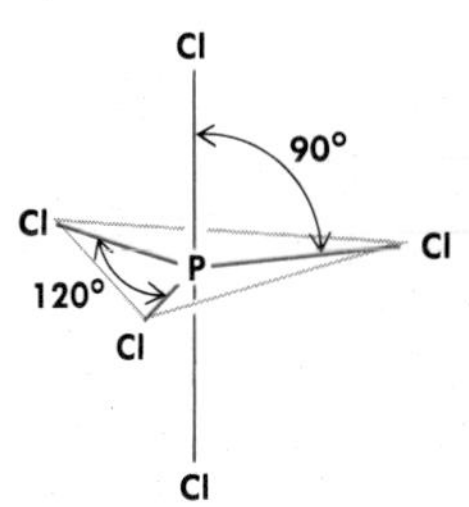

(the positive core of the central atom) so that they are equidistant from the center as well as from one another is by adopting a regular pentagonal arrangement. Such a regular pentagonal arrangement, however, corresponds to a relatively strong repulsion of five electron pairs for one another (the bond angle being only $360°/5 = 72°$), and hence is energetically unfavorable. Thus a compromise is reached, and the trigonal bipyramidal arrangement observed in PCl_5 molecules is the most favorable. In fact, all molecules in which a central element with a symmetrical core is surrounded by five bond pairs have a trigonal bipyramidal structure. Besides PCl_5, other molecules with this structure are the gaseous halides of the Group V elements, such as $PF_{5(g)}$ and $SbCl_{5(g)}$.

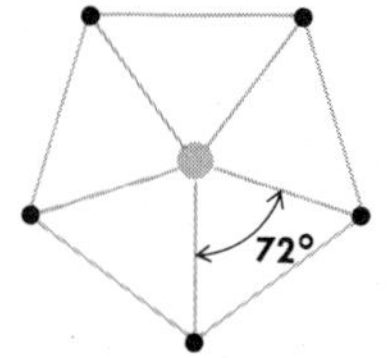

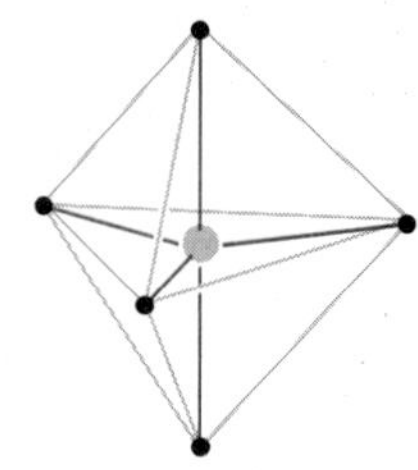

THE IODINE TRICHLORIDE MOLECULE, ICl_3. Assume that the molecule of iodine trichloride, ICl_3, results from the union of an iodine atom, in its valency state, with three chlorine atoms, each in its valency state (which is also the ground state). In this case the iodine atom has three unpaired electrons and two lone pairs, and each chlorine atom has one unpaired electron and three lone pairs:

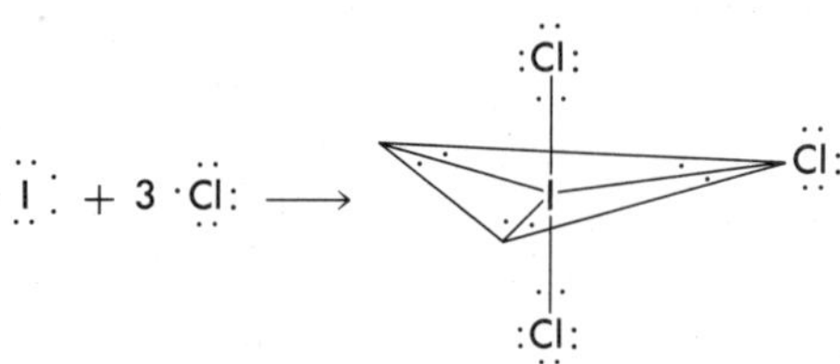

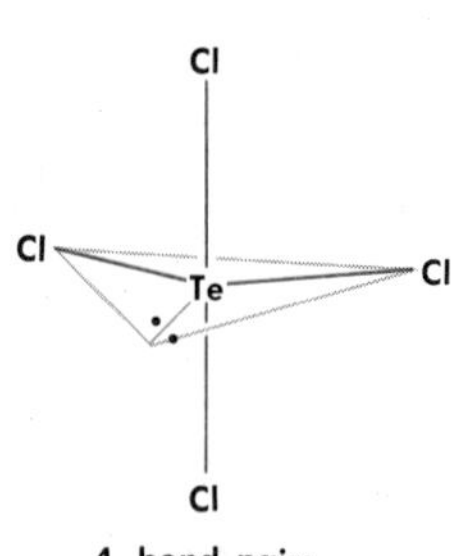

4 bond pairs
1 lone pair

Notice that each of the three chlorine atoms of ICl_3 has an octet of electrons, but the central iodine atom is surrounded by ten electrons. Experiments show that the ICl_3 molecule is T-shaped, as illustrated in the margin; such a stereochemistry may be thought to result from a trigonal bipyramidal arrangement of five electron pairs, similar to that of PCl_5, but with two lone pairs in place of two bond pairs in the equatorial plane. In fact, we may think of the I atom as being at the center of a triangle, with one Cl atom occupying a corner of the triangle, and the other two Cl atoms above and below the plane of this triangle. Also associated with the central I atom are the two lone pairs occupying the other two corners of the triangle in the equatorial plane. The T-shaped arrangement of the atoms in the ICl_3 molecule is evidence of the lone pair effect; in fact, if it were not for the presence of the two lone pairs in the central I atom, the ICl_3 molecule would be expected to have a regular trigonal planar stereochemistry.

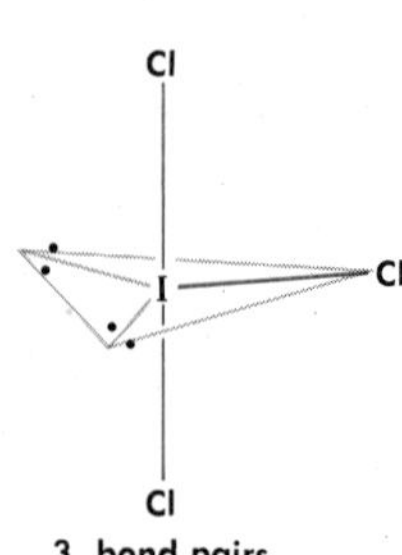

3 bond pairs
2 lone pairs

In general, if we wish to predict the stereochemistry of a molecule in which the central atom has a symmetrical core and is surrounded by five electron pairs (one or more being lone pairs), we must first keep in mind that the five electron pairs will assume a trigonal bipyramidal arrangement. Then, we consider that in this trigonal bipyramidal arrangement each of the three equatorial electron pairs has two neighbors at 120°, and two other neighbors at 90°, while each of the two axial electron pairs have three closer neighbors at 90°, and one at 180°. Repulsion between neighboring electron pairs is, of course, weaker at 120° angles than at 90° angles. On these bases it can be calculated that the minimum overall electrostatic repulsion exists when one, two, or three lone pairs occupy the *equatorial* positions of the trigonal bipyramid. The diagrams in the margin illustrate these conclusions for the molecules of: (a) tellurium tetrachloride, $TeCl_4$, (four bond pairs, one lone pair); (b) iodine trichloride, ICl_3 (three bond pairs, two lone pairs); and (c) the triodide ion, I_3^-, (two bond pairs, three lone pairs).

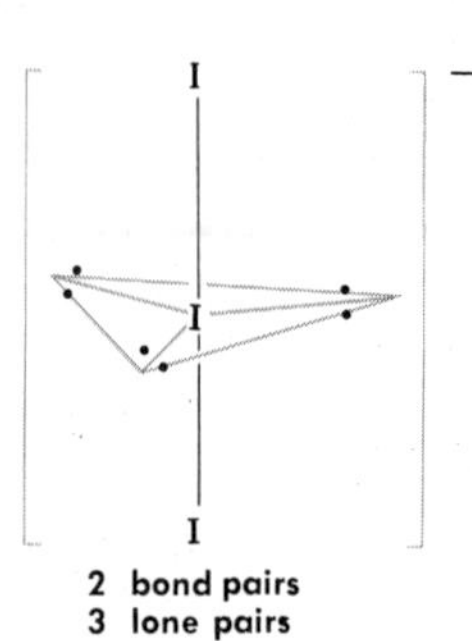

2 bond pairs
3 lone pairs

MOLECULES WITH A CENTRAL ATOM HAVING A SYMMETRICAL CORE AND SIX ELECTRON PAIRS

THE SULFUR HEXAFLUORIDE MOLECULE, SF_6. Imagine that the gaseous SF_6 molecule is formed by the combination of a sulfur atom in its valency state with six unpaired valence electrons, :S:, and of six fluorine atoms, each having one unpaired electron and three lone pairs, ·F:

:S: + 6 ·F: ⟶ (SF₆ electron-dot formula: S bonded to six :F: atoms)

As the electron-dot formula shows, in the SF_6 molecule there are six bond pairs around the central S atom, (whereas each F atom has its usual four outer electron pairs). Experiments reveal that the SF_6 molecule is octahedral, with the S atom at the center and a F atom at each of the six vertices of a regular octahedron. The six F atoms are all equivalent, all being equidistant from the central S atom and from the adjacent F atoms. Also, each F—S—F bond angle is 90°.

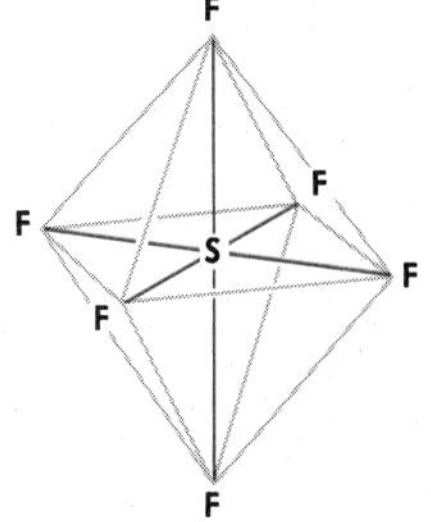

In the sulfur hexafluoride molecule, SF_6, the central S atom, which has a symmetrical core (an argon-like configuration, $1s^2$, $2s^2\ 2p^6$, $3s^2\ 3p^6$) is surrounded by six bond pairs. On the basis of the electrostatic repulsions among these six bond pairs we indeed expect the S atom to be at the center of a regular octahedron with the F atoms at the corners, because in such an arrangement the six bond pairs are as far apart from one another as possible. Notice that this octahedral structure is the most symmetrical three-dimensional arrangement in which six atoms (or groups) can be arranged about a central atom, and this octahedral arrangement also creates the maximum separation between the six bond pairs.

Most molecules and ions in which a central atom has a symmetrical core and is surrounded only by six bond pairs exhibit this octahedral stereochemistry, regardless of the nature of the central atom or of the kinds of atoms, or group of atoms, bonded to it. Thus the neutral molecule SF_6, the positive ion $[Zn(H_2O)_6]^{++}$, and the negative ion $[SiF_6]^{=}$ are all octahedral. It should be emphasized at this point, however, that this octahedral stereochemistry is *regular* only when the six atoms or groups bonded to the central atom are all identical. If the six atoms or groups surrounding the central atom are not all identical, the stereochemistry is still essentially octahedral, but is distorted to a smaller or larger extent. An example is the $[PF_5(OH)]^-$ ion, shown in the margin.

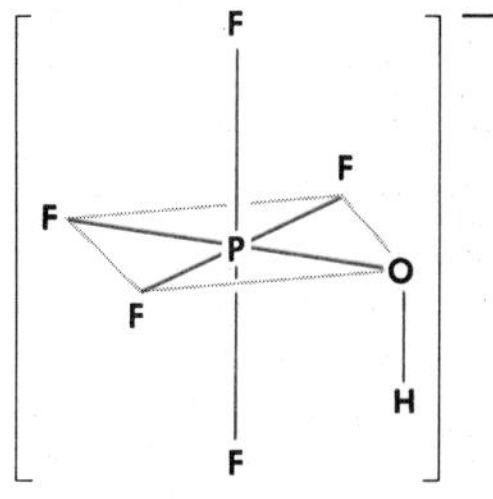

MOLECULES IN WHICH THE CENTRAL ATOM HAS SIX ELECTRON PAIRS, ONE OR MORE OF WHICH ARE LONE PAIRS

THE IODINE PENTACHLORIDE MOLECULE, ICl_5. Assume that the molecule of iodine pentachloride, ICl_5, results from the combination of an iodine atom in a valency state having five unpaired electrons and one lone pair, :I:, with five chlorine atoms, each having one unpaired electron and three lone pairs:

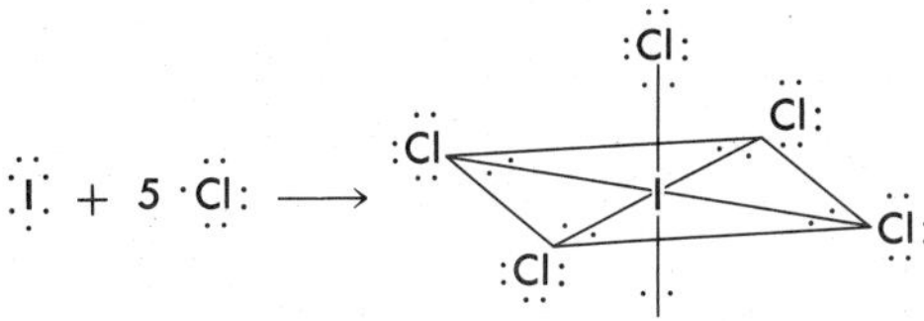

The central I atom of ICl_5 has a symmetrical core and a total of six electron pairs—five bond pairs, and one lone pair in its valence shell. As we know, these six electron pairs tend to arrange themselves octahedrally around the core of the central atom.

Now, in a regular octahedral arrangement, all six positions are equivalent. Therefore, if in a molecule, AX_6, a lone pair is substituted for a bond pair, the resulting molecule, AX_5, is expected to have a square pyramidal shape. In fact, experiments indicate that the ICl_5 molecule has a square pyramidal stereochemistry. The I atom is at the center of a square, at each corner of which there is a Cl atom. Above and below the plane of this square are the fifth Cl atom and the lone pair, respectively. In ICl_5, all five Cl atoms are equidistant from the central I atom, but their geometric positions are not equivalent, because four of the Cl atoms are opposite to one another, but the fifth Cl atom is opposite to the lone pair. Another example of a square pyramidal molecule is bromine pentafluoride, BrF_5.

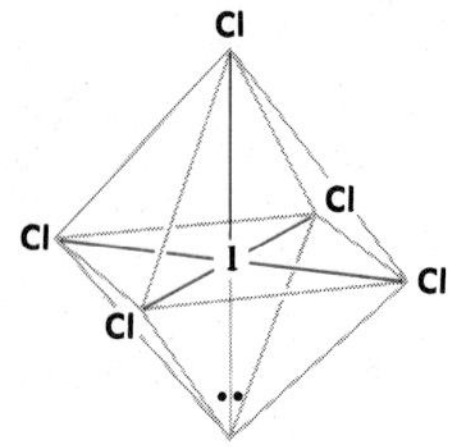

Let us now imagine that in the octahedral molecule AX_6 we substitute two lone pairs for two bond pairs. In the resulting AX_4 molecule, these two lone pairs will tend to occupy positions opposite to one another, because the repulsion between a lone pair and a bond pair in adjacent positions is smaller than that between two adjacent lone pairs. For brevity, opposite positions in an octahedral arrangement are called *trans* positions (from the Latin *trans* = across), and adjacent positions are called *cis* positions (from the Latin *cis* = on the same side). Thus an AX_4 molecule in which the central atom has a symmetrical core, four bond pairs, and two lone pairs will have a square planar structure, with the two lone pairs *trans* to one another, as shown in the margin. Examples are the xenon tetrafluoride molecule, XeF_4, and the tetrachloroidide ion, ICl_4^-.

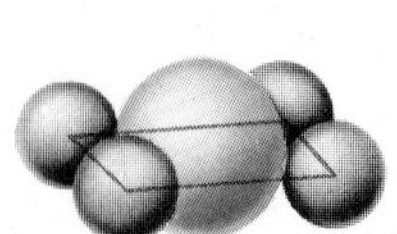

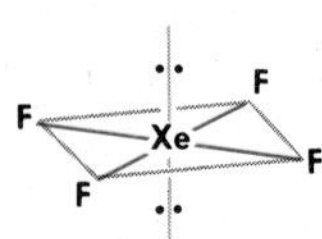

We may conclude this section by emphasizing that the concept of the electrostatic repulsion between electron pairs, repulsion which increases in the order bond pair–bond pair < bond pair–lone pair < lone pair–lone pair, is very helpful in rationalizing the stereochemistry of those molecules in which the central atom has a symmetrical core (a filled electron shell underlying the valence electrons). Also, this concept may guide us in predicting the shape of any molecule in which the central atom has a symmetrical core.

14-4 The Coordinate Covalent Bond

We know that a covalent bond consists of a pair of electrons shared by two atoms. In all our examples so far, one of the electrons in the pair was supplied by one atom, and the other electron was supplied by the other atom. In some covalent bonds, however, one of the two atoms supplies *both* electrons. A covalent bond formed in this way is called a *coordinate covalent bond,* or simply a *coordinate bond.* The interaction between NH_3 and BF_3 to form NH_3BF_3 is a good illustration of the coordinate covalent bond.

AMMONIA-BORON TRIFLUORIDE, NH_3BF_3

It is an experimental fact that when gaseous boron trifluoride, BF_3, and gaseous ammonia, NH_3, are brought together, they react chemically to form the solid compound H_3NBF_3. Thus, an electronic interaction between these two molecules has taken place. What happens is that the nitrogen atom of ammonia shares its lone electron pair with the boron atom of BF_3, so that both the N atom and the B atom attain a total of eight electrons in the resulting compound, H_3NBF_3. Using electron-dot formulas, we can represent the reaction as follows:

```
   H          :F:               H :F:
H:N:  +        B       ⟶     H:N:B:F:
   H       :F:   :F:            H :F:
```

And what about the stereochemistry of the H_3NBF_3 molecule? Experiments show that this molecule may be represented as two tetrahedra joined together in the manner shown in the margin. In one of the two tetrahedra the N atom is at the center, with a H atom at each of three corners and the B atom at the fourth corner. In turn, the B atom is at the center of the other tetrahedron, with a F atom at each of three corners and the N atom at the fourth corner. As we said, the chemical change in the reaction between NH_3 and BF_3 to form H_3NBF_3 consists of the sharing of the original lone pair of the nitrogen atom with the boron atom. This electron pair, shared between the N and B atoms but originally belonging only to the N atom, constitutes a *coordinate covalent bond* between the N and B atoms. Notice that a coordinate covalent bond differs from an ordinary covalent bond only in that *both electrons* are contributed by *one atom*, rather than one electron by each of two atoms, as in an ordinary covalent bond.

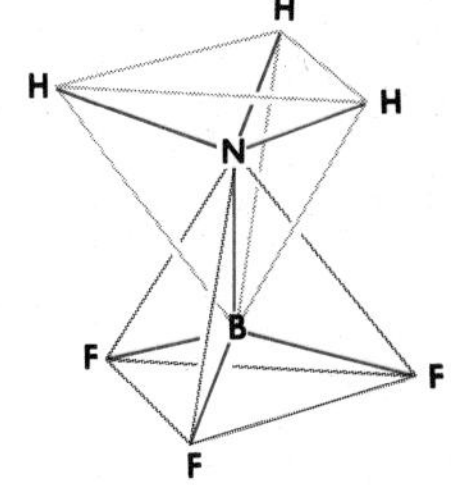

DONOR AND ACCEPTOR ATOMS

In the reaction of NH_3 with BF_3, the nitrogen atom supplies both electrons. An atom that supplies or, as we often say, "donates" an electron pair to another atom forming a coordinate covalent bond is called a *donor* atom. The atom that accepts the electron pair is called an *acceptor* atom. Thus in the reaction considered above, the N atom is the donor atom, and the B atom is the acceptor atom. In general, *any atom which has a lone pair of electrons in its valence shell can act as a donor to a suitable acceptor.* Conversely, *any atom which does not have the maximum possible number of electron pairs in its valence shell can act as an acceptor from a suitable donor.*

The most common donors are the halogen atoms, generally as the (monoatomic) halide ion, $:\ddot{\underset{..}{X}}:^-$; the oxygen atom, both as the monoatomic oxide ion, $:\ddot{\underset{..}{O}}:^=$, and in covalent ions and compounds such as the hydroxide ion, $:\ddot{\underset{..}{O}}:H^-$, and the water molecule, $:\dot{\underset{.}{O}}H_2$; the nitrogen atom of ammonia, $:NH_3$; and the phosphorus and arsenic atoms in compounds such as phosphorus trifluoride, $:PF_3$, and arsenic trichloride, $:AsCl_3$.

The most common acceptors are the metal ions, both those with a symmetrical core, such as $Ag^+([Ar]\ 4s^2\ 4p^6\ 4d^{10})$, and those which do not have a symmetrically filled inner electron shell, such as $Co^{+3}([Ne],\ 3s^2\ 3p^6\ 3d^6)$. The Group IIIB elements, boron, B; aluminum, Al; and gallium, Ga, can also act as electron-pair acceptors when they are present in molecules (for example, the trihalides, BCl_3, AlF_3, $GaCl_3$) in which they do not attain their maximum possible electron-pair coordination number. A very special electron-pair acceptor is H^+, the hydrogen ion. As we know, the H^+ ion, which is the bare nucleus of the hydrogen atom (the proton) is unique among all positive ions in that it has no electron cloud and hence is extremely small (about 10^{-5} A diameter). Consequently, the tendency of the proton to accept an electron pair is extremely strong; in fact, the bare proton does not exist as such except in very special cases.

To summarize: two conditions are necessary for the formation of a coordinate covalent bond. (1) One atom, molecule, or ion must have an electron pair available for donation. (2) One atom, molecule, or ion must be capable of accepting this electron pair. Compounds containing coordinate covalent bonds are extremely common. They are generally called *coordination compounds,* or *complex compounds,* or simply, *complexes,* and their formulas often are enclosed in square brackets.

We know that an "ordinary" covalent bond is represented schematically either as a (shared) electron pair or as a solid line joining the symbols of the bonded atoms. A covalent coordinate bond is sometimes represented as a short arrow pointing from the donor to the acceptor atom. Thus, the formula of the coordination compound, $[H_3NBF_3]$ may be written as:

```
H          F
  \       /
H—N → B—F
  /       \
H          F
```

Often, as we shall see later, there is no clear-cut distinction between coordination compounds containing one or more coordinate bonds and "simple" compounds containing "ordinary" covalent bonds. In these cases, we usually represent all covalent bonds simply as solid lines joining the bonded atoms.

COVALENT BONDS IN POLYATOMIC IONS

As we have seen, monoatomic positive and negative ions are formed when a neutral atom gives up or takes on one or more electrons. Polyatomic (positive or negative) ions may be considered to result from the union of one or more neutral atoms (or a molecule) with one or more monoatomic ions of appropriate electrical charge. Generally, in polyatomic ions each of the original atoms or monoatomic ions achieves the electron configuration of a noble gas through the formation of covalent bonds, often of the coordinate kind. As an illustration, let us consider the electronic structure of some polyatomic (or complex) ions.

THE DISULFIDE ION, $[S_2]^=$. We have seen that an ion which possesses a lone pair of electrons may share this lone pair with a suitable acceptor atom forming a complex ion. For example, the (mono)sulfide ion, $:\ddot{\underset{..}{S}}:^=$, formed when a sulfur atom takes on two electrons, can react with a neutral sulfur atom in its valence state, $\ddot{\underset{..}{S}}:$, to give the disulfide ion:

$$:\ddot{\underset{..}{S}}:^= + \ddot{S}: \longrightarrow \left[:\ddot{\underset{..}{S}}:\ddot{\underset{..}{S}}:\right]^=$$

The two sulfur atoms in the disulfide ion, $[S_2]^=$, are joined by a coordinate covalent bond, resulting from the donation of a lone pair by the (mono)sulfide ion, $S^=$, to the neutral sulfur atom, S. Notice that once the disulfide ion is formed, it is no longer possible to distinguish from which of the two bonded S atoms the S—S bond pair originally came. In other words, the coordinate covalent bond, once formed, is indistinguishable from an "ordinary" covalent bond, and hence it is not possible to consider one of the S atoms as the donor and the other as the acceptor.

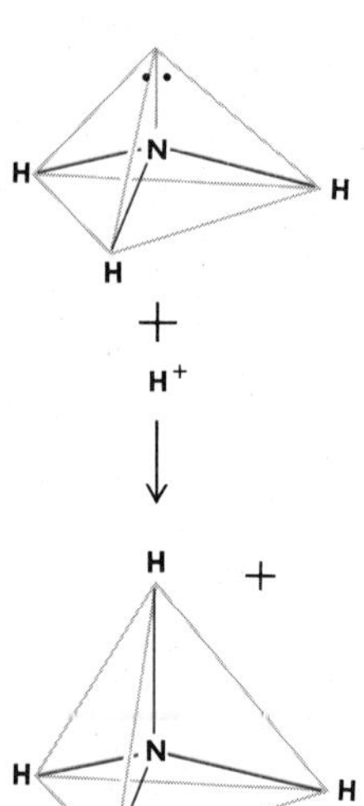

THE AMMONIUM ION, $[NH_4]^+$. A molecule of ammonia, NH_3, can react with a hydrogen ion, H^+, to form an ammonium ion, $[NH_4]^+$, as shown by the equation:

$$H:\ddot{\underset{H}{N}}:H + H^+ \longrightarrow \left[H:\overset{H}{\underset{H}{\ddot{\underset{..}{N}}}}:H\right]^+$$

The chemical change in this reaction consists of the sharing of the original lone pair of the nitrogen atom of $:NH_3$ with the hydrogen ion, H^+. The product of this chemical change is the ammonium ion, NH_4^+. The diagram in the margin shows that when the pyramidal NH_3 molecule shares its lone electron pair with a proton, H^+, the resulting NH_4^+ ion is tetrahedral.

THE TETRAFLUOROBORATE ION, $[BF_4]^-$. The fluoride ion, $:\ddot{\underset{..}{F}}:^-$, may act as a donor by sharing one of its lone pairs of electrons with the central boron atom of the boron trifluoride molecule, BF_3, to form the complex ion, $[BF_4]^-$:

```
   ..                        [     ..     ]-
  :F:                        [    :F:     ]
   ..         ..             [  .. .. ..  ]
   B     +   :F:-   ——→      [ :F:B:F:    ]
 ..   ..      ..             [  .. .. ..  ]
:F.  .F:                     [    :F:     ]
 ..   ..                     [     ..     ]
```

The diagram in the margin shows that when the planar trigonal BF_3 molecule forms a coordinate covalent bond with a fluoride ion, F^-, the resulting BF_4^- ion is tetrahedral.

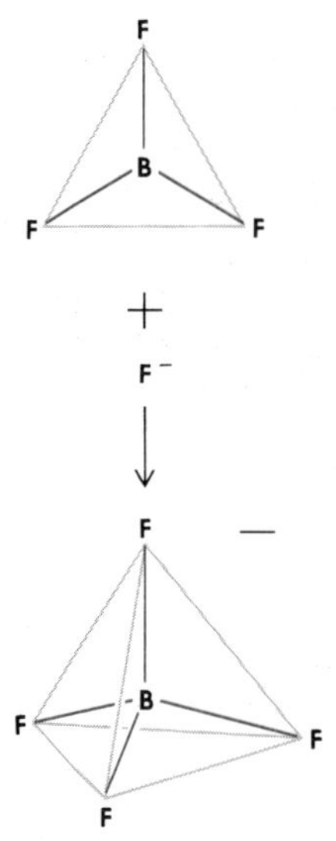

In the $[S_2]^=$, $[NH_4]^+$, and $[BF_4]^-$ complex ions just discussed, the ionic charge comes originally from the monoatomic ion from which the complex is formed. After the complex ion has been formed, however, the charge belongs to the complex ion as a whole and can no longer be localized on the original ion. In the $[S_2]^=$ ion, for example, each sulfur atom is equivalent and shares equally in the double negative charge. And in the $[NH_4]^+$ ion the single positive charge does not belong to any one hydrogen atom; rather, it is distributed equally among all four equivalent hydrogen atoms. Similarly, in the $[BF_4]^-$ ion, the single negative charge is distributed equally among the four equivalent fluorine atoms. Notice also that in the $[NH_4]^+$ ion the four N—H covalent bonds are all equivalent and indistinguishable, and similarly in the $[BF_4]^-$ ion the four B—F bonds are equivalent and indistinguishable. Once these complex ions are formed, therefore, we can no longer distinguish which of the (identical) bond pairs came originally from the donor atom—in other words, we can no longer distinguish the "coordinate" covalent bond from the "ordinary" covalent bonds. Hence in the formulas of these complex ions all bonds are shown simply as solid lines (ordinary covalent bonds).

THE SULFATE ION, $[SO_4]^=$. Consider the sulfate ion as resulting from the union of one sulfur atom, four oxygen atoms and two additional electrons which provide the dinegative charge of the ion. Alternatively, we may consider the sulfate ion to be the aggregate of one sulfur atom, three oxygen atoms, and one oxide ion, $O^=$. We may also think of the sulfate ion as formed by the reaction of an oxide ion, $O^=$ (the donor), with a sulfur trioxide molecule, SO_3 (the acceptor). Regardless of how we may think the sulfate ion to be formed, its stereochemistry and electron distribution are the same. The central sulfur atom of $SO_4^=$ is tetrahedrally surrounded by four bond pairs, each of the four oxygen atoms having one bond pair and three lone pairs. The double negative charge results from the fact that one S atom and four O atoms together have a total of $6 \times 5 = 30$ electrons in their valence shells, whereas the $SO_4^=$ ion has a total of 32 electrons (4 bond pairs and $4 \times 3 = 12$ lone pairs).

14-5 Molecules with Multiple Bonding

In the molecules considered so far, the atoms are linked to one another by "single covalent bonds," each bond consisting of only one electron pair concentrated along the line connecting the nuclei of the two bonded atoms. On the other hand, for many other molecules the physical and chemical properties indicate that the covalent link between two bonded atoms consists of the sharing of two, or three, electron pairs, and is therefore a "multiple" (double or triple) bond. Just as a single covalent bond is represented by a single line, so double and triple covalent bonds are represented, respectively, by double lines and triple lines—for example, H—Cl, O=C=O, and N≡N.

THE COVALENT DOUBLE BOND. A *covalent double bond,* or simply a *double bond,* is formed by the sharing of two pairs of electrons between two atoms. Double bonds exist, for example, in the molecules of carbon dioxide, CO_2, and sulfur monoxide, SO.

In carbon dioxide, CO_2, the Group IV carbon atom and the Group VI oxygen atom have four and six electrons, respectively, in their valence shells. Here is the schematic representation of the union of one C atom (in its combining state having four unpaired electrons) with two O atoms, each having two unpaired electrons and two lone pairs in their valence shells:

$$:\!C\!: + 2\,\ddot{O}\!: \longrightarrow \;\dot{\dot{}}O\!::\!C\!::\!O\dot{\dot{}}$$

From the electron-dot formula of CO_2 we see that each oxygen atom shares two pairs of electrons with the carbon atom, and as a result the carbon atom and the two oxygen atoms attain the stable configuration of eight electrons each (an octet).

Laboratory experiments show that the CO_2 molecule is linear, with the C atom and the two O atoms on the same straight line. In this respect, therefore, CO_2 differs from the other triatomic molecules we have considered in the previous sections, H_2O, H_2S, and SCl_2, all of which are bent. As we shall soon see, the stereochemistry of the linear CO_2 molecule can again be simply explained on the basis of the electron-pair–electron-pair repulsion.

:S::O:

The sulfur monoxide molecule, SO, is an example of a diatomic molecule that contains a covalent double bond (two pairs of shared electrons), as shown in margin.

THE COVALENT TRIPLE BOND. A chemical linkage that involves the sharing of three pairs of electrons by two atoms is called a *covalent triple bond,* or simply a *triple bond.* Examples of molecules containing a triple bond are the nitrogen molecule, N_2, and the hydrogen cyanide molecule, HCN.

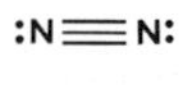

In a molecule of nitrogen gas, N_2, each Group V nitrogen atom, N, has five electrons in its outermost shell, and it is three electrons short of the stable electron arrangement of neon. Each nitrogen atom can attain this stable arrangement by sharing three of its electrons with another nitrogen atom to form three bond pairs. The chemical combination of two nitrogen atoms, N, to form a molecule, N_2, may be shown schematically as follows:

$$2\,:\!\dot{N}\cdot \longrightarrow \;:\!N\vdots\vdots N\!:$$

In the hydrogen cyanide molecule, HCN, we have an example of a molecule which contains both a single covalent bond, the H—C bond, and a triple covalent bond, the C≡N bond. The electron-dot equation for the formation of the HCN molecule from its isolated atoms in their valency states follows:

$$H\cdot + \cdot\dot{\underset{\cdot}{C}}\cdot + \cdot\dot{\underset{\cdot}{N}}\!: \longrightarrow H\!:\!C\vdots\vdots N\!:$$

In the covalent compound HCN, the H atom has a stable two-electron (helium-like) configuration, and the C and N atoms have a stable eight-electron (neon-like) configuration. The HCN molecule is another example of a linear triatomic molecule.

STEREOCHEMISTRY OF MOLECULES CONTAINING MULTIPLE BONDING

So far in our discussion of the stereochemistry of covalent compounds we have considered only compounds with single covalent bonds. Let us now extend our discussion to covalent compounds containing double or triple bonds. Consider, as an example the carbon dioxide molecule, CO_2, in which each of the O atoms is bound to the central C atom by a double covalent bond. The electron cloud of this double bond must naturally be concentrated between the two linked atoms—the C atom and the O atom—just as is the electron cloud of an ordinary single bond. From the viewpoint of the electrostatic interaction between electron pairs, therefore, a double bond can be regarded as a "more concentrated" single bond, so that for the purpose of predicting the stereochemistry of a molecule we can simply assume that the two electron pairs of a double bond will behave as a single bond pair. Thus, in the CO_2 molecule we may assume to have virtually two bond pairs. Now, two bond pairs (and no lone pairs) associated with the central C atom having a symmetrical core should result, according to our rules, in a linear stereochemistry.

In fact, as we already have mentioned, experiments show that the CO_2 molecule is linear.

Let us consider another example. In the hydrogen cyanide molecule, HCN, there is a single covalent bond between the H atom and the C atom, and a triple covalent bond between the N atom and the C atom, H—C≡N. From the viewpoint of the electrostatic repulsion between electron pairs, a triple bond can also be regarded as a more concentrated single bond, so for the purpose of predicting molecular stereochemistry we may regard a triple bond simply as a single bond pair. Hence we may assume that in HCN there are only two bond pairs (and no lone pairs) associated with the central C atom having a symmetrical core. The HCN molecule should then be expected to be—and in fact it is—a linear molecule.

We may then state the following simple rule. In molecules with multiple bonds the stereochemistry is determined by the number of bonds (either single or multiple), plus the number of lone pairs, associated with the central atom having a symmetrical core.

14-6 Resonance Structures

The molecules and ions we have been considering so far in this chapter have structures which could be represented satisfactorily by a single electron-dot formula. There are many molecules and polyatomic ions, however, whose electron structures cannot be represented this way. Let us consider a simple example, the nitrate ion, NO_3^-. Experiments show that the nitrate ion, NO_3^-, is shaped like an equilateral triangle. The nitrogen atom lies at the center of the triangle, each oxygen atom occupies one corner, and the central nitrogen atom and the three oxygen atoms all lie in the same plane. The distance from the central nitrogen atom to each oxygen atom is the same. Consequently, each oxygen atom is identical to the other two oxygen atoms. Let us consider electron-dot representations of the nitrate ion, NO_3^-. This ion may be equally well represented by structures I, II, and III (see margin illustrations). In these three representations the numbers next to the oxygen atoms are intended only as "labels" for the three oxygen atoms; the atoms themselves, of course, are identical.

Notice that in structure I the link between the nitrogen atom and the oxygen atom labeled 1 is a double bond consisting of four electrons, two contributed by each atom. Each of the other nitrogen-oxygen bonds consists of only a single pair of electrons. All the nitrogen-oxygen bonds are identical. Thus, the double bond can be placed between the oxygen 2 atom and the nitrogen atom, as in structure II, or between the oxygen 3 atom and the nitrogen atom, as in structure III. The actual electron structure of the NO_3^- ion is best pictured as a *blend* of the electronic structures I, II, and III, which are therefore called the *contributing structures,* or *resonance structures,* of the NO_3^- ion. Notice that the nitrate ion has *only one electron configuration,* and it is simply for the purpose of representation that we describe it as a hybrid of the three equivalent resonance structures I, II, and III.

The three resonance structures of the nitrate ion differ from one another in the position of the double N═O bond; we sometimes express this by saying that the NO_3^- ion contains two single bonds and a resonating double bond. Actually, however, the three N—O bonds are identical. Each bond has a character intermediate between a single and double bond—more specifically, each bond may be considered to have a "$\frac{1}{3}$ double-bond character" (because there is one double bond resonating among three possible equivalent positions). We can visualize the actual bonding in the NO_3^- ion by a simple exercise. Write structures I, II, and III one on top of the other; a blend of these three contributing structures results in *one* hybrid form that represents the actual bonding in the NO_3^- ion.

THE DINITROGEN MONOXIDE MOLECULE, N_2O. Here is another example of the way in which several electronic structures are blended into one hybrid form. The molecule of the compound dinitrogen monoxide (nitrous oxide), N_2O, may be represented by two non-equivalent resonance structures:

I. :N::N::O: II. :N⋮⋮N:Ö:

In structure I we have a double bond between the two nitrogen atoms, and a double bond between one nitrogen atom and the oxygen atom. In structure II we have a triple bond between the two nitrogen atoms and a single bond between one nitrogen atom and the oxygen atom. Each of the atoms in these resonance structures has an octet of electrons.

THE CARBON MONOXIDE MOLECULE. A molecule of carbon monoxide, CO, contains one carbon atom and one oxygen atom joined covalently. The oxygen atom has six electrons in its outermost shell, and the carbon atom has four electrons in its outermost shell. The oxygen and carbon atoms need only share one electron pair to be covalently bonded, :C:Ö: , but since a double bond is stronger than a single bond (p. 313), the CO molecule will be more stable if the C and O atoms share two electron pairs, :C::O: , in a double bond. In this structure, both the C and the O atoms still have, on the average, the same amount of negative charge they had as isolated atoms. (If we divide up each bond pair so that one electron belongs to the C atom and one electron belongs to the O atom, the C atom ends up with four valence electrons, and the O atom ends up with six valence electrons.) Hence, the *formal charge* on both the C and the O atoms is zero, even though the *effective charge* may be different from zero owing to the greater electronegativity of the O atom with respect to the C atom (p. 315). Finally, it is possible to think of the C and O atoms as being linked by a triple bond, :C⋮⋮O:. This formula should be the most favorable, if the only factor determining the stability of the molecule were the number of electron pairs shared between the C and O atom. However, the sharing of three bond pairs in the above structure results in a *formal charge* of $+1$ on the O atom, and a formal charge of -1 on the C atom. (If we divide each electron pair so that one electron of the pair is counted as belonging to each bonded atom, the C atom ends up with five electrons, instead of four, and the oxygen atom also ends up with five electrons, instead of its usual six.) Thus the structure, $\overset{(-1)}{:C}\vdots\vdots\overset{(+1)}{O:}$, is unfavorable in that it tends to place an excess of negative charge on the C atom, which is, however, the less electronegative of the two.

The actual structure of carbon monoxide, as determined from experimental observation of the carbon-to-oxygen distance (1.13 A) and of the dipole moment of the gaseous CO molecule, is neither :C::O: nor :C⋮⋮O:, but a hybrid of these two resonance forms, the latter contributing only to a minor extent to the overall electron distribution. Thus carbon monoxide is a molecule which well illustrates two important points in connection with the electronic structure of molecules and polyatomic ions: (a) The actual electron configuration of a molecule, which is most stable, often results from a balance of various contrasting factors; (b) when non-equivalent resonance structures contribute to the actual electron configuration of a molecule, these various resonance structures may all contribute equally, or one (or more) may predominate.

HYDROGEN CHLORIDE. As we know, the bonding between hydrogen and chlorine in the gaseous HCl molecule is essentially covalent. However, because the H and Cl atoms exert different attractions on the electron cloud of the bond pair (the Cl atom exerting the stronger attraction), the covalent bond has a polar character. A satisfactory way to describe the H—Cl bond is to consider it to be a blend of a covalent bond formed by a pair of electrons shared equally by hydrogen and chlorine atoms, H:Cl:, and of an ionic bond between the hydrogen ion, H^+, and the chloride ion, $:Cl:^-$. Another way of putting it is to say that the two types of bonds, covalent and ionic, both contribute in varying proportions to the *actual* bond between the atoms. We can then represent the electron structure of the HCl molecule as a hybrid between the two resonance structures as shown in the margin. The covalent structure contributes about 80% to the actual bond, and the ionic structure contributes about 20%. This does *not* mean that 80% of the HCl molecules in a sample of HCl gas have the covalent structure, and 20 per cent have the ionic structure. In any sample of hydrogen chloride gas, the hydrogen chloride molecules are held together by exactly the same kind of bond—a bond that is neither purely covalent nor purely ionic, but a blend of the two extreme types. We can visualize the actual bond of the HCl molecule by a simple exercise: Write structure (a) eight times, placing one representation on top of another. Now, on top of these write structure (b) twice. The blend of all the contributing structures produces *one* hybrid form that represents the actual bond of the hydrogen chloride molecule. These contributing structures (a) and (b) are also called *resonance structures.*

H:Cl:

(a)

$H^+:Cl:^-$

(b)

Exercises

14-1 (a) Explain how atoms of elements may enter into chemical combination to form covalent compounds. Define a covalent *sigma* (σ) bond.

14-2 By means of electron-dot formulas explain the following reactions. (a) The reaction of two fluorine atoms to form a fluorine molecule. What constitutes the real chemical change in this reaction? (b) The reaction of hydrogen atoms with bromine atoms to form hydrogen bromide molecules. What constitutes the real chemical change in this reaction?

14-3 By means of electron-dot formulas, represent the following: (a) hydrogen atom, (b) chlorine atom, (c) nitrogen atom, (d) phosphorus atom, (e) aluminum atom, (f) carbon atom, (g) bromine atom, (h) sulfur atom, (i) the alkali-metal atoms, (j) the alkaline-earth metal atoms, (k) the noble-gas atoms.

14-4 By means of electron-dot formulas, write equations to explain the following. (a) The reaction of a sodium atom with a chlorine atom to form ionic sodium chloride. (b) The reaction of a chlorine atom with a chlorine atom to form a covalent chlorine molecule. (c) The reaction of a strontium atom with an oxygen atom to form ionic strontium oxide. (d) The reaction of two hydrogen atoms with an oxygen atom to form a covalent water molecule. (e) The reaction of a phosphorus atom with three chlorine atoms to form a molecule of phosphorus trichloride. (f) The reaction of a nitrogen atom with three hydrogen atoms to form a covalent ammonia molecule.

14-5 Write electron-dot formulas and sketch the stereochemistry of the following entities: (a) $[AgBr_2]^-$, (b) $HgCl_2$, (c) BCl_3, (d) NCl_3, (e) CCl_4, (f) CH_4, (g) CH_3Br, (h) CH_3OH, (i) $[N(CH_3)_4]^+$, (j) H_3O^+, (k) NH_2^-, (l) ICl, (m) SCl_2.

14-6 Write the electron-dot formulas and sketch the stereochemistry of the following entities: (a) $SbCl_5$, (b) PF_5, (c) I_3^-, (d) SF_6, (e) $[SiF_6]^=$, (f) $[SiF_5(OH)]^=$, (g) $[PbCl_6]^=$, (h) $[Zn(H_2O)_6]^{++}$, (i) $[Ca(NH_3)_6]^{++}$.

14-7 Write the electron-dot formulas and sketch the stereochemistry of the following ions: (a) $(BF_4)^-$, (b) $S^=$, (c) OH^-, (d) $(SO_4)^=$, (e) $(PO_4)^{\equiv}$, (f) $(NH_4)^+$, (g) $(ClO_4)^-$, (i) $(IO_4)^-$.

14-8 Explain the nature of a coordinate bond. Give an example other than those presented in the chapter.

14-9 In the formation of a coordinate bond, what characteristic must an atom, ion, or molecule possess to act as (a) a donor, (b) an acceptor?

14-10 By means of electron-dot formulas, write equations to explain the reactions of certain atoms to form a covalent molecule having (a) a double bond, (b) a triple bond.

14-11 Draw the electron-dot formulas of the following molecules: (a) H_2SO_4, (b) H_2SO_3, (c) H_3PO_4, (d) $HClO_4$, (e) NH_3BCl_3.

14-12 Explain in your own words what you understand by the term "resonance structures."

14-13 Write the resonance structures of the chlorate ion, ClO_3^-.

14-14 Summarize in your own words the following concepts and illustrate each by referring to specific compounds: (a) ionic compound formation, (b) covalent compound formation, (c) coordinate covalent compound formation.

14-15 In the nitrite ion, NO_2^-, the nitrogen atom lies at one corner of a triangle with oxygen atoms at the other two corners. Each nitrogen-to-oxygen distance is the same. (a) Sketch the geometrical structure of the nitrite ion. (b) The nitrite ion has two equal contributing structures. Draw the electron-dot formulas for these two equivalent structures.

14-16 In the $CO_3^=$ ion the central carbon atom and the three oxygen atoms surrounding it are all in the same plane. All the oxygen-carbon-oxygen angles are the same, and each oxygen atom in the $CO_3^=$ ion is identical to the other two oxygen atoms. The carbonate ion, $CO_3^=$, has three equivalent contributing structures. Draw the electron-dot formulas of these three equivalent contributing structures.

THE ELECTRONIC THEORY OF CHEMICAL BONDING: III. THE VALENCE BOND APPROACH

15

In the preceding chapter we learned a set of rules that permits us to predict the stereochemistry of any polyatomic molecule or ion in which the central atom has a symmetrical core simply by considering the number of both bond pairs and lone pairs that surround the central atom. In this chapter we shall consider how the stereochemistry of a polyatomic molecule or ion may be related to the atomic orbitals involved in the formation of the covalent bonds. This approach to the study of covalent molecules and polyatomic ions is called the *valence bond method* and is very useful in correlating stereochemistry and electron configuration. The valence bond approach is best suited to those polyatomic molecules and ions in which the central atom has a symmetrical core, but it also applies fairly well to those molecules in which the central atom has a unsymmetrical core—that is, a partially unfilled underlying electron shell. At the end of this chapter we shall also begin to study the energy aspects of the formation and breaking of covalent bonds, a topic which we shall discuss in greater detail in the next chapter and which will help us to gain a better insight into the nature of the covalent bonds themselves.

15-1 Stereochemistry of Compounds and Hybridization of Atomic Orbitals

LINEAR MOLECULES—TWO BOND PAIRS AND *sp* HYBRIDIZATION

Consider first the gaseous $BeCl_2$ molecule, which, as we have already seen, may be thought to be formed from the union of a Be atom and two Cl atoms, $\cdot Be \cdot + 2\ \cdot\ddot{\underset{..}{Cl}}: \longrightarrow :\ddot{\underset{..}{Cl}}:Be:\ddot{\underset{..}{Cl}}:$. The electron configuration of the central Be atom in the ground state, in its valency state, and in the $BeCl_2$ molecule are shown in Fig. 15-1. In the formation of the $BeCl_2$ molecule according to the above electron-dot equation, the unpaired $3p$ electron of each chlorine atom pairs up with one of the two unpaired electrons (one $2s$ and one $2p$ electron) of the Be atom in its valency state to form two bond pairs. Experiments indicate that in the $BeCl_2$ molecule the two Be—Cl bonds are equivalent, so we conclude that the two electrons as well as the two orbitals of Be involved in the formation of the two Be:Cl bonds must be equivalent. We express this condition by saying that the $2s$ orbital and the $2p$ orbital of the central Be atom mix, or *hybridize*, to form two equivalent $2s\ 2p$ *hybrid orbitals*—or simply two equivalent *sp* hybrid orbitals. (Notice that the symbolism *sp* is used to indicate these hybrid orbitals because they result from the mixing of one *s* and one *p* orbital.) We would arrive at the same conclusion if we thought of the $BeCl_2$ molecule as being formed from a Be^{+2} ion and two Cl^- ions, $Be^{+2} + 2:\ddot{\underset{..}{Cl}}:^- \longrightarrow :\ddot{\underset{..}{Cl}}:Be:\ddot{\underset{..}{Cl}}:$. In this case, each of the two $:\ddot{\underset{..}{Cl}}:^-$ ions donates one of its lone pairs to the Be^{+2} ion. Each of the two equivalent Be—Cl bonds may then be thought to result from the overlap of a completely filled $3p$ orbital of a Cl^- ion with one of the two empty equivalent $2s\ 2p$ hybrid orbitals of the Be^{+2} ion. The *sp* hybridization is represented in Fig. 15-1(a) by the line enclosing the $2s$ and the $2p$ orbitals. The central Be atom of $BeCl_2$ has a total of six electrons, two in the $1s$ core, and four electrons, shared with the two Cl atoms, in its $2s\ 2p$ hybrid orbitals.

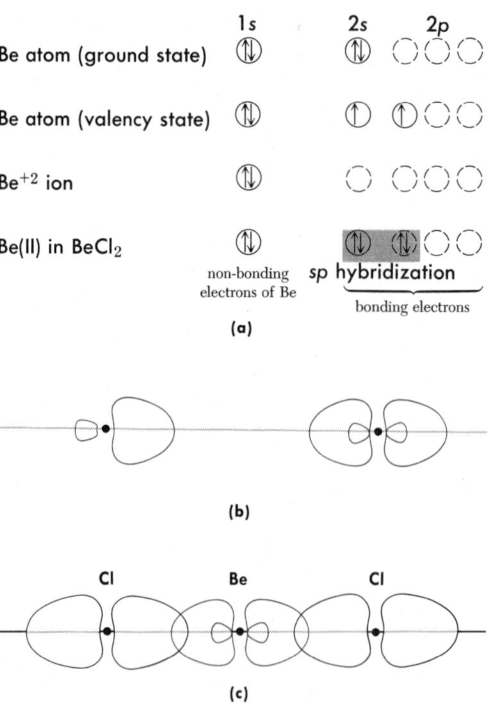

FIGURE 15-1 (a) Electron configuration of Be, Be^{+2}, and Be(II) in the $BeCl_2$ molecule. (b) Boundary line of the spatial distribution of the electron density of *sp* hybrid orbitals. (c) Overlap of atomic orbitals, giving rise to the Be—Cl bonds in the $BeCl_2$ molecule.

In turn, each of the two Cl atoms has a total of 18 electrons—ten in its core ($1s^2$, $2s^2\ 2p^6$) and eight in its valence shell; of these eight valence electrons, two electrons in a $3p$ orbital are shared with the Be atom. The $1s^2$ electrons of Be and the $1s^2$, $2s^2\ 2p^6$, $3s^2\ 3p^2\ 3p^2$ electrons of each Cl that are not used in the Be—Cl bonds of the $BeCl_2$ molecule are called *non-bonding electrons* and belong essentially to their respective and individual atoms. The electrons in the two $2s\ 2p$ hybrid orbitals of Be, each overlapping with a $3p$ orbital of a Cl atom, are the *bonding electrons* of the $BeCl_2$ molecule.

Calculations show that for any atom, and for any value of the principal quantum number, n, the two equivalent sp hybrid orbitals are directed from the (central) atom along a straight line, in agreement with the observed linear stereochemistry of the $BeCl_2$ molecule. The spatial distribution of the electron density or, as we say, the "shape" of the two sp hybrid orbitals is shown as boundary lines in Fig. 15-1(b). In general, any molecule or ion in which the central atom uses sp hybrid orbitals in bond formation has a linear stereochemistry about this central atom.

PLANAR TRIGONAL MOLECULES—THREE BOND PAIRS AND sp^2 HYBRIDIZATION

Let us now consider the BF_3 molecule, which we may assume is formed from the union of a B atom, $\cdot\dot{\mathrm{B}}\cdot$, and three F atoms, $:\ddot{\underset{..}{\mathrm{F}}}\cdot$. The outer electron configuration of the B atom in its ground state, in the valency state (for this reaction), and in the BF_3 molecule are shown in Fig. 15-2(a). In the valency state the B atom has three unpaired electrons, one in the $2s$ orbital and one in each of two equivalent $2p$ orbitals. In forming the BF_3 molecule, each of these three unpaired electrons of boron pairs up with an unpaired $2p$ electron of a F atom to form a B:F bond pair. As we have already discussed, the BF_3 molecule has a regular trigonal planar shape (F—B—F angles, 120°) with three equivalent B—F bonds. It follows that the three orbitals of B involved in the bonding must also be equivalent, and we express this by saying that the $2s$ orbital, and two of the $2p$ orbitals, hybridize to form three equivalent $2s\ 2p^2$—or simply sp^2—hybrid orbitals. Calculations show that three sp^2 hybrid orbitals are directed from the central atom to the corners of an equilateral triangle, and are shaped as shown in Fig. 15-2(b).

Each of the three B—F bond pairs of BF_3 may be thought to result from the overlap of a $2p$ orbital of a F atom with one of the three $2s\ 2p^2$ hybrid orbitals of B (Fig. 15-2(c)). You can verify, as an exercise, that we would have arrived at an identical electron representation of the BF_3 molecule if we had considered it to be formed from the union of a B^{+3} ion and three $:\ddot{\underset{..}{\mathrm{F}}}:^-$ ions.

In general, all molecules in which a central atom with a symmetrical core uses equivalent sp^2 hybrid orbitals for bonding have an equilateral triangular (planar) stereochemistry about this central atom.

FIGURE 15-2 (a) Electron configuration of B, B^{+3}, and B(III) in the BF_3 molecule. (b) sp^2 hybrid orbitals. (c) Overlap of atomic orbitals, giving rise to the B—F bonds in BF_3.

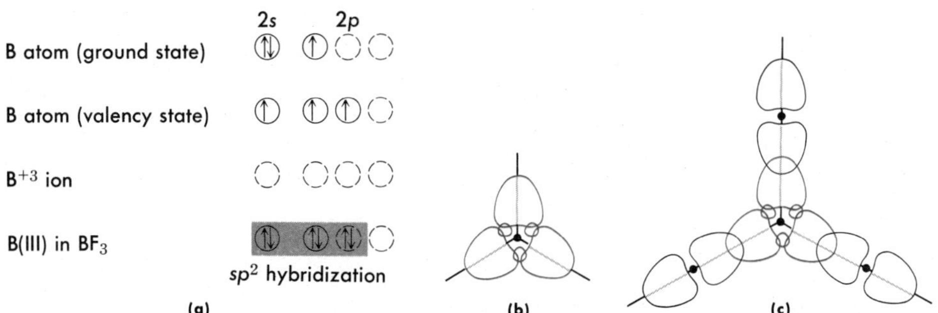

TETRAHEDRAL MOLECULES—FOUR BOND PAIRS. Consider the molecule of methane, CH_4, which we may imagine to be formed from a C atom and four H atoms,

$$\cdot\dot{\underset{\cdot}{C}}\cdot + 4\,\cdot H \longrightarrow H:\overset{H}{\underset{H}{\overset{\cdot\cdot}{\underset{\cdot\cdot}{C}}}}:H$$

The electron configuration of the C atom in its ground state, in its valency state for this reaction, and in the CH_4 molecule are shown in Fig. 15-3(a). The valency state has four unpaired electrons, and may be thought to derive from the ground state by promotion of one electron from the $2s$ orbital to the empty $2p$ orbital. In the formation of the CH_4 molecule, according to the above reaction, each of these four unpaired electrons of carbon pairs up with the unpaired $1s$ electron of a hydrogen atom, forming a C:H bond pair. Experimentally, we find that the four C—H bonds of the CH_4 molecule are equivalent, and consequently the orbitals of the central carbon atom involved in the bonding must also be equivalent. We then conclude that in CH_4 the $2s$ and the three $2p$ orbitals of carbon hybridize to form four equivalent $2s\,2p^3$—or simply sp^3—hybrid orbitals. The sp^3 hybrid orbitals have the shape and orientation shown in Fig. 15-3(b) and are often called tetrahedral orbitals, because they are directed from the central atom to the corners of a regular tetrahedron.

Let us now consider two other tetrahedral entities, the $[NH_4]^+$ cation and the $[ZnCl_4]^{-2}$ anion. In the $[NH_4]^+$ cation, formed when ammonia donates its lone pair to a proton, $H_3N: + H^+ \longrightarrow [NH_4]^+$, the four N—H bonds are found experimentally to be equivalent. We conclude that in $[NH_4]^+$ the central N atom utilizes four equivalent sp^3 hybrid orbitals, each of which overlaps with the $1s$ orbital of an H atom to form an N—H bond.

The $[ZnCl_4]^{-2}$ ion can be thought to be formed either by the reaction $Zn^{+2} + 4\,Cl^- \longrightarrow [ZnCl_4]^{-2}$ or by the reaction $ZnCl_2 + 2\,Cl^- \longrightarrow [ZnCl_4]^{-2}$. In the first reaction, each of the four $:\overset{\cdot\cdot}{\underset{\cdot\cdot}{Cl}}:^-$ ions donates a lone pair to the Zn^{+2} ion, which has a symmetrical core, forming a Zn—Cl bond pair. The four Zn—Cl bond pairs of $[ZnCl_4]^{-2}$ may be thought to occupy the four lowest available orbitals of the Zn^{+2} ion—namely, the one $4s$ and the three $4p$ orbitals, mixed to form four equivalent sp^3 hybrid orbitals (Fig. 15-4). In the second reaction, each of the two Cl^- ions donates a lone pair to the Zn(II) of the linear $ZnCl_2$ molecule, and we may assume that these two electron pairs enter the lowest available orbitals of Zn(II) in $ZnCl_2$—namely, the two empty $4p$ orbitals. But in $[ZnCl_4]^{-2}$ all four Zn—Cl bonds are equivalent, so we conclude that in forming this ion the two bonding sp hybrid orbitals and the two empty p orbitals of Zn(II) in $ZnCl_2$ hybridize to form four

FIGURE 15-3 (a) Electron configuration of C and C(IV) in the CH_4 molecule. (b) sp^3 hybrid orbitals. (c) Overlap of atomic orbitals to form the C—H bonds in CH_4.

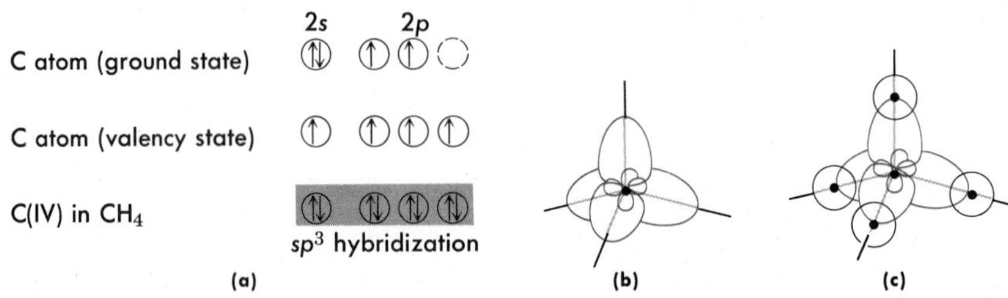

equivalent sp^3 orbitals. This example again illustrates that for each compound the orbitals involved in bond formation are the same regardless of how the compound is formed.

The type of hybridization, sp^3, present in the $[ZnCl_4]^{-2}$ anion is the same as that in the $[NH_4]^+$ cation and in the neutral molecule, CH_4. Thus the theoretical concept of hybridization of atomic orbitals offers an explanation for the experimental fact that these species, $[ZnCl_4]^{-2}$, $[NH_4]^+$ and CH_4, though differing in charge and chemical properties, all have the same tetrahedral stereochemistry.

TRIGONAL PYRAMIDAL MOLECULES—THREE BOND PAIRS AND ONE LONE PAIR

We have seen in Chapter 14 that the ammonia molecule, NH_3, has a trigonal pyramidal shape with three equivalent N—H bonds and H—N—H angles of 107°. Again, this shape can be related to the type of orbitals used in bonding by the central N atom. Because the three N—H bonds of NH_3 are found experimentally to be equivalent, so must be the three orbitals of the N atom involved in their formation. Also, since the H—N—H bond angles are very close to the tetrahedral value of 109.5°, we may assume that in the NH_3 molecule the central N atom utilizes four sp^3 non-equivalent hybrid orbitals—three equivalent orbitals for the three N:H bond pairs and one orbital for the lone pair. Thus we see that from the viewpoint of the orbitals used by the central N atom for its outer electrons (bonding or non-bonding), the NH_3 molecule and the $[NH_4]^+$ ion are closely related. However, in the $[NH_4]^+$ ion the four sp^3 hybrid orbitals of the N atom are all equivalent, because they are used to form four equivalent N—H bonds, whereas in the NH_3 molecule the four sp^3 hybrid orbitals are not equivalent—three orbitals being used for the three bond pairs, and the fourth for the lone pair. Also, the H—N—H angle (107°) of NH_3 will be smaller than the regular tetrahedral H—N—H angle (109.5°) observed in $[NH_4]^+$, because, as we know, the lone pair of NH_3 repels the three N—H bond pairs more strongly than a fourth bond pair does in $[NH_4]^+$. Figure 15-5 shows the hybrid orbitals used in bonding in the NH_3 molecule.

Another trigonal pyramidal molecule is the hydronium ion, $[H_3O]^+$, which again has three bond pairs and one lone pair around the central O atom. The electron configuration of the O atom in the ground and in the valency state and in the $[H_3O]^+$ ion are shown in Fig. 15-6, together with the sp^3 non-equivalent orbital hybridization of the central O atom.

FIGURE 15-4 **(a) Electron configuration of Zn, Zn^{+2}, and Zn(II) in $ZnCl_2$ and $[ZnCl_4]^{-2}$. (b) Overlap of atomic orbitals to form the Zn—Cl bonds of $[ZnCl_4]^=$.**

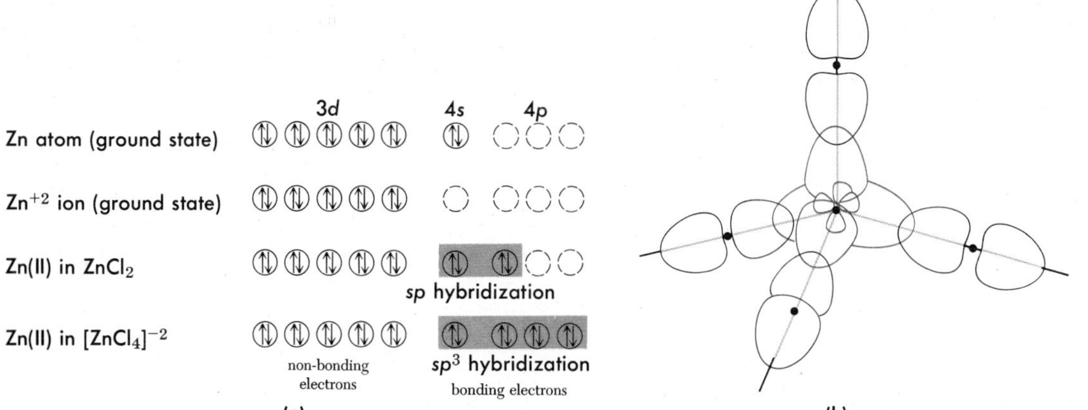

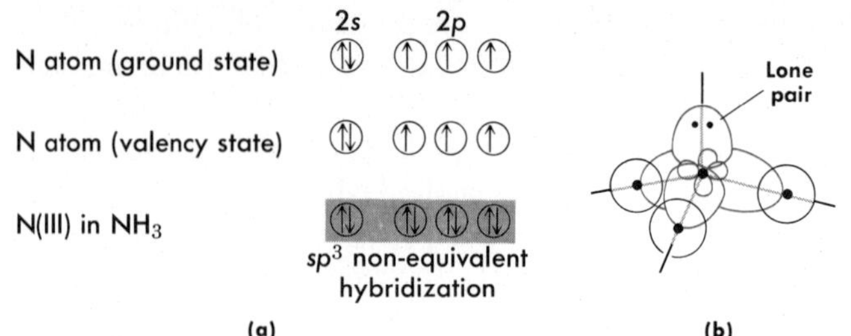

FIGURE 15-5 (a) Electron configuration of N and N(III) in the NH_3 molecule. (b) Bonding and non-bonding outer orbitals in NH_3.

BENT MOLECULES—TWO BOND PAIRS AND TWO LONE PAIRS

lone pair
bond pair
lone pair
H:O:
H
104.5°
bond pair

We know that the water molecule, H_2O, is angular with an H—O—H angle of 104.5° and two equivalent O—H bonds. We must conclude that the orbitals of oxygen involved in bonding with the two H atoms are equivalent. Thus, the O atom of the H_2O molecule may be thought to use four non-equivalent sp^3 hybrid orbitals, two for the O—H bond pairs and two for the lone pairs. The two bonding orbitals are equivalent to one another but differ somewhat from the two non-bonding orbitals, which also are equivalent. However, the directions in space of the four hybrid orbitals remain essentially tetrahedral. As we know, the lone-pair–lone-pair repulsion is stronger than the lone-pair–bond-pair repulsion, so the two O—H bonds of H_2O are pushed closer together (H—O—H angle, 104.5°) than the three N—H bonds of NH_3 (H—N—H angle, 107°). Figure 15-7 shows the electron configuration and orbital hybridization of the O atom in the H_2O molecule.

SQUARE PLANAR MOLECULES—dsp^2 HYBRIDIZATION

Let us now consider the stereochemistry of those molecules in which the central atom is linked to four atoms or groups of atoms, (that is, the central atom has a coordination number of 4 but does not have a symmetrical core. An example is the $[PtCl_4]^{-2}$ ion, which we may visualize as being formed from the union of a Pt^{+2} ion and four Cl^- ions. The $[PtCl_4]^{-2}$ ion is found experimentally to be planar, with the Pt atom at the center and the Cl atoms at the corners of a square. The four Pt—Cl bonds are equivalent and each of the Cl—Pt—Cl bond angles is 90°. The stereochemistry of the $[PtCl_4]^{-2}$ ion can be explained in terms of the hybridization of the atomic orbitals of the central Pt(II). The outer electron configurations of the isolated Pt atom of the Pt^{+2} ion, and of Pt(II) in the $[PtCl_4]^{-2}$ complex ion are shown in Fig. 15-8(a). We see that the Pt^{+2} ion *does not have a symmetrical core, because its 5d orbitals contain eight instead of ten electrons.* If these eight electrons are all paired up in four of the five $5d$ orbitals, as in the valency state of the Pt^{+2} ion for this reaction, then one $5d$ orbital is empty and hybridizes with the one $6s$ and two (of the three) $6p$ orbitals to form four equivalent dsp^2 hybrid orbitals. These four *dsp^2 hybrid orbitals are directed from the central Pt(II) toward the corners of a square, and therefore are called square planar hybrid*

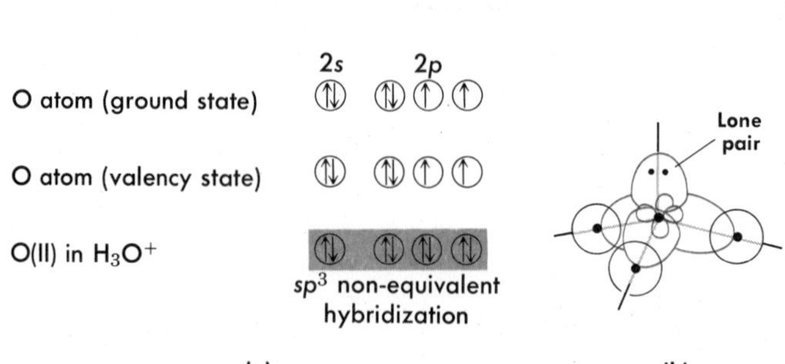

FIGURE 15-6 (a) Electron configuration of O and O(II) in the H_3O^+ ion. (b) Outer orbitals in H_3O^+.

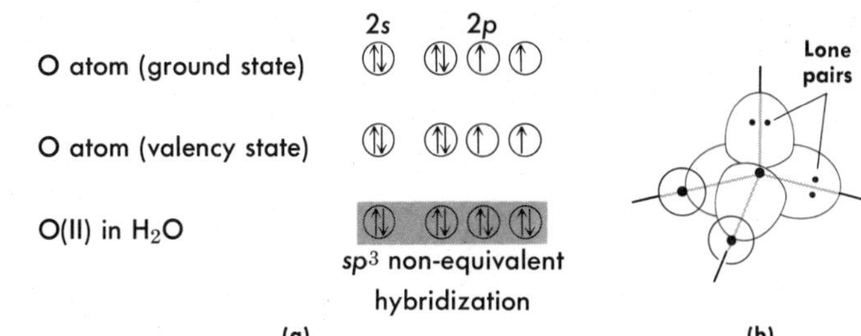

FIGURE 15-7 (a) Electron configuration of O and O(II) in the H_2O molecule. (b) Outer orbitals in the H_2O molecule.

orbitals. In the $[PtCl_4]^{-2}$ ion, each of the four Pt—Cl bonds results from the overlap of an empty $5d,6s6p^2$ hybrid orbital of Pt(II) with a filled $3p$ orbital of a Cl^- ion. In general, atoms or ions which, in their valency state, have one empty d orbital in the penultimate shell can form square planar molecules using dsp^2 hybrid orbitals. Other examples are $[Pd^{II}Cl_4]^{-2}$, $[Ni^{II}(CN)_4]^{-2}$, and $[Au^{III}Br_4]^-$.

FIVE ELECTRON PAIRS—sp^3d HYBRIDIZATION

FIVE BOND PAIRS—TRIGONAL BIPYRAMIDAL MOLECULES. There are only relatively few molecules in which a central atom with a symmetrical core is associated with five bond pairs only. These molecules, as we know, have a trigonal bipyramidal stereochemistry, and a typical example is the gaseous PCl_5 molecule. We may think of the PCl_5 molecule as being formed by the union of an isolated P atom, in a valency state having five outer unpaired electrons, with five Cl atoms, each with one unpaired electron and three lone pairs. The electron configurations of the P atom in its ground state, in the valency state for this reaction, and in PCl_5 are shown in Fig. 15-9(a). Since the outer $3s$ and $3p$ orbitals of the P atom (a total of four orbitals) are not sufficient to accommodate the five unpaired electrons of this valency state, one of the lowest-lying higher-energy vacant orbitals of phosphorus—the $3d$ orbitals—becomes occupied. *The mixing of one 3s, three 3p, and one 3d orbital of the central P atom produces five (non-equivalent) sp^3d hybrid orbitals, directed from the center to the corners of a trigonal bipyramid.* Each of these five $3s3p^33d$ hybrid orbitals of P overlaps with a $3p$ orbital of Cl, forming one of the P—Cl bonds. The spatial distribution of the sp^3d hybrid orbitals is shown in Fig. 15-9(b), and the atomic orbitals involved in the bonding of the PCl_5 molecule are shown in Fig. 15-9(c). Notice that each P:Cl bond may be thought to result from the overlap of a $3s3p^33d$ hybrid orbital of P with a $3p$ orbital of Cl.

We have already discussed, in Section 14-3, the streochemistry of those molecules which have a total of five bond pairs associated with an atom which has

FIGURE 15-8 (a) Structural formula of the $[PtCl_4]^=$ complex ion. (b) Electron configuration of Pt, Pt^{+2}, and Pt(II) in $[PtCl_4]^{-2}$. (c) Orbitals involved in bonding.

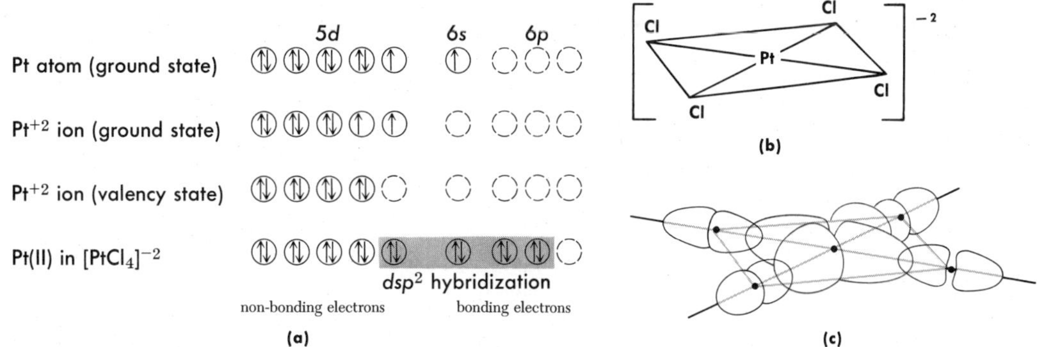

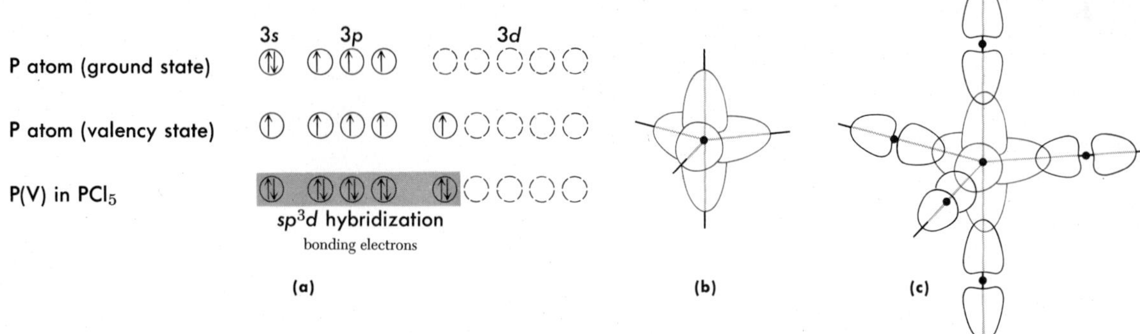

FIGURE 15-9 (a) Electron configuration of the P atom and of P(V) in the PCl_5 molecule. (b) Spatial distribution of the sp^3d hybrid orbitals. (c) Overlap of the atomic orbitals to form the P—Cl bonds of the PCl_5 molecule.

a central symmetrical core, one of more being lone pairs. In all these compounds the central atom is considered to use five non-equivalent sp^3d hybrid orbitals. The diagrams in the margin illustrate the orbitals of both the lone pairs and the bond pairs for the same compounds we considered as examples on p. 284.

$TeCl_4$

SIX BOND PAIRS AND sp^3d^2 OCTAHEDRAL HYBRIDIZATION

Molecules in which six bond pairs are associated with a central atom having a symmetrical core are octahedral (p. 285). And if the six atoms or groups linked to the central atom are identical, the molecule has a *regular octahedral* stereochemistry. To provide six equivalent orbitals for these six equivalent bond pairs, the one *ns*, the three *np*, and two of the *nd* orbitals of the central atom hybridize to form six *sp^3d^2 hybrid orbitals.* These six sp^3d^2 hybrid orbitals are directed from the center to the corners of a regular octahedron, Fig. 15-10(a), in agreement with the observed stereochemistry of six-coordinated molecules with a symmetrical core. An example is the sulfur hexafluoride molecule, SF_6, in which each of the six $3s\,3p^3\,3d^2$ hybrid orbitals of the S atom (Fig. 15-10(b)) overlaps with one of the $2p$ orbitals of a F atom to form a covalent S:F bond.

ICl_3

Another example of a molecule in which the central atom has a coordination number of 6 and a regular octahedral stereochemistry is the complex ion $[Zn(NH_3)_6]^{+2}$. This ion is formed by passing NH_3 gas over a crystalline Zn(II) salt: $Zn^{+2} + 6\ NH_3 \longrightarrow [Zn(NH_3)_6]^{+2}$. We expect the $[Zn(NH_3)_6]^{+2}$ ion will have a regular octahedral shape, in agreement with experimental observations, because in $[Zn(NH_3)_6]^{+2}$ the central Zn(II) ion has a symmetrical core (d^{10}), six bond pairs (each donated by one of the six $:NH_3$ molecules), and no lone pairs. The electron con-

I_3^-

FIGURE 15-10 Spatial distribution of the electron density in the six sp^3d^2 hybrid orbitals. (b) Electron configurations of S and S(VI) in SF_6.

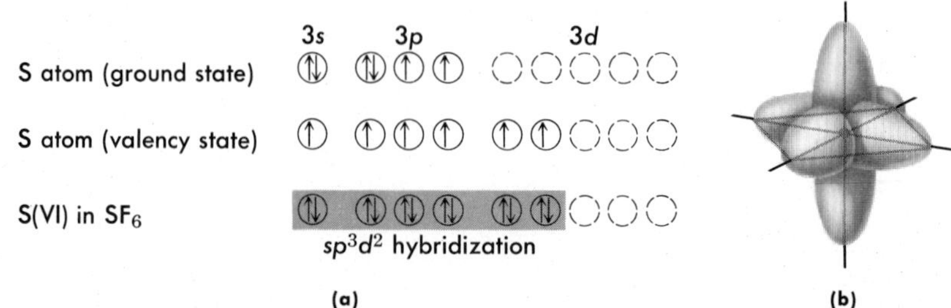

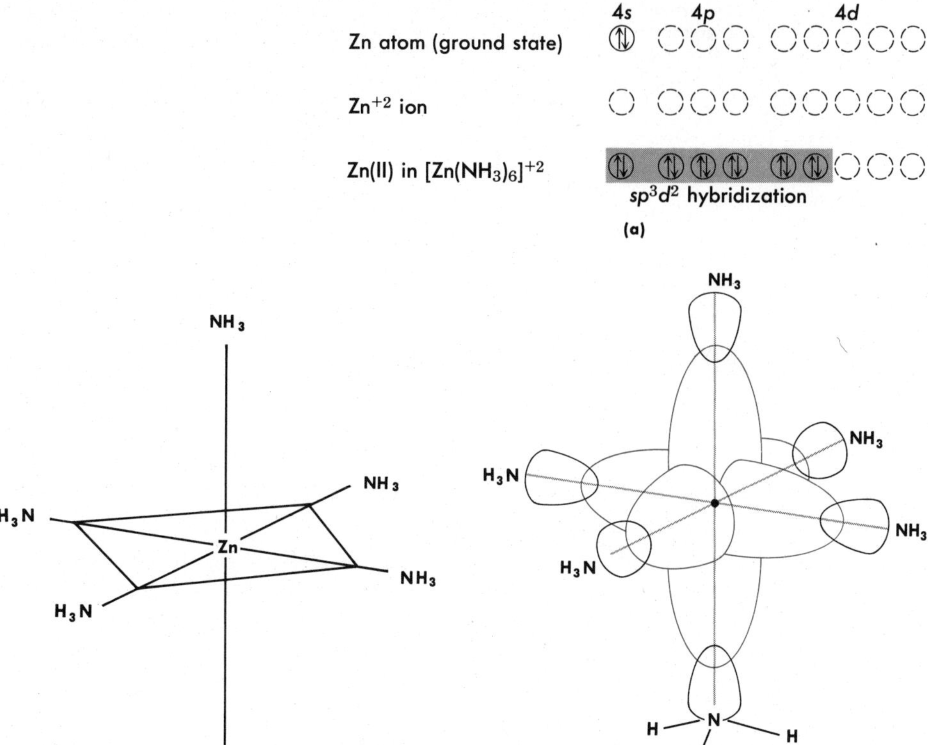

FIGURE 15-11 (a) Electron configurations of Zn, Zn^{+2}, and Zn(II) in $[Zn(NH_3)_6]^{+2}$. (b) Structural formula of the $[Zn(NH_3)_6]^{+2}$ ion. (c) Orbitals involved in the $H_3N{\rightarrow}Zn$ coordinate bonds.

figuration of the isolated Zn atom, of the Zn^{+2} ion and of Zn(II) in $[Zn(NH_3)_6]^{+2}$ are shown in Fig. 15-11(a). As schematically represented in the diagram, the one 4*s*, the three 4*p*, and two of the 4*d* orbitals of Zn(II) hybridize to form six equivalent $4s4p^34d^2$ orbitals, which accept the six electron pairs donated by the six $:NH_3$ molecules. Each bond pair may be thought to occupy one of the six sp^3d^2 hybrid orbitals of the central Zn(II) and also one of the four sp^3 hybrid orbitals of the N atom of the coordinated NH_3 molecule. Figure 15-11(c) shows the overlap of these hybrid orbitals in the $H_3N{\rightarrow}Zn$ bonds.

15-2 Atomic Orbitals Involved in Multiple Bonds. Pi Bonds.

In previous sections we have discussed the atomic orbitals which are involved in the formation of compounds in which the atoms are joined by single covalent bonds. Let us now see how we can visualize the formation of multiple bonding between atoms on the basis of the overlap of atomic orbitals. As an illustration, consider the linear CO_2 molecule, in which, as we know, each oxygen atom is linked to the central carbon by a covalent double bond, ($\dot{\underset{\cdot}{O}}::C::\dot{\underset{\cdot}{O}}$).

The orbitals involved in the formation of the two C=O double bonds may be visualized as follows. (1) The C atom in its valency state for the formation of CO_2 may be thought to have four unpaired electrons: C, $1s^2$, $2s^1\ 2p^1\ 2p^1\ 2p^1$; in turn, each of the two O atoms has, as usual, two unpaired electrons: O, $1s^2$, $2s^2\ 2p^2\ 2p^1\ 2p^1$. Now, the 2*s* orbital and one of the 2*p* orbitals of carbon hybridize to form two linear *sp* hybrid orbitals, and each of these *sp* hybrid orbitals overlaps with a

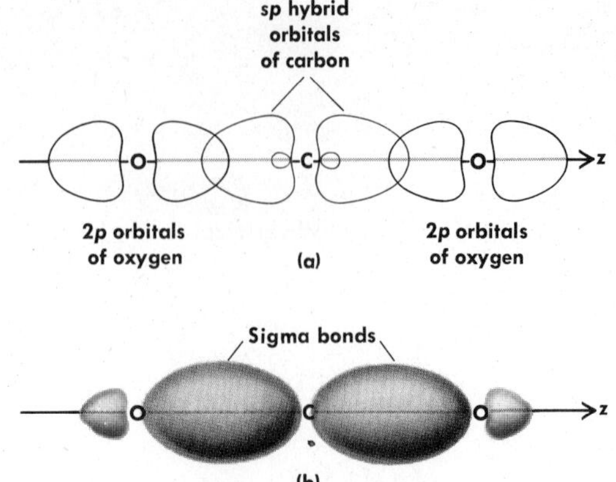

$2p$ orbital of an oxygen atom to form a covalent carbon-to-oxygen bond, as schematically represented in the margin. We see that for the two carbon-to-oxygen bonds thus formed, the distribution of the electron density is maximum along the C—O internuclear axis (the axis of the CO_2 linear molecule), and also is cylindrically symmetrical about this axis. Thus, each of the two carbon-to-oxygen bonds considered here is a *sigma* bond (p. 275). (2) The C atom is left with two unpaired electrons, each in one of the two remaining $2p$ orbitals; in turn each O atom has one unpaired electron in a $2p$ orbital. We know that for an atom the three p orbitals are at right angles to one another; and, it can be shown by calculation that if one of the p orbitals is mixed with an s orbital to form a linear sp hybrid orbital, the two remaining p orbitals will be perpendicular to each other and to the direction of this sp hybrid orbital. For the C atom of CO_2, the relative orientations of the sp hybrid orbitals and of the two p orbitals (each with an unpaired electron) are shown in the margin (assuming the axis of the CO_2 molecule to be the z Cartesian axis). Each of the unpaired electrons in these p orbitals of carbon can now interact with the unpaired electron in a similarly oriented p orbital of one of the oxygen atoms, resulting in the pairing-up of the two electrons and the formation of a covalent bond. Each of the bond electron pairs thus formed may be thought to occupy a *bonding orbital of CO_2*, resulting from the combination of a $2p$ orbital of carbon with a similarly oriented $2p$ orbital of oxygen. The shape of these bonding orbitals, and the atomic orbitals from which they are formed, are shown as follows (the two C—O bonds are drawn separately for clarity).

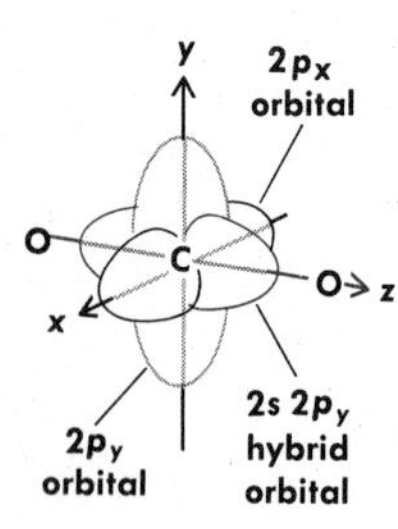

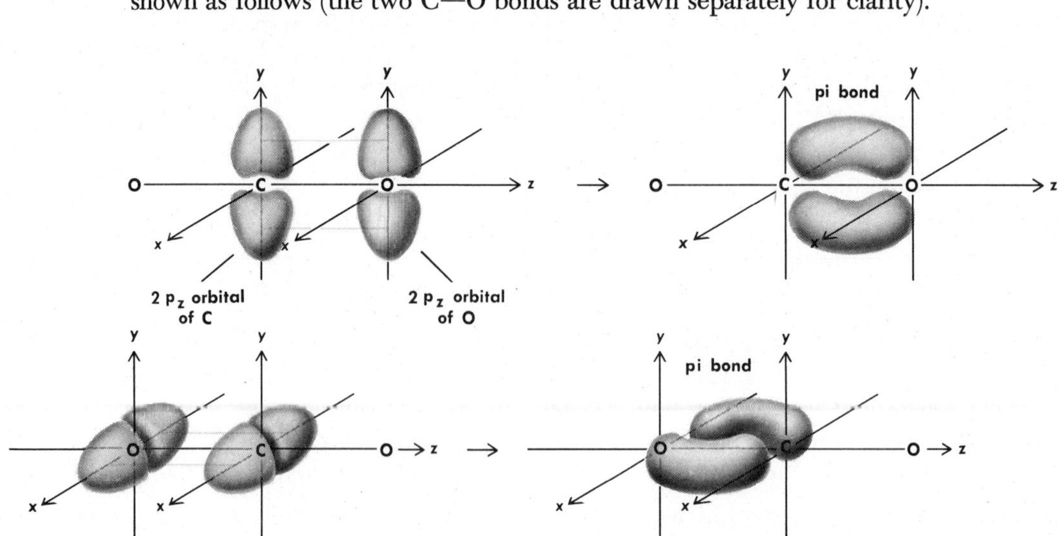

The diagrams show that in these two C—O bonds, the electron density of the bond pair is concentrated between the two bonded atoms, just as in the usual kind of bond, the sigma bond, that we have already considered. There is, however, a fundamental difference. The electron cloud of the bond pair is *not* concentrated along the carbon-to-oxygen internuclear axis, and is *not* cylindrically symmetrical about that axis. In fact, these diagrams show that the electron density of these C—O bond pairs may be described as two "banana-like" regions that lie on opposite sides of the internuclear axis. *A covalent bond whose electron density is not concentrated along the internuclear axis, but lies off this axis in two identical regions on opposite sides of this axis is called a* π *bond (read, pi-bond).* Thus in the molecule of carbon dioxide each O atom is bonded to the central C atom by two different bonds: (1) a σ bond, whose electron density lies chiefly along the C—O internuclear axis and is cylindrically symmetrical about this axis; (2) a π bond, whose electron density is concentrated in two "banana-like" regions at opposite sides of the C—O internuclear axis.

In general, *whenever two atoms are linked by a double bond, one of the bonds is of the* σ *type and the other of the* π *type. Similarly, whenever two atoms are linked by a triple bond, one bond is of the* σ *type and two are of the* π *type.* An example is the nitrogen molecule, N_2 (N≡N). The N_2 molecule, as we know, may be thought to be formed by the union of two N atoms, each having three unpaired valency electrons: N, $1s^2$, $2s^2$ $2p_x^1$ $2p_y^1$ $2p_z^1$. The three $2p$ orbitals of each N atom are directed at right angles to one another, and their interaction to form one σ N—N bond, and two π N—N bonds is schematically represented just below. Notice that here again, as in the case of the CO_2 molecule, the distributions of the electron density of the bonding electron pairs extend *"at right angles" to one another and to the* σ *bond.*

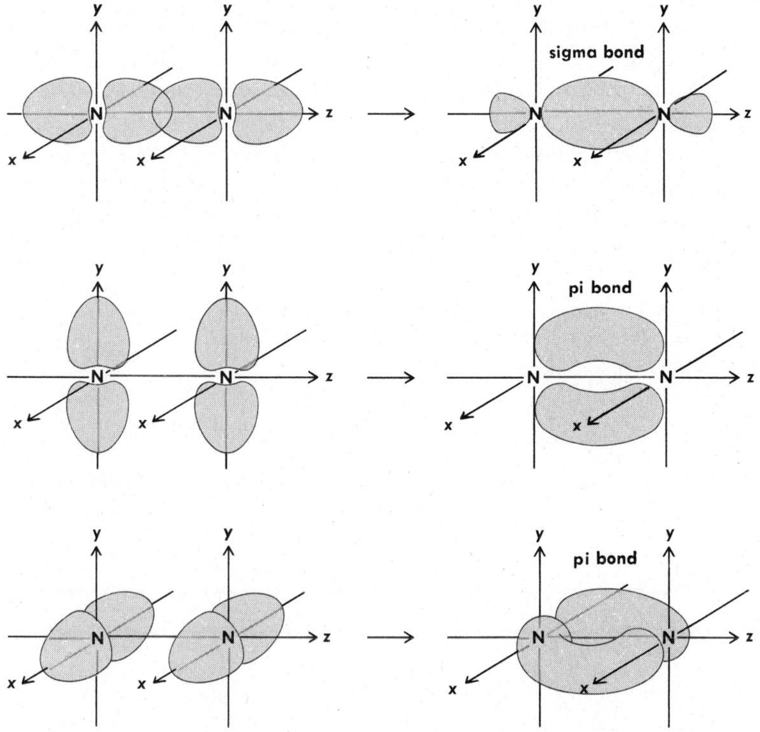

From this pictorial description of multiple bonds we can now understand why, for the purpose of predicting the stereochemistry of molecules, a multiple bond (one σ bond plus one or two π bonds) is considered to act as a more concentrated single (σ) bond. In fact, the electron-cloud density of the π bonds is concentrated *around* the axis of the σ bond, and hence will repel the electron clouds of other bond pairs or lone pairs in much the same way that a σ bond does.

15-3 Atomic Orbitals Involved in Resonance Structures

On p. 291 we discussed the nitrate ion, NO_3^-, as a simple example of a compound whose formula can be best represented by (three) resonance structures. Let us now discuss this same ion from the standpoint of the orbitals involved in the bonding. We know from experiments that the NO_3^- ion is planar, with the N atom at the center and the three O atoms at the corners of an equilateral triangle; also, the three O atoms are equivalent, and so are the three N—O bonds. To account for the regular triangular shape of NO_3^-, we proceed on the basis that the three N—O σ bond pairs occupy three equivalent sp^2 hybrid orbitals of the central N atom. Also, the N atom of NO_3^- has an empty $2p$ orbital, so that any one of the three O atoms can share a lone pair (in a π coordinate bond) with the N atom. Since the three N—O bonds of NO_3^- are equivalent, this π bond is not "localized" between the N atom and one particular O atom, for if it were, this O atom would be different from the other two. The π bond, then, is "delocalized"—that is, it is distributed equally among all three N—O bonds so that the π electrons are considered to be spread over the entire NO_3^- ion (Fig. 15-12.)

In general, a bond which resonates among different positions in a molecule or ion is always a π bond, as we have just seen in the case of the NO_3^- ion. Sigma bonds do not resonate among different positions because, as we know, the electron cloud of a σ bond is concentrated along the axis connecting the nuclei of the bonded atoms, and therefore has a fixed (relative) position in any molecule or ion. In other words, the orientation in space of the bonds determines the relative positions of the atoms (the nuclei) in the molecule—its stereochemistry. *The π bond, on the other hand, has no relationship with the stereochemistry of the molecule. When we say that a π bond resonates among different positions in a molecule, we simply mean that a bond electron pair is not localized in a fixed position between two atoms but rather is spread in a bonding orbital involving more than two atoms and sometimes the entire molecule.*

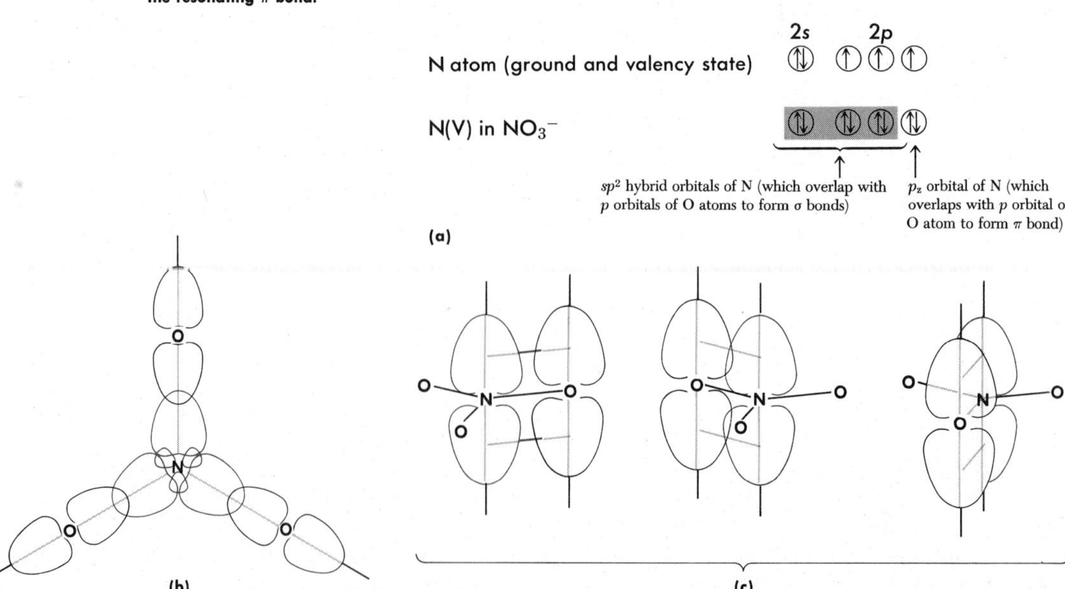

FIGURE 15-12 (a) Electron configurations of N and N(V) in the NO_3^- ion. (b) Overlapping orbitals forming the σ bonds. (c) Overlapping orbitals forming the resonating π bond.

In general, in a molecule an atom will be associated with a number of electron pairs (or occasionally a single electron) in its outer shell. These electron pairs may be bonding pairs—of the σ or of the π type—or lone pairs. *The stereochemistry of the molecule is determined by the number of σ bond pairs and of lone pairs associated with each atom—more particularly with the central atom of the molecule—* according to the rules given on pages 280, 283. The presence of the π bond pairs does not affect the stereochemistry, but it enhances the bond strength and often imparts characteristic reactivity to a compound.

In a molecule which contains σ bond pairs, lone pairs, and π bond pairs, these various kinds of electron pairs are distributed among the available atomic orbitals in the following way. (a) The σ bond pairs and the lone pairs occupy the lowest available atomic orbitals, appropriately mixed to form hybrid orbitals. (b) The π bonds occupy the next lowest available atomic orbitals (p or d orbitals). Thus, the stereochemistry of a molecule is related to the type of hybrid orbitals used by the central atom to accommodate the σ bond pairs and the lone pairs. The distortion from regular symmetry is determined by three factors: (1) the central atom does not have a symmetrical core, (2) both σ bond pairs and lone pairs are associated with the central atom, and (3) the atoms or groups bonded to the central atom are not all identical.

Table 15-1 summarizes what we have seen in the previous sections in regard to the stereochemistry of molecules, and lists some examples.

15-4 The Strength of Covalent Bonds

So far in this chapter we have concerned ourselves with the schematic representation of the electron structure of covalent molecules and polyatomic ions, with their stereochemistry, and with the atomic orbitals involved in the formation of the covalent bonds. Let us now turn to another fundamental aspect of the study of covalent compounds—the quantity of energy involved in breaking or making covalent bonds. The energy absorbed when a covalent bond breaks to form the isolated partner atoms, each carrying one of the electrons of the original bond pair, represents a direct measure of the strength of the bond being considered. The more energy required to break a given bond under a given set of conditions, the stronger the bond.

BOND DISSOCIATION ENERGIES

We shall start by considering the energy changes involved in the dissociation of a gaseous diatomic molecule into its two separate gaseous atoms. For a covalent diatomic molecule, A—A or A—B, we may define the *bond energy as the energy required to dissociate 1 mole of gaseous* A_2, *or* AB *molecules into two moles of gaseous* A *atoms, or into 1 mole of gaseous* A *atoms plus 1 mole of gaseous* B *atoms, respectively.* By convention, we consider both the gaseous molecules (reactant) and the gaseous atoms (product) to be at 25°C and 1 atm pressure, and in their ground (lowest-energy) states. The bond dissociation energy is therefore the enthalpy change, ΔH, of the dissociation reaction.

$$A{:}A_{(g)} \longrightarrow A\cdot_{(g)} + \cdot A_{(g)}$$
$$A{:}B_{(g)} \longrightarrow A\cdot_{(g)} + \cdot B_{(g)}$$

$\Delta H_{\text{dissociation}}$ at 25°C and 1 atm = bond dissociation energy

We could also define the dissociation energy of a gaseous diatomic molecule A_2, or AB, as the enthalpy change involved in the process by which 1 mole

TABLE 15-1 STEREOCHEMISTRY OF MOLECULES AND IONS HAVING A CENTRAL ATOM WITH A SYMMETRICAL CORE

	Formula	*C.N.*	*Number Bond Pairs*	*Number Lone Pairs*	*E.P.C.N.**	*Stereochemistry*	*Hybridiz.*	*Examples*
Molecules with only bond pairs	AB_2	2	2	None	2	Linear B—A—B	*sp*	$BeCl_{2(g)}$, $HgCl_{2(g)}$, $[AgCl_2]^-$, $[Ag(NH_3)_2]^+$
	AB_3	3	3	None	3	Trigonal planar	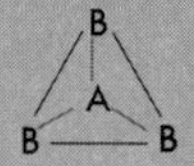 sp^2	$BF_{3(g)}$, $BCl_{3(g)}$
	AB_4	4	4	None	4	Tetrahedral	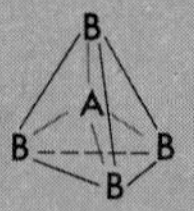 sp^3	CH_4, CCl_4, $[NH_4]^+$, $[BF_4]^-$, $[ClO_4]^-$, $[SO_4]^=$
	AB_5	5	5	None	5	Trigonal bipyramidal	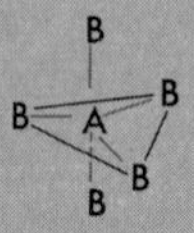 sp^3d	$PF_{5(g)}$, $PCl_{5(g)}$, $AsF_{5(g)}$
	AB_6	6	6	None	6	Octahedral	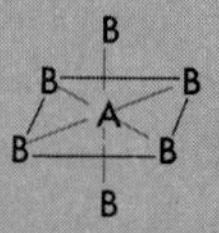 sp^3d^2	SF_6, $[SiF_6]^=$, $[Zn(H_2O)_6]^{++}$
Molecules with lone pairs	AB_2	2	2	2	4	Bent	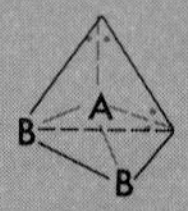 sp^3	$H_2O_{(g)}$, NH_2^-, $SCl_{2(g)}$
	AB	1	1	3	4	Linear	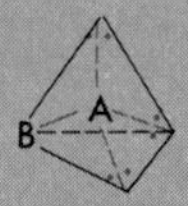 sp^3	ICl
	AB_2	2	2	3	5	Linear	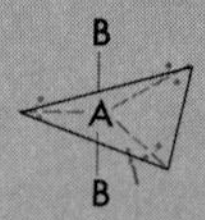 sp^3d	I_3^-
	AB_3	3	3	1	4	Trigonal pyramidal	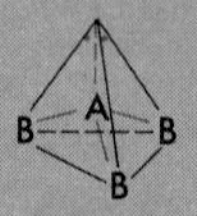 sp^3	$NH_{3(g)}$, H_3O^+, $PCl_{3(g)}$
	AB_3	3	3	2	5	T-shaped	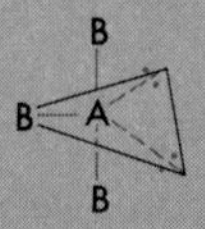 sp^3d	$ICl_{3(g)}$
	AB_4	4	4	1	5	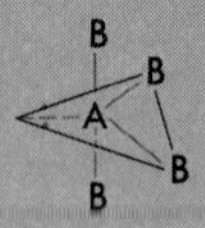	sp^3d	$TeCl_{4(g)}$
	AB_4	4	4	2	6	Square planar	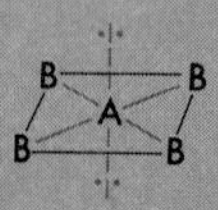 sp^3d^2	ICl_4^-, $XeF_{4(g)}$
	AB_5	5	5	1	6	Square pyramidal	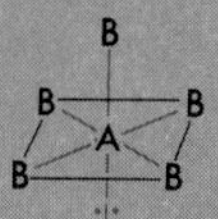 sp^3d^2	$ICl_{5(g)}$

* Notice that the electron-pair coordination number (E.P.C.N.) is equal to the number of bond pairs plus the number of lone pairs.

of covalent A:A or A:B *bonds*, present in 1 mole of A_2 or AB molecules, are broken to form 2 moles of gaseous atoms in their ground state, at 25°C and 1 atm.

BOND ENERGY OF THE $H_{2(g)}$ MOLECULE. As an example consider the dissociation of 1 mole of gaseous hydrogen molecules, H_2, into gaseous hydrogen atoms, H, at 25°C and 1 atm. The dissociation reaction requires 104.2 kcal per mole of $H_{2(g)}$ dissociated:

$$H_{2(g)} \longrightarrow 2\,H_{(g)} \qquad \Delta H = +104.2 \text{ kcal/mole } H_{2(g)} \text{ molecules}$$

As we know, the covalent hydrogen-to-hydrogen bond in the H_2 molecule results from the sharing of an electron pair by both hydrogen nuclei (H:H). When the H:H bond breaks, each hydrogen atom carries away a single electron, $H{:}H \longrightarrow H\cdot + \cdot H$, and if we assume that each hydrogen atom is formed in its ground state, this electron is in the 1*s* orbital. Therefore, 104.2 kcal is the quantity of energy which must be supplied at 25°C and 1 atm to break down 1 mole of gaseous H_2 molecules to 2 moles of gaseous H atoms, all in the 1*s* state (the ground electronic state) and at 25°C and 1 atm. Now if the electron of each hydrogen atom formed in the dissociation reaction is not in its ground state, but is in any one of the possible excited states, then of course more energy than 104.2 kcal is required to dissociate 1 mole of $H_{2(g)}$ to these higher-energy hydrogen atoms.

Assume, for example, that the H atoms formed in the dissociation of the H_2 molecules are in the first excited state, $2s^1$, rather than in the ground state, $1s^1$. The energy required for the dissociation process is then the energy required to dissociate each gaseous H_2 molecule to two gaseous H atoms in the $1s^1$ state, *plus* the energy required to promote the electron of each H atom from the $1s^1$ state to the $2s^1$ state.

$$H_{2(g)} \longrightarrow 2\,H_{(g)}\ (1s^1) \text{ ground state} \qquad \Delta H = +104.2 \text{ kcal/mole } H_{2(s)}$$
$$H_{2(g)} \longrightarrow 2\,H_{(g)}\ (2s^1) \text{ excited state} \qquad \Delta H = +574.2 \text{ kcal/mole } H_{2(g)}$$

The promotion energy for the process $H(1s^1)$ ground state $\longrightarrow$ $H(2s^1)$ excited state is $\Delta H = +235.0$ kcal/mole of H atoms. Hence, the total energy required for the dissociation, $H_2 \longrightarrow 2\,H(2s^1)$ excited state, is $(104.2 + 2 \times 235.0) = 574.2$ kcal/mole $H_{2(g)}$ at 25°C and 1 atm. This energy is more than five times greater than that required to dissociate the H_2 molecules to two H atoms in their ground state. Thus we must always keep in mind that in defining the dissociation energy of a diatomic molecule (as well as of any polyatomic molecule) we assume that the atoms formed are in their ground states. Table 15-2 lists the bond dissociation energies of a number of diatomic homonuclear molecules.

BOND ENERGIES OF THE $LiH_{(g)}$ AND $HF_{(g)}$ MOLECULES. An example of a diatomic molecule made up of two unlike atoms which again dissociates to yield the atoms in their ground states is *gaseous* lithium hydride, $LiH_{(g)}$.

$$LiH_{(g)} \longrightarrow Li_{(g)} + H_{(g)} \qquad \Delta H = +58 \text{ kcal/mole } LiH_{(g)} \text{ molecules}$$
$$Li{:}H_{(g)} \longrightarrow Li\cdot_{(g)} + \cdot H_{(g)} \qquad \Delta H = +58 \text{ kcal/mole Li:H } \textit{bonds} \text{ in } LiH_{(g)} \text{ molecules}$$

When the Li:H covalent bond breaks, we assume that each of the resulting Li and H atoms is in its ground state, $H(1s^1)$ and $Li(1s^2, 2s^1)$. Another example is gaseous hydrogen fluoride, HF.

$$H{:}\ddot{\underset{..}{F}}{:}_{(g)} \longrightarrow H\cdot_{(g)} + {:}\ddot{\underset{..}{F}}{:}_{(g)} \qquad \Delta H = +134 \text{ kcal/mole } HF_{(g)}$$

As this electron-dot equation indicates, the product atoms are formed in their ground-state electron configurations, $H(1s^1)$ and $F(1s^2, 2s^2\,2p^2\,2p^2\,2p^1)$. It is interesting to point out here that the bond dissociation energy of the H:F covalent bond of gaseous hydrogen fluoride is the highest so far known for any single covalent bond and, as we shall see in later chapters, is often used as a reference value for covalent bond energies.

BOND ENERGY OF THE $BeH_{(g)}$ MOLECULE. Now let us proceed one step further and consider the dissociation of a diatomic covalent molecule for which it is reasonable to assume that the product atoms are *not* in their ground electron state. As an example, we may consider the gaseous BeH molecule, which is formed from beryllium and hydrogen in a gas discharge tube. This diatomic BeH molecule, although uncommon, is a very simple and convenient example, because it may help us to visualize the process by which more complicated polyatomic molecules are dissociated into atoms.

Experiments show that when 1 mole of gaseous BeH molecules dissociates into their gaseous Be and H atoms, each in its ground electron state and at 25°C and 1 atm, a rather large quatity of energy is absorbed:

TABLE 15-2 BOND DISSOCIATION ENERGIES OF SOME DIATOMIC MOLECULES OF ELEMENTS (KCAL/MOLE)

Molecule	Dissociation Energy
$H_{2(g)}$	104.2
$Li_{2(g)}$	24.6
$Na_{2(g)}$	17.4
$K_{2(g)}$	11.8
$Rb_{2(g)}$	10.8
$Cs_{2(g)}$	10.4
$Cu_{2(g)}$	47.0
$Ag_{2(g)}$	39.0
$Au_{2(g)}$	52.0
$O_{2(g)}$	119.1
$N_{2(g)}$	226.0
$F_{2(g)}$	38.0
$Cl_{2(g)}$	57.9
$Br_{2(g)}$	46.1
$I_{2(g)}$	36.1

$$BeH_{(g)} \longrightarrow Be_{(g)} + H_{(g)} \qquad \Delta H = +51 \text{ kcal/mole } BeH_{(g)} \text{ molecules}$$

Let us now see how we can interpret this experimental value of the dissociation energy in terms of the Be:H bond energy. Because the gaseous Be atom has two valence electrons ($2s^2$), the electron-dot formula of the BeH molecule is (·Be:H). Notice that in this molecule the beryllium atom has one unpaired electron, and therefore we might consider BeH as a molecule-radical. When the Be:H covalent bond of the BeH gaseous molecule breaks, one electron of the original bond pair remains with the H atom in its ground state ($1s^1$), while the other electron remains with the Be atom. It is reasonable to assume that at first this electron remains in the same orbital of beryllium which was involved in the covalent Be:H bond, so that the Be atom formed in the dissociation may be assumed to be, at least momentarily, in an excited electron state, Be: $1s^2$, $2s^1\,2p^1$ (or simply ·Be·). When this excited state of the gaseous Be atom spontaneously converts to the more stable (lower-energy) ground state ($1s^2$, $2s^2$), a quantity of energy is liberated, equal to the promotion energy of the process:

$$\underset{\text{(ground state)}}{Be(1s^2, 2s^2)} \longrightarrow \underset{\text{(excited state)}}{Be(1s^2, 2s^1\,2p^1)} \qquad \Delta H = +63 \text{ kcal/mole Be atoms}$$

Thus the experimentally measured dissociation energy of BeH, $\Delta H = +51$ kcal/mole, is *less* than the energy actually required to break the covalent Be:H bond, because energy is *liberated* when the Be atom first formed in the dissociation converts from the excited (valency) state to the ground state. We can conclude that we would need ($+51 + 63 =$) $+114$ kcal/mole $BeH_{(g)}$ to dissociate the Be—H bond of the $BeH_{(g)}$ molecule, at 25°C and 1 atom if the $Be_{(g)}$ atom remained in its valency state. Notice that this problem does not arise for the $H_{(g)}$ atom, because for hydrogen the valency and ground states coincide.

$$\cdot Be{:}H \longrightarrow \underset{\text{(valency state)}}{Be(1s^2, 2s^2\,2p^1)} + \underset{\text{(valency-ground state)}}{H(1s^1)}$$

If we assume that there is no simultaneous rearrangement of the electron configuration of each bonded atom when the Be:H bond breaks, we can obtain an estimate of the energy of the bond holding the atoms together—what we call the *intrinsic bond energy.*

BOND ENERGY OF DIAMOND. Now let us consider the dissociation of a crystal of diamond into its constituent atoms. As we know, diamond consists of a three-dimensional covalent lattice of carbon atoms (p. 177) and its formula may be represented as $C_{n(s)}$ where n is the number of C atoms in the crystal. If we consider a diamond crystal composed of 1 mole of C atoms (n = Avogadro's number), then the process of dissociation into gaseous atoms (atomization) may be represented as follows:

$$C_{n(\text{s, diamond})} \longrightarrow n\, C_{(g)} \qquad \Delta H = +172.1 \text{ kcal/mole C atoms in diamond}$$

We know that in the crystal of diamond each C atom is tetrahedrally surrounded by four other C atoms and is bound to each of these four surrounding C atoms by an electron pair bond, as represented for one carbon atom by the diagram at the right. When the crystal of diamond is dissociated into its atoms, this C atom we are considering (as well as all other C atoms of the crystal) retains its four valence electrons, because when a C:C covalent bond is broken each partner C atom retains one of the two electrons of the original bond pair. Let us assume that each C—C bond is broken in such a way that each separate C atom has the same electron configuration (valency state) as in the diamond crystal. In this valency state of the carbon atom, each of the four outer electrons is unpaired and occupies one of the outer (n = 2) orbitals of carbon, resulting in the excited state electron configuration, C: $1s^2$, $2s^1\, 2p_x^1\, 2p_y^1\, 2p_z^1$. Now, the ground state electron configuration of the carbon atom is C: $1s^2$, $2s^2\, 2p_x^1\, 2p_y^1$, so that the excited carbon atoms first formed in the dissociation of diamond spontaneously convert to the more stable ground state, with liberation of energy:

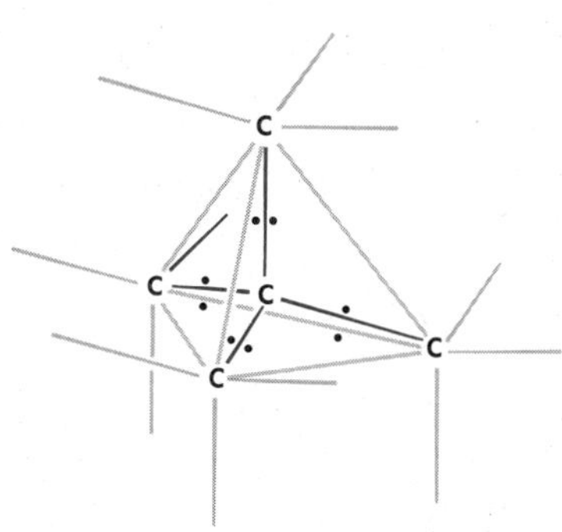

$$\underset{\text{(excited state)}}{C(1s^2,\, 2s^1\, 2p_x^1\, 2p_y^1\, 2p_z^1)} \longrightarrow \underset{\text{(ground state)}}{C(1s^2,\, 2s^2\, 2p_x^1\, 2p_y^1)} \qquad \Delta H = -96.5 \text{ kcal/mole C atoms}$$

Thus for diamond the energy required to break completely all C—C bonds while leaving the gaseous C atoms in their excited valency state is the sum of the heat of dissociation into gaseous atoms (heat of atomization) and the promotion energy from the ground state ($1s^2$, $2s^2\, 2p_x^1\, 2p_y^1$) to the excited state ($1s^2$, $2s^1\, 2p_x^1\, 2p_y^1\, 2p_z^1$) that is, (172.1 + 96.5 =) 268.6 kcal/mole C atoms in diamond.

Let us now see what this energy value means in terms of the intrinsic bond energy of the C—C bonds in diamond. When we break any one C—C bond, we partially free two C atoms, so that for the purpose of calculation we may say that we break one-half of a bond per each of the formerly bonded C atoms. Because each C atom in diamond forms four covalent bonds with four equivalent C atoms, on the average we have to break $4 \times \frac{1}{2} = 2$ bonds per each C atom in order to break up completely a diamond crystal into its gaseous C atoms. In other words, we may consider that 1 mole of diamond contains 2 moles of carbon-to-carbon covalent bonds. It follows that the (average) intrinsic bond energy for the C—C bond of diamond is one-half the energy required to break up diamond into gaseous C atoms in their valency state—namely, 268.6/2 = 134.3 kcal/mole of C—C bonds (in diamond).

In general, *the intrinsic bond energy represents the energy required to break the bond(s) of the structural unit (molecules, ion, or crystal) of a substance in such a way that the resulting gaseous atoms have an electron configuration similar to that present in the parent molecule, ion, or crystal.* On the other hand, the heat of dissociation of a substance into gaseous atoms in their ground state at 25°C and 1 atm (heat of atomization) equals the overall heat change involved when the structural unit of the substance is atomized into its gaseous atoms, each in its ground state electron configuration and at 25°C and 1 atm.

AVERAGE BOND ENERGY

Let us consider the gaseous covalent compound, methane, CH_4. We know from experiments that the methane molecule, CH_4, is a regular tetrahedron with each carbon-to-hydrogen distance (C—H) equal to 1.09 A and each hydrogen-carbon-hydrogen angle (H—C—H) equal to 109°28′.

On this basis we may conclude that the four C—H bonds of CH_4 are identical in all their properties, and in particular have the same bond energy. Experiments establish that the quantity of energy required to atomize (dissociate) 1 mole of gaseous CH_4 molecules into gaseous atoms in their ground state, and at 25°C and 1 atm, is 398.0 kcal/mole of $CH_{4(g)}$ dissociated:

$$CH_{4(g)} \longrightarrow C_{(g)} + 4\ H_{(g)} \qquad \Delta H = +398.0 \text{ kcal/mole } CH_{4(g)} = \text{heat of atomization}$$

This is the quantity of energy required to break completely all four C—H bonds of each gaseous methane molecule in 1 mole of methane, CH_4. If we then divide this quantity of energy by the number of C—H bonds in each CH_4 molecule, we obtain the (average) energy required to break 1 mole of C—H bonds (in methane): 398.0 kcal/4 moles of C—H bonds = 99.5 kcal/1 mole of C—H bonds. This value may be considered to be the *average bond dissociation energy* of the C—H bonds of methane, $CH_{4(g)}$, and is a measure of the average strength of the C—H bond in methane. If now the decomposition of gaseous methane, $CH_{4(g)}$, is carried out by four successive steps, we find experimentally that the energy absorbed in each step varies from one step to another.

Dissociation Step	*ΔH (kcal/mole of CH bond broken)*	*Species Dissociating*
1. $CH_{4(g)} \longrightarrow CH_{3(g)} + H_{(g)}$	+102.0	$(H_3C{:}H)$
2. $CH_{3(g)} \longrightarrow CH_{2(g)} + H_{(g)}$	+105.0	$(H_2\dot{C}{:}H)$
3. $CH_{2(g)} \longrightarrow CH_{(g)} + H_{(g)}$	+108.0	$(H\dot{\underset{\cdot}{C}}{:}H)$
4. $CH_{(g)} \longrightarrow C_{(g)} + H_{(g)}$	+ 83.0	$(\cdot\dot{\underset{\cdot}{C}}{:}H)$
Net Reaction: $CH_{4(g)} \longrightarrow C_{(g)} + 4\ H_{(g)}$	*Total* $\Delta H = +398.0$ kcal/mole $CH_{4(g)}$	

The average C—H bond dissociation energy of methane, one-fourth of the total ΔH value of the step-by-step process, is: $(\frac{1}{4} \times 398.0) = 99.5$ kcal, which agrees with the value obtained from the heat of atomization of $CH_{4(g)}$. We see from these values that when methane, CH_4, is dissociated step-by-step, the energy required to break successively each C—H bond depends on the electron structure, and in particular on the number of (C:H) bond pairs and on the number of unpaired electrons associated with the C atom of the particular species being dissociated.

In step 1 the species being dissociated is the CH_4 molecule (four C:H bond pairs around the central C atom). The breaking of any one of the four equivalent C:H bonds requires +102.0 kcal/mole.

In step 2 the species which dissociates is the $\cdot CH_3$ radical (three C:H bond pairs and one unpaired electron about the C atom) the breaking of any one of the three equivalent C:H bonds now requires a slightly different energy (105.0

TABLE 15-3 SOME SINGLE-BOND DISSOCIATION ENERGIES

Bond	Dissociation Energy, ΔH, in kcal/mole of bonds broken
H—H (in molecular hydrogen, H_2)	104.2
H—Cl (in gaseous hydrogen chloride, HCl)	103.0
O—H (in ethanol, CH_3CH_2O—H)	110.6
O—O (in hydrogen peroxide, H_2O_2)	33.2
C—H (in methane, CH_4)	99.29
C—H (in ethane, H_3C—CH_3)	99.29
C—H (in propane, CH_3—CH_2—CH_3)	98.73
C—C (in propane, CH_3—CH_2—CH_3)	82.20

kcal/mole). In the third step, the breaking of either one of the two equivalent C:H bonds of the $\cdot\dot{C}H_2$ species again requires a slightly different energy (108 kcal), because here the central carbon atom has two C:H bond pairs and two unpaired electrons. Finally, in the last step, the remaining C:H bond is broken from a species, $\cdot\dot{\underset{\cdot}{C}}H$, in which the carbon atom has only one C:H bond pair (the one to be broken) and three unpaired electrons. In this case we may expect that the influence of the environment is more marked, and in fact only 83 kcal are required. Unlike the average bond dissociation energy, the successive bond dissociation energies of a compound usually cannot be experimentally determined.

In general, when experimental evidence shows that the nature of a certain bond is about the same in different compounds, we may expect and in fact observe that the dissociation energy of the bond is very nearly the same (within say 5%). For example, the average dissociation energy of the C—H bond in CH_4 is 99.5 kcal/mole of bonds, while the average obtained from dozens of different hydrocarbons and other organic compounds is 98.8 kcal/mole of C—H bonds. Similarly, 79.3 kcal are needed to break 1 mole of single carbon-to-carbon (C—C) bonds in ethane H_3C—CH_3, and 83.1 kcal/mole is the average dissociation energy of the C—C bond for a number of different organic compounds containing C—C single bonds. Table 15-3 lists the average values of dissociation energy (bond strength) of some covalent single bonds for a number of different but structurally related molecules. Table 15-4 similarly gives the (average) bond dissociation energies for some covalent double and triple bonds; the single bond values are also included for comparison. Notice that 83 kcal/mole are required to break a C—C single (sigma) bond, whereas 146 kcal/mole, that is, only an additional 63 kcal/mole, are required to break completely a C=C double bond (one sigma bond plus one pi bond); and 200 kcal/mole, that is, only an additional 54 kcal/mole more, are required to break completely a C≡C triple bond (one sigma bond plus two pi bonds). Thus, although a C≡C triple bond is stronger than a C=C double bond, and the double bond in turn is stronger than a C—C single bond, we see from the above values of the bond dissociation energies that a C—C sigma bond is stronger, by 25 per cent or more, than a C—C pi bond. And this is indeed what we would expect, considering that in the pi bond the overlap of the atomic orbitals is such that there is relatively low electron density along the bond axis.

TABLE 15-4 SOME MULTIPLE-BOND DISSOCIATION ENERGIES

Bond	ΔH_{diss} (kcal/mole) of bonds broken
C—C (comparison)	83.2
C=C	146.8
C≡C	200.6
N—N (comparison)	38.4
N=N	98.0
N≡N	225.8

15-5 The Electronegativity Scale of the Elements

In Chapter 14 we qualitatively defined the electronegativity of an atom, A, as its tendency to attract to itself an electron pair shared with an unlike partner atom, B, in a covalent bond. Thus defined, the electronegativity of an atom is always a relative property. We have also seen that, in general, a bond between two unlike atoms, A and B, has a polar character, because the bond electron pair is displaced toward the more electronegative atom. The greater the difference in electronegativity between A and B, the more ionic the A—B bond. If we use the symbol X_A to designate the electronegativity of A, and X_B to indicate the electronegativity of B, then the ionic character of the bond, to a first approximation, depends on the difference $X_B - X_A$. If X_B is very much larger than X_A, then the A—B bond is essentially ionic—for example, NaCl. If X_B and X_A are equal, the bond is purely covalent—for example, H_2 or Cl_2. So it is very useful to know the values of the electronegativities of the elements, since from these values we can predict whether the bonding between two elements will be purely ionic, purely covalent, or of an intermediate character, and in this latter case, which atom will represent the negatively charged end of the dipolar bond.

The electronegativity of an atom is not, in general, a directly measurable quantity. However, a fairly inclusive list of the relative electronegativities of the elements has been compiled by Professor Linus Pauling, winner of the Nobel Prize for chemistry in 1954, on the basis of the experimentally determined values of the bond dissociation energies. Let us take the diatomic heteronuclear molecule of gaseous hydrogen chloride, HCl, to illustrate Pauling's method. The bond dissociation energies of the heteronuclear HCl molecule, and of the homonuclear diatomic molecules, H_2 and Cl_2, are:

$$\Delta H_{diss}\ H_2 = +104.2 \text{ kcal/mole } H_2 \text{ molecules}$$
$$\Delta H_{diss}\ Cl_2 = +57.9 \text{ kcal/mole } Cl_2 \text{ molecules}$$
$$\Delta H_{diss}\ HCl = +103.0 \text{ kcal/mole HCl molecules}$$

Now, we can reasonably assume that, if the bonding in the HCl molecule were covalent, the bond dissociation energy of HCl would be very close to the average of the bond dissociation energies of the H_2 and Cl_2 molecules. That is, since in the homonuclear H_2 molecule the bond electron pair is shared equally between the two identical H atoms, we may say that each H atom contributes to the strength of the H—H bond by a quantity of energy equal to half the bond dissociation energy: $104.2/2 = 52.1$ kcal/mole H atoms. Similarly, we may say that each Cl atom contributes to the strength of the Cl—Cl bond by $57.9/2 = 29.0$ kcal/mole Cl atoms. Thus, if the hydrogen-to-chlorine bond in HCl were purely covalent, with the bond electron pair equally shared between the H and Cl atom, the strength of the HCl bond (its dissociation energy) would be expected to be $52.1 + 29.0 = 81.1$ kcal/mole HCl bonds. But, as we have seen, the experimentally determined bond dissociation energy of HCl is much higher, 103.0 kcal/mole HCl bonds. This increase in the bond dissociation energy is attributed to the polar character of the HCl bonds, or in other words, to the contribution of an ionic resonance form to the electronic structure of the HCl molecule (p. 292). This increase in bond strength is taken as a measure of the difference in electronegativity between the H atom and the Cl atom. In a similar manner we can arrive at the electronegativity differences for a large number of heteronuclear bonds. To obtain the relative values of the electronegativity of the elements, it is then sufficient to assign arbitrarily a certain value of electronegativity to an element and to take this element as the reference. The element which was selected as the reference is hydrogen, and the value of the electronegativity assigned to it is 2.1. This value was selected so that the difference in electronegativity between any two elements would be as close as possible to the experimentally determined value of the dipole moment of the bond between the two atoms. The Pauling electronegativity values are given in Table 15-5. Remember that these numerical values are only relative, and that increasing values represent increasing electron-attracting ability.

Pauling's electronegativity values, with some exceptions, are closely proportional to the average of the first ionization energy of the element in question and its electron affinity (both measured in kcal/mole). This average has been proposed by Professor R. S. Mulliken, winner of the Nobel Prize for Chemistry in 1967, as the *absolute* measure of the electronegativity of the elements.

$$\text{Electronegativity (Mulliken)} = \tfrac{1}{2} \times (\text{first ionization energy} + \text{electron affinity})$$

Mulliken's electronegativity values have the advantage of representing absolute rather than relative values; however, they can be determined only for a limited number of elements because the electron affinities of many elements are not known.

The sum of the first ionization energy and the electron affinity divided by 125 gives an electronegativity value for an element which is close to Pauling's electronegativity values listed in Table 15-5. Here is an example. The first ionization energy of the Cl atom is 300.3 kcal and its electron affinity is 87.3 kcal. Thus, $(300.3 + 87.3)/125 = 3.1$, which corresponds closely to the electronegativity value of 3.0 listed in Table 15-5.

Notice that the greater the electronegativity of an element, the more difficult it is to form its positive ion(s). Fluorine, which has the highest electronegativity, 4.0, requires a very large quantity of energy to form its monopositive ion ($F_{(g)} \longrightarrow F^+_{(g)} + e^-$, ionization energy = 402 kcal/mole F atoms), and in fact does not occur as a positive ion in any stable compound. Conversely, cesium, Cs, which has the lowest electronegativity value, 0.7, of all the elements listed in Table 15-5, also has the least reluctance to form a monopositive ion, only 90 kcal/mole being required for the ionization process $Cs_{(g)} \longrightarrow Cs^+_{(g)} + e^-$. Keep in mind that the electronegativity value of an element—its electron-attracting tendency in a covalent bond—is not rigidly fixed but actually can vary appreciably from one oxidation state to another. Thus, the electronegativities of chlorine in HCl (oxidation number -1) and in $HClO_4$ (oxidation number $+7$) will obviously be different. The values listed in the Table 15-5 must be considered only as indicative average values, susceptible to rather wide variations depending on the oxidation number of the element.

TABLE 15-5 ELECTRONEGATIVITY VALUES OF THE ELEMENTS (PAULING)

H 2.1																	He —
Li 1.0	Be 1.5											B 2.0	C 2.5	N 3.0	O 3.5	F 4.0	Ne —
Na 0.9	Mg 1.2											Al 1.5	Si 1.8	P 2.1	S 2.5	Cl 3.0	Ar —
K 0.8	Ca 1.0	Sc 1.3	Ti 1.5	V 1.6	Cr 1.6	Mn 1.5	Fe 1.8	Co 1.8	Ni 1.8	Cu 1.8	Zn 1.6	Ga 1.6	Ge 1.8	As 2.0	Se 2.4	Br 2.8	Kr —
Rb 0.8	Sr 1.0	Y 1.2	Zr 1.4	Cb 1.6	Mo 1.8	Tc 1.9	Ru 2.2	Rh 2.2	Pd 2.2	Ag 1.9	Cd 1.7	In 1.7	Sn 1.8	Sb 1.9	Te 2.1	I 2.5	Xe —
Cs 0.7	Ba 0.9	57–71 1.1–1.2	Hf 1.3	Ta 1.5	W 1.7	Re 1.9	Os 2.2	Ir 2.2	Pt 2.2	Au 2.4	Hg 1.9	Tl 1.8	Pb 1.8	Bi 1.9	Po 2.0	At 2.2	Rn —
Fr 0.7	Ra 0.9																

ELECTRONEGATIVITY DIFFERENCE AND POLAR CHARACTER OF BONDS

We know that the bonding in chemical compounds varies from 100 per cent covalent to 100 per cent ionic, and most bonds are a blend of the two types. But how can we estimate the relative importance of each type in a given compound? The electronegativity scale is useful for this purpose. In a compound made up of two elements that have *very different* electronegativities, the bond will be largely *ionic*. For example, we can predict that the bonding in the compound sodium chloride is essentially *ionic*, because the sodium atom has a relatively *low* electronegativity (0.9) whereas the chlorine atom has a relatively *high* electronegativity (3.0). When chlorine reacts with sodium, the atom with the high electronegativity (chlorine) will form a negative ion, and the atom with the low electronegativity (sodium) will form a positive ion. In the resulting compound, which consists essentially of positive ions and negative ions, the sodium-to-chlorine bonding is largely ionic. The compound cesium fluoride, CsF, composed of the most electronegative (fluorine) and the least electronegative (cesium) of all elements, also fulfills these conditions even more closely. Cesium fluoride in fact is an almost purely ionic aggregate of Cs^+ ions and F^- ions.

But if there is only a *slight difference* in the electronegativities of the atoms that make up a molecule, the bond will be essentially *covalent*. For example, in the compound CH_4, the carbon atom (2.5) and the hydrogen atom (2.1) have very similar electronegativities and the bonding in this compound is largely covalent. The closer the electronegativity values of any two bonded atoms, the more pronounced the covalent character of the bond between them. For example, nitrogen and chlorine have the same electronegativity value, 3.0, and the compound nitrogen trichloride, NCl_3, contains nitrogen-chlorine bonds that are highly covalent.

15-6 Electronic and Stereochemical Representation of Reactions between Molecules

So far in this chapter we have considered chiefly reactions involving individual atoms, and we have described these reactions by means of electron-dot formulas. For example, the formation of a molecule of hydrogen fluoride from a hydrogen atom and a fluorine atom was represented as $\mathrm{H}. + \cdot\ddot{\underset{\cdot\cdot}{\mathrm{F}}}\!: \longrightarrow \mathrm{H}\!:\!\ddot{\underset{\cdot\cdot}{\mathrm{F}}}\!:$. Actually, however, only a few chemical reactions involve individual atoms; most reactions involve elements in the form of molecules or metallic crystals, as well as compounds in the form of molecules, covalent crystals, or ionic crystals.

The chemical reaction of gaseous hydrogen with gaseous fluorine to form gaseous hydrogen fluoride, for example, involves the reaction of gaseous covalent H_2 molecules with gaseous covalent F_2 molecules to form gaseous covalent HF molecules, $H_{2(g)} + F_{2(g)} \longrightarrow 2\ HF_{(g)}$. Hydrogen gas and fluorine gas at room temperature consist of diatomic molecules, H_2 and F_2. We have seen that the binding together of two hydrogen atoms to form a covalent molecule of H_2, and of two fluorine atoms to form a covalent molecule of F_2, may be expressed simply in terms of electron-dot formulas, $\mathrm{H}\!:\!\mathrm{H}$ and $:\!\ddot{\underset{\cdot\cdot}{\mathrm{F}}}\!:\!\ddot{\underset{\cdot\cdot}{\mathrm{F}}}\!:$, or more explicitly by considering that the bond electron pair occupies a bonding orbital resulting from the combination of appropriate atomic orbitals. For the H_2 molecule, such a bonding orbital derives from the overlap of the 1*s* atomic orbitals of the two bonded H atoms; for the F_2 molecule, the bonding orbital involves the overlap of a 2*p* orbital from each of the two bonded F atoms.

H—H

1s 1s

bond electron pair of H_2

F—F

1s 2s 2p 2p 2p 2p 2p 2p 2s 1s

bond electron pair of F_2

We can express the reaction of covalent H_2 molecules with covalent F_2 molecules to form covalent HF as follows:

$$H:H + :\ddot{F}:\ddot{F}: \longrightarrow 2\,H:\ddot{F}:$$

or:

H—H ⟶ H—F

1s 1s + 1s 2s 2p 2p 2p 2p 2p 2p 2s 1s ⟶ 2 1s 2p 2p 2p 2s 1s

bond electron pair of HF

We see that as a result of this chemical reaction the bond between the two H atoms of the H_2 molecule and the bond between the two F atoms of the F_2 molecule are broken, while a new bond between a H atom and a F atom is formed in each HF molecule.

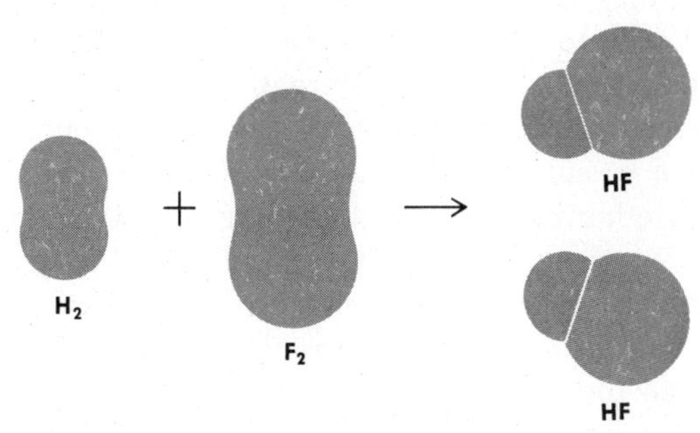

The electron-dot or electron configuration representations of the reaction between H_2 and F_2, and of the other reactions considered in this section, show schematically the meaning of the statement: *A chemical change is one in which the atoms present in the reactants are regrouped by means of electronic interaction to form the products.* Let us now further illustrate, by means of two simple examples, the significance of a chemical reaction in terms of the structure and bonding of all the substances involved.

THE FORMATION OF SODIUM CHLORIDE FROM ITS ELEMENTS. To illustrate the formation of an ionic compound let us consider the chemical reaction between sodium metal and chlorine gas to produce sodium chloride.

$$2\,Na_{(s)} + Cl_{2(g)} \longrightarrow 2\,Na^+Cl^-_{(s)}$$

The atoms of sodium in a crystal of sodium metal are linked together by metallic bonds, and the chlorine atoms in a chlorine molecule are linked together by a covalent bond. When the gaseous chlorine molecules make contact with the atoms of sodium metal, each chlorine atom takes on an electron from a sodium atom to form a chloride ion, Cl^-, and each sodium atom gives up an electron to form a sodium ion, Na^+. These oppositely charged ions then come together to form sodium chloride, a solid ionic compound. The *transfer* of electrons from the sodium atoms to the chlorine atoms may be represented, in terms of electron-dot formulas as follows:

$$2\,Na\cdot + :\ddot{\underset{..}{Cl}}:\ddot{\underset{..}{Cl}}: \longrightarrow 2\,Na^+:\ddot{\underset{..}{Cl}}:^-$$

This electron-dot equation, however, does not describe adequately the reaction between sodium metal and chlorine gas to form solid sodium chloride, a reaction which involves: (1) the breaking of the metallic bonds between the atoms of sodium metal, (2) the breaking of the covalent bond between the two chlorine atoms of each chlorine molecule, (3) the transfer of electrons from sodium atoms to chlorine atoms to form sodium ions and chloride ions, and (4) the formation of the three-dimensional ionic lattice of sodium chloride. Thus, the chemical reaction between sodium metal and chlorine gas is better represented as the sum of the following reactions:

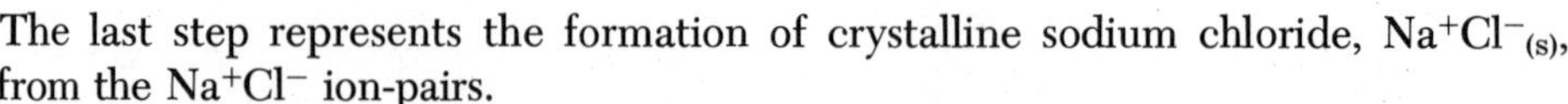

1. $\mathrm{Na_{(metal)}} \longrightarrow \mathrm{Na}\cdot$
2. $:\ddot{\mathrm{Cl}}:\ddot{\mathrm{Cl}}: \longrightarrow :\ddot{\mathrm{Cl}}\cdot + \cdot\ddot{\mathrm{Cl}}:$
3. $\mathrm{Na}\cdot + \cdot\ddot{\mathrm{Cl}}: \longrightarrow \mathrm{Na^+} + :\ddot{\mathrm{Cl}}:^-$ (ion pair)
4. $n(\mathrm{Na^+}:\ddot{\mathrm{Cl}}:^-)$ (ion pair) $\longrightarrow (\mathrm{Na^+}:\ddot{\mathrm{Cl}}:^-)_n$ (crystal)

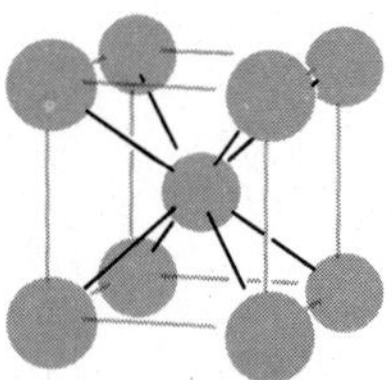

Unit cell of Na metal

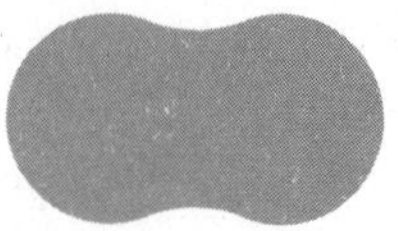

Cl_2 molecule

The last step represents the formation of crystalline sodium chloride, $Na^+Cl^-_{(s)}$, from the Na^+Cl^- ion-pairs.

Let us now consider the stereochemical aspects of the reaction. Solid, crystalline sodium metal, $Na_{(s)}$, has a body-centered cubic structure in which each sodium atom is surrounded by eight closest neighbors. Each Na atom takes part in the metallic bonding with its 3*s* electron. Gaseous chlorine, Cl_2, consists, as we know, of diatomic molecules in which the two Cl atoms are joined together by a σ bond involving a 3*p* orbital of each Cl atom. And crystalline sodium chloride is a three-dimensional lattice of alternating Na^+ and Cl^- ions, arranged in a cubic-face-centered structure. Each Na^+ ion is surrounded octahedrally by six Cl^- ions, and each Cl^- ion is surrounded octahedrally by six Na^+ ions. The Na^+ and Cl^- ions are held together in this lattice by strong mutual electrostatic attractions.

In general, any chemical reaction between an electropositive metal and a diatomic covalent molecule to form an ionic compound may be represented similarly to the reaction of sodium metal with chlorine, although the electron configurations and the crystalline structures of the metal and of the ionic compound, of course, may be different.

THE FORMATION OF AMMONIUM CHLORIDE. The chemical reaction between gaseous, covalent ammonia, $NH_{3(g)}$, with gaseous covalent hydrogen chloride, $HCl_{(g)}$, to form solid ionic ammonium chloride, $NH_4^+Cl^-_{(s)}$, may be represented as follows:

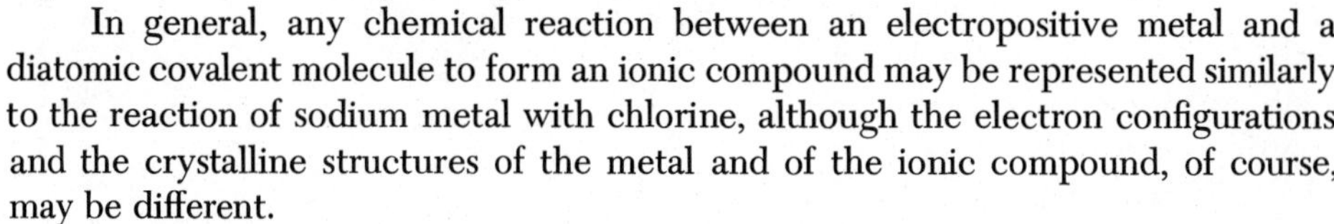

$$\mathrm{H}:\underset{\mathrm{H}}{\ddot{\mathrm{N}}}:\mathrm{H} + \mathrm{H}:\ddot{\mathrm{Cl}}: \longrightarrow \left[\mathrm{H}:\overset{\mathrm{H}}{\underset{\mathrm{H}}{\ddot{\mathrm{N}}}}:\mathrm{H}\right]^+ \quad :\ddot{\mathrm{Cl}}:^-$$

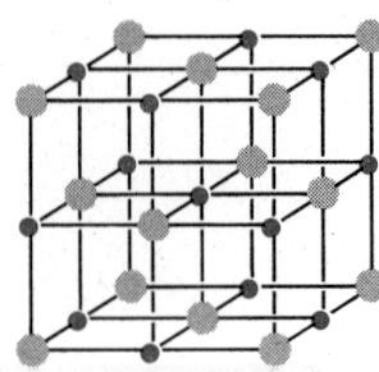

This reaction involves the breaking of the covalent H:Cl bond in the HCl molecule to form a hydrogen ion, H^+, and a chloride ion, Cl^-, the original-bond electron pair remaining attached to chlorine. The hydrogen ion, H^+, then attaches itself (coordinates) to the lone pair of electrons of the nitrogen atom of the NH_3 molecule and a NH_4^+ ion is formed. Finally, the Cl^- ions and the NH_4^+ ions come together and form the three-dimensional lattice of solid ammonium chloride.

We know that the NH_3 molecule is pyramidal, that the NH_4^+ ion is tetrahedral, and that the HCl molecule is, of course, linear. Ionic $NH_4^+Cl^-$ has a body-centered-cubic structure (cesium chloride structure), in which the Cl^- ions alternate with the tetrahedral NH_4^+ ions. We also know that in the ammonia molecule the N atom is linked to each of the three H atoms by a *sigma* bond, which involves the overlap of a sp^3 hybrid orbital of nitrogen with the 1*s* orbital of hydrogen. In HCl the *sigma* hydrogen-to-chlorine bond involves the overlap of the 1*s* orbital of hydrogen with a 3*p* orbital of chlorine. Finally, in the NH_4^+ ion the N atom forms four covalent *sigma* bonds, one to each of the four H atoms. Each bond involves a $2s\,2p^3$ hybrid orbital of nitrogen and the 1*s* orbital of hydrogen. In ammonium chloride, the bonding between the NH_4^+ ions and the Cl^- ions is ionic, but within each individual NH_4^+ ion the bonding is covalent. All this information can be schematically summarized as follows:

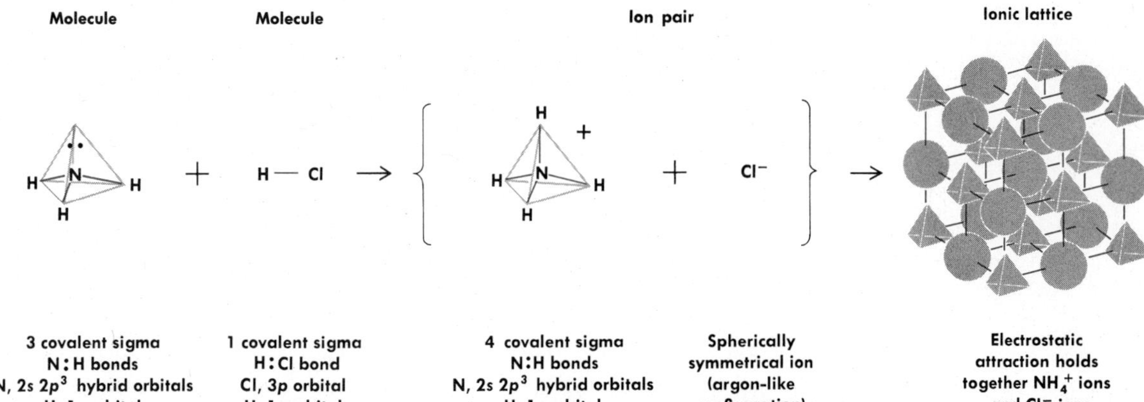

The examples we have discussed in this section illustrate that there are several electronic and structural aspects that must be considered if we wish to realize the meaning of a chemical reaction in terms of bond-making, bond-breaking, and structure. In the following chapters we shall discuss two other very important aspects of chemical reactions—energetics and rates. Only when we consider a reaction in all its aspects—stoichiometry, type of bonding, stereochemistry, energetics, rates and (possibly) mechanism—that is, when we examine what we call "the anatomy of a chemical reaction"—only then can we fully realize its significance and implications. In the later chapters of this book, which deal with the descriptive chemistry of the various groups and series of elements, you will have frequent opportunities to apply this rewarding approach to the study of chemical reactions.

Exercises

15-1 Write the electron-dot formulas, sketch the stereochemistry, and indicate the type of hybridization of the central atom in each of the following:
(a) $BeCl_2$ (vapor), CO_2, N_3^-, N_2O, CNO^-
(b) BF_3, SO_3, $BO_3^{\equiv}$, $CO_3^=$, NO_3^-
(c) SO_2, NOCl, NO_2^-
(d) NH_4^+, BF_4^-, ClO_4^-, $SO_4^=$, $PO_4^{\equiv}$, SiO_4^{-4}, $POCl_3$
(e) H_3O^+, NH_3, ClO_3^-, $SO_3^=$
(f) H_2S, ClO_2^-
(g) SF_6, $SiF_6^=$
(h) NH_3, NH_2^-, NH_4^+

15-2 Write the electron-dot formula for each of the following reactions and sketch the stereochemistry for each di- or polyatomic species (molecule or ion), indicating the hybridization of the central element:
(a) $NH_3 + H^+ \longrightarrow NH_4^+$
(b) $NH_4^+ + OH^- \longrightarrow NH_3 + H_2O$
(c) $NH_3 + HCl \longrightarrow NH_4^+ + Cl^-$
(d) $Na^+ + OH^- + HClO_4 \longrightarrow Na^+ + ClO_4^- + H_2O$

15-3 In the vapor state the formula of the compound dimethyl zinc is CH_3ZnCH_3. (1) Indicate the structure of that part of this molecule which (a) has each C atom attached to the central Zn atom; (b) has three H atoms and a Zn atom attached to a central C atom. (2) Sketch the entire molecule, CH_3ZnCH_3, and indicate the orbitals involved in bonding.

15-4 In the vapor state the formula of the compound dimethyl mercury is CH_3HgCH_3. (1) Indicate the structure of that part of this molecule which (a) has each carbon atom attached to the central Hg atom; (b) has three H atoms and a Hg atom attached to the C atoms. (2) Sketch the entire molecule, CH_3HgCH_3, and indicate the orbitals involved in bonding.

15-5 In solution, the formula of the complex ion, diamine silver(I) is $[Ag(NH_3)_2]^+$. (1) Indicate the structure of that part of this complex ion in which (a) each N atom is attached to the central Ag^+ ion, and (b) three H atoms and a Ag^+ ion are attached to a N atom. (c) Sketch the entire complex ion, $[Ag(NH_3)_2]^+$, and indicate the orbitals involved in bonding.

15-6 (a) The formula of the compound called mercury(II) chloride is $HgCl_2$. Sketch this molecule. (b) The formula of the compound called mercury(I) chloride is Hg_2Cl_2. The two Hg atoms are attached to each other, and, in turn, a Cl atom is attached to each Hg atom. Sketch this molecule. Which orbitals of Hg are involved in bonding?

15-7 What do we mean by "covalent pi (π) bonds"? Give three examples of compounds containing π bonds and sketch the orbitals involved in (a) the π bonds (b) the accompanying σ bonds.

15-8 Give two examples of compounds which have resonating π bonds.

15-9 For which of the molecules (or ions) listed in exercise 15-1 would you expect an appreciable "multiple-bond character"? Explain your answer in each case.

15-10 Explain in your own words the significance of the term "polar molecule." Illustrate with specific examples.

15-11 Compare the strength of the covalent bond between (a) the atoms of each diatomic halogen molecule: F_2, Cl_2, Br_2, and I_2; (b) the atoms of the alkali-metal gaseous molecules Li_2, Na_2, K_2, Rb_2, and Cs_2.

15-12 Define in your own words the term "intrinsic bond energy." Illustrate with two examples.

15-13 When do we use the expression "average bond energy"? Illustrate with two examples.

15-14 Compare a single A—A bond with a double A=A bond and a triple A≡A bond. Which is the strongest bond? And which is the longest bond (the bond with the longest internuclear distance)?

15-15 Is a σ bond between two identical atoms stronger or weaker than a π bond between the same two atoms?

15-16 Explain in your own words the meaning of Pauling's concept of the electronegativity of atoms. Explain its usefulness in predicting the relative ionic and covalent character of the bonding in a given compound.

15-17 What is the general relationship between electronegativity, size, and nuclear charge of an atom?

15-18 Discuss as fully as you can the electronic and stereochemical aspects of the reactions: (a) $SO_{3(g)} + H_2O_{(l)} \longrightarrow H_2SO_{4(l)}$, (b) $2\,K_{(s)} + Br_{2(g)} \longrightarrow 2\,K^+Br^-{}_{(s)}$

ENERGETICS AND CHEMICAL REACTIONS: I. THERMOCHEMISTRY

16

In previous chapters we have often pointed out that physical and chemical processes are accompanied by either the evolution or the absorption of heat. For example, we have seen that heat is always evolved in the neutralization reaction of an acid and a base and also in the combustion reactions of elements, whereas heat is always absorbed when a solid melts to its liquid or when a liquid evaporates to its vapor. In general, all physical or chemical processes involve not only a material change—a change of physical state or chemical constitution—but also an energy change. This energy change can appear not only as heat but also as work—for example, mechanical, electrical, or magnetic work—depending on the particular process considered, or on the conditions under which the process occurs, or both. Two familiar examples of reactions that produce work are: the combustion (with oxygen gas) of gasoline in the cylinder of an automobile, by which the motion of the pistons furnishes the energy (work) to make the automobile run; and the oxidation-reduction reaction of zinc metal with manganese dioxide in certain dry batteries, which provides the electrical energy to light a bulb or operate a radio. We should always be aware of the energy changes which accompany material changes in physical, chemical, and biological processes, because such energy changes furnish some insight into the structural aspects of a process and are often of determining importance in its practical applications. An even more important aspect of the study of the energetics of chemical processes is that the work which a given chemical or physical system is able to provide in a given process may be used to explain why some processes occur spontaneously and others do not.

The branch of science which deals with the energy changes accompanying physical and chemical processes is called *thermodynamics,* from the Greek, meaning the movement of heat. We shall be concerned chiefly, of course, with the thermodynamics of chemical systems. First of all we shall state some *fundamental definitions* and *concepts.*

16-1 The Thermodynamic System and Its Surroundings

A thermodynamic *system* comprises any substance or substances under consideration. For example, 1 mole of a given gas under specified conditions of volume, pressure, and temperature can be considered a system. A given quantity of water at a given temperature and pressure may be a system, and so may a known quantity of solid carbon (graphite) together with a known quantity of oxygen gas at 25°C and 1 atm, or a mixture of known quantities of zinc metal powder and manganese dioxide at a specified temperature and pressure. The *surroundings* consist of everything outside the system under consideration. In theory, the rest of the universe constitutes the surroundings, but for practical reasons we generally limit our attention to that small part of the universe which is somehow affected by the changes occurring in the system. A *closed system* does *not* exchange *matter* with its surroundings, but may exchange *energy* in some form—heat, for example. An *isolated system* exchanges *neither matter nor energy* with its surroundings.

STATE OF A SYSTEM

We often speak of a system as being in a given state, and we say that a system is fully characterized when its state is specified. This means that when the system is under a given set of conditions, all the properties of the system—its state—can be specified unequivocally. For example, if our system is an ideal gas, its state is determined by any three of these four properties: temperature, T; pressure, P; volume, V; and number of moles, n. We say "any three" because the fourth property can be derived from the ideal gas law, $PV = nRT$, or from the van der Waals equation, $\left(P + \frac{a}{V^2}\right)(V - b) = RT$ for 1 mole of gas. Notice that it is not necessary to specify every property of the gas in order to characterize its state, since the number of moles of the gas, together with any two of the three properties, T, P, and V, is sufficient to determine all other properties of the gaseous system. For example, if we know the volume occupied by a given number of moles of a gas at a given temperature and pressure, we then know the density (molecular weight/molecular volume).

For a system composed of a specified number of moles of a pure liquid or a pure solid, the temperature and pressure again are generally sufficient to completely identify the state of a stable system—that is, a system which is in a state of equilibrium. Thus, if we consider 1 mole of liquid water at 20°C and under a total pressure of 1 atm, we can find from tables of physical constants that the density is 1.0 g/cm^3, and consequently we know that 1 mole (18.0 g) of liquid H_2O occupies a volume of 18.0 cm^3. We also find that the vapor pressure of water at 20°C is 17.5 torr. (This means that of the total pressure (760 torr) exerted on the liquid water, water vapor itself exerts 17.5 torr.) Also, we find that the heat capacity of liquid water is 18.0 cal/mole $\times$ deg, and so forth. For solids, however, there is the possibility that different crystalline modifications may exist indefinitely, even though only one form is stable. In this case the crystalline form must also be specified. Thus, for a solid such as carbon, which exists in two crystalline modifications, graphite and diamond, of which graphite is the more stable one, we must state not only the temperature, pressure, and number of moles, but also whether the carbon is in the form of graphite or diamond. In fact, at the same temperature (25°C) and pressure (1 atm), graphite and diamond differ greatly in some of their properties: graphite is an opaque, gray, soft, and flaky substance, whereas diamond appears as transparent, colorless, and extremely hard crystals.

Finally, when the system is a mixture of two or more substances in equilibrium, we must specify, together with the temperature and pressure, the quantity of each substance present. For solutions, we generally specify their concentrations. Thus, two aqueous solutions of sodium chloride at 25°C and 1 atm, the one containing 1 g NaCl in 1 l. of water, and the other containing 10 g of NaCl in 1 l. of water, constitute two systems which differ appreciably in their properties (for example, vapor pressure, osmotic pressure, and electrical conductivity) even though both solutions are made up of the same substances (NaCl and H_2O) and are at the same temperature and total pressure.

It may be useful here to remark that the term "a pressure of, say, 1 atm" commonly used in defining the state of a system, may actually indicate somewhat different concepts for different systems. If we consider a closed system, such as a gas in a container of fixed volume, the specified pressure is the pressure exerted by the system (gas) itself. If, on the other hand, we have an open system in equilibrium with its surroundings, the total pressure acting on the system is that of the atmosphere plus any vapor pressure that the system itself may exert. For example, when we say that liquid water (which is appreciably volatile) is at 25°C and 1 atm, this 1 atm *total* pressure results from the actual atmospheric pressure plus the vapor pressure of water at 25°C. But when we say that solid carbon (which has no appreciable vapor pressure even at extremely high temperatures) is at 25°C and 1 atm, we simply mean that the atmospheric pressure acting on the solid carbon is 1 atm. These differences should be kept in mind throughout the following discussion, where the total value of the pressure is usually indicated without further specification.

To summarize: the state of a (thermodynamic) system is generally identified when we know (1) all the substances composing the system, (2) the quantity and physical state—gas, liquid, solid, and if necessary crystalline form—of each of these substances, and (3) the temperature and pressure of the system.

TRANSFORMATION OF A SYSTEM. Transformation generally indicates any process by which a system passes from a specified initial state to a specified final state. Any chemical reaction represents a transformation of a system; the initial state of the system is composed of the reactants, the final state is composed of the products. Any physical process which changes the state of the system—for example, the condensation of a gas to its liquid—also represents a transformation. When we describe a transformation, we must always specify the initial and final states of the system, and generally it is necessary to specify also the conditions under which the transformation actually occurs. In addition, we must always state the quantity of energy (heat or work or both), that the system exchanges with its surroundings during the transformation.

EXTENSIVE AND INTENSIVE PROPERTIES. As we mentioned in Chapter 2 a system may have extensive properties and intensive properties. An *extensive property* depends on the quantity of material composing the system. Mass and volume are extensive properties of matter (or a system) with which we are already familiar; the quantity of heat exchanged in a process is an extensive property of that process. For example, we know that if 1 mole of an ideal gas occupies a volume of 22.4 l. at 0°C and 1 atm, 2 moles will occupy $(2 \times 22.4) = 44.8$ l. Similarly, if 1 mole of a substance liberates x calories when it decomposes under given conditions, 2 moles of the same substance under the same conditions will liberate $2x$ calories when they decompose; also, if $10x$ calories are produced when a certain quantity of this substance decomposes, again under the same conditions, we may conclude that the quantity of substance decomposed is 10 moles. An *intensive property* is independent of the quantity of material considered. Temperature is an intensive property, because the temperature of a body does not depend on its size.* Another example of an intensive property is density, which for a given substance depends only on the state of the substance (temperature, pressure), not on its quantity. For example, all samples of aluminum, whether 1 g or 100 g, or any other amount, have the same density—2.70 g/cm^3 at 20°C and 1 atm pressure. Notice that the density, which is the ratio of mass to volume, is an intensive property although both mass and volume are extensive properties. Pressure is another intensive property which is the ratio of two extensive properties: pressure = force/area. It is generally true that the ratio of two extensive properties is an intensive one.

MACROSCOPIC CHARACTER OF THERMODYNAMICS

A thermodynamic system is a system (real or ideal) of macroscopic size —for example, a measurable volume of a gas or a quantity of a liquid or of a solid that can be weighed. Thermodynamics is concerned with heat and work energies exchanged between the system and its surroundings during any transformation which causes measurable, macroscopic changes in the system. Such a transformation could, for example, be a chemical reaction, or a change in physical state, such as fusion or vaporization. The conclusions and principles of thermodynamics are not based on any theory of the structure of matter; they have general validity. Actually, our theories of structure and bonding have been developed in such a way as to account for the macroscopic properties defined in the study of thermodynamics. Thus, while our structural theories in time may change and improve, the thermodynamic laws are firmly established.

16-2 The Law of the Conservation of Energy and the First Law of Thermodynamics

EXCHANGE OF HEAT BETWEEN SYSTEM AND SURROUNDINGS

We know that there are many different kinds of energy, such as heat energy, radiation (light) energy, and work energy—mechanical, electrical, and magnetic. Furthermore, from the Law of Conservation of Energy, we know that for the type of physical and chemical processes we are considering, energy is neither created nor destroyed; we know too that if a given quantity of a certain form of energy disappears, an equivalent quantity of energy appears under different forms. Heat energy is often considered in a separate class from all other kinds of energy, because experiments have shown that heat cannot always be converted *completely* to one or more of the other forms of energy, whereas each of the other forms of energy can be completely converted one to another as well as to heat. Notice that this statement does *not* contradict the Law of Conservation of Energy, because the law merely implies that whenever heat is actually converted to another form of energy, an equivalent amount of the other form of energy appears. In studying this chapter, bear in mind that energy is classified for convenience either as "heat" or as "work," work including all other forms of energy which are completely interconvertible.

As we learned in Chapter 9, heat flows under a difference of temperature—a *temperature gradient.* Heat energy is transferable from one system to another, or from one to another part of the same system. If we bring two bodies at different temperatures into contact, we find experimentally that the temperature of the originally

* Remember, however, that we can speak appropriately of temperature only when we are dealing with a large collection of atoms or molecules, not one single atom (molecule) or even just a few (p. 116). Of course, even the smallest particle of matter for which temperature is measurable by ordinary means—for example, a small drop of water—consists of millions and millions of molecules!

warmer body gradually falls, while that of the originally colder body gradually increases, until finally the two bodies (regardless of their relative sizes) attain the same temperature, intermediate between their original temperatures. Similarly, whenever a system at a given temperature is in thermal contact with its surroundings at a different (higher or lower) temperature, heat is exchanged between the system and its surroundings. It is customary to consider the surroundings as having an infinite capacity to absorb or lose heat without temperature change; thus the temperature of the system gradually approaches that of the surroundings rather than some intermediate temperature. (Thermal equilibrium is established between the surroundings and the system.) When a system exchanges a certain quantity of heat, q, with its surroundings, by convention this quantity is considered to be positive when heat is taken on by the system. On the other hand, when the system gives up heat to its surroundings, q is conventionally taken to be negative. We use these conventional signs because we consider the exchange of energy from the *system's point of view*, so that we call "positive" any heat acquired by the system, and "negative" any heat lost by the system.

INTERNAL ENERGY AND HEAT TRANSFER

Let us consider a system in thermal contact with its surroundings and assume that a certain quantity of heat energy is transferred to the system from the surroundings but that no exchange of energy in any other form occurs between them. Notice that this transfer of heat from the surroundings to the system represents a thermodynamic transformation. According to the Law of Conservation of Energy, the quantity of heat given up by the surroundings is equal to the quantity of heat which the system has gained and stores in some way. Obviously, this quantity of heat acquired and retained by the system must cause some change in the state of the system itself. Regardless of what the nature of such a change may be, the heat energy acquired has served to increase the *internal energy* of the system.

The internal energy, E, of a system depends only on its state. It follows that the *change* in the internal energy of a system in going from an initial state to a final state is the internal energy of the *final* state minus the internal energy of the *initial* state. Thus, if for the transformation being considered, E_i is the internal energy of the system in the initial state (before heat is transferred to the system) and E_f is the internal energy of the system in the final state (after the heat transfer), then the increase in the internal energy of the system, ΔE, in going from its initial state to its final state is equal to the heat, q, absorbed by the system. In symbols:

$$\Delta E = E_f - E_i = q$$

According to our convention, q in this case is positive because it represents heat energy gained by the system. On the other hand, when a certain quantity of heat is given up by the system to its surroundings in passing from a specified initial state to a specified final state, while no other form of energy is exchanged, then by our convention q is negative because it represents heat energy lost by the system. In this case the internal energy of the system in the final state, E_f, is less than that in the initial state, E_i, and ΔE represents the decrease of the internal energy of the system in the transformation considered.

The relationship $\Delta E = E_f - E_i = q$ holds in general for any type of system which exchanges only heat energy with its surroundings. If the system absorbs heat (q is a positive quantity), the energy of the system increases (ΔE is a positive quantity); if the system gives up heat (q is a negative quantity), the energy of the system decreases (ΔE is a negative quantity). The relationship $\Delta E = q$, however, provides no information about the nature of the internal energy of the system. To help us visualize what changes may be occurring in the system as a result of the heat transfer, and how such changes may be interpreted in terms of the change in internal energy of the system, let us consider a very simple system composed of a collection of ideal monoatomic gas molecules enclosed in a cylinder of fixed volume, V, at an initial pressure, P_i, and at an initial temperature, T_i. If the surroundings transfer to this system a quantity of heat and this quantity of heat remains stored in the gas, the final pressure, P_f, and the final temperature, T_f, will be higher than the initial pressure and temperature. As we have already discussed in Chapter 8, the only change that can be brought about by adding energy to an ideal monoatomic gas at constant volume is an increase in the average kinetic translational energy of its molecules, and this increase is exactly equal to the quantity of heat energy taken on by the gas from its surroundings. We also know that this increase in kinetic translational energy manifests itself as an increase in both the temperature and pressure of the gas. Hence for a simple system consisting of an ideal monoatomic gas, maintained at constant volume, the increase in internal energy which results from the absorption of a quantity of heat from the surroundings simply represents the increase in the average translational kinetic energy of the gas molecules.

Keep in mind that, regardless of the nature of the system under consideration, the Law of Conservation of Energy tells us that whenever the surroundings transfer a certain number of calories of heat to a system, the internal energy of the final state of the system will be greater than the internal energy of the initial state of the system by the same number of calories. And whenever the system transfers a certain number of calories to its surroundings, the internal energy of the final state of the system will be less than the internal energy of the initial state of the system by exactly this number of calories. These conclusions hold, of course, only when no other exchange of energy in any form takes place.

INTERNAL ENERGY AND WORK ENERGY

Let us now consider a transformation in which the surroundings perform a certain amount of work on the system, but in which there is no exchange of energy in any other form between the system and the surroundings. For example, if our system is again an ideal monoatomic gas confined in an insulated cylinder with a movable, weightless, and frictionless piston, we—as part of the surroundings—can perform work on the system by pushing down the piston. In fact, to push down the piston a certain distance, d, we must apply a force, f, sufficient to overcome the pressure exerted by the gas inside the cylinder. The work performed on the system equals force $\times$ distance, and in symbols, $w = f \times d$. If this quantity of work energy, w, is transferred from the surroundings to the system and is retained by the system, the Law of Conservation of Energy tells us that the system must gain a quantity of energy exactly equal to w. Notice again that this quantity of work energy is conventionally assumed to be a positive quantity (w is a positive number) because it represents energy *acquired* by the system. Thus, the increase in the internal energy of the system in passing from the initial state of internal energy, E_i (before work was performed on the system by the surroundings) to the final state of internal energy, E_f (after work was performed), is exactly equal to the work energy performed on the system by the surroundings. In symbols:

$$\Delta E = E_f - E_i = w$$

In this case, work is performed by the surroundings on the system (w is a positive quantity), hence the energy of the system increases (ΔE is a positive quantity). When work is performed by the system on the surroundings and no exchange of energy in any other form takes place, the energy of the system decreases (ΔE is a negative quantity) because by our convention w is a negative quantity. Regardless of our concept of the nature of a system, the Law of Conservation of Energy tells us that any work done on the system is converted into an equivalent amount of energy of some other kind, or kinds, and is stored by the system; any work done by the system is performed at the expense of an equivalent amount of the internal energy of the system.

FIRST LAW OF THERMODYNAMICS. Now let us consider a system which passes from a specified initial state of internal energy, E_i, to a specified final state of internal energy, E_f, by a transformation involving an exchange of energy *both as heat and as work* between the system and its surroundings. According to the Law of Conservation of Energy, the change in the internal energy of a system in passing from a specified initial state to a specified final state is equal to the heat exchanged plus the work done during the transformation.

Change in internal energy of system	=	Energy as *heat* exchanged between system and surroundings	+	Energy as *work* exchanged between system and surroundings
ΔE	=	q	+	w

As usual, in this expression, $\Delta E = E_f - E_i$; also, both q and w are positive quantities when they represent a gain of energy by the system, and both are negative quantities when they represent a loss of energy by the system. The Law of Conservation of Energy, when expressed in the form $\Delta E = q + w$ is called the *First Law of Thermodynamics.**

As an application of the First Law of Thermodynamics let us consider a simple example of *a system which gives up* 20.5 kcal of heat to its surroundings ($q = -20.5$ kcal) while *the surroundings perform on the system* an amount of work equivalent to 22.0 kcal ($w = +22.0$ kcal). Notice that for simplicity the heat and work energy values in this example are expressed in the same unit, the kilocalorie. Of course, if the energies involved were expressed in different units, we would first have to convert them to the same unit in order to carry out the calculation. From the First Law of Thermodynamics,

$$\Delta E = q + w \qquad \text{or} \qquad \Delta E = -20.5 \text{ kcal} + 22.0 \text{ kcal} = +1.5 \text{ kcal}$$

Thus the internal energy of the system in its final state is greater by +1.5 kcal than the internal energy of the system in its initial state. Notice that the First Law of Thermodynamics permits us to calculate the change in the internal energy for any transformation of any system, without taking into consideration the physical or chemical structure of the system in its initial and final states, or the kind of transformation which has occurred.

INTERPRETING CHANGES IN INTERNAL ENERGY FOR SYSTEM CONSISTING OF A REAL GAS

We know that for an ideal monoatomic gas an increase or a decrease in the internal energy simply means an increase or a decrease in the translational kinetic energy of the gas molecules. If we now consider an ideal gas composed of diatomic or polyatomic molecules, we know that its molecules not only move about in space in a random translational motion, but also rotate about their centers of mass. Furthermore, the atoms composing each diatomic or polyatomic molecule can vibrate with respect to one another about their equilibrium positions, so that the interatomic bonds alternately shorten and lengthen. The translational, rotational, and vibrational motions of diatomic gas molecules were shown in Fig. 9-15; here, Fig. 16-1 represents schematically the various possible components of the translational, rotational, and vibrational motions of a non-linear triatomic gas molecule. Any more general motion of the molecule can be shown to be a superposition of these fundamental motions. As we have seen in our discussion of gases (p. 157), diatomic and polyatomic gas molecules possess not only kinetic translational energy but also kinetic rotational energy and

* Note that here and throughout this book the *work done on the system* is a positive quantity; however, another convention also in use assumes the *work done by the system* on the surroundings to be a positive quantity. Accordingly, the First Law of Thermodynamics is then written: $\Delta E = q - w$.

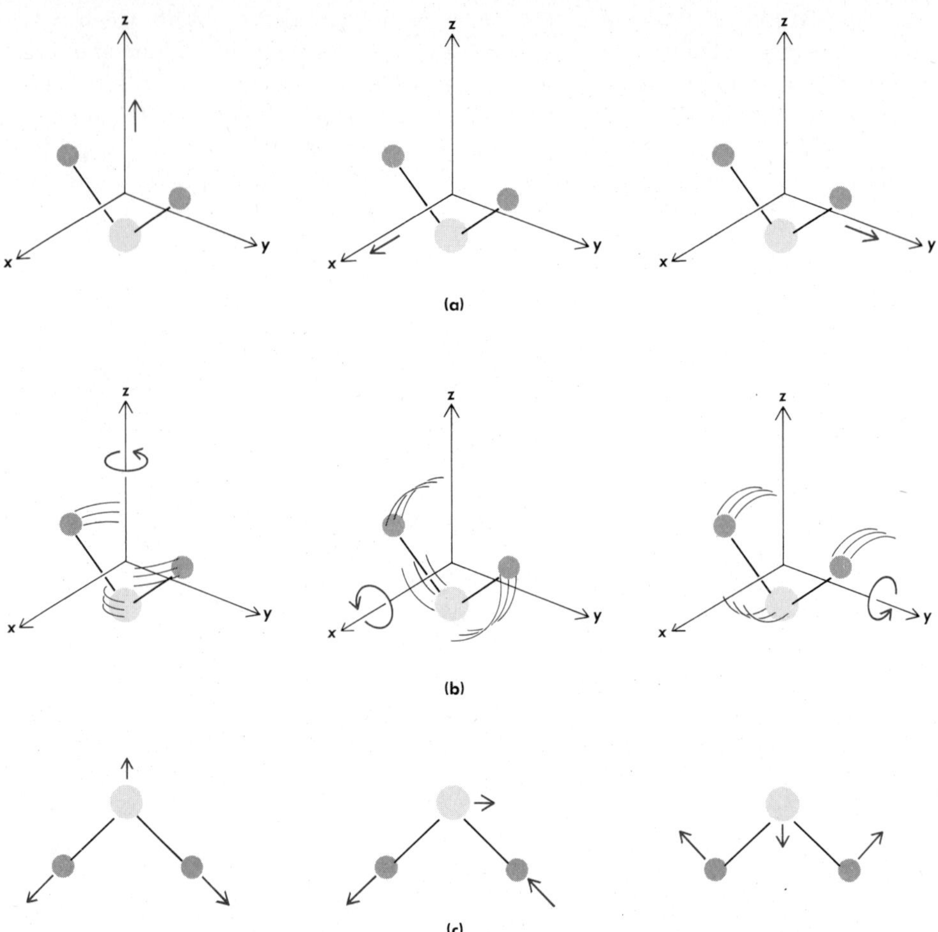

FIGURE 16-1 The components of the possible motions of a non-linear triatomic gas molecule, (a) translational, (b) rotational, and (c) vibrational, illustrate how thermal internal energy can be stored by these molecules. The origin of the Cartesian axes is placed at the center of mass of the molecule.

vibrational energy which is both kinetic and potential. Thus when a gaseous system consisting of ideal diatomic or polyatomic molecules takes on a certain quantity of energy from its surroundings, this energy may be stored by the system as one, two, or all three of these kinds of energy. An increase in the internal energy of the system may therefore involve an increase not only in translational energy but also in rotational and vibrational energies. In fact, as a diatomic or polyatomic gas takes on increasingly larger quantities of energy from its surroundings, its translational kinetic energy increases together with its rotational and vibrational energies until finally (usually at a very high temperature) the vibrational energy becomes so great that the bonds between the atoms of the molecules break and the molecules dissociate into the individual gaseous atoms. In general, for any kind of system, we can always consider its internal energy to be made up of two parts—one part which we indicate as *thermal energy* and which includes the translational, rotational, and vibrational energy of the molecules, and one part which represents the *chemical bond energy*, where the term "bond" includes all kinds of bonding: covalent, ionic, and metallic, as well as intermolecular interactions such as hydrogen-bonding, and van der Waals attractions. For any system which undergoes any transformation from an initial state of internal energy, E_i, to a final state of internal energy, E_f, the change in internal energy, $\Delta E = E_f - E_i$, results in general from a change in both the thermal energy and chemical bond energy. For any transformation in which the temperature of the final state is the same as the temperature of the initial state, the change in the thermal energy of the system is negligible as compared with the change in chemical bond energy arising from the breaking, or making, or both, of chemical bonds of all kinds.

16-3 Expansion Work for Reactions at Constant Pressure

Before we can proceed to apply the First Law of Thermodynamics to the study of chemical reactions, we must consider more closely the significance of the two energy terms—the heat, q, and the work, w, exchanged between the system and its surroundings—whose sum is equal to the change in internal energy, $\Delta E = q + w$.

Let us first focus our attention on the work done by the surroundings on the system (w is positive), or by the system on the surroundings (w is negative). As we have said, such work can be of several kinds, such as mechanical, electrical, and magnetic. However, electrical and magnetic work come into play only in rather particular cases; for example, electrical work is performed when a reaction occurs in an electrochemical cell, and magnetic work when the system is generally surrounded by a magnetic field so that when a reaction occurs the *magnetic* properties of the system undergo change. For most chemical reactions we need only consider a particular kind of mechanical work—the work done when the system expands or contracts against an opposing pressure. Now most ordinary reactions in a laboratory occur under atmospheric pressure—which to a first approximation we may consider to have a constant value of 1 atm. So we may for the present limit our considerations to the work done when the volume of the system changes from an initial value, V_i, to a final value, V_f, under a constant pressure of 1 atm. This kind of mechanical work is generally called *"pressure-volume" work.*

To learn how the pressure-volume work can be calculated, let us consider the simple case of a system whose volume increases by 1 l. in going from the initial state to the final state, $\Delta V = V_f - V_i = 1$ l., while the pressure remains constant at exactly 1 atm. Such a system could be, for example, a quantity of liquid water vaporizing at its boiling point of 100°C under a constant pressure of (exactly) 1 atm—the vaporization of about 0.033 mole (0.59 g) of liquid water would result in a volume increase of 1 l., if water vapor at 100°C and 1 atm behaved as an ideal gas. Let us assume that the vaporization of water takes place in a closed cylinder with a movable, leakproof, and frictionless piston of area a (Fig. 16-2). We know that work = force × distance (in symbols, $w = f \times d$) and that pressure, P, = force per unit area ($P = f/a$). In our case, P is the pressure (assumed to be exactly 1 atm) exerted by the atmosphere on the area (a = 100 cm^2) of the outer side of the piston. Hence, $f = P \times a = 1$ atm × 100 cm^2. If the volume of the system increases by 1 l.—that is, 1,000 cm^3, as the result of the formation of water vapor from liquid water, the distance, d, the piston must move is 10 cm—that is, $V_f - V_i = \Delta V = a \times d$. According to our convention, when ΔV is a positive quantity (the volume increases), the work, w, is a negative quantity, because it represents the energy expended by the system in pushing back the piston a distance d against the constant opposing atmospheric pressure:

FIGURE 16-2 Expansion of an ideal gas against a constant opposing pressure, P.

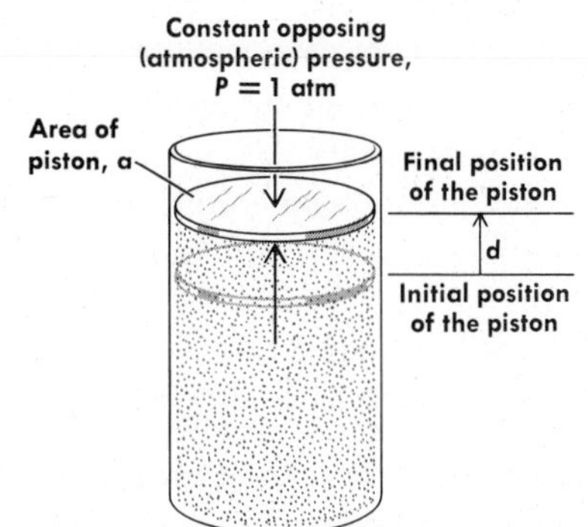

$w = -(f \times d) = -P \times a \times d = -P\,\Delta V = -(1 \text{ atm} \times 100 \text{ cm}^2 \times 10 \text{ cm}) = -1 \text{ atm} \times 1{,}000 \text{ cm}^3 = -1 \times 1 \text{ l.} \times \text{atm} = -1 \text{ l.} \times \text{atm}$.

This quantity of pressure-volume work, $w = -P\,\Delta V = -1$ l. $\times$ atm (read: minus 1 liter-atmosphere), is the energy involved whenever the volume of any system changes by 1 l. under a constant opposing pressure of 1 atm. In the particular case of an ideal gas system which expands or contracts under a constant opposing pressure and *at constant temperature* there is no change in the internal energy of the system. So if the gas expands, the quantity of energy required to perform the pressure-volume work against the opposing pressure (w is negative) has to be supplied to the system by its surroundings in the form of an equivalent quantity of heat (q is positive). If the gas contracts, the energy supplied by the surroundings in performing the pressure-volume work against the pressure exerted by the gas itself must be returned from the gas to its surroundings in the form of heat (w is positive, q is negative). As you can verify, the pressure-volume work does *not* depend on the temperature at which the expansion occurs (provided such temperature remains constant during the expansion), nor does it depend on the quantity of gas considered, or on the initial pressure of the gas, inside the piston.

Generally, in problems involving the First Law of Thermodynamics, it is necessary to express the pressure-volume work in calories or kilocalories. The conversion factor between the unit of energy, *l.* $\times$ *atm*, and the unit of energy, *cal*, is 1 l. $\times$ atm = 24.2 cal; this value, 24.2 cal, also represents the work energy involved in the change of volume of 1 l. for any system under a constant outside pressure of 1 atm.

Try to remember these numerical values of w, because from them you can calculate easily the work done on or by a system in any transformation involving a volume change at 1 atm pressure. For example, if the volume of any system increases by, say, 20 l. under a constant opposing pressure of 1 atm, the work done by the system is $w = -20$ l. $\times$ 1 atm $= -20$ l. $\times$ atm. And if we wish to express the work in calories: $w = (-20$ l. $\times$ atm$) \times 24.2$ cal/l. $\times$ atm $= -484$ cal. In a similar manner we can calculate the quantity of pressure-volume work that a system must perform whenever 1 mole of any gas at 25°C and 1 atm, assumed to behave ideally, is formed by a chemical reaction or by evaporation of its liquid or solid. Examples of such transformations are:

1. $N_2O_{4(g)}$(25°C, 1 atm) $\longrightarrow$ 2 $NO_{2(g)}$(25°C, 1 atm)
2. $H_2O_{(l)}$ (25°C, 1 atm) $\longrightarrow$ $H_2O_{(g)}$ (25°C, 1 atm)
3. $I_{2(s)}$ (25°C, 1 atm) $\longrightarrow$ $I_{2(g)}$ (25°C, 1 atm)

If we assume that each of the gaseous substances in the above reactions behaves ideally, then 1 mole of each gaseous substance at 25°C and 1 atm occupies a volume of 24.4 l. For reaction (1), therefore, $\Delta V = V_f - V_i = 24.4$ l., and the pressure-volume work is $w = -24.4$ l. $\times$ atm or $w = -590.5$ cal $\cong -0.6$ kcal. For transformation (2), the initial volume is the molar volume of liquid water, $V_i = 18.0$ cm^3, and the final volume is $V_f = 24.4$ l.; the initial volume is therefore negligible with respect to the final volume, so that $\Delta V = V_f = 24.4$ l. and again, with good approximation, $w \cong -0.6$ kcal. The same consideration holds for transformation (3), where V_i is the molar volume of solid iodine, that is, $V_i = 51$ cm^3. In general, since the molar volume of liquids and solids is usually very small with respect to that of gases under the same conditions of temperature and pressure, we may neglect it when calculating the pressure-volume work of a vaporization process, or its reverse, the condensation of a vapor.

We will conclude this section by summing up the important concepts concerning the work involved in chemical reactions:

1. For most reactions, unless specifically stated otherwise, work of the pressure-volume kind alone is to be considered.

2. All reactions which are accompanied by a volume change under an opposing pressure involve pressure-volume work. And if the opposing pressure *could be made* equal to zero, the pressure-volume work would also be zero.

3. Since volume changes in solids and liquids are generally small, we generally neglect any pressure-volume work in reactions involving only solids and liquids.

4. For reactions in which gases are involved, changes in volume are likely to involve a significant pressure-volume work. If the opposing pressure is constant, this work can be calculated from the expression $w = -P\,\Delta V$; for reactions at $P = 1$ atm the value of w can be obtained directly by recalling that each 1 l. volume change involves 24.2 cal of work, or equivalently, that at 25°C each mole of ideal gas formed involves approximately 0.6 kcal of work. As we shall see later, this is a relatively small quantity of energy compared with the energy changes involved in the breaking and making of chemical bonds.

HEAT EXCHANGED IN TRANSFORMATIONS AT CONSTANT PRESSURE—ENTHALPY

We have considered in the preceding section the work involved in transformations at constant pressure; now let us consider the other energy term which appears in the First Law, namely, the heat exchanged between the system and its surroundings. The first condition necessary for such an exchange is that the system and its surroundings be in thermal contact. Of course, if the system is thermally insulated, there can be no exchange of heat with the surroundings.

Let us focus our attention on the most common kind of chemical transformation, a transformation at a constant pressure, P, in which no work is done except the unavoidable pressure-volume work, $w = -P\,\Delta V$. For such transformations, the First Law, $\Delta E = q + w$ can be written as:

$$\Delta E = q - P\,\Delta V \qquad \text{(when } P = \text{constant)}$$

Notice that, since P is always a positive quantity, the term $P\,\Delta V$ has a negative sign if the work is done by the surroundings on the system (the system contracts, $\Delta V = V_f - V_i$ is negative) and it has a positive sign if the work is done by the system on the surroundings (the system expands, $\Delta V = V_f - V_i$ is positive). And the heat exchanged, q, is simply the heat of the transformation considered at constant pressure; as we already know, this is called "the enthalpy change" of the transformation, ΔH. Thus for any transformation at constant pressure, and involving only pressure-volume work, we may write the First Law as:

$$\Delta E = \Delta H - P\,\Delta V \qquad \text{and,} \qquad \Delta H = \Delta E + P\,\Delta V$$

This last expression tells us that the enthalpy change of a system during a chemical reaction (the heat of reaction at constant temperature and pressure) is simply the change in the internal energy of the system plus the pressure-volume work. And since the pressure-volume work is negligible for reactions involving only solids and liquids, and is generally relatively small for reactions involving gases, the heat of reaction, which can be determined experimentally, is an approximate measure of the change in internal energy of a system (thermal energy + chemical bond energy) for reactions at constant temperature and pressure. Hence the value of the enthalpy change, ΔH, is very important in studying a given reaction, especially since ΔE cannot be measured directly. But before we can proceed to apply these considerations to specific examples of reactions, we must define further the character of enthalpy changes.

First, since $\Delta H = \Delta E + P\,\Delta V$, where ΔE and ΔV depend only on the initial and final states of the system ($\Delta E = E_f - E_i$ and $\Delta V = V_f - V_i$) and P is constant, we conclude that ΔH too depends only on the initial and final states of the system, and not on the path by which the system has actually passed from one state to the other. Hence, $\Delta H = H_f - H_i$, and the enthalpy, H, of a system is a function of the state of the system.

Second, if we wish the ΔH of a reaction to furnish the most significant information about the chemical nature of a reaction (bond-breaking and bond-making energies), we must arrange the conditions of the reaction so that the thermal part of the internal energy of the system remains practically unchanged. This condition, as we have seen, is achieved if the temperature of the final state is equal to the temperature of the initial state, or as we often say, for reactions at constant temperature. At constant temperature and pressure, the major changes that occur in the system are structural changes—all kinds of bond-breaking and bond-making processes, including changes in physical state—such as fusion, vaporization, crystallization, and liquefaction. The ΔH of the reaction, then, is a direct measure of the net energy effect of such structural changes.

16-4 Thermochemistry

The quantitative study of the enthalpy (heat) changes which accompany chemical reactions is generally called *thermochemistry*. Thermochemistry is concerned chiefly with the heats of chemical reactions, and with the manner in which the heat of a given reaction depends on the conditions (physical state, concentration, temperature, and pressure) of the reactants and products. A comparison of the heats of different reactions under the same conditions of temperature and pressure is also often useful, as we shall discuss later. The quantitative enthalpy relationships with which thermochemistry is concerned are based solely on the Law of Conservation of Energy and are therefore valid for any given chemical change under consideration, regardless of our structural interpretation of the chemical change itself. However, thermochemical data can help us to understand which are the more significant energy factors in a chemical process, and to check the validity of our speculations about them. For these reasons, thermochemistry is very important in our study of chemical reactions.

THERMOCHEMICAL EQUATIONS AND STANDARD ENTHALPIES. When we indicate the enthalpy changes which accompany a chemical reaction, it is important to state specifically the number of moles of all the substances (reactants and products) which take part in the reaction, their physical form (gas, liquid, or solid, including the crystalline form of the solid, if more than one exists), and finally the temperature and pressure of the initial and final states of the reacting system. During a reaction, the temperature of the system may actually rise or fall and so may the pressure, but these changes will not affect the value of ΔH, which is the enthalpy change of the reaction *when the final state of the system (the products) has returned to the temperature and pressure of the initial state of the system.* In fact, as we know, the enthalpy of a system is a thermodynamic function (a function of state), so that the enthalpy change accompanying a reaction, $\Delta H = H_f - H_i$, is independent of any intermediate *state or states.*

Here are two examples of thermochemical equations. The first example is the reaction of solid carbon as graphite, $C_{(s,gr)}$, with oxygen gas, $O_{2(g)}$, to form carbon dioxide gas, $CO_{2(g)}$:

1. $C_{(s,gr)}$ (25°C, 1 atm) + $O_{2(g)}$ (25°C, 1 atm) $\longrightarrow$ $CO_{2(g)}$ (25°C, 1 atm)
$\Delta H = -94.1$ kcal/mole $CO_{2(g)}$

The second example is the neutralization of a strong acid with a strong base in aqueous solution:

2. $H^+_{(aq)}$ (25°C, 1 atm, 1*M*) + $OH^-_{(aq)}$ (25°C, 1 atm, 1*M*) $\longrightarrow$ $H_2O_{(l)}$ (25°C, 1 atm)
$\Delta H = -13.6$ kcal/mole-equation

In these thermochemical equations the subscripts indicating the physical form of each substance, and the values of the temperature and pressure given in parentheses alongside the symbols and formulas are very cumbersome; however they are necessary because the indicated enthalpy change holds only for the specified states and conditions. In these examples we have chosen reactions involving 1 mole of each of the reactants and 1 mole of the product. In most chemical reactions, however, different numbers of moles of the various reactants and products are involved. In these cases, unless otherwise stated, the value of ΔH represents the enthalpy change for the complete reaction of the number of moles indicated in the equation or, as we may say, per "mole-equation." Here are three examples which illustrate the importance of specifying in thermochemical equations both the number of moles reacting and the physical state of the reactants and products:

3. $C_{(s,dia)}$ (25°C, 1 atm) + $O_{2(g)}$ (25°C, 1 atm) $\longrightarrow$ $CO_{2(g)}$ (25°C, 1 atm)
$\Delta H = -94.6$ kcal/mole-equation

4. 2 $H_{2(g)}$ (25°C, 1 atm) + $O_{2(g)}$ (25°C, 1 atm) $\longrightarrow$ 2 $H_2O_{(l)}$ (25°C, 1 atm)
$\Delta H = -136.6$ kcal/mole-equation

5. $H_{2(g)}$ (25°C, 1 atm) + $\frac{1}{2}$ $O_{2(g)}$ (25°C, 1 atm) $\longrightarrow$ $H_2O_{(l)}$ (25°C, 1 atm)
$\Delta H = -68.3$ kcal/mole-equation

The enthalpy change of reaction 3 may also be expressed as follows: $\Delta H = -94.6$ kcal/mole of $CO_{2(g)}$ formed, or $\Delta H = -94.6$ kcal/mole $C_{(s,dia)}$ reacted, or $\Delta H = -94.6$ kcal/mole $O_{2(g)}$ reacted. For reaction 4, $\Delta H = -136.6$ kcal/2 moles $H_2O_{(l)}$ formed, or $\Delta H = -136.6$ kcal/2 moles $H_{2(g)}$ reacted, or $\Delta H = -136.6$ kcal/(1) mole $O_{2(g)}$ reacted. Finally, for reaction 5, $\Delta H = -68.3$ kcal/(1) mole $H_2O_{(l)}$ formed, or $\Delta H = -68.3$ kcal/(1) mole $H_{2(g)}$ reacted, or $\Delta H = -68.3$ kcal/$\frac{1}{2}$ mole $O_{2(g)}$ reacted. Although equations 4 and 5 both represent the combination of hydrogen with oxygen to form liquid water, the values of ΔH are different because in reaction 4 we consider *twice* the number of moles as in reaction 5, and accordingly the value of ΔH for 4 is *twice* that for 5.

THE STANDARD STATE OF A SUBSTANCE. To avoid specifying in each case the physical state, temperature, and pressure of each of the reactants and products of a thermochemical reaction, it is convenient to choose for each substance at a given temperature a reference state, called the *standard state.* Then, any enthalpy change for a reaction involving only substances in their standard states is called a *standard enthalpy change,* at the specified temperature and is indicated as $\Delta H°$ (read: ΔH-zero). Here is how we choose the standard states of substances at a specified temperature:

1. *Pure Solids.* The standard state is the (most) stable crystalline form at 1 atm.
2. *Pure Liquids.* The standard state is the liquid at 1 atm.
3. *Pure gases.* The standard state is the gas (assumed to behave ideally) at 1 atm.
4. *Solutions.* (a) *Solvent:* The standard state of the solvent is the pure (liquid) solvent at 1 atm. (b) *Solute:* The standard state of the solute is that in which the *activity* of the solute in solution is equal to unity. The activity of a solute in solution varies, in general, with the concentration; for each solute and each solvent, an activity = 1 is attained at a well-specified concentration. As a first approximation, however, we assume that all solutes have an activity equal to unity in molar (1 *M*) solution at 1 atm. Thus, the standard state of a solute is taken (approximately) as that with 1 *M* concentration at 1 atm.

Now, we can look back at equations 1 to 5 written above. We see that in equations 1, 2, 4, and 5 all reactants and products appear in their *standard states* at the specified temperature (25°C); hence we speak of the *standard* enthalpy of reaction, $\Delta H°$, at 25°C.

The *standard enthalpy change*, $\Delta H°$, of a given reaction at a specified temperature is defined as the enthalpy change for that reaction when each of the reactants and products is in its *standard state* at that temperature.

We shall now proceed to consider the enthalpy changes for some important and common types of transformations and explain them on the basis of our structural interpretation of matter and material changes. For simplicity we shall commonly use the terms *enthalpy*, or *heat of reaction* to mean the *enthalpy change* for that reaction.

ENTHALPY OF ATOMIZATION (ΔH_{atomiz}). The enthalpy of atomization is the energy involved in the transformation of 1 mole of a substance into its gaseous atoms, at the same temperature and pressure. Energy is always required to transform any substance—solid, liquid, or gas—into its gaseous atoms, so that the enthalpy of atomization, ΔH_{atomiz}, is always positive (heat is absorbed by the system). For example, 25.9 kcal are required to atomize 1 mole of crystalline sodium metal, $Na_{(s)}$, at 25°C and 1 atm, to its gaseous atoms, $Na_{(g)}$, also at 25°C and 1 atm:

$$Na_{(s)} \longrightarrow Na_{(g)} \qquad \Delta H_{atomiz} = +25.9 \text{ kcal/mole Na atoms}$$

Notice that in this example both the reactant, $Na_{(s)}$, and the product, $Na_{(g)}$, are at 25°C and 1 atm. In practice, most substances can be atomized only at very high temperatures, or at very low pressures, or both, so that a direct measure of their ΔH_{atomiz} cannot be obtained under standard conditions of temperature and pressure. However, it is possible to calculate from the experimental value of the heat of atomization obtained at any temperature and pressure what value ΔH_{atomiz} would have at any other specified temperature and pressure, and in particular at 25°C and 1 atm. Thus, regardless of the actual temperature and pressure at which a substance is atomized, we define the *enthalpy of atomization of a substance* (element or compound) as the energy required to change 1 mole of the substance in its stable state at 25°C and 1 atm to its gaseous atoms, also at 25°C and 1 atm. The values of the enthalpies of atomization of the elements are given in Table 16-1.

ENTHALPY OF DISSOCIATION (ΔH_{diss}). This term is generally used to indicate the energy involved in the dissociation of a gaseous covalent molecule into its individual gaseous atoms at the same temperature and pressure as the original molecule. For example: $Cl_{2(g)} \longrightarrow 2\ Cl_{(g)}$, $\Delta H_{diss} = +28.92$ kcal/mole $Cl_{2(g)}$. We have already discussed the heats of dissociation of both diatomic and polyatomic molecules, and

TABLE 16-1 ENTHALPIES OF ATOMIZATION, ΔH_{atomiz}, OF THE ELEMENTS (KCAL/MOLE OF ATOMS) AT 25°C AND 1 ATM*

H 52.1																	He 0.0
Li 38.6	Be 78.2											B 135	C 170.9	N 113.0	O 59.6	F 18.9	Ne 0.0
Na 25.9	Mg 33.3											Al 78.0	Si 107.4	P 79.8	S 65.6	Cl 28.9	Ar 0.0
K 21.3	Ca 42.2	Sc 91.0	Ti 112.5	V 122.8	Cr 94.8	Mn 67.0	Fe 99.7	Co 101.6	Ni 102.8	Cu 81.1	Zn 31.2	Ga 65.4	Ge 90.0	As 72.4	Se 49.7	Br 26.7	Kr 0.0
Rb 19.5	Sr 39.1	Y 101.3	Zr 145.4	Nb 172.8	Mo 158.2	Tc 150	Ru 155.5	Rh 133.2	Pd 90.1	Ag 68.0	Cd 26.8	In 58.2	Sn 72.0	Sb 63.2	Te 44.8	I 25.5	Xe 0.0
Cs 18.7	Ba 41.7	La 102.5	Hf 146.0	Ta 186.8	W 201.8	Re 185.7	Os 188.2	Ir 159.8	Pt 135.1	Au 87.5	Hg 14.6	Tl 43.0	Pb 46.8	Bi 49.5	Po 34.5	At —	Rn 0.0
Fr —	Ra —																

* The intensity of the background color in this table roughly parallels the values of ΔH_{atomiz}.

their relationship to bond strengths in the chapter on chemical bonding (p. 307). For those elements which exist at 25°C and 1 atm as gaseous diatomic molecules, the enthalpy of dissociation is the same as the enthalpy of atomization given in Table 16-1.

ENTHALPY OF IONIZATION. We know that energy must always be supplied to remove an electron from a gaseous atom to form its monopositive gaseous ion, and that an even larger quantity of energy must be supplied to remove one or more additional electron(s) from the monopositive gaseous ion. Thus the enthalpy change, ΔH, for the removal of an electron from either a neutral atom or a positive ion always has a positive value:

$$\left.\begin{array}{llll} H_{(g)} & \longrightarrow H^+_{(g)} & + e^- & \Delta H = \text{1st ionization energy of hydrogen} \\ & & & \quad = +313.0 \text{ kcal/mole-equation} \\ Na_{(g)} & \longrightarrow Na^+_{(g)} & + e^- & \Delta H = \text{1st ionization energy of sodium} \\ & & & \quad = +118.0 \text{ kcal/mole-equation} \\ Na^+_{(g)} & \longrightarrow Na^{++}_{(g)} & + e^- & \Delta H = \text{2nd ionization energy of sodium} \\ & & & \quad = +1{,}090.0 \text{ kcal/mole-equation} \end{array}\right\} \text{at } 25^\circ\text{C, 1 atm}$$

Notice that the ΔH of ionization of a gaseous atom $M_{(g)}$, to form a gaseous positive ion, $M^+_{(g)}$, is simply the *ionization energy* of the element M, which we already discussed in Chapter 13, (p. 255). Conversely, the enthalpy change involved in the process by which a gaseous atom takes on an electron to form a gaseous mononegative ion is simply the *electron affinity* of the element, also discussed in Chapter 13 (p. 262):

$$\left.\begin{array}{ll} H_{(g)} + e^- \longrightarrow H^-_{(g)} & \Delta H = \text{electron affinity of hydrogen} \\ & \quad = -17.0 \text{ kcal/mole-equation} \\ Cl_{(g)} + e^- \longrightarrow Cl^-_{(g)} & \Delta H = \text{electron affinity of chlorine} \\ & \quad = -85.1 \text{ kcal/mole-equation} \end{array}\right\} \text{at } 25^\circ\text{C, 1 atm}$$

Notice, again, that the values of the ionization energies and electron affinities of elements are generally given for the process at 25°C and 1 atm, even though such reactions do not in practice occur under these conditions.

ENTHALPY OF FUSION (ΔH_{fus}), VAPORIZATION (ΔH_{vap}), AND SUBLIMATION (ΔH_{subl}). These terms indicate the energy involved in transforming 1 mole of a solid to its liquid, of a liquid to its vapor, and of a solid to its vapor, respectively. Again, both the reactant and the product of the transformation are at the same temperature and pressure. We know that for any fixed value of the pressure, and in particular for $P = 1$ atm, the fusion and sublimation of a solid and the vaporization of a liquid—and their reverse processes, the freezing of a liquid or gas and the liquefaction of a gas—occur for each substance at a well-defined characteristic temperature (the melting, sublimation, and boiling point of the substance at the specified pressure). The heats of fusion, sublimation, and vaporization are therefore determined experimentally for transformations occurring at non-standard temperatures. The heats of fusion and vaporization at 25°C and 1 atm, which are often given in tables of thermochemical data, are calculated values.

Energy is always required to transform a solid to its liquid or vapor, and a liquid to its vapor, at the same temperature. Consequently, ΔH_{fus}, ΔH_{subl}, and ΔH_{vap} are always positive. As an example, consider ice melting to water at 0°C and 1 atm, and water vaporizing to steam at 100°C and 1 atm:

$$\begin{array}{lll} H_2O_{(s)} \text{ (0°C, 1 atm)} \longrightarrow H_2O_{(l)} \text{ (0°C, 1 atm)} & \Delta H_{fus} = +1.44 \text{ kcal/mole } H_2O \\ H_2O_{(l)} \text{ (100°C, 1 atm)} \longrightarrow H_2O_{(g)} \text{ (100°C, 1 atm)} & \Delta H_{vap} = +9.72 \text{ kcal/mole } H_2O \end{array}$$

If a certain quantity of heat energy is required to melt 1 mole of a solid or to evaporate 1 mole of a liquid, this same quantity of heat will be liberated when the liquid solidifies or the gas liquefies. Hence the heat of solidification of a substance is equal to its heat of fusion, but with a minus sign, and similarly the heat of liquefaction of a gas is equal to its heat of vaporization, with a minus sign. For example, the enthalpy change for the condensation of 1 mole of H_2O gas to its liquid at 100°C and 1 atm is $\Delta H_{condensation} = -9.72$ kcal/mole H_2O.

For the elements which in the gaseous state exist as isolated atoms, the heat of sublimation, ΔH_{subl}, is the same as the heat of atomization, ΔH_{atomiz}. But for some other elements, which sublime to give diatomic or polyatomic molecules, the heat of sublimation differs from the heat of atomization. For example, when solid iodine $I_{2(s)}$ sublimes at 25°C and 1 atm, gaseous diatomic molecules $I_{2(g)}$ are formed:

$$I_{2(s)} \longrightarrow I_{2(g)} \qquad \Delta H_{subl} = +14.9 \text{ kcal/mole } I_{2(g)} \text{ molecules}$$

But when solid iodine, $I_{2(s)}$, is atomized at 25°C and 1 atm, gaseous isolated $I_{(g)}$ atoms are formed:

$$I_{2(s)} \longrightarrow 2\,I_{(g)} \qquad \Delta H_{atomiz} = +51.0 \text{ kcal/2 moles } I_{(g)} \text{ atoms}$$

Notice that to make a meaningful comparison between the heats of these two reactions, we must compare the values of ΔH for equations involving *the same number of moles of iodine atoms.* We then see that less energy is required to sublime 1 mole of crystalline iodine to its molecules, $I_{2(g)}$, than to atomize it to its atoms, $2\,I_{(g)}$. Of course the difference in the ΔH values of these two processes, $51.0 - 14.9 = 36.1$ kcal/mole of $I_{2(g)}$, is the energy required to dissociate 1 mole of gaseous $I_{2(g)}$ molecules into their gaseous atoms at 25°C and 1 atm:

$$I_{2(g)} \longrightarrow 2\,I_{(g)} \qquad \Delta H_{diss} = +36.1 \text{ kcal/mole } I_{2(g)} \text{ molecules}$$

The enthalpies of fusion, sublimation, or vaporization of some common substances are given in Table 16-2.

ENTHALPY OF SOLUTION (ΔH_{soln}). The enthalpy of solution of a substance is the quantity of heat exchanged (given off or absorbed) when 1 mole of the substance is dissolved in a stated amount of solvent at a given temperature and pressure. The enthalpy of solution of a substance is therefore the heat involved in the formation of a solution of 1 mole of the substance (solute) in a given solvent and at a specified concentration, temperature, and pressure. We must always specify the concentration of the solution formed, because the quantity of heat involved in dissolving 1 mole of a given solute in a given solvent depends on the amount of solvent, or in other words, on the concentration of the resulting solution.

In considering enthalpies of solution, it is convenient to express the quantities of both the solute and solvent on a mole basis, so that the dissolving of the solute in the solvent may be represented by an ordinary stoichiometric equation. For example,

TABLE 16-2 ENTHALPIES OF FUSION, SUBLIMATION, AND VAPORIZATION (KCAL/MOLE) OF SOME COMMON SUBSTANCES

Transformation	ΔH at 1 atm and 25°C	ΔH at 1 atm and at equilibrium temperature of transformation
$H_2O_{(s)} \longrightarrow H_2O_{(l)}$		1.44 (0.0°C)
$H_2O_{(l)} \longrightarrow H_2O_{(g)}$	+10.5	9.72 (100.0°C)
$Br_{2(l)} \longrightarrow Br_{2(g)}$	+7.3	
$CH_3OH_{(l)} \longrightarrow CH_3OH_{(g)}$	+8.9	
$CCl_{4(l)} \longrightarrow CCl_{4(g)}$	+7.9	7.3 (76.7°C)
$I_{2(s)} \longrightarrow I_{2(g)}$	+14.9	
$Hg_{(l)} \longrightarrow Hg_{(g)}$	+14.5	
$SO_{2(l)} \longrightarrow SO_{2(g)}$	+6.1	5.9 (−10.0°C)

when 1 mole of gaseous hydrogen chloride, $HCl_{(g)}$, is dissolved in 50 moles of water, 50 H_2O, at 25°C and 1 atm (1 l. of water is approximately 55.5 moles of water), 17.56 kcal are evolved. We may represent this by the equation:

$$HCl_{(g)} + 50\ H_2O_{(l)} \longrightarrow HCl \cdot 50\ H_2O\ (soln) \qquad \Delta H_{soln} = -17.56\ kcal/mole\text{-}equation$$

In this equation we have represented the product—this particular solution of hydrochloric acid—as $HCl \cdot 50\ H_2O$ (soln). We could also have written $HCl_{(aq)}$ (50 H_2O), but in one way or another we must specify the mole ratio of the solute (HCl) to the solvent (H_2O). Note that if the solution is prepared in a Dewar flask, so that no heat can be exchanged with the surroundings, the heat of solution of HCl gas ($\Delta H_{soln} = -17.56$ kcal for this case) is sufficient to raise the temperature of the system from its initial value of 25°C to approximately 42°C. (The heat capacity of water and most water solutions is about 1 kcal/l. = 18 cal/mole.) Since in this example there are about 50 moles (about 1 l.) of solution, the 17.56 kcal evolved in the reaction will raise the temperature by about 17°C.

Let us now consider the dissolving of 1 mole of a solid substance (solute) again in 50 moles (about 1 l.) of liquid water (solvent), at 25°C and 1 atm:

$$1\ mole\ solute_{(s)} + 50\ H_2O_{(l)} \longrightarrow 1\ mole\ solute \cdot 50\ H_2O\ (soln)$$

For the following ionic solids the values of ΔH_{soln} (kcal/mole of solute) are: NaOH, −10.16; NaCl, +0.89; NH_4Cl, +3.75. Notice that for the same molar concentration, the ΔH_{soln} of crystalline NaOH has a rather large negative value, that of crystalline NaCl has a very small but positive value, and that of crystalline NH_4Cl has an appreciable positive value. Experimentally, we find that when we add 1 mole of each of these salts to 50 moles of $H_2O_{(l)}$ in a Dewar flask, all three salts spontaneously dissolve but the NaOH solution warms up considerably, whereas the solution of NaCl remains practically at the same temperature, and the NH_4Cl solution becomes cooler. Table 16-3 gives the enthalpies of solution of some common ionic compounds.

The following example illustrates that the heat of solution for a given amount of a given solute in a given solvent depends upon the number of moles of the solvent. The experimentally determined ΔH_{soln} values for 1 mole of $HCl_{(g)}$ in water at 25°C and 1 atm are: for 25 moles of H_2O (approx. $\frac{1}{2}$ l.), −17.32 kcal; for 50 moles of H_2O (approx. 1 l.), −17.56 kcal; for 5,000 moles H_2O (approx. 10 l.), −17.95 kcal; and the extrapolated value for an infinite number of moles of water ($\infty\ H_2O$) is −18.00 kcal. The enthalpy of solution of HCl at infinite dilution is simply the ΔH of the following reaction:

$$HCl_{(g)} + \infty\ H_2O_{(l)} \longrightarrow HCl \cdot \infty\ H_2O\ (soln) \qquad \Delta H_{soln,\infty} = -18.00\ kcal/mole\ HCl_{(g)}$$

As the number of moles of water increases, the heat of solution of $HCl_{(g)}$ approaches (that is, can be extrapolated to) a final value at infinite dilution, $\Delta H_{soln,\infty} = -18.00$

TABLE 16-3 ENTHALPIES OF SOLUTION, ΔH_{soln}, OF SOME IONIC COMPOUNDS IN VARIOUS AMOUNTS OF WATER AT 25°C AND 1 ATM

ΔH_{soln} (kcal/mole of solute)					Moles of H_2O per 1 mole of solute
$HCl_{(g)}$	$H_2SO_{4(l)}$	$NaOH_{(s)}$	$NaCl_{(s)}$	$NH_4Cl_{(s)}$	
−17.56	−17.53	−10.16	+0.89	+3.75	55 (1 l.)
−17.69	−17.68	−10.11	+0.98	+3.75	100 (about 1.8 l.)
−17.78	−17.91	−10.11	+1.02	+3.73	200 (about 3.5 l.)
−17.89	−18.78	−10.15	+1.00	+3.69	1,000 (about 18 l.)
−17.95	−20.18	−10.20	+0.97	+3.65	5,000 (about 90 l.)

Moles H_2O	ΔH_{soln}
25	+0.726
50	+0.892
100	+0.982
400	+1.020
1000	+1.004
5000	+0.972

kcal/mole $HCl_{(g)}$. It follows that if we add 25 moles of H_2O to 1 mole of HCl already dissolved in 25 moles of H_2O at 25°C—that is, if we dilute the initial solution to half its original concentration—then (17.56 − 17.32 =) 0.24 kcal are liberated. This is the *enthalpy of dilution* for this particular dilution process. In general, the heat of dilution depends on the concentration of both the final and initial solutions. For example, if we now dilute a solution containing 1 mole of HCl in 50 moles of H_2O to a solution containing 1 mole of HCl in 100 moles of H_2O—half again the original concentration—the heat evolved is only (17.69 − 17.56 =) 0.13 kcal. As another example of how the heat of solution depends on concentration, in the margin we see that for NaCl the heat of solution first increases as the dilution increases, reaches a maximum for about 1 mole NaCl in 400 mole of water, and then slightly decreases. And the extrapolated value for an infinite number of moles of H_2O (∞ H_2O) is $\Delta H_{soln,\infty} = +0.930$ kcal/mole NaCl.

STANDARD ENTHALPY OF FORMATION, ΔH°_{form}. The standard enthalpy of formation of a compound is defined as the heat involved in the reaction by which 1 mole of the compound is formed from its elements, each element initially in its standard (most stable) state and at the same temperature as the compound formed. All elements in their standard states are conventionally assigned a heat of formation equal to zero. The *standard enthalpies of formation*, ΔH_{form}, of compounds are usually given at 25°C. Throughout this book we shall always consider standard enthalpies of formation of compounds at 25°C—unless we state explicitly that the reaction occurs under different conditions. However, for the sake of brevity we shall often omit the word "standard."

The following examples illustrate some points of interest in regard to the standard enthalpies of formation of compounds at 25°C and 1 atm:

1. $H_{2(g)} + \frac{1}{2} O_{2(g)} \longrightarrow H_2O_{(g)}$ $\qquad \Delta H^\circ_{form} = -57.8$ kcal/mole $H_2O_{(g)}$
2. $H_{2(g)} + \frac{1}{2} O_{2(g)} \longrightarrow H_2O_{(l)}$ $\qquad \Delta H^\circ_{form} = -68.3$ kcal/mole $H_2O_{(l)}$
3. $C_{(s,gr)} + O_{2(g)} \longrightarrow CO_{2(g)}$ $\qquad \Delta H^\circ_{form} = -94.1$ kcal/mole $CO_{2(g)}$
4. $C_{(s,gr)} + 2\,H_{2(g)} \longrightarrow CH_{4(g)}$ $\qquad \Delta H^\circ_{form} = -17.9$ kcal/mole $CH_{4(g)}$
5. $\frac{1}{2} H_{2(g)} + \frac{1}{2} N_{2(g)} + C_{(s,gr)} \longrightarrow HCN_{(g)}$ $\qquad \Delta H^\circ_{form} = +30.7$ kcal/mole $HCN_{(g)}$

Notice that all these equations are written in terms of 1 mole of the product. Reactions (1) and (2) show that the heat of formation varies according to the physical state of the compound formed; for water, the difference between the heat of formation of $H_2O_{(g)}$ (−57.8 kcal) and the heat of formation of $H_2O_{(l)}$ (−68.3 kcal) is −10.5 kcal. These additional −10.5 kcal evolved in the formation of liquid water are, of course, the heat of condensation of $H_2O_{(g)}$ at 25°C and 1 atm, or as we have seen, the heat of vaporization of liquid water at 25°C and 1 atm with its sign changed: $H_2O_{(l)} \longrightarrow H_2O_{(g)}$, $\Delta H_{vap} = +10.5$ kcal/mole H_2O at 25°C and 1 atm. Thus when we give the heat of formation of a compound we must always be careful to specify its physical state.

Equation 3 involves as a reactant an element, carbon, which exists in two crystalline forms, diamond and graphite. Since the normal state of carbon at 25°C and 1 atm is graphite, this is the form of carbon which appears in the equation. If we considered carbon in the form of diamond as one of the reactants, the thermochemical equation would be:

6. $C_{(s,diamond)} + O_{2(g)} \longrightarrow CO_{2(g)}$ $\qquad \Delta H = -94.6$ kcal/mole $CO_{2(g)}$ (25°C, 1 atm)

In this case the ΔH value would not be, according to our convention, the standard heat of formation of CO_2, because the reacting element is carbon as diamond, rather than as graphite. Notice that the difference between the ΔH values for reactions 3 and 6 is the ΔH of the allotropic transformation of diamond to graphite:

$$C_{(s,diamond)} \longrightarrow C_{(s,graphite)} \qquad \Delta H = -0.5 \text{ kcal/mole carbon (25°C, 1 atm)}$$

Finally, equations 4 and 5 illustrate that the heat of formation of a compound is defined regardless of whether the compound can actually be prepared from its elements by the reaction shown, or is obtained by a different route. Both CH_4 and HCN, in fact, are not prepared by the indicated reactions.

For ions in aqueous solution the values cannot be determined in the same way as for pure substances, the reason being that we cannot have a system made up solely of a certain kind of ions of one sign, and our thermochemical measurements necessarily involve ionic compounds which consist of at least two kinds of ions—positive ions and negative ions. For ions in solution, then, we use relative values of ΔH°_{form} obtained by taking conventionally the ΔH°_{form} of the $H^+_{(aq)}$ ion at 1 molar (1*M*) concentration and at 25° and 1 atm to be equal to zero: ΔH°_{form} for $H^+_{(aq,1M)} = 0$. The relative values of the ΔH°_{form} of ions in solution can be used, just as the ΔH_{form} values of pure compounds can, to calculate ΔH° values of reactions, because the arbitrary factor introduced by taking ΔH°_{form} for $H^+_{(aq,1M)} = 0$ cancels out in all cases.

In the next chapter we shall learn that *at room temperature* the heat of formation of a compound is often the more important energy factor in determining whether the compound has or has not the capacity to decompose spontaneously into its elements. In general, if ΔH°_{form} of a compound has an appreciably large negative value, *at room temperature* the compound does not have the capacity to decompose into its elements, or as we briefly say, is stable toward decomposition into its elements. On the other hand, if ΔH°_{form} has an appreciably large positive value, the compound tends to decompose spontaneously into its elements *at room temperature.* The standard enthalpies of formation of a number of common substances are listed in Table 16-4, page 340.

HESS' LAW

We have seen that the enthalpy, *H*, of a system is a thermodynamic property which depends only on the state of the system—its chemical constitution, physical state, temperature, and pressure. Hence the *change* in enthalpy, ΔH, accompanying a given transformation depends only on the initial and the final states of the system, and not on the actual sequence of states followed by the system during the transformation. This same conclusion was reached by the chemist and physician Germain Hess (1802–1850) on the basis of experimental observations many years before the concept of enthalpy as a function of state was developed. Hess' Law states that the total heat change involved in a chemical reaction is independent of the intermediate stages through which the reaction proceeds or may be thought to proceed, and depends only on the chemical nature and physical conditions of the reactants and products. We have already implicitly applied this law several times in the previous pages—for example, in calculating the heat of vaporization of water at 25°C and 1 atm and the heat transformation of diamond to graphite. Hess' Law enables us to calculate enthalpy changes for reactions which cannot be carried out directly in the laboratory and/or which do not allow the direct determination of their enthalpy changes. This is the case, for example, for the reaction of formation of most compounds from their elements in their stable states at 25°C and 1 atmosphere pressure. If we can put together any sequence of intermediate reactions which, when added together, will result in the desired reaction, then the sum of all the ΔH values for all the intermediate reactions will supply the ΔH of the desired reaction, which we cannot measure directly. As an example, consider the reaction of graphite, $C_{(s,gr)}$, with hydrogen gas, $H_{2(g)}$, to form methane gas, $CH_{4(g)}$, at 25°C and 1 atm:

$$C_{(s,gr)} + 2\,H_{2(g)} \longrightarrow CH_{4(g)} \qquad \Delta H^\circ = -17.9 \text{ kcal/mole } CH_{4(g)}$$

Since we do not know as yet how to carry out this reaction in the laboratory quantitatively, we cannot measure directly its ΔH value, which is the heat of formation of methane gas; however, we can calculate it easily from the information given in Table 16-5. We see, in fact, that we can obtain the desired net equation: $C_{(s,gr)} + 2\ H_{2(g)} \longrightarrow CH_{4(g)}$, by adding the following from Table 16-5: equation (1) as written; equation (2) also as written but multiplied by 2; and finally the *reverse* of equation (3). Notice that when an equation is "reversed," ΔH reaction remains numerically the same, but its sign changes. The intermediate reactants and products then cancel out as shown and only the reactants and products of the desired net equations remain.

TABLE 16-4 STANDARD ENTHALPIES (HEATS) OF FORMATION, ΔH°_{form}, OF SOME SUBSTANCES AT 25°C

A. PURE SUBSTANCES

Substance (state)	ΔH°_{form} (kcal/mole)	Substance (state)	ΔH°_{form} (kcal/mole)	Substance (state)	ΔH°_{form} (kcal/mole)	Substance (state)	ΔH°_{form} (kcal/mole)
$Ag_2O_{(s)}$	−7.3	$CO_{2(g)}$	−94.1	$HCl_{(g)}$	−22.1	$NH_{3(g)}$	−11.0
$AgF_{(s)}$	−48.5	$CH_{4(g)}$	−17.9	$HBr_{(g)}$	−8.7	$NH_4NO_{3(s)}$	−87.3
$AgCl_{(s)}$	−30.4	$CH_3Cl_{(g)}$	−19.6			$(NH_4)_2SO_{4(s)}$	−281.9
$AgBr_{(s)}$	−23.8	$CCl_{4(g)}$	−25.5	$HI_{(g)}$	+6.2	$NH_4Cl_{(s)}$	−75.4
$AgI_{(s)}$	−14.9	$CCl_{4(l)}$	−33.3				
		$CS_{2(g)}$	+27.5	$Hg_{(l)}$	0.0	$Na_2O_{(s)}$	−99.4
$Al_2O_{3(s)}$	−399.1	$CS_{2(l)}$	+21.0	$Hg_{(g)}$	+14.5	$NaOH_{(s)}$	−102.0
$AlF_{3(s)}$	−355.8			$HgO_{(s)}$	−21.7	$NaF_{(s)}$	−136.5
$AlCl_{3(s)}$	−166.2	$CaO_{(s)}$	−151.9	$Hg_2Cl_{2(s)}$	−63.3	$NaCl_{(s)}$	−98.6
$AlBr_{3(s)}$	−125.8	$CaH_{2(s)}$	−45.1	$HgCl_{2(s)}$	−55.0	$NaBr_{(s)}$	−86.0
$AlI_{3(s)}$	−75.2	$CaCl_{2(s)}$	−190.0			$NaI_{(s)}$	−68.0
		$CaCO_{3(s)}$	−288.4	$I_{2(s)}$	0.0		
$B_2O_{3(s)}$	−302.2	$Cl_{2(g)}$	0.0	$I_{2(g)}$	+14.9	$O_{2(g)}$	0.0
$BCl_{3(g)}$	−94.5	$Cl_{(g)}$	+29.0	$I_{(g)}$	+25.5	$O_{3(g)}$	+34.0
$BCl_{3(l)}$	−100.0						
		$CsF_{(s)}$	−126.9	$KCl_{(s)}$	−104.2	$P_{(s,white)}$	0.0
$BaO_{(s)}$	−133.4	$CsCl_{(s)}$	−103.5	$KClO_{3(s)}$	−93.5	$P_{(s,red)}$	−4.4
$BaCl_{2(s)}$	−205.6			$KNO_{3(s)}$	−117.8	$PCl_{3(g)}$	−66.7
$BaSO_{4(s)}$	−350.2	$Cu_2O_{(s)}$	−39.8			$PCl_{5(g)}$	−95.3
		$CuO_{(s)}$	−37.1	$Li_2O_{(s)}$	−142.4		
$BeO_{(s)}$	−146.0			$LiH_{(g)}$	+30.7	$S_{(s,rhombic)}$	0.0
$BeCl_{2(s)}$	−112.0	$F_{2(g)}$	0.0			$S_{(s,monoclinic)}$	+0.1
$Br_{2(l)}$	0.0	$F_{(g)}$	+18.3	$MgO_{(s)}$	−143.8	$SO_{2(g)}$	−71.0
$Br_{2(g)}$	+7.3			$MgF_{2(s)}$	−263.5	$SO_{3(g)}$	−94.4
$Br_{(g)}$	+26.7	$H_{2(g)}$	0.0				
		$H_2O_{(g)}$	−57.8	$NO_{(g)}$	+21.6	$SiO_{2(s)}$	−205.4
$C_{(s,gr)}$	0.0	$H_2O_{2(g)}$	−32.3	$NO_{2(g)}$	+8.1		
$C_{(s,dia)}$	+0.5	$H_2O_{(l)}$	−68.3	$N_2O_{(g)}$	+19.5		
$CO_{(g)}$	−26.4	$HF_{(g)}$	−64.2	$N_2O_{4(g)}$	+2.3		

B. IONS IN 1-MOLAR AQUEOUS SOLUTION*

Ion	ΔH°_{form} (kcal/mole)	Ion	ΔH°_{form} (kcal/mole)	Ion	ΔH°_{form} (kcal/mole)	Ion	ΔH°_{form} (kcal/mole)
$Ag^{+}_{(aq)}$	+25.3	$Cu^{+}_{(aq)}$	+12.4	$K^{+}_{(aq)}$	−60.6	$PO^{-3}_{4(aq)}$	−306.9
$Al^{+++}_{(aq)}$	−125.4	$Cu^{++}_{(aq)}$	+15.4	$Li^{+}_{(aq)}$	−66.5	$S^{=}_{(aq)}$	+10.0
$Ba^{++}_{(aq)}$	−128.7	$F^{-}_{(aq)}$	−78.7	$Mg^{++}_{(aq)}$	−110.4	$HS^{-}_{(aq)}$	−4.2
$Br^{-}_{(aq)}$	−28.9	$Fe^{++}_{(aq)}$	−21.0	$NH^{+}_{4(aq)}$	−31.7	$Rb^{+}_{(aq)}$	−58.9
$CO^{=}_{3(aq)}$	−161.6	$Fe^{+++}_{(aq)}$	−11.4	$NO^{-}_{3(aq)}$	−49.4	$SO^{=}_{3(aq)}$	−149.2
$HCO^{-}_{3(aq)}$	−165.2			$Na^{+}_{(aq)}$	−57.3	$SO^{=}_{4(aq)}$	−216.9
$CN^{-}_{(aq)}$	+36.1	$H^{+}_{(aq)}$	0.0	$Ni^{++}_{(aq)}$	−15.3	$Sr^{++}_{(aq)}$	−13.4
$Ca^{++}_{(aq)}$	−129.8			$OH^{-}_{(aq)}$	−54.9	$Zn^{++}_{(aq)}$	−36.4
$Cl^{-}_{(aq)}$	−40.0	$I^{-}_{(aq)}$	−13.4				
$Cs^{+}_{(aq)}$	−59.2						

* The ΔH°_{form} of ions in solution are conventionally taken relative to that of $H^{+}_{(aq)}$, assumed to be zero.

Thus, the sum of the ΔH values of the intermediate reactions gives us the ΔH value of the desired reaction.

Reaction 1:	$C_{(s,gr)} + \cancel{O_{2(g)}} \longrightarrow \cancel{CO_{2(g)}}$	$\Delta H = -94.1$ kcal/mole $C_{(s,gr)}$
2 × reaction 2:	$2\ H_{2(g)} + \cancel{O_{2(g)}} \longrightarrow \cancel{2\ H_2O_{(l)}}$	$\Delta H = -136.6$ kcal/2 mole $H_{2(g)}$
Reverse of reaction 3:	$\cancel{CO_{2(g)}} + \cancel{2\ H_2O_{(l)}} \longrightarrow CH_{4(g)} + \cancel{2\ O_{2(g)}}$	$\Delta H = +212.8$ kcal/mole $CO_{2(g)}$
Desired net reaction:	$C_{(s,gr)} + 2\ H_{2(g)} \longrightarrow CH_{4(g)}$	

The net ΔH for the desired reaction is:

$$\Delta H = (-94.1 - 136.6 + 212.8 =) -17.9 \text{ kcal/mole } CH_{4(g)}$$

Notice that we can cancel 1 mole of $CO_{2(g)}$ on the right-hand side of the first equation with 1 mole of $CO_{2(g)}$ on the left-hand side of the third equation, because when 1 mole of $CO_{2(g)}$ is produced in the first equation from its elements in their standard state, 94.1 kcal are given off; on the other hand, when 1 mole of $CO_{2(g)}$ is decomposed to its elements in their standard state, 94.1 kcal are absorbed. Consequently, both the moles of $CO_{2(g)}$ and their enthalpy values cancel. The same reasoning holds for the 2 moles of $H_2O_{(l)}$ which appear on the opposite sides of the second and third equations. Similarly, the 2 moles of $O_{2(g)}$ which appear, one each, on the left-hand sides of the first and second equations cancel the 2 moles of $O_{2(g)}$ on the right-hand side of the third equation. The resulting net equation tells us that when both the initial and final states of the system are at 25°C and 1 atm, the final state consisting of 1 mole of $CH_{4(g)}$ has an enthalpy lower by 17.9 kcal than the initial state, which consists of 1 mole of $C_{(s,gr)}$ and 2 moles of $H_{2(g)}$.

The use of Hess' Law in the above example is quite cumbersome. By applying the principle of Hess' Law, however, we can rapidly and simply calculate the ΔH value of any reaction, if we know the values of the $\Delta H^\circ_{\text{form}}$ of all the substances—reactants and products—involved. The $\Delta H^\circ_{\text{form}}$ of most common substances have been determined and we have listed a number of them in Table 16-4. Remember that, by convention, all elements in their standard state at 25°C and 1 atm are assigned a $\Delta H^\circ_{\text{form}}$ equal to zero. Here are some examples of how to calculate the ΔH° of a reaction from the $\Delta H^\circ_{\text{form}}$ of the reactants and products. Consider the reaction of gaseous sulfur dioxide, $SO_{2(g)}$, with oxygen gas, $O_{2(g)}$, to form gaseous sulfur trioxide, $SO_{3(g)}$:

TABLE 16-5 ENTHALPIES OF REACTIONS AT 25°C AND 1 ATM*

Reaction			ΔH(kcal/mole-equation)
1. $C_{(s,gr)} + O_{2(g)}$	$\longrightarrow$	$CO_{2(g)}$	−94.1
2. $H_{2(g)} + \frac{1}{2} O_{2(g)}$	$\longrightarrow$	$H_2O_{(l)}$	−68.3
3. $CH_{4(g)} + 2\ O_{2(g)}$	$\longrightarrow$	$CO_{2(g)} + 2\ H_2O_{(l)}$	−212.8
4. $CH_{4(g)} + Cl_{2(g)}$	$\longrightarrow$	$CH_3Cl_{(g)} + HCl_{(g)}$	−25.6
5. $CH_{4(g)} + 4\ Cl_{2(g)}$	$\longrightarrow$	$CCl_{4(g)} + 4\ HCl_{(g)}$	−97.5
6. $NaOH_{(aq)} + HCl_{(aq)}$	$\longrightarrow$	$NaCl_{(aq)} + H_2O_{(l)}$	−13.8
7. $NH_{3(aq)} + HCl_{(aq)}$	$\longrightarrow$	$NH_4Cl_{(aq)}$	−12.8
8. $NH_{3(g)} + HCl_{(g)}$	$\longrightarrow$	$NH_4Cl_{(s)}$	−42.1
9. $Ag^+_{(aq)} + Cl^-_{(aq)}$	$\longrightarrow$	$AgCl_{(s)}$	−15.5
10. $PCl_{3(g)} + Cl_{2(g)}$	$\longrightarrow$	$PCl_{5(g)}$	−28.6
11. $Zn_{(s)} + Cu^{++}_{(aq)}$	$\longrightarrow$	$Zn^{++}_{(aq)} + Cu_{(s)}$	−51.8
12. $Mg_{(s)} + Pb^{++}_{(aq)}$	$\longrightarrow$	$Mg^{++}_{(aq)} + Pb_{(s)}$	−110.8

* All species in solution have 1 *M* concentration.

$$
\begin{array}{llll}
\textit{Reaction:} & SO_{2(g)} + \tfrac{1}{2} O_{2(g)} \longrightarrow SO_{3(g)} & & \\
\Delta H^\circ_{form}: & -71.0 \quad 0 \qquad -94.4 & & \\
\Delta H^\circ_{reaction}: & = \Delta H^\circ_{form} \text{ of all products } - \Delta H^\circ_{form} \text{ of all reactants} & & \\
 & = \Delta H^\circ_{form}\, SO_{3(g)} - (\Delta H^\circ_{form}\, SO_{2(g)} + \tfrac{1}{2}\, \Delta H^\circ_{form}\, O_{2(g)}) & & \\
 & = \quad -94.4 \quad - \quad (-71.0 \quad + \quad 0) = & & -23.4 \text{ kcal/mole-equation}
\end{array}
$$

As another example let us consider the reaction of methane gas, $CH_{4(g)}$, with chlorine gas, $Cl_{2(g)}$, to form gaseous methyl chloride, $CH_3Cl_{(g)}$:

$$
\begin{array}{llll}
\textit{Reaction:} & CH_{4(g)} + Cl_{2(g)} \longrightarrow CH_3Cl_{(g)} + HCl_{(g)} & & \\
\Delta H^\circ_{form}: & -17.9 \quad 0 \qquad -19.6 \quad -22.1 & & \\
\Delta H^\circ_{reaction}: & = \Delta H^\circ_{form} \text{ of all products } - \Delta H^\circ_{form} \text{ of all reactants} & & \\
 & = \quad (-19.6 - 22.1) \quad - \quad (-17.9) = & & -23.8 \text{ kcal/mole-equation}
\end{array}
$$

ENTHALPY DIAGRAM OF A REACTION

We can represent schematically the enthalpy change which accompanies a reaction of a given system by an *enthalpy diagram* in which the initial and final states of the system are shown as relative enthalpy levels. Enthalpy diagrams can be used for any kind of transformation of any system, and are very useful in helping us to visualize the magnitudes of the enthalpy changes involved in the various steps of a transformation, and also in comparing the magnitudes of the enthalpy changes of different transformations.

In order to construct an enthalpy diagram for a given reaction of a given system, we need first to choose as the reference a certain state of the system, to which we assign arbitrarily an enthalpy value of zero (zero enthalpy level). Each other state of the system then has a fixed relative value, which is determined by the value of the enthalpy change involved in bringing the system from the zero enthalpy state to the state considered. As an example, consider the dissociation of $\frac{1}{2}$ mole of chlorine gas molecules, $Cl_{2(g)}$, to their gaseous atoms, $Cl_{(g)}$.

$$\tfrac{1}{2}\, Cl_{2(g)} \longrightarrow Cl_{(g)} \qquad \Delta H = +28.9 \text{ kcal/mole-equation}$$

If we choose as the zero reference level the initial state of the system, the $\frac{1}{2}$ mole of $Cl_{2(g)}$ molecules, then the enthalpy level of the final state composed of 1 mole of $Cl_{(g)}$ atoms is automatically fixed at +28.9 kcal (Fig. 16-3), since it takes exactly this amount of energy to bring the system from the initial to the final state.

Since in our study of a chemical reaction we are interested in the enthalpy change of the system in passing from its initial to its final state, we can choose as the zero enthalpy level the state of the system which is most convenient for the particular type of reaction under consideration. We should point out here that we have to choose our reference level arbitrarily, because we do not know how to determine the *absolute* enthalpies of substances, and in fact all we can obtain from experiments is the enthalpy *difference* involved when systems undergo transformations.

FIGURE 16-3 Enthalpy diagram of the dissociation of $Cl_{2(g)}$ at 25°C and 1 atm.

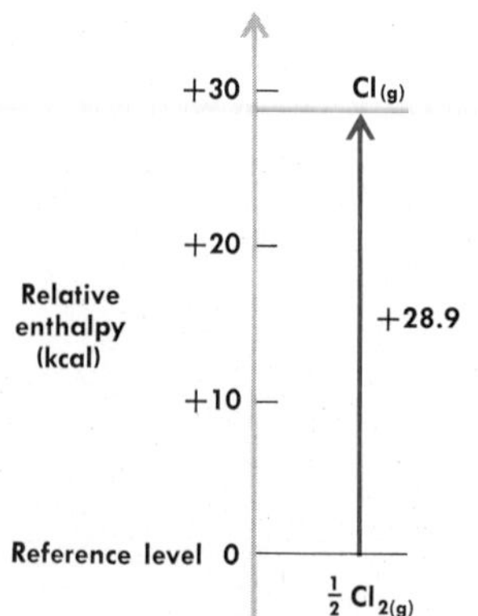

ENTHALPY DIAGRAM FOR THE COMBUSTION OF GRAPHITE. Figure 16-4 represents the enthalpy changes involved in the combustion of (1) graphite, $C_{(s,gr)}$, (2) diamond, $C_{(s,diam)}$, and (3) carbon monoxide gas, $CO_{(g)}$, to form carbon dioxide gas, $CO_{2(g)}$, at 25°C and 1 atm pressure:

$$1.\ C_{(s,gr)} + O_{2(g)} \longrightarrow CO_{2(g)} \qquad \Delta H = -94.1 \text{ kcal/mole-equation}$$
$$2.\ C_{(s,diam)} + O_{2(g)} \longrightarrow CO_{2(g)} \qquad \Delta H = -94.6 \text{ kcal/mole-equation}$$
$$3.\ CO_{(g)} + \tfrac{1}{2}\,O_{2(g)} \longrightarrow CO_{2(g)} \qquad \Delta H = -67.7 \text{ kcal/mole-equation}$$

Notice that in each of these three reactions the final states (products) are all the same, namely 1 mole of $CO_{2(g)}$. The initial states (reactants) are also fundamentally the same since each state represents 1 mole of carbon atoms combined in some way and 2 moles of oxygen atoms combined in some way. However, the initial states differ from one another in the *manner* in which the 1 mole of carbon atoms and the 2 moles of oxygen atoms are bound. By convention we assign the zero enthalpy value to the particular state in which the 1 mole of carbon atoms are combined as graphite (graphite being the standard state of carbon at 25°C and 1 atm) and the 2 moles of oxygen atoms are combined in the form of gaseous diatomic molecules, $O_{2(g)}$. The state in which 1 mole of carbon atoms are combined as diamond and the oxygen atoms again as $O_{2(g)}$ is assigned a higher enthalpy level. The difference between the level of the system $\{C_{(s,diam)} + O_{2(g)}\}$ and that of the system $\{C_{(s,gr)} + O_{2(g)}\}$ being the ΔH of the transformation $C_{(diam)} \longrightarrow C_{(gr)}$. We see from the diagram that since $CO_{2(g)}$ has the same enthalpy value regardless of how it is formed, the enthalpy of combustion of diamond is more negative than that of graphite by an amount precisely equal to the enthalpy difference between diamond and graphite.

We know that graphite, $C_{(s,gr)}$ can be burned completely and quantitatively in the presence of oxygen gas, $O_{2(g)}$, to form carbon dioxide, $CO_{2(g)}$, so we can determine experimentally the quantity of heat liberated in the reaction ($\Delta H = -94.1$ kcal/mole $CO_{2(g)}$). We also know that graphite can be burned to produce gaseous carbon monoxide, $C_{(s,gr)} + \frac{1}{2}\,O_{2(g)} \longrightarrow CO_{(g)}$. However, we cannot determine experimentally the heat of this reaction, because when graphite is burned, even under as carefully controlled conditions as possible, some carbon dioxide is always formed. Hence, the direct experimental measurement of the heat evolved in the reaction cannot give us an accurate value of the heat of combustion of graphite to carbon monoxide. Fortu-

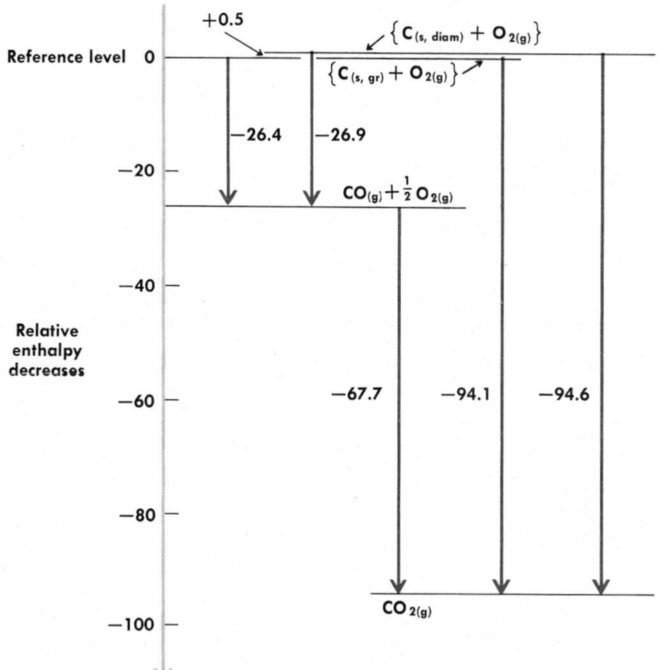

FIGURE 16-4 Enthalpy diagram for the combustion of graphite, diamond, and carbon monoxide gas at 25°C and 1 atm.

nately, however, we can separate carbon monoxide from the small quantity of carbon dioxide formed in the combustion by absorbing the latter in water under high pressure. In fact, $CO_{2(g)}$ is very soluble in water under high pressure, whereas $CO_{(g)}$ is only slightly soluble. Thus we obtain pure carbon monoxide, which can then be burned completely in oxygen to give pure $CO_{2(g)}$. The heat evolved in this combustion is the ΔH of the reaction:

$$CO_{(g)} + \tfrac{1}{2}\,O_{2(g)} \longrightarrow CO_{2(g)} \qquad \Delta H = -67.7 \text{ kcal/mole } CO_{2(g)}$$

From Fig. 16-4 we can now *calculate* that

$$C_{(s,gr)} + \tfrac{1}{2}\,O_{2(g)} \longrightarrow CO_{(g)} \qquad \Delta H = -26.4 \text{ kcal/mole } CO_{(g)}$$

In general, if the series of reactions shown in an enthalpy diagram represents a complete cycle—that is, if each reaction shown can be obtained by summation of the others—the diagram permits us to calculate graphically, just as we can do arithmetically by Hess' Law, the ΔH of any one of the reactions represented. Actually, Hess' Law and enthalpy diagrams are simply two different ways—the one arithmetical and the other graphical—of expressing the concept that the enthalpy of a system is a function of state.

THE INTERPRETATION OF THE ENTHALPIES OF REACTIONS

It is generally instructive to know not only the quantity of heat involved in a given reaction, but also where such heat (energy) comes from, or where it goes. We shall now illustrate with some examples how we can use enthalpy diagrams to interpret from a structural viewpoint the enthalpy changes involved in a reaction. Notice that our reasoning, in this and in the following section, is again based on the statement that the total enthalpy change of a reaction is independent of the path which the reaction follows, or may be thought to follow.

REACTION OF H_2 GAS WITH HALOGENS. Let us consider the reaction of hydrogen gas, $H_{2(g)}$, with gaseous fluorine, $F_{2(g)}$, or chlorine, $Cl_{2(g)}$, to form the corresponding hydrogen halide gas, $HF_{(g)}$, or $HCl_{(g)}$, all reactants and products being at 25°C and 1 atm. If for convenience we represent the halogen simply as X (X = F, Cl), we have:

$$\tfrac{1}{2}\,H_{2(g)} + \tfrac{1}{2}\,X_{2(g)} \longrightarrow HX_{(g)} \qquad \Delta H^\circ = \begin{cases} -64.2 \text{ kcal/mole } HF_{(g)} \\ -22.1 \text{ kcal/mole } HCl_{(g)} \end{cases}$$

Now, with the help of enthalpy diagrams, we shall try to establish which structural factors are responsible for the difference in the $\Delta H^\circ_{\text{form}}$ of gaseous hydrogen fluoride and hydrogen chloride. Since hydrogen, fluorine, and chlorine exist as stable gaseous diatomic molecules at 25°C and 1 atm, and since all elements in their stable state are assigned a $\Delta H^\circ_{\text{form}}$ equal to zero, we place the initial system $\{\tfrac{1}{2}\,H_{2(g)} + \tfrac{1}{2}\,X_{2(g)}\}$ on the zero level of the enthalpy diagram (Fig. 16-5). Next, we place at the appropriate level in the diagram the final system, $HX_{(g)}$. Since we know from experiments that 64.2 kcal/mole and 22.1 kcal/mole are *evolved* when $HF_{(g)}$ and $HCl_{(g)}$, respectively, are formed from their elements in their stable states, the final system will have a *negative* enthalpy on our scale, precisely -64.2 kcal/mole for $HF_{(g)}$ and -22.1 kcal/mole for $HCl_{(g)}$. As far as the enthalpy change of the reaction is concerned, we may imagine the initial state of the system $\{\tfrac{1}{2}\,H_{2(g)} + \tfrac{1}{2}\,X_{2(g)}\}$ to be changed to the final state of the system, $HX_{(g)}$, not directly as in the above reaction but by the following steps, each involving both reactants and products at 25°C and 1 atm:

Step 1: The $\tfrac{1}{2}$ mole of gaseous hydrogen molecules, $\tfrac{1}{2}\,H_{2(g)}$, is decomposed to 1 mole of gaseous hydrogen atoms, $H_{(g)}$. The ΔH of this process is $+52.1$ kcal (one-half of the experimentally determined dissociation energy of the $H_{2(g)}$ molecules

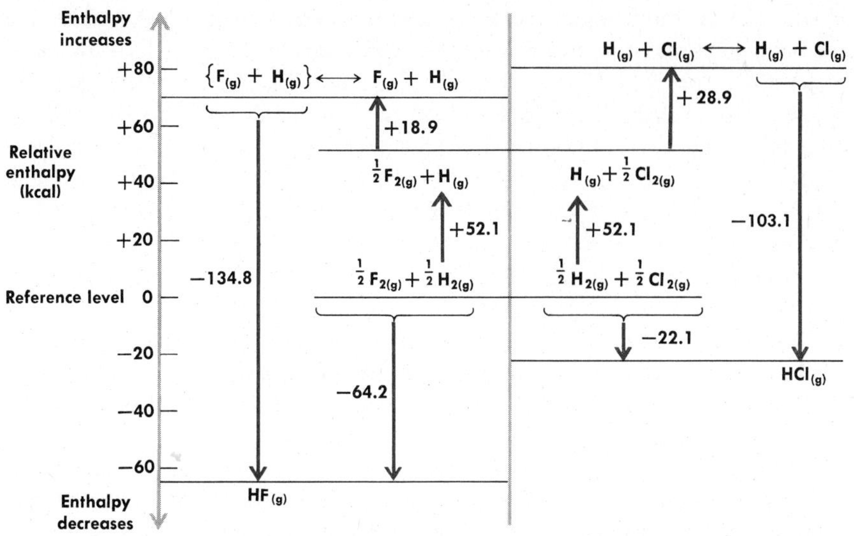

FIGURE 16-5 Enthalpy diagram for the formation of $HF_{(g)}$ and $HCl_{(g)}$ at 25°C and 1 atm.

$+104.2$ kcal/mole $H_{2(g)}$). The $\frac{1}{2}$ mole of gaseous halogen molecules $\frac{1}{2}X_{2(g)}$, remain unchanged. Consequently, the final state of this first step, which consists of 1 mole of $H_{(g)}$ atoms and $\frac{1}{2}$ mole of $X_{2(g)}$ molecules, is assigned a relative enthalpy level of $+52.1$ kcal.

Step 2: The $\frac{1}{2}$ mole of gaseous halogen molecules, $\frac{1}{2}X_{2(g)}$, is decomposed into 1 mole of its gaseous atoms, $X_{(g)}$. The ΔH for this process is one-half of the experimentally determined dissociation energy of the halogen molecule being considered; for $F_{2(g)}$, $\Delta H = \frac{1}{2} \times +37.8 = +18.9$ kcal/$\frac{1}{2}$ mole $F_{2(g)}$; for $Cl_{2(g)}$, $\Delta H = \frac{1}{2} \times +57.8 = +28.9$ kcal/$\frac{1}{2}$ mole $Cl_{2(g)}$. During this step, the 1 mole of $H_{(g)}$ atoms remains unchanged. Thus the final system of step (2), which consists of 1 mole of $H_{(g)}$ atoms and 1 mole of $X_{(g)}$ atoms, is assigned a relative enthalpy level of $(+52.1 + 18.9) = +71.0$ kcal for X = F, and of $(+52.1 + 28.9) = +81.0$ kcal for X = Cl.

To help you follow these changes on the diagram, step (1), which consists of the atomization of $H_{2(g)}$, is indicated by an arrow pointing from the hydrogen molecules to the hydrogen atoms, $\frac{1}{2}H_{2(g)} \longrightarrow H_{(g)}$. Similarly, step (2), which consists of the dissociation reaction, $\frac{1}{2}X_{2(g)} \longrightarrow X_{(g)}$, is indicated by an arrow pointing from $\frac{1}{2}X_{2(g)}$ to $X_{(g)}$. Notice that the enthalpy change for both step (1) and step (2) has a positive sign, since the system *takes on* energy from its surroundings, so the arrow is pointing upward toward increasing values of the enthalpy.

Step 3: The 1 mole of $H_{(g)}$ atoms and the 1 mole of $X_{(g)}$ atoms combine to form 1 mole of covalent gaseous $HX_{(g)}$ molecules, and in the process heat energy is given off by the system to its surroundings. Notice that the energy liberated by the system in this step is equal in absolute value, but opposite in sign, to the *bond dissociation* energy of the covalent hydrogen halide molecule. The bond dissociation energies are: $HF_{(g)}$, $+134.8$ kcal/mole; $HCl_{(g)}$, $+103.0$ kcal/mole. Hence the ΔH of step (3) is -134.8 kcal/mole $HX_{(g)}$ for X = F, and -103.1 kcal/mole $HX_{(g)}$ for X = Cl. This means that the enthalpy of the system during step (3) decreases, and accordingly the arrow for the transformation points downward, toward decreasing values of the enthalpy.

Let us now compare steps 1, 2, and 3 for the reactions of hydrogen, $H_{2(g)}$, with fluorine, $F_{2(g)}$, and chlorine, $Cl_{2(g)}$, respectively. Step (1) involves only the dissociation of the H_2 molecules, and is the same for the two reactions. Step (2) involves only the dissociation of the halogen molecule, and the energy involved therefore depends on the halogen considered. For this step the ΔH is smaller for X = F (+18.9 kcal/$\frac{1}{2}$ mole $F_{2(g)}$) than for X = Cl (+28.9 kcal/$\frac{1}{2}$ mole $Cl_{2(g)}$): hence the system $\{H_{(g)} + Cl_{(g)}\}$ has an enthalpy level higher than the system $\{H_{(g)} + F_{(g)}\}$ by (28.9 − 18.9) = 10.0 kcal/mole. Step (3) represents the formation of a covalent bond between a H atom and a halogen atom: the heat evolved is a measure of the strength of the H—X bond, and, as we can see, the H:F bond is stronger than the H:Cl bond, by (134.8 − 103.1 =) 31.7 kcal/mole H—X bond. Hence the formation of the H—X bond tends to lower the enthalpy level of the $\{H_{(g)} + X_{(g)}\}$ system both for X = F and X = Cl, but this lowering is greater for X = F. We may summarize by saying that the heat of formation of $HF_{(g)}$ is higher than the heat of formation of $HCl_{(g)}$ because of the lower dissociation energy of $F_{2(g)}$ with respect to $Cl_{2(g)}$ and of the greater strength of the H—F covalent bond with respect to that of H—Cl; this latter factor is relatively more important than the former.

An enthalpy diagram such as that of Fig. 16-5 expresses the same kind of relationship between material and energy changes as the Born-Haber cycle considered in Chapter 13. Thus the advantage of the enthalpy diagram is that it shows at a glance the relative magnitude of the various energy factors involved in a reaction because the length of each arrow representing a transformation is proportional to the heat involved in the transformation itself. For this reason enthalpy diagrams are especially helpful to the beginning student.

16-5 Variation of Enthalpy with Temperature

The enthalpy, H, of a system under constant pressure always increases with the temperature as shown by the following considerations. For any system which undergoes a transformation at constant pressure and involves only pressure-volume work, we have the relationship: $\Delta E = \Delta H - P\,\Delta V$. The internal energy of a system is directly proportional to its temperature, so an increase in temperature means that ΔE is positive. Since most systems expand when the temperature increases ($P\,\Delta V$ is positive), we conclude that an increase in temperature means an increase in the enthalpy of the system (ΔH is positive)—that is, H_{final} is greater than $H_{initial}$.

We have already learned that the quantity of heat required to increase by 1 degree the temperature of 1 mole of any specified substance under a constant pressure is the molar heat capacity of that substance at constant pressure, C_p. Thus, for a system consisting of a pure substance, the value of ΔH is related to the heat capacity, C_p, by the expression, $\Delta H = C_p \times \Delta T$, where $\Delta T = T_f - T_i$. In this expression C_p is assumed to have a constant value within the considered range of temperature (T_i to T_f). Actually, the heat capacity at constant pressure, C_p, is almost independent of temperature for solid and liquid substances, provided the range of temperature considered is not very wide; for gases, however, it may vary appreciably. The value of C_p has been experimentally determined for many substances over a wide range of temperature by measuring the quantity of heat that a known quantity of the substance must absorb to increase its temperature by 1 degree, from a temperature T_i to (T_i + 1), and then applying the above expression, $\Delta H = C_p \times \Delta T$.

Figure 16-6 shows how the relative enthalpy, H, of water increases with the temperature from 0°K (the absolute zero of temperature, −273°C) to well above the boiling point of liquid water, say 473°K (200°C), under a constant pressure of 1 atm. On the ordinate axis are the relative enthalpy values of water, and on the abscissa is the absolute temperature. Notice that we must speak of the relative value of the enthalpy, since there is no way to determine its absolute value; in fact, all we can obtain from experimental observation is an *enthalpy change*. In the diagram, the sloping section OA represents the increase in enthalpy of solid water (ice) as its temperature rises from 0°K to 273°K—the melting point of ice. When ice begins to

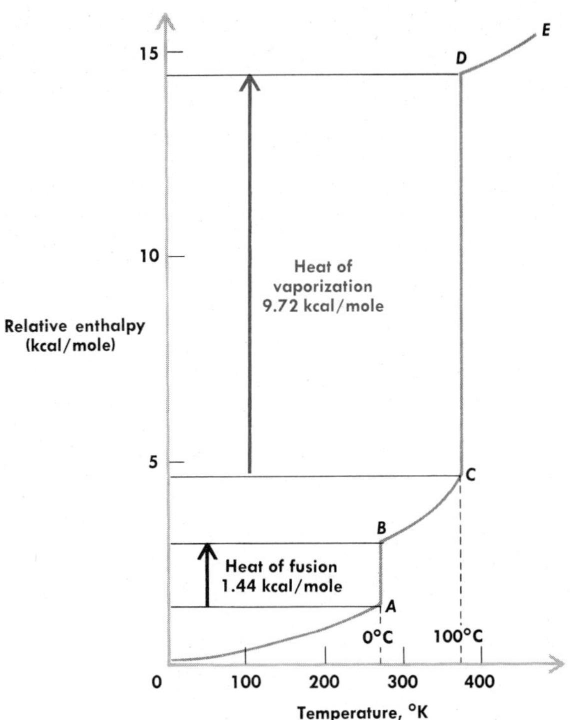

FIGURE 16-6 Variation of the relative enthalpy of water with temperature at a constant pressure of 1 atm.

melt, the temperature remains constant as long as both solid and liquid are present in the system—and all the heat absorbed is used to bring about the change $H_2O_{(s)} \longrightarrow H_2O_{(l)}$, at $P = 1$ atm and $T = 273°K$. Thus we have an increase in enthalpy at constant temperature, shown by the vertical section *AB*, which represents the latent heat of fusion of ice ($\Delta H_{fus} = +1.44$ kcal/mole). The enthalpy of liquid water then increases along an almost straight line from 273° to 373°K (section *BC*), since the heat capacity of liquid water is almost constant ($C_p \cong 18$ cal/mole $\times$ deg), until at 373°K the liquid begins to boil to form its vapor. The temperature then again remains constant as long as there are both liquid and gas in the system, and again the enthalpy increases at this constant temperature, as shown by the vertical straight line *CD*. This increase in enthalpy at constant temperature is the latent heat of vaporization of water, $\Delta H_{vap} = +9.72$ kcal/mole H_2O. After all the water has passed to the gaseous state, the enthalpy increases again gradually, as shown by *DE*.

For all substances the increase in enthalpy with increasing temperature follows a pattern similar to that shown for H_2O, although of course the values of the relative enthalpies of different substances at the same temperature may vary appreciably, especially since the melting and boiling points may differ by as much as 1,000 degrees or more for different kinds of substances.

One very important consequence of the fact that the enthalpies of different stances vary with increasing temperature according to similar patterns is that the ΔHs of reactions vary relatively little with temperature, as long as the reactants and products do not undergo changes in physical state. For example, consider the thermal dissociation reaction, $CaCO_{3(s)} \longrightarrow CaO_{(s)} + CO_{2(g)}$. The ΔH ($= H_{products} - H_{reactants}$) of this reaction at 25°C is +42.4 kcal/mole-equation. As the temperature increases, so do the relative enthalpies of both the initial state $\{CaCO_{3(s)}\}$ and the final state $\{CaO_{(s)} + CO_{2(g)}\}$ of the system. However, since $CaCO_3$ and CaO remain solids and CO_2 remains a gas throughout the temperature interval considered, the *difference* between the enthalpy of the products and that of the reactant varies only slightly. In fact, the ΔH of the reaction actually decreases by less than 3 kcal/mole-equation over a range of 800 degrees ($\Delta H_{1,000°K} = +40.0$ kcal/mole-equation).

Exercises

16-1 What is meant by the terms: (a) "system" and (b) "surroundings" as used in thermodynamics?

16-2 What properties define the state of a stable system composed of (a) only one pure substance; (b) a mixture of two gases; (c) a liquid in contact with an insoluble solid (for example, a piece of gold immersed in water); (d) solid carbon and oxygen gas; (e) a solution of potassium bromide, K^+Br^-, in water; (f) a water solution of sliver nitrate, $Ag^+NO_3^-$, and calcium nitrate, $Ca^{++}(NO_3^-)_2$?

16-3 What does the term "transformation" mean? Give an example of a transformation involving each of the following systems: (a) One mole of hydrogen gas in a closed container of fixed volume. (b) Liquid water in an open container and in contact with a source of heat (which is part of the surroundings). (c) A mixture of 3 moles of H_2 gas and 2 moles of N_2 gas. (d) A piece of zinc metal in contact with a solution of hydrochloric acid.

16-4 Which of the following changes involves an "isolated system" and which a "closed system"? (a) Heat is absorbed by a gas in a thermally insulated vessel. (b) A quantity of gas is removed from a cylinder. (c) Heat is absorbed by a gas enclosed in a vessel of fixed volume while some of the gas escapes through a valve. (d) The quantity of gas enclosed in a vessel of variable volume does not change, nor is heat or any other form of energy taken on or given up by the gas, but expansion into an evacuated space occurs.

16-5 Heat energy is taken on by a given quantity of an ideal gas enclosed in a vessel of constant volume. (a) Is the ΔE of this transformation positive or negative? (b) Describe qualitatively the change (if any) of the following macroscopic properties: (1) temperature, (2) pressure, and (3) density. (c) Give a microscopic interpretation of these macroscopic changes, assuming the ideal gas to be (1) monoatomic, (2) diatomic.

16-6 (a) Does the internal energy of the system increase, decrease, or remain constant, in the following transformations? (b) Would the value of ΔE be different for a monoatomic gas from that for a diatomic gas? Explain your answer. (1) One mole of an ideal gas in a thermally insulated vessel expands into a vacuum, resulting in a doubling of the volume. (2) One mole of an ideal gas takes on 40.2 kcal of heat and 48.3 l. $\times$ atm of work are done on it by its surroundings. (3) One mole of a real gas in a closed system gives up 14.6 kcal to its surroundings while performing 36.3 l. $\times$ atm of work on its surroundings.

16-7 One mole of N_2 gas enclosed in a fixed-volume vessel takes on 0.15 kcal of heat energy from its surroundings. (a) In what respect does the final state of the system differ from the initial state? (b) Does the internal energy of the system increase, decrease, or remain constant?

16-8 Which are the various energy terms that constitute the internal energy of a real gas such as (a) argon, Ar, (b) oxygen, O_2, (c) carbon dioxide, CO_2, and (d) methane, CH_4.

16-9 The following transformations occur at a constant pressure of 1 atm. For each transformation, state whether any appreciable pressure-volume work is involved and whether such work is a positive or a negative quantity according to our convention.

(a) 1 mole $H_2O_{(l)}$, 25°C $\longrightarrow$ 1 mole $H_2O_{(l)}$, 45°C

(b) 1 mole $H_2O_{(s)}$, 0°C $\longrightarrow$ 1 mole $H_2O_{(l)}$, 0°C

(c) 1 mole $H_2O_{(l)}$, 100°C $\longrightarrow$ 1 mole $H_2O_{(g)}$, 100°C

(d) $Zn_{(s)} + Br_{2(l)} \longrightarrow ZnBr_{2(s)}$

(e) $Zn_{(s)} + Cl_{2(g)} \longrightarrow ZnCl_{2(s)}$

(f) $N_2O_{4(g)} \longrightarrow 2\ NO_{2(g)}$

(g) $3\ H_{2(g)} + N_{2(g)} \longrightarrow 2\ NH_{3(g)}$

(h) $KClO_{3(s)} \longrightarrow KCl_{(s)} + \frac{3}{2}\ O_{2(g)}$

16-10 For each of the following transformations, indicate whether the internal energy of the system increases, decreases, or remains constant. Explain your answer in each case. (a) {1 mole ideal gas, 273°K, 1 atm} $\longrightarrow$ {1 mole ideal gas, 200°K, 0.4 atm}. (b) N moles of ideal gas take on 50 kcal of heat and also give up 242 l. $\times$ atm of work to the surroundings. (c) N moles of ideal gas in an isolated system effuse to occupy an evacuated space. (d) N moles of real gas in an isolated system effuse to occupy an evacuated space. (e) {1 mole ideal gas, 1 atm, 500°K} $\longrightarrow$ {1 mole ideal gas, 2 atm, 500°K}. (f) {1 mole ideal gas, 2 atm, 600°K} $\longrightarrow$ {1 mole ideal gas, 1 atm, 300°K}.

EXERCISES

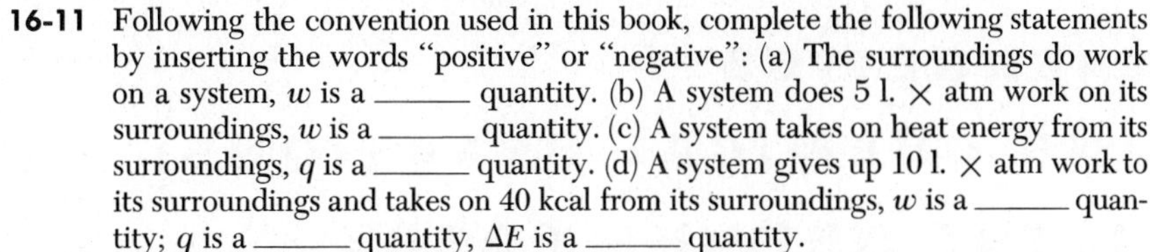

16-11 Following the convention used in this book, complete the following statements by inserting the words "positive" or "negative": (a) The surroundings do work on a system, w is a ______ quantity. (b) A system does 5 l. × atm work on its surroundings, w is a ______ quantity. (c) A system takes on heat energy from its surroundings, q is a ______ quantity. (d) A system gives up 10 l. × atm work to its surroundings and takes on 40 kcal from its surroundings, w is a ______ quantity; q is a ______ quantity, ΔE is a ______ quantity.

16-12 Does the internal energy of the system increase, decrease, or remain constant for the following reactions, at 25°C and 1 atm? (Remember that the pressure-volume work is about −0.6 kcal per each mole of gas produced in a reaction at standard conditions.)

(a) $Fe_{(s)} + S_{(s)} \longrightarrow FeS_{(s)}$ $\Delta H = -22.7$ kcal/mole-equation
(b) $3\ Fe_{(s)} + 2\ O_{2(g)} \longrightarrow Fe_3O_{4(s)}$ $\Delta H = -267.0$ kcal/mole-equation
(c) $N_2O_{(g)} \longrightarrow N_{2(g)} + \frac{1}{2}\ O_{2(g)}$ $\Delta H = -19.5$ kcal/mole-equation
(d) $N_{2(g)} + 3\ F_{2(g)} \longrightarrow 2\ NF_{3(g)}$ $\Delta H = -29.3$ kcal/mole-equation
(e) $N_{2(g)} + 3\ Cl_{2(g)} \longrightarrow 2\ NCl_{3(l)}$ $\Delta H = +55.0$ kcal/mole-equation

16-13 With respect to each of the following pairs of reactions indicate which one involves the greater enthalpy change.

(a) $2\ H_{2(g)} + O_{2(g)} \longrightarrow 2\ H_2O_{(g)}$ or $2\ H_{2(g)} + 2\ O_{(g)} \longrightarrow 2\ H_2O_{(g)}$
(b) $n\ Na_{(g)} \longrightarrow \frac{n}{2}\ Na_{2(g)}$ or $n\ Na_{(g)} \longrightarrow Na_{n(s)}$
(c) $Cl_{(g)} + Na_{(g)} \longrightarrow Na^+Cl^-_{(g)}$ or $Cl^-_{(g)} + Na^+_{(g)} \longrightarrow Na^+Cl^-_{(g)}$
(d) $2\ Na^+_{(g)} + 2\ Cl^-_{(g)} \longrightarrow 2\ Na^+Cl^-_{(s)}$ or $2\ Na_{(s)} + Cl_{2(g)} \longrightarrow 2\ Na^+Cl^-_{(s)}$
(e) $C_{(s,gr)} + O_{2(g)} \longrightarrow CO_{2(g)}$ or $C_{(s,dia)} + O_{2(g)} \longrightarrow CO_{2(g)}$
(f) $CH_{4(l)} + 2\ O_{2(g)} \longrightarrow CO_{2(g)} + 2\ H_2O_{(g)}$ or $CH_{4(g)} + 2\ O_{2(g)} \longrightarrow CO_{2(g)} + 2\ H_2O_{(g)}$
(g) $CH_{4(l)} + 2\ O_{2(g)} \longrightarrow CO_{2(g)} + 2\ H_2O_{(g)}$ or $C_{(g)} + 4\ H_{(g)} + 2\ O_{2(g)} \longrightarrow CO_{2(g)} + 2\ H_2O_{(g)}$

16-14 Using the enthalpy values in the appropriate tables, draw enthalpy diagrams showing the relative enthalpy levels of the initial state (reactants) and the final state (products), as well as of the various intermediate states, for the following reactions at 25°C and 1 atm:

(a) $Na_{(s)} + \frac{1}{2}\ F_{2(g)} \longrightarrow Na^+F^-_{(g)}$
(b) $CH_{4(g)} \longrightarrow C_{(s,gr)} + 2\ H_{2(g)}$
(c) $CH_{4(g)} \longrightarrow C_{(s,gr)} + 4\ H_{(g)}$
(d) $CH_{4(g)} \longrightarrow C_{(g)} + 4\ H_{(g)}$
(e) $Mg_{(s)} + \frac{1}{2}\ O_{2(g)} \longrightarrow Mg^{++}O^{=}_{(s)}$

16-15 Describe how the enthalpy of a system changes with increasing temperature.

16-16 Ice melts to liquid water at a constant temperature of 0°C and constant pressure of 1 atm. Does the enthalpy of the system increase, decrease, or remain constant in this transformation?

16-17 Using the values of ΔH_{form} listed in Table 16-4, calculate the change in enthalpy for the following reactions at 25°C and 1 atm:

(a) $S_{(s,rhombic)} + O_{2(g)} \longrightarrow SO_{2(g)}$
(b) $S_{(s,monoclinic)} + O_{2(g)} \longrightarrow SO_{2(g)}$
(c) $2\ Cs_{(s)} + F_{2(g)} \longrightarrow 2\ CsF_{(s)}$
(d) $H_{2(g)} + 2\ F_{(g)} \longrightarrow 2\ HF_{(g)}$
(e) $2\ NO_{2(g)} \longrightarrow N_2O_{4(g)}$
(f) $Mg_{(s)} + \frac{1}{2}\ O_{2(g)} \longrightarrow MgO_{(s)}$
(g) $2\ HgO_{(s)} \longrightarrow 2\ Hg_{(l)} + O_{2(g)}$
(h) $2\ Li_{(s)} + H_{2(g)} \longrightarrow 2\ LiH_{(s)}$
(i) $CaCO_{3(s)} \longrightarrow CaO_{(s)} + CO_{2(g)}$
(j) $2\ H_2O_{(l)} \longrightarrow 2\ H_{2(g)} + O_{2(g)}$

16-18 Calculate approximately the pressure-volume work involved in the following transformations, and state the appropriate sign of w.

(a) $10\ H_2O_{(l)}$, 25°C, 1 atm $\longrightarrow$ $10\ H_2O_{(g)}$, 25°C, 1 atm
(b) $2\ NH_{3(g)}$, 25°C, 1 atm $\longrightarrow$ $N_{2(g)} + 3\ H_{2(g)}$, both products at 25°C, 1 atm

ENERGETICS AND CHEMICAL REACTIONS: II. THE DRIVING FORCE OF A CHEMICAL REACTION

17

We know that the enthalpy change, ΔH, of a reaction helps us to understand the relative importance of the various energy factors involved in reactions, and in some cases may also help us to estimate the relative strengths of the chemical bonds present in compounds. In addition, for any transformation in which the initial and final pressure is the same and in which the only work involved is of the pressure-volume kind, the relationship $\Delta E = \Delta H - P\,\Delta V$ permits us to calculate easily the change in the internal energy of the system, ΔE, which accompanies the transformation. But neither the value of ΔH nor the value of ΔE alone can give us an answer to one of the fundamental questions of chemistry: why do some systems have the capacity to react spontaneously and others do not? And what is the criterion which decides whether a given system does or does not have the capacity to undergo spontaneously a specified transformation?

In earlier chapters we have encountered many examples of spontaneous transformations—for example, the reaction of $H_{2(g)}$ with $F_{2(g)}$ to form $HF_{(g)}$; the combustion of graphite to form CO_2; the reaction of acetic acid, $CH_3COOH_{(aq)}$, with sodium carbonate, $Na_2CO_{3(aq)}$, to form sodium acetate, $CH_3COONa_{(aq)}$, carbon dioxide, $CO_{2(g)}$, and water; and the dissolution in water of ionic compounds such as $NaCl_{(s)}$ and $NH_4Cl_{(s)}$—and we have seen that for some of these reactions ΔH is negative but for others ΔH is positive. Thus, the formation of $HF_{(g)}$ and the combustion of graphite are both exothermic reactions (ΔH is negative), whereas the reaction of acetic acid with sodium carbonate, and the dissolving in water of $NaCl_{(s)}$ and $NH_4Cl_{(s)}$ are both endothermic (ΔH is positive).

We have also seen that, if an exothermic or endothermic reaction takes place in a thermally isolated system (for example, in a Dewar flask), so that no heat is exchanged with the surroundings, then the temperature of the system increases or decreases, respectively. For example, consider that the exothermic reaction $\frac{1}{2}H_{2(g)} + \frac{1}{2}F_{2(g)} \longrightarrow HF_{(g)}$ is carried out in a thermally isolated cylinder under a constant pressure of 1 atm starting with the reactants at 25°C. All the heat evolved in the reaction, $\Delta H° = -64.2$ kcal/mole $HF_{(g)}$ at 25°C and 1 atm, remains in the system and goes to increase its internal thermal* energy (no pressure-volume work is done because there is no change in the number of moles of gas and therefore the volume remains constant). Hence the temperature of the system increases. Conversely, for an endothermic reaction—such as the dissolution in water of $NH_4Cl_{(s)}$—if the required quantity of heat ($\Delta H = +3.75$ kcal/mole NH_4Cl in 1 l. H_2O at 25°C) is not furnished to the system by the surroundings, then the system itself will provide it by "giving up" some of its own thermal internal energy. Consequently, the temperature of the system will decrease. Thus, a spontaneous endothermic process such as the dissolution of the salt $NH_4Cl_{(s)}$ in water occurs with a decrease in the internal energy of the system—more specifically, a decrease of the *thermal* part of the internal energy—and in fact the resulting solution is cooler than the substance from which it is formed.

We may conclude that neither the heat evolved or absorbed in a reaction at constant temperature nor the change in temperature which accompanies a reaction when no energy, either as heat or as work, is exchanged with the surroundings may by themselves serve to rationalize the spontaneous character of a transformation. If, therefore, we wish to answer the fundamental question we posed before—"What is the criterion which decides whether a given system has or does not have the capacity to undergo spontaneously a specified transformation?"—we must look for some other property (or properties) of the system whose change in a tranformation may be related to the capacity of the system to undergo the specified transformation *spontaneously*. In the following sections we shall discuss this important problem in some detail. The discussion will necessarily be lengthy but, as we will see, the results will be extremely rewarding for the understanding of all chemical reactions.

17-1 Different Paths of a Transformation

A system can, in general, pass from a specified initial state to a specified final state by very many paths. For each of these paths the First Law of Thermodynamics, $\Delta E = q + w$, is of course equally valid, and ΔE has the same value since the initial and final states are the same for all paths; but the heat, q, and the work, w, exchanged between the system and the surroundings vary from one path to another. Let us consider as an example a very simple and by now familiar kind of transformation—the expansion of an ideal gas at constant temperature.

EXPANSION OF AN IDEAL GAS AT CONSTANT TEMPERATURE BY THREE DIFFERENT PATHS

Let us consider the expansion of 1 mole of an ideal gas from an initial state of temperature $T = 25°C$ (298°K), volume $V_i = 12.2$ l., and pressure $P_i = 2$ atm, to a final state *at the same temperature* but twice the initial volume,

* In the preceding chapter we considered the internal energy of a system as being made up of two parts, the *thermal* energy (which includes the translational, vibrational, and rotational motions of the particles of the system) and the *bond* energy (which includes all types of bonding, both within the individual particles and among them).

$V_f = 24.4$ l., and of course half the initial pressure, $P_f = 1$ atm. We can think of many different paths by which the system can pass from the specified initial state to the specified final state, and for each path the change in the internal energy, ΔE, of the system, the heat, q, absorbed by the system from the surroundings, and the work, w, performed by the system, are related by the First Law: $\Delta E = q + w$. For the particular transformation we are considering, the temperature of the ideal gas in the initial state is the same as that in the final state, so there is no change in the internal energy of the system as a result of the expansion: $\Delta E = E_f - E_i = 0$. Hence, for this particular transformation: $q + w = 0$ or: $q = -w$, where, according to our usual convention, q has a positive sign when it represents heat absorbed by the system from the surroundings, and w has a negative value when it represents work done by the system on the surroundings.

Now let us consider separately three paths by which the system may be thought to expand from the specified initial state ($T = 25°$C, $V_i = 12.2$ l., $P_i = 2$ atm) to the specified final state ($T = 25°$C, $V_f = 24.4$ l., $P_f = 1$ atm).

EXPANSION BY PATH 1. The ideal gas expands into an evacuated space and is thermally isolated from the surroundings. As we know, a gas tends to occupy all the volume made available to it, that is to say, the expansion of a gas into an evacuated space is a *spontaneous process*. We can visualize this transformation as taking place in an insulated cylinder equipped with a weightless, frictionless piston, initally loaded with sufficient weights to keep the gas at the initial volume, V_i (Fig. 17-1a). Then the weights on the piston are suddenly and completely removed (the opposing pressure becomes zero) and the piston is pushed back by the expanding gas to a pre-set position corresponding to the final volume, V_f. Alternatively, and more practically, we can visualize the transformation to occur in the set-up illustrated in Fig. 17-1(b). Since in either case the external pressure opposing the expansion of the gas is zero, no work is done by the system on the surroundings, and $w = 0$. Also, since the expansion is carried out in such a way that no heat is exchanged between the gas and the surroundings, $q = 0$. Hence, $\Delta E = 0$, and also—for an ideal gas—$\Delta T = 0$. It is interesting to note that for real gases, under conditions which approach ideal behavior, an expansion into an evacuated space does not involve a significant temperature change (the very small temperature drop which is generally observed indicates a loss of kinetic energy to compensate for the increase of the potential energy of the van der Waals attractions).

EXPANSION BY PATH 2. The ideal gas, confined in the cylinder with a movable, weightless, and frictionless piston, expands against a *constant* opposing pressure of 1 atm (the atmospheric pressure), while taking on heat energy from the surroundings. Again, the expansion of a gas against a constant opposing pressure lower than the pressure of the gas itself, is a process which occurs spontaneously. Since the final temperature of the ideal gas is equal to the initial temperature, and accordingly the change in internal energy during the expansion is zero ($\Delta E = 0$), all the heat, q, taken on by the

FIGURE 17-1 Spontaneous expansion of an ideal gas into an evacuated space without exchange of heat with the surroundings.

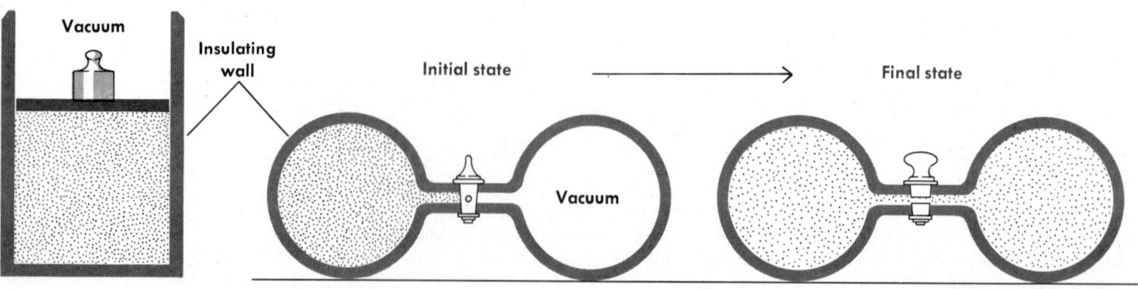

system from the surroundings in going from the initial to the final state is converted into the pressure-volume work, w, expended by the system in overcoming the constant opposing atmospheric pressure. As we know, this pressure-volume work, done by the system on the surroundings in passing from the initial to the final state under a constant opposing pressure, P, is given by the formula, $w = -P\,\Delta V$. Thus:

$$w = -[P(V_f - V_i)] = -[1 \text{ atm} \times (24.4 \text{ l.} - 12.2 \text{ l.})] = -[1 \text{ atm} \times 12.2 \text{ l.}] = -12.2 \text{ l.} \times \text{atm}$$

Recall that 1 l. $\times$ atm at 25°C = 24.2 cal. Hence the work done by the system on the surroundings may be also expressed as:

$$w = -12.2 \text{ (l.} \times \text{atm)} \times 24.2 \text{ cal}/1 \text{ (l.} \times \text{atm)} = -295.2 \text{ cal.}$$

The negative sign indicates that this quantity of work is done by the system on the surroundings, and hence represents energy lost by the system.

We have stated that both in the initial and in the final states of the transformation the system is in thermal equilibrium with (at the same temperature as) the immediate surroundings—which could be, for example, a constant temperature bath surrounding the cylinder. How can we visualize that the system absorbs heat from the surroundings? As the gas just begins to expand against the constant pressure of the atmosphere and in so doing performs some work on the surroundings, its internal energy may begin to decrease and the gas may begin to cool down just slightly; some heat then would flow spontaneously from the surroundings to the momentarily cooler system, maintaining its temperature constant. Such a process may be thought to be repeated continuously throughout the expansion. So, when the final state of the transformation is reached, the system has absorbed from the surroundings a certain quantity of heat, and simultaneously it has done on the surroundings an equivalent amount of work while the system itself remains finally at the initial temperature.

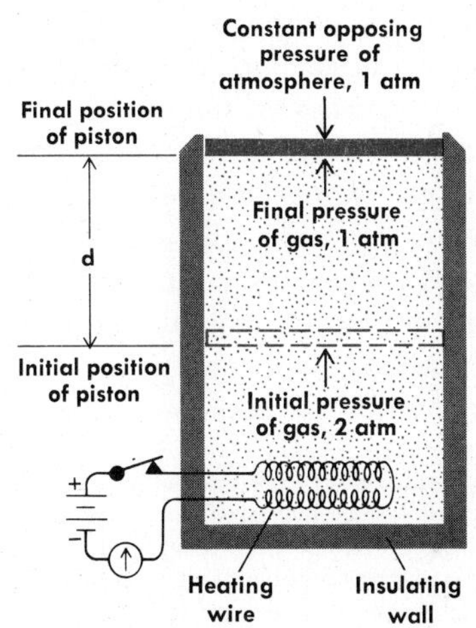

FIGURE 17-2 Expansion of an ideal gas against a constant opposing pressure of 1 atm while taking on heat from its surroundings (heating wire).

If we carry out the transformation under the experimental conditions just described, we cannot measure conveniently the quantity of heat absorbed by the system. This may be done, however, if we modify the experimental set-up in such a way that the cylinder containing the gas is now thermally isolated from the surroundings, for example, in a Dewar flask, but an electrically heated wire of known and constant resistance is passed through the gas (Fig. 17-2). In this case we can determine experimentally the heat absorbed by the system by measuring the applied voltage and the quantity of electricity (current $\times$ time, Ch. 23) which passes through the heating wire during the process. Notice that this change of experimental set-up does not in any way alter the system under consideration. In fact, we have only changed some details of the surroundings in order to measure more easily the heat taken on by the system during the expansion.

EXPANSION BY PATH 3. Again—as in path 2—we imagine the ideal gas to be confined in a thermally isolated cylinder closed by a movable, weightless, and frictionless piston, and equipped with a heating wire. This time, however, we consider the gas to pass from the specified initial state to the specified final state by taking on heat from the surroundings while expanding against a gradually decreasing external pressure virtually equal at every instant to the gradually decreasing pressure exerted by the ideal gas.

Such a transformation might occur as follows. In the very first moment of the transformation, the pressure exerted by the gas on the underside of the piston is exactly 2.000 atm whereas the outside pressure acting on the top-side of the piston is only very slightly lower than 2.000 atm; this outside pressure results from the constant atmospheric pressure, assumed to be 1.000 atm, plus an added weight which exerts on the piston a pressure only very slightly lower than one atmosphere. We can obtain such conditions by placing on top of the piston a quantity of very fine sand (Fig. 17-3) that exerts a pressure just very slightly less than $14.7/\text{lbs/in}^2 = 1.000$ atm, say 0.999 atm. Then the total pressure exerted on the top of the piston—the atmospheric pressure (1.000 atm) plus the pressure exerted by the sand (0.999 atm)—would be 1.999 atm, which is slightly less than the pressure (2.000 atm) exerted by the gas confined in the cylinder. The gas would then undergo spontaneously a very small expansion—what we may call an "element of expansion"—against this opposing pressure, and thus the system would perform a very small quantity of work—an "element of work"—on the surroundings. We could arrange conditions so that, as the gas expands slightly and pushes up the piston a tiny distance, a very small amount of sand flows over from the top of the cylinder. As the expansion proceeds, the pressure exerted by the sand on the piston slowly and continuously decreases (because the quantity of sand decreases), just as the pressure exerted by the gas on the underside of the piston slowly and continuously diminishes (because the volume of the gas increases).* At all moments during the process, the pressure exerted by the gas on the underside of the piston is almost, but not quite, counterbalanced by the opposing pressure of the atmosphere plus the pressure exerted by the sand. Therefore, we may consider the gas

* An alternative experimental set-up for this spontaneous gradual expansion of an ideal gas against a gradually decreasing opposing external pressure could be obtained by placing on top of the thermally isolated piston an appropriate quantity of a substance—for example, naphthalene, the substance of which moth-balls are made—which is capable of slowly vaporizing at the temperature of the experiment. Initially the atmospheric pressure and the pressure exerted by the solid naphthalene are sufficient to counterbalance the pressure of the gas inside the cylinder, but as some naphthalene slowly vaporizes, the total pressure on the piston very slightly decreases and the gas begins to expand. As more and more naphthalene slowly vaporizes, the gas continues to expand in a slow, continuous process, since the pressure exerted on the top-side of the piston by the constant atmospheric pressure and the slowly decreasing weight of solid naphthalene is just sufficient, at every instant, to counterbalance the pressure of the gas itself on the underside of the piston.

FIGURE 17-3 Expansion of an ideal gas against a gradually decreasing opposing pressure, just slightly lower than pressure of gas, while taking on heat from its surroundings (heating wire).

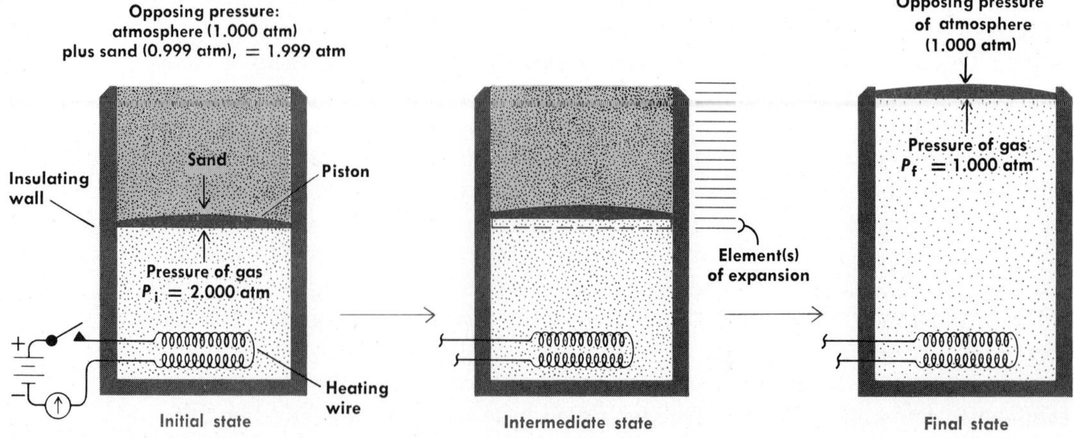

to be very *nearly in equilibrium* with the surroundings throughout the entire expansion, and we may express this by saying that the expansion takes place through a continuous series of extremely small *quasi-static* expansion steps.

The expansion of the gas carried out in this manner is spontaneous, since the gas expands against an opposing pressure which at each instant is smaller—however, infinitesimally so—than the pressure exerted by the gas itself. Since the system does an extremely small amount of work on the surroundings at each instant during the expansion, it must simultaneously absorb from the surroundings an equivalent, extremely small amount of heat in order to maintain a constant internal energy (temperature). Notice that we may consider the system to be in thermal equilibrium with the surroundings, not only at the initial and final states of the expansion, but virtually throughout the entire expansion process, and yet the system spontaneously absorbs from the surroundings a certain quantity of heat and transforms it into an equivalent quantity of pressure-volume work. We can measure the total quantity of heat absorbed by the system in the process of expansion by making use, as in path 2, of an electrically heated wire as the source of heat. For the expansion of an ideal gas at constant temperature, the change in internal energy is zero, $\Delta E = 0$; therefore, by measuring the quantity of heat absorbed, q, we also know the quantity of work, w, performed by the system. The quantity of work done by the system on the surroundings during the expansion can also be calculated independently, either graphically or mathematically, as explained in Appendix 17-1. Here we shall use the result of those calculations:

$$w = -nRT \ln \frac{V_f}{V_i} = -2.303\, nRT \log \frac{V_f}{V_i}$$

In this formula n is the number of moles of the ideal gas, R is the ideal gas constant ($R = 1.987$ cal/mole $\times$ deg), T is the absolute temperature, V_f is the final volume, and V_i is the initial volume of the gas. For our example: initial state ($V_i = 12.2$ l., $T = 298°$K) $\longrightarrow$ final state ($V_f = 24.4$ l., $T = 298°$K):

$$\begin{aligned} w &= -\left[2.303 \times 1 \text{ mole} \times 1.987 \text{ cal/mole} \times \text{deg} \times 298 \text{ deg} \times \log \frac{24.4 \text{ l.}}{12.2 \text{ l.}}\right] \\ &= -[(2.303 \times 1.987 \times 298) \text{ cal} \times \log 2] \\ &= -1263.65 \text{ cal} \times 0.301 = -380.36 \text{ cal} \end{aligned}$$

Here again the minus sign indicates that this amount of energy as work is expended by the system during the transformation.

COMPARISON OF THE VALUES OF q AND w FOR THE THREE PATHS. We may summarize the results of the preceding section by comparing the values of ΔE, q, and w (Table 17-1) for the expansion of our ideal gas system from the same specified initial state to

TABLE 17-1 ENERGY CHANGES FOR AN ISOTHERMAL TRANSFORMATION OF AN IDEAL GAS

Path	Internal Energy Change, ΔE	Heat Exchanged, q	Work Performed w
1. Expansion into vacuum	0	0	0
2. Expansion against constant opposing external pressure (1 atm)	0	+295.2 cal	−12.2 l. × atm = −295.2 cal
3. Expansion against continuously "equal" opposing pressure	0	+380.36 cal	−17.0 l. × atm = −380.36 cal

the same specified final state, by the three different paths just considered. First, we notice that the change in internal energy, ΔE, is the same for the three paths (in fact as we already know the internal energy, E, of the system is a thermodynamic function, that is to say, it depends only on the state of the system and hence ΔE does not depend on the path by which the final state is reached). Furthermore, since the system under consideration is an ideal gas and there is no change in temperature from the initial to the final state, the change of internal energy for all three cases is zero; $\Delta E = 0$.

In each of the three paths the First Law of Thermodynamics, $\Delta E = q + w$, is of course obeyed. In path 1, however, the system neither absorbs heat from nor does work on the surroundings, whereas in paths 2 and 3 the system absorbs heat from the surroundings while it itself does mechanical pressure-volume work on the surroundings. In paths 2 and 3, therefore, the system converts heat energy into an equivalent quantity of work energy. In both path 2 and path 3 all the heat taken on by the system from the surroundings is completely converted into work done on the surroundings by the system (since $\Delta E = 0$); however, in path 3 more heat is taken on, and consequently more work is done by the system, than in path 2.

THE MAXIMUM WORK

If we were to explore all possible paths by which the ideal gas system considered in the preceding sections can go from the specified initial state to the specified final state, we would find that the magnitude of the work done by the system when expanding against a gradually decreasing external pressure becomes greater (w has increasingly larger negative values) as the difference between the external opposing pressure and the pressure exerted by the gas itself decreases. At the limit—when the process is (as it virtually is in path 3) a continuous sequence of infinitesimally small elements of expansion against an opposing external pressure which is at all times equal to that of the expanding gas—the work involved reaches its greatest negative value. Hence, in no other path does the system perform on the surroundings a quantity of work greater than or even equal to that performed in path 3. Notice that in this idealized path 3, the piston is moving, at each instant, against the *maximum possible external pressure* that will still permit it to move in that direction; therefore, the work, w, has the largest negative value for path 3.

We can express this by saying that in path 3 the system performs on the surroundings the *maximum amount of work it is capable of doing in this particular transformation.* Consequently in path 3 the system also takes on from the surroundings the maximum quantity of heat possible for this transformation, which it then converts to (the maximum amount of) work. Notice that whereas the change in the internal energy, ΔE, does not depend on the path of the transformation (E is a thermodynamic function of state) *both q and w do depend on the path.* Thus in path 1 the system performed *no* work on the surroundings in changing from its initial state to its final state, although initially it had the capacity to do so—in fact, it had the capacity to do maximum work of -380.36 cal. In path 2 the system did some work, precisely -1 (l. $\times$ atm) $= -295.2$ cal, but this is less than the maximum quantity of work that it had the capacity to do in going from the initial to the final state. In path 3 the system actually performed all the work, -380.36 cal, that it had the capacity to do, that is, the maximum possible work.

As in each of the three paths considered here, whenever *a system has the capacity to do work in passing from a specified initial state to a specified final state at the same temperature, then the transformation can take place spontaneously.* It must be emphasized, that the spontaneity of a transformation is related to the *capacity* of the system to do work in passing isothermally from the specified initial state to the specified final state and *not to the work actually done* by the system while undergoing the transformation along a particular path (for example, path 1 above).

REVERSIBLE TRANSFORMATIONS. Let us consider again the expansion of an ideal gas carried out by path 3. If at a certain instant we were to increase the outside opposing pressure by an extremely small amount, so that the outside pressure would become just greater than the pressure of the gas itself, then the gas inside the cylinder would undergo a very small quasi-static contraction. We could realize these conditions, for example, by putting back on the top of the piston a little of the sand that had just fallen off (or some solid naphthalene). By such slight variance of the external pressure which opposes the pressure exerted by the gas itself, we can at any given instant reverse the transformation of the system by path 3 from an expansion to a contraction. Hence we generally say that such a transformation (either expansion or contraction) is carried out reversibly, or—more simply—is a *reversible transformation.* This term, "reversible transformation" (or "reversible process") states concisely that the transformation considered passes through an infinite series of quasi-static steps and that, in each of these steps, the system is virtually in equilibrium with the surroundings. We saw in the previous section that, for the expansion of an ideal gas, the greatest amount of work is done by the system on the surroundings through the reversible path 3. In general, of all possible transformations of a system passing from an initial state to a final state *at the same temperature,* the reversible transformation involves the greatest amount of work.

17-2 A Criterion of Spontaneity at Constant Temperature: Maximum Work

In the previous section we saw that if a system has the *capacity* to do work on the surroundings (w is negative) while undergoing a certain transformation at constant temperature, then this transformation can occur spontaneously. In a similar manner, we can reason that if a system *does not have the capacity to do work* on the surroundings while passing isothermally from a specified initial state to a specified final state, then the system *cannot* undergo such a transformation *spontaneously.* The transformation can be forced to take place, but to do so the surroundings have to perform work on the system (w has to be positive). For example, 1 mole of an ideal gas occupying a volume of 24.4 l. at a pressure of 1 atm and at 298°K, in a set-up such as that described in path 3 and shown in Fig. 17-3, will not contract spontaneously to half its initial volume if the temperature remains constant. We can effect this contraction, however, by applying a gradually increasing pressure on the piston. If we operate reversibly, so that the transformation consists of a series of infinitesimally small, "quasi-static" elements of contraction, then the work that the surroundings must expend to carry out the transformation is $w = +380.36$ cal. Note that this is the same quantity of work, but with the sign changed, that the system performs on the surroundings during the reversible expansion by path 3.

In general, the work involved when a system passes reversibly, and at a constant temperature, from a specified initial to a specified final state can be used as a guiding principle to decide whether this transformation can or cannot occur spontaneously. If the work, w, is done by the system (negative sign), then the transformation is *thermodynamically permitted;* if the work is done by the surroundings (positive sign) the transformation is *thermodynamically forbidden.*

In the isothermal transformation of a system from a specified initial state to a specified final state the maximum work is a measure of how much the *capacity for work* of the system has changed in the transformation. If the maximum work is positive (work done by the surroundings on the system), the capacity for work of the system has increased in the transformation; if the maximum total work is negative (work done by the system on the surroundings), then the capacity for work of the system has decreased. Now, the *maximum* work for a specified transformation of a given system,

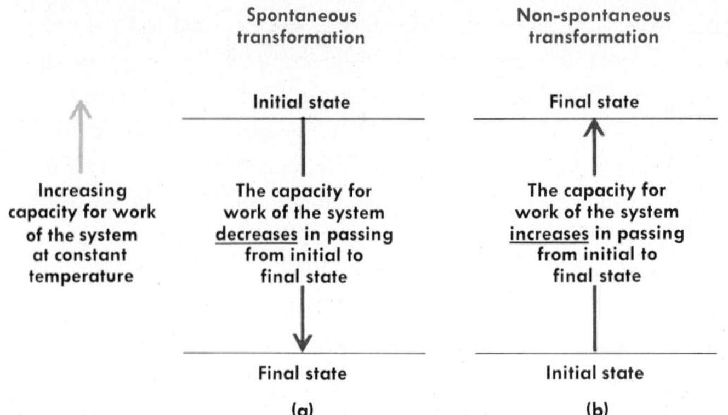

FIGURE 17-4 Graphic representation of the change in "capacity for work" of a system in (a) spontaneous and (b) non-spontaneous processes at constant temperature.

and hence the change in "capacity for work," depends not on the path of the transformation but only on the final and initial states. We may conclude, therefore, that the "capacity for work" of a system is a *thermodynamic function*—just like the internal energy or the enthalpy of the system. These considerations are summarized in the diagram of Fig. 17-4.

THE USEFUL WORK

We saw in Chapter 16 (p. 329) that, in general, the work done on or by a system during a transformation can be divided into two parts: (1) the pressure-volume work, and (2) any other type of work, for example, electrical or magnetic. The pressure-volume work is, of course, zero for transformations at constant volume (volume of the final system = volume of the initial system) or when the system expands into a vacuum (opposing pressure = zero). On the other hand, for all transformations of the system in which the volume changes against an opposing pressure, the pressure-volume work is mandatory and unavoidable. When the system expands or contracts, for example, under a constant atmospheric pressure, this mandatory pressure-volume work is $w = -P\,\Delta V$, w being, according to our convention, negative if the system expands and positive if the system contracts.

The pressure-volume work represents the *minimum work* involved when a system undergoes a given transformation under constant pressure. Any other work, such as electrical or magnetic, is *optional work*, in the sense that we can always arrange the path of a transformation so that no such work is done. Alternately, we may arrange the path of the transformation so as to have any amount of optional work, up to a maximum value, which is the difference between the maximum total work for the transformation considered and the unavoidable pressure-volume work. The optional work is commonly called *useful work* because it can be utilized to some practical purpose. Note, on the other hand, that we cannot make any use of the pressure-volume work done by the system in transformations at atmospheric pressure—such work represents a "fee" to be paid for any volume change under the constant opposing atmospheric pressure. For any given transformation at constant temperature and under a constant opposing pressure, the pressure-volume work is a constant quantity, $-P\,\Delta V$; hence the useful work has the greatest value when the total work is greatest, that is, when the system passes reversibly from its initial to its final state. Thus for any transformation at constant temperature we can write:

$$w_{\text{total max}} = w_{\text{useful max}} + w_{\text{unavoidable}}$$

$$w_{\text{total max}} = w_{\text{useful max}} + w_{\text{pressure-volume}}$$

And if the pressure is also constant we have:

$$w_{\text{total max}} = w_{\text{useful max}} - P\,\Delta V$$

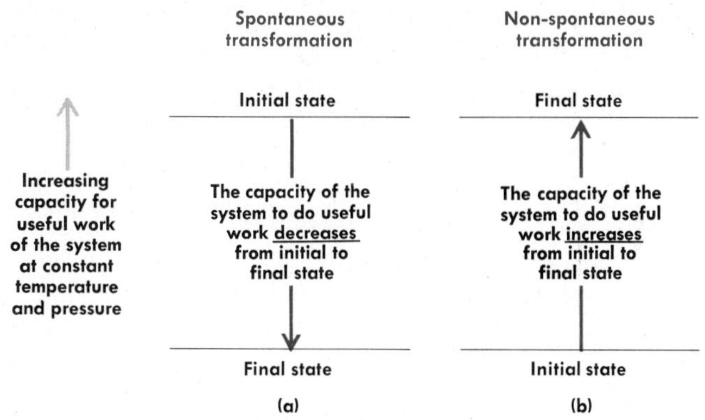

Spontaneous transformation | Non-spontaneous transformation

Increasing capacity for useful work of the system at constant temperature and pressure

(a) Initial state → Final state: The capacity of the system to do useful work <u>decreases</u> from initial to final state

(b) Initial state → Final state: The capacity of the system to do useful work <u>increases</u> from initial to final state

FIGURE 17-5 Graphic representation of the change in "capacity for useful work" of a system in (a) spontaneous and (b) non-spontaneous processes at constant temperature and pressure.

17-3 Spontaneity of Transformations at Constant Temperature and Pressure

We have learned that the maximum total work (of any or all types) involved in a transformation at constant temperature is a thermodynamic function which is a measure of the spontaneity of the transformation considered. Similarly, the maximum useful work—which is also a thermodynamic function of state—represents the change in the capacity of the system to do useful work (any work besides the unavoidable pressure-volume work) when passing from a specified initial state to a specified final state at constant temperature and pressure. The maximum useful work is also a measure of the spontaneity of the transformation. These considerations are summarized in the diagram of Fig. 17-5.

For most chemical reactions, which take place under a constant atmospheric pressure, we use $w_{\text{useful max}}$ rather than $w_{\text{total max}}$ as the criterion of spontaneity, because then we do not have to take into account the pressure-volume work. Since both $w_{\text{total max}}$ and $w_{\text{useful max}}$ are thermodynamic functions of state, by using either one as the criterion of spontaneity, we need only to know the initial and final states of the system. Thus, we do not have to concern ourselves with the path followed by the transformation, which is often most difficult to assess. This is the fundamental reason for our trying to discuss the energy aspects of transformations in terms of "thermodynamic functions" rather than of more readily measurable quantities such as the heat and the work actually involved in the transformation.

If we can determine the value of $w_{\text{useful max}}$ for a given process, we can then predict whether such a process can or cannot occur spontaneously—that is, whether such a process is thermodynamically permitted or forbidden. Unfortunately, it is usually very difficult to measure $w_{\text{useful max}}$ directly, and actually for some reactions it cannot be measured. Thus, if we are to adopt $w_{\text{useful max}}$ as a criterion of spontaneity for reactions which occur at constant temperature and pressure, we must find a way to express $w_{\text{useful max}}$ in terms of more readily measurable thermodynamic functions. We shall consider this problem in the following sections.

HEAT EXCHANGED IN A REVERSIBLE PROCESS, q_{rev}

For an isothermal transformation of an ideal gas, the First Law of Thermodynamics is written as follows:

$$1.\quad \Delta E = q + w = 0, \qquad \text{or } w = -q$$

If the transformation is carried out reversibly, we have:

$$2.\quad w_{\text{total max}} = -q_{\text{rev}}$$

$$3.\quad \overbrace{w_{\text{useful max}} + w_{\text{pressure-volume}}}^{w_{\text{total max}}} = -q_{\text{rev}}$$

And if the reversible isothermal transformation also occurs under a constant opposing pressure, P, then $\Delta E = \Delta H - P\,\Delta V = 0$ (see Chapter 16, p. 331), and $w_{\text{pressure-volume}} = -P\,\Delta V = -\Delta H$. By substituting this value of $w_{\text{pressure-volume}}$ in expression 3 we have:

$$4.\ w_{\text{useful max}} - \Delta H = -q_{\text{rev}}$$

$$5.\ w_{\text{useful max}} = \Delta H - q_{\text{rev}}$$

The $w_{\text{useful max}}$ is thus expressed as the sum of two terms. One of these terms, ΔH, can be measured directly or calculated as we learned in Chapter 16, whereas the other term, q_{rev}, is not generally easy to measure directly. Thus we must now try also to express q_{rev} in terms of some thermodynamic function (or functions).

17-4 Entropy of a System

In this section we shall introduce a new thermodynamic function, the *entropy* of the system, and we shall see that it is directly proportional to q_{rev}. As we have often done in previous sections, we shall develop our argument using as an example a very simple particular system; yet our conclusions will have general validity.

Let us again consider the isothermal expansion of an ideal gas, for which $\Delta E = 0$ and hence $q = -w$. If the isothermal expansion takes place reversibly (that is, under a gradually decreasing opposing external pressure, almost equal at every instant to the pressure exerted by the gas), then, as given on p. 355 and explained in Appendix 17-1, the pressure-volume work is expressed

$$w_{\text{pressure-volume, rev}} = -nRT \times \ln \frac{V_f}{V_i}$$

And since for this transformation the pressure-volume work is the only kind of work involved, we also have:

$$q_{\text{rev}} = -w_{\text{pressure-volume, rev}} = nRT \times \frac{V_f}{V_i}$$

Let us now use this expression to calculate q_{rev} for the isothermal expansion of 1 mole of an ideal gas from an initial volume, $V_i = 12.2$ l., to a final volume, $V_f = 2\,V_i = 24.4$ l., for three different values of the temperature T—say, 273°K (0°C), 298°K (25°C), and 373°K (100°C):

At 273°K: $$q_{\text{rev}} \text{ at } 273^\circ\text{K} = nRT \times \ln \frac{V_f}{V_i}$$
$$= 273^\circ\text{K} \times nR \ln 2$$
$$= 273^\circ\text{K} \times 1 \text{ mole} \times 1.98 \text{ cal/mole} \times \text{deg K} \times 2.303 \log 2$$
$$= 273^\circ\text{K} \times 1.4 \text{ cal/deg K}$$

We may write this result also as:

$$\frac{q_{\text{rev}} \text{ at } 273^\circ\text{K}}{273^\circ\text{K}} = 1.4 \text{ cal/deg K per 1 mole of gas}$$

At 298°K: $$q_{\text{rev}} \text{ at } 298^\circ\text{K} = nRT \times \ln \frac{V_f}{V_i}$$
$$= 298^\circ\text{K} \times nR \ln 2$$
$$= 298^\circ\text{K} \times 1 \text{ mole} \times 1.98 \text{ cal/mole} \times \text{deg K} \times 2.303 \log 2$$
$$= 298^\circ\text{K} \times 1.4 \text{ cal/deg K}$$

or, $$\frac{q_{\text{rev}} \text{ at } 298^\circ\text{K}}{298^\circ\text{K}} = 1.4 \text{ cal/deg K per 1 mole of gas}$$

At 373°K similarly:

$$\frac{q_{rev} \text{ at } 373°K}{373°K} = 1.4 \text{ cal/deg K per 1 mole of gas}$$

A similar result would be obtained for any temperature we may wish to choose. In general, for any reversible volume change of an ideal gas at a constant temperature T, the *ratio* $\frac{q_{rev} \text{ at } T°}{T°}$ is constant, and its value can be shown to depend only on *the initial and final states of the system.* This statement, which we arrived at by considering a particular transformation—the isothermal expansion of an ideal gas—can be shown to be valid in general for any transformation at constant temperature.

Since we know that any property of a system whose change during a transformation depends only on the initial and final states is a thermodynamic function, we can define a new thermodynamic function, the *entropy* of the system. Entropy is indicated by the symbol S, and its change in any transformation at constant temperature T is: $\Delta S = \frac{q_{rev}}{T}$. Since T always has a positive value, ΔS is positive (the entropy, S, of the system increases) when the system absorbs heat from the surroundings (q is positive); and vice versa, the entropy, S, of the system decreases (ΔS is negative) when the system gives up heat to the surroundings (q is negative). It follows from the above definition that the entropy, S, of a system is expressed in units of energy divided by degrees of (absolute) temperature. And since thermodynamic calculations usually use the mole as the basis for quantity of substance, ΔS is expressed in units of cal/mole $\times$ deg K. This unit is often referred to as the "entropy unit," *e.u.*

To put our symbolic expression, $\Delta S = \frac{q_{rev}}{T}$, into words, for any transformation at constant temperature the entropy change, ΔS, is equal to the heat exchanged by the system with the surroundings under reversible conditions, q_{rev}, divided by the absolute temperature, T, at which the heat is exchanged. It follows that for the same value of q_{rev}, the value of ΔS becomes smaller and smaller as the temperature is raised. In other words, for any given value of q_{rev}, ΔS is inversely proportional to the absolute temperature, T.

In the following sections we shall digress to consider the significance of an entropy change—and hence of entropy itself—from the point of view of a microscopic interpretation of the structure of the system.

THE RELATIONSHIP BETWEEN ENTROPY AND DISORDER

Let us again focus our attention on the isothermal expansion of 1 mole of an ideal gas. As the gas expands from its initial to its final volume, its molecules spread out to occupy the greater volume uniformly (Fig. 17-1), so that in the final state, as compared with the initial state, each molecule can occupy at each instant any one of a much larger number of possible positions in space. Thus the initial and final states of the system differ by a property—the number of ways in which the molecules can be arranged in the available volume—which increases as the volume increases. We may say that, as a result of the isothermal expansion, the system has become more disordered, in the sense that the probability of finding a given molecule of the gas inside a small specified element of volume has decreased.

The entropy of a system increases when its volume increases at constant temperature, and on this basis alone, we can conclude that the entropy of a system, S, and the disorder of the positional arrangement of the molecules of the system must somehow be related. It can be shown mathematically—although we shall not consider this here—that the entropy, S, of the system is a measure of the number of ways in which the molecules of the system can be arranged in the available volume. Thus, as the entropy of a system increases, so does its disorder—and vice versa, any transformation which brings about an increase in the disorder of the system results in an increase of its entropy (ΔS is positive). These conclusions, even though obtained here for a specific example—the isothermal expansion of an ideal gas—are of general validity and apply to any transformation of any system.

Having arrived at the conclusion that the entropy of a system increases as its disorder does, we can now understand that an increase in temperature always results in an increase in entropy. We know (see Chapter 9, Fig. 9-14) that each value of the temperature, T, has a particular corresponding distribution of molecular velocities and kinetic energies, and that an increase in temperature has the effect of both increasing the value of the average energy and flattening the energy-distribution curve. In other words, as the temperature is raised the possible range of kinetic energies broadens, and there is a greater "spreading" of the gas molecules among all possible values of the energy. Figure 17-6 illustrates this statement and shows that the range of energies comprising a given fraction—let us say about 90 per cent—of the molecules of the system becomes wider as the temperature increases. An increase in temperature therefore, corresponds to an increase in the number of possible kinetic energy values which each molecule may assume, and to a decrease of the average probability of finding a given molecule in a given interval of energy. The system becomes energetically more disordered as the temperature increases. This increase of energetic disorder—increase in the number of possible distributions of the gas molecules among the various values of the kinetic energy—may again be expressed as an increase in the *entropy* of the system.

Let us summarize by saying: *Entropy*, S, is a thermodynamic function which is a measure of the disorder of the system—a disorder which may be thought of as having a two-fold character, a *positional disorder* (disorder of molecular arrangement) related to the possible arrangements of the molecules in space, and an *energetic disorder*, (disorder of energy distribution) related to the possible distributions of the energies among all the molecules of the system. In other words, the entropy of a system is a measure of the number of distinguishable states available to the molecules of the system, if we take the word "state" to refer to the distribution of the molecular positions as well as to the distribution of the molecular energies.

As the temperature becomes lower, the entropy of any system decreases, since both the positional and the energetic disorder decrease; in fact, at the lowest possible temperature, the absolute zero, 0°K, the entropy of any substance in the form of a perfect crystal is taken to be zero.

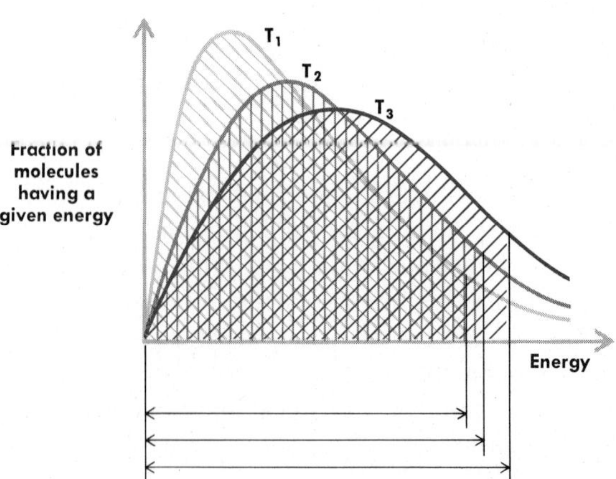

FIGURE 17-6 Energy range comprising about 90 per cent of the molecules of an ideal gas at three successively higher temperatures, T_1, T_2, and T_3.

ENTROPY CHANGES FOR TRANSFORMATIONS INVOLVING CHANGES OF TEMPERATURE

We have seen that for transformations at constant temperature we can express the entropy change, ΔS, in terms of two measurable macroscopic properties of the system, its constant absolute temperature T and the heat q_{rev} absorbed by the system when the transformation is carried out under reversible conditions. If, in a similar way, we try to express the entropy change for a transformation at variable temperatures as a function of some macroscopic property of the system, we find that the situation is far more complicated. In fact, the system now absorbs heat from the surroundings at different temperatures during the transformation, and, as we have seen before, the increment of entropy corresponding to the absorption of a given quantity of heat is inversely proportional to the temperature at which the heat is absorbed.

If the transformation occurs under reversible conditions through a sequence of infinitesimally small successive steps, in each of which the system exchanges with the surroundings, a very small quantity of heat—an "element of heat" at a virtually constant temperature, we can write for each infinitesimally small step:

$$\text{Infinitesimally small entropy change} = \frac{\text{"element of heat"}}{\text{temperature at which "element of heat" is absorbed}}$$

The value of ΔS for the specified transformation is then the sum of the very small entropy changes of all the individual steps; the method of calculating this entropy change is discussed in Appendix 17-2.

CHANGES IN ENTROPY ACCOMPANYING CHANGES IN PHYSICAL STATE

The melting of a solid into its liquid is an important transformation in which the entropy of the system increases at a constant temperature, because of an increase in the disorder of both molecular and energy distribution. Let us consider, as the initial state of a system, say 1 mole of a solid at its melting point and under a constant atmospheric pressure of 1 atm. When a quantity of heat is supplied from the surroundings to the system, some of the solid begins to change to its liquid, and as we know, the temperature remains constant. As more and more heat is supplied from the surroundings to the system, more solid passes to the liquid form until at last virtually all the solid has melted. The temperature remains the same as in the initial state throughout the entire transformation. If we stop supplying heat to the system at this moment, all the solid will have been transformed to its liquid, at constant temperature (*the temperature of fusion*) and under a constant pressure (1 atm):

$$\text{Solid } (T_{fusion}, P = 1 \text{ atm}, V_{solid}) \longrightarrow \text{Liquid } (T_{fusion}, P = 1 \text{ atm}, V_{liquid})$$

In this case $q_{rev} = \Delta H_{fus}$, so the increase in entropy for this melting process at constant temperature and pressure is:

$$\Delta S_{fus} = \frac{q_{rev}}{T_{fus}} = \frac{\Delta H_{fus}}{T_{fus}}$$

How can we use our structural knowledge of matter to interpret the fact that a substance has more entropy in the liquid state than in the solid state? First, we know that in the solid the structural units (molecules, atoms, or ions) of the substance are arranged in an orderly array in the crystal lattice. These structural units can vibrate in the crystal about their equilibrium positions, but apart from this motion the crystalline solid is essentially a well-ordered system.* In a liquid, on the other hand, the structural

* Of course both in the solid state and in liquid state the atoms of each di- or polyatomic unit can vibrate with respect to one another *within* each unit itself. However, these *intra*molecular vibrations are about the same in the solid and liquid states of a substance and we neglect any change in them in the transformation.

units are more or less free to move about in the space occupied by the liquid, and we know that because of their extremely frequent collisions with one another they actually move along random zig-zag paths. Thus any given substance is more disordered in the liquid state than in the solid state, and the increase in disorder—increase in entropy—in passing from the solid to the liquid state at constant temperature is two-fold. First, there is an increase in the positional disorder since the spatial arrangement of molecules is far more disordered in the liquid than in the solid; second, the distribution of thermal energy of the molecules in the solid is fairly ordered since within the crystal lattice only some particular motions are possible, which in the liquid is random and follows a distribution curve of the type shown in Chapter 9, Fig. 9-14. Thus the entropy of any substance always increases upon melting at constant temperature.

A similar argument holds for the transformation of a liquid to its vapor. For the vaporization of a liquid at constant temperature and pressure, the entropy increase is:

$$\Delta S_{\mathrm{vap}} = \frac{q_{\mathrm{rev}}}{T_{\mathrm{vap}}} = \frac{\Delta H_{\mathrm{vap}}}{T_{\mathrm{vap}}}$$

For a large variety of substances the values of the entropy changes in going from liquid to vapor all lie within a rather narrow range. Many other common processes result in an increase in the entropy of a system at constant temperature and pressure, and in future chapters we shall discuss several of them in detail. Here we simply summarize the most common among such processes: (a) The fusion of a solid to its liquid. (b) The vaporization of a solid or liquid. (c) The mixing of two or more substances to form a solution. Two particularly important examples are the diffusion of two gases through one another and the dissolution of an ionic solid in water. (d) An increase of volume. An especially important case is that of a chemical reaction (under constant atmospheric pressure) in which there is an increase in the number of moles of gaseous substances. For example: $2\,NH_{3(g)} \longrightarrow N_{2(g)} + 3\,H_{2(g)}$; and $CaCO_{3(s)} \longrightarrow CaO_{(s)} + CO_{2(g)}$. (e) All chemical reactions for which the "mixed-up-ness" of the products is greater than that of the reactants, even though the volume of the system does not appreciably increase. Examples are: $H_{2(g)} + Cl_{2(g)} \longrightarrow 2\,HCl_{(g)}$; and $C_{(s,gr)} + O_{2(g)} \longrightarrow CO_{2(g)}$. (f) An increase in temperature of a substance.

ENTROPY-TEMPERATURE DIAGRAMS

An increase in the temperature of a system always contributes to increasing its entropy, and the way in which the entropy varies with the temperature is particularly interesting if we consider a system composed of a pure substance, because then the entropy is a measure of the molecular disorder. Figure 17-7 shows how the entropy of water increases with temperature under a constant pressure of 1 atm.

Let us assume that we start with water in the solid state—at the absolute zero of temperature, $T = 0°K$. At this lowest possible temperature, water in the form of a perfect crystal of ice is in a state of maximum molecular order; not only does each H_2O molecule occupy a fixed position in the crystal lattice, but also the vibrational motions are reduced to a minimum. Hence we conventionally assign an entropy value of zero, $S = 0$, to water in this state of perfect crystal at 0°K. As the temperature gradually increases from 0°K up to 273°K (0°C) there is a gradual increase of entropy—represented by the sloping line OA—a result of increased vibrational motions of the H_2O molecules in the crystal lattice. At 273°K ice begins to melt to liquid water, and as we know, the temperature remains constant as long as both ice and liquid water are present. The entropy rises vertically (at constant temperature) along AB, and we know that this increase in entropy is

$$\Delta S_{\mathrm{fus}} = \frac{\Delta H_{\mathrm{fus}}}{T_{\mathrm{fus}}} = \frac{1436\ \mathrm{cal/mole}}{273\ \mathrm{deg}} = 5.3\ \mathrm{cal/mole} \times \mathrm{deg}$$

This increase of entropy during the fusion process at constant temperature is accounted for by greater molecular disorder of the liquid state as compared to the crystalline state. From 273° to 373°K (100°C) the entropy again increases gradually as the molecular disorder of liquid water increases, until finally at 373°K and 1 atm liquid water begins to pass to the gaseous state. Again, as long as the system is composed of both liquid and gaseous water, the temperature remains constant and the entropy increase (represented by the vertical line CD) is:

$$\Delta S_{vap} = \frac{\Delta H_{vap}}{T_{vap}} = \frac{9710 \text{ cal/mole}}{373 \text{ deg}}$$
$$= 26.0 \text{ cal/mole} \times \text{deg}$$

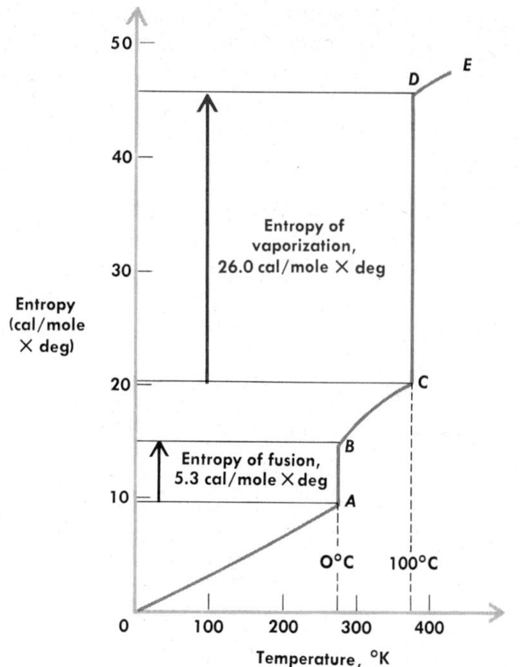

FIGURE 17-7 Variation of the entropy of water with temperature at constant pressure of 1 atm.

Above 373°K, the entropy of gaseous water again increases gradually with temperature, as both the positional disorder (volume) and the energetic disorder (temperature) of the $H_2O_{(g)}$ molecules increase.

STANDARD ENTROPY OF A SUBSTANCE

For any pure substance under a constant pressure, the entropy increases as the temperature rises, in the manner discussed in the preceding section. *If we take the entropy of a perfectly crystalline substance at 0°K to be zero,* then we can determine experimentally the entropy of that pure substance in any physical state at any temperature. The entropy values of most common substances in their standard states (p. 333) at 25°C have been determined and are referred to as Standard Entropy values, S° (read: S-zero). For ions in aqueous solution, the absolute values of the entropy cannot be determined in the same way as for pure substances; the reason is that we cannot have a system made up solely of a certain kind of ions of one sign, and our measurements necessarily involve ionic compounds, which consist of positive and negative ions. For ions in solution, then, we use relative S° values. These are derived from the convention that the entropy of the $H^+_{(aq)}$ ion is zero when its activity is equal to unity. As a first approximation, when the concentration of the H^+ ion is 1-molar (1 *M*) at 25° and 1 atm, then S° for $H^+_{(aq,1M)} = 0$. The relative values of the S° of ions in solution can be used, just as the absolute S° values of pure substances, to calculate ΔS° of reactions, because the arbitrary factor introduced by taking S° for $H^+_{(aq,1M)} = 0$ cancels out in all cases. A number of S° values are listed in Table 17-2.

17-5 The Free Energy of a System

We shall now return to the problem we were considering before we digressed to define and discuss the concept of entropy—namely, how to express in terms of readily accessible thermodynamic functions the *maximum useful work* involved when a system passes at constant temperature and pressure from a specified initial state to a specified final state. The importance of such maximum useful work, as we have seen,

TABLE 17-2 STANDARD ENTROPIES, S°, OF SOME SUBSTANCES AT 298°K (25°C)

A. PURE SUBSTANCES

Substance (state)	S° *(cal/mole × deg)*
$Ag_{(s)}$	+10.2
$Ag_2O_{(s)}$	+29.1
$AgF_{(s)}$	+20.0
$AgCl_{(s)}$	+23.0
$AgBr_{(s)}$	+25.6
$AgI_{(s)}$	+27.3
$Al_{(s)}$	+6.8
$Al_2O_{3(s)}$	+12.2
$AlF_{3(s)}$	+15.9
$AlCl_{3(s)}$	+26.3
$AlBr_{3(s)}$	+49.0
$AlI_{3(s)}$	+48.0
$B_{(s)}$	+1.6
$B_2O_{3(s)}$	+12.9
$BCl_{3(g)}$	+69.3
$BCl_{3(l)}$	+50.0
$Ba_{(s)}$	+16.0
$BaO_{(s)}$	+16.8
$BaCl_{2(s)}$	+30.0
$BaSO_{4(s)}$	+31.6
$Be_{(s)}$	+2.3
$BeO_{(s)}$	+3.4
$BeCl_{2(s)}$	+21.5
$Br_{2(l)}$	+36.4
$Br_{2(g)}$	+58.6
$Br_{(g)}$	+41.8
$C_{(s,gr)}$	+1.4

Substance (state)	S° *(cal/mole × deg)*
$C_{(s,dia)}$	+0.6
$CO_{(g)}$	+47.3
$CO_{2(g)}$	+51.1
$CH_{4(g)}$	+44.5
$CH_3Cl_{(g)}$	+56.0
$CCl_{4(g)}$	+73.9
$CCl_{4(l)}$	+51.2
$CS_{2(g)}$	+56.8
$CS_{2(l)}$	+36.1
$Ca_{(s)}$	+9.9
$CaO_{(s)}$	+9.5
$CaH_{2(s)}$	+10.0
$CaCl_{2(s)}$	+27.2
$CaCO_{3(s)}$	+22.2
$Cl_{2(g)}$	+53.3
$Cl_{(g)}$	+39.5
$Cs_{(s)}$	+19.8
$CsF_{(s)}$	+19.8
$CsCl_{(s)}$	+23.9
Cu	+8.0
$Cu_2O_{(s)}$	+22.4
$CuO_{(s)}$	+10.2
$F_{2(g)}$	+48.6
$F_{(g)}$	+37.9
$H_{2(g)}$	+31.2
$H_2O_{(g)}$	+45.1

Substance (state)	S° *(cal/mole × deg)*
$H_2O_{(l)}$	+16.7
H_2O_2	+54.2
$HF_{(g)}$	+41.5
$HCl_{(g)}$	+44.6
$HBr_{(g)}$	+47.4
$HI_{(s)}$	+49.3
$Hg_{(l)}$	+18.2
$Hg_{(g)}$	+41.8
$HgO_{(s)}$	+16.8
$Hg_2Cl_{2(s)}$	+46.8
$HgCl_{2(s)}$	+34.5
$I_{2(s)}$	+27.9
$I_{2(g)}$	+62.3
$I_{(g)}$	+43.2
$K_{(s)}$	+15.2
$KCl_{(s)}$	+19.8
$KClO_{3(s)}$	+34.2
$KNO_{3(s)}$	+32.9
$Li_{(s)}$	+6.7
$Li_2O_{(s)}$	+9.1
$LiH_{(g)}$	+40.8
$Mg_{(s)}$	+7.8
$MgO_{(s)}$	+6.4
$MgF_{2(s)}$	+13.7
$N_{2(g)}$	+45.8
$NO_{(g)}$	+50.3

Substance (state)	S° *(cal/mole × deg)*
$NO_{2(g)}$	+57.5
$N_2O_{(g)}$	+52.6
$N_2O_{4(g)}$	+72.7
$NH_{3(g)}$	+46.0
$NH_4Cl_{(s)}$	+22.6
$(NH_4)_2SO_{4(s)}$	+52.6
$Na_{(s)}$	+12.2
$Na_2O_{(s)}$	+17.4
$NaOH_{(s)}$	+15.3
$NaF_{(s)}$	+12.3
$NaCl_{(s)}$	+17.4
$NaBr_{(s)}$	+20.0
$NaI_{(s)}$	+21.8
$O_{2(g)}$	+49.0
$O_{3(g)}$	+56.8
$P_{(s,white)}$	+10.6
$PCl_{3(g)}$	+74.6
$PCl_{5(g)}$	+84.3
$S_{(s,rhombic)}$	+7.6
$S_{(s,monoclinic)}$	+7.8
$SO_{2(g)}$	+59.4
$SO_{3(g)}$	+61.2
$Si_{(s)}$	+4.5
$SiO_{2(s)}$	+10.0

B. IONS IN 1-MOLAR AQUEOUS SOLUTION*

Ion	S° *(cal/mole × deg)*
$Ag^+_{(aq)}$	+17.7
$Al^{+3}_{(aq)}$	−74.9
$Ba^{++}_{(aq)}$	+3.0
$Br^-_{(aq)}$	+19.3
$CO_{3(aq)}$	−12.7
$HCO_{3(aq)}$	+22.7
$CN^-_{(aq)}$	+28.2
$Ca^{++}_{(aq)}$	−13.2
$Cl^-_{(aq)}$	+13.2

Ion	S° *(cal/mole × deg)*
$Cs^+_{(aq)}$	+31.8
$Cu^+_{(aq)}$	−6.3
$Cu^{++}_{(aq)}$	−23.6
$F^-_{(aq)}$	−2.3
$Fe^{++}_{(aq)}$	−27.1
$Fe^{+++}_{(aq)}$	−70.1
$H^+_{(aq)}$	0.0

Ion	S° *(cal/mole × deg)*
$I^-_{(aq)}$	+26.1
$K^+_{(aq)}$	+24.5
$Li^+_{(aq)}$	+3.4
$Mg^{++}_{(aq)}$	−28.2
$NH^+_{4(aq)}$	+27.0
$NO^-_{3(aq)}$	+35.0
$Na^+_{(aq)}$	14.4
$Ni^{++}_{(aq)}$	−38.1
$OH^-_{(aq)}$	−2.6

Ion	S° *(cal/mole × deg)*
$PO^{\equiv}_{4(aq)}$	−52.0
$SO^{=}_{3(aq)}$	+10.4
$SO^{=}_{4(aq)}$	+4.1
$HS^-_{(aq)}$	+14.6
$S^{=}_{(aq)}$	+5.3
$Sr^{++}_{(aq)}$	−9.4
$Zn^{++}_{(aq)}$	−25.4

* The S° values of ions in solution are conventionally taken relative to that of the $H^+_{(aq)}$ ion, assumed equal to zero. Hence the S° value of an ion in 1-molar solution is negative or positive, depending on whether its value is smaller or larger than that of the H^+ ion.

is that it represents a criterion of spontaneity. If $w_{\text{useful max}}$ is negative (work is done by the system) the transformation can take place spontaneously: if $w_{\text{useful max}}$ is positive (work is done on the system) the transformation is not spontaneous and in fact work must be expended to carry it out. In our previous discussion we had arrived at the following expression for the maximum useful work involved in transformations at constant temperature and pressure:

$$w_{\text{useful max}} = \Delta H - q_{\text{rev}}$$

Now the heat exchanged by a system in a reversible transformation at a given constant temperature is equal to the product of the absolute temperature, T, and the change in entropy, ΔS, of the system:

$$q_{\text{rev}} = T\,\Delta S$$

Hence the useful work for any transformation at constant T and P:

$$w_{\text{useful max}} = \Delta H - T\,\Delta S$$

For transformations which occur at constant temperature and under constant pressure, we have finally managed to express the maximum useful work as the difference of two terms each involving only thermodynamic quantities which depend only on the initial and final states of the system, and can be readily measured or calculated. The term ΔH, as we know from Chapter 16, is often measurable directly, and it can be obtained from tables of heats of reaction, or calculated from Hess' Law (p. 339) or enthalpy diagrams (p. 342). And in the $T\,\Delta S$ term, T is the absolute temperature at which the process occurs, and ΔS is the entropy change from the initial to the final state, which can be usually obtained directly, or calculated, from tables of entropy values.

As we stated in section 17.2, $w_{\text{useful max}}$ represents the change in the "capacity of the system to do useful work" in passing at constant temperature and pressure from a specified initial to a specified final state. This *capacity of the system to do useful work when in a given state is called the Gibbs free energy,* after the American scientist J. Willard Gibbs, and is indicated as G. We have, therefore:

$$w_{\text{useful max}} = G_{\text{final}} - G_{\text{initial}} = \Delta G \quad \text{and} \quad \Delta G = \Delta H - T\,\Delta S$$

These expressions tell us that when a system passes at constant temperature and pressure from a specified initial state to a specified final state, the change in the free energy of a system, $\Delta G = G_{\text{final}} - G_{\text{initial}}$, is equal to the maximum useful work involved in the transformation. Therefore, if $w_{\text{useful max}}$ is positive (work done on system), the free energy of the system increases in the transformation (ΔG is positive). Conversely, if $w_{\text{useful max}}$ is negative (work done by system), the free energy of the system decreases (ΔG is negative). Also, at constant temperature and pressure, the free energy change, ΔG, is equal to the change in the enthalpy, ΔH, minus the product of the absolute temperature T and the entropy change, ΔS. Notice that, as both ΔH and ΔS depend only on the initial and final states of the system, and not on the path followed in the transformation, so does ΔG. In fact, the free energy, G, is a thermodynamic function as are the enthalpy H and entropy S. (Note the use of a capital letter to indicate a thermodynamic function of state, in this case the capacity to do useful work.)

Let us consider the units involved in the equation: $\Delta G = \Delta H - T\,\Delta S$. If we express ΔH in cal/mole, T in deg K, and ΔS in cal/mole $\times$ deg, then ΔG is expressed in cal/mole. We may say that ΔG represents the quantity of energy (per mole) which is "free to do useful work," when a system passes, at constant temperature and pressure, from a specified initial to a specified final state (hence the name Gibbs "free energy").

We saw earlier (p. 356) that for reactions which can take place spontaneously, the $w_{\text{useful max}}$ has a negative value (the work is done by the system). It follows that a *system is capable of passing spontaneously from an initial state of higher free energy to a final state of lower free energy.* Therefore, for a spontaneous transformation there is a decrease in the free energy of the system, and ΔG has a negative value. Conversely, if the value of ΔG for a designated transformation is positive, the system cannot pass spontaneously from the initial state (lower free energy) to the final state (higher free energy). In this case, if we still want the transformation to take place, we—as part of the surroundings—must spend energy to do work of some form on the system. We see, then, that the sign of ΔG for a given transformation tells us directly whether or not the transformation as written can proceed spontaneously. These considerations are valid, in general, for any kind of transformation—physical process or chemical reaction—which occurs at constant temperature and pressure. In the following sections, we shall concern ourselves primarily with the application of the concept of free energy to the study of chemical systems and their reactions.

The ΔG values for some specific processes are often designated by placing the abbreviated name of the process as a subscript after the symbol ΔG, just as we do for the ΔH values. For example, we write ΔG_{fus}, ΔG_{vap}, and ΔG_{diss} to indicate, respectively, the free energy change of a fusion, a vaporization process, and the dissociation of a molecular substance into its isolated atoms.

STANDARD FREE ENERGY OF FORMATION, $\Delta G^\circ_{\text{form}}$, OF A COMPOUND

This term is used to indicate the free energy change of the reaction in which a specified compound, at a certain temperature and pressure, is formed from its elements in their standard state (p. 333) at that same temperature. By convention, all elements in their standard state are assigned a $\Delta G^\circ_{\text{form}}$ equal to zero. Thus, for example, the $\Delta G^\circ_{\text{form}}$ of CO_2 at 25°C, -94.3 kcal/mole $CO_{2(g)}$ indicates the free energy change for the reaction, $C_{(s,gr)} + O_{2(g)} \longrightarrow CO_{2(g)}$, if each of the substances involved (reagents and product) are at 25°C and 1 atm.

As we shall see in the following sections, the $\Delta G^\circ_{\text{form}}$ of compounds are of great interest in the study and understanding of the chemical behavior of compounds. The values of $\Delta G^\circ_{\text{form}}$ for a number of compounds at 25°C are given in Table 17-3.

TABLE 17-3 STANDARD FREE ENERGY OF FORMATION, $\Delta G^\circ_{\text{form}}$, OF SOME SUBSTANCES AT 298°K (25°C)*

Substance (state)	$\Delta G^\circ_{\text{form}}$ *(kcal/mole)*	*Substance (state)*	$\Delta G^\circ_{\text{form}}$ *(kcal/mole)*	*Substance (state)*	$\Delta G^\circ_{\text{form}}$ *(kcal/mole)*	*Substance (state)*	$\Delta G^\circ_{\text{form}}$ *(kcal/mole)*
$Ag_2O_{(s)}$	-2.6	$Ca^{++}_{(aq)}$	-132.2	$HgCl_{2(g)}$	-44.0	NaH	$+24.8$
		$CaH_{2(s)}$	-35.8			$NaCl_{(s)}$	-92.2
$Al_2O_{3(s)}$	-376.8	$CaCO_{3(s)}$	-269.8	$Li_2O_{(s)}$	-133.8	$Na_2CO_{3(s)}$	-250.4
$Al^{+++}_{(aq)}$	-115.0			$Li^{+}_{(aq)}$	-70.2		
		$Cu_2O_{(s)}$	-34.4	$LiH_{(s)}$	$+24.2$	$O_{3(g)}$	$+31.1$
$B_2O_{3(s)}$	-118.7	$Cu^{++}_{(aq)}$	$+15.5$			$OH^{-}_{(aq)}$	-37.6
		$CuO_{(s)}$	-30.4	$MgO_{(s)}$	-136.1		
$BaO_{(s)}$	-126.3					$PH_{3(g)}$	$+6.2$
		$H^{+}_{(aq)}$	0.0	$NH_{3(g)}$	-4.0		
$BeO_{(s)}$	-139.0	$H_2O_{(g)}$	-54.6	$NH^{+}_{4(aq)}$	-19.0	$SO_{2(g)}$	-71.8
		$HCl_{(g)}$	-22.8	$N_2O_{(g)}$	$+24.8$	$SO_{3(g)}$	-88.5
$CO_{2(g)}$	-94.3			$NO_{(g)}$	$+20.7$	$SO^{=}_{4(aq)}$	-177.3
$CCl_{4(g)}$	-15.3	$KCl_{(s)}$	-97.6	$N_2O_{4(g)}$	$+23.5$	Zn^{++}	-39.1
$CCl_{4(l)}$	-16.4	$K^{+}_{(aq)}$	-67.5	$NO_{2(g)}$	$+12.4$		
$CS_{2(g)}$	$+15.5$	$KClO_{3(s)}$	-69.3				
$CS_{2(l)}$	$+15.2$	$KH_{(s)}$	$+25.1$	$Na^{+}_{(aq)}$	-62.6		
				$Na_2O_{(s)}$	-90.6		
$CaO_{(s)}$	-144.4	$Hg_2Cl_{2(s)}$	-50.3	$Na_2O_{2(s)}$	-107.8		

* Ions are in 1-molar aqueous solution, relative to the H^+ ion as the reference.

CALCULATION OF THE $\Delta G°$ OF A REACTION FROM TABULATED VALUES OF $\Delta G°_{form}$

We now know that the free energy of a system, G, is a thermodynamic function and hence that the ΔG of a reaction depends only on the final and initial states of the system, and not on the path by which the system actually passes from the initial to the final state. Therefore, we can calculate easily the $\Delta G°$ of any reaction if we know the values of the $\Delta G°$ of formation of all the substances which appear in the reaction equation (reactants and products). This type of calculation is analogous to that discussed in some detail for the calculation of $\Delta H°_{reaction}$ from the $\Delta H°_{form}$ of the reactants and products; the following examples illustrate this:

a. Consider the reaction of solid copper(II) oxide, $CuO_{(s)}$, with hydrogen gas, $H_{2(g)}$, to give metallic copper, $Cu_{(s)}$, and water vapor, $H_2O_{(g)}$, at 25°C:

Reaction:	$CuO_{(s)}$ +	$H_{2(g)}$ $\longrightarrow$	$Cu_{(s)}$ +	$H_2O_{(g)}$
$\Delta G°_{form}$ (kcal/mole) =	−30.4	0	0	−54.6

$\Delta G°_{reaction} = \Delta G°_{form}$ of all products $-$ $\Delta G°_{form}$ of all reactants

$\Delta G°_{reaction} = -54.6 - (-30.4) = -24.2$ kcal/mole-eqn

The $\Delta G°_{reaction}$ has a negative value, hence the reaction is thermodynamically permitted—that is, it is capable of occurring spontaneously under the specified conditions (25°C; crystalline CuO and Cu metal at 1 atm; gaseous H_2 and water vapor, $H_2O_{(g)}$, each at 1 atm).

b. Consider the reaction of solid sodium carbonate, $Na_2CO_{3(s)}$, with hydrogen chloride gas, $HCl_{(g)}$, to form sodium chloride, $NaCl_{(s)}$, and carbon dioxide, $CO_{2(g)}$, and water vapor, $H_2O_{(g)}$, each reactant and product being at 25°C and 1 atm:

Reaction:	$Na_2CO_{3(s)}$ +	2 $HCl_{(g)}$ $\longrightarrow$	2 $NaCl_{(s)}$ +	$CO_{2(g)}$ +	$H_2O_{(g)}$
$\Delta G°_{form}$ (kcal/mole) =	−250.4	2(−22.8)	2(−92.2)	−94.3	−54.6

$\Delta G°_{reaction} = \Delta G°_{form}$ of all products $-$ $\Delta G°_{form}$ of all reactants

$$\Delta G°_{reaction} = \{2(-92.2) - 94.3 - 54.6\} - \{-250.4 + 2(-22.8)\}$$
$$= -184.4 - 94.3 - 54.6 + 250.4 + 45.6 = -333.3 + 296.0$$
$$= -37.3 \text{ kcal/mole-eqn}$$

Thus, the reaction can proceed spontaneously, under the specified conditions, in the direction shown by the equation.

c. Consider the reaction of solid zinc metal, $Zn_{(s)}$, with a 1 *M* aqueous solution of hydrogen ions, $H^+_{(aq,1M)}$ (for example 1 *M* hydrochloric acid) at 25°C:

Reaction:	$Zn_{(s)}$ +	2 $H^+_{(aq,1M)}$ =	$Zn^{++}_{(aq,1M)}$ +	$H_{2(g)}$
$\Delta G°_{form}$ (kcal/mole) =	0	0	−39.1	0

$\Delta G°_{reaction} = \Delta G°_{form}$ of $Zn^{2+}_{(aq,1M)} = -39.1$ kcal/mole-eqn

The reaction is thermodynamically permitted; and in fact, as we know, zinc metal dissolves in acidic solutions with the evolution of hydrogen gas.

17-6 Spontaneous Reactions

The guiding principle for deciding whether a physical or chemical transformation can take place spontaneously at constant temperature and pressure is: *any system tends to go from a state of higher free energy to a state of lower free energy.* Hence a system can pass spontaneously from its initial to its final state if the transformation involves a *decrease* in the free energy of the system (ΔG is negative). In other words, a transformation tends to proceed spontaneously in that direction which brings the system to a state of minimum free energy. Since the change in free energy at constant temperature and pressure is given by the expression $\Delta G = \Delta H - T\,\Delta S$, the capacity of a given system to undergo spontaneously a specified transformation depends on two independent energy terms—the ΔH energy term and the $T\,\Delta S$ energy term*—each having its own sign and magnitude for the transformation considered. A negative value of ΔH (exothermic reaction) is favorable to spontaneity; on the other hand, since the $T\,\Delta S$ term is preceded by a minus sign in the expression $\Delta G = \Delta H - T\,\Delta S$, a *positive* value of ΔS (disordering reaction) is favorable to spontaneity (T, the absolute temperature, is always positive). We can summarize these considerations:

$$\Delta G = \Delta H - T\,\Delta S$$

ΔH *enthalpy term:*	Exothermic reaction:	ΔH negative and favorable to spontaneity.
	Endothermic reaction:	ΔH positive and unfavorable to spontaneity.
ΔS *entropy term:*	Disordering reaction:	ΔS positive and favorable to spontaneity.
	Ordering reaction:	ΔS negative and unfavorable to spontaneity.

Hence the actual value of ΔG for a given transformation at constant temperature and pressure depends on the relative values, favorable or unfavorable to spontaneity, of the ΔH and $T\,\Delta S$ energy terms. The following cases are possible:

Case 1. The reaction is exothermic (ΔH is negative) and also results in an increase of the entropy of the system (ΔS is positive). Both the ΔH energy term and the $T\,\Delta S$ energy term, therefore, are favorable to a spontaneous transformation, and, of course, the reaction has the capacity to take place spontaneously under the specified conditions of constant temperature and pressure. An example is the reaction of hydrogen gas, $H_{2(g)}$, with *liquid* bromine, $Br_{2(l)}$, to form hydrogen bromide gas, $HBr_{(g)}$ at 25°C:

$$\tfrac{1}{2}\,H_{2(g)} + \tfrac{1}{2}\,Br_{2(l)} \longrightarrow HBr_{(g)} \quad \begin{cases} \Delta H^\circ = -8.7 \text{ kcal/mole } HBr_{(g)} \\ T\,\Delta S^\circ = +4.1 \text{ kcal/mole } HBr_{(g)} \end{cases}$$

$$T\,\Delta S^\circ = 298 \text{ \sout{deg}} \times (+0.014 \text{ kcal/mole } HBr_{(g)} \times \text{\sout{deg}}) = +4.1 \text{ kcal/mole } HBr_{(g)}$$

$$\Delta G^\circ = \Delta H^\circ - T\,\Delta S^\circ = -8.7 - (+4.1) = -12.8 \text{ kcal/mole } HBr_{(g)}$$

The negative value of ΔG° indicates that the reaction has the capacity to occur spontaneously at 25° when each of the reactants as well as the product is in its standard state ($H_{2(g)}$ at 1 atm, $Br_{2(l)}$ at 1 atm, $HBr_{(g)}$ at 1 atm). The magnitude of ΔG° is a measure of the capacity of the system as written to react under these conditions.

Case 2. The reaction is exothermic but results in *a decrease* in entropy (greater order) of the system. The ΔH energy term is favorable to a spontaneous transformation (ΔH is negative), whereas the $T\,\Delta S$ energy term is unfavorable ($T\,\Delta S$ is negative, that is, the entropy, S, of the system decreases in passing from the initial to the final state). In this case, the reaction is capable of proceeding spontaneously if the favorable ΔH energy term outweighs the unfavorable $T\,\Delta S$ energy term. Conversely, if the magnitude of the favorable ΔH term is smaller than that of the unfavorable $T\,\Delta S$ term, the reaction cannot take place spontaneously. In this case the unfavorable $T\,\Delta S$ term outweighs the favorable ΔH term.

As an example, consider the reaction: $\tfrac{1}{2}\,N_{2(g)} + \tfrac{3}{2}\,H_{2(g)} \longrightarrow NH_{3(g)}$, $\Delta H^\circ = -11.0$ kcal/mole $NH_{3(g)}$ (favorable to spontaneity), $T\,\Delta S^\circ = -7.1$ kcal/mole $NH_{3(g)}$ (unfavorable to spontaneity). Hence, $\Delta G^\circ = -11.0 - (-7.1) = -3.9$ kcal/mole $NH_{3(g)}$. This negative ΔG° value means that this chemical reaction can occur spontaneously (at 25°, under the conditions specified in defining ΔG°).

Case 3. The reaction is endothermic but results in an increase in the entropy, that is, in a more disordered state of the system. The ΔH energy term is unfavorable

* Notice that whereas the entropy change, ΔS, is not itself an energy term, as indicated by its units which are cal/mole × deg, the product of the absolute temperature, T, by the change in entropy, ΔS, is an energy term: T deg × ΔS cal/mole × deg = $T\,\Delta S$ cal/mole.

(ΔH is positive), whereas the $T\,\Delta S$ energy term is favorable to a spontaneous transformation ($T\,\Delta S$ is positive because the entropy, S, of the system increases in the transformation). Again, in this case, the relative magnitudes of the favorable energy term, $T\,\Delta S$, and of the unfavorable energy term, ΔH, decide whether the free energy change, ΔG, has a negative or positive value, that is, whether the reaction can or cannot occur spontaneously. Here are two illustrative examples:

a. For the dissolution of ammonium sulfate in water at 25°C to form a solution containing 1 mole of $(NH_4)_2SO_4$ in 55 moles (about 1 liter) of water, the data are:

$$(NH_4)_2SO_{4(s)} + 55\ H_2O_{(l)} \longrightarrow \{2\ NH_{4(aq)} + SO^{=}_{4(aq)}\} \cdot 55\ H_2O;$$
$$\Delta H^\circ = +2.0 \text{ kcal/mole-eqn};\ T\,\Delta S = +4.6 \text{ kcal/mole-eqn}$$

Hence: $\Delta G = \Delta H - T\,\Delta S = +2.0 - (+4.6) = -2.6$ kcal/mole-equation, (ΔG negative, favorable to spontaneity). In fact 1 mole (132.1 g) of crystalline $(NH_4)_2SO_4$ at 25°C dissolves in 55 moles (1 liter) of water at 25°C. Actually in this example the $T\,\Delta S$ entropy term is so favorable that $(NH_4)_2SO_{4(s)}$ dissolves in water up to about 5.8 moles/liter, although the resulting solution becomes appreciably cooler if no heat is taken on from the surroundings. Ammonium sulfate stops dissolving when the solution reaches a concentration of 5.8 moles/liter, because, as we shall discuss in detail in Chapters 24 and 25, the ΔG of a process involving solutions depends on the concentration of the solutions. In this case, the (negative) value of ΔG gradually decreases in magnitude as the solution becomes more concentrated. Finally, when a certain concentration is reached, $\Delta G = 0$, and the dissolution process stops.

b. As another example, consider the dissociation of solid calcium carbonate, $CaCO_{3(s)}$, into solid calcium oxide, $CaO_{(s)}$, and carbon dioxide gas, $CO_{2(g)}$ at 25°C:

$$CaCO_{3(s)} \longrightarrow CaO_{(s)} + CO_{2(g)};\quad \Delta H^\circ = +42.5 \text{ kcal/mole } CaCO_{3(s)}$$
$$T\,\Delta S^\circ = +11.5 \text{ kcal/mole } CaCO_{3(s)}$$

For this endothermic reaction the value of the unfavorable ΔH° energy term is larger than that of the favorable $T\,\Delta S^\circ$ energy term, so that their difference is positive: $\Delta G^\circ = \Delta H^\circ - T\,\Delta S^\circ = +42.2 - 11.54 = +30.66$ kcal/mole $CaCO_{3(s)}$. Consequently the reaction is thermodynamically forbidden (energetically unfavorable), and in fact it does not occur spontaneously at 25°C.

Case 4. The last general case concerns those reactions for which the enthalpy term ΔH and the entropy term $T\,\Delta S$ are both unfavorable; obviously, such reactions cannot take place spontaneously. Rather, if the "products" were brought into contact with one another, they would have the capacity to transform spontaneously into the "reactants."

Consider as an example the formation of the gas, $N_2O_{(g)}$ from nitrogen gas, $N_{2(g)}$, and oxygen gas, $O_{2(g)}$, each gas being at 25°C and 1 atm:

$$N_{2(g)} + \tfrac{1}{2}\,O_{2(g)} \longrightarrow N_2O_{(g)};\ \Delta H^\circ = +19.5 \text{ kcal/mole } N_2O_{(g)};\ T\,\Delta S^\circ = -5.4 \text{ kcal/mole } N_2O_{(g)}$$

Thus, for the reaction as written: $\Delta G^\circ = \Delta H^\circ - T\,\Delta S^\circ = +19.5 - (-5.4) = +24.9$ kcal/mole $N_2O_{(g)}$. This positive value of ΔG° tells us that $N_2O_{(g)}$ cannot be formed spontaneously from its elements at 25°C and 1 atm.

$$N_{2(g)} + \tfrac{1}{2}\,O_{2(g)} \longrightarrow N_2O_{(g)} \qquad \Delta G^\circ = +24.9 \text{ kcal/mole } N_2O_{(g)}$$

Rather, $N_2O_{(g)}$ is unstable at this temperature and has the capacity to dissociate into nitrogen gas, $N_{2(g)}$ and oxygen gas, $O_{2(g)}$:

$$N_2O_{(g)} \longrightarrow N_{2(g)} + \tfrac{1}{2}\,O_{2(g)} \qquad \Delta G^\circ = -24.9 \text{ kcal/mole } N_2O_{(g)}$$

CALCULATION OF ΔG° VALUES FROM TABULATED VALUES OF ΔH° AND S°

Let us now illustrate by some examples how we can predict whether a given reaction is capable of proceeding spontaneously (when each reactant and product is in its standard state at 25°C) on the basis of the $\Delta G°$ of the reaction calculated from values of $\Delta H°_{form}$ and standard entropy values, $S°$ (Tables 16-4 and 17-2).

Example 1. First let us consider the reaction $H_{2(g)}$ with $Cl_{2(g)}$ to form $HCl_{(g)}$, all substances being at 25°C and 1 atm. To calculate the $\Delta G°$ of this reaction we need to know the values of $\Delta H°$ and $\Delta S°$ at the temperature, $T = 298°K$. For this particular example, the $\Delta H°$ of the reaction is simply the $\Delta H°_{form}$ of $HCl_{(g)}$, given directly in Table 16-4; $\Delta H°_{form}\ HCl_{(g)} = -22.1$ kcal/mole. The value of $\Delta S°$ for the reaction is given by the sum of the standard entropies of all the products minus the sum of the standard entropies of all reactants (Table 17-2). A convenient way to calculate $\Delta S°_{reaction}$ is to write under the formula of each reactant and product the corresponding value of the standard entropy, $S°$, obtained from Table 17-2, multiplying each value by its appropriate coefficient:

Reaction:	$\frac{1}{2} H_{2(g)}$ +	$\frac{1}{2} Cl_{2(g)}$ ⟶	$HCl_{(g)}$
S° (cal/mole × deg K):	$\frac{1}{2} \times 31.2$	$\frac{1}{2} \times 53.3$	44.6

$$\begin{aligned}\Delta S° &= S°_{HCl(g)} - \{\tfrac{1}{2} S°_{H_2(g)} + \tfrac{1}{2} S°_{Cl_2(g)}\}\\ &= 44.6 - \{(\tfrac{1}{2} \times 31.2) + (\tfrac{1}{2} \times 53.3)\}\\ &= 44.6 - 15.6 - 26.6\\ &= 44.6 - 42.2 = +2.4 \text{ cal/mole} \times \text{deg}\end{aligned}$$

In calculating $\Delta G°$, we must remember to express both $\Delta H°$ and $T\,\Delta S°$ in the same energy unit, say kcal. Thus we have:

$$\begin{aligned}\Delta G° = \Delta H° - T\,\Delta S° &= -22.1 \text{ kcal/mole} - 298 \text{ deg} \times 2.4 \times 10^{-3} \text{ kcal/mole} \times \text{deg}\\ &= -22.1 \text{ kcal/mole} - 0.7 \text{ kcal/mole} = -22.8 \text{ kcal/mole}\end{aligned}$$

We find that $\Delta G°$ has a negative value (the standard free energy of the system decreases) in passing from the initial state, $\{\frac{1}{2} H_{2(g)} + \frac{1}{2} Cl_{2(g)}\}$, to the final state, 1 $HCl_{(g)}$, at 298°K and 1 atm. Hence the reaction is capable of taking place spontaneously under the specified conditions of temperature and pressure. We also notice that $\Delta H°$ (−22.1 kcal/mole) and $T\,\Delta S°$ (+0.7 kcal/mole) both contribute favorably to the spontaneity of the reaction. However, the value of $T\,\Delta S°$ is very small compared with $\Delta H°$. Actually the $T\,\Delta S°$ term contributes to $\Delta G°$ about 3 per cent of its value (0.7/22.8 = 0.03). Thus, in this example, $\Delta H°$ alone can give us with good approximation an estimate of the capacity of the reaction to take place spontaneously.

Example 2. Consider the reaction between nitrogen monoxide gas, $NO_{(g)}$, and oxygen gas, $O_{2(g)}$, to form nitrogen dioxide gas, $NO_{2(g)}$, each substance again being at 25°C and 1 atm. To calculate the $\Delta G°$ of this reaction, we can use the same general scheme. Under the formula of each reactant and product appearing in the chemical equation, we write the values of $\Delta H°_{form}$ and of the standard entropies, $S°$, each multiplied by the appropriate coefficient:

Reaction:	$NO_{(g)}$ +	$\frac{1}{2} O_{2(g)}$ ⟶	$NO_{2(g)}$
$\Delta H°_{form}$ (kcal/mole):	+21.6	0	+8.1
S° (cal/mole × deg K):	+50.3	$\frac{1}{2}$(+49.0)	+57.5

From these values we calculate $\Delta H°$ and $\Delta S°$ of the reaction considered:

$$\begin{aligned}\Delta H°_{reaction} &= +8.1 - (+21.6) = -13.5 \text{ kcal/mole-eqn}\\ \Delta S°_{reaction} &= +57.5 - \{+50.3 + \tfrac{1}{2}(49.0)\} = -17.3 \text{ cal/mole-eqn} \times \text{deg}\end{aligned}$$

Hence:

$$\begin{aligned}T\,\Delta S° &= 298 \text{ deg} \times (-17.3 \text{ cal/mole-eqn} \times \text{deg}) = -5130 \text{ cal/mole-eqn}\\ &= -5.13 \text{ kcal/mole-eqn; and, } \Delta G° = \Delta H° - T\,\Delta S°\\ \Delta G° &= -13.5 - (-5.13) = -8.37 \text{ kcal/mole-eqn}\end{aligned}$$

Therefore this exothermic reaction can proceed spontaneously under the specified conditions, because the favorable $\Delta H°$ term overcomes the unfavorable $T\,\Delta S°$ term.

Example 3. Consider the dissolution of potassium nitrate in water (both at 25° C) to form a solution containing 1 mole of KNO_3 (101 g) in 1 liter (about 55 moles) of water. We can write the reaction as follows, using the ΔH°_{form} and S° values* of Tables 16-4 and 17-2, respectively:

Reaction:	$KNO_{3(s)} + 55\ H_2O_{(l)}$	$\longrightarrow$	$\{K^+_{(aq)}$	$+\ NO^-_{3(aq)}\} \cdot 55\ H_2O_{(l)}$
ΔH°_{form} (kcal/mole):	$-117.8 + 55\,(-68.3)$		-60.6	$-49.4 + 55\,(-68.3)$
S° (cal/mole × deg):	$+32.9 +$ ~~$55\,(+16.7)$~~		$+24.5$	$+35.8 +$ ~~$55\,(+16.7)$~~

From these values we obtain:

$$\Delta H^\circ = +7.80 \text{ kcal/mole-eqn}$$
$$\Delta S^\circ = +24.5 + 35.8 - 32.9 = +27.4 \text{ cal/mole-eqn} \times \text{deg}$$
$$T\,\Delta S^\circ = 298 \text{ deg} \times +27.4 \text{ cal/mole} \times \text{deg} = +8.16 \text{ kcal/mole-eqn}$$
$$\Delta G^\circ = \Delta H^\circ - T\,\Delta S^\circ = +7.80 - 8.16 = -0.56 \text{ kcal/mole-eqn}$$

From this negative value of ΔG° we can predict that the dissolution of 1 mole of KNO_3 in 1 l. of H_2O is spontaneous, even though the solution formed, if thermally isolated, would be found to cool down from 25°C to about 17°C. (Recall that the absorption or loss of 1 kcal results in a change in temperature of approximately 1°C for 1 liter of water or of a water solution of a salt. Thus a 25° − 17° = 8°C decrease in temperature corresponds to the positive ΔH° value of 7.80 (about 8) kcal.)

17-7 Considerations on the Stability of Compounds

We have seen that the value of the free energy of formation, ΔG_{form}, of a compound represents a criterion of its stability toward decomposition into its elements under specified conditions of temperature and pressure. If the ΔG of the formation reaction is negative, then the ΔG of the reverse reaction—the dissociation of the compound into its elements—is positive, and hence the compound does *not* have the capacity to decompose into its elements. On the other hand, a positive ΔG_{form} means that the compound has the capacity to decompose into its elements, although often such a thermodynamically permitted decomposition may not actually occur at a detectable rate, for kinetic reasons which are examined in Chapter 25. In discussing the stability of compounds we must keep in mind another possibility: in fact, a given compound, which under specified conditions of temperature and pressure does not have the capacity to decompose into *its elements* and is also carefully excluded from the presence of any substance that could be a possible reactant, may still have the capacity to "decompose" by undergoing various kinds of reactions "by or with itself." For example, it may undergo decomposition to form different compounds, or disproportionation (self-oxidation-reduction), or polymerization (union of many single molecules to form a large molecule). We have already encountered in previous chapters several such cases of decomposition of a compound by reaction "by or with itself." Two common examples are:

1. *Decomposition to form compounds.* Consider the decomposition of solid potassium chlorate, $KClO_{3(s)}$, to solid potassium chloride, $KCl_{(s)}$, and oxygen gas, $O_{2(g)}$, at 25°C. From the data of ΔH°_{form} and S° given in Tables 16-4 and 17-2 we can write:

Reaction:	$KClO_{3(s)}$	$\longrightarrow$	$KCl_{(s)}$	$+\ \frac{3}{2}\,O_{2(g)}$
ΔH°_{form} (kcal/mole):	-93.5		-104.2	0
S° (cal/mole × deg K):	$+34.2$		$+19.8$	$\frac{3}{2}\,(+49.0)$

* Notice that we can cancel the ΔH°_{form} and the S° values of the 55 moles of $H_2O_{(l)}$ which appear on both sides of the equation, if we assume, as a first approximation, that the enthalpy and entropy of pure water do not differ much from those of water in the presence of the dissolved salt.

From these data we calculate:

$$\begin{aligned} \Delta H^\circ &= -104.2 - (-93.5) = -10.7 \text{ kcal/mole-eqn} \\ \Delta S^\circ &= \tfrac{3}{2}(49.0) + 19.8 - 34.2 = +59.1 \text{ cal/mole-eqn} \times \text{deg} \\ T\,\Delta S^\circ &= 298 \text{ deg} \times (+59.1) \text{ cal/mole} \times \text{deg} = +17.7 \text{ kcal/mole-eqn} \\ \Delta G^\circ &= \Delta H^\circ - T\,\Delta S^\circ = -10.7 - 17.7 = -28.4 \text{ kcal/mole-eqn} \end{aligned}$$

If, on the other hand, we had considered the decomposition of $KClO_{3(s)}$ into its elements in their standard states at 25°C:

$$KClO_{3(s)} \longrightarrow K_{(s)} + \tfrac{1}{2} Cl_{2(g)} + \tfrac{3}{2} O_{2(g)}$$

we would have found, by a similar procedure, $\Delta G^\circ = +63.3$ kcal/mole-equation. We may therefore conclude that $KClO_{3(s)}$ at 25°C and 1 atm cannot spontaneously decompose to its elements, but it does have the capacity to decompose to $KCl_{(s)}$ and $O_{2(g)}$. Pure $KClO_{3(s)}$ does not actually decompose into $KCl_{(s)}$ and $O_{2(g)}$ until the temperature is raised substantially above room temperature because of the high energy of activation for this reaction (Chapter 25).

2. *Disproportionation.* Let us consider hydrogen peroxide in the gaseous form, $H_2O_{2(g)}$. From the data in Tables 16-4 and 17-2 we find (and you may wish to verify this as an exercise) that the free energy of formation of $H_2O_{2(g)}$ at 25°C and 1 atm is negative ($\Delta G^\circ_{form} = -24.5$ kcal/mole of $H_2O_{2(g)}$), so that $H_2O_{2(g)}$ under these conditions is not capable of decomposing to $H_{2(g)}$ and $O_{2(g)}$. However, for the disproportionation of $H_2O_{2(g)}$ to form $H_2O_{(g)}$ and $O_{2(g)}$, ΔG° is negative and therefore favorable to reaction. In fact, from the data in Tables 16-4 and 17-2 we have:

Reaction:	$H_2O_{2(g)}$ $\longrightarrow$	$H_2O_{(g)}$ +	$\tfrac{1}{2} O_{2(g)}$
ΔH°_{form} (kcal/mole):	-32.3	-57.8	0
S° (cal/mole × deg K):	$+54.2$	$+45.1$ +	$\tfrac{1}{2}(49.0)$

Hence:

$$\begin{aligned} \Delta H^\circ &= -57.8 + 32.3 = -25.5 \text{ kcal/mole-eqn} \\ \Delta S^\circ &= 45.1 + 24.5 - 54.2 = +15.4 \text{ cal/mole-eqn} \times \text{deg} \\ T\,\Delta S^\circ &= 298 \text{ deg} \times 15.4 \text{ cal/mole} \times \text{eqn} \times \text{deg} \cong +4.6 \text{ kcal/mole-eqn} \\ \Delta G^\circ &= \Delta H^\circ - T\,\Delta S^\circ = -25.5 - 4.6 = -30.1 \text{ kcal/mole-eqn} \end{aligned}$$

Thus $H_2O_{2(g)}$ can undergo disproportionation into $H_2O_{(g)}$ and $O_{2(g)}$.

In general, therefore, we may say that a given compound is stable under specified conditions of temperature and pressure if it does not have the capacity to (1) undergo decomposition to its elements, (2) "react with or by itself" to form other compounds, and (3) react with any other substances which may be present—for example, oxygen and water vapor of the atmosphere. Relatively few compounds meet all these three requirements of thermodynamic stability. Organic substances, to give a very important example, are unstable with respect to combustion with atmospheric oxygen ($\Delta G_{combustion}$ is negative). Thus, the paper on which this page is printed could (thermodynamically) burst into flame at room temperature! Fortunately for us, the combustion of organic substances does not actually occur in air at ordinary temperature and pressure because of a kinetic factor—the high activation energy of such combustion reactions—as we shall discuss in Chapter 25.

INFLUENCE OF TEMPERATURE ON THE ΔG OF A REACTION

The value of the free energy change, ΔG, for a specified reaction, and hence the capacity of the reaction to take place spontaneously, depends markedly on the temperature at which the reaction occurs. For a reaction at constant temperature and under constant pressure, $\Delta G = \Delta H - T\,\Delta S$. This expression tells us that the value of the temperature must influence the value of ΔG, because not only is the $T\,\Delta S$ energy term directly proportional to absolute temperature, T, but also both ΔH and ΔS, have a characteristic temperature dependence, as we have previously learned. If we assume, as a first approximation, that the values of the enthalpy and entropy changes, ΔH and ΔS, of a given reaction, do not vary appreciably within a certain interval of temperature, then we see that a change of the temperature at which the reaction takes place can alter the balance between the ΔH and $T\,\Delta S$ energy terms so as to change not only the magnitude but also the sign of ΔG. In other words, a reaction which is thermodynamically forbidden (ΔG = positive) at a certain temperature and pressure, can at a higher temperature be thermodynamically permitted (ΔG = negative). As an illustration, consider the dissociation of calcium carbonate, $CaCO_{3(s)}$, to form calcium oxide, $CaO_{(s)}$, and carbon dioxide, $CO_{2(g)}$, at 1 atm pressure. We have seen that at 25°C (298°K) this reaction is thermodynamically forbidden, since $\Delta G = \Delta H - T\,\Delta S = +30.66$ kcal/mole-equation, the unfavorable (positive) value of ΔG being due to the large positive (unfavorable) ΔH value of this endothermic reaction. We know, however, that at 1 atm pressure $CaCO_{3(s)}$ completely dissociates into $CaO_{(s)}$ and $CO_{2(g)}$ when the temperature reaches 825°C (1,098°K). This means that an increase in the temperature from 298°K to 1098°K has so increased the $T\,\Delta S$ term that the favorable entropy change finally outweighs the unfavorable enthalpy change, and the dissociation of $CaCO_{3(s)}$ becomes a spontaneous reaction. It is interesting to note that the ΔH of this reaction does not appreciably vary with the temperature between 25°C ($\Delta H = +42.5$ kcal/mole) and 825°C ($\Delta H = +40.0$ kcal/mole). Similarly, by using entropy-temperature diagrams of the kind shown in Fig. 17-7 for H_2O, we would find that the ΔS of the reaction also has not changed appreciably; thus the change from a (thermodynamically) forbidden to a permitted reaction is predominantly the result of the effect of the absolute temperature, T, on the magnitude of the $T\,\Delta S$ energy term.

The following holds generally for any reaction in which the entropy of the system increases (disordering reaction): if the reaction cannot occur spontaneously at a given temperature because of a large unfavorable ΔH value (strongly endothermic reaction), a rise in temperature will make the favorable $T\,\Delta S$ factor relatively more important. Consequently, there is always a certain temperature—even though it is sometimes an extremely high one—at which the favorable $T\,\Delta S$ term finally outweighs the unfavorable ΔH term, so that the reaction becomes thermodynamically permitted. However, these considerations should not lead us to believe that simply by raising the temperature we may always obtain the *desired product(s)* from a reaction with a favorable ΔS and an unfavorable ΔH. In fact, as the temperature increases, other *different* reactions (and hence other *different* products) may become even *more* favorable than the desired one—so that at a higher temperature the reactants would undergo (partially or totally) these more favorable reactions.*

One kind of endothermic reaction which can always be obtained spontaneously, provided the temperature is high enough, is the dissociation of substances (elements and compounds) into their atoms (atomization). In the process of atomization of a substance, the products always have greater entropy than the reactant, and the process always results in an increase in entropy (ΔS is positive). Of course, a large quantity of energy is usually required for an atomization reaction (ΔH_{atomiz} has a large positive value), because atomization involves the breaking of the strong chemical bonds which hold together the atoms of the reactant in the molecule, or in the ionic crystal, or in the metallic state. On the other hand, no bonds of any type are formed in the products, which are isolated gaseous atoms. Hence with regard to the spontaneous atomization of a substance, the ΔH term is unfavorable, and the ΔS term is favorable. At room temperature, almost all atomization processes are thermodynamically forbidden; how-

* As we shall see in Chapter 25, at relatively low temperatures—let us say up to room temperature and slightly above—a thermodynamically permitted reaction may actually not take place because its activation energy is too high, so that the reaction rate is too slow to be detectable. At sufficiently higher temperatures, however, all thermodynamically permitted processes do occur, because the average thermal energy of the reactants is great enough to overcome the activation-energy barrier.

ever, as the temperature increases the relative importance of the favorable $T\,\Delta S$ energy term gradually increases until finally the atomization becomes a thermodynamically permitted reaction, and hence *does* take place.

These considerations explain the very interesting fact, established by spectral observations, that in the hottest stars no compounds of any kind can be detected, since at the high temperatures of the stars, matter exists (is thermodynamically stable) only as a (gaseous) plasma consisting of gaseous atoms, their positive ions, and electrons.

THE CRITERION OF SPONTANEITY FOR TRANSFORMATIONS WHICH INVOLVE CHANGES IN TEMPERATURE AND/OR PRESSURE

We have discussed at great length the application of ΔG as the criterion of spontaneity for transformations of any kind—chemical reactions as well as changes of physical state—which take place under conditions of constant temperature and pressure. The emphasis we have placed on such conditions is justified by the fact that most chemical reactions and changes of state of interest to us do in fact occur under a constant pressure—the pressure of the atmosphere. The condition of constant temperature is more difficult to realize for reactions which are either strongly exothermic or strongly endothermic. However, ΔG is a thermodynamic function of state, and it depends only on the initial and final states of the system; therefore, in order to calculate ΔG from the expression $\Delta G = \Delta H - T\,\Delta S$ the only condition which must be satisfied is that the temperature and pressure of the final state be the same as those of the initial state (even though during the reaction their values may have varied). There are, however, many important processes in which the final state and the initial state differ in temperature or pressure or both. For these reactions, the capacity of the system to do useful work is still the criterion of spontaneity. However, this useful work can no longer be calculated by the expression $\Delta G = \Delta H - T\,\Delta S$, which holds only for constant T and P. The necessary calculation is rather complicated and we shall not consider it here. We can, however, apply a simple criterion of spontaneity for at least one important kind of process that is not isothermal. In general, for any reaction which occurs in a closed and thermally insulated container of constant volume—so that the system exchanges neither matter nor energy of any kind with the surroundings—the change in the *entropy* of the system is the criterion of spontaneity. If the entropy of the system increases, the transformation is spontaneous. Examples are the mutual diffusion of two ideal gases, the mixing of two completely miscible liquids, and the transfer of heat from a hot to a cold body.

17-8 Structural and Thermodynamic Aspects of Chemical Reactions

We have learned in earlier chapters that chemical changes involve the redistribution of the atoms of the reactants to form the products, accompanied by the absorption or liberation of energy; we have also studied the facts and theories concerning the structure of molecules, ions, and compounds. In the present chapter we have learned that the thermodynamic factors ΔH and $T\,\Delta S$ together determine whether or not a specified reaction is capable of taking place spontaneously under specified conditions of constant temperature and pressure. Now we shall illustrate with some examples how the structural and the thermodynamic principles, considered together, give us a fuller and more detailed understanding of the changes which take place in chemical reactions. For each example we shall first consider the experimental facts, and then we shall interpret these facts in terms of structures, chemical bond theories, and energetics. We shall, in other words, consider what we may call the "anatomy of a chemical reaction."

EXAMPLE 1. REACTION OF $H_{2(g)}$ WITH $Cl_{2(g)}$ TO FORM $HCl_{(g)}$

Consider first the simple, familiar reaction of hydrogen gas, $H_{2(g)}$, with chlorine gas, $Cl_{2(g)}$, to form gaseous hydrogen chloride, $HCl_{(g)}$. Let us show schematically the various aspects of this reaction as symbolized by the net chemical equation:

Reaction:

$$\tfrac{1}{2}\,H_{2(g)} + \tfrac{1}{2}\,Cl_{2(g)} \longrightarrow HCl_{(g)} \qquad \begin{cases} \Delta H^\circ = -22.1 \text{ kcal/mole } HCl_{(g)} \\ \Delta G^\circ = -22.8 \text{ kcal/mole } HCl_{(g)} \\ \Delta S^\circ = +2.4 \text{ cal/mole} \times \text{deg} \end{cases}$$

Stoichiometry:

$\tfrac{1}{2}$ mole $H_{2(g)}$	$\tfrac{1}{2}$ mole $Cl_{2(g)}$	1 mole $HCl_{(g)}$
1.01 g hydrogen	35.45 g chlorine	36.46 g hydrogen chloride
~12.2 l. $H_{2(g)}$ at 25°C, 1 atm	~12.2 l. $Cl_{2(g)}$ at 25°C, 1 atm	~24.4 l. $HCl_{(g)}$ at 25°C, 1 atm

Physical State:

Colorless gas, composed of diatomic molecules. Very sparingly soluble in water (the solution is neutral).	Green-yellow gas composed of diatomic molecules. Moderately soluble in water.	Colorless gas composed of diatomic molecules, H—Cl. Extremely soluble in water to give a colorless acidic solution, containing $H^+_{(aq)}$ ions and $Cl^-_{(aq)}$ ions.

Structure:

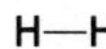

H—H

Covalent radius of $H_{(g)}$ atom

0.37 A 0.37 A

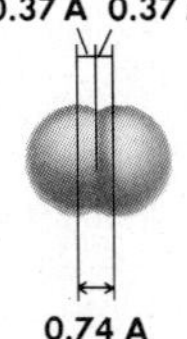

0.74 A

H—H internuclear distance in $H_{2(g)}$

Cl—Cl

Covalent radius of $Cl_{(g)}$ atom

0.99 A 0.99 A

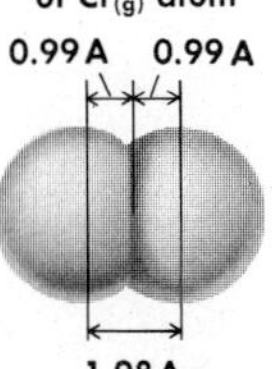

1.98 A

Cl—Cl internuclear distance of $Cl_{2(g)}$

H—Cl

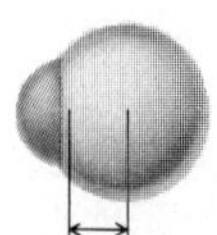

1.28 A

HCl internuclear distance in $HCl_{(g)}$

Bonding:

H:H	Cl:Cl	H:Cl
Purely covalent (identical atoms)	Purely covalent (identical atoms)	Covalent with marked dipolar character owing to different electronegativities of H($\chi_H = 2.1$) and Cl($\chi_{Cl} = 3.0$), as well as to different sizes of H and Cl atoms

Atomic Orbitals Involved in Bonding:

Each H atom uses the 1*s* orbital. The bond electron-pair is considered to occupy a sigma-bonding orbital resulting from the overlap of the 1*s* orbital of one H atom with the 1*s* orbital of the other H atom.	Each Cl atom uses a 3*p* orbital. The bond electron-pair is considered to occupy a sigma-bonding orbital resulting from the overlap of a 3*p* orbital of one Cl atom with a 3*p* orbital of the other Cl atom.	The H atom uses a 1*s* orbital, the Cl uses a 3*p* orbital. The bond-electron pair is considered to occupy a sigma-bonding orbital resulting from the overlap of the 1*s* orbital of the H atom with a 3*p* orbital of the Cl atom.

Thus the chemical reaction $\frac{1}{2} H_{2(g)} + \frac{1}{2} Cl_{2(g)} \longrightarrow HCl_{(g)}$, consists of the breaking of both the covalent bond between the two H atoms of each H_2 molecule and the covalent bond between the two Cl atoms of each Cl_2 molecule, while a new bond between a H atom and a Cl atom is formed in each HCl molecule.

As we have discussed in detail in the section on enthalpy diagrams (Chapter 16, p. 342), the formation of $HCl_{(g)}$ from $H_{2(g)}$ and $Cl_{2(g)}$ can be *imagined* to take place by three steps: *Step 1*—the dissociation of the covalent gaseous H_2 molecules into gaseous $H_{(g)}$ atoms; *Step 2*—the dissociation of covalent gaseous $Cl_{2(g)}$ molecules into gaseous chlorine atoms $Cl_{(g)}$; *Step 3*—the combination of the $H_{(g)}$ and $Cl_{(g)}$ gaseous atoms to form covalent $HCl_{(g)}$ molecules. Notice that both Steps 1 and 2 represent bond-breaking processes; consequently, energy must be supplied to the system from an external source to make the reaction occur (ΔH is positive). On the other hand, Step 3 is a bond-making process and hence energy is liberated (ΔH is negative). Enthalpy changes of the bond-breaking processes go as follows:

Step 1.

$\Delta H = +52.1$ kcal/mole of H atoms at 25°C, 1 atm. (This is half the bond dissociation energy of the $H_{2(g)}$ molecule.)

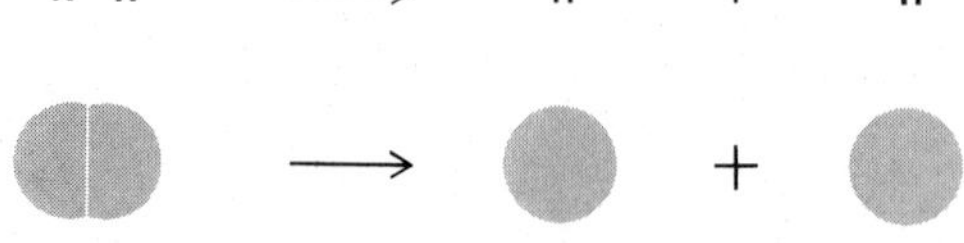

Step 2.

$\Delta H = +28.9$ kcal/mole $Cl_{(g)}$ atoms at 25°C, 1 atm. (This is half the bond dissociation energy of the $Cl_{2(g)}$ molecule.)

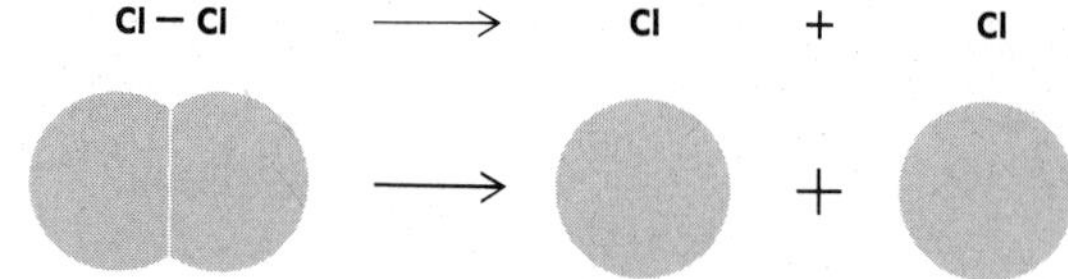

Step 3.

$\Delta H = -103.1$ kcal/mole $HCl_{(g)}$ molecules at 25°C and 1 atm. (This is the H—Cl bond energy of gaseous hydrogen chloride.)

The net enthalpy change for the reaction, $\frac{1}{2} H_{2(g)} + \frac{1}{2} Cl_{2(g)} \longrightarrow HCl_{(g)}$ is therefore: $\Delta H° = +52.1 + 28.9 - 103.1 = -22.1$ kcal/mole-equation when both the reactants and the products are at 25°C and 1 atm. This is shown graphically in the enthalpy diagram of Fig. 17-8.

FIGURE 17-8 Enthalpy diagram for the formation of $HCl_{(g)}$ at 25°C from the elements in their standard states.

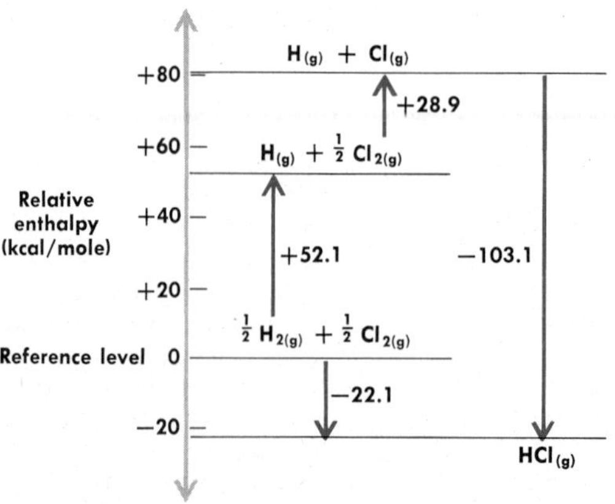

We can see that for the reaction $\frac{1}{2} H_{2(g)} + \frac{1}{2} Cl_{2(g)} \longrightarrow HCl_{(g)}$, which involves only gases, the number of moles on both sides of the equation is the same. Therefore, there is no change in the volume, V, of the system ($\Delta V = 0$), because both the pressure and the number of moles of the gas (assumed to behave ideally) are constant. Hence, there is no pressure-volume work

—nor is any other kind of work involved in the process. From the First Law of Thermodynamics, $\Delta E = q + w = \Delta H - P\,\Delta V$ (for reactions at constant pressure and temperature), we see that the internal energy of the system decreases by exactly the amount of heat evolved in the reaction: $\Delta E = \Delta H = -22.1$ kcal/mole $HCl_{(g)}$. This decrease in the internal energy of the system (−22.1 kcal/mole) arises almost entirely from the difference in bond energies between the product $HCl_{(g)}$ and the reactants, $\{\frac{1}{2}\,H_{2(g)} + \frac{1}{2}\,Cl_{2(g)}\}$. In fact, that part of the internal energy of the system which is thermal in nature remains unchanged provided that the temperature of the product is the same as that of the reactants.

In this reaction involving gaseous reactants and gaseous products there is no volume change, and hence no essential entropy change arising from a change in the number of possible positional arrangements of the gaseous molecules (which are assumed to behave ideally). Thus the entropy change for the reaction, at 25°C and 1 atm, is due only to the difference between the standard entropies of the gaseous product and the sum of the standard entropies of the gaseous reactants. The entropy change of the reaction is: $\Delta S^\circ_{\text{reaction}} = S^\circ_{\text{products}} - S^\circ_{\text{reactants}}$.

$$\begin{aligned}\Delta S^\circ_{\text{reaction}} &= +S^\circ_{HCl(g)} - \{\tfrac{1}{2}\,S^\circ_{H_2(g)} + \tfrac{1}{2}\,S^\circ_{Cl_2(g)}\}\\ &= +44.6 - \{\tfrac{1}{2}(31.2) + \tfrac{1}{2}(53.3)\} = +2.4 \text{ cal/deg} \times \text{mole eqn}\end{aligned}$$

We see that the entropy change is very small. For this reaction, therefore, the value of ΔH°, being relatively so much larger than that of $T\,\Delta S^\circ$, determines the value of the free energy change of the reaction, $\Delta G^\circ = \Delta H^\circ - T\,\Delta S^\circ$, and tells us directly whether the reaction is spontaneous (ΔG° negative) or not (ΔG° positive).

$$\begin{aligned}\Delta G^\circ &= \Delta H^\circ - T\,\Delta S^\circ = -22.1 - (298^\circ \times 2.4 \times 10^{-3})\\ &= -22.1 - (0.7) = -22.8 \text{ kcal/mole}\end{aligned}$$

It is important to point out, here, that even though $H_{2(g)}$ and $Cl_{2(g)}$ have the capacity to react spontaneously at 25°C and 1 atm forming $HCl_{(g)}$, the reaction actually does not occur at a detectable rate as long as the reactants are kept in the dark. But as soon as the $H_{2(g)}/Cl_{2(g)}$ mixture is exposed to sunlight, or heated in the presence of platinum gauze as a catalyst, the reaction occurs rapidly and completely. Finally, we must point out once more that an enthalpy diagram is only a convenient scheme to follow the energy changes involved in a process. Therefore the sequence of paths 1, 2, and 3 shown in Fig. 17-8 does not intend to—and in fact, *does not*—represent the actual path (the "mechanism") by which the reaction takes place. The actual mechanism of the reaction between $H_{2(g)}$ and $Cl_{2(g)}$ at room temperature in the presence of sunlight will be discussed in detail in Chapter 25.

To conclude, we see that in order to have a complete picture of a chemical process we should consider not only the structural and thermodynamic aspects of the reaction, but also the *rate* at which the reaction proceeds, and the *mechanism* by which the reactants are actually transformed into the products. We shall study these latter two factors in Chapter 25.

EXAMPLE 2. THE COMBUSTION OF Mg METAL IN O_2 GAS

Our second example is another familiar reaction between two elements, the reaction of magnesium metal with oxygen gas. We know that magnesium metal, $Mg_{(s)}$, burns in O_2 gas (or in air) with a strongly exothermic reaction which produces crystalline magnesium oxide, $MgO_{(s)}$, as a white powder. The equation of this reaction, together with the summary of the pertinent structural and thermodynamic data, follows:

Reaction:

$$Mg_{(s)} + \tfrac{1}{2}\,O_{2(g)} \longrightarrow MgO_{(s)} \qquad \left\{\begin{aligned}\Delta H^\circ &= -143.8 \text{ kcal/mole } MgO_{(s)}\\ \Delta S^\circ &= -\ \ 24.9 \text{ cal/mole} \times \text{deg}\\ \Delta G^\circ &= -136.1 \text{ kcal/mole } MgO_{(s)}\end{aligned}\right.$$

Physical State and Structure:

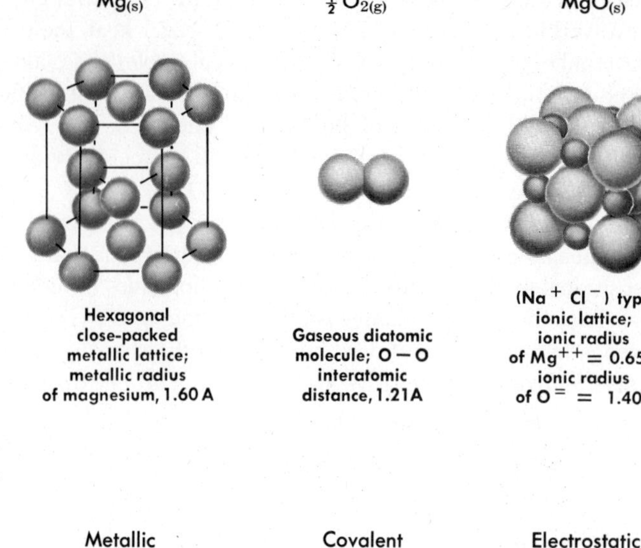

Bonding:

Let us consider these structures individually. The structure of magnesium metal, $Mg_{(s)}$, consists of a hexagonal, closed-packed lattice of magnesium atoms, each magnesium atom having 12 equidistant equivalent neighbors. In this metallic crystal the two outer electrons of each magnesium atom are "shared" by the cores of many neighboring magnesium atoms, giving rise to what is called "metallic bonding." That is to say, metallic magnesium consists of a three-dimensional network in which the cores of the magnesium atoms occupy the hexagonal close-packed positions, and are held together by the ($3s^2$) electrons shared by the neighboring magnesium atoms in multicenter bonds. The gaseous oxygen molecule, O_2, is a diatomic molecule in which the two oxygen atoms share one pair of electrons in a sigma-bonding orbital and another pair of electrons in a pi-bonding orbital; each oxygen atom also has two lone pairs of electrons. Finally, magnesium oxide, MgO, whether present in the form of the powdery solid obtained by the direct combustion of magnesium metal, or of the well-crystallized material ob-

FIGURE 17-9 Enthalpy diagram for the reaction, $M_{g(s)} + \frac{1}{2}O_{2(g)} \longrightarrow M_gO_{(s)}$, at 25°C and 1 atm.

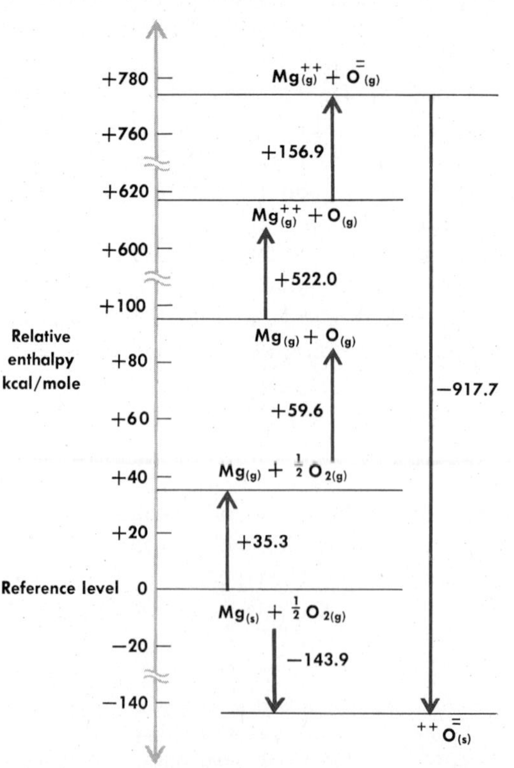

tained by fusion of the powdered magnesium oxide and subsequent gradual cooling, has a crystalline structure. The crystalline structure of magnesium oxide is of the Na^+Cl^- (rock-salt) type—that is, the Mg^{++} ions and the $O^=$ ions are arranged in a face-centered cubic ionic lattice, similar to that of Na^+Cl^- (with Mg^{++} in place of Na^+, and $O^=$ in place of Cl^-).

Now we will consider the enthalpy diagram (Fig. 17-9) for the combustion of magnesium metal and the structural aspects of each single step by which the combustion may be *imagined* to take place:

Step 1.

Atomization of magnesium metal (bond-breaking process):
$\Delta H_{\text{Step 1}} = \Delta H_{\text{atomization}} = +35.3$ kcal/mole $Mg_{(g)}$ atoms

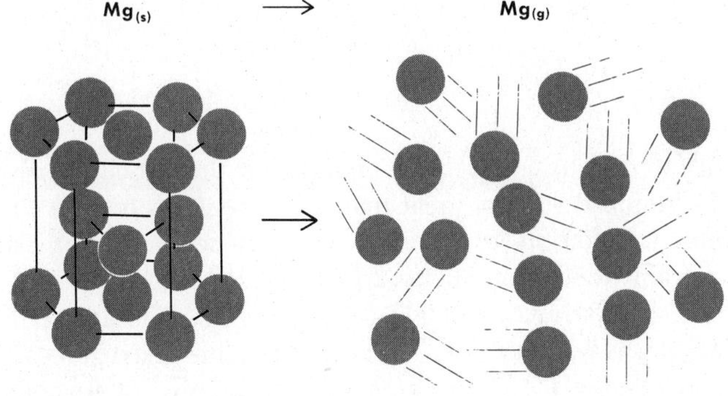

Step 2.

Dissociation of each gaseous oxygen molecule into two gaseous oxygen atoms (bond-breaking process): $O_{2(g)} \longrightarrow 2\ O_{(g)}$:

$$\Delta H_{\text{Step 2}} = \tfrac{1}{2}\,\Delta H_{\text{dissociation}} \text{ of } O_{2(g)} = \frac{+119.2}{2} = 59.6 \text{ kcal/mole } O_{2(g)}$$

1.21 A ⟶ 0.73 A + 0.73 A

Step 3.

Ionization of each magnesium atom: $Mg_{(g)} \longrightarrow Mg^{++}{}_{(g)} + 2\ e^-$:

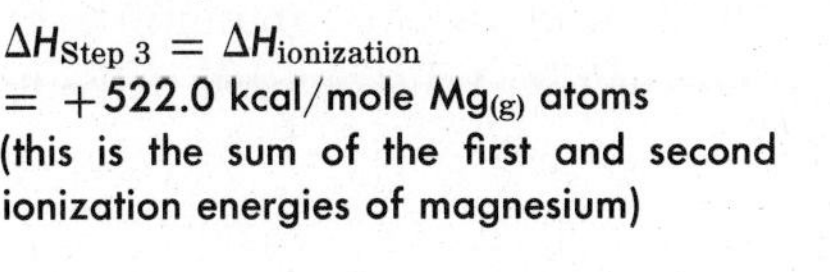

$\Delta H_{\text{Step 3}} = \Delta H_{\text{ionization}}$
$= +522.0$ kcal/mole $Mg_{(g)}$ atoms
(this is the sum of the first and second ionization energies of magnesium)

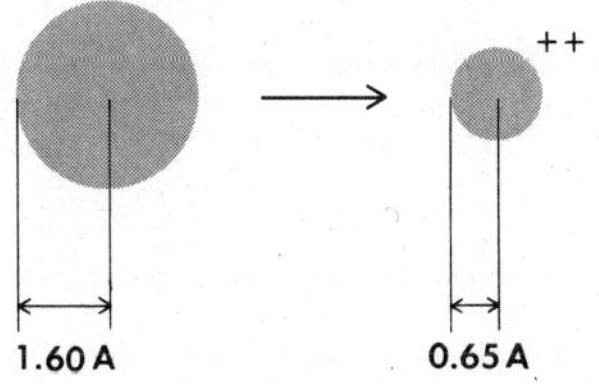

Step 4.

Reaction of each O atom with two electrons to form an oxide ion, $O^=$; thus $O_{(g)} + 2\ e^- \longrightarrow O^=_{(g)}$:

$\Delta H_{\text{Step 4}} = \Delta H_{\text{electron affinity}}$
$= +156.9$ kcal/mole $O_{(g)}$ atoms

0.73 A ⟶ 1.40 A

Step 5.

Reaction of $Mg^{++}_{(g)}$ with $O^{=}_{(g)}$ to form ionic solid $Mg^{++}O^{=}_{(s)}$ (bond-making process):

$$Mg^{++}_{(g)} + O^{=}_{(g)} \longrightarrow Mg^{++}O^{=}_{(s)}:$$

$\Delta H_{\text{Step 5}} = -917.7$ kcal/mole $MgO_{(s)}$ (this is the lattice energy of MgO with its sign changed)

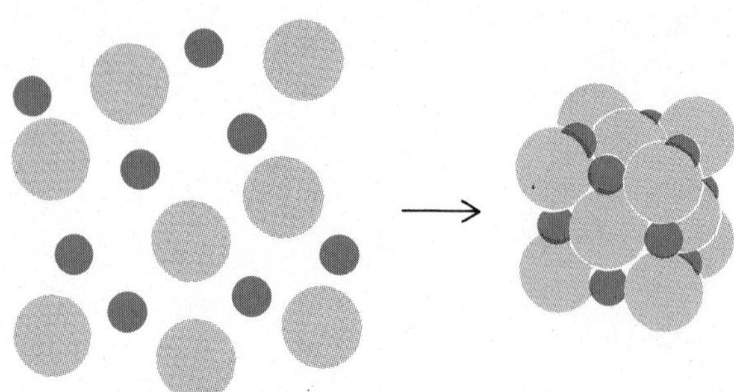

Notice that steps 1 to 4 all require energy, but the lattice energy of crystalline MgO released in step 5 is so very great that it compensates for the energy absorbed in all other steps. In addition, it makes the reaction strongly exothermic, therefore contributing favorably to its spontaneity: $\Delta H° = -917.7 + (35.3 + 59.6 + 522.0 + 156.9) = -917.7 + 773.8 = -143.9$ kcal/mole $MgO_{(s)}$. The $\Delta S°$ term, on the other hand, is unfavorable, as we would expect, because $\frac{1}{2}$ mole of oxygen gas "disappears." However, the unfavorable $T\,\Delta S°$ energy term is small (-7.7 kcal/mole $MgO_{(s)}$) compared with the large favorable $\Delta H°$ energy term (-143.9), and in fact magnesium metal is capable of reacting spontaneously with oxygen gas at a temperature of 25°C and 1 atm.

Magnesium does not burn in air or oxygen at room temperature, however, so to start the combustion we must first raise the temperature of magnesium to its ignition temperature. At that point magnesium burns very rapidly, and indeed violently, with the evolution of a large quantity of heat and the emission of a very intense white light (the familiar "magnesium flash bulb" used in photography). Again, this is an example of a thermodynamically permitted, strongly exothermic reaction, but one that does not occur at an appreciable rate at room temperature because of a very high activation energy.

EXAMPLE 3. THE COMBUSTION OF GRAPHITE

As a last example, consider the combustion of carbon (graphite) with oxygen gas to form carbon dioxide gas. The thermodynamic and structural data are listed below; the enthalpy diagram is in Fig. 17-10.

Reaction:

$$C_{(s,\text{graphite})} + O_{2(g)} \longrightarrow CO_{2(g)} \qquad \begin{cases} \Delta H° = -94.1 \text{ kcal/mole } CO_2 \\ \Delta S° = -\ 0.7 \text{ cal/mole} \times \text{deg} \\ \Delta G° = -94.3 \text{ kcal/mole } CO_2 \end{cases}$$

Physical State and Structure:

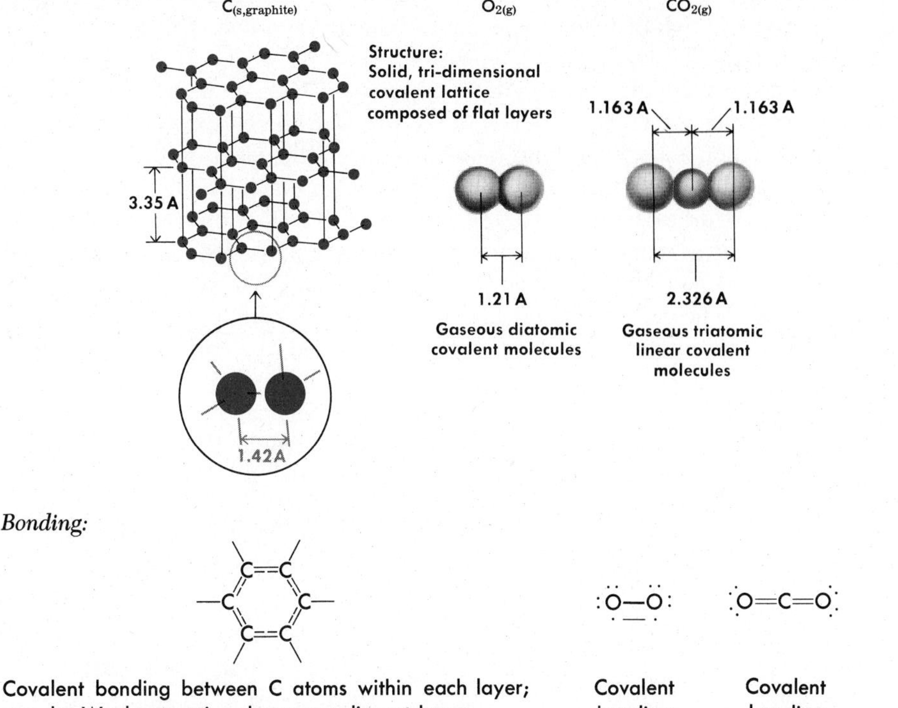

Bonding:

Covalent bonding between C atoms within each layer; van der Waals attractions between adjacent layers.

Covalent bonding

Covalent bonding

Let us consider these structures and bondings individually. Carbon, in the form of graphite, has a hexagonal, close-packed structure in which each carbon atom of a given layer is bonded equally to the three equivalent carbon atoms which surround it in a regular triangular arrangement. The distance between any two C atoms in a given plane is 1.42 A, whereas the distance between the closest-neighbor carbon atoms in separate planes is 3.35 A. Each carbon atom in a layer is strongly bound to each of the three surrounding carbon atoms by covalent bonds, whereas neighboring carbon atoms of adjacent planes are only loosely held by van der Waals forces. Each C atom is considered to form three *sigma* bonds with its three neighbors in the plane, using $2s2p^2$ equivalent hybrid orbitals (trigonal planar hybridization). In addition, each C atom forms a *pi* bond with one of its three neighbors—and this pi bond resonates among the three equivalent positions, I, II, and III:

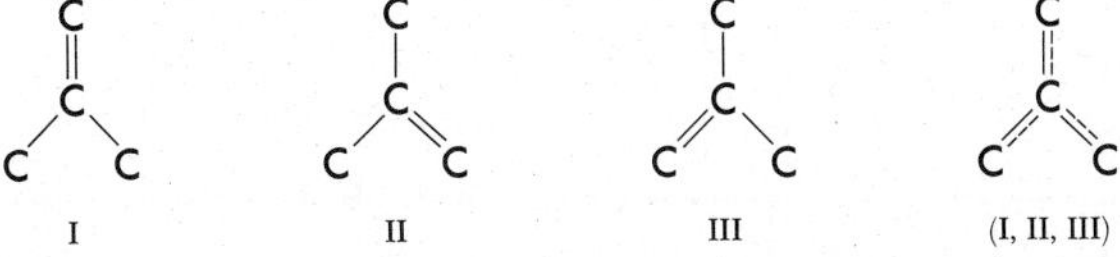

The unhybridized $2p_z$ orbital of each C atom is involved in this resonating *pi* bond.

The structure and bonding of the $O_{2(g)}$ molecule was previously discussed in Example 2. The gaseous carbon dioxide molecule, $CO_{2(g)}$ is linear, with the C atom at the center; each oxygen atom forms a double bond (one sigma bond and one pi bond) with the C atom. The C atom utilizes $2s2p$ linear hybrid orbitals for the σ bonds with the two O atoms, and the remaining two $2p$ orbitals for the π bonds. The O atoms utilize $2p$ orbitals for both the σ and π bonds. The carbon-oxygen link in CO_2 is a double bond, so the energy of the carbon-oxygen bond is very great. In fact, as the enthalpy diagram of Fig. 17-10 shows, the carbon-oxygen bond energy, $-384.1/2$ kcal/mole of C—O bonds, is the main factor which determines the large negative value of the ΔH°_{form} of $CO_{2(g)}$.

We see from the equation, $C_{(s,gr)} + O_{2(g)} \longrightarrow CO_{2(g)}$, that since 1 mole of a gas is present in the reactants as well as in the product, the entropy change accompanying the reaction is negligible and hence has very little effect on the spontaneity of the reaction ($T\,\Delta S^\circ = -0.2$ kcal/mole $CO_{2(g)}$). Consequently, the high negative value of ΔH° (-94.1 kcal/mole $CO_{2(g)}$) in this case tells us that this reaction can take place spontaneously at room temperature. As in the examples considered above, however, graphite does not burn in air at room temperature, although its oxidation is thermodynamically favorable. To start the combustion of graphite, we must first raise its temperature to a rather high value; then, once started, the combustion proceeds rapidly and spontaneously. Again, this high activation energy is related to both the high value of the heat of atomization of graphite ($\Delta H_{atomiz} = +170.9$ kcal/mole) and the high dissociation energy ($\Delta H_{diss} = +119.2$ kcal/mole) of the $O_{2(g)}$ molecule.

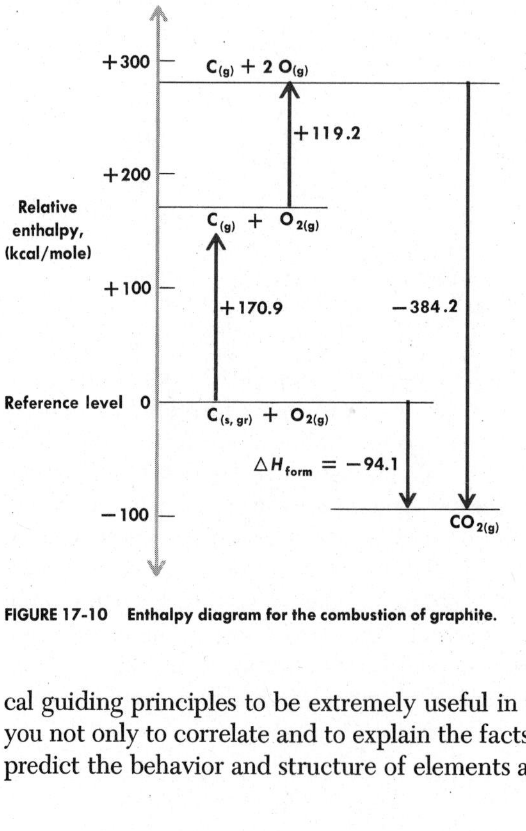

FIGURE 17-10 Enthalpy diagram for the combustion of graphite.

The examples we have just considered emphasize that chemistry is first of all an experimental science, and that experimental data such as structure, stereochemistry, internuclear distances, bond energies, and enthalpies of reaction, constitute the basis of our study of chemical behavior. However, a rationalization of the experimental facts in terms of bond theories and thermodynamic principles is essential to the understanding of chemistry. In fact, you will find these theoretical guiding principles to be extremely useful in the future chapters, as they will help you not only to correlate and to explain the facts that you will be learning, but also to predict the behavior and structure of elements and compounds still unknown to you.

Exercises

17-1 Give an example of a transformation which can occur by different paths, and specify at least two such paths (do not use the same example discussed in section 17-1).

17-2 Define a "reversible transformation" and illustrate with two examples, specifying the experimental conditions in sufficient detail.

17-3 If a system undergoes a transformation from a specified initial state to a specified final state by different paths, which of the following energy terms will depend on the path? (a) The change in internal energy of the system, ΔE; (b) the change in enthalpy, ΔH; (c) the work, w, involved in the transformation; (d) the heat, q, exchanged between the system and the surroundings.

17-4 If a given system has the capacity to perform work on the surroundings in passing isothermally from a specified initial state to a specified final state by several different paths, what are the general conditions under which the system will actually perform the greatest quantity of work? Illustrate your answer with an example.

17-5 Define the "capacity for total work" and the "capacity for useful work" of a system undergoing a transformation at constant temperature and pressure. How are the maximum total work and the maximum useful work related to one another?

17-6 Does the maximum useful work that a system is capable of doing when passing at constant pressure and temperature from a specified initial state to a specified final state depend on the path by which the system actually undergoes the transformation? Explain your answer.

17-7 What do we mean when we say that the capacity for useful work of a system is a thermodynamic function of state?

17-8 By which idealized path can we obtain the maximum useful work from a system which passes isothermally and at constant pressure from a specified initial state to a specified final state?

17-9 Discuss the use of the free energy change, ΔG, as a criterion of spontaneity for transformations which occur at constant temperature and pressure.

17-10 What is the meaning of the expressions: "thermodynamically permitted," and "thermodynamically forbidden" reactions?

17-11 If no work of any kind is involved in a given transformation at constant temperature, which thermodynamic function can be taken as the criterion of spontaneity for that transformation?

17-12 A system undergoes a given isothermal, reversible transformation at various temperatures, and at each temperature, T, it absorbs a different quantity of heat, q_{rev}. How does q_{rev} depend on the temperature T? Write the expression which relates q_{rev} and T for any isothermal reversible process.

17-13 Discuss the significance of the entropy of a system (a) in terms of thermodynamic properties, (b) in terms of our microscopic interpretation of the structure and behavior of matter.

17-14 List the most common processes in which the entropy of the system increases at constant temperature. Explain this increase in entropy in terms of the change of the "positional disorder," or "energetic disorder," or both.

17-15 For a pure substance (element or compound) how does the entropy increase with the temperature? Illustrate your answer with a sketch and explain the significance of the observed trend. How can you calculate the entropy change, ΔS, of any given reaction involving substances (elements or compounds) in their standard state at 25°C, if you know: (a) the standard entropies, S°, of all the reactants and products, (b) the heat exchanged by the system with the surroundings when the reaction is carried out under reversible conditions?

17-16 For each of the following reactions predict, on the basis of the number of moles and the physical states of the reactants and products, whether the entropy (1) definitely increases, (2) definitely decreases, (3) probably changes slightly.

(a) $S_{6(g)} \longrightarrow 6\ S_{(g)}$
(b) $H_2O_{(s)} \longrightarrow H_2O_{(l)}$
(c) $I_{2(g)} \longrightarrow I_{2(s)}$
(d) $C_2H_5OH_{(g)} \longrightarrow C_2H_5OH_{(l)}$
(e) $Na_{(s)} \longrightarrow Na_{(g)}$
(f) $P_{4(s)} + 5\ O_{2(g)} \longrightarrow P_4O_{10(s)}$
(g) $2\ Cl_{(g)} \longrightarrow Cl_{2(g)}$
(h) $K^+Br^-_{(g)} \longrightarrow K^+_{(g)} + Br^-_{(g)}$
(i) $HCl_{(g)} + NH_{3(g)} \longrightarrow NH_4^+Cl^-_{(s)}$
(j) $2\ N_{2(g)} + 3\ H_{2(g)} \longrightarrow 2\ NH_{3(g)}$
(k) $K^+Cl^-_{(s)}$ + water $\longrightarrow K^+_{(aq)} + Cl^-_{(aq)}$

17-17 For each of the following sets of data, indicate whether a system has the capacity to do useful work in undergoing the specified transformation at constant temperature and pressure. If the system has the capacity to do useful work, indicate also whether the value of this work energy, w, is greater or less than that of the heat energy, (enthalpy) ΔH, involved in the transformation.

(a) ΔG is negative, and ΔS is positive
(b) ΔG is positive, and ΔH is negative
(c) ΔG is negative, and $T\,\Delta S$ is positive
(d) ΔG is negative, and ΔS is negative
(e) ΔH is negative, and ΔS is positive

17-18 Discuss whether a general transformation with each of the following thermodynamic characteristics has, or does not have, the capacity to take place spontaneously. Explain your answer in each case. (a) The ΔH energy factor is favorable (to spontaneity); the $T\,\Delta S$ energy factor is favorable (to spontaneity). (b) The ΔH energy factor is unfavorable; the entropy, S, of the system decreases. (c) The transformation is endothermic and the $T\,\Delta S$ energy factor is unfavorable. (d) The ΔH energy is unfavorable; the $T\,\Delta S$ energy factor is unfavorable. (e) The transformation is exothermic and the entropy S of the system increases. (f) The reaction is exothermic; the entropy of the initial state is greater than the entropy of the final state of the system. (g) The enthalpy, H, of the system decreases, and the entropy, S, of the system increases in passing from the initial to the final state.

17-19 For each of the following sets of thermodynamic data, indicate whether the system has or does not have the capacity to pass spontaneously from the initial to the final state at constant pressure and temperature. (a) ΔH is negative and $T\,\Delta S$ is positive; the magnitude of ΔH is greater than the absolute value of $T\,\Delta S$. (b) ΔH is positive and ΔS is negative. (c) ΔH is positive and $T\,\Delta S$ is positive; the magnitude of $T\,\Delta S$ is greater than that of ΔH. (d) ΔH is positive and $T\,\Delta S$ is positive; the magnitude of $T\,\Delta S$ is smaller than that of ΔH. (e) ΔH is negative and ΔS is positive.

17-20 Given the general chemical reaction: $2\ Y_{(s)} + X_{2(g)} \longrightarrow 2\ YX_{(s)}$
Indicate for which of the following set of data the reaction can take place spontaneously at 25°C. If the reaction does not take place at 25°C indicate (1) whether it can take place spontaneously at a higher temperature, if each substance is still at 1 atm pressure, and (2) estimate approximately at which minimum temperature the reaction would begin to have the capacity to take place spontaneously (neglect as a first approximation the change of ΔH and ΔS with temperature).
(a) $\Delta H^\circ = +24.2$ kcal/mole $YX_{(s)}$ and $\Delta S^\circ = +6.4$ cal/mole $\times$ deg
(b) $\Delta H^\circ = -50.6$ kcal/mole $YX_{(s)}$ and $\Delta S^\circ = -4.8$ cal/mole $\times$ deg
(c) $\Delta H^\circ = +20.8$ kcal/mole $YX_{(s)}$ and $\Delta S^\circ = -7.1$ cal/mole $\times$ deg
(d) $\Delta H^\circ = -30.8$ kcal/mole $YX_{(s)}$ and $\Delta S^\circ = -3.2$ cal/mole $\times$ deg
(e) $\Delta H^\circ = +\ 6.2$ kcal/mole $YX_{(s)}$ and $\Delta S^\circ = +8.4$ cal/mole $\times$ deg

17-21 None of the transformations with the sets of thermodynamic data listed below has the capacity to take place spontaneously at 25°C. Discuss which of these transformations may, however, have the capacity to take place at a higher temperature. Explain your answer.
(a) ΔH° is positive, and $T\,\Delta S^\circ$ is positive
(b) ΔH° is negative, and $T\,\Delta S^\circ$ is negative
(c) ΔH° is positive, and ΔS° is positive
(d) ΔH° is positive, and ΔS° is negative

17-22 In regard to question 17-21, can you think of a general reaction that each system would be able to undergo, provided the temperature could be raised to any desired value, however high?

17-23 Do all reactions which are "thermodynamically permitted" at room temperature actually take place at room temperature? Explain your answer.

17-24 What general conditions must be satisfied for a certain substance (element or compound) to be thermodynamically stable?

17-25 Following the general outline of Section 17-8, discuss the "anatomy" of the following processes, involving reactants and products at 25°C and 1 atm:
(a) $Na_{(s)} + \frac{1}{2}\,Cl_{2(g)} \longrightarrow NaCl_{(s)}$
(b) $I_{2(g)} + H_{2(g)} \longrightarrow 2\ HI_{(g)}$
(c) $SO_{2(g)} + \frac{1}{2}\,O_{2(g)} \longrightarrow SO_{3(g)}$
(d) $PCl_{3(g)} + Cl_{2(g)} \longrightarrow PCl_{5(g)}$
(e) $NaCl_{(s)}$ + water $\longrightarrow Na^{+}_{(aq,1M)} + Cl^{-}_{(aq,1M)}$

Problems

17-1 (a) Calculate the pressure-volume work (per mole-equation) involved in the reaction; $NH_4Cl_{(s)} \longrightarrow NH_{3(g)} + HCl_{(g)}$ at 150°C and 1 atm. (b) Describe a type of apparatus which may be used to carry out this reaction again at 150°C but under reversible pressure conditions (under an opposing pressure just slightly lower at each instant than that of the system itself). (c) Calculate the pressure-volume work performed by the system on the surroundings if the reaction is carried out reversibly at 150°C.

17-2 One mole of liquid water is completely vaporized at 100°C, in a cylinder closed by a weightless, frictionless piston to which is applied: (a) a constant pressure of 1 atm, (b) a pressure which is at each instant just very slightly less than that of the water vapor itself, and gradually increases to a maximum value of 1 atm. Calculate the work done by the system in each case.

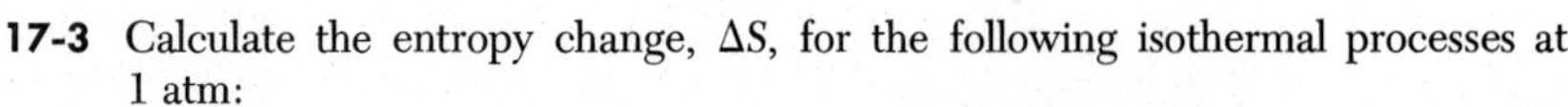

PROBLEMS

17-3 Calculate the entropy change, ΔS, for the following isothermal processes at 1 atm:

(a) $H_2O_{(s)} \longrightarrow H_2O_{(l)}$ $\Delta H_{fus} = +1.44$ kcal/mole at 0°C
(b) $H_2O_{(l)} \longrightarrow H_2O_{(g)}$ $\Delta H_{vap} = +9.82$ kcal/mole at 100°C
(c) $I_{2(s)} \longrightarrow I_{2(g)}$ $\Delta H_{subl} = +14.9$ kcal/mole at 25°C
(d) $MgCl_{2(s)} \longrightarrow MgCl_{2(l)}$ $\Delta H_{fus} = +10.3$ kcal/mole at 712°C
(e) $LiCl_{(s)} \longrightarrow LiCl_{(l)}$ $\Delta H_{fus} = +3.2$ kcal/mole at 610°C
(f) $HF_{(l)} \longrightarrow HF_{(g)}$ $\Delta H_{vap} = +1.8$ kcal/mole at 19°C
(g) $HCl_{(l)} \longrightarrow HCl_{(g)}$ $\Delta H_{vap} = +3.86$ kcal/mole at −85°C

17-4 Calculate the standard entropy change, $\Delta S°$, for the following reactions at 25°C (use values in Table 17-2).

(a) $Al_{(s)} + \frac{3}{2} F_{2(g)} \longrightarrow AlF_{3(s)}$
(b) $Al_{(s)} + \frac{3}{2} Cl_{2(g)} \longrightarrow AlCl_{3(s)}$
(c) $PCl_{3(g)} + Cl_{2(g)} \longrightarrow PCl_{5(g)}$
(d) $KClO_{3(s)} \longrightarrow KCl_{(s)} + \frac{3}{2} O_{2(g)}$
(e) $Cu_2O_{(s)} + H_{2(g)} \longrightarrow 2\ Cu_{(s)} + H_2O_{(g)}$
(f) $CS_{2(l)} + 3\ O_{2(g)} \longrightarrow CO_{2(g)} + 2\ SO_{2(g)}$
(g) $CuO_{(s)} + H_{2(g)} \longrightarrow Cu_{(s)} + H_2O_{(g)}$

17-5 Calculate the entropy changes for the following *non-isothermal* processes, using the equation given in Appendix 17-2. (a) 1 mole of the monoatomic noble gas argon, Ar, enclosed in a container of fixed volume is cooled from 200°K to 100°K. (b) 2 moles of the diatomic gas nitrogen, N_2, initially at 25°C and 1 atm, absorb from the surroundings 20 cal of heat energy. The heat capacity of N_2 at constant volume is $C_v = 5$ cal/mole × deg.

17-6 For the following reactions at 25°C (1) calculate the value of $\Delta G°$ from the given values of $\Delta H°$ (Tables 16-2 and 16-4) and $S°$ (Table 17-2). (2) Discuss the relative contribution of the $\Delta H°$ and $T\,\Delta S°$ energy terms to the value of the $\Delta G°$ of the reaction. (3) Predict whether the reaction has or does not have the capacity to take place spontaneously at 25°C, and explain your answer in terms of the significance of the $\Delta H°$ and $\Delta S°$ (or $T\,\Delta S°$) terms.

(a) $PCl_{5(g)} \longrightarrow PCl_{3(g)} + Cl_{2(g)}$
(b) $H_{2(g)} + Br_{2(g)} \longrightarrow 2\ HBr_{(g)}$
(c) $H_{2(g)} + Br_{2(l)} \longrightarrow 2\ HBr_{(g)}$
(d) $2\ NaOH_{(s)} \longrightarrow Na_2O_{(s)} + H_2O_{(l)}$
(e) $H_2S_{(g)} + O_{2(g)} \longrightarrow H_2O_{(g)} + SO_{2(g)}$
(f) $Ag_{(s)} + \frac{1}{2} O_{2(g)} \longrightarrow AgO_{(s)}$
(g) $2\ CuO_{(s)} \longrightarrow Cu_2O + \frac{1}{2} O_2$
(h) $H_2SO_{4(l)} \longrightarrow H_2O_{(l)} + SO_{3(g)}$

17-7 Calcium oxide, $CaO_{(s)}$, is a good dehydrating agent forming $Ca(OH)_{2(s)}$. Explain this fact by considering the equation: $CaO_{(s)} + H_2O_{(g)} \longrightarrow Ca(OH)_{2(s)}$, for which the energy term $\Delta H = -26.1$ kcal/mole-equation and the energy term $T\,\Delta S = +10.6$ kcal/mole-equation at 25°C and 1 atm.

SOLUTIONS: I

18

In this chapter and in the next, we shall discuss the fundamental concepts of solubility, some of which we already introduced in Chapter 10 in order to explain the solvent properties of water. In this chapter we shall consider both the effect of various factors on the solubility of substances and equilibrium conditions of solubility. And since the formation of a solution from a solute and a solvent is best interpreted on the basis of the enthalpy change, ΔH, and the entropy change, ΔS, which accompany the process of dissolution, we shall discuss solubility in terms of the fundamental thermodynamic equation, $\Delta G = \Delta H - T\,\Delta S$. In the next chapter we shall consider the quantitative relationships among the most important properties of solutions.

18-1 Definition of Solution

When a pure substance has been subdivided so that its particles are of molecular, atomic, or ionic size, it is in a state of *molecular dispersion*. A homogeneous molecular dispersion of two or more substances is called a *solution*. You may recall that homogeneity does not imply only uniformity of appearance, but also, and more specifically, the impossibility of separating the individual component substances by simple mechanical means. In a solution the individual *components* are subdivided into particles of molecular size, and can only be separated by physical processes—for example, diffusion, evaporation, and crystallization. It is customary to discuss solutions in terms of *solvent* and *solute* (one or more), the solvent being that component which retains its original physical state after the solutes are added. When the components of a solution are in the same physical state as the solution itself (for example, two gases that mix to give a gaseous solution, or two miscible liquids that give a liquid solution), the differentiation between solvent and solute ceases to be meaningful. Even in this case, however, it is common to apply the name "solvent" to the component which is present in greater proportion in the solution.

PHYSICAL STATES OF SOLUTIONS. Ordinarily, we think of solutions as a mixture of a solid in a liquid. Actually, however, solutions can exist in any one of the three states of matter—gaseous, liquid, and solid—as can the solvent and solute. Since for each possible physical state of the solvent—and hence of the solution—the solute may be a solid, a liquid, or a gas, we have, in all, nine kinds of solutions, which differ according to the physical state of their components (Table 18-1).

18-2 Solutions of Gases in Gases

All gaseous mixtures are, in effect, solutions of gases in gases. We shall discuss these simple solutions first, because some of their fundamental characteristics apply to all other solutions.

IDEAL-GAS SOLUTIONS

Suppose we mix samples of two ideal gases, A and B. Since ideal-gas molecules exert no attraction on one another, no interactions exist among the molecules of gas A alone or among the molecules of gas B alone or among the molecules of A and of B together. Consequently, when two ideal gases mix at constant temperature and pressure, no change in the internal energy of the system occurs and the enthalpy change is zero ($\Delta E = 0$, hence $\Delta H = P\,\Delta V = 0$ because V is constant). The important change which takes place when the two gases are mixed is that the entropy of the system increases (ΔS is positive). For the mixing of two ideal gases, the fundamental equation, $\Delta G = \Delta H - T\,\Delta S$, becomes simply $\Delta G = -T\,\Delta S$, and ΔG is negative because the entropy, S, of the system increases as a result of the mixing. Thus it is because of the favorable $T\,\Delta S$ energy factor that, according to the laws of thermodynamics, the mixing of two ideal gases can occur.

TABLE 18-1 KINDS OF SOLUTIONS

Solution	*Solute in Solvent*	*Example*
Gaseous	Gas in gas	Air: $O_{2(g)}$ + noble gases in $N_{2(g)}$
	Liquid in gas	Moist nitrogen gas: $H_2O_{(l)}$ in $N_{2(g)}$ at 25°C, 1 atm
	Solid in gas	Iodine, $I_{2(s)}$, in nitrogen, $N_{2(g)}$, at 25°C, 1 atm
Liquid	Gas in liquid	Ammonia, $NH_{3(g)}$, in water, $H_2O_{(l)}$, at 25°C, 1 atm
	Liquid in liquid	Acetic acid, $CH_3COOH_{(l)}$, in water, $H_2O_{(l)}$
	Solid in liquid	Potassium nitrate, $KNO_{3(s)}$, in water, $H_2O_{(l)}$
Solid	Gas in solid	Hydrogen, $H_{2(g)}$, in palladium, $Pd_{(s)}$, at 25°C and 1 atm
	Liquid in solid	Mercury, $Hg_{(l)}$, in copper, $Cu_{(s)}$
	Solid in solid	Metal alloys (for example, $Cu_{(s)}$ in $Ag_{(s)}$)

In a solution of two ideal gases, A and B, the intermolecular attractions among the A molecules, among the B molecules, and also between the A and B molecules, are all the same—zero. And if we assume that gases A and B are composed of point molecules (or of molecules of equal size), then the molecules of A and B will be distributed in the gaseous solution with the greatest possible randomness—that is, the maximum entropy of the system possible under the specified conditions of volume and temperature. The gaseous mixture of two ideal gases is an example of an *ideal solution. In an ideal solution the interactions among all kinds of (like and unlike) molecules present in the solution are equal, and the molecular distribution has the maximum degree of ramdomness.* For any ideal solution, the forces acting among the molecules of component A are the same as those acting among the molecules of component B, and among the molecules of A and B. Therefore, the following dissolution process is not accompanied by an enthalpy change ($\Delta H = 0$):

$$\text{A (alone)} + \text{B (alone)} \longrightarrow \{\text{A} + \text{B}\} \text{ (solution)}$$

This simple discussion of the mixing of two ideal gases to form an ideal gaseous solution summarizes the fundamental concepts which permit us to understand the phenomenon of solubility for all kinds of solutions. In fact the formation of real solutions, as we shall now see, simply involves some variations of the enthalpy and entropy factors considered for ideal solutions, owing to the different interactions and different sizes of the molecules of the various real substances.

SOLUTIONS OF REAL GASES

We know that all real gases will mix in any proportion to form a homogeneous mixture (a real gaseous solution). A real solution of two real gases—for example, a mixture of oxygen gas, $O_{2(g)}$, and hydrogen gas, $H_{2(g)}$—is unlike an ideal gaseous solution in that the van der Waals oxygen-oxygen and hydrogen-hydrogen interactions differ slightly—as indicated by the different numerical values of the van der Waals correction factor a for hydrogen gas and oxygen gas (see Table 9-2). They differ also from the van der Waals oxygen-hydrogen interactions. Furthermore, the molecular sizes of $O_{2(g)}$ and $H_{2(g)}$ differ appreciably—as indicated, again, by the different values of van der Waals correction factor b for these two gases (Table 9-1). From the experimental values of b, the molecular radius of $O_{2(g)}$ is calculated to be 1.7 A, and that of $H_{2(g)}$ is calculated to be 1.4 A.

As a result of the slight differences in the van der Waals intermolecular forces for different real-gas molecules, the mixing of two real gases is accompanied by a very small but well-defined enthalpy change. As usual the ΔH of the mixing process results from the difference between the internal energy of the final system (a solution of $H_{2(g)} + O_{2(g)}$) and that of the initial system ($H_{2(g)}$ alone plus $O_{2(g)}$ alone), the temperature and total volume of the system being constant. In turn, the change in internal energy simply reflects the difference in the van der Waals potential energy of the gaseous solution as compared with that of the two separated gaseous components. We can conclude that, in general, the attractions between like molecules are somewhat stronger than the attractions between unlike molecules, because the mixing of two different gases is usually accompanied by an increase in van der Waals potential energy, and hence by a positive—but very small—enthalpy change. The mixing of two real gases to form a real gaseous solution has therefore a positive, unfavorable ΔH value. Since this small unfavorable ΔH term is still more than compensated for by the favorable $T\,\Delta S$ term, the mixing of real gases is a spontaneous process. In fact, experiments show that if two real gases originally at the same temperature are allowed to diffuse through one another—for example, in a thermally isolated set-up similar to that shown in Fig. 8-15—the temperature of the final homogeneous gaseous solution is slightly lower than that of the original separated gases. This lowering of the temperature indicates that some of the thermal energy of the gases has been converted to van der Waals potential energy—in other words, that it has been spent to overcome the intermolecular attractions, which are slightly greater in the isolated gases than in their mixture. Actually, the lowering of the temperature which results from the mixing of two real gases indicates the existance of van der Waals intermolecular attractions.

18-3 Solutions of Liquids and Solids in Gases

Now that we have considered solutions formed by mixing two gaseous substances, let us turn to the two other types of gaseous solutions—a liquid in a gas (for example, water in air) and a solid in a gas (for example, iodine in air). In dealing with the dissolving of a liquid or of a solid in a gas, we must of course take into consideration the enthalpy change, ΔH, involved in the mixing of two different gases, as discussed above. In addition, we must take into account the heat required to change the liquid or solid solute to a gas consisting of the same species that will be present in the resulting gaseous solution. In other words, the dissolution of a liquid or a solid occurs by two successive steps, as schematically shown below:

Step 1.

Solid Solute: solid $\longrightarrow$ gas (solute) ΔH_{subl} (or ΔH_{atomiz}) = positive, unfavorable

Liquid Solute: liquid $\longrightarrow$ gas (solute) ΔH_{vap} = positive, unfavorable

Step 2.

gas (solute) + gas (solvent) $\longrightarrow$ gas (solution) ΔH_{mixing} = positive, generally, but very small

Suppose we wish to form a solution of water in air, at 25°C and 1 atm, starting with liquid water and dry air, both at 25°C and 1 atm. First, we need to supply energy to the initial system in order to vaporize the liquid water to gaseous, monomeric H_2O molecules. We must supply an additional small quantity of energy to compensate for the van der Waals attractions, whose sum is greater for $H_2O_{(g)}$ and air separately than for their solution. Since the ΔH_{vap} of liquid water is quite large (10.5 kcal/mole at 25°C), the total enthalpy change for the formation of the solution of H_2O in air at 25°C represents a significant *unfavorable* energy term in the equation $\Delta G = \Delta H - T\,\Delta S$.

Similarly for the dissolution of a solid in a gas, the total enthalpy term includes the large, unfavorable heat of sublimation, ΔH_{subl} (or heat of atomization, ΔH_{atomiz}), of the solid to form the species that will be present in the gaseous solution. For example, for a solution of iodine in air we are interested in the ΔH_{subl} for the process: $I_{2(s)} \longrightarrow I_{2(g)}$. The gaseous I_2 molecules then mix with the air molecules to form a homogeneous gaseous solution. Again, even though ΔH_{subl} is an unfavorable energy term, the favorable positive ΔS_{mixing} is sufficient to compensate, at appropriate temperatures, for the unfavorable ΔH, and solid iodine sublimes to give a solution of iodine vapor in air.

SOLUTIONS OF LIQUIDS IN GASES

How can our general considerations of the energy factors involved in the formation of real gaseous solutions help us understand the solubility of liquids in gases?

Assume we have a known quantity of liquid water at 25°C and 760.0 torr (1 atm) and we bring it into contact with a known quantity of dry air*, also at 25°C and 760.0 torr. We maintain the system closed at the same constant temperature and volume. If we follow (for example, with a balance) the changes over time of the weight

* Air regarded simply as a mixture of O_2 and N_2.

of *liquid* water, we observe at first a slow decrease; since the system is closed, this means simply that some liquid water evaporates, forming a gaseous solution with the air. But after some time the weight of the liquid reaches a certain value and remains constant from then on. At the same time, if we measure with a sensitive manometer the pressure of the air-water vapor mixture in the system, we observe an initial gradual increase from the original value, 760.0 torr, to 783.8 torr, where it remains constant. How do we explain this behavior in terms of the change in free energy of the system? At the start, when all H_2O molecules are in the liquid phase and the gas phase contains only O_2 and N_2 molecules, the evaporation of some water to form a gaseous solution with the air results in a very dramatic increase in the disorder of the system—that is, a large entropy increase. At the beginning, therefore, the favorable entropy change of the process is large enough to compensate for the unfavorable enthalpy term—which includes the heat of vaporization of water at 25°C and 1 atm, and the enthalpy of mixing of the resulting water vapor with air ($O_{2(g)}$ 20 per cent, $N_{2(g)}$ 80 per cent). Thus, the favorable $T\,\Delta S$ energy term more than compensates for the unfavorable ΔH term, and the free energy change of the process, $\Delta G = \Delta H - T\,\Delta S$, is negative. Therefore, the process can occur spontaneously. As more water molecules continue to pass from the liquid phase to the gas phase, forming a solution of water vapor and air, any further evaporation still results in an increase of the entropy of the system, but the entropy change becomes progressively smaller. This is so because we are going from a disordered system to one which is only slightly more disordered. When the concentration of $H_2O_{(g)}$ in the air has reached a certain fixed value (for this temperature), the further evaporation of a very small quantity of water will involve a favorable entropy change, ΔS, such that the favorable $T\,\Delta S$ energy change exactly counterbalances the unfavorable enthalpy change, ΔH, involved in the evaporation of the liquid and the mixing of the resulting $H_2O_{(g)}$ with air:

$$T\,\Delta S_{\text{vap}} + T\,\Delta S_{\text{mixing}} = \Delta H_{\text{vap}} + \Delta H_{\text{mixing}}$$

At this moment, therefore, $\Delta G = \Delta H - T\,\Delta S = 0$. The system has now reached a *state of equilibrium*, and if the temperature and pressure remain constant, the quantity of liquid water and the quantity of gaseous water dissolved in the air remain constant thereafter. Any further *net* evaporation of water is now thermodynamically forbidden (ΔG would be positive). After a state of equilibrium is reached, the air in contact with the liquid water contains the maximum possible concentration of dissolved H_2O molecules—and, as we know, the air is *saturated with water vapor.* (We should mention here that some $O_{2(g)}$ and $N_{2(g)}$ molecules are dissolved in the liquid water, so that equilibrium really exists between a liquid solution of O_2 and N_2 in water and a gaseous solution of H_2O in air. We shall consider the solubility of gases in liquids in section 18-4. Actually, since the extent to which $N_{2(g)}$ and $O_{2(g)}$ dissolve in water at 25°C and 1 atm is very small, we may neglect the matter here.)

It is important to keep in mind that during the process we have just described, our system—at the constant temperature of 25°C—takes from the surroundings a quantity of heat equal to the ΔH of the process (the volume is constant, hence no pressure-volume work is involved). If the system were thermally isolated so that no heat could be transferred from the surroundings to the system, the weight of liquid water would still decrease, but simultaneously the temperature of the system would decrease below 25°C, because now the evaporation of water would occur at the expense of the kinetic energy of the liquid water and of the air in contact with it. A new equilibrium state would be reached, at a lower temperature than 25°C and with a smaller concentration of water vapor in the air (at a lower temperature, the $T\,\Delta S$ term becomes equal to the ΔH term for a smaller concentration of H_2O in the air).

We may summarize these considerations as follows: Liquid water dissolves in dry gaseous air spontaneously—the process involves a positive (unfavorable) ΔH and a positive (favorable) ΔS—and reaches a state of equilibrium corresponding, for each value of the temperature, to a fixed concentration (or partial pressure) of water in air. At equilibrium, the air is saturated with water vapor (and the liquid water is saturated with air). At equilibrium the favorable $T\,\Delta S$ term is exactly sufficient to counterbalance the unfavorable ΔH term. Hence $\Delta G = 0$ and any further *net* evaporation or condensation of water is thermodynamically forbidden. This discussion of the energy factors involved in the dissolving of water is applicable to other liquids. Each liquid has its own vapor pressure—that is, its own equilibrium concentration in the confined space above it—because the heat of vaporization differs from one liquid to another and so do the intermolecular interactions of their vapors. In general, the lower the (unfavorable) ΔH_{vap} of a liquid, the more volatile the liquid. For each liquid the vapor pressure always increases with rising temperature (see Chapter 10, Section 10-2) because the $T\,\Delta S$ term, which favors vaporization, increases proportionately to the absolute temperature, whereas ΔH_{vap} does not vary much with the temperature. Hence the equilibrium state, $\Delta H = T\,\Delta S$, is reached for increasingly higher concentrations of the liquid solute in the gaseous solution.

SOLUTIONS OF SOLIDS IN GASES

Considerations of vapor pressure can also be applied to explain the solubility of solids in gases. Since for any substance the heat required for the process *solid* $\longrightarrow$ *gas* is appreciably greater than that required for the process *liquid* $\longrightarrow$ *gas*, solids have lower vapor pressures than their liquids. And, as we would expect, the solids with the highest vapor pressures are those with the lowest values of ΔH_{subl} and ΔH_{atomiz}—that is, those solids in which the intermolecular forces holding together the particles (molecules or atoms) in the crystal lattice are relatively weak. Again, as for liquids, the vapor pressure of solids increases with temperature because the higher the temperature, the greater the $T\,\Delta S$ term which favors the vaporization.

18-4 Solutions of Gases in Liquids

All gases are somewhat soluble in all liquids, although often the concentration at saturation may be extremely small. The solubility of a given gas in a given liquid again depends on the balance of the ΔH and $T\,\Delta S$ energy terms, since at equilibrium (saturation) $\Delta G = 0$ and $\Delta H = T\,\Delta S$. But for solutions of gases in liquids the magnitudes of the values of the individual terms, ΔH and ΔS, are quite different from those we considered for solutions of liquids in gases.

Let us first discuss the simplest case—a solution of an ideal gas in a liquid. It is convenient to consider the process as consisting of a sequence of *imaginary* steps, which help us to evaluate the various energy factors that contribute to make the net process thermodynamically permitted or forbidden. Thus, we may consider that, the gas first condenses to its liquid phase, which then mixes with the liquid solvent.

Step 1. Liquefaction of gas:

$$\text{gas} \longrightarrow \text{liquid (solute)}$$

$\Delta H_{\text{liquefaction}}$ is favorable; $\Delta S_{\text{liquefaction}}$ is unfavorable

Step 2. Mixing of liquid (solute) with liquid (solvent):

$$\text{liquid (solute)} + \text{liquid (solvent)} \longrightarrow \text{liquid (solution)}$$

ΔH_{mixing} can be favorable or unfavorable; ΔS_{mixing} is favorable

Step 1, as we know, has a favorable ΔH. Heat is always evolved in the condensation of a gas to its liquid because for any substance the energy of the intermolecular attractions is greater in the liquid than in the gaseous state. Step 1 has an unfavorable ΔS term however, because for any pure substance the liquid state is more ordered than the gaseous state. Step 2 always has a favorable entropy term (ΔS_{mixing} is large and positive), whereas the ΔH_{mixing} may be positive or negative depending on whether the sum of the intermolecular attractions in the solution is larger or smaller than the sum of the intermolecular attractions in the two separate liquid components. The values of $\Delta H_{liquefaction}$ and $\Delta S_{liquefaction}$ depend only on the gas considered; whereas ΔH_{mixing} and ΔS_{mixing} depend both on the gas (solute) and on the liquid solvent. Thus the relative tendencies of various gases to dissolve in a certain liquid depend chiefly on their ΔH_{vap} ($\Delta H_{vap} = -\Delta H_{liquefaction}$) and on the energy of the interactions between the molecules of each gas and the molecules of the liquid. Since the heats of vaporization of gases that do not form associated liquids (Chapter 10) do not differ much from one another, the different solubilities of various gases in the same liquid reflect the different energies of the solute-solvent intermolecular attractions. Similarly the different solubilities of a given gas in various liquids simply reflect the different strengths of the interactions between the dissolved molecules of the gas and the molecules of the various liquid solvents. For each gas and each solvent, finally, the solubility will depend on the temperature and on the pressure, since both these factors influence the total ΔS of the process of dissolution.

We shall now apply these general considerations to some specific examples. Since water is the most common solvent in the laboratory, in industry, and in biological processes, we shall use as examples solutions of gases in water; our considerations, however, hold true for all solutions of gases in liquids.

Experiments reveal that the amount of a gas that will dissolve in a given amount of water depends on three factors: (1) the nature of the gas, (2) the temperature of the solution, and (3) the pressure of the gas above the solution. Let us discuss the effect of each of these factors on the ΔH and ΔS terms for the dissolution of the gas in water.

THE EFFECT OF THE NATURE OF THE GAS ON SOLUBILITY. When certain gases, such as hydrogen, oxygen, and nitrogen, are brought into contact with water, a small amount of the gas dissolves to form a solution in which the dissolved molecules remain essentially unchanged. For example, hydrogen molecules dissolved in water are the same strongly bonded covalent molecules, H—H, that are present in the gas. Hydrogen, oxygen, and nitrogen gases are only slightly soluble in water because, although the polar molecules of water strongly attract one another, they offer only relatively slight attraction for the non-polar molecules of these gases. The enthalpy change, ΔH, for the mixing of the liquefied gas and liquid water has a large positive (unfavorable) value because a great deal of energy is required to break up the strong interactions among the polar water molecules—in order to make room for the non-polar molecules of the solute, H_2, O_2, or N_2. That even these gases are somewhat soluble in water shows, however, that the gain of entropy in the mixing process (to the extent that it does take place) is still large enough to make dissolving thermodynamically favorable.

Sometimes dissolution in water is accompanied by some fundamental chemical changes—for example, hydrogen chloride gas, $HCl_{(g)}$, dissolves in water to form hydrated hydrogen ions, $H^+{}_{(aq)}$, and hydrated chloride ions, $Cl^-{}_{(aq)}$, that is, hydrochloric acid. In such cases the enthalpy change of the mixing process usually becomes favorable to dissolution, because the net sum of all intermolecular interactions in solution is greater than that of the gas and water taken separately. The gas therefore dissolves with evolution of heat; in the case of HCl, the heat evolved is 17.56 kcal/mole of $HCl_{(g)}$ dissolved in 1 liter of $H_2O_{(l)}$ at 25°C and 1 atm. For the dissolution of hydrogen chloride in water, both the enthalpy and the entropy of mixing have large favorable values, and in fact HCl gas is very soluble in water. In general, all gases which are very soluble in water undergo appreciable chemical change when dissolved in water.

THE EFFECT OF TEMPERATURE ON SOLUBILITY. Temperature has a marked effect on the amount of a gas that will dissolve in a given amount of water. In general, *the* *solubility of all gases decreases as the temperature increases.* Consequently, most gases may be removed from solution simply by boiling (of course, some solvent may also evaporate together with the dissolved gas). Of the various energy factors involved in the dissolution of a gas in water, those most affected by a change of temperature are the unfavorable $T\,\Delta S$ of the condensation of the gas and the favorable $T\,\Delta S$ of the mixing process. Thus, the decrease of gas solubility with increasing temperature indicates that the unfavorable $T\,\Delta S$ of the condensation process becomes more and more important as the temperature rises.

THE EFFECT OF PRESSURE ON SOLUBILITY. The greater the pressure of a gas in contact with a liquid, the greater the solubility of the gas. That is to say, the greater the concentration of the gas molecules above a liquid, the greater the concentration of gas molecules in solution. For gases that do not react chemically with water—for example, O_2, N_2, and H_2—a quantitative relationship exists between solubility and gas pressure. This relationship, called Henry's Law, is discussed in the following chapter.

18-5 Solutions of Liquids in Liquids

As we have seen, all gases will mix to form solutions, regardless of the proportions in which they are present. All gases are *completely miscible* with one another. There are many pairs of liquids—for example, alcohol and water; benzene and toluene; and ether and acetone—which are also completely miscible. On the other hand, many liquids do not mix at all when they are brought into contact; such liquids are insoluble in one another, or *immiscible.* Water and mercury provide an example of immiscible liquids.

Between these two solubility limits are various liquids that mix with one another to form solutions only in certain proportions—such liquids are partially soluble in one another, or *partially miscible.* The different solubility limits of various pairs of liquids arise from the differences in their intermolecular attractions. Liquids with very similar molecular structures, and hence similar intermolecular attractions, are usually completely miscible—and their solutions approximate the behavior of ideal solutions. For such pairs of very similar liquids, the ΔS_{mixing} provides the favorable driving force for the mixing process. Although two liquids—for example, water and phenol—have different structures, if the intermolecular attractions among the molecules of each liquid alone do not differ too greatly from those between the molecules of the two liquids in the solution, then partial miscibility may occur. The ΔH_{mixing} is unfavorable to the formation of the solution, because the water molecules attract one another more strongly than they attract the phenol molecules, and in turn the phenol molecules attract one another more strongly than they attract the water molecules. However, the ΔH_{mixing} is not very great, and the favorable $T\,\Delta S$ term makes partial solubility possible. In general, whenever two partially miscible liquids, A and B, are brought together, three results are possible depending on the relative quantities of A and B. (1) Liquid A may completely dissolve in liquid B, forming a solution of A (solute) in B (solvent). (2) Liquid B may completely dissolve in A forming a solution of B (solute) in A (solvent). In these cases the two liquids are present in proportions within their mutual solubility limits, and a homogenous solution is formed. (3) If the liquids A and B are present in proportions exceeding their mutual solubility limits, two solutions are then obtained, a solution of A (solute) in B (solvent), and a solution of B (solute) in A (solvent). These two solutions form separate layers. For example, the solubility limits for water and phenol at 25°C are: 8 per cent phenol in water, and 75 per cent phenol in water (percentages are expressed in grams). It follows that if we mix 5 g of phenol with 95 g of water at 25°C we obtain a single solution where water is the solvent. If we mix 10 g of water with 90 g of phenol we also obtain a single solution, where now phenol is the solvent. But if we mix 60 g of phenol with 40 g of water, at 25°C, we obtain two liquid layers. One is a saturated solution of phenol in water containing

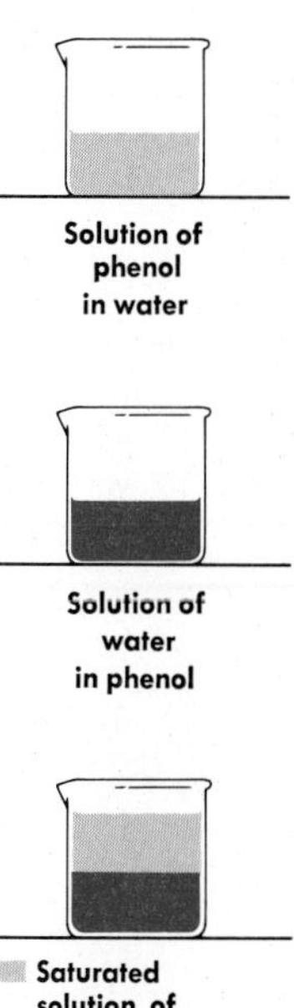

8 per cent phenol, and the other is a saturated solution of water in phenol containing 75 per cent phenol.

Liquids are completely immiscible when their intermolecular forces are both very strong and very different in nature. For example, the intermolecular forces that hold together water molecules in the liquid state are quite strong ($\Delta H_{vap} = 10.5$ kcal/mole H_2O at 25°C and 1 atm) and even stronger are the forces that hold together the atoms of liquid mercury ($\Delta H_{atomiz} = 14.65$ kcal/mole Hg at 25°C, 1 atm). But these intermolecular forces are of very different kinds. The water molecules are held together in the liquid state by van der Waals forces and hydrogen bonding, whereas the atoms of mercury are held together in the liquid state by metal bonding. Thus, the attractions that H_2O molecules and Hg atoms exert for each other are not comparable with those they exert for themselves, and the ΔH_{mixing} is so very large and unfavorable that it completely overcomes the favorable effect of the entropy of mixing.

18-6 Solutions of Solids in Liquids

Solutions of solids in liquids, and especially in water, are among the most common and important in the laboratory, in industry, and in biological processes. For this reason we shall consider the properties and structural aspects of these solutions in some detail.

In discussing the solubility of solids in liquids it is convenient to distinguish between solids which have a molecular lattice and those which have an essentially ionic lattice.

SOLUTIONS OF MOLECULAR SOLIDS

As an illustration, let us consider the dissolution of crystalline iodine in liquid water. We have learned in Chapter 10 that solid iodine is a molecular crystal composed of diatomic molecules, I_2. In the crystal, the shortest internuclear distance between separate I_2 molecules is about twice the internuclear distance within the I_2 molecule itself, and the van der Waals attractions among the I_2 molecules are relatively weak, as shown by the low heat of sublimation ($\Delta H_{subl} = 5.78$ kcal/mole I_2 at 25°C, 1 atm).

Suppose we add a very tiny crystal of solid iodine to a given volume of water at a given temperature. Gradually the steel-gray iodine crystal dissolves; the liquid surrounding the crystal turns yellow, and this color gradually spreads throughout the solution. This spreading is brought about both by the diffusion of the dissolved iodine molecules from regions of higher iodine concentration to regions of lower iodine concentration, and by the diffusion of water molecules from regions of higher water concentration to regions of lower water concentration. Finally, the tiny crystal of iodine dissolves completely, and the solution attains a uniform light yellow color. (Any given solution tends to approach uniform concentration by means of diffusion, as we shall discuss in section 18-10.) If we add more iodine crystals to our solution, the dissolution process continues until the iodine in solution reaches its maximum possible concentration at that particular temperature. The solution is now saturated with respect to iodine; the solid iodine in contact with the solution and the dissolved iodine present in the solution are in equilibrium. At 25°C and 1 atm, a saturated solution of iodine in water contains 0.30 g of iodine in 1 liter of solution. If we continue to add iodine crystals to the saturated solution, the added crystals simply fall to the bottom of the container and fail to dissolve.

In order to evaluate the energy factors which determine the limit of solubility of iodine in water, we can consider the dissolution of iodine to take place in two successive steps (at constant temperature and pressure).

Step 1. Crystalline iodine melts to its liquid phase; the enthalpy change is unfavorable (ΔH_{fusion} of iodine $= +1.88$ kcal/mole I_2) but the transformation is accompanied by a favorable ΔS, since the entropy of any substance increases upon melting.

$$I_{2(s)} \longrightarrow I_{2(l)} \qquad \Delta H_{fus} = \text{unfavorable}; \; \Delta S_{fus} = \text{favorable}$$

Step 2. Liquid iodine and liquid water mix to form a homogeneous solution. The entropy increases upon mixing and ΔS_{mixing} is therefore favorable, but the enthalpy change is unfavorable because the attraction of the non-polar iodine molecules for the polar water molecules is weaker than the attractions among the polar water molecules themselves.

$$I_{2(l)} + H_2O_{(l)} \longrightarrow \{I_2 + H_2O\}_{solution} \qquad \Delta H_{mixing} = \text{unfavorable}; \; \Delta S_{mixing} = \text{favorable}$$

Thus, the total enthalpy change for the dissolution of crystalline iodine in water has a rather large positive, unfavorable value. The favorable $T\,\Delta S$ term is sufficient to compensate for the unfavorable ΔH, so that the free energy change is negative and favorable, but small. Therefore, when we mix crystalline iodine and pure liquid water, some iodine dissolves. At room temperature, however, saturation is reached when the iodine concentration in solution is still rather low.

In general, molecular solids made up of non-polar molecules which do not react chemically with water are only slightly soluble in water. In all these cases, the chief factor opposing the dissolution of a non-polar solid in water is the strong attraction of the water molecules for one another; their mutual attraction tends to "exclude" the non-polar molecules of the solute. Non-polar molecular solids which are only slightly soluble in water are generally much more soluble in other liquids, such as alcohol, ether, and carbon tetrachloride. For example, a saturated solution of iodine in alcohol contains 20 g of iodine per 100 ml of alcohol at room temperature. The process by which iodine dissolves in alcohol and in water, however, is exactly the same; the saturated solution again consists of covalent I_2 molecules, dispersed throughout the solution, in equilibrium with covalent I_2 molecules in the iodine crystals. The greater solubility of iodine in alcohol, as well as in ether and carbon tetrachloride, is simply a consequence of the weaker intermolecular attraction holding together the molecules of these solvents, as compared with water. When crystalline iodine is put in contact with these solvents the attractions between the iodine molecules and the solvent molecules can compete more successfully with the forces acting between the molecules of the solvent itself, and $\Delta H_{dissolution}$ is less unfavorable than with water.

SOLUBILITY OF COVALENT CRYSTALS (MACROMOLECULES). We have seen that substances such as diamond, carborundum, and silica consist of a continuous three-dimensional lattice of atoms joined together by strong covalent bonding. For these substances, a great deal of energy is required to break the bonds and form the individual atoms, or groups of atoms, in the gaseous state. In fact, the heats of atomization for elements like carbon as graphite or diamond, and the heats of sublimation for compounds like silicon dioxide, as silica, are very high indeed. This very unfavorable ΔH term is the chief reason for the insolubility of these covalent giant crystals (macromolecules) in all solvents.

DISSOLUTION OF IONIC SOLIDS IN WATER

When an ionic compound such as potassium chloride is gradually added to water, the solid passes into solution and it continues to dissolve until the solution has become saturated. We know that crystalline potassium chloride, K^+Cl^-, consists of K^+ ions and Cl^- ions, arranged in a lattice of the rock-salt type (6:6 crystal coordination) and held together by strong electrostatic forces. Now the question arises, in what form is potassium chloride present in water solution?

Various experimental observations, which we shall discuss in detail in the next chapter, show that an aqueous solution of potassium chloride—and in general of any ionic compound—contains positive ions and negative ions, relatively free from mutual attractions, which are able to move independently about the solution and to give independent chemical reactions. There is also evidence that the positive and negative ions in solution are strongly associated with a certain number of water molecules to form hydrated ions, as we have already briefly discussed earlier in Chapter 13. Thus the dissolution of an ionic salt, such as $K^+Cl^-_{(s)}$, in a polar liquid, such as water, can be considered to take place in two successive (imaginary) steps:

Step 1. The ionic crystal is broken down to form the isolated gaseous ions. A large quantity of heat is required for this process (ΔH = lattice energy). The ΔH of this step, therefore, is greatly unfavorable to dissolution.

$$K^+Cl^-_{(s)} \longrightarrow K^+_{(g)} + Cl^-_{(g)} \qquad \Delta H_{\text{step 1}} = \text{lattice energy; unfavorable}$$

Step 2. The isolated gaseous positive ions, $K^+_{(g)}$, and gaseous negative ions, $Cl^-_{(g)}$, combine with liquid water molecules to form hydrated positive and hydrated negative ions in solution, $K^+_{(aq)}$ and $Cl^-_{(aq)}$. A large quantity of energy is evolved in this process ($\Delta H_{\text{step 2}}$ = Hydration energy of K^+ + Hydration energy of Cl^- = large favorable value).

$$K^+_{(g)} + Cl^-_{(g)} + \text{water}_{(l)} \longrightarrow \{K^+_{(aq)} + Cl^-_{(aq)}\} \text{ solution}$$
$$\Delta H_{\text{step 2}} = \{\Delta H_{\text{hydr}} \text{ of } K^+ + \Delta H_{\text{hydr}} \text{ of } Cl^-\}\text{; favorable}$$

If we now consider the total entropy change for the dissolution process, we see that it must be favorable, since the dissolution of the ionic crystal in water involves the breaking down of the ordered three-dimensional array of K^+ and Cl^- in the crystal lattice, to give more or less independent, hydrated K^+ and hydrated Cl^- ions that move randomly about the entire volume of the solution. Since the ΔS of the dissolution process is generally favorable to the dissolution of an ionic compound in water and does not vary much for different ionic compounds, the marked differences in the solubilities of ionic solids in water depend on the total ΔH of the dissolution process. Thus the solubility of an ionic solid in water depends chiefly on the balance of the following factors: the lattice energy, which is unfavorable to dissolving, and the solvation energy, which is favorable to dissolving. Both of these opposing factors depend, in turn, on the ionic charges and sizes of the ions which make up the compound, and it is very interesting that, in general, the values (both large) of lattice energy and solvation energy are very close in magnitude even though of opposite sign. For example, here are some values (in kcal/mole) of the lattice and hydration energies, respectively, of some common ionic compounds: Li^+F^- (244 vs. 243); Na^+I^- (163 vs. 164); K^+Br^- (160 vs. 155); Rb^+Br^- (154 vs. 149); and Cs^+I^- (140 vs. 132).

As we have learned in an earlier chapter, the lattice energy of an ionic compound is inversely proportional to the sum of the radius of the cation, r_{cation}, and the radius of the anion, r_{anion}, and directly proportional to the product of the electrical charges of the partner ions. That is, the lattice energy decreases as the internuclear distance between neighboring positive and negative ions increases, and increases greatly as the charge of the ions increases. The charge and size of the ions also determine the value of the hydration energy of the compound, the total hydration energy being the sum of the hydration energies of the cation and of the anion. In general, for any ion, the larger the charge/radius ratio, the greater the polarizing power of the ion, and the greater its hydration energy—which is a measure of the mutual attraction of the positive ion for the polar water molecules.

SOLUBILITY TRENDS OF IONIC SOLIDS

These considerations permit us to explain observed trends in the solubility of related ionic compounds. For example, let us look at the series of the lithium halides: LiF, LiCl, LiBr, and LiI, all of which have the sodium chloride crystal structure (crystal coordination number 6:6). The experimentally measured heats of solution of these compounds are LiF (+0.90 kcal/mole); LiCl (−8.6); LiBr (−11.7); and LiI (−14.3). Whereas the heat of solution of LiF is positive, those of the other lithium halides are negative; also the enthalpy of solution increases regularly from the fluoride to the iodide. The enthalpy of solution, as we said above, is the sum of the hydration energy of the Li^+ ion and that of the halide ion, X^-, minus the lattice energy of the salt LiX. The first term, the enthalpy of hydration of the Li^+ ion, is very high (−130 kcal/mole) because the Li^+ is very small (0.60 A) and hence has a high charge/radius ratio. For each compound this term makes a constant, favorable contribution to the enthalpy of solution. As for the heats of hydration of the halide ions, they decrease in going down the family from fluoride to iodide ($\Delta H_{\text{hydration}}$, kcal/mole: $F^- = -113$, $Cl^- = -81$, $Br^- = -73$, $I^- = -62$). We see that variation in the hydration energy of the ions is opposite to that of the heat of solution of their lithium salts; therefore, it must be the lattice energy of these salts which is responsible for the observed trend. We can conclude, in a general way, that the changes in lattice energy along this series are larger than the changes in the solvation energy.

When the ions are in the crystalline state, the electrostatic attractions of the oppositely charged ions decreases as the sum of their radii increases; thus, for a series of similar salts of the same Li^+ cation, the lattice energy decreases as the size of the anion X^- increases. The electrostatic attraction of Li^+ (0.60 A) for the halide ions, X^-, decreases as we go from the small F^- ion (1.36 A) to the increasingly larger Cl^- (1.81 A), Br^- (1.95 A), and I^- (2.16 A) ions. And the lattice energies (in kcal/mole) are: LiF, 244; LiCl, 202; LiBr, 191; LiI, 178. Since the value of the ΔH_{diss} is positive (unfavorable to dissolution) for LiF and negative (favorable) for the other lithium halides, we would expect LiF to be moderately-to-sparingly soluble in water—the driving force for its dissolution being provided solely by the increase in entropy. We can expect the other lithium halides, on the other hand, to be very soluble in water (both ΔH and ΔS being favorable to dissolution); furthermore, the solubility should increase from the chloride to the iodide. And it is indeed so. A similar general trend is observed for the enthalpies of solution (kcal/mole) of the crystalline sodium halides: NaF (+0.6 kcal/mole), NaCl (+1.1), NaBr (+0.2), and NaI (−1.2).

We can summarize these considerations on the solubility of ionic compounds as follows: The entropy change for the dissolution of an ionic compound in a liquid (solvent) is, in general, always favorable to dissolution. An ionic compound will be, therefore, soluble in a given solvent if the ΔH_{diss} is negative and favorable to dissolution, or if the ΔH_{diss} is positive and unfavorable, provided that it is smaller in magnitude than the favorable $T\,\Delta S$ term. The value of ΔH_{diss} of a compound is the sum of its total solvation energy minus its lattice energy. Therefore, a compound will be soluble in a certain solvent at a specified temperature if the magnitude of its solvation energy is greater than that of its lattice energy, or if the lattice energy is slightly larger than the solvation energy but not so much that the difference exceeds the magnitude of the favorable $T\,\Delta S$ term.

We can now understand the solubility trends of a given ionic compound in different solvents. Since the lattice energy is a constant factor and the entropy of the dissolution process is also almost constant, it is the differences in solvation energies which determine the different solubilities. For example, a salt like LiCl is extremely soluble in water, slightly soluble in diethylether, $O(C_2H_5)_2$, and completely insoluble in carbon tetrachloride, CCl_4. This is so because the polar H_2O molecules effectively solvate both the Li^+ cations and the Cl^- anions, whereas the molecules of diethylether solvate effectively only the positive Li^+ ions, which attract a lone pair of electrons of the O atoms of diethylether, $O(C_2H_5)_2$, but do not solvate the anions of Cl^- (since the H atoms of ether do not have a partially positive character as do the H atoms of water). Finally, carbon tetrachloride—a tetrahedral, non-polar covalent molecule—solvates neither the positive Li^+ nor the negative Cl^- ions and hence will not dissolve Li^+Cl^-.

Water is such an exceptionally good solvent for ionic compounds because it can solvate both positive and negative ions. This is a point to keep in mind.

As a useful application of the concept discussed above, let us see how we can choose a salt that will give us a desired solubility of a given ion in a given solvent at a specified temperature. For example, let us assume that we are interested in having a solution of Cl^- ions in alcohol. First, we may try the commonest of chlorides, NaCl; but we find that it does not dissolve to any appreciable extent in alcohol. Which salts can we choose to give us a higher solubility in this solvent? What we should look for is an ionic chloride salt with a relatively low lattice energy and a cation which can be effectively solvated by ethanol. We may think of CsCl which, since Cs^+ has a radius of 1.69 A, has a lower lattice energy than NaCl. It is also true, on the other hand, that Cs^+ has much less tendency to solvate because the charge/radius ratio is smaller than that for Na^+. Experimentally we find that CsCl is soluble in alcohol and thus we see that the solvation energy wins out over the lattice energy.

Another possibility is to use a salt such as tetramethylammonium chloride $[N(CH_3)_4]^+Cl^-$. The tetramethylammonium cation, $[N(CH_3)_4]^+$, may be thought to derive from the ammonium ion $[NH_4]^+$, by substitution of each of the four hydrogen atoms, H, with methyl groups, CH_3. The radius of the $[N(CH_3)_4]^+$ cation (2.60 A) is appreciably larger than those of the Na^+ (0.95 A) and Cs^+ ions (1.69 A), so the lattice energy of its chloride salt is much lower—and the salt dissolves in ethanol to an appreciable extent.

STRUCTURE OF HYDRATED IONS IN SOLUTION

POSITIVE IONS. Back in Chapter 11, when we briefly discussed the structure of hydrated ions in aqueous solutions, we saw that immediately surrounding a metal ion, M^{+n}, there are a number of water molecules held in a definite geometric arrangement, with the partially negative O atoms in direct contact with the positive metal ion. For example, four polar water molecules tetrahedrally surround a lithium ion, $Li^+(OH_2)_4$, and the O atoms of six water molecules octahedrally surround a sodium ion, $Na^+(OH_2)_6$. The highly ordered water molecules directly surrounding the metal ion constitute the primary hydration sphere (Fig. 18-1). Because of the polarizing ability of the metal ion, M^{+n}, not only are the water molecules of the first hydration sphere oriented so that the partially negative oxygen atoms point toward the positive ion, M^{+n}, but also these water molecules are more polar than the molecules of pure water. In fact, since a lone pair of electrons of the O atom of each OH_2 molecule is attracted by the positive ion, M^{+n}, the bond electron pairs shared between the O atom and each of the two H atoms of OH_2 are also displaced towards the O atom more than they are in a molecule of pure water. The result is a greater, partially positive charge on each H atom. Thus the hydrogen atoms of the water molecules of the first hydration sphere exert a greater electrostatic attraction on the oxygen atoms of the OH_2 molecules of the next neighboring layer—what we may call the second hydration sphere.

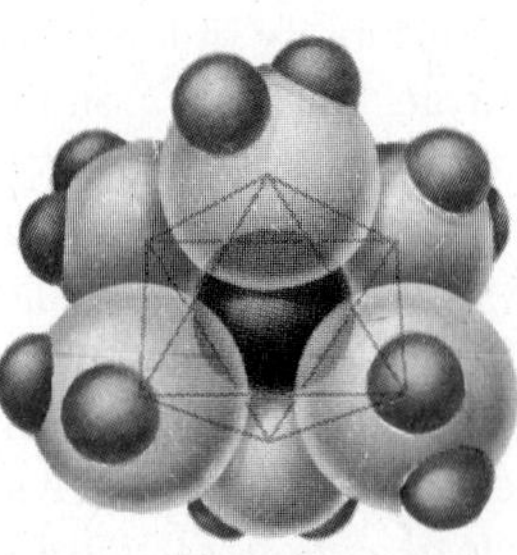

FIGURE 18-1 Primary hydration sphere of M^{+n} ion.

The second hydration sphere of the M^{+n} ion includes a larger number of water molecules than the first sphere does. Thus, we can visualize the central metal ion,

M^{+n}, as polarizing directly the water molecules of the first hydration sphere, and indirectly and less strongly the water molecules of the second hydration sphere. In turn, the partial positive charge of H atoms of the H_2O molecules is less in the second sphere than in the first sphere, but greater than in pure water. Hence the H atoms of the H_2O molecules of the second sphere attract the O atoms of other molecules to form another and still larger layer of oriented water molecules, and so on. Thus does the central metal exert a polarizing and orienting effect, with gradually decreasing strength, on successive layers of oriented water molecules. Of course, at some distance from the central metal ion its polarizing effect becomes too small to have any influence on the orientation or polarity of water molecules. Water molecules that are sufficiently removed from a positive ion, M^{+n}, being unaffected by it, behave just as they do in pure water alone and have the short-ordered arrangement typical of pure liquid water.

In general, the H_2O molecules which surround any positively charged ion in an aqueous solution are subjected to the disordering influence of thermal agitation as well as to two conflicting ordering influences. On the one hand, under the electrostatic attraction of the metal ion's positive charge, they tend to align themselves so that the O atoms are toward the metal ion; on the other hand, they tend to assume the relative positions—each O atom tetrahedrally surrounded by four H atoms—typical of the small clusters present in pure liquid water. Thus the tiny volume of aqueous solution which surrounds each positive ion is in effect composed of three concentric zones. The first zone, immediately surrounding the central positive ion, consists of ordered water molecules, aligned with their O atoms toward the central positive ion and strongly bonded to it. In the intermediate zone the H_2O molecules have a disordered arrangement resulting from the balance between the electrostatic attraction of the central positive ion and the tendency of water molecules to fit into the normal water structure, which allows maximum hydrogen bonding. The third zone consists of water molecules that are practically unaffected by the presence of the metal ion and therefore have the ordered structure characteristic of pure water.

The molecules of the inner zone are held rather strongly by the central positive ion, those of the intermediate zone are held less and less tightly as their distance from the positive ion increases, and finally those of the outer zone are almost unaffected by the positive ion. When a hydrated positive ion moves in solution, it carries along with itself the water molecules of the inner zone, as well as some of the water molecules of the intermediate zone.

For each positive ion, the hydration energy provides a measure of the *total* bond energy between the positive ion and *all* water molecules which are influenced by its charge. The sizes and hydration energies of the monopositive alkali metal ions, each having a noble-gas electron configuration, are listed in the table; you can see that they decrease with increasing ionic radius. Also, as we may expect, for two ions of about the same size and similar noble-gas electron configuration—for example, Ca^{++} (0.99 A) and Na^+ (0.95 A)—the ion with the higher charge will have the greater hydration energy: Ca^{++} -395 kcal/mole; Na^+ -104 kcal/mole. Furthermore, of two metal ions of the same charge and size, the one with a non-symmetrical electron configuration has a greater hydration energy than the one with a noble-gas electron configuration. For example, Cu^+: [Ar]$3d^{10}$; radius, 0.95 A; $\Delta H_{hydration}$, -115 kcal/mole; and Na^+: [Ne]; radius, 0.95 A; $\Delta H_{hydration}$, -104 kcal/mole.

	Ionic Radius, A	$\Delta H_{hydration}$, kcal/mole
Li^+	0.60	-130
Na^+	0.95	-104
K^+	1.33	-84
Rb^+	1.48	-78
Cs^+	1.69	-70

NEGATIVE IONS. A hydrated negative ion in aqueous solution is surrounded by water molecules in hydration zones just as a positive ion is. However, in the first sphere the water molecules in direct contact with the anion X^{-n} are oriented so that their partially positive hydrogen atoms are in contact with the negative central X^{-n} ion. (It is not known whether one or two H atoms of each H_2O molecule are in contact with the X^{-n} ion, that is, whether one only or both or a combination.) Because of the electrostatic attraction of the central negative X^{-n} ion for the hydrogen atoms of water, the oxygen atoms of H_2O molecules have a greater partial negative charge in this first sphere than in pure liquid water. In the second larger hydration sphere, the water molecules are oriented so that their partially positive hydrogen atoms are directed toward the oxygen atoms of the water molecules of the first sphere. Again, the oxygen atoms of H_2O molecules in the second sphere have a greater partial negative charge than those of pure water, even though not as much as those of the H_2O molecules of the first sphere. Thus the central negative ion, X^{-n}, influences directly the first sphere of water molecules and indirectly the second sphere, and also some of the outer spheres of water molecules. At a sufficient distance, the water molecules surrounding a negative ion are unaffected by its negative charge, and exist in the short-ordered arrangement typical of pure water.

When a hydrated negative ion migrates in solution, it tends to carry with it the water molecules in direct contact (first hydration sphere) as well as some of the water molecules of the next spheres. For a negative ion, as for a positive ion, the total energy of the interaction with all the surrounding water molecules will depend on the size, charge, and electron configurations of the negative ion. For example, in the family of mononegative halogen ions, X^-, each having a s^2p^6 (noble gas) outer electron configuration, the hydration energy decreases inversely as the ionic size increases, as shown in the table. The hydration energy of a negative ion, like that of a positive ion, increases with the charge/radius ratio.

	Ionic Radius, A	$\Delta H_{\text{hydration}}$, kcal/mole
F^-	1.36	−113
Cl^-	1.81	− 81
Br^-	1.95	− 73
I^-	2.16	− 62

These considerations hold for solutions of all ionic compounds. In general, the electrostatic attraction exerted by each positive ion and negative ion on the surrounding zones of oriented water molecules is the solution counterpart of the electrostatic attraction exerted in the crystalline $M^{+n}X^{-n}$ by each ion on the surrounding ions of opposite charge. Thus, as we have pointed out, the hydration energy of an ionic compound in solution may be considered to be the counterpart of its lattice energy in the crystal.

SOLID SOLUTIONS

Solutions of gases and liquids in solids are known, but by far the more numerous and practically important solid solutions are those of solids in solids; this category includes the *alloys* (mixtures of two or more metals). The characteristic feature of solid solutions, as compared with gases and liquids, is that the particles—molecules, atoms, or ions—occupy fixed relative positions in a rigid three-dimensional lattice. Therefore, a solid can act as a solvent only when the particles of the solute can be accommodated in the lattice of the solvent, usually by substituting for particles of the solvent but without causing too marked a distortion in the host lattice. For example, the metals silver, Ag, and gold, Au, have the same metallic radius (1.44 A) and the same type (face-centered cubic) of metallic lattice, so silver and gold are miscible in all proportions to form solid solutions, and the enthalpy change, ΔH_{soln}, is very small. Aluminum(III) oxide, Al_2O_3, and chromium(III) oxide, Cr_2O_3, are also soluble in one another in varying proportions, since both have the same type of ionic lattice (*corundum*, Al_2O_3, structure; cation:anion crystal coordination = 6:4), and the Al^{+3} and Cr^{+3} ions have the same ionic charge and similar radii (Al^{+3} = 0.50 A; Cr^{+3} = 0.60 A). Solutions containing less than 8 per cent of Cr_2O_3 in Al_2O_3 constitute the so-called "ruby."

The energy factors involved in the formation of solid solutions from their solid components are essentially the same as for the other types of solutions we have considered in the preceding sections. The major difference between solid solutions and liquid solutions is that the mobility of the particles in a solid solution is extremely limited. At room temperature, the rate of diffusion of particles in the solid state is quite small. Thus the formation of a solid alloy from its solid components may not be appreciable at all, even if the process is thermodynamically favorable. In effect, solid solutions are generally prepared by mixing the components when molten and then cooling the mixture until it crystallizes to give a homogeneous solid.

18-7 Saturated, Unsaturated, Supersaturated Solutions

As we have seen in the preceding sections, in defining a "saturated solution" the key term is *equilibrium*. *A saturated solution is one in which an equilibrium exists between the undissolved solute (gaseous, liquid, or solid) and the solute present in solution.* The concentration of the solute in the solution at equilibrium is the solubility of the solute in the solvent at that given temperature. *The solubility of any substance (gas, liquid, or solid) does not depend on the amount of excess solute that is in contact with the solution. In fact, the same equilibrium concenration is found in a saturated solution whether a very small or a very large amount of the undissolved solute is in contact with the solution.*

If a solution contains less dissolved solute than the equilibrium concentration, the solution is *unsaturated*. In an unsaturated solution, the amount of solute present in solution may vary from a mere trace to a concentration just under that of a saturated solution. Of course, there is no excess undissolved solute in contact with an unsaturated solution, or else some of the excess solute would dissolve and equilibrium would eventually be attained.

A solution that contains more solute than is present at equilibrium under similar experimental conditions is *supersaturated*. Such a solution is not stable, especially when in contact with any undissolved solute. In fact, supersaturated solutions tend to reach a state of equilibrium; upon standing, some of the solute will eventually separate out of solution and the concentration of the solution will attain the saturation value. However, without a disturbance or some solid in contact a supersaturated solution may remain so for quite a long time.

A supersaturated solution and an unsaturated solution are similar in that neither has the equilibrium concentration. However, an unsaturated solution cannot, by itself, attain the equilibrium state (saturated) because there is not enough solute in the system, whereas a supersaturated solution can, and usually will, spontaneously attain the equilibrium state, simply by giving off the excess of dissolved solute. Thus unsaturated solutions exist only because of a lack of solute in the system, whereas supersaturated solutions exist because the change: supersaturated solution $\longrightarrow$ saturated solution + undissolved solute, even though thermodynamically favorable, may involve a relatively high activation energy (Ch. 26) and so will occur only very slowly.

In comparisons of saturated, unsaturated, and supersaturated solutions, the saturated solution is regarded as the standard of reference, because both an unsaturated and a supersaturated solution will tend to form a saturated solution when conditions permit. For example, when crystals of a salt are added to an unsaturated solution or to a supersaturated solution of the salt, both tend to approach equilibrium conditions. The *unsaturated* solution approaches equilibrium by *dissolving* some crystals and the *supersaturated* solution approaches equilibrium by *depositing* some crystals.

Supersaturated solutions of gases in liquids are quite common. Carbonated beverages, for example, are supersaturated solutions of carbon dioxide in water under relatively high pressure. When the bottles are uncapped, some of the gas escapes, but the remaining solution can remain supersaturated with respect to the dissolved carbon dioxide for some time. Supersaturated solutions of solid substances can be obtained by slowly evaporating the solvent from an unsaturated solution, or lowering the temperature of an unsaturated solution, provided no solid solute is in contact with the solution. Some substances readily form supersaturated solutions, others form supersaturated solutions only under carefully controlled experimental conditions.

18-8 Dynamic Equilibrium

We have often used the concept of equilibrium in our discussions. In every case we have stated that once a system has reached a state of equilibrium the quantity, physical state, and intensive properties of each substance present in the system remain constant. Notice that this statement mentions only macroscopic—or bulk—properties of the system; it does not give us a microscopic—or molecular—interpretation of what actually happens in a system in a state of equilibrium.

Let us now consider an experiment which can help us to obtain a microscopic picture of a system in equilibrium. Let us assume that we have a saturated solution of potassium chloride in water at 25°C and 1 atm, in the presence of an excess of crystalline $K^+Cl^-_{(s)}$. The system is in equilibrium, and the concentration of the solution remains constant at 35 grams/liter. Now we add to the system a small quantity of solid potassium chloride, containing some radioactive chloride ions, indicated as $\overset{*}{Cl}{}^-$. After some time, we examine both the solution and the crystalline KCl in contact with it. We find that the solution still contains 35 g/l. of KCl but now it too is radioactive. Some of the radioactive $\overset{*}{Cl}{}^-$ of the newly added $K\overset{*}{Cl}_{(s)}$ must have passed into solution even though the solution was already saturated with K^+ and Cl^-. Simultaneously, some of the non-radioactive Cl^- formerly present in the saturated solution must have crystallized out. And, if the system stands a sufficiently long time, we will find that the radioactive $\overset{*}{Cl}{}^-$ will be distributed uniformly not only through the solution but also through the solid in contact with it. In addition, at equilibrium the ratio, radioactive $\overset{*}{Cl}{}^-$/total Cl^-, will be the same in the solution as it is in the crystals. The results would be similar if we added to the original saturated solution a small quantity of KCl containing radioactive potassium ions $\overset{*}{K}{}^+$. Again we would find that the radioactive $\overset{*}{K}{}^+$ distributes itself uniformly throughout the solution and the solid in contact with it, even though the total potassium ion concentration in solution remains constant.

We can therefore conclude that when a saturated solution is in the presence of its solid solute, the solute indeed continuously dissolves but an equal quantity of the dissolved solute simultaneously crystallizes out. *The dissolving and crystallization processes occur at the same rate, so no net change in the concentration of the solution is observed.* But if we label some particles of the solid with a radioactive species, then we can observe experimentally this continuous process of dissolution and simultaneous crystallization by following how the labeled species becomes uniformly distributed throughout the system. Or, as chemists say, we can follow the *exchange* of the labeled species between solid and saturated solution.

It is important to note, here, that the exchange of a labeled (for example, radioactive) species occurs because the ΔH term of the exchange is zero (the radioactive species has the same chemical properties as the non-radioactive one), so that from the enthalpy viewpoint it is the same to have a non-radioactive as a radioactive species in the solution or in the lattice. But since the entropy term favors the most random distribution of every particle of the system, the exchange reaction proceeds until both the radioactive and the non-radioactive species are uniformly distributed throughout the entire system, in both solution and solid.

We must always keep in mind that when a solution is in equilibrium with its solute, there is a continuous exchange of the species of the solute between the undissolved solute and the saturated solution. This exchange does not result in a concentration change although, as we have seen, it can be observed experimentally by labeling the solute. This concept of *dynamic equilibrium* is fundamental to an understanding of all solutions, as well as of many other phenomena to be discussed in the following chapters.

18-9 The Rate and Mechanism of Dissolution

In the preceding sections we have found it convenient to consider the dissolution of a solute into a solvent of different physical state in two successive steps: (1) The solute assumes the same physical state as the solvent, and (2) the solute and the solvent, now both in the same physical state, mix to form a molecular dispersion. It is important to emphasize that these two steps are imaginary. They are of interest only because they help us understand the various energy factors involved in the formation of a solution.

The mechanism by which a solute dissolves in a solvent of different physical state does not, in general, follow those two steps. Rather, the dissolution process involves the direct passage of the molecules of the solute from the physical state of the solute itself to the physical state of the solution. As you may expect, this process takes place at the surface of contact between the solute and the solvent. As an illustration, we shall now consider briefly a likely mechanism by which solids dissolve in liquid solvents.

COVALENT SOLIDS. We will use as our example the covalent solid, iodine. In the process of dissolving, which is indicated by the symbol, $\longrightarrow$, in Fig. 18-2, the water molecules come into contact with the iodine molecules at the surface of the iodine crystals, and by surrounding them exert maximum attraction. These surface iodine molecules then leave the crystal lattice and pass into solution as hydrated iodine molecules, $I_{2(aq)}$. This process of dissolving continues as new layers of I_2 molecules become the crystal surfaces exposed to the water molecules. Since iodine has a large and hence readily polarizable electron cloud, it is reasonable to assume that the partially positive hydrogen atoms of the polar water molecule will be in contact with the iodine molecule in the hydrated $I_{2(aq)}$ molecule. However, it is not known with certainty how the H_2O molecules are oriented about the I_2 molecule in the hydration sphere of $I_{2(aq)}$, or how many H_2O molecules are in direct contact with each I_2 molecule.

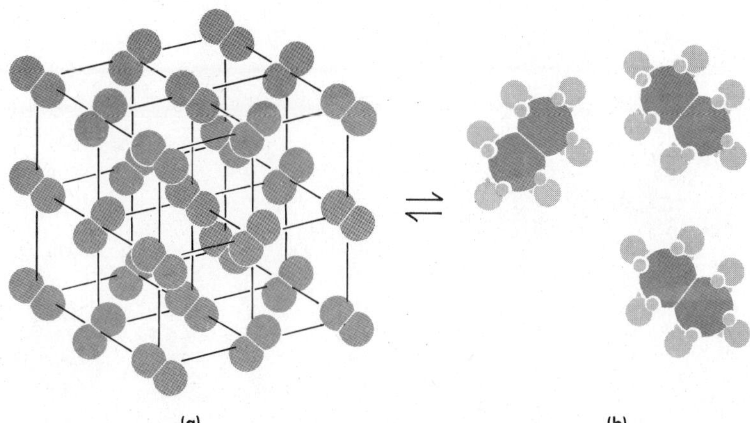

FIGURE 18-2 Schematic representation of a crystal of iodine dissolving in water. (a) Iodine crystal. (b) Hydrated iodine molecules in solution.

Once the hydrated iodine molecules have entered into solution, they gradually diffuse away from the region surrounding the crystals and distribute themselves uniformly throughout the solution. Some of the hydrated iodine molecules, $I_{2(aq)}$ in their random motion within the solution, eventually come again into contact with the surface of the crystals of iodine still present. When this occurs, the iodine molecules, I_2, may separate themselves from the water molecules of the hydration sphere and attach themselves to the surface of the iodine crystal. This crystallization process is represented by the symbol $\longleftarrow$ in Fig. 18-2.

When the solution achieves equilibrium, the rate at which the iodine molecules are leaving the crystal lattice of solid iodine is equal to the rate at which iodine molecules are leaving the solution and redepositing themselves on the crystal lattice. This state of dynamic equilibrium is represented by the symbols $\rightleftharpoons$ in Fig. 18-2.

IONIC SOLIDS. As an example of the mechanism by which an ionic solid dissolves in a polar solvent, let us consider the dissolution of potassium chloride, KCl, in water. When potassium chloride, K^+Cl^-, comes into contact with water, the positively charged potassium ions on the surface of the crystal become surrounded by the partially negative oxygen atoms of the polar water molecules. Similarly, the negatively charged Cl^- ions of the crystal become surrounded by the partially positive hydrogen atoms of the polar water molecules. The attraction of the K^+ ions for the oxygen atoms of water, and of the Cl^- ion for the hydrogen atom of water, is strong enough to compete successfully with the ionic attraction which holds together the oppositely charged ions in the lattice. The K^+ and Cl^- ions detach themselves from the crystal lattice, Fig. 18-3, pass into solution as hydrated ions, $K^+{}_{(aq)}$ and $Cl^-{}_{(aq)}$, and diffuse away from the crystal, tending to distribute themselves uniformly throughout the solution. A new layer of alternating K^+ and Cl^- ions becomes exposed on the surface of the undissolved crystalline K^+Cl^-, and the process of dissolution proceeds. Eventually, some of the hydrated ions in solution will again come into contact with the undissolved crystalline K^+Cl^-. The positive K^+ and negative Cl^- ions can then detach themselves from the surrounding water molecules of the hydrated $K^+{}_{(aq)}$ and $Cl^-{}_{(aq)}$ and redeposit on the crystal lattice. At first, when solid potassium chloride is added to water, more K^+ and Cl^- ions leave the crystal lattice at each moment than are returning to it. Gradually, as the concentration of ions in solution increases, the rate of crystallization and that of dissolving approach each other. When the solution becomes saturated, the rates of dissolution and crystallization become equal, and equilibrium is established.

To summarize: in a *saturated* solution of a solid in a liquid, the rate at which the molecules or ions leave the solid and pass into solution is equal to the rate at which they return to the solid. In an *unsaturated* solution of a solid in contact with the solid

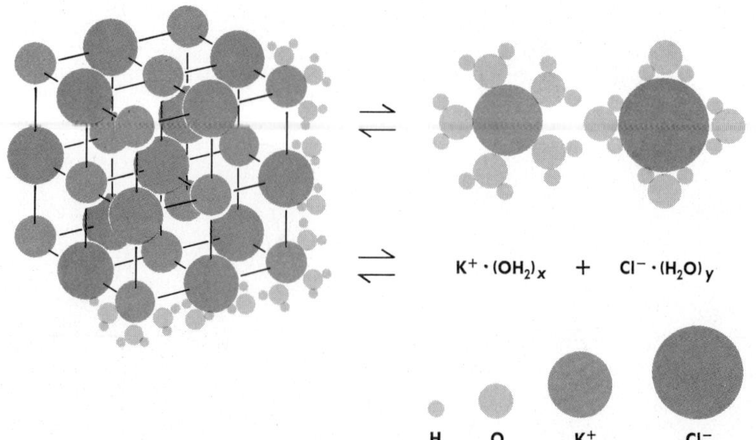

FIGURE 18-3 Schematic representation of a crystal of KCl dissolving in water.

solute, the molecules or ions pass into solution more rapidly than they crystallize out of solution. The two rates gradually approach one another until the solution becomes saturated. At that point they become (are) equal, and dissolution stops occurring as a bulk process.

When a crystal of an ionic solid is added to a *supersaturated* solution, some of the solute crystallizes out because now the dissolved particles find a preformed lattice surface on which they can deposit themselves. Initially the rate of crystallization is greater than the rate of solution; in a very short time, however, equilibrium is established and the two rates become equal.

18-10 Diffusion in Liquid Solution

When a substance dissolves in a liquid the particles of the solute (molecules or ions) diffuse uniformly throughout the entire available volume of the solution much in the same way as the molecules of gases diffuse spontaneously to occupy uniformly all available space. As an example, suppose we have two containers, A and B, separated by a stopcock and filled to the same level, B with pure water and A with a uniform purple aqueous solution of potassium permanganate, $K^+ + MnO_4^-$. (The purple color of solid $K^+MnO_4^-$ and of its water solution is a property of the MnO_4^- ion; the K^+ ion is colorless.) As soon as we open the stopcock we observe that the purple solution in A gradually becomes paler while the solution in B gradually assumes a purple color; actually we can see the color diffuse through the stopcock. Ultimately, the solutions in both A and B will become a uniform red color, indicating that the colored MnO_4^- ions have spontaneously distributed themselves evenly throughout the entire solution. Analysis, or the use of radioactively labeled K^+ ions, shows that the colorless K^+ ions have also distributed themselves uniformly throughout the entire solution. Furthermore, by labeling the water in one of the containers—say, the pure water in B—with molecules containing ^{18}O instead of the common isotope of oxygen, ^{16}O, we can detect that the molecules of the solvent, too, diffuse spontaneously from one container to the other, until maximum randomness of the distribution of all species present —K^+, MnO_4^-, $H_2(^{16}O)$ and $H_2(^{18}O)$—is reached.

We can understand the diffusion of substances in solution on the basis of the same considerations used to explain the diffusion of gases (p. 135). In a liquid solution both the particles (ions, molecules) of the solute and those of the solvent are in continuous random motion. Thus each ion (K^+ and MnO_4^-) and molecule (H_2O) in container A which is close to the stopcock opening has a chance to pass into B. Once entered into B, these ions and molecules from A will diffuse in all directions, in the continuously shifting motion characteristic of the particles of liquids. Similarly, each H_2O molecule near the stopcock opening in container B has a chance to pass into A. And once there, this water molecule will diffuse through the other water molecules of A in its continuously shifting, ceaseless motion. The net result of the exchange between the two containers of all the particles present in solution is, at the beginning, a flow of the solute particles, the K^+ and MnO_4^- ions, from A into B. Then as the concentration of the K^+ and MnO_4^- ions inside B gradually increases, so does the number of these ions which have a chance of returning to container A. As time passes, the *net rate* of flow of the solute particles from A to B decreases, that is the rate at which the K^+ and MnO_4^- ions enter B from A gradually approaches that at which the K^+ and MnO_4^- ions return from B to A. Finally, equilibrium is attained when the rates of departure and return become equal, when the concentration of the solute in A and B is the same. From then on, *no further concentration change results from the continuous exchange of solute and solvent particles between A and B.*

This process of diffusion is a result of the chance behavior of each individual particle of the solution (solvent and solute alike), which, as you will recall, is analogous to the process of diffusion of gases. There is, however, one important difference. In their motion, the particles of a liquid remain in continuous contact and interact strongly with a certain number of neighbors, even though such neighbors may continuously change. Thus a molecule or ion in solution will travel only a very short distance in a certain direction before being influenced to change its course by interactions with other molecules. These interactions explain the relatively slow diffusion of particles in liquids, as compared with the very rapid diffusion of gases, whose molecules are relatively far apart from one another and hence are subjected to weaker intermolecular attractions.

The final equilibrium state for any diffusion process is a homogeneous solution—a solution, that is, in which the distribution of the particles has attained maximum randomness. Diffusion is a spontaneous process for all solutions, and the driving force for the diffusion is provided by the favorable entropy change. Generally there is no appreciable total enthalpy change associated with a diffusion process.

18-11 Factors that Influence the Rate of Dissolution

When a solute is brought into contact with a solvent, the rate of dissolution depends on four factors: (1) the nature of the solute and solvent, (2) the particle size of the solute, (3) the temperature, and (4) the extent to which the solute-solvent mixture is agitated. Since, as we shall see in Chapter 25, these are the chief factors in determining the rate of any heterogeneous process, let us briefly discuss each of them.

1. *Nature of the Solute and Solvent.* As we know, the mixing of two gases is almost instantaneous. The dissolution of two completely miscible liquids is also very fast, but the dissolution of two partially miscible liquids into one another may require a considerable time to reach equilibrium conditions (saturation). The dissolution of liquids and solids in gases and of solids in liquids always requires an appreciable time to reach equilibrium. In these cases, the rate of dissolution varies greatly for various solutes in various solvents. It is not possible, however, to make any generalization about the relation between rate of dissolution and the nature of the solutes and solvents.

2. *Particle Size of the Solute.* The more finely divided the solute is, the greater its rate of dissolution. In order for the solution process to take place at all, the particles (molecules or ions) of the solute and those of the solvent must come into contact. Clearly, then, the larger the contact surface between solute and solvent, the faster will be the rate at which dissolution occurs.

3. *Temperature of the Solution.* A rise in temperature always increases the *rate* of dissolution of any solute in any solvent. The concentration of a solution at saturation (equilibrium) may increase or decrease with the temperature (see section 18-12), but in all cases the state of equilibrium is attained more *rapidly* at higher than at lower temperatures. An increase in temperature increases the rate of dissolution through two cooperative effects: (1) it increases the kinetic energy of the particles of the solute, which therefore have a better chance of escaping the attractions of their like molecules in the pure solute and pass into solution, and (2) it increases the kinetic energy of the particles of the solution (solvent and solute alike) and thus increases the rate of diffusion of the solute throughout the solution until a uniform saturated solution is attained.

4. *Extent to which the Mixture Is Agitated.* When a mixture of solute and solvent is agitated, the solute is brought into more effective contact with the solvent, and the rate of solution is increased. Agitating the mixture increases the contact surface between solute and solvent. For example, if the mixture of a solid and a liquid

solvent is agitated, the crystals of the solid solute do not settle down at the bottom of the container, so that some are covered by others, but each crystal is constantly surrounded by the liquid. Moreover, agitating the solution speeds up the uniform distribution of the dissolved ions or molecules throughout the solution and thus reduces the time required to attain saturation. If the solution is not agitated, the layer of solution in immediate contact with the particles of the solute soon becomes saturated, and further dissolution of the solute then occurs only as fast as the already dissolved particles diffuse from this saturated layer towards regions of the solution which are as yet unsaturated. In other words, the rate of dissolution would be dependent on the rate of diffusion. Agitation of the solution exposes the surface of the solute to fresh parts of the solution, and thus avoids the retarding effects of ordinary diffusion.

18-12 Solubility and Temperature

We have seen that dissolution of a solute (gas, liquid, or solid) in a solvent is generally accompanied by an enthalpy change. Experiments indicate that, whenever the dissolution of a given solute in a given solvent is accompanied by the evolution of heat (ΔH_{soln} is negative), the solubility of that solute in that solvent decreases as the temperature increases. Conversely, if ΔH_{soln} is positive, that is, if heat is absorbed in the dissolution process, the solubility of the solute in the solvent increases as the temperature rises. As we shall see later on, this behavior is explained on the basis of Le Chatelier's Principle in Chapter 24. There is no simple equation by which we can express the relationship between the solubility of a given solute in a given solvent and the temperature; solubility-temperature relationships are commonly represented by experimentally determined graphs, in which solubility is plotted against temperature. Such graphs, examples of which are shown in Figs. 18-4 and 18-5 are called *solubility-temperature curves* or simply *solubility curves.*

A common type of solubility curve is shown in Fig. 18-4; this curve of the solubility of potassium nitrate, KNO_3, in water steepens as the temperature rises. At any given temperature, the solubility of KNO_3 in water has a definite value which can be experimentally determined. At 60°C, for example, a saturated solution of potassium nitrate will contain 108 g of KNO_3 per 100 g of water.

Any point of the solubility curve represents a saturated solution of KNO_3 in water, with the concentration shown by the ordinate and the temperature shown by the abscissa. Any point in the region *under* the curve represents the concentration of an unsaturated solution with the specified concentration and temperature. For example, the point marked x(1) represents an unsaturated solution containing 68 g of KNO_3 dissolved in 100 g of water at 65°C. If the temperature of this solution is gradually lowered, as shown by the broken horizontal line leading left from point x(1), the solution will reach saturation at 42°C. If we continue to lower

FIGURE 18-4 Solubility-temperature curve of KNO_3 in water.

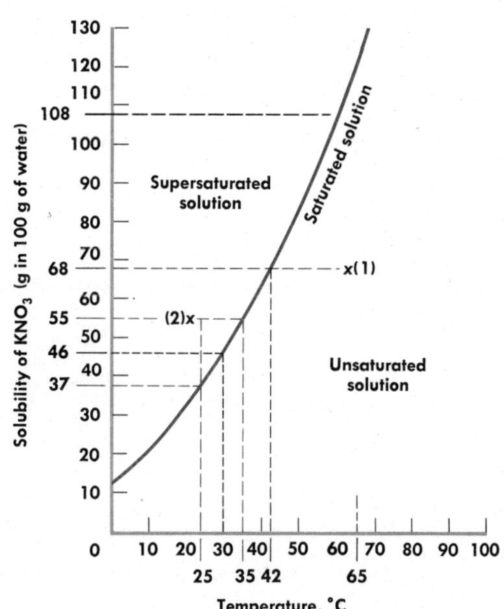

the temperature, KNO_3 will begin to crystallize out of solution. While KNO_3 crystallizes and the temperature decreases, the remaining solution continues to be saturated (even though it does contain less and less dissolved KNO_3) and its concentration is, for each value of the temperature, what is specified by the solubility curve. If, for example, we cool the solution to 30°C, 46 g of KNO_3 will remain in solution, whereas 22 g (68 − 46 = 22 g) of crystalline KNO_3 will separate out of solution.

Similarly, any point in the region *above* the curve represents a supersaturated solution, with the specified concentration and temperature. For example, at the point marked (2)x, the solution would contain 55 g of KNO_3 dissolved in 100 g of water at 25°C, whereas the saturation temperature for this concentration is 35°C. If we were to add a crystal of solid KNO_3 to this supersaturated solution at 25°C, the excess of KNO_3 (55 g − 37 g = 18 g) would suddenly crystallize out of solution, and the concentration of the solution would fall to that of a saturated solution at this temperature (37 g of KNO_3 is 100 g of water). The solubility curves of potassium chloride, KCl; sodium chloride, NaCl; potassium nitrate, KNO_3; sodium sulfate, Na_2SO_4; sodium sulfate decahydrate, $Na_2SO_4 \cdot 10\ H_2O$; and sodium nitrate, $NaNO_3$, are given in Fig. 18-5.

CRYSTALLIZATION FROM SOLUTIONS

Crystalline solids can generally be obtained from their solutions by decreasing the amount of solvent present. If the solvent is volatile—water, for example —evaporation will decrease the amount of solvent present in the solution; thus, when sea water or mineral waters evaporate, the dissolved salts are left behind as crystals. If the solubility of a substance decreases with a fall in temperature, we can bring about crystallization by cooling the solution. The solubility curve for the substance considered will indicate the temperature to which a given solution must be cooled before crystallization will begin; it will also tell whether cooling will be an effective means for obtaining good yields of crystals. For example, cooling will effectively crystallize KNO_3 from its aqueous solutions, for the solubility of KNO_3 decreases markedly with a fall in temperature. On the other hand, cooling would be less suitable for crystallizing KCl from its aqueous solutions, because the solubility of KCl decreases only slightly as temperature is lowered. And lowering the temperature of the solution would be no practical use in the crystallization of NaCl, because the solubility of this salt is almost independent of temperature.

FIGURE 18-5 Solubility-temperature curves of some ionic solids in water.

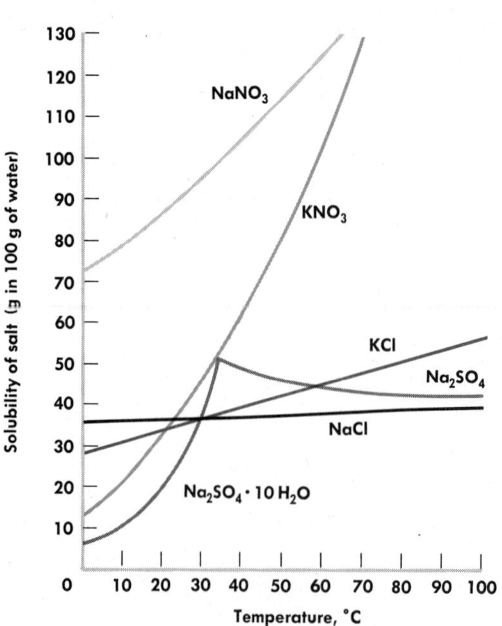

PURIFICATION OF SALTS BY CRYSTALLIZATION. A knowledge of solubility curves is useful when we want to free a salt from small amounts of impurities. Here is an example: Suppose we have some solid KNO_3 contaminated with a small amount—say, 1 per cent—of $NaNO_3$. The solubility curves in Fig. 18-5 show us that at 10°C, $NaNO_3$ is about four times more soluble than KNO_3. So if we dissolve 100 g of impure KNO_3 in 100 g of hot water and then cool the solution to 10°C, the graph shows that 79 g of pure KNO_3 will crystallize out while the 1 g of $NaNO_3$ will remain in solution together with 20 g of unrecovered KNO_3. If the crystals KNO_3 are removed and if we partially evaporate the solution at 10°C, more KNO_3 will crystallize out, substantially free of $NaNO_3$. Such purification of compounds by recrystallization is often used both in the laboratory and in industry.

EXERCISES

Exercises

18-1 (a) Give a general definition of the term "solution." (b) What is the general basis for the differentation between "solvent" and "solute" in a solution? (c) List the possible physical states of solutions, and specify how solutions can be classified according to the physical state of the solute.

18-2 (a) Give a definition of the term "ideal solution." (b) Discuss the energy factors involved in the formation of an ideal gaseous solution. (c) Two ideal gases mix spontaneously because (check one): (1) the enthalpy of mixing, ΔH_{mixing}, is favorable; (2) the ΔH_{mixing} is zero but the entropy of mixing, ΔS_{mixing}, is favorable; or (3) the ΔH_{mixing} is unfavorable but the ΔS_{mixing} is favorable and prevails.

18-3 On the basis of the equation $\Delta G = \Delta H - T\,\Delta S$, discuss the energy factors involved in the formation of a solution of two real gases.

18-4 (a) Explain the phenomenon of the "vapor pressure" of liquids and solids on the basis of the energy factors involved in the dissolution of solids and liquids in gases. (b) Explain why the vapor pressures of solid and liquid substances increase with increasing temperature.

18-5 (a) Hydrogen gas, H_2, is only slightly soluble in water, whereas hydrogen chloride gas, HCl, is very soluble. Explain. (b) Discuss the effect of the nature of a gas on its solubility in various solvents.

18-6 Give a reason why the solubility of all gases in water (a) decreases markedly with increasing temperature, and (b) increases proportionally to the pressure of the gas above the water.

18-7 The solubility of carbon dioxide in water at 20°C is (greater than, less than, the same as) its solubility at 40°C.

18-8 The solubility of oxygen in water at 760 torr is (greater than, less than, the same as) its solubility at 840 torr.

18-9 Give a general explanation why some liquids are completely miscible with one another, others are only partially miscible, whereas still others are completely immiscible.

18-10 When we bring together two partially miscible liquids—for example, water and diethylether—in relative amounts exceeding their mutual solubility limits, two liquid layers are obtained. These two layers consist of: (a) a saturated solution of diethylether in water and pure diethylether, (b) a saturated solution of water in diethylether and pure water, (c) a saturated solution of diethylether in water and a saturated solution of water in diethylether. Check one.

18-11 The liquid organic compound (normal) pentane $CH_3CH_2CH_2CH_2CH_3$ is insoluble in water, whereas the corresponding alcohol, (normal) 1-pentanol, $CH_3CH_2CH_2CH_2CH_2OH$, is somewhat soluble (~3 per cent at room temperature), even though the intermolecular forces acting among the molecules of n-pentane (boiling point, 36°C) are much weaker than those acting among the molecules of n-1-pentanol (boiling point 138°C). Explain in terms of the role played by the —OH group in pentanol.

18-12 Discuss (a) the energy factors, (b) the likely mechanism, and (c) the factors influencing the rate of the dissolution of a solid in a liquid.

18-13 Does the solubility of a solid in water vary appreciably with a change in (a) pressure? (b) temperature?

18-14 Solid iodine is only slightly soluble in water but is appreciably soluble in such non-polar liquids as carbon disulfide, CS_2, and carbon tetrachloride, CCl_4. Explain in terms of the molecular structure and intermolecular interactions of both the solute and the solvent.

18-15 Explain why liquid water is such a good solvent for ionic solids.

18-16 Briefly describe the structure of hydrated positive and negative ions in aqueous solution.

18-17 Sodium chloride, Na^+Cl^-, is insoluble in ethyl alcohol, whereas sodium tetraphenylborate, $Na^+[B(C_6H_5)_4]^-$, is very soluble. Give an explanation in terms of the lattice and hydration energies of the two ionic compounds.

18-18 The enthalpies of dissolution (kcal/mole) of the cesium halides in water are: CsF, −8.4; CsCl, +4.3; CsBr, +6.3; CsI, +8.2. Explain this trend in terms of the lattice energies of these salts and of the hydration energies of the halide ions. Explain why the difference in ΔH_{diss} between CsF and CsCl (4.1 kcal/mole) is greater than the differences between the other successive pairs of halides, CsCl–CsBr (2.0 kcal/mole) and CsBr–CsI (1.9 kcal/mole).

18-19 In general, under what conditions can a solid act as a solvent for another solid? Give two examples of solid solutions.

18-20 Define a "saturated," an "unsaturated," and a "supersaturated" solution and discuss each kind in relation to the equilibrium conditions between undissolved solute and solution.

18-21 What do we mean by the term "dynamic equilibrium"? Illustrate with an example involving a saturated solution.

18-22 Discuss briefly the phenomenon of diffusion in a liquid solution and compare it with the diffusion in the gaseous state. What effect will a rise in temperature have on the rate of diffusion in solution? Explain your answer.

18-23 Describe the changes which occur when the following solutions are slowly cooled: (a) an unsaturated aqueous solution of potassium nitrate, (b) a saturated aqueous solution of potassium nitrate, (c) a supersaturated aqueous solution of potassium nitrate.

18-24 Explain how you would determine the solubility of potassium nitrate in water at a given temperature.

18-25 Explain how you would obtain crystals of potassium permanganate from an aqueous solution of this compound.

18-26 How could you obtain one salt in good purity from a mixture of KNO_3 and KCl? Describe exactly what you would do, giving reference to the solubility curves of Figs. 18-4 and 18-5.

SOLUTIONS: II

19

In this chapter we shall consider some of the methods that are used to express the concentration of a solution, and we shall also discuss certain important properties of solutions that depend on the number rather than kind of particles present. We shall conclude with a survey of the properties and behavior of colloidal systems, which are closely related to solutions in many aspects.

19-1 Methods of Expressing Concentration of a Solution

Of the several methods of expressing the concentration of a solution that have been worked out, some of them in response to specialized needs in the laboratory or in industry, the following are the more commonly used.

WEIGHT/WEIGHT BASIS

One method is based on the relationship between *the weight of the solute and the weight of the solution itself.* Usually, we specify the number of grams of the solute that are dissolved in every 100 g of the solution, that is, the percentage, by weight, of the solute in the solution. For example, the concentration of a solution containing 5 g of NaCl in 95 g of water can be expressed as follows: 5 g/(95 g + 5 g) = 5/100 = 5% NaCl, by weight. Therefore in a 5 per cent by weight solution of NaCl, every 100 g of solution contain 5 g of NaCl and 95 g of water.

WEIGHT/VOLUME BASIS

Another way of expressing concentration is based on the *weight of the solute* dissolved in a *given volume of solvent*, which, for convenience, is taken as 100 ml. For example, 5 g of $AgNO_3$ dissolved in 100 ml of water produces a 5 per cent by weight-volume aqueous solution, on the basis of the weight of the solute and the volume of the solvent.

VOLUME/VOLUME BASIS

In expressing the concentration of a solution of one liquid in another liquid, we often use a method based on the volume of each liquid dissolved in the *total volume of the solution*. For example, a solution made by adding to 5 ml of alcohol enough water to make the *final volume of the solution* 100 ml is called a 5 per cent by volume solution of alcohol in water.

MOLE/VOLUME BASIS, MOLARITY

Another method of expressing the concentration of a solution is to specify the *number of moles of the solute* that are dissolved in *a given volume of solution*. For convenience, we specify the volume of solution as 1 l. (1,000 ml). There are two reasons why this method is particularly convenient: (1) chemical reactions occur according to a fixed ratio of the number of moles of the reactants, and (2) volumes of solutions are easily measured. Since the volume of a liquid is influenced by temperature, however, the concentration of a mole-volume basis changes somewhat as the temperature changes.

A solution that contains 1 mole of a solute dissolved in 1 l. of solution is known as a *1 molar solution*. Thus, a 1 molar solution of NaOH consists of 40 g of NaOH (1 mole = 40 g) dissolved in 1 l. of solution. The *molarity* of the solution is said to be 1, and is usually designated as 1 *M*, the symbol "*M*" being the abbreviation of molarity. The molarity is the ratio of the number of moles of the solute to the *volume* (expressed in liters) occupied by the solution. Thus, a solution prepared by (a) dissolving 20 g of NaOH in 0.5 l. of solution, or by (b) dissolving 4 g of NaOH in 100 ml of solution, or by (c) dissolving 0.040 g of NaOH in 1 ml of solution, all have the same concentration, and all are 1 *M* sodium hydroxide solutions. The expression "1 *M* NaOH," then, simply says that *if* 1 l. of the solution were present, it *would* contain 40 g of sodium hydroxide. The following calculations show that the concentration of these various solutions of NaOH is the same in each case:

$$\frac{40\text{ g}}{1\text{ l. solution}} = \frac{1\text{ mole}}{1\text{ l. solution}} = 1\text{ M}$$

$$\frac{20\text{ g}}{0.5\text{ l. solution}} = \frac{40\text{ g}}{1\text{ l. solution}} = \frac{1\text{ mole}}{1\text{ l. solution}} = 1\text{ M}$$

$$\frac{4\text{ g}}{100\text{ ml solution}} = \frac{4\text{ g}}{0.1\text{ l. solution}} = \frac{40\text{ g}}{1\text{ l. solution}} = \frac{1\text{ mole}}{1\text{ l. solution}} = 1\text{ M}$$

$$\frac{0.040\text{ g}}{1\text{ ml solution}} = \frac{0.040\text{ g}}{0.001\text{ l. solution}} = \frac{40\text{ g}}{1\text{ l. solution}} = \frac{1\text{ mole}}{1\text{ l. solution}} = 1\text{ M}$$

MOLE/WEIGHT BASIS, MOLALITY

In many kinds of chemical calculations, some of which we shall develop later in this chapter, it is convenient to express the concentration of a two-component (solute-solvent) solution as the number of moles of solute dissolved in 1,000 g of solvent. The concentration thus expressed is called "molality" (*m*). It has the advantage of being independent of temperature.

MOLE/MOLE BASIS, MOLE FRACTION

All the above methods of expressing concentration are used to some extent in chemistry. But a more fundamental and widely applicable method of expressing the concentration of solutions is to specify the *number of moles of the solute compared with the total number of moles of all the constituents of the solution*—the total thus includes the number of moles of the solute(s) plus the number of moles of the solvent. The fraction, no. moles of solute/total no. moles of solution, is called the *mole fraction* of the solute considered in the solution. For example, the mole fraction of NaOH in a solution produced by dissolving 40 g of NaOH in 1,800 g of water is:

$$\text{Mole fraction of NaOH} = \frac{40}{40} \Big/ \left(\frac{40}{40} + \frac{1{,}800}{18.0}\right) = 1/(1 + 100) = 1/101$$

Expressing concentrations as mole fractions is especially useful when we deal with certain properties of solutions. As we shall see later in this chapter, some properties can be correlated to the number of moles of both solute and solvent.

PREPARATION OF SOLUTIONS. We know that a 1 molar solution contains 1 mole of a solute dissolved in 1 l. of solution. But let us look more closely at the expression "1 l. of solution." When a solid, liquid, or gas is dissolved in a given volume of a liquid —say, water—the volume of the resulting solution is usually greater than the original volume of the solvent. But there are important exceptions to this general rule. When some substances are added to a given volume of a liquid (solvent), the volume of the resulting solution is *less than* the volume of the solvent alone. And a few solutes cause almost *no change* in the volume of the solvent. Because of these various possibilities we must measure the volume of the *resulting solution—not* the volume of the pure solvent—whenever we wish to prepare a solution with a specified weight-volume or mole-volume concentration (molarity). Chemists have worked out a method of preparation which insures that the resulting solution in each case will have the desired total volume. The most convenient way of doing so is this: We introduce the required quantity of solute into a flask which has a mark to indicate the desired, known volume, and then add some of the liquid solvent. We continue to add liquid, shaking the graduated flask occasionally, to dissolve the solute, until the volume mark is approached. Then we add more liquid drop by drop until the surface of the solution coincides with the mark that indicates the required volume. Finally, we put a stopper in the flask and shake it vigorously to make sure that the solution is homogeneous. Flasks of this kind, which have marks to indicate exactly a certain specified volume, are commonly called *graduated,* or *volumetric, flasks.*

For example, let us consider the preparation of 1 l. of a 1 *M* solution of a sugar, $C_6H_{12}O_6$ (1 mole = 180.16 g). To a liter flask we add 1 mole of sugar and enough water to dissolve the sugar. Then we add more water until the resulting solution has a volume of 1 l. We have thus prepared "1 l. of solution of 1 *M* concentration." Similarly, we can make up a 1 *M* solution of NaCl by introducing 1 mole (58.5 g) of NaCl into a graduated 1 l. flask and, again, adding water until the volume of the solution reaches 1 l. Figure 19-1 illustrates the preparation of a 1-molar solution of a sugar.

ILLUSTRATIVE PROBLEMS

PROBLEM. Calculate the molarity of a solution that contains 0.50 mole of a compound dissolved in 250 ml of solution.

SOLUTION.

$$\frac{0.50 \text{ mole}}{0.25 \text{ l.}} = \frac{2.0 \text{ moles}}{1 \text{ l.}} = 2.0 \text{ molar} = 2\ M$$

PROBLEM. Calculate the molarity of a solution that contains 10.0 g of HCl in 100.0 ml of solution. 1 mole of HCl = 36.5 g.

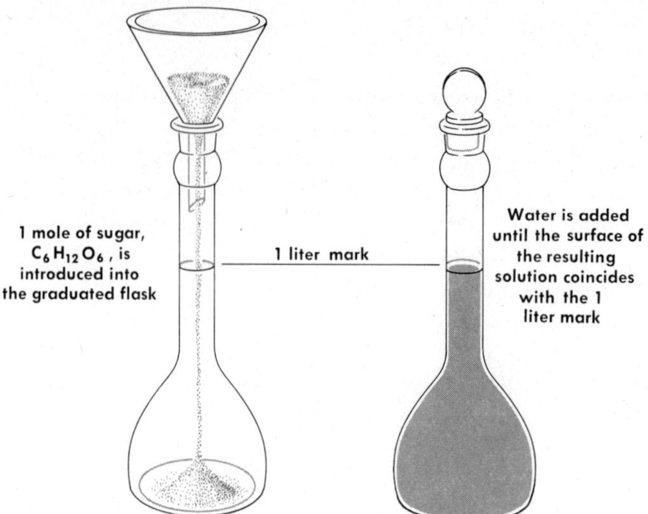
1 mole of sugar,
$C_6H_{12}O_6$, is
introduced into
the graduated flask
1 liter mark
Water is added
until the surface of
the resulting
solution coincides
with the 1
liter mark

FIGURE 19-1 The preparation of a 1 *M* solution of sugar.

SOLUTION. The concentration is $\frac{10.0\text{ g}}{100.0\text{ ml}}$; hence, it is necessary to convert (a) 10.0 g to moles, (b) 100.0 ml to liters.

(a) Conversion of grams to moles:

$$\frac{10.0\text{ g}}{36.5\text{ g/1 mole}} = 10.0\text{ g} \times \frac{1\text{ mole}}{36.5\text{ g}} = 0.274\text{ mole}$$

(b) Conversion of milliliters to liters:

$$\frac{100.0\text{ ml}}{1{,}000\text{ ml/1 l.}} = 100.0\text{ ml} \times \frac{1\text{ l.}}{1{,}000\text{ ml}} = 0.100\text{ l.}$$

(c) Combine to yield molarity:

$$\frac{0.274\text{ mole}}{0.100\text{ l.}} = \frac{2.74\text{ moles}}{1\text{ l.}} = 2.74\ M$$

After some practice, you can solve problems of this sort by combining (a), (b), and (c) in the following set-up:

$$\frac{\dfrac{10.0\text{ g}}{36.5\text{ g/1 mole}}}{\dfrac{100.0\text{ ml}}{1{,}000\text{ ml/1 l.}}} = \frac{10.0\text{ g} \times \dfrac{1\text{ mole}}{36.5\text{ g}}}{100.0\text{ ml} \times \dfrac{1\text{ l.}}{1{,}000\text{ ml}}} = 2.74\ \frac{\text{moles}}{\text{liter}} = 2.74\ M$$

PROBLEM. How many grams of NaCl are needed to prepare 400 ml of a 2 *M* solution? 1 mole of NaCl = 58.5 g.

SOLUTION. A 1 *M* solution contains exactly 1 mole/1 l.; a 1 *M* solution of NaCl contains 58.5 g/1 l.; hence, a 2 *M* solution of NaCl contains 2.00 × (58.5 g/1 l.). Since 2.00 × (58.5 g/1 l.) is the number of grams of NaCl present in 1 l. of 2 *M* solution, the number of grams present in 0.4 l. (400 ml) is 0.400 times this value:

$$2.00 \times (58.5\text{ g/1 l.}) \times 0.400\text{ l.} = 46.8\text{ g}$$

Thus, 46.8 g of NaCl are needed to prepare 400 ml of a 2 *M* solution.

PROBLEM. Calculate the molarity of a solution prepared by dissolving 54.5 g of $Na_2CO_3 \cdot 10\ H_2O$ in enough water to give the resulting solution a volume of 2.41 l. One mole of $Na_2CO_3 \cdot 10\ H_2O$ = 286 g.

SOLUTION. The number of grams of $Na_2CO_3 \cdot 10\ H_2O$ present in 1 mole of $Na_2CO_3 \cdot 10\ H_2O$ is 286 g/1 mole.

$$\frac{54.5\text{ g}}{286\text{ g/1 mole}} = 54.5\text{ g} \times \frac{1\text{ mole}}{286\text{ g}} = 0.190\text{ mole, the number of moles of } Na_2CO_3 \cdot 10\ H_2O \text{ present in 54.5 g of this compound}$$

Thus, $\frac{0.190 \text{ mole}}{2.41 \text{ l.}} = 0.0788 \frac{\text{mole}}{\text{l.}} = 0.0788\ M$

PROBLEM. If we start with 4.23 g of KNO_3 and add water, what must the final volume of the solution be for it to have a concentration of 0.2 *M*? One mole of KNO_3 = 101 g.

SOLUTION. Water must be added to the solution until the resulting solution contains 0.200 mole of KNO_3 per liter of solution. A 1 *M* solution of KNO_3 contains 101 g/1 l.; a 0.2 *M* solution contains 0.200 times this value—that is, $0.200 \times \frac{101 \text{ g}}{1 \text{ l.}}$ = the number of grams of solute in 1 l. of a 0.2 *M* solution; also, $\frac{1 \text{ l.}}{0.200 \times 101 \text{ g}}$ = the number of liters of 0.2 *M* solution that contains 1 g of KNO_3. Therefore, the number of liters of 0.2 *M* solution that contains 4.23 g of KNO_3 is

$$\frac{1 \text{ l.}}{0.200 \times 101 \text{ g}} \times 4.23 \text{ g} = 0.209 \text{ l.}$$

ALTERNATE SOLUTION.

$$\frac{4.2 \text{ g}}{101 \text{ g/1 mole}} = 4.2 \text{ g} \times \frac{1 \text{ mole}}{101 \text{ g}} = 0.0418 \text{ mole of } KNO_3$$

A 0.2 *M* solution is $\frac{0.200 \text{ mole}}{1 \text{ l.}}$ or, $\frac{1 \text{ l.}}{0.200 \text{ mole}}$ = 5, (number of liters of solution that contains 1 mole) and $\frac{1 \text{ l.}}{0.200 \text{ mole}} \times 0.0418 \text{ mole} = 0.209$ l. (number of liters of 0.2 *M* solution that contains 4.23 g of KNO_3).

CHANGES IN CONCENTRATION CAUSED BY ADDING OR REMOVING SOLVENT

Often we find it necessary to dilute a solution of known concentration, usually by adding more solvent to the solution. Conversely, if we want to increase the concentration, we remove some of the solvent. Changing the concentration of a solution by adding or removing some of the solvent is similar to changing the concentration of a gas by increasing or decreasing the volume. The solvent in a solution plays a role similar to that of the volume of a container that is filled by a gas. Decreasing the concentration of a solution by adding solvent, for example, is similar to decreasing the density of a gas by increasing the volume of the container. Also, increasing the concentration of a solution by removing some of the solvent is similar to increasing the concentration of a gas by decreasing the volume of the container.

To show the similarity between the method of calculating the change in the concentration of a solution produced by dilution, and the change in the density of a gas produced by increasing volume, we shall first consider a simple gas problem and then a similar problem involving the dilution of a solution.

ILLUSTRATIVE PROBLEMS

PROBLEM. The density of a gas is 1.4 g/l. Calculate the density of the gas if the temperature and pressure remain constant and the volume is increased from 200 ml to 800 ml.

SOLUTION. Since the new density will be less than the original density, the fraction to correct for the change in volume is "less than 1."

$$\frac{1.4 \text{ g}}{1 \text{ l.}} \times \frac{200 \text{ ml}}{800 \text{ ml}} = 0.35 \frac{\text{g}}{\text{l.}}$$

PROBLEM. An aqueous solution is 1.4 molar. If a 200 ml volume of the solution is diluted with water to 800 ml, calculate the new molarity of the solution.

SOLUTION. Since the molarity will be decreased by the addition of solvent, the correction fraction is "less than 1."

$$1.4\ M \times \frac{200 \text{ ml}}{800 \text{ ml}} = 0.35\ M$$

PROBLEM. To what volume must 150 ml of a gas with a density 0.12 g/l. be changed to decrease the density to 0.075 g/l. at the same temperature and pressure?

SOLUTION. Since the density is decreased, the volume of the gas must be increased, and the correction fraction must be "greater than 1."

$$150 \text{ ml} \times \frac{0.12 \text{ g/l.}}{0.075 \text{ g/l.}} = 240 \text{ ml}$$

PROBLEM. To what volume must 150 ml of a 0.12 molar solution be changed to decrease the concentration to 0.075 molar?

SOLUTION. Since the concentration is decreased, the volume of the solution must be increased, and the correction fraction must be "greater than 1."

$$150 \text{ ml} \times \frac{0.12\ M}{0.075\ M} = 240 \text{ ml}$$

19-2 Colligative Properties of Solutions

The vapor pressure, the boiling and freezing points, and the osmotic pressure of solutions are dependent only on the relative numbers of molecules (or ions) of the solute and of the solvent, provided the solutions are sufficiently dilute. Such properties, which depend only on the *number* of particles present and not on their kind, are called *colligative properties.*

VAPOR PRESSURE OF SOLUTIONS OF NON-VOLATILE SOLUTES. Each pure liquid solvent has a characteristic vapor pressure at any given temperature, as we learned in Chapter 10. The vapor pressure of many solid solutes, on the other hand, is negligible at the temperatures at which they are present in solutions. Such a solute is called a *non-volatile solute.* When a non-volatile solute is dissolved in a liquid solvent, the vapor pressure of the solvent in the resulting solution is always less than the vapor pressure of the pure solvent at the same temperature. Experiments have shown that the decrease in the vapor pressure of the solvent is proportional to the relative number of particles (molecules and ions) of the solute present in a given quantity of solvent. Consequently, the greater the concentration of the non-volatile solute, the greater the lowering of the vapor pressure of the solvent. In other words, at each temperature the tendency of the solvent molecules in a solution to pass from the liquid to the gaseous state decreases as the concentration of the non-volatile solute increases. Thus, at any given temperature, a pure solvent has a higher vapor pressure than a dilute solution, and a dilute solution, in turn, has a higher vapor pressure than a concentrated solution (Fig. 19-2).

What happens when we place a beaker containing a pure solvent and a beaker containing a solution of that solvent side by side in a closed container? Eventually all the pure solvent will pass from its own beaker into the beaker containing the solution (Fig. 19-3). In this figure, the passage of water molecules from a beaker of pure water, through the vapor phase, into a beaker containing an aqueous solution occurs because the vapor pressure (escaping tendency of the molecules) of the pure solvent is greater that that of the solution. Thus, the molecules of the pure solvent have a greater tendency to escape from the liquid to the vapor than have the solvent molecules from the solution.

FIGURE 19-2 The vapor pressure-temperature curves of a pure solvent, a dilute solution, and a concentrated solution.

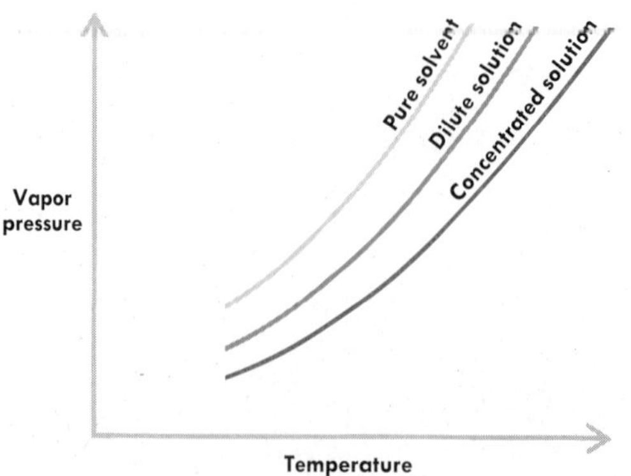

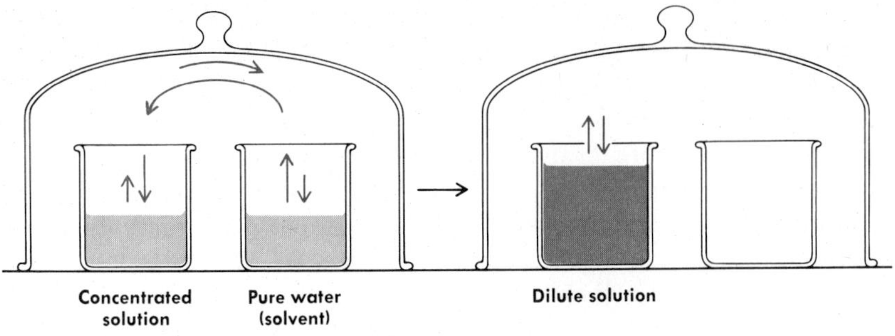

FIGURE 19-3 Schematic representation of the spontaneous passage of water molecules from pure water to an aqueous solution of a non-volatile solute.

The pure solvent and the solution are enclosed in the same container and share, so to speak, the same vapor. The pure solvent and the solution would each tend to establish equilibrium conditions with the vapor above. But since the pure solvent and the solution have different vapor pressures, this is not possible. The pure solvent continues to evaporate, tending to reach the equilibrium value of its vapor pressure, while the solution continues to condense some of the vapor, tending to reach the equilibrium value of its own lower vapor pressure. This spontaneous process continues until all the pure solvent has passed into the solution—only then can the dilute solution establish equilibrium conditions with the vapor inside the closed container.

This same spontaneous passage of solvent from one container to another, through the vapor phase, occurs if we place a beaker containing a dilute solution side by side in a closed container with a beaker containing a concentrated solution of the same non-volatile solute in the same solvent. The transfer of solvent molecules continues until the two solutions reach equal concentrations, as illustrated in Fig. 19-4. Only then is the escaping tendency of the solvent molecules in both beakers the same, and only then are the vapor pressures of the two solutions equal so that equilibrium can finally be attained.

In general, molecules of the solvent will pass from the solution with the higher vapor pressure (from which they have the greater escaping tendency) to the solution with the lower vapor pressure (from which they have the lesser escaping tendency) until the vapor pressures (the escaping tendencies) become equal. *Two solutions can co-exist in a state of equilibrium only when their vapor pressures are equal.* If the vapor pressures of the solutions are not equal, spontaneous changes will take place that tend to make them equal, so as to attain equilibrium.

BOILING POINTS OF SOLUTIONS. The boiling point of a liquid, as we learned earlier (p. 168), is the temperature at which the vapor pressure of the liquid is equal to the pressure of the atmosphere above it. And we know that the vapor pressure of a

FIGURE 19-4 The passage of solvent molecules from a dilute to a concentrated solution.

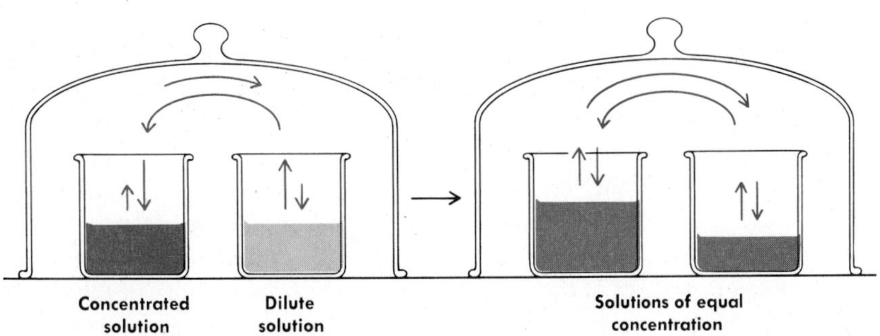

solution is always lower than the vapor pressure of the pure solvent. Consequently, the presence of a non-volatile solute makes the boiling point of a solution higher than that of the pure solvent. Both the solvent and the solution will boil when their vapor pressure is equal to the opposing atmospheric pressure, but this condition is reached at a higher temperature for the solution than for the pure solvent. The vapor pressure of pure water, for example, is 760 torr at 100°C; consequently, when the opposing pressure is 760 torr water boils at 100°C. The vapor pressure of a solution of a non-volatile solute, such as sugar, in water is *less than* 760 torr at 100°C, however; consequently, the solution will not boil at 100°C under an opposing pressure of 760 torr. To make the sugar solution boil, we must increase its vapor pressure to 760 torr. And we can do this only by raising the temperature of the solution above 100°C. The greater the concentration of the solute, the higher we must raise the temperature to make the solution boil. In other words, the boiling point of a solution of a non-volatile solute is always higher than the boiling point of the pure solvent. And the greater the concentration of the solute, the higher the boiling point of the solution.

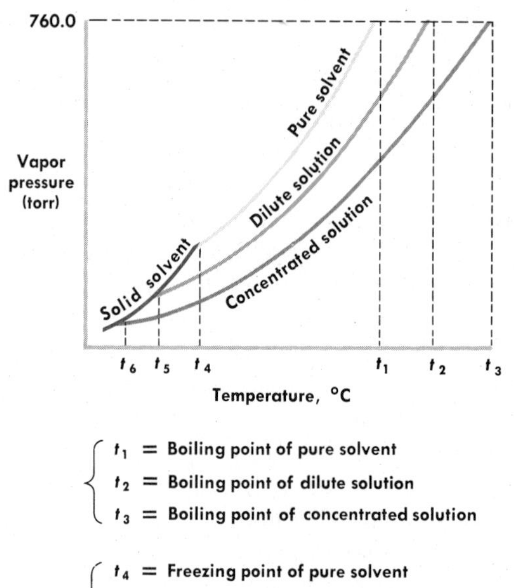

FIGURE 19-5 Vapor pressure, boiling points, and freezing points of a pure solvent, a dilute solution, and a concentrated solution.

The relationship between the vapor pressure and the boiling point of a pure solvent, a dilute solution, and a concentrated solution is shown by the curves in Fig. 19-5. Notice that the normal boiling point (the boiling point when the opposing pressure is 760 torr) of the pure solvent (t_1) is lower than the boiling point of the dilute solution (t_2), which, in turn, is lower than the boiling point of the concentrated solution (t_3). Also, at any given temperature, say t_1, the vapor pressure of the pure solvent (760.0 torr) is greater than the vapor pressure of the dilute solution (501.5 torr), which, in turn, is greater than the vapor pressure of the concentrated solution (268.2 torr).

19-3 Quantitative Treatment of Vapor Pressure, Boiling Point, and Freezing Point

In a solution made up of a non-volatile solute in a liquid solvent, a quantitative relationship exists between the amount of solute present and the extent to which the vapor pressure is lowered, and also the extent to which the boiling point is raised. For a sufficiently *dilute* solution of a non-volatile solute in a liquid solvent, how much the vapor pressure of the solvent is lowered and how much the boiling point is elevated depend only on the number of moles (or molecules) of the solute present in a fixed quantity of solvent. These changes do *not* depend on the *kind* of solute (small molecules, large molecules, ions) or on the *kind* of solvent (polar, non-polar). For a *concentrated* solution, the vapor pressure (and the boiling point) depends not only on the number of particles of the solute present in a given quantity of solvent, but also on the nature of the solute-solvent interactions. We shall limit our considerations to the simpler case of sufficiently dilute solutions. For an example of the difference, 0.1 mole of either fructose, $C_6H_{12}O_6$, or sucrose, $C_{12}H_{22}O_{11}$, both of which are non-volatile solutes, has exactly the same effect on the vapor pressure and the boiling point of 1 liter of water. But in more concentrated solutions, containing say 1 mole/liter, we would observe some minor difference on the effect of the two different solutes.

LIQUID SOLUTIONS OF NON-VOLATILE, NON-DISSOCIATED SOLUTES

VAPOR PRESSURE OF SOLUTIONS—RAOULT'S LAW. Let us look more closely at the relationship between the vapor pressure of a pure solvent, the vapor pressure of its solution, and the *number* of moles of *non-volatile, non-dissociated* solute that are present in the solution. If x moles of a non-volatile, non-dissociated solute dissolved in a given weight of a solvent lowers the vapor pressure a certain amount, then 2x moles of the same solute, or 2x moles of *any other* non-volatile, non-dissociated solute, dissolved in the same quantity of solvent, will lower the vapor pressure twice as much.

It has been found by experiment that at any given temperature, the vapor pressure, *P*, of a dilute solution from which only the pure solvent vaporizes is equal to the vapor pressure of the pure solvent, P^0, at that same temperature, multiplied by the mole fraction of the solvent:

$$P = P^0 \times \frac{n_1}{n_1 + n_2}$$

- P = the vapor pressure of the solution
- P^0 = the vapor pressure of the pure solvent
- n_1 = the number of moles of the solvent
- n_2 = the number of moles of the solute

This expression simply indicates that, for dilute solutions composed of a non-volatile solute and a volatile solvent, the vapor pressure is directly proportional to the mole fraction of the solvent, the proportionality constant being simply the vapor pressure of the pure solvent, P^0, at the same temperature. It is important to emphasize again that this statement, which is generally called *Raoult's Law* from the name of the French scientist who first formulated it in 1886, holds rigorously only for ideal solutions. As a first approximation, however, we can use it to calculate the vapor pressure of the solvent in very dilute non-ideal solutions.

ILLUSTRATIVE PROBLEMS

PROBLEM. Calculate the vapor pressure at 25°C of a solution containing 0.400 mole of sugar dissolved in 500 g of water. (Vapor pressure of water at 25°C is 23.5 torr.)

SOLUTION.

$$\text{v.p. water solution} = \text{v.p. of pure water} \times \frac{\text{moles of water}}{\text{moles of water} + \text{moles of sugar}}$$

$$\text{number of moles of } H_2O = \frac{500\text{ g}}{18.0\text{ g/1 mole}}$$

$$\text{v.p. solution} = 23.5\text{ torr} \times \frac{\dfrac{500\text{ g}}{18.0\text{ g/1 mole}}}{\left(\dfrac{500\text{ g}}{18.0\text{ g/1 mole}}\right) + 0.400\text{ mole}}$$

$$= 23.5\text{ torr} \times \frac{500\text{ g} \times \dfrac{1\text{ mole}}{18.0\text{ g}}}{\left(500\text{ g} \times \dfrac{1\text{ mole}}{18.0\text{ g}} + 0.400\text{ mole}\right)}$$

$$\text{v.p. solution} = 23.2\text{ torr}$$

PROBLEM. Calculate the vapor pressure at 80.2°C of a solution containing (exactly) 0.2 mole of a non-volatile non-dissociated solute dissolved in 250 g of benzene, C_6H_6 (1 mole = 78.1 g). The vapor pressure of benzene at 80.2°C is 760 torr.

SOLUTION.

$$\text{v.p. benzene solution} = \text{v.p. benzene} \times \frac{\text{moles of benzene}}{\text{moles of benzene} + \text{moles of solute}}$$

$$\text{number of moles of benzene} = \frac{250\text{ g}}{78.1\text{ g/1 mole}}$$

$$\text{v.p solution} = 760\text{ torr} \times \frac{\dfrac{250\text{ g}}{78.1\text{ g/1 mole}}}{\left(\dfrac{250\text{ g}}{78.1\text{ g/1 mole}}\right) + 0.200\text{ mole}}$$

$$= 760\text{ torr} \times \frac{250\text{ g} \times \dfrac{1\text{ mole}}{78.1\text{ g}}}{\left(250\text{ g} \times \dfrac{1\text{ mole}}{78.1\text{ g}}\right) + 0.200\text{ mole}}$$

$$\text{v.p. solution} = 718\text{ torr}$$

BOILING-POINT ELEVATION. We have already noted, in a qualitative way, that for a solution consisting of a non-volatile solute in a volatile solvent, the boiling point increases as the vapor pressure of the solution decreases—that is, as the mole fraction of the solute increases. On the basis of experiments, the following quantitative relationship has been worked out between the increase in boiling point and the concentration of the solution: The boiling-point elevation $\Delta t_{\text{b.p.}}$, of a solution is directly proportional to ($\propto$) the number of moles of non-volatile non-dissociated solute dissolved in 1,000 g of solvent:

$$\Delta t_{\text{b.p.}} \propto \frac{\text{moles of solute}}{\text{grams solvent}} \times 1{,}000\text{ g solvent}$$

$$\Delta t_{\text{b.p.}} = K_{\text{b.p.}} \times \frac{\text{moles of solute}}{\text{grams solvent}} \times 1{,}000\text{ g solvent}$$

or:

$$\Delta t_{\text{b.p.}} = K_{\text{b.p.}} \times \frac{\text{grams solute/mol wt solute}}{\text{grams solvent}} \times 1{,}000\text{ g solvent}$$

In these expressions, $K_{\text{b.p.}}$ is a proportionality constant, characteristic of the solvent. For example $K_{\text{b.p.}}$ for water is 0.52°C per mole of solute and is usually referred to as the *molal boiling-point elevation constant* for water. Thus, if 1 mole of any non-volatile non-dissociated solute is dissolved in 1,000 g of water, the boiling point of the solution is raised 0.52°C—that is, to 100.52°C. Similarly, 0.1 mole of a non-volatile non-dissociated solute dissolved in 100 g of water will also increase the boiling point of the solution by 0.52°C. Each solvent has its own boiling-point elevation constant. The $K_{\text{b.p.}}$ constants of four common solvents are given in Table 19.1.

TABLE 19-1 MOLAL BOILING-POINT ELEVATION CONSTANTS, $K_{\text{b.p.}}$

Solvent	Boiling Point at 1 atm	$K_{\text{b.p.}}$
Water	100°C	0.52°C/mole
Alcohol	78.3°C	1.15°C/mole
Acetone	56.5°C	1.67°C/mole
Benzene	80.2°C	2.67°C/mole

ILLUSTRATIVE PROBLEMS

PROBLEM. A solution contains 0.20 mole of glycerol (a non-volatile non-dissociated solute) dissolved in 500 g of water. Determine the normal boiling point (boiling point at 760 torr) of this solution.

SOLUTION. Normal b.p. of solution = b.p. of pure solvent + $\Delta t_{\text{b.p.}}$

$$\Delta t_{\text{b.p.}} = K_{\text{b.p.}} \times \frac{\text{moles solute}}{\text{grams solvent}} \times 1{,}000\text{ g solvent}$$

$$\Delta t_{b.p.} = \frac{0.52°C}{mole} \times \frac{0.20 \text{ mole}}{500 \text{ g } H_2O} \times 1{,}000 \text{ g } H_2O$$

$$\Delta t_{b.p.} = 0.21°C$$

Thus, the normal b.p. of the solution = 100.00°C + 0.21°C = 100.21°C.

PROBLEM. Find the normal boiling point of a solution that contains 27.0 g of the non-volatile non-dissociated solute sucrose, $C_{12}H_{22}O_{11}$ (mol. wt. = 342), dissolved in 150 g of water.

SOLUTION. Normal b.p. solution = b.p. pure solvent + $\Delta t_{b.p.}$

$$\Delta t_{b.p.} = K_{b.p.} \times \frac{\text{moles solute}}{\text{grams solvent}} \times 1{,}000 \text{ g solvent} \qquad \frac{\text{moles solute}}{\text{(sucrose)}} = \frac{27.0 \text{ g}}{342 \text{ g}/1 \text{ mole}}$$

$$\Delta t_{b.p.} = \frac{0.52°C}{mole} \times \frac{\frac{27.0 \text{ g}}{342 \text{ g}/1 \text{ mole}}}{150 \text{ g } H_2O} \times 1{,}000 \text{ g } H_2O$$

$$\Delta t_{b.p.} = 0.27°C$$

Thus, the normal b.p. of the solution = 100.00°C + 0.27°C = 100.27°C.

MOLECULAR-WEIGHT DETERMINATION. Since the elevation of the boiling point of a solution depends on the number of moles of a non-volatile non-dissociated solute present, we can measure the boiling point of a solution and then determine the molecular weight of the solute. Following is an example.

ILLUSTRATIVE PROBLEM

PROBLEM. A solution containing 7.2 g of a non-volatile non-dissociated solute dissolved in 250 g of water boils at 100.26°C. Find the molecular weight of the solute.

SOLUTION.

$$\Delta t_{b.p.} = 100.26°C - 100.00°C = 0.26°C$$

$$\Delta t_{b.p.} = K_{b.p.} \times \frac{\text{grams solute/mol wt solute}}{\text{grams solvent}} \times 1{,}000 \text{ g solvent}$$

Solving for molecular weight of solute:

$$\text{mol wt of solute} = K_{b.p.} \times \frac{\text{grams solute}}{\Delta t_{b.p.}} \times \frac{1{,}000 \text{ g solvent}}{\text{grams solvent}}$$

$$\text{mol wt of solute} = \frac{0.52°C}{mole} \times \frac{7.2 \text{ g}}{0.26°C} \times \frac{1{,}000 \text{ g solvent}}{250 \text{ g solvent}} = \frac{58 \text{ g}}{mole}$$

FREEZING-POINT DEPRESSION. The freezing point (f.p.) of a liquid is the temperature at which the liquid and its solid exist together at equilibrium. Solid and liquid can co-exist at equilibrium only when they have the same vapor pressure. Thus, at the freezing point, the vapor pressure of a solid and its liquid must be the same. Since the presence of a non-volatile non-dissociated solute lowers the vapor pressure of a solution, it also lowers its freezing point.

Experiments reveal that the freezing point and the concentration of the solution are related by a simple quantitative expression similar to what we have just learned for the b.p. elevation. One mole of a non-volatile non-dissociated solute dissolved in 1,000 g of a solvent lowers the freezing point of that particular solvent by a constant amount. This amount, called the *molal freezing-point depression constant,* has

TABLE 19-2 MOLAL FREEZING-POINT DEPRESSION CONSTANTS $K_{f.p.}$

Solvent	Freezing Point at 1 atm	$K_{f.p.}$
Water	0.0°C	1.86°C/mole
Benzene	5.5°C	5.12°C/mole
Phenol	40°C	7.3°C/mole
Camphor	180°C	40.0°C/mole

a characteristic value for each solvent, and, like the boiling point constant, it is independent of the nature of the non-dissociated solute. The lowering of the freezing point, $\Delta t_{f.p.}$, of a solution may be expressed in symbol as:

$$\Delta t_{f.p.} = K_{f.p.} \times \frac{\text{moles solute}}{\text{grams solvent}} \times 1{,}000 \text{ g solvent}$$

where $\Delta t_{f.p.}$ = freezing-point depression (the decrease in the freezing point of solvent)

$K_{f.p.}$ = a proportionality constant characteristic of the solvent. For example, $K_{f.p.}$ for water is 1.86°C per mole of solute

Thus, 1 mole of any non-volatile non-dissociated solute dissolved in 1,000 g of water lowers the freezing point of the water by 1.86°C, and 1 mole of any non-volatile non-dissociated solute dissolved in 1,000 g of benzene lowers the freezing point of benzene by 5.12°C. Table 19-2 gives the molal freezing-point constants of some liquids commonly used as solvents.

ILLUSTRATIVE PROBLEMS

PROBLEM. Calculate the freezing point of a solution that contains 6.84 g of sucrose (1 mole = 342 g) dissolved in 250 g of water.

SOLUTION. f.p. solution = f.p. pure solvent − $\Delta t_{f.p.}$

$$\Delta t_{f.p.} = K_{f.p.} \times \frac{\text{moles solute}}{\text{grams solvent}} \times 1{,}000 \text{ g solvent} \qquad \text{moles solute (sucrose)} = \frac{6.84 \text{ g}}{342 \text{ g/1 mole}}$$

$$\Delta t_{f.p.} = \frac{1.86°\text{C}}{\text{mole}} \times \frac{\dfrac{6.84 \text{ g}}{342 \text{ g/1 mole}}}{250 \text{ g } H_2O} \times 1{,}000 \text{ g } H_2O$$

$$\Delta t_{f.p.} = \frac{1.86°\text{C}}{\text{mole}} \times 0.08 \text{ mole} = 0.15°\text{C}$$

Thus, the freezing point of the solution = 0°C − 0.15°C = −0.15°C.

PROBLEM. Find the freezing point of a solution that contains 0.2 mole of a non-dissociated solute dissolved in 1,200 g of benzene. The freezing point of benzene is 5.5°C, and the molal freezing-point constant for benzene is 5.12°C.

SOLUTION. f.p. solution = f.p. pure solvent − $\Delta t_{f.p.}$

$$\Delta t_{f.p.} = K_{f.p.} \times \frac{\text{moles solute}}{\text{grams solvent}} \times 1{,}000 \text{ g solvent}$$

$$\Delta t_{f.p.} = \frac{5.12°\text{C}}{\text{mole}} \times \frac{0.2 \text{ mole}}{1{,}200 \text{ g benzene}} \times 1{,}000 \text{ g benzene}$$

$$\Delta t_{f.p.} = 0.85°\text{C}$$

Thus, the freezing point of the solution = 5.5°C − 0.85°C = 4.65°C.

PROBLEM. The freezing point of a solution containing 18 g of a non-dissociated solute dissolved in 200 g of water is −0.93°C. Find the molecular weight of the solute.

SOLUTION.

$$\Delta t_{f.p.} = K_{f.p.} \times \frac{\text{moles solute}}{\text{grams solvent}} \times 1{,}000 \text{ g solvent}$$

$$\Delta t_{f.p.} = K_{f.p.} \times \frac{\text{grams solute/mol wt solute}}{\text{grams solvent}} \times 1{,}000 \text{ g solvent}$$

Solving for molecular weight of solute:

$$\text{mol wt of solute} = K_{f.p.} \times \frac{\text{grams solute}}{\Delta t_{f.p.}} \times \frac{1{,}000 \text{ g solvent}}{\text{grams solvent}}$$

$$\text{mol wt of solute} = \frac{1.86°\text{C}}{\text{mole}} \times \frac{18 \text{ g}}{0.93°\text{C}} \times \frac{1{,}000 \text{ g } H_2O}{200 \text{ g } H_2O}$$

$$\text{mol wt of solute} = \frac{180 \text{ g}}{\text{mole}}$$

Let us now consider a solution of a solid, non-volatile solute that dissociates upon dissolution—for example, a soluble ionic compound. In such a solution, the solute is present in the form of solvated positive and negative ions. And if the solution is sufficiently dilute, the ions will act independently, for they are too far apart to be affected appreciably by their mutual electrical interactions. Thus, as far as the colligative properties of the solution are concerned, *each ion in a highly dilute solution has the same effect as a molecule would have.* Clearly, then, 1 mole of an ionic compound that upon dissolution produces 2 *moles of ions* will have twice the effect of 1 mole of a non-ionic substance that produces only 1 mole of *molecules.* For example, 1 mole of NaCl in a very dilute solution produces $2 \times (6.02 \times 10^{23})$ independent ions, whereas 1 mole of glucose produces only $1 \times (6.02 \times 10^{23})$ independent molecules. Thus, when dissolved in the same volume of water to give a very dilute solution, an amount of NaCl will lower the freezing point of the solution almost twice as much as an equimolar amount of glucose. Similarly, 1 mole of an ionic solute that produces 3 moles of ions will have approximately 3 times as much effect on the colligative properties of its solutions as an equimolar amount of a non-ionic solute.

Now all that we have just said holds true for *very dilute* solutions of ionic solutes, where the individual ions are more or less independent of one another. In more concentrated solutions of ionic solutes, however, where the ions are closer together, they cannot behave with as much independence, for the attractive forces between the oppositely charged ions become relatively stronger. In these less dilute solutions of ionic compounds, therefore, the presence of the solute has less effect on the four colligative properties—vapor pressure, boiling point, freezing point, and osmotic pressure—than it does in a very dilute solution. As the concentration is increased, the attractive forces between the oppositely charged ions in the solution become progressively stronger and in effect reduce the number of independent particles present. Consequently, the relative effect of the solute on the colligative properties become less and less.

Table 19-3 gives the ratios between the *observed* values for the lowering of the freezing point and the values *calculated on the assumption* that the individual particles are moving with complete freedom. These ratios are for NaCl and $MgSO_4$ solutions between 0.005 and 0.5 molal. Notice that as the concentration of the solutions increases from left to right, the ratios become steadily lower than the theoretical value of 1.00. This is to be expected, because the closer together the ions are, the greater the attractive forces between them. Notice, too, that the ratio decreases more rapidly for the salt $MgSO_4$, which has more highly charged ions, $(Mg^{++} + SO_4^{=})$, than NaCl $(Na^+ + Cl^-)$. The greater the charge on the ions, the greater the deviation from the theoretical ratio of 1.00, because, as we know from Coulomb's Law, the forces of attraction between ions are directly proportional to their charges.

EFFECTIVE CONCENTRATION. In a 0.5 molal solution of sodium chloride, the lowering of the freezing point is only 91 per cent of the value calculated on the assumption

TABLE 19-3 OBSERVED CHANGES IN RATIO: OBSERVED F.P. DEPRESSION, CALCULATED F.P. DEPRESSION

Salt	Concentration				
	0.005 molal	0.02 molal	0.05 molal	0.1 molal	0.5 molal
NaCl	0.975	0.96	0.945	0.94	0.91
$MgSO_4$	0.845	0.77	0.71	0.66	0.54

that the ions have complete freedom of motion. This means that in a 0.5 molal solution, the mutual interference between the Na^+ ions and the Cl^- ions is such that the *average* individual ion moves with only 91 per cent of the freedom it would have in a very dilute solution. We may express this condition by saying that the *effective concentration* (more correctly, the *activity*) *of free sodium ions* and *free chloride ions* is 91 per cent of 0.5 molal (0.5*m*).

If we know the effective concentration (activity) of a solution, we can calculate how much its freezing point has been lowered. For example, we can calculate the freezing-point lowering for a 0.5*m* aqueous solution of NaCl as follows:

$$(0.5 \times 1.86°\mathrm{C} + 0.5 \times 1.86°\mathrm{C}) \times 0.91 = 1.69°\mathrm{C}$$

COLLIGATIVE PROPERTIES OF SOLUTIONS OF COMPOUNDS WHICH DISSOCIATE ONLY PARTIALLY

Some compounds undergo only partial dissociation into ions when they are put into solution, and thus consist mostly of molecules, with relatively few ions in equilibrium with them. For example, pure acetic acid, CH_3COOH, is a covalent compound, but when it is dissolved in water it ionizes to a slight extent to form a few hydrated hydrogen and acetate ions. Actually, only about 1 per cent of a 1-molal solution of acetic acid ionizes. The observed freezing-point lowering of solutions of acetic acid agrees with this low percentage of ionization. Therefore, a 1-molal solution of acetic acid would exhibit colligative properties only slightly different from those calculated on the basis of the presence of only CH_3COOH molecules. The same behavior holds for all solutions of those compounds—called *weak electrolytes*—which dissociate only partially in solution.

SOLUTIONS OF TWO LIQUIDS

What happens in a solution in which both components are volatile liquids? How does the presence of one liquid affect the vapor pressure of the other? And what is the total vapor pressure of the solution, and hence its boiling and freezing point? The answer is relatively simple only when the two liquids are very similar to one another in chemical composition and molecular size, and therefore form a mixture that closely approaches an ideal solution (p. 389). An example is a mixture of two hydrocarbons: (normal) pentane, C_5H_{12}, and (normal) hexane, C_6H_{14}, which are "consecutive" members of the saturated hydrocarbon family (Chapter 36). Both of these hydrocarbons consist of non-polar, chain-like molecules of approximately the same size and with approximately the same kind and magnitude of intermolecular interactions. If we mix pentane with hexane, almost no heat is evolved or absorbed (ΔH of mixing $\cong 0$), and there is no appreciable change of the total volume. For such a solution, the vapor pressure, P, of each component in the solution is simply proportional to the mole fraction, the proportionality constant being the vapor pressure, P^0, of the pure component at the same temperature:

$$P_{\mathrm{pentane}} = P^0_{\mathrm{pentane}} \times \frac{n_{\mathrm{pentane}}}{n_{\mathrm{pentane}} + n_{\mathrm{hexane}}}$$

$$P_{\mathrm{hexane}} = P^0_{\mathrm{hexane}} \times \frac{n_{\mathrm{hexane}}}{n_{\mathrm{pentane}} + n_{\mathrm{hexane}}}$$

The variation of the vapor pressure of each component with the concentration (mole fraction) is shown graphically in Fig. 19-6(a). The total vapor pressure of the solution at this temperature will be the sum of the vapor pressures of the individual components:

$$P_{\mathrm{solution}} = P_{\mathrm{pentane}} + P_{\mathrm{hexane}}$$

As you can verify by applying the above expressions, the total pressure of the solution

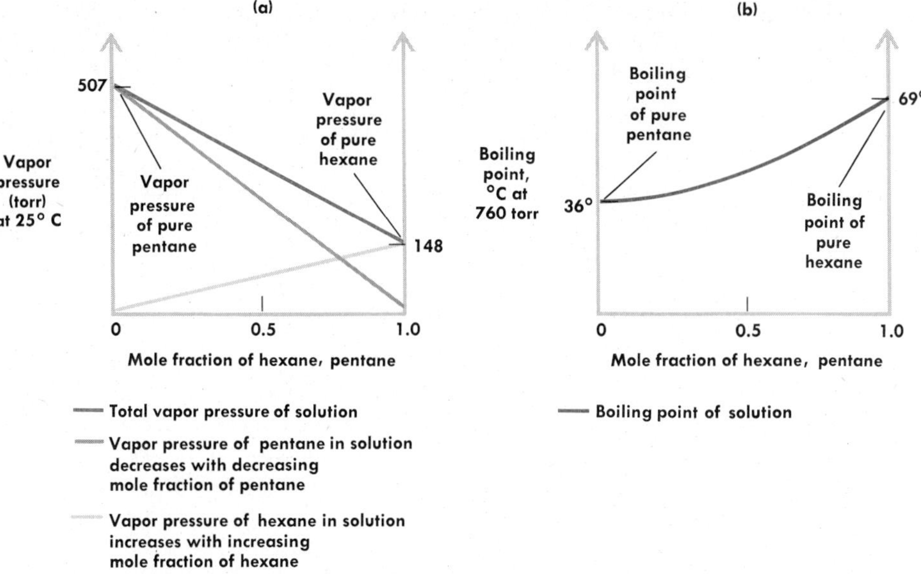

FIGURE 19-6 (a) Vapor pressure—mole fraction diagram for a (ideal) solution of two volatile liquids. (b) Boiling point of the solution versus mole fraction.

for any ratio of the two components is greater than the vapor pressure of the less volatile component (hexane) alone, but smaller than that of the more volatile component (pentane) alone, as shown in Fig. 19-6(a). A liquid mixture of pentane + hexane will boil when its pressure, $P = P_{\text{pentane}} + P_{\text{hexane}}$, equals the value of the opposing atmospheric pressure. The temperature at which this value of the total pressure is reached increases, of course, as the concentration of the less volatile liquid in the mixture increases, as shown in Fig. 19-6(b). Two other pairs of liquids whose mixtures follow these simple rules are carbon tetrachloride–benzene, and benzene–toluene. Most pairs of miscible liquids, however, show marked deviations from the behavior of ideal solutions, and their vapor pressure and boiling points obey more complicated relationships, which cannot be expressed by simple formulas. For example, the vapor pressure of the two components for a mixture of water, H_2O, and ethanol, C_2H_5OH, at 20°C vary with the concentration of the mixture in an irregular manner, as shown by graphs of Fig. 19-7.

FIGURE 19-7 Variations of vapor pressures with mole fractions for a (non-ideal) solution of water and ethanol, C_2H_5OH, at 20°C.

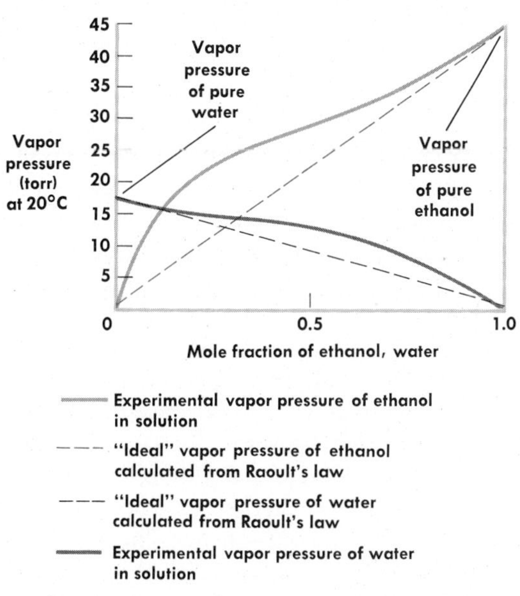

LIQUID SOLUTIONS OF GASEOUS SOLUTES

Next let's turn to a solution of a gas in a liquid. If the solution is very dilute, the pressure of the gas above the solution and the mole fraction of the gas dissolved in the solution are related by the following expression:

$$P_{gas} = k \times \frac{n_{gas\ dissolved}}{n_{gas\ dissolved} + n_{solvent}}$$

Notice that this expression, generally called *Henry's Law,* is very similar to Raoult's Law for the vapor pressure of each volatile liquid component of a dilute solution of two liquids. Actually, Henry's Law was first formulated in a slightly different manner by the English scientist William C. Henry (1775–1836). Henry investigated how the solubility of a gas in a liquid increases, at any given temperature, when the pressure of the gas above the liquid is increased, and observed that at any given temperature the mass of a gas dissolved in a specified mass of a liquid is directly proportional to the pressure of the gas above the solution. For example, at 1 atm pressure, 0.1 g of a certain gas will dissolve in a given weight of water to form a saturated solution. Now if the pressure of the gas above the solution is doubled, the concentration of the gas in the saturated solution will also be doubled. Thus, if the pressure is increased to 2 atm, 0.2 g of the gas will dissolve in the same weight of water. Henry expressed this experimental observation as follows:

$$\frac{n_{gas\ dissolved}}{n_{solvent}} = \text{constant} \times \text{pressure of gas above solution}$$

In symbols: $n_{gas\ dissolved}/n_{solvent} = k'P_{gas}$

For very dilute solutions, $n_{gas\ dissolved}$ is very small compared with $n_{solvent}$, so that the total number of moles of solution is approximately equal to the number of moles of solvent alone. The expression $n_{gas\ dissolved}/n_{solvent} = k'P_{gas}$ can be written as:

$$P_{gas} = k \times \frac{n_{gas\ dissolved}}{n_{gas\ dissolved} + n_{solvent}}$$

Henry found that the proportionality between the solubility of a gas and the gas pressure above the solution held only for very slightly soluble gases, for example for H_2, O_2, and N_2 in water at room temperature. This is so, of course, because only for slightly soluble gases is a saturated solution dilute enough to follow with good approximation the general law expressed by the formula.

19-4 Osmosis

Osmosis is the process by which a liquid solvent passes through a semi-permeable membrane, a material that permits the passage of the molecules of a solvent but prevents the passage of the molecules of a solute. Certain parchment papers, many natural membranes such as the walls of plant and animal cells, and some gelatinous inorganic compounds act as semi-permeable membranes. When we separate, by means of a semi-permeable membrane, a solution from its pure solvent, or two solutions of unequal concentration from each other, some of the solvent alone flows through the membrane from the pure solvent to the solution, or from the dilute solution to the concentrated solution, tending to equalize the concentrations. Here again we see at work a general principle that we have encountered before: a system tends to achieve the equilibrium state of maximum disorder—that is, maximum entropy—compatible with the other energy factors involved.

OSMOTIC PRESSURE. Let us assume that we have two aqueous solutions of sodium chloride, one concentrated and one dilute, contained in two vessels having long, narrow, graduated necks. The two vessels are separated by a porous glass partition impregnated with phenol. Phenol, C_6H_5OH, is an organic liquid that acts as a semi-permeable membrane for this particular system, because water is somewhat soluble in phenol, and hence can diffuse through it, but sodium chloride is not. At the beginning of our experiment, the level of the liquid in both vessels is the same, that is, the same pressure is exerted on the porous glass wall by the weight of the two liquids in the two containers. If the solutions were of equal concentration, the same number of water molecules would, at each instant, diffuse in both directions through the phenol-impregnated porous glass wall. But since our two solutions are of unequal concentrations and there are, statistically, more water molecules near the porous glass wall in the dilute than in the concentrated solution, there is a greater probability that the water molecules pass from the dilute to the concentrated solution than *vice versa*. As a result, there is a net flow of water molecules from the dilute solution to the concentrated solution. And if we replace the dilute NaCl solution with pure water, an even greater flow of water molecules will pass through the glass to the concentrated solution as shown schematically in Fig. 19-8.

As the flow of water molecules from the pure solvent in container A to the solution in container B proceeds, the level of the liquid in B rises in the graduated neck while the level of the liquid in A decreases. Gradually, therefore, the pressure exerted on the porous glass partition increases by the extra amount of liquid in container B. The flow of solvent molecules from B to A then also gradually increases, and tends to counterbalance more and more effectively the extra flow of solvent molecules from A to B until equilibrium is attained. At equilibrium, equal numbers of solvent molecules pass in each instant from A to B as from B to A, through the porous wall, and the pressure of the extra amount of liquid in B equals the "pressure" that tends to push molecules of the solvent from the dilute solution into the more concentrated solution. This "pressure" is the *osmotic pressure* of the solution. (The term "osmosis" comes from the Greek word for "a push.")

For our experimental set-up (Fig. 19-8) the osmotic pressure of the solution can be measured simply by mutiplying the difference of liquid level, Δl, in the two containers at equilibrium by the density of the solution, d:

$$\text{pressure of extra amount of liquid in B} = \text{osmotic pressure in A} = \Delta l \times d$$

ISOTONIC SOLUTIONS. If there is no net transfer of the solvent between two solutions separated by a semi-permeable membrane, the osmotic pressure of the solutions is equal and the solutions are said to be *isotonic*. This term comes from the Greek word *isotonos*, meaning "same tone" or "same tension," hence the same osmotic pressure.

OSMOSIS AND DIFFUSION. The phenomenon of the net flow of the solvent molecules through a semi-permeable membrane resembles, in many ways, the diffusion of gases and liquids, which we have discussed in detail on p. 135 and p. 419, respectively. In osmosis, as in diffusion, the driving force of the process, ΔG, results chiefly from the

FIGURE 19-8 Experimental observation of osmotic pressure.

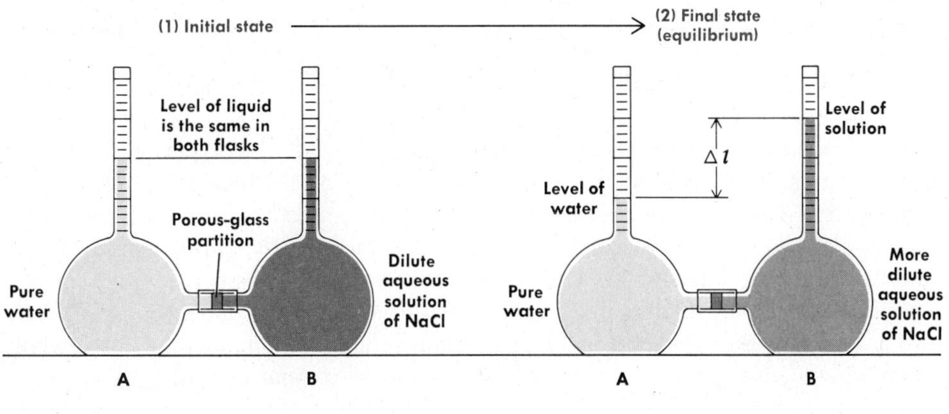

tendency of the system to attain the maximum possible entropy. And in osmosis, as in diffusion, we can visualize the process on the basis of the ceaseless random movement of the liquid molecules and their greater probability of passing from the dilute to the concentrated salt solution. But there is a fundamental difference between osmosis and diffusion. In the latter, the final state of the system—the state of equilibrium—is attained when complete mixing is achieved, and the system consists of a single, homogeneous solution. In osmosis, on the other hand, the final state of the system—equilibrium—still consists of two distinct phases, the pure solvent and the solution, or two solutions of different concentrations. In the example of osmosis considered above, gravity is the force which opposes complete equilibration of the concentration within the system.

QUANTITATIVE EXPRESSION OF THE OSMOTIC PRESSURE

For a very dilute solution of a non-dissociated solute, the osmotic pressure, which we indicate by the symbol π, is directly proportional to the molar concentration of the solute, M:

$$\pi = k \times M = k \times n/V$$

As usual, n is the number of moles of non-dissociated solute present in V liters of solution, and k is a proportionality constant which depends on the temperature. For very dilute solutions, k is, with very good approximation, equal to RT, so the osmotic pressure may be expressed as: $\pi = RT\,n/V$. Thus, we may write:

$$\text{Ideal-solution equation: } \pi V = nRT$$

In this equation all symbols have the same meaning and are expressed in the same units as in the ideal-gas equation:

$$\text{Ideal-gas equation: } PV = nRT$$

For example, if the osmotic pressure is expressed in atmospheres, the volume in liters, and the temperature, as usual, in degrees Kelvin, then the constant R has the value 0.082 l. $\times$ atm/°K $\times$ mole.

The equation $\pi V = nRT$ is generally called the van't Hoff equation, from the Dutch scientist J. H. van't Hoff, who first correlated the osmotic pressure with the thermodynamic properties of solutions. From the van't Hoff equation we can rapidly calculate that the osmotic pressure has really quite large values. For example, a 0.1 M solution of a non-dissociated solute at 0°C has an osmotic pressure of approximately 2.2 atm. Thus, natural semi-permeable membranes often burst under the effect of osmotic pressure. Just as for real gases the deviation from the behavior expressed by the equation, $PV = nRT$, represents a measure of their non-ideality, so for real solutions the extent by which the observed osmotic pressure deviates from the value calculated from the equation $\pi V = nRT$ is a measure of the non-ideality of the solution.

Another significant similarity between gases and solutions is that both deviate more and more from ideality as the molecules (gas molecules or solute molecules) become more crowded, that is, as the pressure of the gas, or the concentration of the solution, increases.

OSMOTIC PRESSURE OF SOLUTIONS OF IONIC SUBSTANCES. We know that, when a substance dissociates into ions upon dissolution, the colligative properties of the resulting solution depend on the number of moles of ions effectively present. For such a solute, the van't Hoff equation, $\pi V = nRT$, becomes: $\pi V = i\,nRT$, where i is the number of moles of ions which actually result from the ionic dissociation of 1 mole of solute. For a solute which ionizes completely into ions in very dilute solution (where we can neglect the interactions among the ions), the correction factor "i" is a whole number. For example, for a very dilute solution of sodium chloride ($Na^+ + Cl^-$),

$i = 2$, and for a very dilute solution of sodium sulfate ($2\ Na^+ + SO_4^=$), $i = 3$. If the solution is not dilute, so that ion-ion interactions become appreciable, then i will be less than the number expected for complete dissociation. Again, as we discussed for the boiling-point elevation and freezing-point depression of ionic solutions, the ratio between the experimentally determined value of i, obtained by measuring the osmotic pressure, π, and the value of i expected theoretically for complete dissociation, gives us a measure of the mutual ion-ion interaction in the solution.

19-5 Colloids

In Chapter 18 we learned that a homogeneous molecular dispersion of two or more substances in any physical state, solid, liquid, or gaseous, is called a *solution.* Thus, in a solution the dispersed particles are of molecular size. In a *suspension,* such as finely divided sand in water, the dispersed particles are much larger than molecules —actually they consist of many thousands or even millions of molecules. Initially, the particles are suspended more or less uniformly throughout the liquid, but in time they settle to the bottom of the container. They may be separated from the liquid by means of gravity (that is, simply by letting them settle out), by centrifugation, or by filtration.

Between these two extreme types of dispersion are many cases in which the dispersed particles are *larger than molecules* but *not large enough to settle out under the influence of gravity.* These intermediate instances of dispersion are called *colloidal systems* or *colloids,* and in this section we shall introduce some of their very interesting chemical and physical properties.

SIZES OF COLLOIDAL PARTICLES

A colloidal system, then, contains dispersed particles that are intermediate in size between the particles in a solution and the particles in a suspension. What, specifically, do we know about the actual sizes of colloidal particles? We know that simple molecules are a few angstroms in diameter (an angstrom, you will remember, is equal to 10^{-7} mm). Colloidal particles are much larger, ranging in size from about 10 A to 1,000 A. The sizes of colloidal particles are often expressed in microns (μ) or millimicrons ($m\mu$), as well as in angstrom units (A). A micron, μ, is one-millionth of a meter (10^{-6} m $= 10^{-3}$ mm). (The prefix micro means one-millionth.) A millimicron, $m\mu$, is one-thousandth of a micron; thus, 1 $m\mu = 10^{-9}$ m $= 10^{-6}$ mm. Therefore, the size of colloidal particles range from 1 $m\mu$ to 100 $m\mu$.

Now the chief factor that determines whether one substance (the dispersed phase) dispersed in another (the dispersion medium) will give rise to a true solution, or a colloidal system, or an ordinary suspension is the *size* of the dispersed particles. If the dispersed particles are of molecular size, we have a solution. If the dispersed particles are much larger than 1 μ, we have a suspension. And if the dispersed particles are between 1 $m\mu$ and 100 $m\mu$ in diameter we have a colloidal system. In some cases—for example, with certain dyes and polymers—the dispersed particles may consist of single molecules that are so large that the resulting solution exhibits many of the properties of a colloidal system.

VISIBILITY OF PARTICLES. Ordinary molecules and ions, which are only a few angstrom units in diameter, cannot be seen by means of a microscope. These particles are called *submicroscopic.* The particles in a suspension may be too small to be seen by the naked eye, but they are always large enough to be seen through an ordinary microscope. Particles of this sort are termed *microscopic.* Colloidal particles may be seen with an instrument known as the ultramicroscope, designed in 1912 by the German scientist, Richard Zsigmondy. In an ordinary microscope, the observer views the object through the eye piece; the rays of light that reach his eye come directly from the object itself. In the ultramicroscope, on the other hand, the observer views the object at *right angles* to the illuminating beam. What the viewer actually sees is light *scattered* by small particles too small to be seen with the ordinary microscope. Such particles are called *ultramicroscopic.*

THE TYNDALL EFFECT. Here is a simple experiment to illustrate the relation between particle size and visibility. To one beaker we add a solution of sugar or salt in water, and to a second beaker we add a colloidal dispersion in water. When we look at the two beakers with our naked eye, and even when we examine them through a microscope, we find that both the solution and the colloidal system appear clear. Now we focus a powerful beam of light, *B*, down to a narrow beam by means of a lens, *L*, and pass it through both containers, as in Fig. 19-9. And we examine the beakers in a darkened room with our eye at right angles to the beam of light. When we look at the solution (a), we do not observe the light passing through. But when we look at the colloidal system (b), we find that the colloidal particles dispersed in the water reveal the path of light as a bright cloudy beam. This is another example of the *Tyndall effect* which we already encountered in Chapter 9, in our discussion of gases. The explanation of the Tyndall effect in a colloidal system is quite simple. Neither the molecules of the water, nor the molecules of the sugar, nor the ions of the salt in solution are large enough to scatter the light beam. But in the colloidal system the dispersed particles are large enough to scatter the light, each colloidal particle appearing as an extremely small bright speck, and the multitude of these bright specks showing up as a beam of light.

BROWNIAN MOVEMENT. We found in Chapter 9 that very small particles suspended in gases or liquids move about ceaselessly in a random fashion, following continuously shifting zig-zag paths. The movement of such small suspended particles is known as the *Brownian movement,* (p. 150). Like *all suspensions* whose particles are small enough, colloidal systems exhibit the Brownian movement, which results from the continuous bombardment of each suspended particle by the molecules of the liquid.

VARIOUS KINDS OF COLLODIAL SYSTEMS

Even though the most common and important colloids consist of colloidal particles of a solid dispersed in a liquid medium, there are other significant types —such as those consisting of solid or liquid particles dispersed in a gas, or of liquid particles dispersed in a liquid.

AEROSOL. Aerosol indicates a colloidal dispersion of solid or liquid particles in a gas, and is therefore, a general term that includes fog, mist, and clouds in which the dispersed particles are of colloidal size. The dispersed particles can be separated from an aerosol by the Cottrell process, which is largely applied in industry to purify gases from furnaces and chemical plants. In this process, the colloidal particles of the aerosol "fumes" are first given an electrical charge and then passed between oppositely charged electrodes. The charged particles are attracted to the electrode of opposite charge; when they come into contact with the electrode, they are discharged and are deposited as dust. The cleaned gases are then permitted to pass on.

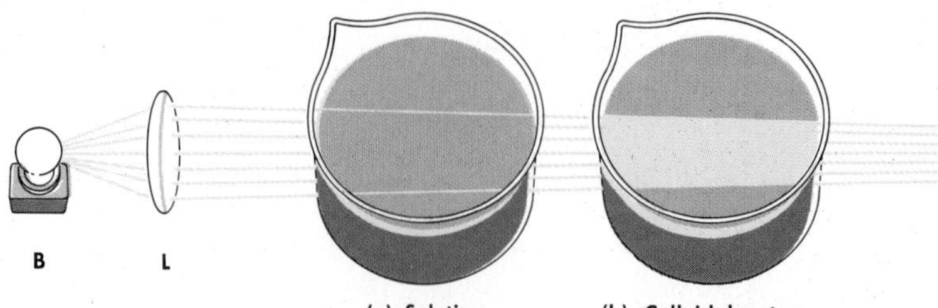

FIGURE 19-9 The Tyndall effect.

SOLS. A colloidal dispersion of a solid in a liquid is called a sol. A convenient way of classifying sols is on the basis of the relative attraction between the dispersed particles and the liquid dispersion medium. When the colloidal particles exert only a very slight attraction for the liquid dispersion medium, the sol is said to be *lyophobic* (this term comes from a Greek word meaning "liquid-fearing"). If, as is often the case, water is the dispersion liquid, these colloids are called *hydro*phobic ("water-fearing"). Examples of hydrophobic sols are colloids of the metals, sulfur, arsenious sulfide and other metal sulfides, and silver iodide; in general these are substances in which each particle is a very small fragment of the crystalline metallic or ionic lattice of the substance. Lyophobic *sols* are only slightly more viscous than the dispersion liquid itself. When the solvent of a lyophobic system is evaporated, it is usually very difficult to convert the solid particles back into sols by adding some of the dispersion solvent again.

The term *lyophilic* (from the Greek meaning "liquid-loving") applies to sols whose particles exert a very strong attraction for the liquid dispersion medium. When water is the dispersion liquid, these colloids are called *hydrophilic.* Lyophilic sols are much more viscous than the dispersion liquid itself, and the addition of a small quantity of an electrolyte does not cause the colloidal particles to coagulate—that is, lyophilic sols are much more stable than lyophobic sols. After we have separated the solid dispersed particles of a lyophilic colloid from the dispersion medium by precipitation or by evaporation of the liquid, we can generally re-form the colloidal dispersion by adding some of the dispersion liquid again. Compounds that most readily form lyophilic sols are those with high molecular weight, and as a rule each colloidal particle of these compounds consists of a large, single molecule. The chief lyophilic substances are such naturally occurring ones as starch, proteins, and gums; others are soaps and specially prepared metasilicic acid, H_2SiO_3.

EMULSIONS. A colloidal system in which both the dispersed substance and the dispersion medium are liquids is known as an *emulsion.* Cream, for example, is an emulsion that consists of particles of liquid fat dispersed in water.

When we shake two immiscible liquids together, the best we can hope for is only a weak and unstable emulsion. An oil-in-water emulsion prepared in this way, for example, soon separates into two layers. But we can stabilize the emulsion *by adding a third substance.* Thus, when we add egg white to olive oil and water and then shake the mixture, we get a stable emulsion. The colloidal particles of oil are coated with a film of egg white, which prevents them from coagulating. The egg white is known as an *emulsifying agent.* In general, an emulsifying agent is a substance that leads to the formation of a stable emulsion when it is added to a mixture of two immiscible liquids. Soap, for example, is a well-known emulsifying agent that permits grease to form a stable colloidal emulsion in water.

GELS. We have seen that hydrophilic sols are more viscous than the dispersion liquid. If a sufficient amount of a hydrophilic dispersed substance is present, a gel forms when the system is cooled or when some of the dispersion liquid is evaporated. A hot hydrophilic sol, so long as it is not too dilute, usually sets to a stiff, apparently homogeneous gel, or jelly, when it is cooled. When the system is warmed, the gel changes back to a sol. A soap solution, or a 2 per cent solution of gelatin, in warm water, for example, is fluid, but when the solution is cooled it sets to a stiff gel. When the gel is warmed, it liquefies. This process may be repeated any number of times.

COLLOIDS IN EVERYDAY LIFE. A great many colloidal systems occur in nature and are of great importance in biological processes. Many man-made colloidal systems are also important in our everyday life. An example is colloidal silver bromide, which is the photosensitive substance of photographic films. In the preparation of the sols of silver bromide, gelatin is added to the solution in which silver bromide is being formed from its ions. The gelatin coats the colloidal AgBr particles and prevents coagulation, acting as a "protective colloid." This stable sol of AgBr, is then used to coat a sheet of cellulose acetate, forming a photographic film. Fruit jellies, which are generally formed when a fruit juice is boiled with sugar, are common examples of colloidal systems. What happens is that a carbohydrate, pectin, which is present in the fruit, forms a gel when the mixture is cooled.

VAPOR PRESSURE, BOILING POINT, AND FREEZING POINT OF COLLOIDAL SYSTEMS

In contrast with true solutions, the vapor pressure, boiling point, and freezing point of a solid-in-liquid colloidal system are only very slightly different from those of the pure solvent. Since the average weight of colloidal particles is extremely large—on a molecular basis, of course—the mole fraction of colloidal particles in a colloidal system is always exceedingly small. And since the variation of the colligative properties—vapor pressure, boiling point, and freezing point—depends on the mole fraction of the dissolved material, you can see that the colligative properties of a colloidal system are almost the same as those of the solvent alone. This same effect is observed in a true solution containing exceedingly large molecules of solute—in protein solutions, for example.

Exercises

19-1 How would you prepare 250 ml of a 0.4 *M* solution of $KClO_3$?

19-2 The vapor pressure of water at 20°C is (the same as, greater than, less than) the vapor pressure of any aqueous sugar solution at the same temperature.

19-3 Explain your answer in 19-2.

19-4 Beaker A contains water and beaker B contains a water solution of calcium chloride. (a) Which liquid has the higher vapor pressure? (b) If a bell jar is placed over the two beakers, explain any visible changes and any changes in concentration that may take place.

19-5 For each of the following pairs of solutions, which solution will obey more closely Raoult's Law? Explain your answer. (a) A 0.1 *M* solution of sugar in water, or a 0.1 *M* solution of ammonia, NH_3, in water. (b) A 1 *M* aqueous solution of urea $(NH_2)_2CO$ (an organic compound that does not dissociate), or a 1 *M* aqueous solution of hydrochloric acid? (c) A 1 *M* or a 0.1 *M* solution of glucose, $C_6H_{12}O_6$, in water.

19-6 We add some toluene (b.p. 110.6°C at 1 atm) to pure benzene (b.p. 80.2°C at 1 atm). (a) How is the vapor pressure of benzene affected? (b) Is the total vapor pressure of the mixture lower or higher than that of pure benzene at the same temperature? (c) Will the mixture boil at a temperature higher or lower than pure benzene? (d) Explain your answers in (a), (b), and (c).

19-7 Flask A is filled to the volume mark with a solution of sugar in water; flask B is filled to the same mark with pure water. The two flasks are connected through a tube equipped with a stopcock and a semipermeable membrane. (a) What happens when we open the stopcock? (b) What happens when we open the stopcock and also remove the semipermeable membrane?

19-8 Which of the solutions of Exercise 19-5 will follow more closely van't Hoff's Law of osmotic pressure? ($\pi V = (i)\, nRT$)

19-9 Explain and illustrate the following terms: (a) colloidal particles, (b) the Brownian movement, (c) Tyndall effect, (d) dialysis, (e) gel, (f) lyophobic, (g) lyophilic, (h) hydrophobic, (i) coagulation, (j) electrophoresis, (k) emulsifying agent, (l) aerosol.

19-10 Indicate how you could determine by three different experimental procedures if a given system is (a) an ordinary suspension or a colloidal suspension, (b) a true solution or a colloidal dispersion.

19-11 A sol of iron(III) hydroxide, made by dissolving a little iron(III) chloride in a large volume of hot water, moves to the negative electrode. (a) What is the sign of the charge on the sol? (b) What ion do you think is adsorbed on the surface of the colloidal iron(III) hydroxide?

19-12 In what respects are lyophobic sols and lyophilic sols (a) similar and (b) different?

19-13 Can you give a simple explanation of why colloidal clay in a river precipitates when it reaches the ocean?

Problems

PROBLEMS

19-1 How many grams of solute are present in 260 ml of a 4.2-molar solution of KCl?

19-2 Calculate the molarity of the following solutions: (a) 1 mole of NaCl dissolved in 500 ml of solution. (b) 4.2 g mol wt of $CuSO_4 \cdot 5\,H_2O$ dissolved in 2.5 l. of solution. (c) 20.4 g of $NaHCO_3$ dissolved in 600 ml of solution. (d) 6.5 g of $H_2C_2O_4 \cdot 2\,H_2O$ dissolved in 400 ml of solution.

19-3 How many moles of $AgNO_3$ are present in 400 ml of a 0.5 *M* solution?

19-4 Calculate the number of moles of solute present in 2.6 l. of a 1.4 *M* solution of (a) NaOH, (b) $ZnCl_2$, (c) H_3PO_4.

19-5 How many grams of $(NH_4)_2SO_4$ are required to prepare 4 l. of a 1 *M* solution?

19-6 What is the molarity of the following acid solutions? (a) Hydrochloric acid solution with a density of 1.20 g/ml and 40.0 per cent (by weight) of HCl. (b) Sulfuric acid solution with a density of 1.84 g/ml and 93.1 per cent (by weight) of H_2SO_4. (c) Nitric acid solution with a density of 1.2 g/ml and 32.3 per cent (by weight) of HNO_3.

19-7 How many moles of Al^{+++} ions are present in a solution of 3 moles of $Al_2\,(SO_4)_3$ dissolved in water?

19-8 How many (a) moles of zinc chloride, (b) grams of zinc ions are present in 400 ml of a 0.1 *M* solution of zinc chloride?

19-9 Calculate (1) the molality and (2) the mole fraction of the solute in the following: (a) the solutions of problem 19-6, (b) a 2 per cent (by weight) solution of LiCl in water. (c) A 10 per cent (by weight) solution of $AgNO_3$ in ethanol, C_2H_5OH.

19-10 Calculate the vapor pressure at 25°C of the following aqueous solutions: (a) 10 per cent (by weight) aqueous solution of glucose ($C_6H_{12}O_6$) in water (v.p of pure water at 25°C = 23.5 torr), (b) 10 per cent (by weight) aqueous solution of the ionic compound LiBr, (c) a solution containing 0.01 mole of iodine, I_2, in 400 g of acetone (v.p. of acetone at 8°C = 100 torr), (d) a solution containing 0.35 g of silver perchlorate, $AgClO_4$ in 1,000 g of benzene, C_6H_6 (v.p. of C_6H_6 at 26°C = 100 torr).

19-11 Calculate the boiling-point elevation for the solutions of problem 19-10. (See Table 19-1 for $K_{b.p.}$ values.)

19-12 Calculate the freezing-point depression for the solutions of problem 19-10 (a), (b), and (d). (See Table 19-2 for $K_{f.p.}$ values.)

19-13 Calculate the vapor pressure at 50°C of a mixture of 1 mole of carbon tetrachloride, CCl_4 and 0.5 moles of benzene, C_6H_6; assume the mixture to behave ideally (v.p. of CCl_4 at 50°C = 305 torr: v.p. of C_6H_6 at 50°C = 270 torr).

19-14 Calculate the osmotic pressure of the following solutions: (a) An aqueous solution containing exactly 0.001 mole of NaOH in 500 ml of water at 25°C. (b) A 0.01-molar aqueous solution of the organic compound urea, $(NH_2)_2CO$, which does not dissociate in solution. The temperature is 50°C. (c) A solution containing 0.020 g of silver nitrate, $Ag^+(NO_3{}^-)$, in 200 ml of acetone at 10°C.

ACIDS, BASES, AND SALTS

20

In this chapter we shall consider the classification of inorganic compounds into three main groups: acids, bases, and salts. Then we shall discuss the characteristic properties of each group. Finally, we shall look at several theories that have been advanced to account for these properties.

20-1 Acids

The name "acid" (from the Latin *acidus,* meaning sour) was given to a class of compounds that have, *in aqueous solution,* these properties: (1) a characteristic sour taste; (2) the ability to change the color of litmus (a vegetable dye) from blue to red; (3) the ability to react with certain metals to liberate H_2 gas; (4) the ability to react with the hydroxides and oxides (bases, see Section 20-2) of metals to form a salt and water.

For the present we shall limit our discussion of acids to aqueous solutions, and we shall define an acid as *a substance that yields hydrogen ions, H^+, when it is dissolved in water.* This definition was framed by Svante Arrhenius (1859–1927), Professor of Physics at the University of Stockholm, and the approach to the study of acids and bases which we shall consider in the first part of this chapter is called the *Arrhenius theory.* That all acids *contain* hydrogen was first recognized by Claude Louis Berthollet (1748–1822), a French chemist, in 1798. Berthollet's research disproved Lavoisier's belief (p. 73) that all acids contain oxygen, but it did *not* anticipate Arrhenius' definition, which introduced the idea of *ions.*

Some of the common acids are HCl, HNO_3, H_2SO_4, and H_3PO_4. In aqueous solutions these acids dissociate (ionize) extensively to produce hydrated hydrogen ions, $H^+_{(aq)}$, and hydrated anions characteristic of the parent acid. Although for brevity we usually say that a solution of an acid contains "hydrogen ions," which we write simply as H^+, we must keep in mind that these are *hydrated* hydrogen ions (p. 201), and that they can be represented by any one of the notations listed here in the margin. For example, we can write the dissociation (ionization) of HCl in water, showing the hydration of the H^+ ions and also of the Cl^- ions, as:

H^+

$H^+_{(aq)}$

H_3O^+

$H^+(H_2O)_x$

$H^+ \cdot H_2O$

$$HCl + \text{water} \longrightarrow H^+_{(aq)} + Cl^-_{(aq)}$$

For simplicity, however, we often represent these ions without their water of hydration:

$$HCl \xrightarrow{H_2O} H^+ + Cl^-$$

Acids such as HCl, which ionize almost completely in dilute aqueous solution, are regarded as *strong acids*. An acid that ionizes only slightly in water is called a *weak acid*. Acetic acid, CH_3COOH, is an example of a weak acid, and vinegar is essentially a dilute aqueous solution of acetic acid.

Those substances which ionize in aqueous solution to yield hydrated H^+ ions (hydrated protons) are sometimes referred to as *proton* or *Arrhenius acids*. In short, an Arrhenius acid is a substance that has the ability to yield a proton.

20-2 Bases

The name "base" was given to a class of compounds characterized by: (1) the soapy feeling of their aqueous solutions; (2) their ability to restore the original blue color of litmus that has been turned red by acids, (3) their ability to react with acids to form salts.

For the present we shall limit our discussion of bases to aqueous solutions, and we shall define a base *as a substance that yields OH^- ions when dissolved in water.* The OH^- ions may be present in the original compound, as in NaOH, or they may be produced when a compound such as Na_2O reacts with water. Here is the reaction of the base Na_2O with water:

$$Na_2O + H_2O \longrightarrow 2\ NaOH \longrightarrow 2\ Na^+ + 2\ OH^-$$

Oxides such as Na_2O, which react with water to form bases, are called *basic oxides*. The oxides of the more electropositive metals are all basic oxides. A basic hydroxide, $M(OH)_n$, that dissociates almost completely in aqueous solution to form M^{n+} and OH^- is called a *strong base*. Examples are the compounds NaOH, KOH and $Ba(OH)_2$.

A convenient way of approaching acids and bases is to compare their composition with the composition of water, HOH. If the OH of a water molecule, H—OH, is replaced by an electronegative element, X, the resulting compound is an acid, represented by the general formula HX, for example, HCl. If the H of a water molecule, H—OH, is replaced by an electropositive element, M, the resulting compound is a *base*, represented by the general formula MOH, for instance, NaOH. If the H of a water molecule is replaced by M, and the OH by X, the resulting ionic compound is a *salt*, represented by the general formula MX, for example, NaCl.

20-3 Neutralization of Acids and Bases

Acids and bases react with one another to form (1) water and (2) ionic compounds known as salts; this general reaction is called a *neutralization reaction*. An example is the reaction of the base, sodium hydroxide, NaOH, with the acid, hydrochloric acid, HCl, to form water, H_2O, and the salt, sodium chloride, NaCl:

$$Na^+ + OH^- + H^+ + Cl^- \longrightarrow H_2O + Na^+ + Cl^-$$

The ability of acids and bases to neutralize one another depends on the tendency of the hydrogen ion, H^+, of the acid to combine with the hydroxide ion, OH^-, of the base to form un-ionized water, H_2O. The positive ions of the base and the negative ions of the acid have only a minor effect on the neutralization reaction. Consequently, we can describe all neutralization reactions between aqueous solutions of acids and bases by means of this simple equation:

$$H^+ + OH^- \longrightarrow H_2O$$

When a dilute aqueous solution of a strong acid, such as HCl or HNO_3, which is almost completely ionized, is mixed with a dilute aqueous solution of a strong base, such as NaOH or KOH, which is also almost completely ionized, the neutralization reaction is exothermic. In all such cases the ΔH of reaction is virtually the same:

$$\left.\begin{array}{l} H^+ + \cancel{Cl^-} + \cancel{Na^+} + OH^- \longrightarrow \cancel{Na^+} + \cancel{Cl^-} + H_2O \\ H^+ + \cancel{Cl^-} + \cancel{K^+} + OH^- \longrightarrow \cancel{K^+} + \cancel{Cl^-} + H_2O \\ H^+ + \cancel{NO_3^-} + \cancel{Na^+} + OH^- \longrightarrow \cancel{Na^+} + \cancel{NO_3^-} + H_2O \\ H^+ + \cancel{NO_3^-} + \cancel{K^+} + OH^- \longrightarrow \cancel{K^+} + \cancel{NO_3^-} + H_2O \end{array}\right\} \Delta H = -13.8 \frac{\text{kcal}}{\text{mole-eqn}}, \text{ at } 25^\circ C$$

These equations emphasize that the *essential or net chemical change* is in each case the union of H^+ ions and OH^- ions to form un-ionized water, H_2O, while the anions of the acid originally present in the acid solution and the cations of the base originally present in the basic solution remain unchanged. Accordingly, as we have said, the heat of neutralization is approximately the same in each case, and is in effect the ΔH of the reaction *of hydrogen ions, H^+, and hydroxyl ions, OH^-, in forming molecular water, H_2O:*

$$H^+_{(aq)} + OH^-_{(aq)} \longrightarrow H_2O_{(l)} \qquad \Delta H = -13.8 \text{ kcal/mole } H_2O$$

20-4 Equilibrium between H^+, OH^-, and H_2O. *pH*

We have already learned in Chapter 11 that pure water contains a very small but detectable, equal number of H^+ ions and OH^- ions in equilibrium with H_2O molecules. Experimental evidence of the presence of these H^+ and OH^- ions, which are formed by the ionization of the water, is the ability of pure water to conduct an electric current to a slight but measurable degree. The ionization of water can be expressed as follows:

$$H_2O_{(l)} \rightleftharpoons H^+_{(aq)} + OH^-_{(aq)}, \text{ or simply, } H_2O \rightleftharpoons H^+ + OH^-$$

Pure water always contains equal concentrations of H^+ ions and OH^- ions, because one H^+ ion and one OH^- ion are formed for each water molecule, H_2O, that ionizes. Any solution that contains equal concentrations of H^+ ions and OH^- ions is *neutral.* A solution that contains a higher concentration of H^+ ions than of OH^- ions is *acidic.* And a solution that has a higher concentration of OH^- ions than of H^+ ions is *basic.*

At 25°C the concentration of both the H^+ ions and OH^- ions in water is 1×10^{-7} moles of ions/l. *In any aqueous solution* at 25°C, either acidic, basic, or neutral, the *product* of the concentration of the H^+ ions, expressed in moles/l., and of the OH^- ions, expressed in moles/l., is essentially a constant, and is equal to 1×10^{-14}. Using brackets to express concentration in moles/l., we write: $[H^+] \times [OH^-] = 1 \times 10^{-14}$. To summarize:

Acidic solution	*Neutral solution*	*Basic solution*
$[H^+] > [OH^-]$	$[H^+] = [OH^-]$	$[OH^-] > H^+$
$[H^+] > 1 \times 10^{-7}$	$[H^+] = 1 \times 10^{-7}$	$[OH^-] > 1 \times 10^{-7}$
$[OH^-] < 1 \times 10^{-7}$	$[OH^-] = 1 \times 10^{-7}$	$[H^+] < 1 \times 10^{-7}$

Since in any aqueous solution the product of the H^+ ion concentration and the OH^- ion concentration is a constant, if we know the concentration of either of these ions in a solution, we can easily calculate the concentration of the other. Actually, we could express the acidity or basicity of a solution in terms of the concentration of either the H^+ ion or the OH^- ion. But it is customary to use the H^+ ion concentration.

pH. The acidity or basicity of solutions is frequently expressed in terms of a function of the H^+ ion concentration called *pH*. The *pH* of a solution is defined as,

$$pH = -\log [H^+]$$

Thus, if the $[H^+]$ of a solution is 10^{-7} (that is, a neutral solution), the *pH* is:

$$pH = -\log [H^+] = -\log 10^{-7} = -(-7) = 7$$

If the H^+ is 10^{-3} (an acidic solution), the $pH = -\log 10^{-3} = -(-3) = 3$. Of course, if the $[H^+]$ is not exactly a power of 10, the *pH* of the solution is not expressed as an integral number, but as a decimal number. For example, if $[H^+] = 2 \times 10^{-3}$ moles/l., the *pH* of the solution is:

$$pH = -\log [H^+] = -\log [2 \times 10^{-3}] = -\log 2 + 3.000 = 3.000 - 0.301 = 2.699 \cong 2.7$$

If we know the OH^- ion concentration but not the H^+ ion concentration of a solution, we can still calculate the *pH* by using the relationship $[H^+] \times [OH^-] = 1 \times 10^{-14}$. For example, if the $[OH^-]$ is 10^{-4}, the $[H^+]$ is equal to $10^{-14}/10^{-4}$, or 10^{-10}, and the $pH = -(-10) = 10$. In a neutral solution the $[H^+] = 10^{-7}$ and the $pH = 7$; in an acidic solution the $[H^+]$ is greater than 10^{-7} and the *pH* is less than 7; in a basic solution the $[H^+]$ is less than 10^{-7} and the *pH* is greater than 7.

To sum up, then, we can express the acidity or basicity of a solution in terms of its H^+ ion concentration, or of its OH^- ion concentration, or of its *pH*. Table 20-1 illustrates these three methods.

20-5 Weak Acids

Pure, anhydrous, acetic acid is, at room temperature, a liquid consisting of covalent CH_3COOH molecules. When acetic acid is dissolved in water, it ionizes only partially into hydrogen ions, H^+, and acetate ions, CH_3COO^-. Thus, an aqueous solution of acetic acid contains un-ionzed CH_3COOH molecules, as well as H^+ ions and CH_3COO^- ions. Actually, in a 0.1 *M* acetic acid solution, about 99 per cent of the

TABLE 20-1 EXPRESSING ACIDITY OR BASICITY OF AQUEOUS SOLUTIONS

	$[H^+] \times [OH^-] = 10^{-14}$			
Solution	$[H^+]$	$[OH^-]$	pH	*Nature of Solution*
0.01 *M* HCl	10^{-2}	10^{-12}	2	acidic
10^{-5} *M* HCl	10^{-5}	10^{-9}	5	acidic
H_2O (pure water)	10^{-7}	10^{-7}	7	neutral
10^{-5} *M* NaOH	10^{-9}	10^{-5}	9	basic
0.01 *M* NaOH	10^{-12}	10^{-2}	12	basic

original CH_3COOH molecules remain as CH_3COOH molecules, and only about 1 per cent is ionized to form ions. In a solution of acetic acid at constant concentration and temperature, the H^+ ions and the CH_3COO^- ions are continuously recombining to form CH_3COOH molecules, but an equal number of CH_3COOH molecules are continuously ionizing to form H^+ and CH_3COO^- ions, so that the proportion of molecules to ions remains constant. We say that an equilibrium is established, as expressed by the following equation:

$$CH_3COOH \rightleftharpoons H^+ + CH_3COO^-$$

Covalent substances of this sort, which produce relatively few H^+ ions in solution, are called weak acids. In aqueous solution weak acids ionize only partially, giving rise to an equilibrium mixture of covalent molecules of the acid and relatively few H^+ ions and anions of the acid. Table 20-2 lists some weak acids, together with the extent of their ionization under similar conditions.

The extent to which a weak acid ionizes in aqueous solution increases as the solution becomes more and more dilute. For example, the percentage of acetic acid molecules that ionize in an aqueous solution increases from about 1.3 per cent in a 0.1 *M* solution to about 4.3 per cent in a 0.01 *M* solution, because in the more dilute solution the H^+ ions and the CH_3COO^- ions have less opportunity to come together and form covalent CH_3COOH molecules. Although the percentage of ionization is higher in the more dilute solution, the concentration of H^+ and CH_3COO^- ions is still greater in the more concentrated solution ($[H^+] = [CH_3COO^-] = 1.3$ per cent $\times$ 0.1 *M*) than in the dilute solution ($[H^+] = [CH_3COO^-] = 4.3$ per cent $\times$ 0.01 *M*).

Notice that even though the un-ionized acetic acid molecule (the hydrogen acetate molecule), CH_3COOH, contains a total of four hydrogen atoms, only one of them can be ionized (is ionizable). Studies of the structure of this molecule show that the three hydrogen atoms bonded to a covalent carbon atom are not ionizable at all, whereas the fourth hydrogen atom bonded to an oxygen atom is ionizable (p. 449).* This hydrogen atom, however, does not ionize completely but gives rise to the equilibrium we have just discussed: $CH_3COOH \rightleftharpoons H^+ + CH_3COO^-$.

20-6 Strength and Capacity of Acids

As we have seen, a strong acid ionizes in dilute solution almost completely, and a weak acid ionizes only slightly. Thus, the concentration of H^+ ions in a water solution of a strong acid is relatively high; in a water solution of a weak acid of some molarity it is relatively low. In certain reactions, however, solutions of strong acids and weak acids produce the same over-all effect. For example, equal volumes of solutions of hydrochloric acid and acetic acid at the same molarity, require exactly

* Writing the formula of the acetic acid molecule as CH_3COOH rather than as $C_2H_4O_2$ helps to clarify this distinction.

TABLE 20-2 SOME WEAK ACIDS AND THEIR PERCENTAGE IONIZATION IN 0.1 *M* AQUEOUS SOLUTION AT 25°C.

Acid	*Formula*	*% Ionization*	*Equilibrium Reaction*
Acetic acid	CH_3COOH	1.3	$CH_3COOH \rightleftharpoons H^+ + CH_3COO^-$
Formic acid	$HCOOH$	4.3	$HCOOH \rightleftharpoons H^+ + HCOO^-$
Cyanic acid	$HCNO$	3.4	$HCNO \rightleftharpoons H^+ + CNO^-$
Hydrogen sulfide	H_2S	0.1	$H_2S \rightleftharpoons H^+ + HS^-$;
			$HS^- \rightleftharpoons H^+ + S^=$

the same volume of sodium hydroxide in order to be neutralized, even though the H^+ ion concentration is quite different in the two solutions. This is so because both solutions have *the same number (of moles) of "replaceable hydrogen"* (free hydrogen ions plus un-ionized, but ionizable, hydrogen).

In the aqueous solution of hydrochloric acid (which is ionized almost completely into H^+ ions and Cl^- ions), the OH^- ions of the base react extremely rapidly with the H^+ ions of the acid to form un-ionized water:

$$H^+ + \cancel{Cl^-} + \cancel{Na^+} + OH^- \longrightarrow H_2O + \cancel{Na^+} + \cancel{Cl^-}$$

In the aqueous solution of acetic acid, however, which contains covalent CH_3COOH molecules in equilibrium with H^+ ions and CH_3COO^- ions, the neutralization reaction may be thought to occur in either of two ways: (1) The OH^- ions react with the H^+ ions to form water. *But as the H^+ ions are removed,* additional acetic acid molecules, CH_3COOH, *ionize* to form more H^+ ions and more CH_3COO^- ions. This combined reaction *continues* until all the OH^- ions have been neutralized. (2) Both the H^+ ions and the acetic acid molecules react directly with the OH^- ions of the base to form un-ionized water. Regardless of the mechanism, however, the net effect is the same—acetic acid molecules, CH_3COOH, are used up, the OH^- ions of the base are neutralized, and CH_3COO^- ions and H_2O are formed, the cations of the base remaining unchanged in solution:

$$CH_3COOH + \cancel{Na^+} + OH^- \longrightarrow CH_3COO^- + \cancel{Na^+} + H_2O$$

Thus we see that the behavior of the solutions of an acid depends on two different and unrelated properties—the strength and the capacity of the acid. The *strength* of an acid is a measure of the instantaneous hydrogen ion concentration, $[H^+]$, in a solution of the acid at a specified concentration and temperature. This instantaneous hydrogen ion concentration can be measured, for example, by immersing a hydrogen electrode in the solution or by determining the color of a suitable indicator added to the acid solution. On the other hand, the *capacity* of an acid is the number of "replaceable hydrogen atoms" in one molecule of the acid—that is, the number of hydrogen atoms in the parent acid molecule which can react with the hydroxide ions of a base to form water. The number of "replaceable hydrogen atoms" can be determined, for example, by titration of the acid solution with a base (p. 446). For instance, a 1 *M* aqueous solution of hydrogen chloride, HCl, has a very much greater—almost 100 times greater—instantaneous hydrogen ion concentration than a 1 *M* aqueous solution of hydrogen acetate, CH_3COOH, but both solutions have the same capacity to neutralize a basic solution (both HCl and CH_3COOH contain one replaceable hydrogen atom per molecule).

20-7 Ions that Act as Acids

In addition to neutral *molecules* that act as acids, certain *ions* can also act as acids. An aqueous solution of sodium hydrogen sulfate, $NaHSO_4$, like an aqueous solution of HCl, has chemical properties that can be attributed to hydrated hydrogen ions —in other words, the solution is acidic. The $NaHSO_4$ is completely dissociated into Na^+ ions and HSO_4^- ions in solution, and the HSO_4^- ions are ionized further into H^+ and $SO_4^=$ ions:

$$HSO_4^- \rightleftharpoons H^+ + SO_4^=$$

For example, if 1 mole of $NaHSO_4$ is dissolved in water to form 1 l. of a 1 *M* solution, approximately 13 per cent of the HSO_4^- ions in turn ionize into hydrated H^+ ions and $SO_4^=$ ions. The remaining 87 per cent exist as undissociated HSO_4^- ions. The HSO_4^- ion must be regarded as an acid, because the formation of H^+ ions is characteristic of acids.

Other "ion acids" that undergo partial ionization in aqueous solution to form H^+ ions are HSO_3^-, $H_2PO_4^-$, and $HPO_4^=$:

$$HSO_3^- \rightleftharpoons H^+ + SO_3^= \qquad H_2PO_4^- \rightleftharpoons H^+ + HPO_4^= \qquad HPO_4^= \rightleftharpoons H^+ + PO_4^{\equiv}$$

The anions HSO_3^-, $H_2PO_4^-$, and $HPO_4^=$ are ionized only slightly in water and consequently they are *weak acids.*

20-8 Hydrolysis

In the preceding examples, we have been considering acidic and basic solutions in which the H^+ ion or the OH^- ion is formed directly from the acid or base as a result of ionization. But H^+ ions and OH^- ions can be formed in another way: *from the reaction of an ion with water.* This general type of reaction is called *hydrolysis,* and we shall now discuss it in some detail.

CATIONS THAT ACT AS ACIDS. The NH_4^+ ion is a common cation that reacts with water, though only slightly, to produce a hydrated H^+ ion. To understand this reaction, we must remember that water itself is ionized to a slight but significant extent into H^+ ions and OH^- ions. When the ionic compound NH_4Cl is dissolved in water, the crystal breaks down, and hydrated NH_4^+ ions and Cl^- ions are formed. Some of the NH_4^+ ions react with the OH^- ions of the water to form H_2O and NH_3. Thus, an excess of H^+ ions is left in the solution, which consequently is acidic:

$$\begin{array}{ccl} H_2O \rightleftharpoons H^+ + & OH^- & \\ & + & \\ & NH_4^+ & \rightleftharpoons NH_3 + H_2O \end{array}$$

Some hydrated cations, such as $[Fe(H_2O)_6]^{+++}$, $[Al(H_2O)_6]^{+++}$, and $[Cu(H_2O)_6]^{++}$ also produce hydrated H^+ ions when dissolved in water, so that their aqueous solutions are acidic. For these compounds, the hydrolysis consists essentially of the expulsion of a hydrogen ion from one of the water molecules attached to the metal ion in the hydrated ion; we can represent it as follows:

$$[Fe(H_2O)_5(HOH)]^{+++} \rightleftharpoons [Fe(H_2O)_5(OH)]^{++} + H^+$$

Thus the hydrated iron(III) ion, $[Fe(H_2O)_6]^{+++}$, is an acid, because it yields H^+ ions when it is dissolved in water, but since the resulting concentration of H^+ ions is low, the $[Fe(H_2O)_6]^{+++}$ ion is a weak acid. Notice that water (the solvent) is directly involved in the above reaction, even though it does not appear in the net equation, because it serves to hydrate the proton which is expelled from the hydrated metal ion. Actually, the reaction may well be described as a competition for this proton between a water molecule of the hydrated metal ion and a water molecule of the solvent:

$$[Fe(H_2O)_5(HOH)]^{+++} + H_2O \rightleftharpoons [Fe(H_2O)_5(OH)]^{++} + H_3O^+$$

Simple equations to represent similar reactions for the hydrated ions $[Zn(H_2O)_4]^{++}$ and $[Al(H_2O)_6]^{+++}$ follow:

$$[Zn(H_2O)_4]^{++} \rightleftharpoons [Zn(H_2O)_3(OH)]^+ + H^+$$
$$[Al(H_2O)_6]^{+++} \rightleftharpoons [Al(H_2O)_5(OH)]^{++} + H^+$$

These hydrated metal ions also are weak acids, because they yield a low H^+ ion concentration when they are dissolved in water.

ANIONS THAT ACT AS BASES. The negative ions of some salts react with water to produce hydroxide ions, OH^-. Since the formation of hydroxide ions is characteristic of bases, such negative ions are regarded as bases. For example, when sodium acetate, CH_3COONa, dissolves in water, it dissociates almost completely into Na^+ ions and CH_3COO^- ions; some of these CH_3COO^- ions combine with the H^+ ions from the water to form undissociated CH_3COOH molecules. Since this reaction effectively ties up the H^+ ions, the concentration of OH^- exceeds that of the H^+ ions:

$$\begin{array}{ccc} H_2O & \rightleftharpoons & H^+ + OH^- \\ & & + \\ & & CH_3COO^- \rightleftharpoons CH_3COOH \end{array}$$

The H^+ ions (formed from the ionization of the water) combine with the CH_3COO^- ions because acetic acid is a weak acid and consequently tends to exist mostly as undissociated CH_3COOH molecules. In general, a salt of any weak acid will react with water to form OH^- ions in the same way as the CH_3COO^- ion does.

Other examples of ions that act as bases in aqueous solution are HCO_3^-, $CO_3^=$, $PO_4^{\equiv}$, $SO_3^=$, HS^-, $S^=$, and CN^-. Thus, an aqueous solution of Na_2CO_3 produces OH^- ions and H_2CO_3 molecules, as shown by the following equation:

$$\cancel{2\,Na^+} + CO_3^= + 2\,H_2O \rightleftharpoons \cancel{2\,Na^+} + H_2CO_3 + 2\,OH^-$$

An equilibrium exists between the carbonate ions, $CO_3^=$, and the water molecules on the one hand, and the hydroxide ions and the un-ionized carbonic acid molecules, H_2CO_3, on the other. The $CO_3^=$ ion is a base, because it yields OH^- ions in water. But it is a weak base, because the resulting concentration of OH^- ions is small.

Here are the equations for the essential reactions that occur between water and the other anions that we have mentioned:

$$HCO_3^- + H_2O \rightleftharpoons H_2CO_3 + OH^- \qquad HS^- + H_2O \rightleftharpoons H_2S + OH^-$$
$$PO_4^{\equiv} + H_2O \rightleftharpoons HPO_4^= + OH^- \qquad S^= + H_2O \rightleftharpoons HS^- + OH^-$$
$$SO_3^= + H_2O \rightleftharpoons HSO_3^- + OH^- \qquad CN^- + H_2O \rightleftharpoons HCN + OH^-$$

Because the hydrolysis of the salt of a strong base and a weak acid produces a basic solution, such a salt may be used to neutralize an acid; Na_2CO_3, for example, will neutralize an acid such as hydrochloric acid according to the following reaction:

$$2\,H^+ + \cancel{2\,Cl^-} + \cancel{2\,Na^+} + CO_3^= \rightleftharpoons H_2CO_3 + \cancel{2\,Na^+} + \cancel{2\,Cl^-}$$

The resulting H_2CO_3 then decomposes to yield CO_2 and H_2O.

To summarize: the reaction of the solvent, water, with either the cation of a salt to give H^+, or with the anion of a salt to give OH^- is called in general "the hydrolysis of the salt." The hydrolysis of a salt of a weak base and a strong acid produces an acid solution:

$$M^+ + X^- + H_2O \rightleftharpoons MOH + X^- + H^+$$

The hydrolysis of a salt of a strong base and a weak acid produces a basic solution:

$$M^+ + X^- + H_2O \rightleftharpoons M^+ + HX + OH^-$$

The weaker the acid or base involved, the greater the extent of the hydrolysis. For example, H_2CO_3 is a weaker acid than CH_3COOH. Thus, Na_2CO_3 is hydrolyzed (reacts with water to produce OH^- ions) to a much greater extent than does CH_3COONa.

20-9 Monobasic and Polybasic Acids, Monoacid and Polyacid Bases

Some common acids, such as HCl, HNO_3, and CH_3COOH, contain only one replaceable (acidic) hydrogen atom per molecule. When dissolved in water, 1 mole of each of these acids has the capacity to produce 1 mole only of hydrated H^+. Consequently, these and similar acids are called *monobasic acids.*

Some other common acids, on the other hand, contain two, three, or even more replaceable hydrogen atoms per molecule of acid. Sulfuric acid, H_2SO_4, for example, contains two acidic hydrogen atoms per molecule. When dissolved in water, 1 mole of H_2SO_4 can produce 2 moles of H^+, and in order to neutralize the resulting solution, 2 moles of OH^- are required. Consequently, this and similar acids are called *dibasic acids.* One mole of an acid such as H_3PO_4, which contains three acidic hydrogen atoms per molecule, can neutralize 3 moles of OH^-, so this acid is called a *tribasic acid.* Acids that contain two, three, or more acidic hydrogen atoms per molecule are known as *polybasic acids.*

Similarly, bases such as NaOH and KOH that produce 1 mole of OH^- ions per 1 mole of base are termed *monoacid bases.* Bases such as $Ca(OH)_2$ and $Mg(OH)_2$ that produce 2 moles of OH^- ions per 1 mole of base are *diacid bases.* And bases such as $Al(OH)_3$ and $Cr(OH)_3$ that produce 3 moles of OH^- ions per 1 mole of base are *triacid bases.* Bases that contain two, three, or more moles of hydroxide groups per mole of base are known as *polyacid bases.*

Now let us compare the strength of polybasic acids with the strength of the acid ions that are formed by the ionization of these acids. A polybasic acid molecule ionizes to form a H^+ ion more readily than its acid ion does. And an acid anion of lower negative charge ionizes more readily to form a H^+ ion than an acid ion of higher negative charge. For example, a neutral molecule of phosphoric acid, H_3PO_4, ionizes more readily to form a H^+ ion than does the negatively charged dihydrogen phosphate ion, $H_2PO_4^-$, which in turn ionizes more readily than the hydrogen phosphate ion, $HPO_4^=$.

1. $H_3PO_4 \rightleftharpoons H^+ + H_2PO_4^-$
2. $H_2PO_4^- \rightleftharpoons H^+ + HPO_4^=$
3. $HPO_4^= \rightleftharpoons H^+ + PO_4^{\equiv}$

Step 1 represents the *primary ionization,* step 2 the *secondary ionization,* and step 3 the *tertiary ionization.* Thus, the extent of ionization of a polybasic acid is as follows:

$$\text{Primary ionization} > \text{secondary ionization} > \text{tertiary ionization}$$

The reverse way of saying this is that the trinegative ion $PO_4^{\equiv}$ has a greater attraction for a positively charged H^+ ion than does the dinegative $HPO_4^=$ ion, which in turn has a greater attraction for a positively charged H^+ ion than does the mononegative $H_2PO_4^-$ ion.

20-10 Molar and Normal Solutions of Acids and Bases

We learned in Chapter 19 that we can conveniently express the concentration of any solution in terms of its molarity, *M*—the number of moles of solute per liter of solution. If we know the molarity and the volume of a given acid solution, and the molarity of a given base solution, we can calculate the volume of the base solution required to neutralize the acid solution, provided we know the equation for the neutralization reaction. Let us consider the neutralization of HCl by NaOH:

$$HCl + NaOH \longrightarrow NaCl + H_2O$$

This equation tells us that 1 mole of HCl will neutralize 1 mole of NaOH. And it follows that 1 l. of a 1 *M* HCl solution, which contains 1 mole of HCl, will exactly neutralize 1 l. of a 1 *M* NaOH solution, which contains 1 mole of NaOH. Also, 1 l. of a 1 *M* HCl solution will neutralize 2 l. of a 0.5 *M* NaOH solution, or 0.5 l. of a 2 *M* NaOH solution, because these quantities of basic solution each contain 1 mole of NaOH. Notice that a given volume of a solution of the monoacid base NaOH will exactly neutralize an equal volume of the monobasic acid HCl, if the acidic and basic solutions have the same molarity.

The concentrations of solutions of acids and bases can also be expressed conveniently in terms of equivalent weights. *The equivalent weight of an acid* is the weight in grams of the acid which contains 1 mole of replaceable hydrogen atoms. Similarly, *the equivalent weight of a base* is the weight in grams of the base which contains 1 mole of replaceable hydroxide ions. According to this definition of equivalent weight, if 1 mole of an acid produces exactly 1 mole of replaceable hydrogen atoms, then the formula weight of the acid is also the equivalent weight of the acid. Examples are HCl, HNO_3, HBr. If 1 mole of an acid, such as H_2SO_4, contains 2 moles of replaceable hydrogen atoms, then 1 mole contains 2 equivalent weights of the acid, and $\frac{1}{2}$ mole of the acid contains 1 equivalent weight. Similarly, if 1 mole of a base contains 2 moles of replaceable hydroxide ions, such as $Ba(OH)_2$, then 1 mole of the base contains 2 equivalent weights, and $\frac{1}{2}$ mole of the base contains 1 equivalent weight. Likewise, for an acid that has three replaceable hydrogen atoms (e.g., H_3PO_4), and for a base which has three replaceable OH^- ions (e.g., $Al(OH)_3$), the equivalent weight is one-third of one mole of the acid or base. Table 20-3 gives the formula weights and the equivalent weights of a number of acids and bases.

TABLE 20-3 EQUIVALENT WEIGHTS OF SOME ACIDS AND BASES

Compound	Formula Weight	Equivalent Weight*
HBr	80.92	80.92/1 = 80.92
CH_3COOH	60.05	60.05/1 = 60.05
H_3PO_4	97.99	97.99/3 = 32.66
$NaHSO_4$	120.06	120.01/1 = 120.06
NaH_2PO_4	119.98	119.98/2 = 59.99
KOH	56.10	56.11/1 = 56.11
$Mg(OH)_2$	58.33	58.33/2 = 29.16
NH_4OH	35.05	35.05/1 = 35.05
$Al(OH)_3$	78.00	78.00/3 = 26.00

* The equivalent weight is the formula weight divided by (a) the number of replaceable H atoms, or (b) the number of OH groups in each formula.

A solution that contains 1 equivalent weight of a substance per liter is a 1 normal solution. The *normality* of a solution—usually designated by the symbol *N*—is the number of equivalent weights of solute per liter of solution. Since 1 eq wt of any acid will neutralize 1 eq wt of any base, a given volume of 1 normal solution of *any* acid will exactly neutralize the same volume of a 1 normal solution of *any* base. This also holds for the neutralization of a base by an acid.

Now let us illustrate with two examples the methods for calculating the volume of an acidic solution of known normality that will exactly neutralize a known volume of a basic solution of known normality, and vice versa.

ILLUSTRATIVE EXAMPLES

PROBLEM. What volume of a 0.33 *N* solution of an acid is required to neutralize 27 ml of a 0.44 *N* solution of a base?

SOLUTION. The "greater or less than" method used in calculating gas problems (see p. 118) may also be used for neutralization problems. The volume of the acid in our example must be *greater than* 27 ml, for the volume of the weaker acidic solution required to neutralize the stronger basic solution must be greater than 27 ml.

$$V = 27 \text{ ml} \times \frac{0.44 \text{ N}}{0.33 \text{ N}} = 36 \text{ ml}$$

PROBLEM. The neutralization of 30 ml of a 0.2 *N* solution of $Ca(OH)_2$ requires 40 ml of a given acid. Calculate the normality of the acid.

SOLUTION. The normality of the acid in our example must be *less than* 0.2 *N*, for a greater volume (40 ml) is required to neutralize the volume (30 ml) of the base:

$$N = 0.20 \text{ N} \times \frac{30 \text{ ml}}{40 \text{ ml}} = 0.15 \text{ N}$$

TITRATION

Assume that we have a basic solution of known normality and an acidic solution of unknown normality. If we measure experimentally the volume of the basic solution that is required to neutralize exactly a given volume of the acidic solution, we can calculate the normality of the acidic solution, as we have seen in the above examples. This operation is called "titration." But how can we tell when we have added just the right volume of the basic solution to neutralize exactly the acidic solution? One method is to add a trace of some chemical compound—an indicator—that will change color when an equivalent quantity of the base has been added.

INDICATORS. In general, an indicator is a very weak acid or a very weak base that has a particular color when present as the undissociated molecule and a different color when present in its ionic form. For example, the indicator methyl orange is red when present in an acidic solution as the undissociated molecule HIn,* but it is orange-yellow when present in a basic solution as the ions In^- and H^+. Another common indicator, phenolphthalein, is colorless in its acidic form (in acid solution) and red in its ionic form (in basic solution). For each indicator, the characteristic change in color occurs at a particular value of the *pH*. Hence, by using a rather wide selection of indicators we can estimate the H^+ ion concentration of a given solution within fairly narrow limits. Table 20-4 gives the names and the acidic and basic colors of three commonly used indicators, together with the range of the H^+ ion concentrations within which the characteristic acidic $\rightleftharpoons$ basic color change occurs.

TITRATION CURVES. The process of adding a basic solution of known normality to an acidic solution of unknown normality (or vice versa) until the solution has become exactly neutralized is known as *titration*. Now let us consider the titration of an aqeuous solution of a strong acid, such as hydrochloric acid, H^+Cl^-, by an aqueous solution of a strong base, such as sodium hydroxide, Na^+OH^-. In the original solution of the strong acid the instantaneous concentration of the H^+ ions is equal to the total concentration of the acid. For example, if the solution of hydrochloric acid is 0.1 molar (0.1 *M*) or 0.1 normal (0.1 *N*), the H^+ ion concentration is also 0.1 *M* or 1×10^{-1} *N* and the *pH* of the solution is therefore 1. Now, as we add drop-by-drop a solution of the strong base, say 0.1 *M* or 0.1 *N* sodium hydroxide, the added OH^- ions of the base neutralize an equal number of the H^+ of the acid, forming water molecules, H_2O. Thus, as the OH^- ions are first added, the concentration of the H^+ ions in the solution decreases but the number of the H^+ ions remaining in solution is still very great. If we plot the instantaneous H^+ concentration on a log scale, or the *pH* of the solution, against the number of equivalent weights of base added (Fig. 20-1), we first obtain a curve which slopes only slightly. But when the number of equivalent weights of base (OH^-) added begins to approach the number of equivalent weights of acid (H^+) originally present in the solution to be titrated, the instantaneous

* The *abbreviation* In is used here to denote the anion of the dissociated indicators.

TABLE 20-4 COLOR CHANGES OF THREE INDICATORS AND THEIR H^+ ION CONCENTRATION RANGE

	Color in Solution	
Indicator	*Acidic*	*Basic*
Methyl orange	red, $[H^+] = 10^{-3}$	yellow, $[H^+] = 10^{-5}$
Litmus	red, $[H^+] = 10^{-5}$	blue, $[H^+] = 10^{-7}$
Phenolphthalein	colorless, $[H^+] = 10^{-8}$	red, $[H^+] = 10^{-10}$

concentration of hydrogen ions begins to decrease more sharply. Finally, as the end-point of the titration (100 per cent neutralization) is reached, the H^+ concentration drops very markedly and abruptly. In fact, the OH^- ions in the last drop of basic solution added near the end-point of the titration first neutralize the few remaining H^+ ions and then change the character of the solution from acidic (excess H^+ over neutrality, $[H^+] = 10^{-7}$) to basic (excess OH^- over neutrality, $[OH^-] = 10^{-7}$). At the end-point, therefore, the titration curve rises very sharply, as the H^+ concentration changes abruptly from about 10^{-3} to about 10^{-11} ($[H^+] = 10^{-11}$ when $[OH^-] = 10^{-3}$, because $[H^+] \times [OH^-] = 10^{-14}$ in any aqueous solution). If, after reaching the end-point, we keep adding the basic solution, the H^+ ion concentration continues to drop, but now much more slowly, and we again have a slightly sloping curve. To determine the end-point of the titration of a strong acid with a strong base (or vice versa), we can use either an indicator such as methyl orange which changes color when the solution is still somewhat acidic but very close to neutrality, or one such as phenolphthalein which changes color when the solution is already somewhat basic but still very close to neutrality, or any other indicator in the intermediate $[H^+]$ range. Alternatively, we can use a *pH*-meter (see next section and Chapter 22).

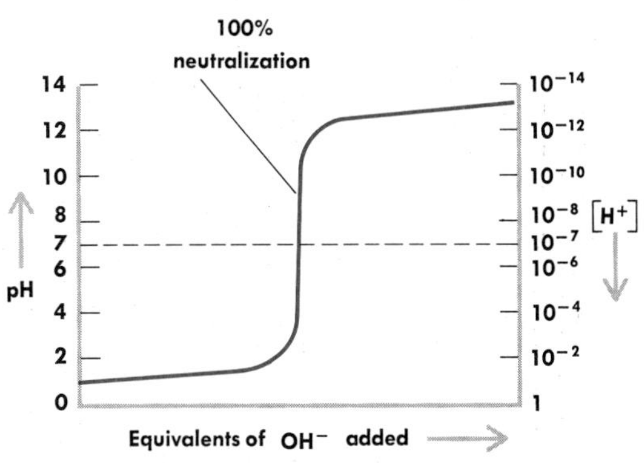

FIGURE 20-1 Neutralization curve for the titration of a strong acid with a strong base, using methyl orange or phenolphthalein as an indicator.

MEASUREMENT OF THE STRENGTH OF AN ACID

As we have seen, the greater the extent to which an acid, *HA*, ionizes to yield (hydrated) protons, H^+, and (hydrated) anions, A^-, the stronger the acid. Hence the strength of an acid in water solution is a measure of how much the following equilibrium reaction is displaced to the right:

$$HA + H_2O \rightleftharpoons H^+ + A^-$$

Consequently, one way to determine the strength of an acid is to measure the instantaneous hydrogen ion concentration in a solution of the acid. We can do so with indicators—as we have already discussed—but we can do so more accurately with an instrument called a *pH*-meter. A *pH*-meter is essentially a combined energy cell (Ch. 22) consisting of a hydrogen electrode immersed in the solution whose acidity we wish to measure and joined to a standard reference electrode. The electromotive force of this combined cell depends on the concentration of hydrogen ions in the solution, and the instrument is calibrated to give us the reading directly in units of *pH*. We shall discuss the principle of the *pH*-meter in more detail in Chapter 21.

The relative strengths of different acids in the same solvent and at the same concentration can also be obtained by measuring the *electrical conductivity* of their solutions. The electrical conductivity increases as the number of H^+ ions and A^- ions present in solution increases—that is, as the ionization of the dissolved acid increases.

20-11 Normal Salts, Acid Salts, and Basic Salts

When polybasic acids and polyacid bases are neutralized completely and the resulting solutions are concentrated, the salts that separate in crystalline form contain no replaceable hydrogen atoms or hydroxide ions, for all these ions have taken part in the neutralization reaction. Salts that do not contain any acidic hydrogen atoms or hydroxide ions are called *normal salts.* Examples are Na_2SO_4, $CaSO_4$, and K_3PO_4.

If we do not completely neutralize a polybasic acid, the salt produced, called an *acid salt,* will still contain replaceable hydrogen atoms. Consider, for example, the partial neutralization of 1 mole of H_2SO_4 by 1 mole of NaOH. If all the NaOH reacts, two possibilities arise: (1) One-half mole of H_2SO_4 may be completely neutralized to form H_2O and the salt, Na_2SO_4, leaving $\frac{1}{2}$ mole of H_2SO_4 unreacted; or (2) 1 mole of NaOH may react with the total 1 mole of H_2SO_4 to form H_2O and the salt $NaHSO_4$, sodium hydrogen sulfate. The second reaction is the one that actually takes place, and the resulting salt, $NaHSO_4$, is an *acid salt.*

Why is the acid salt of sulfuric acid, $NaHSO_4$, formed, rather than the normal salt, Na_2SO_4? The reason is that H_2SO_4 ionizes almost completely into H^+ ions and HSO_4^- ions in water solutions at moderate concentration:

$$H_2SO_4 \longrightarrow H^+ + HSO_4^-$$

In this primary ionization (p. 444) sulfuric acid is a strong acid, comparable, for example, to hydrochloric acid under the same conditions. On the other hand, the HSO_4^- ion in the sulfuric acid solution has only a slight tendency to ionize further into H^+ and $SO_4^=$ ions, so that in its secondary ionization sulfuric acid behaves as a weak acid.

Thus, when we add a base drop-by-drop to a sulfuric acid solution, the base will first react with the H^+ ions, and not with the HSO_4^- ions. Then, if we keep on adding the base, the OH^- ions will neutralize the HSO_4^- ions to form $SO_4^=$ ions and H_2O:

$$H^+ + HSO_4^- + OH^- \longrightarrow H_2O + HSO_4^-$$
$$HSO_4^- + OH^- \longrightarrow H_2O + SO_4^=$$

Similarly, when polyacid bases react with appropriate amounts of acids, the salts that are formed contain hydroxide groups (OH^-). Consider, for example, the reaction of 1 mole of $Pb(OH)_2$ with 1 mole of HCl, and the reaction of 1 mole of $Bi(OH)_3$ with 1 mole of HNO_3:

$$Pb(OH)_2 + HCl \longrightarrow H_2O + Pb(OH)Cl$$
$$Bi(OH)_3 + HNO_3 \longrightarrow H_2O + Bi(OH)_2NO_3$$

Salts such as $Pb(OH)Cl$ and $Bi(OH)_2NO_3$, which contain the hydroxide group (OH^-), are called *basic salts,* because they can react further with H^+ ions to form H_2O and the corresponding salts, $PbCl_2$ and $Bi(NO_3)_3$.

$$Pb(OH)Cl + HCl \longrightarrow H_2O + PbCl_2$$
$$Bi(OH)_2NO_3 + 2HNO_3 \longrightarrow 2H_2O + Bi(NO_3)_3$$

20-12 Structural Formulas and Acidic and Non-Acidic Hydrogen

In such common acids as HCl, HBr, HI, and HNO_3, which contain only one hydrogen atom per molecule, the hydrogen atom must obviously be an acidic hydrogen atom.

In acids that contain more than one hydrogen atom, however, not all of the hydrogen atoms are necessarily acidic. In acids that contain oxygen (called oxoacids), for example, only the hydrogen atoms that are bonded to an oxygen atom are acidic. If we know the structural formula of an oxoacid, we can tell which hydrogen atoms are bonded to oxygen atoms and thus can determine the number of acidic hydrogen atoms present. As an illustration, consider the electron-dot formulas and structural formulas of the monobasic oxoacids HNO_3 and CH_3COOH, and of the dibasic oxoacid H_2SO_4:

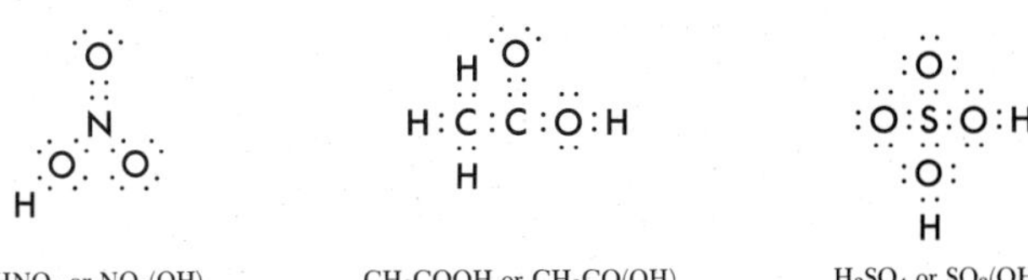

HNO_3 or $NO_2(OH)$ CH_3COOH or $CH_3CO(OH)$ H_2SO_4 or $SO_2(OH)_2$

Notice that in the structural formulas of HNO_3 and H_2SO_4, each hydrogen atom is bonded to an oxygen atom. Consequently, each hydrogen atom in these acids is capable of ionizing to a hydrated H^+ ion when the acids are dissolved in water. Thus, HNO_3 is a monobasic acid and H_2SO_4 is a dibasic acid. The structural formula of acetic acid, on the other hand, shows that one hydrogen atom is bonded to an oxygen atom, while the other three hydrogen atoms are bonded to a carbon atom. Thus, acetic acid contains one acidic hydrogen and three non-acidic hydrogen atoms, and is therefore a monobasic acid.

Another interesting example of this general rule is the series of acids of phosphorus: phosphoric acid, H_3PO_4; phosphorous acid, H_3PO_3; and hypophosphorous acid, H_3PO_2. Their electron-dot formulas and the structures are:

H_3PO_4 or $PO(OH)_3$ H_3PO_3 or $HPO(OH)_2$ H_3PO_2 or $H_2PO(OH)$

In phosphoric acid, H_3PO_4, each hydrogen atom is attached to an oxygen atom, and hence is a replaceable hydrogen atom. Phosphoric acid is therefore a *tribasic* acid. But in H_3PO_3, phosphorous acid, only two of the three hydrogen atoms present are bonded to oxygen atoms. These two hydrogen atoms are capable of ionizing into H^+ ions. The *third* hydrogen atom, however, is bonded to the phosphorus atom and is *not* capable of ionizing into a H^+ ion. And in H_3PO_2, hypophosphorous acid, only one of the three hydrogen atoms is bonded to an oxygen atom, whereas each of the other two hydrogen atoms is bonded to the phosphorous atom. Consequently, since only one hydrogen atom is available to form a H^+ ion, H_3PO_2 is a monobasic acid. Regardless of whether an acid is mono-, di-, or tribasic, its stereochemistry always follows regularly the rules given in Chapter 14, p. 279. Thus, in the molecule of hydrogen nitrate (nitric acid), HNO_3, the central N atom, is bonded to the three O atoms situated at the corners of a triangle that is almost equilateral. Also, the N—O—H bond angle is about 105°, as is usual for an O atom (symmetrical core) with two bond (electron) pairs and two lone (electron) pairs. On the same basis, we understand why the hydrogen sulfate molecule, H_2SO_4, is a tetrahedron, with the S atom at the center, an O atom at each of two corners, and an OH group at each of the other two corners. Again, the S—O—H angle is roughly 105°. In the hydrogen acetate molecule, CH_3COOH, the C atom, labeled C_1, forms four sigma bonds and lies at the center of a tetrahedron with a H atom at each of three corners and the other C atom, C_2, at the fourth corner. On the other hand, the C_2 atom, which forms only three sigma bonds, is at the center of a triangle, one corner being occupied by C_1, another corner by an O atom, and the third corner by an OH group. The molecules of the three acids—H_3PO_4, H_3PO_3, and H_3PO_2—all have a tetrahedral arrangement of four sigma bond pairs about the central P atom (which has a symmetrical core and no lone pairs). However, in H_3PO_4 the P atom is bonded to four O atoms, in H_3PO_3 the P atom is bonded to three O atoms and one H atom, and in H_3PO_2 the P atom is bonded to two O atoms and two H atoms. In every case, the P—O—H bond angle is about 105°, as predictable on the basis of the lone pair-lone pair repulsion.

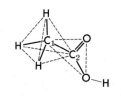

20-13 Acidic or Basic Character of Hydroxide Compounds—Amphoteric Hydroxides

An OH group present in an oxoacid ionizes to form a H^+ ion. But an OH group present in a metal hydroxide produces an OH^- ion. Thus, the metal hydroxides as well as the oxoacids—which may be considered as the hydroxides of the non-metallic elements—contain OH groups. However, in general, the hydroxides of metallic elements produce OH^- ions in solution, whereas the hydroxides of non-metallic elements produce H^+ ions in solution.

Whether the hydroxide of an element, (general formula: EOH) behaves like an acid or like a base depends on how the hydroxide dissociates when dissolved in water. If the dissociation produces a H^+ ion, the hydroxide is an acid; if the dissociation produces an OH^- ion, the hydroxide is a base. This distinction can be represented schematically as follows:

(a) *Dissociation as base*	(b) *Dissociation as acid*
E | $:\ddot{O}:$H	E$:\ddot{O}:$ | H
The electron pair is retained by the oxygen atom, and the ions E^+ and $:\ddot{O}:H^-$ are formed.	The electron pair is retained by the oxygen atom, and the ions $E:\ddot{O}:^-$ and H^+ are formed.

If the element (or group of elements) E of the hydroxide EOH is a very electronegative non-metal—which gives up electrons only with difficulty—the hydroxide dissociates as an acid; if E is a very electropositive metal—which gives up electrons with relatively little difficulty—then the hydroxide EOH dissociates as a base. Thus the "hydroxides of the halogens"—for example, hydrogen perchlorate, $HClO_4$ (or $ClO_3(OH)$); hydrogen chlorate, $HClO_3$ (or $ClO_2(OH)$); and hydrogen bromate, $HBrO_3$ (or $BrO_2(OH)$)—dissociate as acids in water, yielding respectively, $H^+ + ClO_4^-$ (perchloric acid); $H^+ + ClO_3^-$ (chloric acid); and $H^+ + BrO_3^-$ (bromic acid). On the other hand, the hydroxides of the very electropositive alkali and alkaline-earth metals dissociate as bases (i.e., NaOH gives $Na^+ + OH^-$, and $Ba(OH)_2$ gives Ba^{++} and 2 OH^-). Finally, the hydroxides of the less electropositive metals, such as $Zn(OH)_2$ and $Al(OH)_3$, even though they are insoluble in water, dissolve in (react with) aqueous acid solutions, thus indicating their ability to dissociate as bases:

$$Zn(OH)_{2(s)} + 2\ H^+_{(aq)} \longrightarrow Zn^{++}_{(aq)} + 2\ H_2O_{(l)}$$

However, these less electropositive metal hydroxides also dissolve in aqueous solutions of bases, thus indicating their ability to act as acids. For example, $Zn(OH_2)$ dissolves in aqueous solutions containing OH^- ions to form $[Zn(OH)_4]^=$:

$$Zn(OH)_{2(s)} + 2\ OH^-_{(aq)} \longrightarrow [Zn(OH)_4]^=_{(aq)}$$

Thus, the less electropositive metals such as zinc and aluminum have hydroxides that can behave as both acids and bases; these are called amphoteric (from the Greek for "both") hydroxides and the metals are called amphoteric metals.

20-14 Trends in the Strengths of Acids and Bases

As we know the strength of an acid, or of a base, is the extent to which the acid or base is ionized in solution. In general the strength of an acid, or of a base, may be related to its formula and structure. Let us consider the strength of bases first. As we know, bases dissociate to form positive metal ions and negative OH^- ions. The larger the size of the positive ion and the smaller its charge, the greater the tendency of the base to dissociate. The reason is clear: A large ion with a low positive charge has less attraction for the electron pair of the negative OH^- ion than does a small ion with a high positive charge.

The hydroxides of the alkali metals, MOH, form strong bases, and their strength increases as the size of the alkali-metal ion increases. For example, KOH is a stronger base than NaOH, because the monopositive K^+ ion is larger than the monopositive Na^+ ion. Also, among metals of a same periodic series, NaOH is a strong base, $Mg(OH)_2$ is a weaker base, and $Al(OH)_3$ is an even weaker base, because the ions Na^+, Mg^{++}, Al^{+++} become both progressively smaller in size and higher in positive charge.

Now let us compare the strengths of acids that have similar electronic structures. We find that the greater the oxidation number of the central non-metallic element, the stronger the acid. For example, in H_2SO_4, sulfuric acid, the S atom has oxidation number +6, and in H_2SO_3, sulfurous acid, the S atom has oxidation number +4. Consequently, the pull exerted by the S atom on all electron pairs it shares with oxygen atoms is greater in H_2SO_4 than in H_2SO_3. As a result, the pull exerted in turn by an O atom of an OH group on the electron pair it shares with the hydrogen atom is greater in H_2SO_4 than in H_2SO_3. When the bond electron pair shared by the oxygen atom and the hydrogen atom is pulled closer to the oxygen atom, the oxygen-to-hydrogen bond is weakened because the H atom's share of the electron pair is decreased. An H atom which shares less of the electron-pair bond has an increased tendency to leave the electron pair completely to the O atom, thus becoming a hydrogen ion, H^+. This tendency of the H atom to give up its share in the electron pair is greater in $H_2S^{+6}O_4$ than in $H_2S^{+4}O_3$. In other words, a H atom can break away, as a H^+ ion, more readily in H_2SO_4 than in H_2SO_3. The relative strengths of three series of oxoacids with similar electronic structures are listed in Table 20-5.

H:Ö:S^{+4}:Ö:
:Ö:
H
H_2SO_3
or
$SO(OH)_2$

:Ö:
H:Ö:S^{+6}:Ö:
:Ö:
H
H_2SO_4
or
$SO_2(OH)_2$

We can draw some useful generalizations from Table 20-5. Let us write the formulas of the oxoacids of a given element, E, in the general form $EO_m(OH)_n$—m is the number of oxygen atoms and n the number of hydroxide groups bound to the central element E. Table 20-5 shows that the strength of the first ionization of an acid

TABLE 20-5 RELATIVE STRENGTHS OF THREE SERIES OF OXOACIDS

Name	Formula	Structural Formula	Acid Strength	
Hypochlorous	$H\overset{+1}{Cl}O$	Cl(OH)	very weak	↓ acid strength increases
Chlorous	$H\overset{+3}{Cl}O_2$	ClO(OH)	weak	
Chloric	$H\overset{+5}{Cl}O_3$	$ClO_2(OH)$	strong	
Perchloric	$H\overset{+7}{Cl}O_4$	$ClO_3(OH)$	strong	
Sulfurous	$H_2\overset{+4}{S}O_3$	$SO(OH)_2$	weak	↓ acid strength increases
(Meta) phosphoric	$H\overset{+5}{P}O_3$	$PO_2(OH)$	strong	
Sulfuric	$H_2\overset{+6}{S}O_4$	$SO_2(OH)_2$	strong	
Chloric	$H\overset{+5}{Cl}O_3$	$ClO_2(OH)$	strong	
Acetic	CH_3COOH	$CH_3CO(OH)$	weak	↓ acid strength increases
Monochloroacetic	$ClCH_2COOH$	$ClCH_2CO(OH)$	moderate	
Dichloroacetic	$Cl_2CHCOOH$	$ClCH_2CO(OH)$	strong	
Trichloroacetic	CCl_3COOH	$CCl_3CO(OH)$	strong	

increases as the number m of the O atom increases. A qualitative explanation is that each electronegative "m oxygen atom" attached to the central E atom in the acid $EO_m(OH)_n$ tends to draw to itself the electron pair of the O↶:E covalent bond. Consequently the central E atom has a partial positive charge and tends to draw to itself the electron pair of the E↶:OH covalent bonds. In turn, the O atom of the OH group tends to attract more strongly the electron pair of the O↶:H bond, so the H atom of the OH group is more readily ionized. This effect is represented in the margin for the weak acid ClO(OH) (i.e. chlorous acid, $H\overset{+3}{Cl}O_2$); the curved arrows ↶ indicate the displacement of the electron pair of the covalent bonds. On this basis we would expect the following acids, which have no "m oxygen atoms," to be very weak: hypochlorous acid, $H\overset{+1}{Cl}O$ or Cl(OH); boric acid, $H_3\overset{+3}{B}O_3$ or $B(OH)_3$; and silicic acid, $H_4\overset{+4}{Si}O_4$ or $Si(OH)_4$. And indeed these are extremely weak acids, regardless of the oxidation number of the central element.

The acids in the third section of Table 20-5 have the general formula RCO(OH), which is characteristic of *carboxylic acids.* The first acid listed—acetic acid, $CH_3CO(OH)$—is, as expected, a weak acid ($m \doteq 1$). However, the following acids, in which one, two, and three H atoms of the CH_3 group are replaced by more electronegative Cl atoms, are increasingly stronger. Trichloroacetic acid is indeed a strong acid, about as strong as HCl. The explanation for the regular increase in acid strength along this series of carboxylic acids is similar to the explanation just discussed for the acids of the $EO_m(OH)_n$ type. The electronegative Cl atoms of the chloroacetic acids have the effect of pulling electrons away from the O atom of the OH group, so that the O atom in turn exerts a greater attraction on the electron pair of the covalent O:H bond, as compared to acetic acid itself, and the H atom becomes more readily ionizable. This effect is schematically shown in the margin. The analogy with $HClO_2$, previously described, is evident.

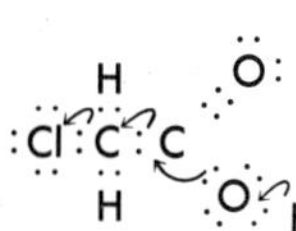

The trends we have just discussed hold in general for both monobasic and polybasic acids. For polybasic acids, of course, the strength decreases for successive ionization steps, as we saw on p. 444.

20-15 The Proton Theory of Acids and Bases

The Arrhenius definitions of acid and base that we have been using so far in this chapter apply only to aqueous solutions; these definitions emphasize the presence of H^+ ion in acids and the presence of OH^- ions in bases. In 1923, a somewhat more general definition, applicable to solutions in any solvent, was proposed independently by a Danish chemist, J. N. Bronsted (1879–1947), and an English chemist, T. M. Lowry, (1874–1936). According to this more general definition, known as the *proton theory, an acid is any hydrogen-containing substance which can give up a proton, H^+; a base is any substance which can take up a proton.* Using symbols, if HA is an acid and B is a base, we can represent the general reaction between a Bronsted acid and a Bronsted base as follows:

$$HA + B \rightleftharpoons A^- + BH^+$$

Examples of Bronsted acids are: HCl, $HClO_4$, H_3O^+, NH_4^+, $[Fe(H_2O)_6]^{+3}$, HSO_4^-, HCO_3^-, and CH_3COOH. We see, then, that a Bronsted acid may be a neutral molecule, a positive ion, or a negative ion. Examples of Bronsted bases are: OH^-, CH_3COO^-, Cl^-, NH_3, and H_2O. With the acetate ion, CH_3COO^-, as an example of a Bronsted base, the general proton-accepting reaction is shown below on the left. For comparison, the reaction in aqueous solutions is shown on the right:

$$\underset{\text{base}}{CH_3COO^-} + \underset{\text{proton}}{H^+} \longrightarrow CH_3COOH \qquad \underset{\text{base}}{CH_3COO^-} + \underset{\text{proton (hydrated)}}{H^+(H_2O)} \longrightarrow CH_3COOH + H_2O$$

Similarly, for a Bronsted acid such as HCl, the general proton-yielding reaction and the reaction in aqueous solution are:

$$\underset{\text{acid}}{HCl} \longrightarrow \underset{\text{proton}}{H^+} + Cl^- \qquad \underset{\text{acid}}{HCl} + H_2O \longrightarrow \underset{\text{proton (hydrated)}}{H^+(H_2O)} + Cl^-$$

As the equations show, whenever a Bronsted base takes on a proton the product formed is a Bronsted acid; and, conversely whenever a Bronsted acid gives up a proton the product formed is a Bronsted base. Thus in terms of the Bronsted definition, whenever an acid reacts with a base the corresponding base and the corresponding acid are formed. The acid and its corresponding base are called *conjugate,* as are the base and its corresponding acid. Table 20-6 gives a list of some Bronsted acid-base reactions; notice that for every acid there is a conjugate base and for every base a conjugate acid, and also that some substances can act both as acids and as bases.

For any conjugate acid-base system in water solution the following general equilibrium exists:

$$\underset{(\text{acid}_1)}{HA} + \underset{(\text{base}_2)}{H_2O} \rightleftharpoons \underset{(\text{acid}_2)}{H^+(H_2O)} + \underset{(\text{base}_1)}{A^-}$$

This general equation shows implicitly that water plays a dual role in the Bronsted acid-base theory; in fact in any neutralization reaction in aqueous solution, H_2O behaves both as a Bronsted acid and as a Bronsted base:

$$\underset{(\text{acid}_1)}{H^+(H_2O)} + \underset{(\text{base}_2)}{OH^-} \rightleftharpoons \underset{(\text{acid}_2)}{H_2O} + \underset{(\text{base}_1)}{H_2O}$$

As we see from Table 20-6, there are also other compounds that can either give up or take on a proton under specified conditions; such substances are called *amphiprotic.* The most common amphiprotic substances besides H_2O are the acid-ions of polybasic acids—for example, HCO_3^-, HSO_4^-, and $H_2PO_4^-$.

THE RELATIVE STRENGTHS OF BRONSTED ACIDS AND BASES

In Table 20-6 the acids are listed from bottom to top in order of increasing strength—that is, increasing tendency to give up a proton. For example, $HClO_4$

TABLE 20-6 SOME BRONSTED ACID-BASE SYSTEMS

(strength of acid increases ↑ — strength of base increases ↓)

Acid	⇌	Base	+	Proton
$HClO_4$	⇌	ClO_4^-	+	H^+
HCl	⇌	Cl^-	+	H^+
H_2SO_4	⇌	HSO_4^-	+	H^+
H_3O^+	⇌	H_2O	+	H^+
HSO_4^-	⇌	$SO_4^=$	+	H^+
H_3PO_4	⇌	$H_2PO_4^-$	+	H^+
$Fe(H_2O)_6^{+3}$	⇌	$Fe(H_2O)_5OH^{+2}$	+	H^+
$Al(H_2O)_6^{+3}$	⇌	$Al(H_2O)_5OH^{+2}$	+	H^+
H_2CO_3	⇌	HCO_3^-	+	H^+
H_2S	⇌	HS^-	+	H^+
$H_2PO_4^-$	⇌	$HPO_4^=$	+	H^+
$Cu(H_2O)_6^{+2}$	⇌	$Cu(H_2O)_5OH^+$	+	H^+
NH_4^+	⇌	NH_3	+	H^+
HCN	⇌	CN^-	+	H^+
HCO_3^-	⇌	$CO_3^=$	+	H^+
HPO_4^{-2}	⇌	PO_4^{-3}	+	H^+
HS^-	⇌	$S^=$	+	H^+
H_2O	⇌	OH^-	+	H^+
OH^-	⇌	$O^=$	+	H^+

is the strongest of all the acids, and in a dilute aqueous solution it is virtually completely ionized:

$$HClO_4 + H_2O \rightleftharpoons H^+(H_2O) + ClO_4^-$$

Since $HClO_4$ is a very strong acid, its corresponding conjugate base, the ClO_4^- ion, is very weak—that is, it has only a very slight tendency to take on a proton and re-form $HClO_4$. Similarly, HCl and H_2SO_4 are very strong acids and their conjugate bases, the ions Cl^- and HSO_4^-, are very weak bases. Thus even though there is theoretically an equilibrium between an acid and its conjugate base, a strong acid in dilute aqueous solution can be considered to be, for all practical purposes, completely ionized. For this reason we generally write the equation simply with the arrow pointing to the right; for example, for the acid HCl in water we write:

$$\underset{\text{acid}_1}{HCl} + \underset{\text{base}_2}{H_2O} \longrightarrow \underset{\text{acid}_2}{H^+(H_2O)} + \underset{\text{base}_1}{Cl^-}$$

As we go *down* the table the acids become weaker; their acidic H atoms are more and more strongly bound, and consequently their conjugate bases become stronger. Thus a weak acid near the bottom of the table—for example, HCN—has only a slight tendency to give up its strongly bound H atom; its conjugate base, the CN^- ion, is very strong because it has a great tendency to take on a proton and re-form HCN. Strong acids, then, have weak conjugate bases and weak acids have strong conjugate bases, and vice versa. Thus, of all the bases listed in Table 20-6, the one at the very bottom, OH^-, is the strongest, and the one at the very top, ClO_4^-, is the weakest. And in general a base near the bottom of the table—for example, the CN^- ion (of a salt such as Na^+CN^-)—reacts extensively with water (hydrolyzes) to form the very weak acid HCN and the stronger base OH^-:

$$CN^- + H_2O \rightleftharpoons HCN + OH^-$$

On the other hand, a base near the top of the table, for example the Cl^- ion (or a salt such as Na^+Cl^-) does not react to any appreciable extent with water to form the strong acid HCl.

INFLUENCE OF THE SOLVENT ON THE STRENGTH OF ACIDS

Some acids exhibit similar properties in different solvents. For example, trichloroacetic acid, CCl_3COOH, which, as we have seen, is structurally similar to acetic acid, CH_3COOH, is a strong acid in water solution and an equally strong acid in benzene, C_6H_6. Usually, however, an acid exhibits different properties when dissolved in widely different solvents. For example, when gaseous hydrogen chloride, HCl, is dissolved in water, the resulting solution is strongly acidic and is an excellent conductor of electric current, since HCl is almost completely ionized into hydrated H^+ and Cl^- ions. On the other hand, when HCl is dissolved in benzene, C_6H_6, the resulting solution does not conduct an electric current, indicating that HCl is not ionized to any appreciable extent.* Consequently, as we would expect, the chemistry of hydrogen chloride is markedly different in water solution from what it is in benzene solution. In water solution the chemistry of hydrogen chloride is that of the strongly hydrated $H^+(H_2O)_x$ and $Cl^-(H_2O)_y$ ions, whereas in benzene solution it is that of the covalent HCl molecule, only weakly solvated (through van der Waals forces) by the C_6H_6 molecules of benzene.

In general, when we consider the ionization of acids—or of any substance that on dissolving yields ions—we must always be aware of the important role played by the solvent. In fact, the strength of an acid, HA, in a given solvent (*solv*) depends

* We shall see in Chapter 23 that any liquid or solution containing ions is an *electrolyte*, and "conducts" an electric current.

largely on the tendency of the solvent molecules to solvate both the proton, H^+, and the anion A^-:

$$HA + (x + y)\ solv \rightleftharpoons H^+(solv)_x + A^-(solv)_y$$

If we consider a number of strong acids, such as HCl, HBr, HNO_3, $HClO_4$, and H_2SO_4, we find that all are equally strong in aqueous solution, because the solvent H_2O molecules have such a great tendency to take on the available proton that any difference in the tendency of the acids to give up the proton does not become apparent. On the other hand, in pure acetic acid, CH_3COOH, the molecules do not have as strong a tendency to take on a proton from an acid, according to the equilibrium $CH_3COOH + HA \rightleftharpoons CH_3COOH_2^+ + A^-$. So, when acetic acid is the solvent the differences in the ability of the acids listed above to give up a proton become evident, and experiments show that these acids decrease in strength in the order: $HClO_4 > HBr > H_2SO_4 > HCl > HNO_3$. For these acids, water is a *leveling solvent,* and acetic acid is a *differentiating* solvent. In general, a solvent which is a strong Bronsted base tends to be a leveling solvent for acids, and conversely a solvent which is a weak Bronsted base tends to be a differentiating solvent for acids. Of course, water is a leveling solvent in part because the H_2O molecules solvate the anions of the acids more strongly than do the molecules of acetic acid, and in part because the higher dielectric constant of water (80), which decreases the electrostatic attraction between the oppositely charged ions in solution, also favors the ionization of the dissolved acids.

20-16 The Electron-Pair Concept of Acids and Bases

A very general acid-base concept that can be applied to all solvents and even to acid-base neutralization in the absence of solvents was suggested in 1916 by the American scientist G. N. Lewis. According to the Lewis definition, *an acid is a substance that accepts an electron pair, and a base is a substance that donates an electron pair.* First, let us see how this definition applies to the kinds of reactions in aqueous solution that we have so far considered in this chapter. Take HCl in water:

$$HCl + H_2O \rightleftharpoons H_3O^+ + Cl^- \quad \text{or} \quad H:\ddot{\underset{..}{Cl}}: + :\ddot{\underset{\substack{..\\ H}}{O}}:H \rightleftharpoons H:\ddot{\underset{\substack{..\\ H}}{O}}:H^+ + :\ddot{\underset{..}{Cl}}:^-$$

We see that in this reaction the H_2O molecule donates a lone pair of electrons, so H_2O is a Lewis base. The proton of the HCl molecule accepts this electron pair, so the proton is a Lewis acid. An even simpler example is the reaction of a proton, H^+, and a hydroxide ion, OH^-, to produce water, H_2O.

$$\underset{\substack{\text{Lewis acid,}\\ \text{Bronsted acid,}\\ \text{Arrhenius acid}}}{H^+} + \underset{\substack{\text{Lewis base,}\\ \text{Bronsted base,}\\ \text{Arrhenius base}}}{:\ddot{\underset{..}{O}}:H^-} \rightleftharpoons H:\ddot{\underset{\substack{..\\ H}}{O}}:$$

Let us now see how the Lewis definition applies to a different kind of reaction—one that does not involve a solvent. Consider the reaction of HCl gas with NH_3 gas to form solid ionic $NH_4^+Cl^-$.

$$HCl_{(g)} + NH_{3(g)} \rightleftharpoons NH_4^+Cl^-_{(s)}$$

$$\underset{\text{Lewis acid}}{H:\ddot{\underset{..}{Cl}}:} + \underset{\text{Lewis base}}{:\overset{\substack{H\\ ..}}{\underset{\substack{..\\ H}}{N}}:H} \rightleftharpoons \left[H:\overset{\substack{H\\ ..}}{\underset{\substack{..\\ H}}{N}}:H\right]^+ + :\ddot{\underset{..}{Cl}}:^-$$

Notice again that NH_3 is a Lewis base because it donates an electron pair, and HCl is an acid because the proton, H^+, accepts a share of this electron pair, forming a coordinate covalent bond. Thus a molecule or ion which can take on a proton from a Bronsted acid, and is therefore a Bronsted base, can also share an electron pair from a Lewis acid and be a Lewis base. These examples illustrate that the definition of Lewis acid and base also includes the Bronsted and Arrhenius definitions. In addition, the Lewis concept can be extended to other substances which are not included by the Bronsted definition. For example, in the reaction between gaseous NH_3 and gaseous BF_3 ($NH_3 + BF_3 \longrightarrow H_3N{\rightarrow}BF_3^-$), NH_3 is a Lewis base and, BF_3 is a Lewis acid, as shown in the following schematic representation:

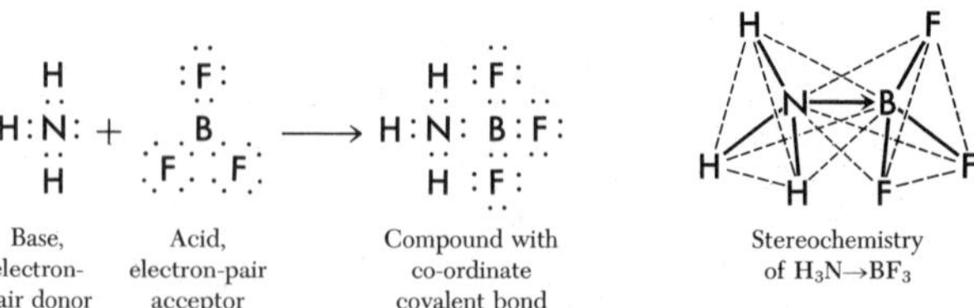

Base, electron-pair donor — Acid, electron-pair acceptor — Compound with co-ordinate covalent bond — Stereochemistry of $H_3N{\rightarrow}BF_3$

However, this reaction would not be included in either the Arrhenius or the Bronsted classification of acid-base reactions, since no protons are exchanged between the reactants.

Another example of a Lewis acid-base reaction not included in the Bronsted definition is the dissolution in water of solid ionic silver nitrate, $Ag^+NO_3^-$. When silver nitrate is dissolved in water, each Ag^+ ion reacts with two water molecules, $:OH_2$, to form the hydrated complex cation $[Ag(H_2O)_2]^+$, that is, $[Ag(OH_2)_2]^+$.

$$Ag^+ + \cancel{NO_3^-} + 2\ {:}OH_2 \rightleftharpoons [Ag({:}OH_2)_2]^+ + \cancel{NO_3^-}$$

Similarly, if silver nitrate is dissolved in an aqueous solution of ammonia, two ammonia molecules ($:NH_3$) coordinate to the Ag^+:

$$Ag^+ + \cancel{NO_3^-} + 2\ {:}NH_3 \longrightarrow [Ag({:}NH_3)_2]^+ + \cancel{NO_3^-}$$

And in an aqueous solution of potassium cyanide, $K^+({:}CN)^-$, the complex anion $[Ag({:}CN)_2]^-$ is formed:

$$Ag^+ + \cancel{NO_3^-} + \cancel{2K^+} + 2\ ({:}CN)^- \rightleftharpoons \cancel{2K^+} + [Ag({:}CN)_2]^- + \cancel{NO_3^-}$$

In all these examples the Ag^+ ion is an electron-pair acceptor, hence a Lewis acid, whereas $:OH_2$, $:NH_3$, and $:CN^-$ are electron-pair donors, hence Lewis bases.

In addition to the silver ion, Ag^+, many other metal ions, (especially those of the transition metals, see Chapter 34) can act as electron-pair acceptors (Lewis acids), forming complexes with many different molecules and ions; for example, $[Cu(OH_2)_6]^{++}$, $[Co(NH_3)_6]^{+++}$, $[Fe(CN)_6]^{\equiv}$, and $[Fe(H_2O)_6]^{+++}$. The proton, H^+, can also accept an electron pair from Lewis bases, such as those mentioned above, $:OH_2$, $:NH_3$, and $:CN^-$; the reactions form $H_3O^+(H^+{\leftarrow}OH_2)$; $NH_4^+(H^+{\leftarrow}NH_3)$; and $HCN(H^+{\leftarrow}CN^-)$, respectively. In fact, since the proton, H^+, has an enormous tendency to accept a share of an electron pair from any donor molecule or ion, we can consider it a "super metal ion."

To summarize: According to the Lewis concept, in an acid-base reaction a lone electron-pair of the base is accepted by the acid, resulting in a covalent link, $B: + A \longrightarrow B{:}A$. Lewis acids are those molecules or ions which can accommodate additional electron pairs. Examples are BCl_3, H^+, SO_3, $AlCl_3$, Ag^+, Cu^{++}, Fe^{+++}, SO_2, $SnCl_4$. Lewis bases are molecules or ions which can donate a lone electron pair to an acceptor and form a coordinate covalent bond. Examples are, $:NH_3$, $:OH_2$, $:CN^-$, $:OH^-$, $:N(CH_3)_3$, and $:F^-$.

20-17 Summary of Reactions of Acids and Bases

A summary of the more important reactions of acids and bases, discussed in this and earlier chapters, is presented in Table 20-7. In addition, acids and bases act as catalysts (Chapter 26) in many different kinds of chemical and biological processes. As we know, biological systems are aqueous systems, and the presence of the amphiprotic solvent water, together with the acidity of the solutions, plays an important role in their reactions. For example, many organic compounds used as drugs are either weak acids or weak bases, and their biological action depends on which form of the compound, molecular or ionized, is present in solution (compare the action of indicators). Since the biological activity of these drugs depends to some extent on the *pH* of the solution, it may be necessary to adjust the H^+ ion concentration (*pH*) to assist the activity. As another example, many proteins—which are very-high-molecular-weight compounds resulting from the condensation of many molecules of amino acids—are extremely sensitive to the H^+ ion concentration (*pH*) of their solutions.

TABLE 20-7 SOME IMPORTANT REACTIONS OF ACIDS AND BASES

Reaction	*Discussion*
Electropositive metal + acid $\longrightarrow$ metal salt + H_2 $M + HA \longrightarrow MA + H_2$ (unbalanced equation) eg., $Zn + H_2SO_4 \longrightarrow ZnSO_4 + H_2$	M = Pb and metals above it in electromotive series. HA = non-oxidizing agent.
Electropositive metal hydroxide + acid $\longrightarrow$ H_2O + metal salt $MOH + HA \longrightarrow H_2O + MA$ (unbalanced equation) eg., $KOH + HCl \longrightarrow H_2O + KCl$	M = metal ions with small positive charge—i.e., Na^+, K^+, Mg^{++}.
Electropositive metal oxide + acid $\longrightarrow$ H_2O + metal salt $MO + HA \longrightarrow H_2O + MA$ (unbalanced equation) eg., $MgO + 2\,HCl \longrightarrow H_2O + MgCl_2$	M = metal ions with small positive charge—i.e., Na^+, K^+, Mg^{++}.
Certain metal salts + acid $\longrightarrow$ acid or acid salts + metal salt $MHCO_3 + HA \longrightarrow H_2CO_3 + MA$ $2\,MCO_3 + 2\,HA \longrightarrow M(HCO_3)_2 + MA_2$ $MCO_3 + 2\,HA \longrightarrow H_2CO_3 + MA_2$ $MHS + HA \longrightarrow H_2S + MA$ $2\,MS + 2\,HA \longrightarrow M(HS)_2 + MA_2$ $MS + 2\,HA \longrightarrow H_2S + MA_2$	Acid HA must be stronger than acid produced. Whether acid salt, or acid plus metal salt, is formed depends on concentration of HA.
Metal + alkali-metal hydroxide + H_2O $\longrightarrow$ complex metal anion $M + M'OH + H_2O \longrightarrow M'M(OH)_x + H_2$ (unbalanced equation) eg., $Zn + 2\,NaOH + 2\,H_2O \longrightarrow Na_2[Zn(OH)_4] + H_2$	M = Zn, Al, Sn; M' = alkali-metal ion.
Polybasic acid + base $\longrightarrow$ acid salt, or normal salt + H_2O eg., $H_2SO_4 + NaOH \longrightarrow NaHSO_4 + H_2O$ $H_2SO_4 + 2\,NaOH \longrightarrow Na_2SO_4 + 2\,H_2O$	Whether acid salt, or normal salt plus water, is formed depends on relative amounts of polybasic acid and base mixed.
Acid + polyacid base $\longrightarrow$ basic salt, or normal salt + H_2O eg., $HCl + Ca(OH)_2 \longrightarrow Ca(OH)Cl + H_2O$ $2\,HCl + Ca(OH)_2 \longrightarrow CaCl_2 + 2\,H_2O$	Whether basic salt, or normal salt plus water, is formed depends on relative amounts of acid and polyacid base mixed.
Polybasic acid + polyacid base $\longrightarrow$ acid salt, or normal salt + H_2O eg., $2\,H_2SO_4 + Ca(OH)_2 \longrightarrow Ca(HSO_4)_2 + 2\,H_2O$ $H_2SO_4 + Ca(OH)_2 \longrightarrow CaSO_4 + 2\,H_2O$	Whether acid salt, or normal salt, is formed depends on relative amounts of polybasic acid and polyacid base mixed.

Exercises

20-1 Explain the meaning of the terms "strong" and "weak" as applied to acids and bases.

20-2 Give examples of a strong acid, a strong base, a weak acid, a weak base.

20-3 Classify aqueous solutions of the following in order of decreasing acid strength:
(a) (1) H_2CO_3, (2) CH_3COOH, (3) HCl, (4) H_2S, (5) H_2O.
(b) (1) Na_2O, (2) CO_2, (3) HCl, (4) SO_2.
(c) (1) P_4O_{10}, (2) CO_2, (3) HNO_3, (4) SO_3, (5) SO_2.
Classify aqueous solutions of the following in order of decreasing basic strength:
(d) (1) MgO, (2) SiO_2, (3) Al_2O_3, (4) P_4O_{10}, (5) Na_2O.
(e) (1) $Ca(OH)_2$, (2) KOH, (3) $Al(OH)_3$, (4) $Mg(OH)_2$, (5) $Zn(OH)_2$.

20-4 A solution of acetic acid is pink in the presence of the indicator methyl orange. When solid sodium acetate is added to the acid solution, the color changes to yellow. Explain.

20-5 A 0.1 *N* solution of H_2CO_3 and a 0.1 *N* solution of HCl turn different colors when the same indicators are added to them. Explain.

20-6 We want to dissolve a precipitate, $Pb(OH)_2$, in an acid solution to produce a *clear solution.* Suggest two acids that will achieve this and write equations for the reactions involved.

20-7 Which solution has the higher HSO_4^- ion concentration: (a) 0.1 *M* H_2SO_4, or (b) 0.1 *M* $NaHSO_4$? Explain your answer.

20-8 List the following solutions in order of increasing H^+ ion concentration: (a) 0.2 *M* CH_3COOH, (b) 0.2 *M* HCl, (c) 0.2 *M* HNO_2, (d) 0.2 *M* H_2SO_4.

20-9 Write equations for the equilibria present in an aqueous solution of (a) H_2SO_4, (b) H_3PO_4.

20-10 (a) The covalent hypothetical acids HA, HB, and H_2C are dissolved in water. A is smaller than B, and B is smaller than C. Arrange these acids in order of increasing strength. Explain your answer. (b) Arrange the hypothetical acids, HZO, HZO_2, HZO_3, and HZO_4 in order of increasing strength. Explain your answer.

20-11 Would you expect equimolar solutions (say 0.1 *M*) of hydrochloric acid and acetic acid to show the same quantitative effect on the freezing point of water? Explain your reasons.

20-12 Arrange in order of decreasing acidity (assume 1 *M* solutions): (a) CH_3COOH, (b) $CH_3COO^-Na^+$, (c) $Na^+HSO_4^-$, (d) $H^+ + Cl^-$, (e) $Na^+HCO_3^-$, (f) Na^+Cl^-.

20-13 Are all solutions of normal salts neutral, or can they be acidic or basic? Consider Na^+Cl^-, $Na_2{}^+SO_4{}^=$, $Na_3{}^+PO_4{}^{-3}$, $NH_4{}^+Cl^-$, $CH_3COO^-Na^+$.

20-14 What is an acid and what is a base according to (a) the Arrhenius definition, (b) the Bronsted definition, and (c) the Lewis definition?

20-15 List the following as Lewis acids or bases (or both): (a) NH_3, (b) H_2O, (c) $CO_3{}^=$, (d) BF_3, (e) $(CH_3)_3N$, (f) Ag^+, (g) Co^{++}, (h) H^+, (i) $O^=$, (j) OH^-, (k) NH_2^-, (l) SO_3.

20-16 Take three hypothetical acids, HA, HB, and HC; in water a 0.1 *M* solution of HA is 1 per cent ionized, that of HB is 2 per cent ionized, and that of HC is 3 per cent ionized. (a) Write the equation for the chemical equilibrium that exists in water for each of these acids. (b) Which solution has the highest *pH*? (c) Which solution has the highest H^+ ion concentration? (d) Which substance is the strongest Bronsted acid? (e) Which substance is the strongest Bronsted base? (f) Which substance is the weakest Bronsted acid? (e) Which substance is the weakest Bronsted base?

Problems

20-1 (a) How many ml of a 0.400 *M* HCl solution are required to neutralize 34.6 ml of a 0.600 *M* NaOH solution?
(b) How many ml of a 0.600 *M* H_2SO_4 solution are required to neutralize 40 ml of a 0.400 *M* KOH solution?
(c) How many ml of a 0.400 *M* H_3PO_4 solution are required to neutralize 60 ml of a 0.300 *M* KOH solution?

PROBLEMS

20-2 (a) A solution contains 0.1 mole of $HC_2H_3O_2$ dissolved in 0.5 l. Calculate the molarity of the solution. (b) 500 ml of a solution contain 0.1 mole of $HC_2H_3O_2$. The solution is diluted with water to the 1-l. mark. Calculate the molarity of the resulting solution. (c) A 250-ml solution of H_2SO_4 has a strength of 0.2 *M*. The solution is diluted with water to 1 l. What is the molarity of the solution so formed? (d) If 0.3 mole of acetic acid is present in 150 ml of solution, calculate the molarity of the solution.

20-3 (a) Compare the concentrations and the numbers of grams of solute present in (1) 250 ml of a 1 *M* NaOH solution and in (2) 100 ml of a 1 *M* NaOH solution. (b) If 4 moles of a salt are dissolved in 2.5 l. of solution, how many moles are present in 500 ml of this solution? (c) How many moles of acid are required to make 125 ml of a 0.5 *M* solution? (d) To what volume must 125 ml of a 2 *M* solution of HCl be diluted to make the solution of 0.05 *M*?

20-4 Assume 100 per cent ionization. Calculate the molar concentrations of the ions present in the following solutions: (a) 0.01 *M* HCl, (b) 0.1 *M* NaOH, (c) 0.01 *M* $Ba(OH)_2$, (d) 0.0001 *M* Ag_2SO_4, (e) 0.0001 *M* $Ca_3(PO_4)_2$.

20-5 Two hundred fifty ml of a solution of 0.2 *M* NaOH are added to 500 ml of a solution of 0.1 *M* HCl. Calculate the concentration of the resulting solution. Assume that the total volume of the resulting solution is 750 ml.

20-6 Three hundred ml of a solution of 0.2 *M* KOH are added to 200 ml of a solution of 0.4 *M* H_2SO_4. Calculate the concentration of the resultisng solution. Assume that the volumes of the solutions are additive.

20-7 (a) What is the *pH* of a solution that has a H^+ ion concentration of 0.001 g ions/l.? (b) If the *pH* of a solution is 3.0, what is the concentration of H^+ ions in gram ions/liter? (c) Compare the H^+ ion concentration in a solution of $pH = 3$ with the H^+ ion concentration in a solution of $pH = 5$.

20-8 Calculate (1) the H^+ ion concentration, (2) the OH^- ion concentration, and (3) the *pH* of (a) 0.1 *N* HCl, (b) 10 *N* HCl, (c) 5 *N* NaOH, (d) pure water, and (e) 4 *M* H_2SO_4.

BALANCING OXIDATION–REDUCTION EQUATIONS

21

Back in Chapter 6 we discussed oxidation-reduction equations in which one or more electrons given up by one atom, ion, or molecule are taken on by another atom, ion, or molecule. We found that in any oxidation-reduction reaction the total number of electrons given up by the substance which is oxidized is always equal to the total number of electrons taken on by the substance which is reduced, so that the reaction consists essentially of a transfer of electrons from one reactant to another. The reactant that gives up electron(s)—the reductant—is oxidized and the reactant that takes on electron(s)—the oxidant—is reduced.

Oxidation-reduction reactions are very important in chemistry, and equations for these reactions often involve coefficients that cannot be worked out by the usual trial-and-error method of balancing. Consequently, a systematic method must be followed in balancing oxidation-reduction equations.

21-1 Electron-Transfer Method

One convenient procedure is the *electron-transfer* method. The basis for this, as for every method of balancing oxidation-reduction equations, is the fact that oxidation-reduction is a "co-operative" action. That is, whenever a substance is oxidized, another substance is simultaneously reduced, and the number of electrons gained by the oxidant in the oxidation process must equal the number of electrons lost by the reductant in the reduction process. If we know the number of electrons per atom, ion, or molecule taken on and given off by, respectively, the oxidant, and the reductant, then we can determine the ratio of the numbers of atoms, ions, or molecules of the oxidant and of the reductant, bearing in mind that the total number of electrons gained by the oxidant must equal the total number of electrons lost by the reductant.

In order to balance an oxidation-reduction equation it is necessary to indicate the oxidation number of each element that undergoes a change in oxidation number. As we have seen in Chapter 5, the oxidation numbers of monoatomic positive and negative *ions* are equal to the ionic charge. For example, the oxidation number of the sodium ion, Na^+, is $+1$, and the oxidation of the calcium ion, Ca^{++}, is $+2$; similarly, the oxidation number of the chloride ion, Cl^-, is -1, and that of the sulfide ion, $S^=$, is -2. For covalent compounds we assign a positive or negative oxidation number to each atom according to the rules on page 55; the more electronegative atom(s) are assigned a negative oxidation number, and the less electronegative atom(s) are assigned a positive oxidation number. For example, in the covalent compound HCl, the electron pair shared by the two atoms is assigned to the more electronegative atom, chlorine. The chlorine atom then has an oxidation number of -1, and the hydrogen atom has an oxidation number of $+1$. Similarly, in the complex ion MnO_4^-, each of the shared electron pairs is *assigned* to the oxygen atoms. Each oxygen atom then has an oxidation number of -2, and the manganese atom has an oxidation number of $+7$.

$\overset{+1}{H}:\overset{-1}{\ddot{Cl}}:$

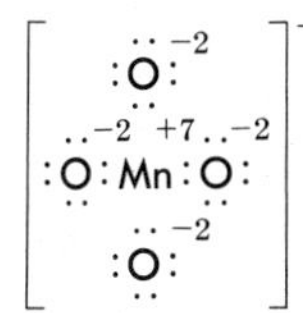

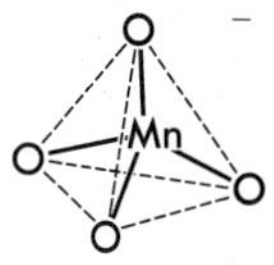

As our first example of the electron-transfer method for balancing oxidation-reduction equations, let us take the reaction between aluminum metal, Al, and a solution of silver nitrate, $AgNO_3$, which produces aluminum nitrate, $Al(NO_3)_3$, and metallic silver, Ag. In writing balanced equations we are concerned with the quantities—the moles—of the reactants and products, and not necessarily with their state. Thus, for example, for 1 mole of silver nitrate in aqueous solution we write $AgNO_3$ rather than $Ag^+_{(aq)} + NO^-_{3(aq)}$. To write the balanced equation for the reaction in question, we follow these six steps:

Step 1. Write the formulas for the reactants and the products.

$$Al + AgNO_3 \longrightarrow Al(NO_3)_3 + Ag$$

Step 2. Underline the symbols of those elements that are involved in the transfer of electrons and indicate by a superscript their oxidation numbers (p. 62). Remember that an element in the free state is assigned an oxidation number of zero—for example, $\overset{0}{Al}$.

$$\overset{0}{\underline{Al}} + \overset{+1}{\underline{Ag}}(NO_3) \longrightarrow \overset{+3}{\underline{Al}}(NO_3)_3 + \overset{0}{\underline{Ag}}$$

Step 3. For each of the underlined elements, indicate the numbers of electrons transferred. In this reaction, for example, an atom of aluminum with an oxidation number of zero, $\overset{0}{Al}$, gives up three electrons and becomes an aluminum ion with an oxidation number of $+3$, $\overset{+3}{Al}$. And a silver ion with an oxidation number of $+1$, $\overset{+1}{Ag}$, takes on an electron and is reduced to an atom of metallic silver with an oxidation number of zero, $\overset{0}{Ag}$. Here is a simple way of indicating these transfers:

$$\overset{0}{\underline{Al}} + \overset{+1}{\underline{Ag}}(NO_3) \longrightarrow \overset{+3}{\underline{Al}}(NO_3)_3 + \overset{0}{\underline{Ag}}$$

(Ag → Ag: $(1\ e^-)$; Al → Al: $(3\ e^-)$)

Step 4. Make the total number of electrons taken on by one reactant equal to the total number of electrons given up by the other. Since electrons are merely transferred, the number of electrons given up by one element must be equal to the number of electrons taken on by another element. This means that for each $\overset{0}{\text{Al}}$ that becomes $\overset{+3}{\text{Al}}$, 3 $\overset{+1}{\text{Ag}^+}$ must become 3 $\overset{0}{\text{Ag}}$. This balanced transfer of electrons may be represented as follows:

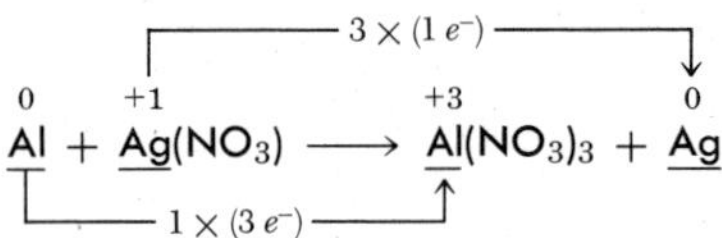

Step 5. Write the correct coefficients for the reactants and products that contain elements which have changed in oxidation number.

$$1\ Al + 3\ Ag(NO_3) \longrightarrow 1\ Al(NO_3)_3 + 3\ Ag$$

In this example the number of symbols of the elements that did not change in oxidation number also balances, and, so the whole equation is correctly balanced. The usual manner of representing the equation is:

$$Al + 3\ Ag(NO_3) \longrightarrow Al(NO_3)_3 + 3\ Ag$$

Step 6. Check the balanced equation to make sure that the same number of each kind of symbol is present on each side of the equation.

Now let us consider the balancing of some more complicated equations.

ILLUSTRATIVE EXAMPLES

STATEMENT. Solid manganese dioxide reacts with an aqueous solution of potassium bromide in the presence of sulfuric acid to produce bromine, manganese(II) sulfate, potassium sulfate, and water.

PROBLEM. Write the balanced equation for this reaction.

SOLUTION. *Step 1.* Write the formulas for the reactants and the products.

$$MnO_2 + KBr + H_2(SO_4) \longrightarrow Br_2 + Mn(SO_4) + K_2(SO_4) + H_2O$$

Step 2. Underline the symbols of those elements that *change* in oxidation number, and indicate their oxidation numbers.

$$\underset{}{\overset{+4}{\underline{Mn}}}O_2 + K\overset{-1}{\underline{Br}} + H_2(SO_4) \longrightarrow \overset{0}{\underline{Br}}_2 + \overset{+2}{\underline{Mn}}(SO_4) + K_2(SO_4) + H_2O$$

Step 3. Indicate the transfer of electrons.

$$\overset{+4}{\underline{Mn}}O_2 + K\overset{-1}{\underline{Br}} + H_2(SO_4) \longrightarrow \overset{0}{\underline{Br}}_2 + \overset{+2}{\underline{Mn}}(SO_4) + K_2(SO_4) + H_2O$$

(Mn: $(2\ e^-)$; Br: $(1\ e^-)$)

Step 4. Make the number of electrons given up by the reductant equal to the number of electrons taken on by the oxidant.

$$\overset{+4}{\underline{Mn}}O_2 + K\overset{-1}{\underline{Br}} + H_2(SO_4) \longrightarrow \overset{0}{\underline{Br}}_2 + \overset{+2}{\underline{Mn}}(SO_4) + K_2(SO_4) + H_2O$$

(Mn: $1 \times (2\ e^-)$; Br: $2 \times (1\ e^-)$)

Step 5. Write the correct coefficients for the reactants and products that contain elements which change in oxidation number.

$$\not{1}\ MnO_2 + 2\ KBr + H_2(SO_4) \longrightarrow \not{1}\ Br_2 + \not{1}\ Mn(SO_4) + K_2(SO_4) + H_2O$$

Step 6. In the equation above, balance by inspection the elements that do not change in oxidation number. In this step it is helpful to consider each polyatomic group as a unit, and to balance all other elements before hydrogen and oxygen. Then balance hydrogen. If the equation is balanced with regard to all the other elements, the number of oxygen symbols on each side of the equation will then balance.

The number of potassium ions, two, on each side, is equal. There are two $(SO_4)^=$ ions in the products, but only one $(SO_4)^=$ ion appears in the reactants. So we place a coefficient of 2 before the reactant: 2 H_2SO_4. The equation now becomes:

$$\not{1}\ MnO_2 + 2\ KBr + 2\ H_2(SO_4) \longrightarrow \not{1}\ Br_2 + \not{1}\ Mn(SO_4) + K_2(SO_4) + H_2O$$

There are four hydrogen symbols in the reactants, but only two hydrogen symbols appear in the products. So we place a coefficient of 2 before the product: 2 H_2O.

$$\not{1}\ MnO_2 + 2\ KBr + 2\ H_2(SO_4) \longrightarrow \not{1}\ Br_2 + \not{1}\ Mn(SO_4) + K_2(SO_4) + 2\ H_2O$$

Now if we check, we find that ten oxygen symbols appear on each side of the equation.

Finally, we check the entire equation thoroughly, making sure that the number of each symbol in the products is equal to the number in the reactants. It is advisable to count the symbols "backward"—that is, from the right of the arrow to the left. Thus, if you have made an error the first time, you are less likely to repeat it in the final check.

STATEMENT. Manganese dioxide oxidizes hydrochloric acid to form manganese(II) chloride, chlorine gas, and water.

PROBLEM. Write the balanced equation for this reaction.

SOLUTION. The reactants and products are:

$$MnO_2 + HCl \longrightarrow MnCl_2 + Cl_2 + H_2O$$

Underline the symbols of the elements that change in oxidation number and indicate their oxidation numbers.

$$\overset{+4}{\underline{Mn}}O_2 + H\overset{-1}{\underline{Cl}} \longrightarrow \overset{+2}{\underline{Mn}}Cl_2 + \overset{0}{\underline{Cl}_2} + H_2O$$

Notice that some of the chloride ions, $\overset{-1}{Cl}$, are oxidized to form chlorine atoms, which combine to yield chlorine gas, $\overset{0}{Cl}_2$, whereas other chloride ions appear in the products unchanged, $Mn\overset{-1}{Cl}_2$. When one of the reactants plays a dual role of this sort, is is convenient to write its formula twice on the left-hand side of the equation:

$$\underline{Mn}O_2 + H\underline{Cl} + HCl \longrightarrow \underline{Mn}Cl_2 + \underline{Cl}_2 + H_2O$$

But notice that only one symbol of the reactant which plays two roles (a dual role) is underlined. First, we balance only the underlined elements.

$$\overset{+4}{\underline{Mn}}O_2 + H\overset{-1}{\underline{Cl}} + HCl \longrightarrow \overset{+2}{\underline{Mn}}Cl_2 + \overset{0}{\underline{Cl}_2} + H_2O$$

$1 \times (2\ e^-)$ (Mn, +4 → +2)

$2 \times (1\ e^-)$ (Cl, −1 → 0)

$$\not{1}\ \underline{Mn}O_2 + 2\ H\underline{Cl} + HCl \longrightarrow \not{1}\ \underline{Mn}Cl_2 + \not{1}\ \underline{Cl}_2 + H_2O$$

Then we balance the other elements by inspection:

$$\not{1}\ \underline{Mn}O_2 + 2\ H\underline{Cl} + 2\ HCl \longrightarrow \not{1}\ MnCl_2 + 1\ \underline{Cl}_2 + 2\ H_2O$$

In this balanced equation the reactant, HCl, acts both as a reducing agent, indicated in the equation as 2 H$\underline{Cl}$, and as an acid, indicated as 2 HCl. The usual manner of writing the equation is:

$$MnO_2 + 4\ HCl \longrightarrow MnCl_2 + Cl_2 + 2\ H_2O$$

If we write this equation in the following form, we see clearly that only two of the four chloride ions are oxidized to form one molecule of chlorine gas:

$$MnO_2 + 4\ H^+ + 4\ Cl^- \longrightarrow Mn^{++} + 2\ Cl^- + Cl_2 + 2\ H_2O$$

21-2 Self-Oxidation-Reduction

Now let us consider a reaction in which one-reactant acts *both* as an oxidizing agent *and* as a reducing agent. An example is the reaction of bromine, Br_2, with a solution of potassium hydroxide, K^+OH^-, to form potassium bromide, K^+Br^-, potassium bromate, $K^+(BrO_3)^-$, and water. The following unbalanced equation gives the reactants and products of this reaction:

$$\overset{0}{\underline{Br}_2} + KOH \longrightarrow K\overset{-1}{\underline{Br}} + K\overset{+5}{\underline{Br}}O_3 + H_2O$$

Notice that bromine, $\overset{0}{Br}_2$, is both oxidized to $K\overset{+5}{Br}O_3$, and reduced to $K\overset{-1}{Br}$. Again, for convenience, we write bromine, which plays a dual role, twice on the left-hand side of the equation:

$$5\,\overset{0}{\underline{Br}_2} + 1\,\overset{0}{\underline{Br}_2} + KOH \longrightarrow 10\,K\overset{-1}{\underline{Br}} + 2\,K\overset{+5}{\underline{Br}}O_3 + H_2O$$

(upper bracket: $10 \times (1\,e^-)$; lower bracket: $2 \times (5\,e^-)$)

$$5\,\underline{Br}_2 + 1\,\underline{Br}_2 + KOH \longrightarrow 10\,K\underline{Br} + 2\,K\underline{Br}O_3 + H_2O$$

Now that we have balanced the elements that have changed in oxidation numbers, we balance the remaining elements by inspection. The number of potassium symbols in the products totals twelve. Thus, the coefficient of KOH in the reactant must also become 12. And the twelve symbols of hydrogen in 12 KOH require six H_2O in the product. The symbols of oxygen also balance, for there are twelve in the reactant and twelve in the products:

$$5\,Br_2 + 1\,Br_2 + 12\,KOH \longrightarrow 10\,KBr + 2\,KBrO_3 + 6\,H_2O$$

or

$$6\,Br_2 + 12\,KOH \longrightarrow 10\,KBr + 2\,KBrO_3 + 6\,H_2O$$

If we divide all the coefficients by 2, we can simplify the equation as follows:

$$3\,Br_2 + 6\,KOH \longrightarrow 5\,KBr + 1\,KBrO_3 + 3\,H_2O$$

21-3 Oxidation-Reduction Reactions Involving Elements with Average Oxidation Numbers

In some compounds where an element appears more than once, this element is assigned an average oxidation number (which may not be a whole number). In balancing oxidation-reduction equations involving such compounds, the procedure outlined above again leads to a correctly balanced equation. Here is an example:

$$Na_2\overset{+2}{\underline{S}_2}O_3 + \overset{0}{\underline{I}_2} \longrightarrow Na_2\overset{+2\frac{1}{2}}{\underline{S}_4}O_6 + Na\overset{-1}{\underline{I}}$$

(upper bracket: $2 \times (1\,e^-)$; lower bracket: $1 \times (2\,e^-)$)

$$2\,Na_2S_2O_3 + I_2 \longrightarrow Na_2S_4O_6 + 2\,NaI$$

In sodium thiosulfate, $(Na^{+1})_2S_2(O^{-2})_3$, if $+1$ is the oxidation number of each sodium and -2 is the oxidation number of each oxygen, then the two sulfur atoms together have an oxidation number of $+4$. Thus each sulfur atom has an *average* oxidation number of $+2$. In sodium tetrathionate, $(Na^{+1})_2S_4(O^{-2})_6$, four sulfur atoms have a total oxidation number of 10 and each sulfur atom has an *average* oxidation number of $\frac{10}{4} = 2\frac{1}{2}$. In the chemical reaction each *two* sulfur atoms of $Na_2S_2O_3$ may be considered to lose one electron in forming $Na_2S_4O_6$.

Now, let us see how average oxidation numbers are used in balancing equations that involve organic compounds. The oxidation of ethyl alcohol, C_2H_5OH, by potassium dichromate, $K_2Cr_2O_7$, in sulfuric acid solution produces acetic acid, $HC_2H_3O_2$; chromium(III) sulfate, $Cr_2(SO_4)_3$; potassium sulfate, K_2SO_4; and water, H_2O. The reactants and products are:

$$C_2H_5OH + K_2Cr_2O_7 + H_2SO_4 \longrightarrow HC_2H_3O_2 + Cr_2(SO_4)_3 + K_2SO_4 + H_2O$$

Carbon has an *average* oxidation number of -2 in C_2H_5OH, and an *average* oxidation number of 0 in $HC_2H_3O_2$:

$$\overset{-2}{\underline{C}_2H_5OH} + K_2\overset{+6}{\underline{Cr}_2}O_7 + H_2SO_4 \longrightarrow H\overset{0}{\underline{C}_2}H_3O_2 + \overset{+3}{\underline{Cr}_2}(SO_4)_3 + K_2SO_4 + H_2O$$

3 × (4 e^-) [C → C]; 2 × (6 e^-) [Cr → Cr]

By the usual steps, we obtain the balanced equation:

$$3\ C_2H_5OH + 2\ K_2Cr_2O_7 + 8\ H_2SO_4 \longrightarrow 3\ HC_2H_3O_2 + 2\ Cr_2(SO_4)_3 + 2\ K_2SO_4 + 11\ H_2O$$

21-4 Ion-Electron or Half-Reaction Method

There are other convenient ways to balance an oxidation-reduction equation. One of these methods, the "ion-electron" or "half-reaction" method, is especially important for us here because it will also serve as an introduction to the topics discussed in the following chapter.

Consider the reaction between aluminum metal and copper(II) chloride to produce copper metal and aluminum chloride. The reactants and products are:

$$Al + CuCl_2 \longrightarrow AlCl_3 + Cu$$

Obviously, we can balance this equation readily enough by inspection:

$$2\ Al + 3\ CuCl_2 \longrightarrow 2\ AlCl_3 + 3\ Cu$$

But we shall use this example to illustrate the ion-electron (half-reaction) method for balancing oxidation-reduction equations. This method involves the following steps:

Step 1. Write the unbalanced equation.

$$Al + CuCl_2 \longrightarrow AlCl_3 + Cu$$

Step 2. Rewrite the unbalanced equation in ionic form.

$$\overset{0}{Al} + Cu^{++} + 2\ Cl^- \longrightarrow Al^{+++} + 3\ Cl^- + \overset{0}{Cu}$$

Rewrite, omitting the ions that do not change in oxidation number. (We thereby obtain the *unbalanced* net ionic equation.)

$$\overset{0}{Al} + Cu^{++} \longrightarrow Al^{+++} + \overset{0}{Cu}$$

Step 3. Indicate the electron changes in the reactants and products.

$$\overset{0}{Al} + Cu^{++} \longrightarrow Al^{+++} + \overset{0}{Cu}$$

2 e^- [Cu^{++} → Cu]; 3 e^- [Al → Al^{+++}]

Step 4. Write equations for the half-reactions—that is, first the oxidation reaction involving electron loss, and then the reduction reaction involving electron gain.

Oxidation half-reaction: $\overset{0}{Al} - 3\ e^- \longrightarrow Al^{+++}$

Reduction half-reaction: $Cu^{++} + 2\ e^- \longrightarrow \overset{0}{Cu}$

Step 5. Balance the two half-reactions so that the number of electrons given up is equal to the number of electrons taken on. Then add the two equations.

$$\begin{array}{lrcl} \textit{Oxidation half-reaction:} & 2\,\overset{0}{Al} - 6\,e^- & \longrightarrow & 2\,Al^{+++} \\ \textit{Reduction half-reaction:} & 3\,Cu^{++} + 6\,e^- & \longrightarrow & 3\,\overset{0}{Cu} \\ \hline & 2\,\overset{0}{Al} + 3\,Cu^{++} & \longrightarrow & 2\,Al^{+++} + 3\,\overset{0}{Cu} \end{array}$$

This is the *balanced* net ionic equation.

Step 6. Now all we have to do is restore with proper coefficients the ions which do not change oxidation number, and which we omitted in Step 2.

$$2\,\overset{0}{Al} + 3\,Cu^{++} + 6\,Cl^- \longrightarrow 2\,Al^{+++} + 3\,\overset{0}{Cu} + 6\,Cl^-$$

Notice that in this last step we have added enough negatively charged ions, Cl^-, on each side of the equation, to balance the charges on the positively charged ions.

Here is another example showing how to obtain the net ionic equation of an oxidation-reduction reaction by making use of two half-reaction equations, one for the oxidation step and another for the reduction step. In the reaction between solid manganese dioxide, MnO_2, and hydrochloric acid ($H^+ + Cl^-$), the reaction products are $MnCl_2$ and H_2O. The reduction product of the MnO_2 is Mn^{++}, and the oxidation product of the Cl^- is Cl_2. Here is how we obtain the equation for the *oxidation half-reaction:*

$$Cl^- \longrightarrow Cl_2$$

First, we balance the Cl symbols on each side of the equation:

$$2\,Cl^- \longrightarrow Cl_2$$

Now we must balance the ionic charges so that the total of these charges on the left-hand side is equal to the total on the right-hand side. To achieve this balance we add two electrons ($2\,e^-$) to the right-hand side of the equation:

1. $$2\,Cl^- \longrightarrow Cl_2 + 2\,e^-$$

For the *reduction half-reaction* we write:

$$MnO_2 \longrightarrow Mn^{++}$$

For this half reaction let us first balance the number of symbols on each side. The left-hand side contains *two* O atoms, but the right-hand side has none. To balance the O symbols, we add two H_2O to the right-hand side because water, H_2O, is the only product which contains oxygen, and two oxygen atoms must be accounted for thus requiring two moles of water, $2\,H_2O$.

$$MnO_2 \longrightarrow Mn^{++} + 2\,H_2O$$

Now we must add four H^+ to the left-hand side so that the number of H symbols on each side balances. Since hydrogen appears in the products as H_2O, and the only hydrogen-containing compound in the reactants is hydrochloric acid, HCl, which supplies hydrogen ions, H^+, we add $4\,H^+$ to the left-hand side of the equation.

$$MnO_2 + 4\,H^+ \longrightarrow Mn^{++} + 2\,H_2O$$

As a general rule, we can balance the number of oxygen atoms by adding two H^+ to one side of the equation for each (excess) oxygen atom of the oxidizing agent, and one H_2O to the other side of the equation. Here we have applied a general rule, which is often used when equations are balanced by the half-equation method. For reactions that take place in acid solution, one of the reagents is the (hydrated) H^+ ion. Usually, another reactant contains oxygen. This oxygen, as well as the hydrogen present in the reactant(s) as H^+ must, of course, appear also on the right side of the arrow. For each oxygen atom on the left side of the equation we shall then write a water molecule, H_2O, on the right side, and conversely for each water molecule on the right, we shall write two H^+ ions on the left.

We have balanced the number of symbols but now we must balance the total ionic charges on each side of the equation. The left-hand side of the equation has a total ionic charge of +4, but the right-hand side has a total charge of only +2. Thus, we add 2 e^- to the left-hand side to make the charges on both sides of the equation equal:

2. $MnO_2 + 4\,H^+ + 2\,e^- \longrightarrow Mn^{++} + 2\,H_2O$

Since the loss and gain of electrons are equal, we can add the equation for the oxidation half-reaction 1 and the equation for the reduction half-reaction 2:

Oxidation half-reaction:	1.	$2\,Cl^-$	$\longrightarrow Cl_2 + 2\,e^-$
Reduction half-reaction:	2.	$MnO_2 + 4\,H^+ + 2\,e^-$	$\longrightarrow Mn^{++} + 2\,H_2O$
Total reaction:	3.	$MnO_2 + 4\,H^+ + 2\,Cl^-$	$\longrightarrow Mn^{++} + Cl_2 + 2\,H_2O$

Equation 3 is also the balanced net ionic equation.

Here is a somewhat more complicated example. In acid (H^+) solution the permanganate ion, MnO_4^-, reacts with hydrogen sulfide, H_2S, to form the Mn^{++} ion and free sulfur, S. Again, as in the previous example, we shall write first the balanced oxidation half-equation, then the balanced reduction half-equation. Finally we add these to obtain the net ionic equation.

Here are the steps in balancing the number of symbols and charges of the equation for the *oxidation* half-reaction:

(1) $H_2S \longrightarrow S$

(2) $H_2S \longrightarrow S + 2\,H^+$

1. (3) $H_2S - 2\,e^- \longrightarrow S + 2\,H^+$

Here are the steps in balancing the number of symbols and charges of the equation for the *reduction* half-reaction:

(1) $MnO_4^- \longrightarrow Mn^{++}$

(2) $MnO_4^- \longrightarrow Mn^{++} + 4\,H_2O$

(3) $MnO_4^- + 8\,H^+ \longrightarrow Mn^{++} + 4\,H_2O$

2. (4) $MnO_4^- + 8\,H^+ + 5\,e^- \longrightarrow Mn^{++} + 4\,H_2O$

Here are the half-equations 1 and 2:

1. $H_2S \longrightarrow S + 2\,H^+ + 2\,e^-$

2. $MnO_4^- + 8\,H^+ + 5\,e^- \longrightarrow Mn^{++} + 4\,H_2O$

To add half-equations 1 and 2, however, the numbers of electrons lost in 1 (the oxidation step) must be equal to the number of electrons gained in 2 (the reduction step). Thus, we multiply half-equation 1 by 5 and half-equation 2 by 2.

Oxidation half-reaction:	1.	$5\,H_2S$	$\longrightarrow 5\,S + 10\,H^+ + 10\,e^-$
Reduction half-reaction:	2.	$2\,MnO_4^- + 16\,H^+ + 10\,e^-$	$\longrightarrow 2\,Mn^{++} + 8\,H_2O$
		$2\,MnO_4^- + 5\,H_2S + 16\,H^+$	$\longrightarrow 2\,Mn^{++} + 5\,S + 8\,H_2O + 10\,H^+$

We may simplify this by subtracting ten hydrogen ions (10 H^+) from each side of the equation to obtain the net ionic equation:

$$2\,MnO_4^- + 5\,H_2S + 6\,H^+ \longrightarrow 2\,Mn^{++} + 5\,S + 8\,H_2O$$

Notice again that for oxidation-reduction reactions that occur in acid (H^+) solution, we balanced the reduction half-equation by adding *two* H^+ ions to that side of the equation for each (excess) oxygen atom of the oxidizing agent present, and added *one* H_2O to the right side of the equation.

OXIDATION-REDUCTION REACTIONS IN BASIC SOLUTIONS

For oxidation-reduction reactions that take place in *acid* solutions we made use of H^+ and H_2O to balance the equations. Similarly, for oxidation-reduction reactions in *basic* solutions we use OH^- and H_2O to balance the equations. Thus the same general procedure is used in balancing oxidation-reduction reactions in acid (H^+) and basic (OH^-) solutions. First we shall work out in detail the balancing of one equation in basic solution, then we shall offer a generalization which simplifies the procedure.

When chlorine gas, Cl_2, is passed into a cold, aqueous solution of potassium hydroxide, $K^+ + OH^-$, the Cl_2 reacts with OH^- (one of the reactants) to form ClO^- and Cl^- (the products). The oxidation half-reaction is:

$$\overset{0}{Cl_2} \longrightarrow \overset{+1}{ClO^-}$$

First, we balance the Cl symbols:

$$\overset{0}{Cl_2} \longrightarrow 2\ \overset{+1}{ClO^-}$$

Since two O symbols (2 ClO^-) are present on the right side, two are needed on the left side. This oxidation-reduction reaction takes place in basic solution, so we know that we can add OH^- (remember we have a $K^+ + OH^-$ solution) to the left side of the equation to balance the (excess) O symbols on the right. We might expect therefore that by adding two OH^- to the left we would balance the half-equation.

$$Cl_2 + 2\ OH^- \longrightarrow 2\ ClO^-$$

This does not work out, however, because for each OH^- that we add to balance the O symbols we also are adding an H symbol. Therefore, we must also add H_2O to the right to compensate for the two H symbols automatically added on the left.

$$Cl_2 + 2\ OH^- \longrightarrow 2\ ClO^- + H_2O$$

Now in balancing the H symbols we have thrown the number of O symbols out of balance. However, if we double the number of both OH^- (4 OH^-) and H_2O (2 H_2O), this half-equation becomes balanced in regard to all the symbols.

$$Cl_2 + 4\ OH^- \longrightarrow 2\ ClO^- + 2\ H_2O$$

Finally, to balance the charges of this half-equation, it is necessary to add two electrons ($2e^-$) to the right side of the equation; the balanced equation for the oxidation half-reaction becomes:

$$Cl_2 + 4\ OH^- \longrightarrow 2\ ClO^- + 2\ H_2O + 2\ e^-$$

Here is a generalization which helps us to reduce the number of steps in balancing such half-equations. In a basic solution, for each O symbol required (on one side of the equation) add *twice* this number of OH^- symbols; then add on the other side of the equation that number of H_2O symbols required to balance the number of H symbols in the added OH^-. For example, the first step above was:

$$Cl_2 \longrightarrow 2\ ClO^-$$

Since the left side requires two O symbols we add twice this number of OH^- (4 OH^-) and then to balance, we add 2 H_2O on the right.

$$Cl_2 + 4\ OH^- \longrightarrow 2\ ClO^- + 2\ H_2O$$

The balanced equation for the reduction step which follows is a very simple one:

$$Cl_2 + 2\,e^- \longrightarrow 2\,Cl^-$$

Finally, the balanced oxidation and reduction half-equations may be combined to obtain the total reaction:

Oxidation half-equation:	$Cl_2 + 4\,OH^-$	$\longrightarrow 2\,ClO^- + 2\,H_2O + 2\,e^-$
Reduction half-equation:	$Cl_2 + 2\,e^-$	$\longrightarrow 2\,Cl^-$
Total reaction:	$2\,Cl_2 + 4\,OH^- + 2\,e^-$	$\longrightarrow 2\,ClO^- + 2\,H_2O + 2\,Cl^- + 2\,e^-$

Cancelling 2 e^- on each side (and dividing through by 2 to simplify), finally gives the balanced net ionic equation:

$$\textit{Net ionic equation:}\quad Cl_2 + 2\,OH^- \longrightarrow ClO^- + H_2O + Cl^-$$

21-5 Products of Oxidation-Reduction Reactions

The second important item related to the balancing of oxidation-reduction reactions is the knowledge of some of the commonly used oxidizing agents and their reduction products. After we know how to balance these equations *and* have memorized several of the common oxidizing agents and their reduction products, then we can write the balanced equations for a great number of oxidation-reduction reactions. Let us consider some of these common oxidizing agents.

TABLE 21-1 THREE COMMON OXIDIZING AGENTS AND THEIR REDUCTION PRODUCTS

Oxidized Form	Reduced Form
$MnO_4^- + H^+$	$Mn^{++} + H_2O$
$Cr_2O_7^= + H^+$	$Cr^{+++} + H_2O$
$MnO_2 + H^+$	$Mn^{++} + H_2O$

TABLE 21-2 THREE COMMON REDUCING AGENTS AND THEIR OXIDATION PRODUCTS

Reduced Form	Oxidized Form
H_2S	$S + 2\,H^+$
I^-	I_2
Br^-	Br_2

To begin, three common oxidizing agents and their reduction products are listed in Table 21-1, and three common reducing agents and their oxidation products are listed in Table 21-2. Each of the reducing agents may be oxidized to the form indicated, by the oxidizing agents listed in Table 21-1. And the oxidizing agents, in turn, are reduced in the process to the forms indicated. For example, if we mix a solution containing MnO_4^- ions and H^+ ions with a solution containing I^- ions, the following reaction occurs (equation not balanced):

$$MnO_4^- + H^+ + I^- \longrightarrow Mn^{++} + H_2O + I_2$$

MnO_4^-	H^+	I^-	Mn^{++}	I_2
oxidizing agent	hydrogen ion	reducing agent	reduction product	oxidation product

Here are several other examples. If we mix a solution containing $KMnO_4$ and H_2SO_4 with a solution of KI, the following reaction occurs (equation not balanced):

$$KMnO_4 + H_2SO_4 + KI \longrightarrow MnSO_4 + H_2O + I_2 + K_2SO_4$$

If we add solid MnO_2 to a solution containing KBr and H_2SO_4, and then heat the resulting solution, the reactants and the products are represented by the following unbalanced equation:

$$MnO_2 + H_2SO_4 + KBr \longrightarrow MnSO_4 + H_2O + Br_2 + K_2SO_4$$

If we added a dilute H_2SO_4 solution containing $Na_2Cr_2O_7$ to an aqueous solution of H_2S, the reactants involved and the products formed are given by the following unbalanced equation:

$$Na_2Cr_2O_7 + H_2SO_4 + H_2S \longrightarrow Cr_2(SO_4)_3 + H_2O + S + Na_2SO_4$$

With the above information we can write the reactants and products for many oxidation-reduction reactions and then balance the equations by the methods described earlier in this chapter.

FURTHER APPLICATIONS OF TABLES 21-1 AND 21-2

In applying the principles we have just discussed, however, we must heed certain precautions. For example, a substance which can act as an oxidizing agent does not always do so exclusively. Some of that substance can indeed act as an oxidizing agent, but a residual amount might react in another way. The same is true of reducing agents. Let us consider an example.

Potassium permanganate, $KMnO_4$, reacts with hydrogen bromide in solution (hydrobromic acid) to form manganese(II) bromide, bromine, potassium bromide, and water. Here is the unbalanced equation (showing reactants and products) for this reaction:

$$KMnO_4 + HBr \longrightarrow MnBr_2 + Br_2 + KBr + H_2O$$

The reactant, hydrogen bromide, $H\overset{-1}{Br}$, acts both as a reducing agent (for it is oxidized to bromine, $\overset{0}{Br}_2$) and as an acid (for bromide ions appear in the product as potassium bromide, $K\overset{-1}{Br}$, and manganese(II) bromide, $MnBr_2$). The balanced equation for this reaction is:

$$2\ K\underline{Mn}O_4 + 10\ H\underline{Br} + 6\ HBr \longrightarrow 2\ \underline{Mn}Br_2 + 5\ \underline{Br}_2 + 2\ KBr + 8\ H_2O$$

or

$$2\ KMnO_4 + 16\ HBr \longrightarrow 2\ MnBr_2 + 5\ Br_2 + 2\ KBr + 8\ H_2O$$

The ionic equation is:

$$2\ K^+ + 2\ MnO_4^- + 10\ H^+ + 10\ Br^- + 6\ H^+ + 6\ Br^- \longrightarrow 2\ Mn^{++} + 4\ Br^- + 5\ Br_2 + 2\ K^+ + 2\ Br^- + 8\ H_2O$$

By canceling out the ions that are common to both sides of the equation, we get the net ionic equation:

$$\cancel{2\ K^+} + 2\ MnO_4^- + 10\ H^+ + 10\ Br^- + 6\ H^+ + \cancel{6\ Br^-} \longrightarrow 2\ Mn^{++} + \cancel{4\ Br^-} + 5\ Br_2 + \cancel{2\ K^+} + \cancel{2\ Br^-} + 8\ H_2O$$

This net ionic equation may also be expressed as follows:

$$2\ MnO_4^- + 16\ H^+ + 10\ Br^- \longrightarrow 2\ Mn^{++} + 5\ Br_2 + 8\ H_2O$$

Notice that sixteen H^+ ions (supplied by the six HBr acting as an acid and by the ten HBr acting as a reducing agent) react with two MnO_4^- ions and ten Br^- ions to form two Mn^{++} ions, five Br_2 molecules, and eight H_2O molecules. This is the essential chemical reaction that takes place.

From the above equation it is clear that ten electrons, $10\ e^-$, are given up for every ten bromide ions, $10\ Br^-$, that are oxidized to form five molecules of bromine, $5\ Br_2$.

$$10\ Br^- \longrightarrow 5\ Br_2 + 10\ e^-$$

On the other hand, it may not be so clear that the reduction of the permanganate ions, MnO_4^- to form manganese(II) ions, Mn^{++}, conforms to the rule that reduction involves the gain of electrons. Let us look more closely at the reduction of the MnO_4^- ions in the presence of H^+ ions.

$$2\ MnO_4^- + 16\ H^+ + 10\ e^- \longrightarrow 2\ Mn^{++} + 8\ H_2O$$

In other words, the ten electrons given up by the ten bromide ions are taken on by the two MnO_4^- ions in the presence of H^+ ions. Thus, one MnO_4^- ion reacts with eight H^+ ions and five electrons to form one Mn^{++} ion and four H_2O molecules:

$$MnO_4^- + 8\ H^+ + 5\ e^- \longrightarrow Mn^{++} + 4\ H_2O$$

The MnO_4^- ion is reduced to the Mn^{++} ion only if (a) five electrons are supplied by a reducing agent, and (b) eight H^+ ions are available to react with the MnO_4^- ion to produce four H_2O. Thus, we find that the MnO_4^- ion reacts in *acid solution* (H^+) to form Mn^{++} and H_2O, as shown in Table 21-1.

21-6 Oxidation-Reduction Couples

The information contained in Tables 21-1 and 21-2 may be combined into a more useful form shown in Table 21-3.

The oxidized and reduced forms of each substance constitute an *oxidation-reduction couple.* In Table 21-3, all six oxidation-reduction couples are written with the reduced form on the left, and the oxidized form on the right. Because the title of Table 21-3 specifies *acid* (H^+) solutions, it is not necessary to include H^+ and H_2O, which are understood to be present in any acidic aqueous solution.

TABLE 21-3 OXIDATION-REDUCTION COUPLES IN ACID SOLUTIONS

	Reduced Form	*Oxidized Form*	
Increasing Reducing Ability ↑	H_2S	S	Increasing Oxidizing Ability ↓
	I^-	I_2	
	Br^-	Br_2	
	Mn^{++}	MnO_2	
	Cr^{+++}	Cr_2O_7	
	Mn^{++}	MnO_4^-	

Table 21-3 is more informative than Tables 21-1 and 21-2 because the oxidants and reductants are listed in order of their relative strengths (of course under specified "standard" conditions). The oxidants, on the right side of the table, are progressively *stronger* as we move *downward.* Not only can MnO_4^-, in acidic (H^+) solution, oxidize Br^- to Br_2, I^- to I_2, and H_2S to S, but it can also oxidize Mn^{++} to MnO_2 and Cr^{+++} to $CrO_7^=$. Also, *any one of the oxidants* (right side) is strong enough to *oxidize any one of the reductants* (left side) which are *above it* in the table. In each case the oxidant is reduced to the species appearing on its left. Conversely, any one of the oxidants is too weak to oxidize those reductants which appear below it on the table. For example, I_2 will oxidize H_2S to S, but cannot oxidize any of the other reducing agents listed in this table. Here is a generalization: In a table of oxidation-reduction couples, any species (ion, atom, molecule) on the right (oxidant) can react with any species on the left (reductant) above it. In each case the product is the other member of the couple. Of course if we wish to point out the reducing properties of a substance, we can equally say that any *reductant* (left-hand side of table) can reduce any *oxidant* which is *below* it on the right-hand side. In general then, any substance on the *left-hand* side of the table will react with any substance *below* it on the right-hand side, and the products are those listed alongside each reactant.

21-7 Predicting Oxidation-Reduction Reactions

A fairly complete list of oxidation-reduction couples is given in Table 21-4 and in the Appendix, Tables I & II. In these tables it is useful to indicate the relative oxidizing and reducing powers of various substances not only by the relative positions of the substances in the table but also by numbers. These numbers are called $E°$ values; we shall discuss their significance in detail in the next chapter. For the moment,

TABLE 21-4 OXIDATION-REDUCTION COUPLES (ALL IONS AT 1*M* CONCENTRATION)

(I) IN ACID SOLUTION

Reduced Form	Oxidized Form	$E°$ (volts)
Al	Al^{+++}	(+1.66)
Zn	Zn^{++}	(+0.76)
Fe	Fe^{++}	(+0.44)
Cd	Cd^{++}	(+0.44)
Cr^{++}	Cr^{+++}	(+0.41)
Co	Co^{++}	(+0.277)
Ni	Ni^{++}	(+0.25)
Cu^{+}	Cu^{++}	(+0.153)
Sn	Sn^{++}	(+0.14)
H_2	$2\,H^+$	(0.00)
H_2S	$S + 2\,H^+$	(−0.14)
Cu	Cu^{++}	(−0.34)
Cu	Cu^{+}	(−0.521)
$2\,I^-$	I_2	(−0.34)
H_2O_2	O_2	(−0.682)
Fe^{++}	Fe^{+++}	(−0.77)
Ag	Ag^{+}	(−0.80)
$2\,Br^-$	Br_2	(−1.06)
Mn^{++}	MnO_2	(−1.23)
$2\,Cr^{+++}$	$Cr_2O_7^{=}$	(−1.33)
$2\,Cl^-$	Cl_2	(−1.36)
Mn^{++}	MnO_4^-	(−1.51)
$2\,H_2O$	$H_2O_2 + 2\,H^+$	(−1.77)
Co^{++}	Co^{+++}	(−1.82)

(II) IN BASIC SOLUTION

Reduced Form	Oxidized Form	$E°$ (volts)
$Mn(+ OH^-)$	$Mn(OH)_2$	(+1.55)
$Cr(+ OH^-)$	$Cr(OH)_3$	(+1.30)
$Mn(OH)_2(+ OH^-)$	MnO_2	(+0.05)

however, we can use these numbers simply to locate couples in these tables. In the Appendix, Table I is used for acidic (H^+) and neutral solutions, whereas Table II is used for basic (OH^-) solutions. Couples from Table I may be combined with those from Table II only when there are no hydrogen ions (H^+) present in the balanced half-reaction. While reading the paragraphs which follow, refer to Table 21-4.

These more extensive tables may be used in exactly the same way that we used Tables 21-3 and 21-4.* For example, MnO_4^- in acid (H^+) solution ($E° = -1.51$) is a strong enough oxidizing agent to oxidize Co^0 to Co^{++} ($E° = +0.277$) because the oxidizing agent, MnO_4^- is *lower* in the table than the reducing agent, Co^0. However, MnO_4^- in acid (H^+) solution is not strong enough to oxidize Co^{++} to Co^{+++} ($E° = -1.82$) because, in this case, the oxidizing agent is *higher* in the table than the reducing agent.

Now that we have predicted that a reaction between MnO_4^- and Co^0 can occur spontaneously to produce Mn^{++} and Co^{++} (in acid solution), we may obtain the balanced net ionic equation for the reaction by properly combining the balanced half-reactions given in Table 21-4.

1. We write the (oxidation) half-reaction for the couple (Co^0, Co^{++}) in the order as written in the table for the *oxidation* process. This is the half-equation having the *more positive* $E°$ value:

Oxidation half-reaction: 1. $Co \longrightarrow Co^{++} + 2\,e^-$ $(E° = +0.277)$

2. We write the half-reaction for the other couple, (Mn^{++}, MnO_4^-):

$$Mn^{++} + 4\,H_2O \longrightarrow MnO_4^- + 8\,H^+ + 5\,e^- \qquad (E° = -1.51)$$

The reverse of this oxidation half-reaction then is the desired reduction half-reaction:

Reduction half-reaction: 2. $MnO_4^- + 8\,H^+ + 5\,e^- \longrightarrow Mn^{++} + 4\,H_2O$ $(E° = +1.51)$

3. We note from half equations 1 and 2 that two electrons ($2\,e^-$) are given up by each Co atom which is oxidized to Co^{++}. Similarly we see from half-equation 2 that five electrons ($5\,e^-$) are taken on by each MnO_4^- ion which is reduced to Mn^{++}. Consequently, half-equation 1 must be multiplied by 5 and half-equation 2 must be multi-

* Assuming that the conditions (temperature, ion concentration, gas pressures) are those for which the tables apply. Conditions other than those specified at the top of each table may change the relative positions of the oxidizing and reducing agents. The effect of non-standard conditions is discussed in the following chapter (page 498).

plied by 2 to balance the number of electrons lost and gained. Now, we can write the balanced half-equations and add them to give the total net equation:

Oxidation half-equation:	1.	$5\ Co \longrightarrow 5\ Co^{++} + 10\ e^-$
Reduction half-equation:°	2.	$2\ MnO_4^- + 16\ H^+ + 10\ e^- \longrightarrow 2\ Mn^{++} + 8\ H_2O$
Net ionic equation:		$5\ Co + 2\ MnO_4^- + 16\ H^+ \longrightarrow 5\ Co^{++} + 2\ Mn^{++} + 8\ H_2O$

As another example we can predict from Table 21-4 that MnO_2 in *basic* (OH^-) solution ($E° = +0.05$) is strong enough to oxidize Cr^0 to $Cr(OH)_3$ ($E° = +1.30$) because in basic solution the oxidizing agent, MnO_2, is lower in the table than the reducing agent, Cr^0. The balanced net ionic equation for this spontaneous reaction may be arrived at as follows:

Oxidation half-equation: $[Cr + 3\ OH^- \longrightarrow Cr(OH)_3 + 3\ e^-] \times 2$

Reduction half-equation: $[MnO_2 + 2\ H_2O + 2\ e^- \longrightarrow Mn(OH)_2 + 2\ OH^-] \times 3$

Total equation:

$$2\ Cr + 6\ OH^- + 3\ MnO_2 + 6\ H_2O + 6\ e^- \longrightarrow 2\ Cr(OH)_3 + 6\ e^- + 3\ Mn(OH)_2 + 6\ OH^-$$

Canceling $6\ e^-$ and $6\ OH^-$ on each side gives:

Net ionic equation: $2\ Cr + 3\ MnO_2 + 6\ H_2O \longrightarrow 2\ Cr(OH)_3 + 3\ Mn(OH)_2$

21-8 *E*° Values and Disproportionation

As we saw earlier, some substances are capable of acting as both oxidizing agents and reducing agents. For example, Cu^+ can either gain one electron to become metallic Cu^0 or lose one electron to become Cu^{++}. In the first case, Cu^+ (of the couple Cu^0, Cu^+) acts as an oxidizing agent and undergoes reduction; in the second case, Cu^+ (of the couple Cu^+, Cu^{++}) acts as a reducing agent and undergoes oxidation.

Table 21-4 lists these two couples in the order: Cu^+, Cu^{++}; $E° = +0.153$; and Cu^0, Cu^+; $E° = -0.521$. Since Cu^+ as an oxidizing agent (right side) is lower in Table 21-4 than Cu^+ as a reducing agent (left side), Cu^+ is strong enough to oxidize Cu^+. We can obtain the balanced net ionic equation by combining the two half-equations:

Oxidation half-equation:	$Cu^+ \longrightarrow Cu^{++} + e^-$
Reduction half-equation:	$Cu^+ + e^- \longrightarrow Cu$
Net ionic equation:	$2\ Cu^+ \longrightarrow Cu^{++} + Cu$

This equation tells us that Cu^+ reacts with Cu^+ (Cu^+ oxidizes and reduces itself) and this is an example of self-oxidation-reduction, or disproportionation. Thus, Cu(I) ions (in acidic or neutral aqueous solutions) are unstable toward oxidation-reduction (disproportionation) and tend to form Cu^{++} ions and Cu metal in a 1:1 mole ratio.

Hydrogen peroxide, H_2O_2, in aqueous acid solution is also unstable toward disproportionation and can oxidize and reduce itself as shown by the relative positions (and *E*° values) of the following couples taken from Table 21-4.

$$H_2O_2 \longrightarrow O_2 + 2\ H^+ + 2\ e^- \qquad E° = -0.682$$

$$2\ H_2O \longrightarrow H_2O_2 + 2\ H^+ + 2\ e^- \qquad E° = -1.77$$

H_2O_2 as an oxidant (right side of table), is lower in the table than H_2O_2 as a reductant (left side of table), and so it is strong enough to oxidize and reduce itself. That is, H_2O_2 disproportionates. The net ionic equation for this spontaneous reaction will be:

° To obtain a reduction half-equation, it is always necessary to reverse the order of the reduced form and the oxidized form given in the equations in the table, since in Table 21-4 all equations are written as oxidation half-equations.

Oxidation half-equation:	H_2O_2	$\longrightarrow$	$O_2 + 2\,H^+ + 2\,e^-$
Reduction half-equation:	$H_2O_2 + 2\,H^+ + 2\,e^-$	$\longrightarrow$	$2\,H_2O$
Total equation:	$2\,H_2O_2 + 2\,H^+ + 2\,e^-$	$\longrightarrow$	$O_2 + 2\,H^+ + 2\,H_2O + 2\,e^-$
Net ionic equation:	$2\,H_2O_2$	$\longrightarrow$	$O_2 + 2\,H_2O$

21-9 Concurrent Reactions

In all the reactions we have considered up to this point, we have found that if we know the reactants and the products, we can balance the equation. We assign proper coefficients to the reactants and products on the basis of the electron changes involved and the law of conservation of mass. But notice that in all the equations so far, only one simple value was possible for each coefficient, for a definite and fixed weight relationship always existed between the reactants and the products. Thus, when only one reaction takes place the systematic method described above for balancing oxidation-reduction equations leads to a single set of coefficients.

But sometimes in a chemical system two or more independent reactions take place, and an equation must be written for the summation of these independent reactions. In such a case, each individual, independent reaction has a single set of coefficients.

For example, if in an oxidation-reduction reaction more than one reduction product is formed at the same time, and if the different products result from independent reactions, we must set up and balance separate equations for each reaction. The reaction of Cu metal with a 1-molar solution of nitric acid produces both NO and NO_2 as reduction products, by two independent reactions. Two different equations must be written:

1. $3\,Cu + 8\,HNO_3 \longrightarrow 2\,NO + 3\,Cu(NO_3)_2 + 4\,H_2O$
2. $Cu + 4\,HNO_3 \longrightarrow 2\,NO_2 + Cu(NO_3)_2 + 2\,H_2O$

The relative amount of copper metal that enters into reaction 1 as compared with reaction 2 depends on many factors, such as temperature and acid concentration. If we were simply to add equations 1 and 2,

$$4\,Cu + 12\,HNO_3 \longrightarrow 2\,NO_2 + 2\,NO + 4\,Cu(NO_3)_2 + 6\,H_2O$$

we would be describing only the case in which, for every three Cu atoms that enter into equation 1, one Cu atom enters into equation 2. Any other ratio of Cu atoms that follows reactions 1 and 2 would yield a different set of coefficients for the combined equation. In cases of this sort we must determine *experimentally* the mole ratio of the products NO and NO_2 formed in the chemical reaction; only on this basis can we indicate the true relationship between them.

Thus, in order to express the true equation for an oxidation-reduction reaction in which more than one reduction product is produced from one reactant, we must know the relative mole quantities of the reduction products as well as the reactants.

Exercises

21-1 In each of the following unbalanced equations, identify (1) the oxidant, (2) the reductant, (3) the substance oxidized, (4) the substance reduced:
(a) $Al + CuSO_4 \longrightarrow Al_2(SO_4)_3 + Cu$
(b) $Fe + Cl_2 \longrightarrow FeCl_3$
(c) $KOH + Cl_2 \longrightarrow KClO_3 + KCl + H_2O$
(d) $MnO_2 + NaCl + H_2SO_4 \longrightarrow MnSO_4 + NaHSO_4 + H_2O + Cl_2$
(e) $KMnO_4 + HCl \longrightarrow KCl + MnCl_2 + Cl_2 + H_2O$
(f) $KMnO_4 + H_2S + H_2SO_4 \longrightarrow K_2SO_4 + MnSO_4 + H_2O + S$
(g) $CuS + HNO_3 \longrightarrow Cu(NO_3)_2 + H_2O + NO_2 + SO_2$
(h) $K_2Cr_2O_7 + HCl \longrightarrow KCl + CrCl_3 + H_2O + Cl_2$

21-2 Using the electron-transfer method, balance the equations in 21-1.

21-3 Rewrite these same equations in ionic form.

21-4 Rewrite these same equations in the net ionic form.

21-5 Using the electron-transfer method, balance the following equations:

(a) $Cu + HNO_3 \longrightarrow Cu(NO_3)_2 + NO + H_2O$

(b) $Br_2 + KOH \longrightarrow KBrO_3 + KBr + H_2O$

(c) $HI + H_2SO_4 \longrightarrow H_2O + H_2S + I_2$

(d) $K_2CrO_4 + H_2S + H_2SO_4 \longrightarrow K_2SO_4 + Cr_2(SO_4)_3 + S + H_2O$

(e) $K_2Cr_2O_7 + FeSO_4 + H_2SO_4 \longrightarrow Cr_2(SO_4)_3 + K_2SO_4 + Fe_2(SO_4)_3 + H_2O$

(f) $H_2S + HNO_3 \longrightarrow H_2O + NO_2 + S$

(g) $K_2Cr_2O_7 + KBr + H_2SO_4 \longrightarrow K_2SO_4 + Cr_2(SO_4)_3 + Br_2 + H_2O$

21-6 Using (a) the electron-transfer method *and* (b) the half-cell reaction method, balance the following equations:

(a) $Cu + H^+ + NO_3^- \longrightarrow Cu^{++} + NO + H_2O$

(b) $S^= + Cr_2O_7^= + H^+ \longrightarrow S + Cr^{+++} + H_2O$

(c) $Zn + H^+ + NO_3^- \longrightarrow Zn^{++} + NH_4^+ + H_2O$

(d) $Cl_2 + H_2O + SO_2 \longrightarrow SO_4^= + Cl^- + H^+$

(e) $Fe^{++} + Cr_2O_7^= + H^+ \longrightarrow Cr^{+++} + Fe^{+++} + H_2O$

21-7 For each pair of possible reactants, locate the oxidant and the reductant in Table I, Appendix, and predict whether or not a spontaneous reaction should occur when they are mixed together in acid (H^+) solution. The numbers in parentheses are $E°$ values which you may use to locate the substances in the table.

(a) Fe^{++} (+0.440) and Ti^{++} (+0.37)

(b) HNO_3 (−0.94) and Sn^{++} (−0.15)

(c) Sn (+0.25) and $(AlF_6)^{\equiv}$ (+2.07)

(d) TiO^{++} (−0.1) and Ni (+0.250)

21-8 Write balanced net ionic equations for each of the following half-reactions. For each, indicate whether an oxidation or a reduction process is involved.

(a) $MoO_2^{++} \longrightarrow Mo^{+++}$ (H^+ solution)

(b) $Os(OH)_4 \longrightarrow OsO_4$ (H^+ solution)

(c) $HXeO_4^- \longrightarrow HXeO_6^{\equiv}$ (OH solution)

(d) $H_3SbO_6^{\equiv} \longrightarrow SbH_3$ (OH solution)

Problems

21-1 On the basis of the couples listed in Table 21-4, which of the following is (1) the strongest oxidant (2) the strongest reductant: Zn, Sn, I^-, Br^-. (All ions at 1 *M* concentration.)

21-2 By reference to Table 21-4, indicate which of the following reactions take place (spontaneously) by completing the equations. If a reaction does not take place write N.R. (1) $Zn + Fe^{++}$, (2) $Cu + I_2$, (3) $Fe^{++} + Br^-$, (4) $Ni + Sn^{++}$, (5) $Fe + Sn^{++}$, (6) $Al + H^+$, (7) $Fe^{+++} + Ag$. (All ions at 1 *M* concentration.)

21-3 On the basis of the couples listed in Table 21-4, write (balanced) half-equations for the following half-reactions in acid solution. (1) The oxidation of Sn to Sn^{++}, (2) the oxidation of Cr^{++} to Cr^{+++}, (3) the oxidation of Cu^0 to Cu^{++}, (4) the oxidation of Br^- to Br_2, (5) the oxidation of Mn^{++} to MnO_2, (6) the oxidation of Cr^{+++} to $Cr_2O_7^=$, (7) the oxidation of Mn^{++} to MnO_4^-. (All ions at 1 *M* concentration.)

21-4 On the basis of the couples listed in Table 21-4, write balanced half-equations for the following *reduction* half-reactions in acid solution. (1) Fe^{++} to Fe^0, (2) Ni^{++} to Ni^0, (3) MnO_2 to Mn^{++}, (4) Br_2 to Br^-, (5) MnO_4^- to Mn^{++}, (6) $Cr_2O_7^=$ to Cr^{+++}, (7) I_2 to I^-, (8) S to H_2S. (All ions at 1 *M* concentration.)

21-5 On the basis of the couples listed in Table 21-4, (a) list all the species (atoms, ions or molecules) which can be *oxidized* in acid solution by (1) Ni^{++}, (2) Fe^{+++} giving in each case the oxidized product; (b) list all the species which can be *reduced* in acid solution by (1) Fe^{++}, (2) Mn^{++}, giving in each case the reduced product. (All ions at 1 *M* concentration.)

21-6 On the basis of the couples listed in Table 21-4, predict which of the following reactions could take place spontaneously in acid solution, listing only the reactants and products. Write N.R. if no reaction is expected. (1) Br and I_2, (2) $Zn + Cr^{++}$, (3) Fe + hydrochloric acid, (4) Zn^{++} and Sn^{++}, (5) iron(II) nitrate and an aqueous solution of Br_2. (All ions at 1 *M* concentration.)

ELECTROCHEMISTRY: I. ENERGY CELLS

Electrochemistry is concerned with the relationships between chemical reactions and electrical energy—and more specifically with two chief facts: (1) chemical processes with the capacity to take place spontaneously can, under appropriate conditions, produce electrical energy, and (2) chemical processes without the capacity to take place spontaneously can occur if an appropriate quantity of electrical energy is supplied under suitable conditions. In this chapter we shall discuss in detail the first point, and we shall learn that, when a spontaneous chemical process occurs in an apparatus called an electrochemical *energy cell,* the free energy released by the system is given off chiefly as electrical energy, which can be utilized for practical purposes such as lighting a bulb or operating a motor. In the next chapter, on the other hand, we shall learn how chemical processes which cannot take place spontaneously can be made to occur by supplying electrical energy to the system in an apparatus called an *electrolytic cell.*

In this chapter we shall first find out how energy cells are constructed and how they operate. Then we shall consider the chemical reactions that occur in the cells, and the significance of the $E°$ values in relation to the spontaneous character of such reactions. Finally, we shall study how changes in the experimental conditions, and especially changes in concentration, affect the voltage of energy cells.

22-1 Standard Half-Cells

An electrochemical half-cell consists of a metallic conductor (usually a metal plate) immersed in a fluid (usually a solution) through which ions and molecules can move. The metal plate is called the *electrode*, and the solution is called the *electrolyte*, of the half-cell.*

In some half-cells, the metal of the electrode is present in the electrolyte as positive ions. For example, a zinc half-cell consists of a plate of zinc immersed into an aqueous solution of hydrated Zn^{++} ions and hence is represented briefly as Zn,Zn^{++}. A metal in contact with a 1 *M* solution† of its cations (ions with positive charges), at a temperature of 25°C and a pressure of 1 atm, constitutes a *standard half-cell* or *standard couple*. Let us examine two standard half-cells of this kind.

THE STANDARD ZINC HALF-CELL, OR Zn,Zn^{++} COUPLE. Consider a zinc plate that is partially immersed in a 1 *M* aqueous solution of hydrated Zn^{++} ions—prepared, for example, by dissolving in water a soluble zinc salt, such as $ZnSO_4$—at 25°C and 1 atm. This system, as shown in Fig. 22-1(a), forms a standard zinc half-cell, or standard Zn,Zn^{++} couple. In this half-cell, no net reaction is occurring. The zinc plate remains unchanged—in particular, its weight remains constant—and the concentration of the Zn^{++} ions in the surrounding solution also remains unchanged. At each instant however, a number of the Zn atoms of the metal plate is oxidized to form Zn^{++} ions which enter into solution, $Zn_{(s)} \longrightarrow Zn^{++}{}_{(aq)} + 2\,e^-$, while simultaneously an equal number of the hydrated Zn^{++} ions of the solution is reduced to form Zn atoms which deposit on the metal plate, $Zn^{++}{}_{(aq)} + 2\,e^- \longrightarrow Zn_{(s)}$. Even though no net reaction is occurring in the half-cell, a *dynamic equilibrium* is established between the zinc atoms, $Zn_{(s)}$, which constitute the electrode, the hydrated $Zn^{++}{}_{(aq)}$ ions present in the solution, and the electrons involved in the reversible oxidation-reduction reaction:

$$Zn_{(s)} \rightleftharpoons Zn^{++}{}_{(aq)} + 2\,e^-$$

Thus there is a continuous exchange of zinc atoms and ions between the surface of the electrode and the surrounding solution, but the concentration of the $Zn^{++}{}_{(aq)}$ ions in solution remains unchanged, and so does the quantity of the Zn metal in the electrode. Notice that, from a electrical viewpoint, the half-cell itself is an open circuit—that is, no electrons flow into or out of it.

THE STANDARD COPPER HALF-CELL, OR Cu,Cu^{++} COUPLE. The standard copper half-cell consists of a plate of copper metal partially immersed in a 1 *M* aqueous solution of hydrated Cu^{++} ions at 25°C and 1 atm, as shown in Fig. 22-1(b). In this system, too, a dynamic equilibrium is established at the contact surface between the electrode (the copper plate) and the electrolyte (the $Cu^{++}{}_{(aq)}$ solution); for every Cu atom of the electrode which is oxidized to form a $Cu^{++}{}_{(aq)}$ ion, a $Cu^{++}{}_{(aq)}$ ion from the solution is simultaneously reduced to a Cu atom which deposits on the surface of the copper electrode: $Cu_{(s)} \rightleftharpoons Cu^{++}{}_{(aq)} + 2\,e^-$. Again, dynamic equilibrium is established but no net reaction occurs in the half-cell. The half-cell itself is an open circuit, for no electrons flow in or out of the system.

Not all half-cells consist of a metallic electrode in contact with a solution containing cations of the same metal. Some half-cells consist of an oxidized and a reduced form of the same element—not necessarily a metal—in contact with the surface of an unreactive electrode. An important example is the hydrogen half-cell described below.

* The term "electrode" comes from a Greek word meaning "pathway for electricity." The term "electrolyte" is used to indicate any fluid—a melt or a solution—containing ions which can undergo chemical reaction under the influence of electrical energy (see next chapter).

† More appropriately, we should say a solution in which the activity of the metal ions is unity (p. 555).

THE STANDARD HYDROGEN HALF-CELL, OR H_2,H^+ COUPLE. The standard hydrogen half-cell, illustrated in Fig. 22-1(c), can be constructed in the following manner. Cover a strip of platinum metal with a layer of finely divided platinum (called "platinum black," because of its color) in order to provide an active surface area for the adsorption of H_2 gas. Immerse this platinum black electrode, with its adsorbed H_2 gas, in a 1 *M* aqueous solution of H^+ ions (for example, a 1 *M* hydrochloric acid solution). Then continuously bubble hydrogen gas, H_2, at 25°C and at a pressure of 1 atm, into the solution surrounding the platinum black electrode. Thus, the standard hydrogen half-cell, also known as the standard H_2,H^+ couple, consists essentially of a platinum black electrode surrounded by a stream of H_2 gas at a constant pressure of 1 atm and in contact with a 1 *M* solution of H^+ ions—all at 25°C. On the surface of the platinum electrode a dynamic equilibrium is established between the H_2 molecules adsorbed on the electrode and the hydrated H^+ ions present in the solution:

$$H_{2(g)} \rightleftharpoons 2\ H^+_{(aq)} + 2\ e^-$$

No net reaction is taking place in the hydrogen half-cell, which is an open circuit.

22-2 Energy Cells

THE COMBINED ZINC-COPPER STANDARD CELL

We can join the standard zinc half-cell and the standard copper half-cell by means of both a salt bridge connecting the two solutions and an external circuit connecting the two metal plates (Fig. 22-2). The *salt bridge* consists essentially of a glass tube filled with an aqueous solution of an appropriate salt, say potassium sulfate, K_2SO_4, and fitted at the ends with two thick porous plugs (made, for example, of sintered glass). This salt bridge keeps the solutions of the two half-cells in contact, so that ions can slowly migrate from one solution to the other through the bridge; at the same time the bridge prevents the solutions from becoming rapidly mixed. The *external circuit* consists essentially of four parts: a metallic conductor (for example, copper wire), a *voltmeter* (an instrument that measures differences of electric potential), a light bulb which glows when an electric current passes through the circuit, and a switch to open and close the circuit. When the switch is closed, the two electrodes of the two half-cells are connected electrically, and with the voltmeter we can measure any difference of electrical potential between them.

When the switch is open, so that the two electrodes are not connected through

FIGURE 22-1 Standard half cells. (a) Zinc; (b) copper; (c) hydrogen.

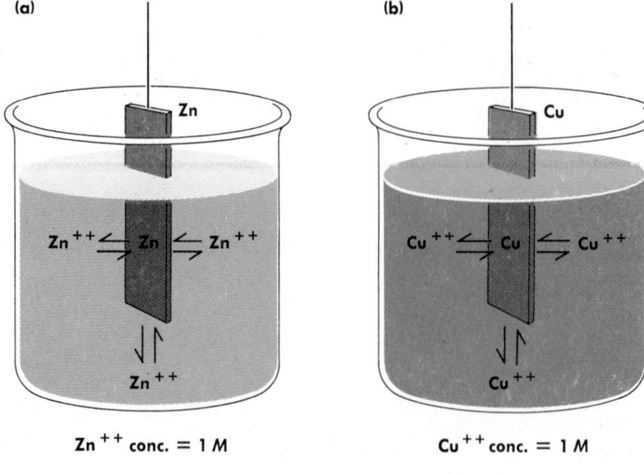

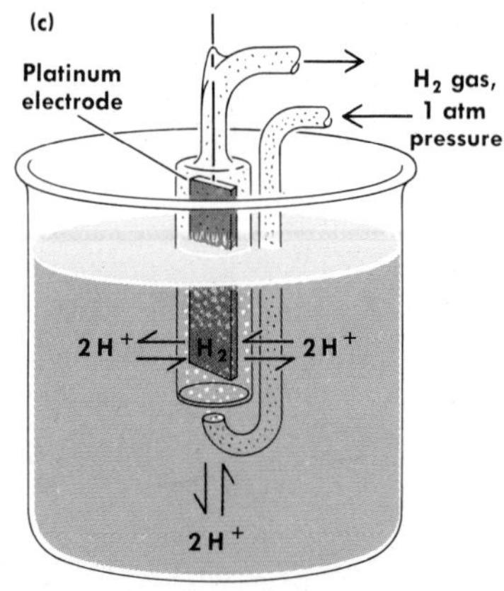

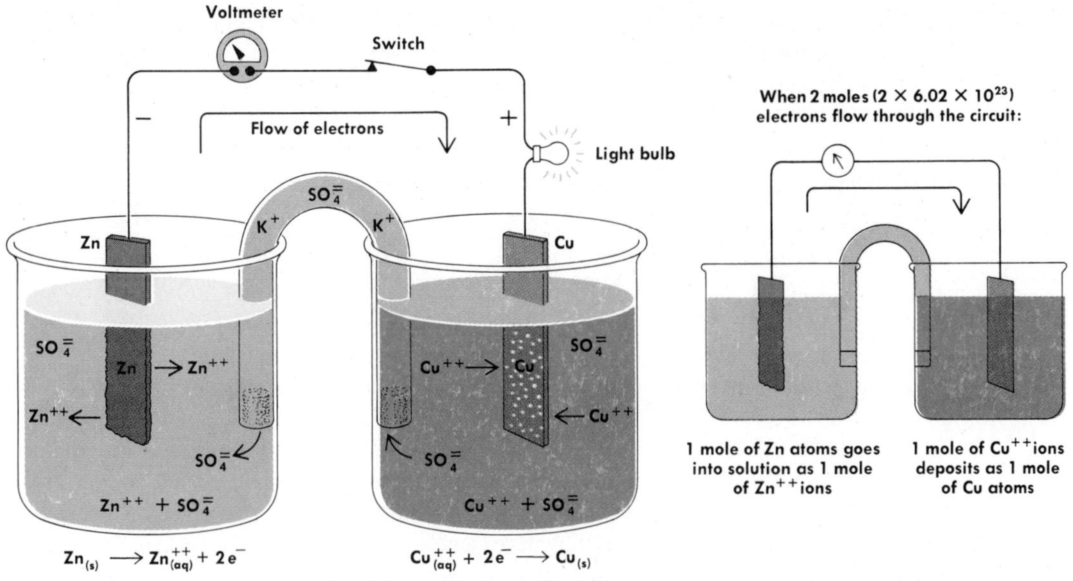

FIGURE 22-2 A zinc-copper cell (with salt bridge).

the external circuit, the light bulb does not glow, the voltmeter does not measure any difference of potential, and no detectable chemical reaction occurs at the electrodes of the two half-cells. But as soon as we close the switch, important changes begin to take place, and we observe the following:

1. At the very instant we close the circuit the light bulb begins to glow, showing that an electrical current flows through the external circuit, and the voltmeter measures a potential difference, a voltage,* of about 1.10 volts.†

2. Just as soon as the circuit is closed and the electrical current begins to flow through the system, some of the Zn metal that makes up the electrode of the zinc half-cell dissolves (is oxidized) to form Zn^{++} ions in solution:

Oxidation half-reaction: $$Zn_{(s)} \longrightarrow Zn^{++}_{(aq)} + 2\ e^-$$

In this oxidation reaction the electrons given up by the zinc atoms of the zinc plate remain behind on this plate. Then, they flow through the metallic wire of the external circuit, to the copper plate of the copper half-cell.

3. Simultaneously, metallic copper, Cu, is deposited at the electrode of the copper half-cell as some of the hydrated Cu^{++} ions of the solution are reduced (by electrons taken from the copper plate itself):

Reduction half-reaction: $$Cu^{++}_{(aq)} + 2\ e^- \longrightarrow Cu_{(s)}$$

We often describe this reduction process by saying that the Cu^{++} ions *"plate out of solution" on the copper electrode.*

4. When the current flows through the circuit, we find that the number of moles of Zn metal that are oxidized during a certain time at the zinc electrode is equal to the number of moles of Cu metal that plate out during the same time at the copper elec-

* In the following sections and throughout the book, the terms "potential difference," "electromotive force," and "voltage" are used interchangeably.

† As the current continues to flow, the potential difference decreases (eventually to zero). We shall discuss this aspect later, on page 481.

trode. Since the half-reactions for the oxidation of the Zn metal and the reduction of the Cu^{++} ion each involve 2 electrons, the electrons given up by the Zn atoms at the zinc electrode must pass through the circuit to the copper electrode, where they reduce the Cu^{++} ions in solution, thus forming metallic Cu which plates out. The reaction of the whole system is represented by the net equation obtained by adding the two half-cell equations which take place at the two electrodes.

Zinc half-cell reaction:	$Zn_{(s)}$	$\longrightarrow Zn^{++}{}_{(aq)} + 2\ e^-$
Copper half-cell reaction:	$Cu^{++}{}_{(aq)} + 2\ e^-$	$\longrightarrow Cu_{(s)}$
Net cell reaction:	$Zn_{(s)} + Cu^{++}{}_{(aq)}$	$\longrightarrow Cu_{(s)} + Zn^{++}{}_{(aq)}$

5. As the above reaction proceeds, an excess of $SO_4^{=}$ ions from the original $CuSO_4$ solution remains momentarily in the solution in the vicinity of the copper half-cell, while an excess of Zn^{++} ions remains momentarily in the solution in the vicinity of the zinc half-cell. In order to remedy the electrical imbalance thus created near each electrode, ions move into and out of the solution of the two half-cells through the connecting salt bridge (which contains a solution of K^+ and $SO_4^{=}$ ions). The excess number of Zn^{++} ions momentarily present in the zinc half-cell solution are balanced by an equal number of dinegative $SO_4^{=}$ ions which leave the salt bridge and enter the zinc half-cell solution. This flow of $SO_4^{=}$ ions toward the zinc half-cell leaves an excess of K^+ ions inside the salt bridge. What happens to this excess of K^+ ions? Do they leave from the other end of the salt bridge, and enter the copper half-cell where they balance the excess $SO_4^{=}$ ions left behind by the plating out of the Cu^{++} ions? Or do the excess $SO_4^{=}$ ions in the copper half-cell enter the salt bridge to balance the excess K^+ ions? Actually, what happens is that some K^+ ions leave the salt bridge and some $SO_4^{=}$ ions enter the salt bridge. These migrations of ions from one half-cell to the other through the salt bridge serve to maintain the electrical neutrality throughout both solutions. Thus, the salt bridge acts not only as a partition which prevents the solutions of the two half-cells from mixing spontaneously, but also as a reservoir of the anions and cations required to maintain electrical neutrality.

A porous partition, for example of sintered glass or unglazed porcelain, can also be used to maintain the solutions of the two half-cells in contact and yet prevent them from becoming rapidly mixed (and reacting directly). Like the salt bridge, the porous partition permits the ions present in the solutions to migrate from one half-cell to the other as required to keep both solutions electrically neutral.

6. As the net reaction, $Zn_{(s)} + Cu^{++}{}_{(aq)} \longrightarrow Cu_{(s)} + Zn^{++}{}_{(aq)}$, occurs in the combined cell, electrons flow from the Zn electrode to the Cu electrode through the external circuit. This flow of electrons constitutes the electric current which passes through the external circuit and makes the bulb light up. Now, electrical energy must always be expended in order to make an electric current flow through a circuit, because the electrical resistance of the circuit must be overcome. So we conclude that the reaction, $Zn_{(s)} + Cu^{++}{}_{(aq)} \longrightarrow Zn^{++}{}_{(aq)} + Cu_{(s)}$, when carried out in a combined cell occurs spontaneously and provides electrical energy—as well as some heat energy that warms the solutions and the wires of the circuit. If, on the other hand, the reaction is carried out simply by mixing the reactants, only heat energy is produced:

$$Zn_{(s)} + Cu^{++}{}_{(aq)} \longrightarrow Zn^{++}{}_{(aq)} + Cu_{(s)} \qquad \Delta H^\circ = -51.8 \text{ kcal/mole-eqn at } 25^\circ\text{C and 1 atm}$$

In the combined zinc-copper standard cell, the *oxidation half-reaction* occurs at the zinc electrode, which is called the *anode* of the combined cell. The copper electrode, where the *reduction half-reaction* takes place, is called the *cathode* of the combined cell. *In general, in any energy cell, the electrode at which the oxidation half-reaction takes place is called the anode, and the electrode at which the reduction half-reaction takes place is called the cathode.* In the zinc-copper energy cell, as in any energy cell, the *anode is the negatively charged electrode,* because in the oxidation half-reaction electrons are given up by the reactant species to the electrode. Conversely, in any energy cell, the *cathode is the positively charged electrode,* because in the reduction half-reaction electrons are taken on by the reactant from the electrode.

We can now see that the reduction of hydrated Cu^{++} ions by metallic zinc, Zn, may be brought about: (1) directly, by bringing metallic zinc into contact with a solution of Cu^{++} ions, as we learned in Chapter 7, and (2) indirectly, through the use of a combined zinc-copper cell. In each case zinc metal, Zn, enters into solution as Zn^{++} ions, and an equal number of Cu^{++} ions plates out as metallic copper, Cu. In the *direct* reaction electrons are transferred from the metallic zinc, Zn, *directly* to the Cu^{++} ions, and heat energy is released ($\Delta H^\circ = -51.8$ kcal/mole-eqn). In the combined cell, the zinc metal enters into solution as Zn^{++} ions in its half-cell, but the electrons travel through an external wire to the copper electrode, where they are taken on by the Cu^{++} ions in solution and Cu is deposited. In this case the electrons are transferred *indirectly* from Zn to Cu^{++}. The same total quantity of energy is released, but here most of it is usable electrical energy rather than only heat energy.

THE ELECTROMOTIVE FORCE OF AN ENERGY CELL

In the previous section we saw that, as soon as we close the switch in the combined Zn,Zn^{++}—Cu,Cu^{++} standard cell (Fig. 22-2), the voltmeter inserted in the external circuit registers a potential difference of 1.10 volts. This potential difference, measured instantaneously upon the closing of the circuit, is called *the electromotive force (e.m.f.) of the combined standard* Zn,Zn^{++}—Cu,Cu^{++} *cell,* and is represented by the symbol E° (read: e-zero). In this symbol, E stands for "electromotive force" and the superscript $^\circ$ means "standard." Thus the E° value for the combined zinc-copper standard cell is 1.10 volts. The voltage indicated by the voltmeter is equal to the E° value of 1.10 volts only so long as both solutions in contact with the electrodes remain at 1 M concentration—that is, before any appreciable quantity of electrical current has passed through the cell. Once the current has begun to flow, the concentration of the solution near the electrodes changes because of the reactions:

Anode reaction: $Zn \longrightarrow Zn^{++} + 2\,e^-$

Cathode reaction: $Cu^{++} + 2\,e^- \longrightarrow Cu$

As the current flows, the concentration of the Zn^{++} ions in the solution near the Zn electrode increases, the concentration of the Cu^{++} ions in the solution near the Cu electrode correspondingly decreases, and the potential difference shown by the voltmeter decreases. In general, the voltage of *any energy cell is always* at maximum when the cell has just begun to operate, then gradually decreases as the cell continues to operate producing electrical energy (we shall discuss this in detail in section 22-3). Eventually, the potential difference between the two electrodes of the cell becomes zero. When this happens, no more current flows through the external circuit, and no further net reactions take place at the electrodes—in short, the cell ceases to operate. Thus, the voltage of an energy cell can be taken as a measure of the tendency of the net cell reaction to occur as written, under the specified conditions of concentration, temperature, and pressure. As the voltage of the combined cell decreases, the capacity of the net cell reaction to occur spontaneously also decreases. In measuring the electromotive force of an energy cell as described in the previous section, we must therefore take the first instantaneous value shown on the voltmeter when the circuit is closed. Also, the voltmeter must have a very high electrical resistance, so that only a negligible quantity of electricity actually passes through the circuit during the time required to take the voltmeter reading.

When we assemble an energy cell for the purpose of measuring its electromotive force at the specified initial concentrations—and not to make use of the electrical energy provided by the net cell reaction—we generally use a potentiometer in the

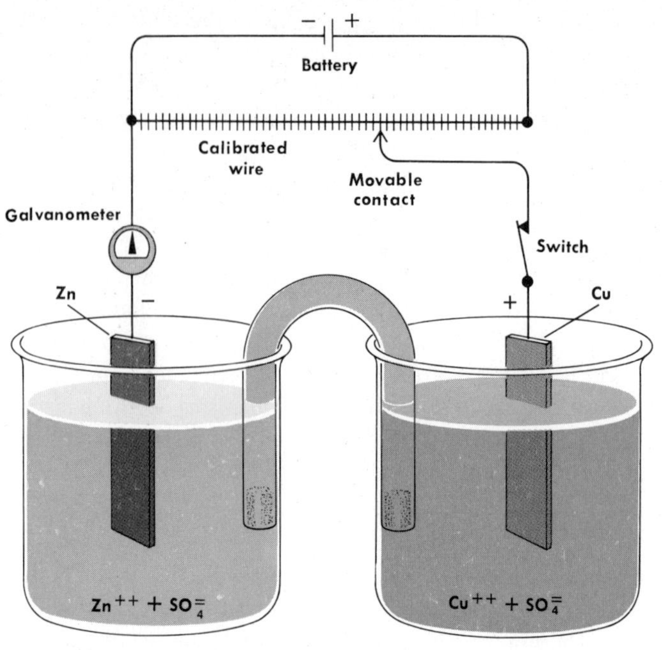

FIGURE 22-3 Measurement of the electromotive force of a zinc-copper energy cell.

external circuit instead of a voltmeter. A *potentiometer* is an instrument that measures the difference in electrical potential between the two electrodes of a cell when current is *not* flowing through the circuit. A potentiometer, as shown in Fig. 22-3, consists essentially of a reference cell of exactly known voltage,* whose electrodes are connected to the ends of a calibrated resistance wire (for example, a high-resistance, thin metal wire of exactly uniform cross section) equipped with a sliding contact. The value of the potential applied by the reference cell between one end of the resistance wire and the sliding contact itself can be read directly alongside the wire. To measure the electromotive force (e.m.f.) of a given cell, we connect one of its electrodes (say, the positive one) to the end of the calibrated resistance wire attached to the positive electrode of the reference cell. We then connect the other (negative) electrode of the cell under study to the sliding contact, and at the same time insert into the circuit a *galvanometer*—an instrument which indicates the passage of an electric current. By successive trials, we adjust the position of the sliding contact along the resistance wire so that, when the circuit is closed, the galvanometer shows no passage of electricity. When this condition is attained, the voltage effectively provided by the reference cell, through the segment of calibrated resistance wire, is exactly equal in magnitude and opposite in sign to the electromotive force of the cell under study. The position of the sliding contact then gives us directly the value of the desired unknown voltage. Using a potentiometer, we can obtain the voltage of the cell when at each electrode the oxidized and reduced forms of the couples are in equilibrium.

22-3 The Electromotive Force of an Energy Cell and the ΔG Value of the Net Cell Reaction

In Chapter 17 we learned that the factor which determines whether or not a given reaction has the capacity to occur spontaneously under the specified conditions is the change of free energy, ΔG, accompanying the reaction. If ΔG is negative

* The voltage of this reference cell must be greater than the voltage of the cell to be measured.

the reaction is spontaneous, whereas if ΔG is positive the reaction cannot occur spontaneously. We have just seen that the standard electromotive force, $E°$, of an energy cell is also a measure of the tendency of the net cell reaction to occur as written under the specified experimental conditions. Since both the electromotive force, E, of a cell and the free energy change, ΔG, of the cell reaction can be used as a criterion of spontaneity, ΔG and E must be related to each other.

We may arrive at the relationship between E_{cell} and $\Delta G_{reaction}$ by the following reasoning. Recall from Chapter 17 that the free energy change, ΔG, which accompanies a given reaction is the *maximum useful work*, $w_{useful\ max}$, that can be exchanged between the system and the surroundings in passing from the initial to the final state (by convention this maximum useful work has a negative sign when it represents work done by the system, that is, energy expended by the system in the process considered): $\Delta G = w_{useful\ max}$. Recall also that the work done by any system in a spontaneous reaction from a given initial state to a given final state has the largest negative value *when the reaction is carried out under reversible conditions*—that is, when the reaction is carried out in such a way that the system is at each instant very nearly in equilibrium with the surroundings.

Let us now apply these general considerations to the reaction that occurs in an energy cell, for example, the Zn,Zn^{++}—Cu,Cu^{++} combined cell. We will adopt the experimental arrangement shown in Fig. 22-3 with the potentiometer set in such a way that the voltage supplied by the reference cell through the slide resistance wire almost, but not quite, counterbalances the electromotive force of the zinc-copper cell. Under these conditions, during each very short time interval only a relatively small number of Zn atoms will oxidize to Zn^{++} ions and go into solution at the zinc half-cell, $Zn \longrightarrow Zn^{++} + 2\,e^-$; simultaneously an equal number of Cu^{++} ions of the copper half-cell will plate out from the solution on the Cu electrode, $Cu^{++} + 2\,e^- \longrightarrow Cu$. Let us assume, for example, that the solution of the zinc half-cell consists of 1,000 liters of a 1 M solution of aqueous Zn^{++} ions and that the solution of the copper half-cell consists of 1,000 liters of a 1 M solution of aqueous Cu^{++} ions. If we let the *standard* combined zinc-copper cell operate long enough for 1 mole of Zn^{++} ions to go into solution at the anode and for 1 mole of Cu^{++} ions to plate out at the cathode, the zinc-copper cell will no longer be exactly a standard cell, but it will still approximate one very closely. In fact, in the zinc half-cell we will have a Zn^{++} ion concentration of 1.001 moles/l. (instead of 1.000 mole/l.) while in the copper half-cell we will have a Cu^{++} ion concentration of 0.999 mole/l. (instead of 1.000 mole/l.). Thus we will have accomplished an electrochemical transformation of the (anodic) oxidation of 1 mole of Zn atoms, the (cathodic) reduction of 1 mole of Cu^{++} ions, and the transfer of 2 moles of electrons from the anode to the cathode through the external circuit, under concentration conditions very close to *standard* conditions. Furthermore, throughout the tranformation the system is electrically very nearly in equilibrium with its surroundings, because the gradually and slightly decreasing potential difference applied by the potentiometer almost exactly counterbalances the gradually and slightly decreasing electromotive force of the cell itself, $E° = 1.10$ v. Therefore, this electrochemical reaction can be compared to the reversible isothermal expansion of an ideal gas against a gradually decreasing, almost equal opposing pressure, which we considered in Chapter 17.

Let us now calculate the maximum useful work done in this reversible electrochemical reaction. We know that to obtain the work done when an electric current flows through a conductor between two points at different potentials we must multiply the quantity of electricity by the potential difference transferred:

$$\text{electrical work} = \text{quantity of electricity} \times \text{potential difference}$$

We learned in a preceding section how to measure the potential difference, but how do we determine this quantity of electricity? First, we see that for the reaction:

Anode half-reaction:	$Zn \longrightarrow Zn^{++} + 2\,e^-$	
Cathode half-reaction:	$Cu^{++} + 2\,e^- \longrightarrow Cu$	
Net cell reaction:	$Zn + Cu^{++} \longrightarrow Zn^{++} + Cu$	

2 moles of electrons are transferred from the anode to the cathode for each mole-equation. The number of moles of electrons (per mole-equation) transferred from the anode to the cathode in an electrochemical process is generally indicated by the symbol n (for the zinc-copper cell, $n = 2$). Now, the quantity of electricity in 1 mole of electrons (6.02×10^{-23} electrons) expressed in coulomb units is 96,500 coulombs; this quantity of electricity called a "Faraday" is expressed by the symbol F.* Thus the quantity of electricity transferred from the anode to the cathode per each mole-equation in the Zn,Zn^{++}—Cu,Cu^{++} cell is: $n \times F = 2 \times 96{,}500$ coulombs. And the electrical work that is done by the electrochemical system when 1 mole-reaction, $Zn + Cu^{++} \longrightarrow Zn^{++} + Cu$, occurs under the specified conditions at a practically constant voltage ($E^\circ = 1.10$ volts) is given by the expression:

$$\textit{Electrical work} = nFE^\circ$$

$$\textit{Electrical work} = 2\text{ (mole electrons/mole-eqn)} \times (96{,}500\text{ coulombs/mole electrons}) \times 1.10\text{ volts}$$

$$\textit{Electrical work} = 2 \times 96{,}500 \times 1.10\text{ coulomb} \times \text{volts/mole-eqn}$$

$$= 212{,}300 = 2.12 \times 10^5\text{ coulomb} \times \text{volts/mole-eqn}$$

We can now substitute this expression of the electrical work—the maximum useful work of the electrochemical reaction—in the general thermodynamic expression, $\Delta G = w_{\text{useful max}}$. Note that the work must be assigned a negative sign because it is energy expended by the electrochemical system in overcoming the resistance of the external circuit.

$$\Delta G^\circ = -\text{electrical work} = -nFE^\circ$$

$$\Delta G^\circ = -2.12 \times 10^5\text{ coulombs} \times \text{volts/mole-eqn}$$

In this equation, ΔG° is expressed in energy units of coulomb $\times$ volts/mole-eqn. To convert this value of ΔG° to the more familiar units of kcal/mole-eqn, we must multiply by the conversion factor: 1 coulomb $\times$ volt $= 2.3901 \times 10^{-4}$ kcal. Thus in general:

$$\Delta G^\circ = -n\left(\frac{\cancel{\text{mole electrons}}}{\text{mole-eqn}}\right) \times F\left(\frac{\cancel{\text{coulombs}}}{\cancel{\text{mole electrons}}}\right) \times E^\circ(\cancel{\text{volts}}) \times 2.3901 \times 10^{-4}\left(\frac{\text{kcal}}{\cancel{\text{coulombs}} \times \cancel{\text{volts}}}\right)$$

$$= -2.3901 \times 10^{-4} \times nFE^\circ\left(\frac{\text{kcal}}{\text{mole-eqn}}\right)$$

Since the Faraday, F, has a constant value, 96,500 coulombs, we can simplify this expression further by including this value in the conversion factor:

$$\Delta G = -(2.390 \times 10^{-4} \times 96{,}500)\,nE = -23.06 \times nE$$

Notice that in this expression ΔG is in kcal/mole-equation and E is in volts.

Units for $\Delta G = -nFE$

ΔG = kcal/mole-eqn	The conversion factor is:
n = moles electrons/mole-eqn	2.3901×10^{-4} kcal = 1 coulomb $\times$ volt
F = coulomb/mole-electrons	
E = volts	

* The charge of a single electron, expressed in coulombs, is 1.602×10^{-19} coulombs. This value, multiplied by Avogadro's number, 6.02×10^{23}, gives the value of the Faraday, 96,500 coulombs: (1.602×10^{-19} coulombs/electron) $\times$ (6.02×10^{23} electrons) $=$ 96,500 coulombs.

For our example of the Zn,Zn^{++}—Cu,Cu^{++} cell, where $n = 2$ and $E° = +1.10$ v, the free energy change is:

$$\Delta G° = -23.06 \times 2 \times 1.10 = -50.7 \text{ kcal/mole-eqn}$$

Keeping in mind the simple expression $\Delta G = -23.06\ nE$, we can interchangeably use the ΔG value of a given reaction (taking place under specified conditions of concentration, pressure and temperature) or the E value of the corresponding energy cell, to predict whether the reaction can occur spontaneously as written. *If ΔG is negative or if E is positive, then the reaction can take place spontaneously.* Conversely, if ΔG is positive (or E is negative), the reaction cannot take place spontaneously.

For a reaction that occurs under standard conditions of concentration (1 *M*), temperature (25°C) and pressure (1 atm), both $\Delta G°_{\text{reaction}}$ (1 *M*, 25°C, 1 atm) and the standard electromotive force, $E°$ are measures of the tendency of the cell reaction to occur spontaneously as written.

In closing this section, we want to note that the quantity of energy $\Delta G = -nFE$ is the *maximum* quantity of energy that can be made available for useful work when "1 mole reaction" takes place in an electrochemical system under reversible conditions, that is, at near-equilibrium conditions. Since, however, electrochemical reactions do not occur under reversible conditions, the electrical work actually obtainable from each mole-reaction is less than the amount given by the above expression.

ENERGY FACTORS INVOLVED IN THE REACTION OF THE STANDARD ZINC-COPPER COMBINED CELL

We saw that the free energy change, $\Delta G°$, for the reaction of the zinc-copper standard cell, Zn,Zn^{++} (1 *M*)—Cu,Cu^{++} (1 *M*) calculated from the relationship $\Delta G° = -nFE°$, is $\Delta G° = -50.7$ kcal/mole-equation. Now we shall discuss this value of $\Delta G°$ in terms of the $\Delta G° = \Delta H° - T\Delta S°$ equation, to evaluate the independent contributions of the enthalpy change, $\Delta H°$, and of the entropy change, $\Delta S°$, to the reaction: $Zn_{(s)} + Cu^{++}{}_{(aq)}$ (1 *M*) $\longrightarrow$ $Zn^{++}{}_{(aq)}$ (1 *M*) $+ Cu_{(s)}$.

The enthalpy change, $\Delta H° = -51.8$ kcal/mole-eqn, is determined directly by measuring the heat evolved when 1 mole of zinc metal is mixed with 1 liter of a 1 *M* solution of Cu^{++} ions (for example, from $CuSO_4$), at 25° and 1 atmosphere. Thus, $\Delta H°$ is negative and favorable to the reaction. Notice that the value of $\Delta H°$ is slightly more negative, by 1.1 kcal/mole-eqn, than the value of $\Delta G°$ (-50.7 kcal/mole-eqn). This means that the $T\Delta S°$ term has a very small unfavorable value ($T\Delta S° = -1.1$ kcal/mole-eqn), or, in other words, the entropy of the system decreases very slightly as the reaction proceeds from left to right. In fact, an independent estimate of $\Delta S°$ for this reaction gives $\Delta S° = -4.0$ cal/mole-eqn $\times$ deg at 25°C. From this value of $\Delta S°$ we calculate $T\Delta S° = -1.2$ kcal/mole-eqn, in good agreement with the value obtained above as the difference between the experimental values of $\Delta H°$ and $\Delta G°$.

We might have predicted a very small entropy change for this reaction because both the initial system and the final system consist of 1 mole of a crystalline metal and 1 mole of dipositive ions in 1 *M* aqueous solution. Also, the two ions, Cu^{++} and Zn^{++} have not only the same ionic charge, +2, but also similar radii ($Cu^{++} = 0.69$ A, $Zn^{++} = 0.74$ A); hence they should have similar hydration spheres in water solution at the same concentration and temperature. Some further insight into the energy factors involved in this reaction is given by the enthalpy diagram of Fig. 22-4. We see that the $\Delta H°$ of reaction, -52 kcal/mole-eqn, results mostly from the difference of the heats of atomization of copper metal and zinc metal ($\Delta H_{\text{atomiz}} = +81$ kcal/mole for Cu, and +31 kcal/mole for Zn), because the other factors almost exactly compensate for one another (total ionization energy in kcal/mole = +646 for Cu, +631 for Zn; ΔH_{hydr} in kcal/mole = -516 for Cu^{++}, -503 for Zn^{++}).

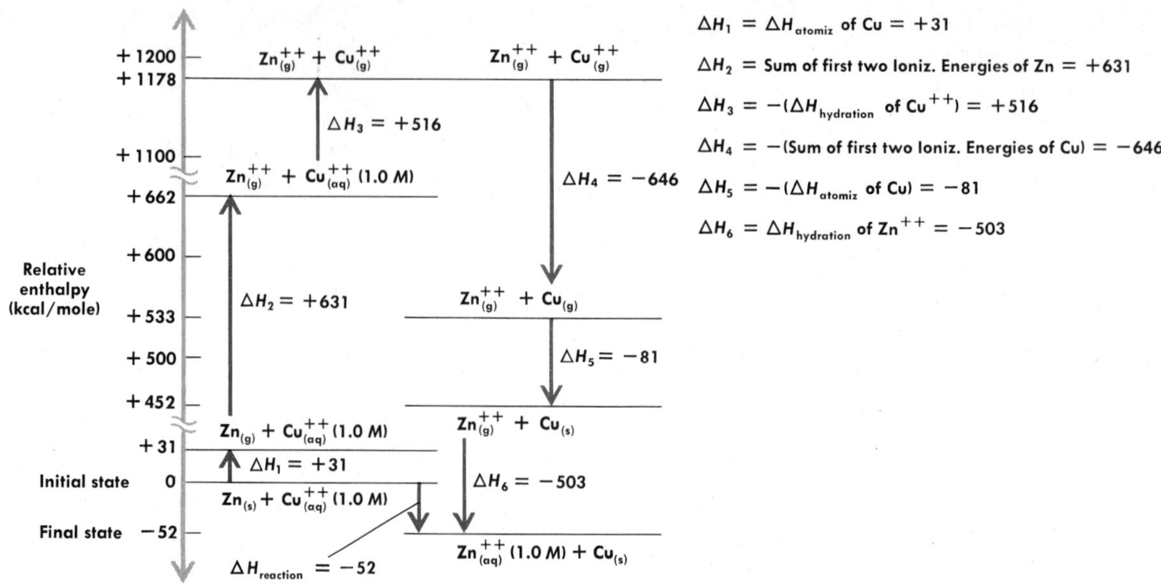

FIGURE 22-4 Enthalpy diagram for the reaction, $Zn_{(s)} + Cu^{++}_{(aq)}$ (1.0 *M*) ⟶ $Zn^{++}_{(aq)}$ (1.0 *M*) + $Cu_{(s)}$ at 25°C and 1 atm.

22-4 Electrode Potentials

The electromotive force (e.m.f.), or voltage, of an energy cell results from the combined action of two half-cells, such as the standard zinc half-cell and the standard copper half-cell. But how can we determine what part of the measured e.m.f. is contributed by each half-cell? We can do so by using as a reference a third half-cell, to which we arbitrarily assign a certain potential, and measuring the e.m.f of the two cells obtained by combining the reference half-cell separately with each of the other half-cells. By convention, the standard hydrogen half-cell (Fig. 21-1(c)) is adopted as the reference half-cell, and is assigned a potential of exactly 0.00 v. This conventionally assigned voltage is the $E°$ value of the $H_{2(g)}$,$H^+_{(aq)}$ couple (see p. 94). The measused e.m.f. of the combined cell consisting of the zinc half-cell and the hydrogen half-cell is the *assigned* potential of the zinc half-cell, and similarly with the copper half-cell. In general, the potential of any half-cell is the e.m.f. of the combined cell consisting of the half-cell in question and the standard hydrogen half-cell. Let us consider in detail a specific example.

THE POTENTIAL OF THE STANDARD ZINC HALF-CELL, OR Zn,Zn^{++} COUPLE. Consider a cell that is made up of a standard zinc half-cell, connected by means of an external wire and a salt bridge to a standard hydrogen half-cell, as illustrated in Fig. 22-5.

When we close the circuit, the balanced potentiometer setting indicates a potential difference of 0.76 v, with the electrons tending to flow from the zinc electrode to the hydrogen electrode. Since the potential of the H_2,H^+ standard half-cell is conventionally taken to be 0.00 v, the measured e.m.f. of 0.76 v is assigned entirely to the Zn,Zn^{++} half-cell. The value, +0.76 v, is then a measure of the tendency of Zn metal to pass into solution as hydrated Zn^{++} ions, when the solution is already 1 *M* with respect to Zn^{++}. Thus, if a current is allowed to pass through the combined cell (a voltmeter is substituted for the potentiometer in the external circuit), in the zinc half-cell some of the Zn metal will go into solution as Zn^{++} ions, and, simultaneously, in the hydrogen half-cell some of the H^+ ions will form H_2 gas. At the same time, the voltage reading on the voltmeter will steadily decrease. The reactions which occur spontaneously at the two half-cells and the net equation for the combined cell follow:

Oxidation half-equation (at anode):	$Zn \longrightarrow Zn^{++} + 2\,e^-$
Reduction half-equation (at cathode):	$2\,H^+ + 2\,e^- \longrightarrow H_2$
Net cell equation:	$Zn + 2\,H^+ \longrightarrow Zn^{++} + H_2$

In the oxidation reaction, the Zn atoms which dissolve to form Zn^{++} ions, give up electrons to the remaining Zn metal of the electrode. In the reduction reaction the H^+ ions in solution remove electrons from the hydrogen electrode, thus permitting an electron flow from the zinc electrode (anode) to the hydrogen electrode (cathode).

We have seen that the e.m.f. of this combined cell is +0.76 v, and since we have conventionally assigned a value of zero to the potential of the hydrogen half-cell, this measured voltage is assigned entirely to the zinc half-cell. This arbitrary assignment of half-cell potentials is unavoidable, because there is simply no way to measure the potential of a single half-cell.

The standard electrode potential of a standard half-cell is the e.m.f. value recorded when that standard half-cell is combined with the standard hydrogen half-cell. The standard electrode potential is generally represented by the symbol $E°$ (read, "E zero"; E for electrode potential; ° for standard). Thus, for the zinc electrode $E° = +0.76$ v. The significance of the positive sign is explained below.

THE POTENTIAL OF THE STANDARD COPPER HALF-CELL, OR Cu,Cu^{++} COUPLE. We can determine the potential of the standard Cu,Cu^{++} half-cell by following the same procedure. The H_2,H^+—Cu,Cu^{++} standard cell is illustrated in Fig. 22-6. For this combined cell the potentiometer reading indicates a e.m.f. of 0.34 v, with the electrons tending to flow from the hydrogen electrode (anode) to the copper electrode (cathode). Consequently, since a potential of zero is assigned to the standard hydrogen half-cell, the potential of the Cu,Cu^{++} half-cell is −0.34 v. The significance of the negative sign is explained below.

FIGURE 22-5 Measurement of the voltage of the standard zinc half-cell.

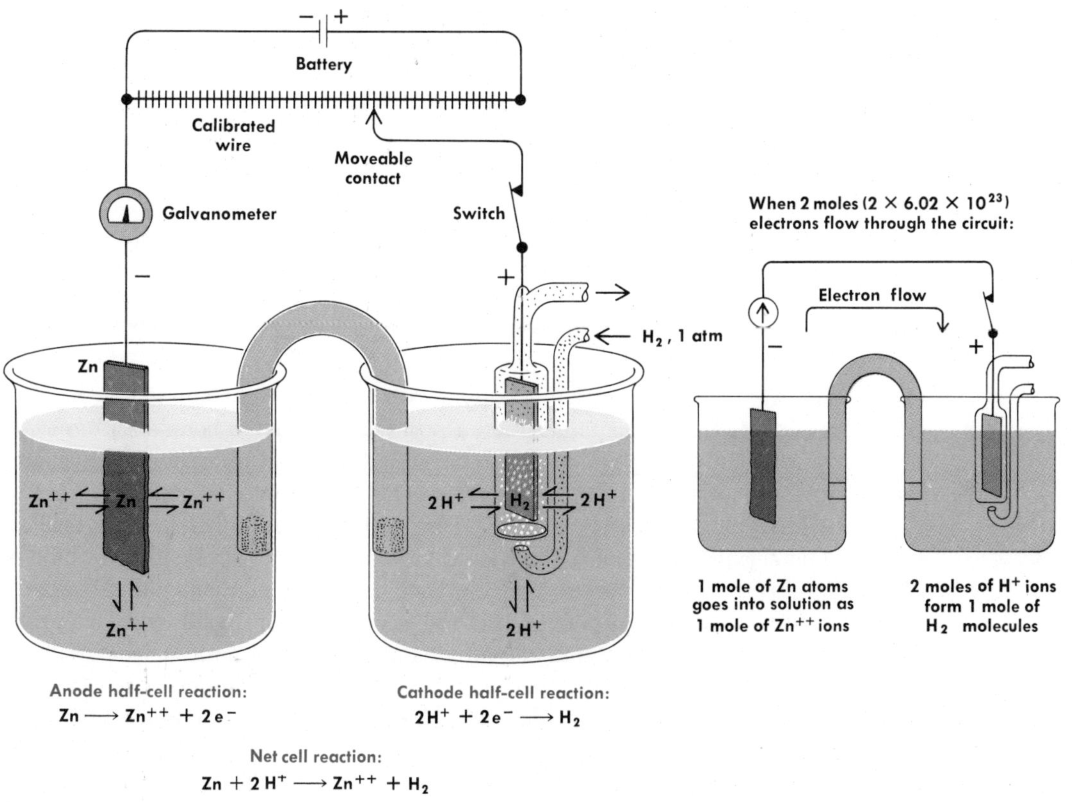

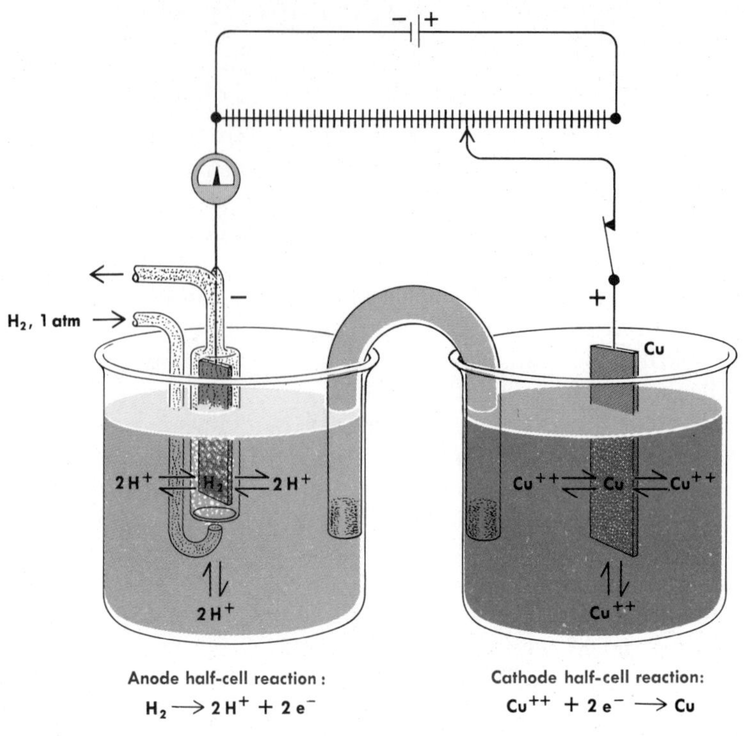

FIGURE 22-6 Measurement of the voltage of the standard copper half-cell.

SIGNS OF HALF-CELL POTENTIALS—OXIDATION POTENTIALS. As we have seen, in the Zn,Zn^{++}—H_2,H^+ combined cell the electrons flow spontaneously from the zinc half-cell to the hydrogen half-cell, whereas in the Cu,Cu^{++}—H_2,H^+ combined cell the electrons flow spontaneously from the hydrogen half-cell to the copper half-cell. The potentials assigned to the Cu,Cu^{++} half-cell and the Zn,Zn^{++} half-cell must therefore have opposite signs, and we arbitrarily assign to one of them a positive sign.

By convention, *the sign of a standard half-cell potential, $E°$, is positive if the electrons tend to flow spontaneously from the (metal) electrode of this standard half-cell, through the external connecting wire, to the (metal) electrode of the standard hydrogen half-cell. The sign of $E°$ is conventionally negative if the electrons tend to flow from the (metal) electrode of the standard hydrogen half-cell, through the external connecting wire, to the (metal) electrode of the standard half-cell being measured.* For example, the Zn,Zn^{++} half-cell has a positive potential of $+0.76$ v and the Cu,Cu^{++} half-cell has a negative potential of -0.34 v.

According to our convention, a couple with a greater tendency to give up electrons than the H_2,H^+ couple is assigned a positive potential, a couple with a lesser tendency is assigned a negative potential. Because the term of reference is the relative tendency of the couple *to give up electrons*—that is, to undergo the oxidation reaction—the potentials thus assigned are called *oxidation potentials.* In this book we shall use *oxidation potentials* throughout. You should keep in mind, however, that it would be equally possible to take as the term of reference the relative tendency of a couple to *take on electrons*—that is, to undergo the reduction reaction. In this case, we would have *reduction potentials,* equal in magnitude but with sign opposite to the *oxidation potentials* we have considered. Since many chemists use reduction potentials, you should remember this distinction when using data on electrode potentials taken from different books.

When two half-cells, one with a positive potential, and the other with a negative potential, are joined together to form a combined cell, the half-cell with the positive potential will have the stronger (relative) tendency to give up electrons and hence will be the anode of the combined cell. The half-cell with the negative potential will have the stronger tendency to take on electrons and so will be the cathode. In the external circuit the electrons will flow from the half-cell with positive potential to the half-cell with negative potential. The e.m.f. of any combination of two half-cells whose potentials have opposite signs is the algebraic difference of the half-cell potentials. For example, when the Zn,Zn^{++} half-cell, with its potential of $+0.76$ v is connected to the Cu,Cu^{++} half-cell, with its potential of -0.34 v, the e.m.f. of the combined cell is $+0.76 - (-0.34) = +1.10$ v.

HALF-CELLS INVOLVING TWO IONS OF THE SAME ELEMENT IN DIFFERENT OXIDATION STATES

Atoms and molecules are not the only particles that can give up electrons in a half-cell reaction. Positive ions of an element in a lower oxidation state, for example, Cr^{++} ions, also can give up electrons to form ions of a higher oxidation state, such as Cr^{+++} ions. We can determine the extent of this tendency by measuring the potential of a half-cell containing the ions of both the lower and higher oxidation states at the same molar concentration. Let us consider the apparatus shown in Fig. 22-7, which illustrates the standard Cr^{++},Cr^{+++} half-cell. This half-cell consists of an inert platinum electrode, immersed in a solution with a 1 *M* concentration of Cr^{++} ions and a 1 *M* concentration of Cr^{+++} ions. (Notice that the solution is covered in order to prevent, as much as possible, the spontaneous oxidation of the Cr^{++} ions to Cr^{+++} ions by the oxygen of air.) To measure the potential of this standard Cr^{++},Cr^{+++} half-cell, we connect it to a standard hydrogen half-cell. The e.m.f. of this combined standard cell, Cr^{++},Cr^{+++}—H_2,H^+, is measured and found to be 0.41 v. We also find that in the Cr^{++},Cr^{+++} half-cell, the Cr^{++} ions are oxidized to form Cr^{+++} ions, whereas at the hydrogen half-cell, the H^+ ions are reduced to form H_2 gas. Hence, the inert platinum electrode of the Cr^{++},Cr^{+++} half-cell is the anode of the combined cell, and the inert platinum electrode of the hydrogen half-cell is the cathode. The flow of electrons in the external circuit then takes place from the (negatively charged) anode (the standard Cr^{++},Cr^{+++} electrode) to the (positively charged) cathode (the standard hydrogen electrode). Therefore, according to the convention we have just discussed, the e.m.f. of the combined cell has a positive value, $+0.41$ v, which means that the Cr^{++},Cr^{+++} half-cell has a greater tendency to give up electrons than does the hydrogen half-cell.

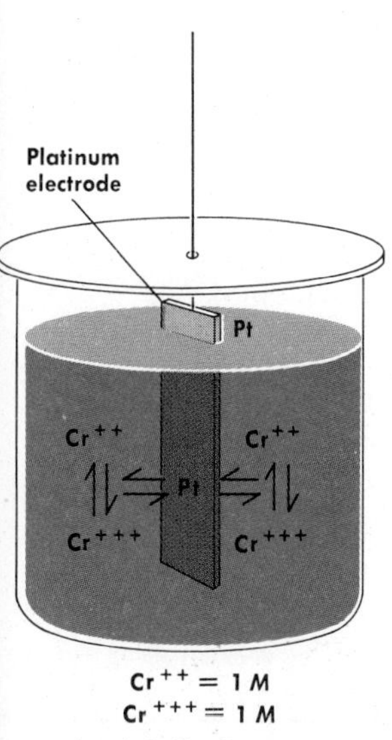

FIGURE 22-7 A Cr^{++}, Cr^{+++} half-cell.

22-5 The Polarity of Electrodes and the Direction of Electron Flow in a Combined Cell

Let us now consider two half-cells, both with a positive potential, joined together to form a combined cell. Here the half-cell with the larger value of the positive potential will have the stronger tendency to *give up* electrons and hence will be the *anode* of the combined cell, while the half-cell with the smaller value of the positive potential will have the stronger tendency to *take on* electrons and hence will be the cathode of the combined cell. For example, if we join together a standard aluminum half-cell, Al,Al^{+++} ($E° = +1.66$ v), and a standard zinc half-cell, Zn,Zn^{++} ($E° = +0.76$ v), the aluminum half-cell, which has the *larger positive potential,* is the anode of this combined cell, whereas the zinc half-cell, which has the *smaller positive potential,* is the cathode. At the aluminum half-cell, aluminum atoms are oxidized to form Al^{+++} ions which pass into solution as $Al^{+++}_{(aq)}$, while simultaneously at the zinc half-cell hydrated Zn^{++} ions are reduced to form Zn atoms which plate out on the zinc electrode. Thus the aluminum electrode, where electrons are given up by Al atoms, is negatively charged, while the zinc electrode, where Zn^{++} ions take on electrons, is positively charged. In the external circuit connecting the two electrodes, the electrons flow from the aluminum electrode, the anode, to the zinc electrode, the cathode.

In a similar way, if we connect two half-cells, both with a negative potential, the half-cell with the *less negative potential* has the greater tendency to *give up* electrons, and the half-cell with the *more negative potential* has the greater tendency to *take on* electrons. Hence, the former is the anode and the latter is the cathode of the combined cell. For example, if we join together a standard bromide-bromine half-cell, Br^-,Br_2, ($E° = -1.07$ v) and a standard chloride-chlorine half-cell, Cl^-,Cl_2, ($E° = -1.36$ v), the (inert) electrode of the bromide-bromine half-cell will be the anode, and the (inert) electrode of the chloride-chlorine half-cell will be the cathode. The spontaneous chemical reactions that occur in the cell are the oxidation of the Br^- ions to form Br_2 molecules and the simultaneous reduction of Cl_2 molecules to form Cl^- ions:

$$Cl_2 + 2\,Br^- \longrightarrow 2\,Cl^- + Br_2$$

Even though both half-cells have negative potentials with respect to the hydrogen electrode, in the combined $Br^-_{(aq)},Br_{2(g)}$—$Cl^-_{(aq)},Cl_{2(g)}$ cell the (inert) electrode of the Cl^-,Cl_2 half-cell is positively charged relative to the (inert) electrode of the Br^-,Br_2 half-cell. So electrons flow in the external circuit from the latter to the former.

RELATIONSHIP BETWEEN $E°$ AND $\Delta G°$ VALUES FOR HALF-CELL REACTIONS

A list of standard oxidation potentials—the $E°$ values—for a number of half-cell reactions is given in Table 22-1. A more complete list is given in the Appendix, Table I. *These E° values represent relative tendencies of the indicated chemical reactions to occur as written, at 25°C and 1 atm, when all reactants and products are present in the system with an activity* = 1 (see "standard states," p. 333). All pure substances—solids, liquids, or gases—are considered to have an activity = 1 (at 25° and 1 atm). And, as we stated in Chapter 16, any ion present in solution is assumed to have an *activity* = 1 (approximately) when its concentration is one mole/l. (at 25°C and 1 atm).

In section 22-3 we saw that the electromotive force of a standard combined cell is related to the free energy change of the net cell reaction by the expression:

$$\Delta G°_{\text{net cell reaction}} = -nFE°_{\text{combined cell}}$$

Now, we know that the standard oxidation potential, $E°$, of any half-cell is simply the e.m.f. of the combined cell in which the standard H_2,H^+ couple is the other half-cell. Thus, the relationship between $E°$ and $\Delta G°$ that we obtained for net cell reactions must also hold for the half-reactions of half-cells:

$$\Delta G°_{\text{half-reaction}} = -nFE°_{\text{couple}}$$

In this expression, n is the number of moles of electrons, per mole-(half)-eqn and F is the Faraday—the quantity of electricity in 1 mole of electrons, that is, 96,500 coulombs. Again, this expression gives $\Delta G°$ in units of coulomb × volts/mole-(half)-eqn;

if we wish to express ΔG° in kcal/mole-(half)-eqn, we must use the conversion factor, 1 coulomb × volt = 2.3901×10^{-4} kcal. Hence:

$$\Delta G^\circ_{\text{half-reaction}} = -nFE^\circ_{\text{couple}}$$

$$\Delta G^\circ_{\text{half-reaction}} = -n(2.390 \times 10^{-4} \times 96{,}500) \times E^\circ_{\text{couple}} = -23.06\, nE^\circ_{\text{couple}}$$

where ΔG° is expressed in kcal/mole-(half)-eqn, and E° is expressed in volts. Table 22-1 lists the ΔG° values of the standard half-cell reactions, alongside the E° values. Notice that the ΔG° values of half-cell reactions are all *relative* values; the half-reaction $\frac{1}{2}\, H_{2(g)} \longrightarrow H^+ + e^-$ is conventionally assigned the value $\Delta G^\circ = 0.000$ kcal/mole-(half)-eqn when the pressure of $H_{2(g)}$ is 1 atm, the activity of the H^+ ions in solution is 1 (1 molar concentration), and the temperature is 25°C. Just as we can measure directly the e.m.f. of a combined cell (E°_{cell}) but not the oxidation potential of an isolated half-cell (E°_{couple}), so we can measure the absolute value of the free energy change accompanying a complete, balanced reaction, but not that of a half-reaction.

Since the values of E°_{couple}, or the related values of the $\Delta G_{\text{half-reaction}}$, both give us a measure of the relative tendency of various couples to give up or take on electrons, both E°_{couple} and $\Delta G^\circ_{\text{half-reaction}}$ values permit us to predict chemical reactions that can occur when we join together, either in a combined cell or simply by mixing, the chemical species that constitute any two given half-cells. In all cases, *the reaction has the capacity to proceed spontaneously in the direction corresponding to the negative value of $\Delta G^\circ_{\text{reaction}}$ and to the positive value of E_{cell}.*

NET CELL EQUATIONS

We will now illustrate with an example how we can obtain the balanced net equation and the e.m.f. value, or reaction potential, for the spontaneous reaction of an energy cell resulting from the combination of any two half-cells.

THE COMBINED Cr^{++},Cr^{+++}—Cu,Cu^{++} CELL. If we connect a standard Cr^{++},Cr^{+++} half-cell with a standard Cu,Cu^{++} half-cell, in which direction will the

TABLE 22-1 SOME STANDARD OXIDATION POTENTIALS (HALF-CELL VOLTAGES) AT 25°C AND CORRESPONDING VALUES OF FREE ENERGY CHANGES

Couple*	Half-reaction	E°, volts	ΔG° (1 M, 25°C, 1 atm), kcal/mole-(half)-eqn.
Al,Al^{+++}	$Al = Al^{+++} + 3e^-$	+1.66	−114.8
Zn,Zn^{++}	$Zn = Zn^{++} + 2e^-$	+0.76	− 35.0
Fe,Fe^{++}	$Fe = Fe^{++} + 2e^-$	+0.44	− 20.3
Cr^{++},Cr^{+++}	$Cr^{++} = Cr^{+++} + e^-$	+0.41	− 9.4
Ni,Ni^{++}	$Ni = Ni^{++} + 2e^-$	+0.24	− 12.0
Sn,Sn^{++}	$Sn = Sn^{++} + 2e^-$	+0.14	− 6.4
H_2,H^+	$H_2 = 2H^+ + 2e^-$	0.00	0.0
H_2S,S	$H_2S = S + 2H^+ + 2e^-$	−0.14	+ 12.0
Cu,Cu^{++}	$Cu = Cu^{++} + 2e^-$	−0.34	+ 15.7
OH^-,O_2	$4OH^- = O_2 + 2H_2O + 4e^-$	−0.40	+ 73.8
I^-,I_2	$2I^- = I_2 + 2e^-$	−0.54	+ 24.9
Fe^{++},Fe^{+++}	$Fe^{++} = Fe^{+++} + e^-$	−0.77	+ 17.7
Ag,Ag^+	$Ag = Ag^+ + e^-$	−0.80	+ 49.3
Br^-,Br_2	$2Br^- = Br_2 + 2e^-$	−1.07	+ 56.7
H_2O,O_2	$2H_2O = O_2 + 4H^+ + 4e^-$	−1.23	+113.4
Mn^{++},MnO_2	$Mn^{++} + 2H_2O = MnO_2 + 4H^+ + 2e^-$	−1.23	+184.2
$Cr^{++},Cr_2O_7^=$	$2Cr^{+++} + 7H_2O = Cr_2O_7^= + 14H^+ + 6e^-$	−1.33	+ 67.7
Cl^-,Cl_2	$2Cl^- = Cl_2 + 2e^-$	−1.36	+ 62.7
Mn^{++},MnO_4^-	$Mn^{++} + 4H_2O = MnO_4^- + 8H^+ + 5e^-$	−1.51	+ 69.6

* All ionic species are present in aqueous solution at an activity of unity, or approximately 1 molar concentration.

electrons tend to flow through the outside circuit? What reactions will tend to take place in each half-cell and what is the net chemical change in the combined cell? And what will be the e.m.f. of the combined cell? Table 22-1 gives us the information:

$$Cr^{++} = Cr^{+++} + e^- \qquad E^\circ = +0.41 \text{ v}$$
$$Cu = Cu^{++} + 2 e^- \qquad E^\circ = -0.34 \text{ v}$$

In the table both half-reactions are written as oxidation processes (electrons are given off when the reactions occur from left to right), so both E° values are *oxidation potentials*. However, the Cr^{++},Cr^{+++} half-cell has a positive voltage, which means that it has a tendency to give up electrons, whereas the standard Cu,Cu^{++} half-cell has a negative voltage, which means that it has a tendency to take on electrons. The direction of electron flow in the external circuit of the combined cell, Cr^{++},Cr^{+++}—Cu,Cu^{++}, therefore, is *from* the Cr^{++},Cr^{+++} half-cell *to* the Cu,Cu^{++} half-cell. When we join these to form a combined cell, an oxidation reaction occurs at the electrode with the more positive oxidation potential (the anode), while a reduction reaction occurs at the other electrode (the cathode). In order to obtain the reduction half-reaction which occurs at the cathode, we must reverse the direction of the equation shown in Table 22-1 (we already saw how to do this in Chapter 20, in balancing oxidation-reduction equations). Remember that when you reverse a half-cell equation, the numerical magnitude of E° remains the same but the sign is changed. Thus the

Oxidation half-equation: $Cu = Cu^{++} + 2 e^- \qquad E^\circ = -0.34$ becomes the
Reduction half-equation: $Cu^{++} + 2 e^- = Cu \qquad E^\circ = +0.34$

We now obtain the net cell equation by adding the two half-cell equations.

Oxidation half-reaction:	$2 Cr^{++} \longrightarrow 2 Cr^{+++} + 2 e^-$	$E^\circ = +0.41$ v
Reduction half-reaction:	$Cu^{++} + 2 e^- \longrightarrow Cu$	$E^\circ = +0.34$ v
Net reaction:	$2 Cr^{++} + Cu^{++} \longrightarrow 2 Cu^{++} + Cu$	$E^\circ_{cell} = +0.75$ v

Before adding these two half-reactions, we must multiply the oxidation half-reaction by two, in order to equalize the gain and loss of electrons. Some beginners make the mistake of also doubling the E° value. Remember, the E° values are determined experimentally and in nature reactions are always balanced. *The experimentally determined E° value results from a balanced reaction.* The e.m.f. of the combined cell, also called *the reaction potential,* is the algebraic sum of the oxidation potential of the anode half-reaction and the reduction potential of the cathode half-reaction: $E^\circ_{cell} = +0.41 \text{ v} + 0.34 \text{ v} = +0.75 \text{ v}$. The *positive sign* of the reaction potential tells us that the (cell) reaction has the capacity to occur spontaneously as written, releasing energy. When we actually set up this cell in the laboratory we find that, as we expect, the concentrations of the Cr^{++} ions and of the Cu^{++} ions do decrease, while the concentration of the Cr^{+++} ions increases. And we find that the (inert) platinum electrode of the Cr^{++},Cr^{+++} half-cell is negatively charged with respect to the copper electrode of the Cu,Cu^{++} half-cell, so that the electrons do flow through a connecting external wire from the chromium half-cell to the copper half-cell.

In calculating a reaction potential, it is helpful to write first the oxidation couple (the couple with the more positive E° value) and below it the reduction couple (the couple with the less positive E° value). The net cell reaction will then have a positive reaction potential (E°_{cell} is positive) and will represent the reaction that can take place spontaneously, with the evolution of energy, when the two half-cells are joined together to form a combined cell. If, for a given reaction, E°_{cell} is negative, the reaction cannot occur spontaneously as written* but will, instead, tend to take place in

* Such a non-spontaneous reaction, can be forced to take place by supplying energy to the system, for example electrical energy, as with an electrolytic cell, which will be discussed in the next chapter.

the reverse direction. It is very important to understand the meaning of electrode and cell reactions, and the significance of the sign of the $E°$ values, because we shall be using them throughout the rest of this book.

THE COMBINED Zn,Zn^{++}—Cr^{++},Cr^{+++} CELL. Now suppose we connect a standard Zn,Zn^{++} half-cell with a standard Cr^{++},Cr^{+++} half-cell. Again we may ask: In which direction will the electrons tend to flow through the outside circuit? What reactions will tend to take place in each half-cell, and what will be the net cell reaction? What will be the e.m.f. of the combined cell? From Table 22-1 we see that both the standard Zn,Zn^{++} half-cell ($E° = +0.76$ v) and the standard Cr^{++},Cr^{+++} half-cell ($E° = +0.41$ v) have a positive potential. However, since the Zn,Zn^{++} half-cell has a *greater positive potential* (+0.76 v) than the Cr^{++},Cr^{+++} half-cell (+0.41 v), electrons will tend to flow from the former to the latter. And a measure of this tendency is the cell voltage, that is, the algebraic difference between the two half-cell potentials: $+0.76 - (+0.41) = +0.35$ v.

Laboratory experiments show that the Zn,Zn^{++} half-cell is negatively charged with respect to the Cr^{++},Cr^{+++} half-cell, so that electrons do actually flow from the zinc half-cell (anode) to the chromium half-cell (cathode). And the net cell reaction is, as usual, obtained by adding the two half-cell reactions.

Anode half-cell reaction:	$Zn \longrightarrow Zn^{++} + 2\,e^-$	$E° = +0.76$ v
Cathode half-cell reaction:	$2\,Cr^{+++} + 2\,e^- \longrightarrow 2\,Cr^{++}$	$E° = -0.41$ v
Net ionic cell reaction:	$Zn + 2\,Cr^{+++} \longrightarrow Zn^{++} + 2\,Cr^{++}$	$E°_{cell} = +0.35$ v

ILLUSTRATIVE PROBLEM

We want to find the net cell reaction and the e.m.f. of the energy cell obtained by combining a standard Zn,Zn^{++} half-cell and a standard Ag,Ag^+ half-cell.

Solution: Table 22-1 provides the following information:

$$Zn = Zn^{++} + 2\,e^- \qquad E° = +0.76 \text{ v}$$
$$Ag = Ag^+ + e^- \qquad E° = -0.80 \text{ v}$$

Here is how we obtain the $E°$ value of the spontaneous net cell reaction. First we write the oxidation half-equation of the couple with the *larger positive* $E°$ value (Zn,Zn^{++}; $E° = +0.76$ v). Then we *reverse* the oxidation half-equation of the couple with the smaller positive $E°$ value, changing the sign of the $E°$ value (Ag,Ag^+; $E° = -0.80$ v reverses to Ag^+,Ag; $E° = +0.80$ v). In this way we obtain the reduction half-equation. Finally, we add the two half-equations so that electrons gained equal electrons lost.

Oxidation (anode) half-reaction:	$Zn \longrightarrow Zn^{++} + 2\,e^-$	$E° = +0.76$ v
Reduction (cathode) half-reaction:	$2\,Ag^+ + 2\,e^- \longrightarrow 2\,Ag$	$E° = +0.80$ v
Net cell reaction:	$Zn + 2\,Ag^+ \longrightarrow Zn^{++} + 2\,Ag$	$E°_{cell} = +1.56$ v

The positive sign of the reaction potential tells us that the reaction has the capacity to proceed spontaneously as written, that is, from left to right; Zn is oxidized to Zn^{++} at the anode and Ag^+ is reduced to Ag at the cathode.

ILLUSTRATIVE PROBLEM

If we add metallic copper to a solution containing Fe^{++} and Cu^{++} ions, both at 1 *M* concentration, will the Fe^{++} ions have the capacity to react with copper metal to form Cu^{++} ions and Fe metal, according to the following equation?

$$Cu_{(s)} + Fe^{++}_{(aq)} \longrightarrow Cu^{++}_{(aq)} + Fe_{(s)}$$

Solution: We can find the answer to this question by either (1) noting the relative positions of the Cu,Cu^{++} and Fe,Fe^{++} couples in Table 22-1, or (2) calculating the reaction potential.

1. The Fe,Fe^{++} couple is higher in Table 22-1 than the Cu,Cu^{++} couple, therefore Fe^{++} is not strong enough to oxidize Cu metal spontaneously.

2. The electromotive force of the Fe,Fe^{++}—Cu,Cu^{++} cell is obtained by changing the sign of $E°$ for the Fe,Fe^{++} couple (since our equation calls for reducing Fe^{++} to Fe) and adding the number thus obtained (−0.44 v) to the $E°$ value for the Cu,Cu^{++} couple: −0.44 v + (−0.34 v) = −0.78 v. The negative sign of the reaction potential, $E°_{cell}$, tells us that the reaction does not have a tendency to take place spontaneously as written. In fact, the reverse reaction, which has a positive $E°_{cell}$, would be the spontaneous one.

ILLUSTRATIVE PROBLEM

A solution contains Fe^{++},Fe^{+++}, and Al^{+++} ions, all at 1 *M* concentration, and then Al metal is added to the solution. Can the following reaction take place spontaneously?

$$Al + 3\ Fe^{+++} \longrightarrow Al^{+++} + 3\ Fe^{++}$$

Solution: Table 22-1 provides the following information:

$$Al = Al^{+++} + 3\ e^- \qquad E° = +1.66\ v$$
$$Fe^{++} = Fe^{+++} + e^- \qquad E° = -0.77\ v$$

We see that Fe^{+++} is a stronger oxidant (lower in the Table) than Al^{+++}, and hence Fe^{+++} will spontaneously oxidize Al to Al^{+++}. Yes, the reaction can take place spontaneously as written when the concentrations of all ions are 1 *M*.

The e.m.f. of the combined Al,Al^{+++}—Fe^{++},Fe^{+++} cell is calculated by changing the sign of $E°$ for the Fe^{++},Fe^{+++} couple (to obtain the reduction potential), and adding the $E°$ value for the Al,Al^{+++} couple: +0.77 v + 1.66 v = +2.73 v. Again, the positive sign of $E°_{cell}$ indicates that the reaction can occur spontaneously as written.

22-6 Fuel Cells

Figure 22-8 shows a cell capable of producing an electric current from the reaction of hydrogen gas with chlorine gas. The anode consists of a plate of platinum metal, covered with platinum black, which has adsorbed $H_{2(g)}$ from a stream of hydrogen gas bubbling continuously about it at a constant pressure of 1 atm. The cathode consists of a carbon plate which adsorbs $Cl_{2(g)}$ from a stream of chlorine gas continuously bubbling about it at 1 atm pressure. A single container accommodates both electrodes because the same electrolyte, an aqueous solution of 1 molar hydrochloric acid ($H^+{}_{(aq)} + Cl^-{}_{(aq)}$), is suitable for both half-cells. The system is maintained at a constant temperature of 25°C. The half-reactions and electrode potentials necessary to calculate the $E°_{cell}$ are obtained from Table 22-1.

During the operation of the cell H^+ ions are oxidized to H_2 gas at the anode, and Cl_2 gas is reduced to Cl^- ions at the cathode.

Anode half-reaction:	$H_2 \longrightarrow 2\ H^+ + 2\ e^-$	$E°$	= 0.00 v
Cathode half-reaction:	$Cl_2 + 2\ e^- \longrightarrow 2\ Cl^-$	$E°$	= +1.36 v
Net cell reaction:	$H_2 + Cl_2 \longrightarrow 2\ H^+ + 2\ Cl^-$	$E°_{cell}$	= +1.36 v

As the net cell reaction shows, this cell converts hydrogen gas, $H_{2(g)}$, and chlorine gas, $Cl_{2(g)}$, into a solution of hydrogen chloride, $HCl_{(aq)}$, at the same time producing electrical energy. The hydrogen-chlorine cell is an example of a *fuel cell.*

In general, a fuel cell is a cell in which the oxidant and reductant are not part of the mechanical structure. Hence, as the cell is used, it does not fall apart; the oxidant and reductant are supplied, from reservoirs external to the structure of the cell itself. Fuel cells show great promise as a very convenient source of electrical power. A

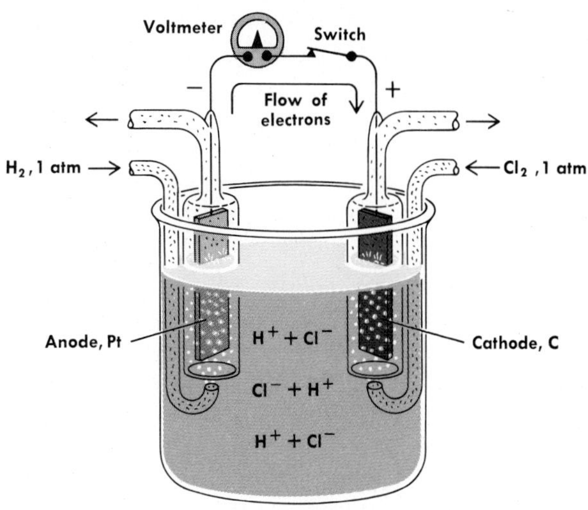

FIGURE 22-8 Reaction of H_2 with Cl_2 to produce electrical energy.

practical important example is the hydrogen-oxygen fuel cell in which these gases react with each other over a platinum catalyst to produce water and electrical energy. The Gemini V was the first spacecraft reported to have used this cell as a source of both electrical power and water.

THE ACID CELL

The acid cell consists of a plate of zinc metal which serves as the anode, and of a graphite rod which serves as the cathode, both immersed in a solution of sulfuric acid and connected externally by a conducting wire. At the zinc anode, atoms of Zn metal are oxidized to form Zn^{++} ions, and at the graphite cathode, H^+ ions are reduced to form H_2 gas. As a result of these simultaneous reactions, electrons tend to pass spontaneously from the zinc anode, through the external circuit, to the graphite cathode. The half-cell reactions and the net cell reaction follow:

Anode half-reaction:	$Zn \longrightarrow Zn^{++} + 2\,e^-$	$E^\circ = +0.76$ v
Cathode half-reaction:	$2\,H^+ + 2\,e^- \longrightarrow H_2$	$E^\circ = 0.00$ v
Net cell reaction:	$Zn + 2\,H^+ \longrightarrow Zn^{++} + H_2$	$E^\circ_{cell} = +0.76$ v

The maximum voltage that this cell can produce is $E^\circ_{cell} = +0.76$ v. When the cell is operating and electrons flow through the external circuit, the electrical energy produced can be utilized to do useful work. As you know, metallic zinc dissolves spontaneously in a solution of H^+ ions, forming Zn^{++} ions and liberating H_2 gas. Therefore, some hydrogen gas will also be evolved at the zinc electrode as a result of the *chemical* reaction between the electrode itself and the electrolyte. Graphite, however, it a better catalyst for the evolution of H_2 gas than zinc metal is; so the major part of the H_2 gas is evolved *electrochemically* at the graphite cathode.

THE DANIELL CELL

The Daniell cell is one of the oldest devices for producing electrical energy by chemical means. It was invented in 1841 by J. F. Daniell, Professor of Physics at King's College, London. The Daniell cell consists essentially of two parts: a copper plate immersed in a saturated solution of $CuSO_4$ and a zinc plate immersed in a dilute $ZnSO_4$ solution. The two solutions are separated by a porous plate to prevent direct contact between the reductant, (metallic zinc, Zn) and the oxidant (Cu^{++} ions). Therefore, the electrons given up by the Zn metal, $Zn \longrightarrow Zn^{++} + 2\,e^-$, must flow through the external wire in order to reach the copper electrode, where they react with the Cu^{++} ions in the solution: $Cu^{++} + 2\,e^- \longrightarrow Cu$. This electron flow (electric current) can serve some practical purpose, for example, lighting an electric bulb or heating a high-resistance wire inserted into the circuit. The net cell reaction of the Daniell cell is: $Zn + Cu^{++} \longrightarrow Zn^{++} + Cu$.

If both the Zn^{++} and the Cu^{++} solutions are initially at 1 *M* concentrations, the maximum initial voltage of the Daniell cell is +1.10 volts (as we calculated on p. 481 for a combined standard Zn,Zn^{++}—Cu,Cu^{++} cell in which the solutions of the two half-cells were in contact through a salt bridge rather than through a porous plate). As we shall see, the voltage of an energy cell depends on the nature of the two combined half-cells, on the concentrations of the solutions in the two half-cells, on the pressure of any gaseous reactants, and finally on the temperature, but *not* on the design of the set-up used in combining the two half-cells. Thus, the electromotive force is the same for the Daniell cell and for the salt-bridge Zn,Zn^{++}—Cu,Cu^{++} cell discussed on p. 498, provided the concentrations and temperature are the same.

22-7 Effect of Non-Standard Concentrations on Cell Potentials

LE CHATELIER'S PRINCIPLE

One of the principles of nature that holds in many different situations is Le Chatelier's principle (see Chap. 24). It states *that if a system is at equilibrium under a certain set of conditions, and we change these conditions, the system will shift its equilibrium position in such a way as to minimize the effect of the imposed changes.*

As we have stated, $E°$ values are measured under equilibrium conditions, that is, when the oxidized and reduced forms of each half-cell are in equilibrium with one another. For example, the standard electrode potential ($E° = +0.76$ v) for the Zn,Zn^{++} couple is measured when the metallic zinc of the electrode is in equilibrium with the hydrated Zn^{++} ions present in solution at a 1 molar concentration and at a temperature of 25°C:

$$Zn \rightleftharpoons Zn^{++} + 2\,e^- \qquad E° = +0.76 \text{ v}$$

Remember that the electrode potential is determined by measuring the voltage (the e.m.f.) of a combined cell consisting of the standard Zn,Zn^{++} half-cell and a standard hydrogen half-cell. Because zinc metal, Zn, gives up electrons with less difficulty than hydrogen gas, H_2 (Zn is a stronger reducing agent than H_2), the zinc electrode becomes negatively charged because of the accumulation of the electrons produced as the reaction $Zn \longrightarrow Zn^{++} + 2\,e^-$ proceeds from left to right. What happens to the magnitude of this negative charge when the concentration of Zn^{++} ions in solution becomes greater than 1 *M*? According to Le Chatelier's principle, the equilibrium at the zinc electrode will shift in a way that will tend to restore the original condition (a lower Zn^{++} concentration)—that is, the equilibrium will shift to the left. When the equilibrium shifts to the left, Zn^{++} ions are reduced to zinc metal, so that fewer electrons are made available—and fewer electrons means a smaller negative charge on the zinc electrode and hence a lower value for the electrode potential. Conversely, if we *decrease* the concentration of Zn^{++} ions in solution *below* 1 *M*, the relative tendency of the zinc electrode to give up electrons forming Zn^{++} ions is *increased*, and the measured electrode potential is *greater than* the $E°$ value of +0.76 v.

Here is another example of the effect of ion concentration on the voltage of a cell. What happens to the voltage of a Zn,Zn^{++}—H_2,H^+ combined cell when we keep the Zn^{++} ion concentration at 1 *M*, but increase the H^+ ion concentration to a value greater than 1 *M*? This increase in the H^+ ion concentration heightens the relative tendency of the H^+ ions to take on electrons, because the equilibrium, $2\ H^+ + 2\ e^- \longrightarrow H_2$, is upset and the reaction is shifted to the right—that is, the tendency for the reaction to occur is increased. Consequently, the tendency of electrons to flow from the zinc half-cell to the hydrogen half-cell is also increased, and the measured voltage of the combined cell becomes *greater than* its $E°$ value of $+0.76$ v. And what happens when we *decrease* the H^+ ion concentration? Then the relative tendency of the hydrogen electrode to take on electrons is lessened, and the voltage of the combined cell is therefore *less than* the $E°$ value of $+0.76$ v.

To summarize: The voltages of combined cells made up of a Zn,Zn^{++} half-cell connected to a H_2,H^+ half-cell, vary with the concentrations of the ions as follows:

Combined Cell	*E (volts)*[*]
Zn,Zn^{++} (1 M) —H_2,H^+ (1 M)	$= +0.76$ v
Zn,Zn^{++} ($<$ 1 M)*—H_2,H^+ (1 M)	$> +0.76$ v
Zn,Zn^{++} ($>$ 1 M) —H_2,H^+ (1 M)	$< +0.76$ v
Zn,Zn^{++} (1 M) —H_2,H^+ ($>$ 1 M)	$> +0.76$ v
Zn,Zn^{++} (1 M) —H_2,H^+ ($<$ 1 M)	$< +0.76$ v

On the basis of these figures we can predict what will happen to the voltage of a combined standard zinc-hydrogen cell that is permitted to operate over a period of time. As we know, when the solution is each half-cell is at 1 *M* concentration, the voltage of the combined cell is $+0.76$. Now, when we close the circuit between the two half-cells, the following spontaneous reaction occurs: $Zn + 2\ H^+ \longrightarrow H_2 + Zn^{++}$. The concentration of the Zn^{++} ions increases, serving to lower the voltage; and the concentration of the H^+ ions decreases, also serving to lower the voltage. Consequently, if we keep the circuit closed, the voltage of the combined cell will fall gradually farther and farther below the $E°$ value, $+0.76$ v, and eventually become zero.

THE NERNST EQUATION

Le Chatelier's principle permits us to predict qualitatively the effect that changes of concentrations have on the values of the electrode and cell voltages. Quantitatively, the value of the electrode potentials of both half-cells and combined cells with non-standard concentrations (but still at the standard temperature of 25°C†) may be calculated from the *Nernst equation.* This equation (see Chapter 25) permits us to obtain reaction potentials and electrode potentials when the activities of the substances involved differ from unity—in particular, when the ion concentrations are different from 1 *M*:

$$E_{\text{cell}} = E^\circ_{\text{cell}} - \frac{0.0591}{n} \times \log Q$$

$$E_{\text{cell}} = E^\circ_{\text{anode}} + E^\circ_{\text{cathode}} - \frac{0.0591}{n} \times \log Q$$

In this expression, E°_{anode} and E°_{cathode} indicate, as usual, the standard electrode potentials of the oxidation half-reaction at the anode and of the reduction half-reaction at the cathode. Also, n is the number of moles of electrons involved in the net cell reaction, and Q is a term which has the same form as the equilibrium quotient (p. 544) of the net cell reaction. *The term Q is the product of the activities of the species on the right side of the cell equation, each raised to a power equal to its coefficient in the balanced equation, divided by the product of the activities of the species on the left side of the equation, each also raised to a power equal to its coefficient.* (Recall that

[*] Remember that the sign $>$ means "is greater than," and the sign $<$ means "is less than."
† At temperatures other than 25°C the factor 0.0591 has a different value.

for pure substances the activity is unity at 25°C and 1 atm, and for solutions the activity of each dissolved species can be expressed approximately as the concentration in moles per liter, at 25°C and 1 atm.) Note that in the Nernst equation the constant 0.0591 is expressed in volt × mole, because both E_{cell} and E°_{cell} are given in volts, n is expressed in moles and log Q has no dimensions.

Let us illustrate the use of the Nernst equation by calculating the electromotive force of a combined cell consisting of a *non-standard* zinc half-cell, where zinc metal is in contact with 0.1 M solution of Zn^{++}, and of a *standard* copper half-cell, where copper metal is in contact with a 1.0 M solution of Cu^{++} ions. First, here again is the E° value for a combined cell consisting of a standard zinc half-cell, Zn,Zn^{++} (1 M), and a standard copper half-cell, Cu,Cu^{++} (1 M)—that is, the combined standard Zn,$Zn^{++}{}_{(1M)}$—Cu,$Cu^{++}{}_{(1M)}$ cell (Table 22-1):

Anode half-reaction:	$Zn \longrightarrow Zn^{++} + 2\,e^-$	$E^\circ_{anode} = +0.76$ v
Cathode half-reaction:	$Cu^{++} + 2\,e^- \longrightarrow Cu$	$E^\circ_{cathode} = +0.34$ v
Net cell reaction:	$Zn + Cu^{++} \longrightarrow Zn^{++} + Cu$	$E^\circ_{cell} = +1.10$ v

We see that two moles of electrons are transferred from the anode to the cathode in the balanced cell reaction, hence $n = 2$. Also, for the particular cell under consideration, the ratio, Q, for the balanced cell reaction has the following form, in which the square brackets indicate the activity of the enclosed species:

$$Q = \frac{[Zn^{++}][Cu]}{[Zn][Cu^{++}]} = \frac{0.1 \times 1}{1 \times 1} = 10^{-1}, \qquad \text{and} \qquad \log Q = -1$$

We now substitute these values into the Nernst equation:

$$E_{cell} = E^\circ_{cell} - \frac{0.0591}{n} \times \log Q$$

$$E_{cell} = +1.10 - \frac{0.0591}{2} \times (-1) = +1.10 + 0.03 = +1.13 \text{ volts}$$

Thus, for the combined cell, Zn,Zn^{++} (0.1 M)—Cu,Cu^{++} (1 M), the electromotive force is $E = +1.13$ v.

Notice that the Nernst equation may be applied rigorously only to a net cell reaction. We may also use it, however, to calculate the electrode potential of a half-reaction for non-standard concentrations. In this case, however, we are really applying the Nernst equation to a combined cell reaction in which the other half-cell is the standard hydrogen half-cell. To calculate a non-standard electrode potential, the Nernst equation takes the form:

$$E_{electrode} = E^\circ_{electrode} - \frac{0.0591}{n} \times \log Q$$

In this expression n is the number of moles of electrons involved in the electrode half-reaction and Q is the ratio of the initial activities (molar concentrations for ionic species) of the oxidized and reduced forms of the couple in equilibrium at the electrode. Thus, for a half-reaction, Q = [oxidized form]/[reduced form.] As an illustration, let us calculate the electrode potential for a half-cell consisting of Zn metal in contact with a 0.1 M solution of its ions. We connect this non-standard zinc half-cell with the standard hydrogen half-cell, and calculate the E°_{cell} as follows. First, here is the E°_{cell} value for the combined standard zinc-hydrogen cell:

Anode half-reaction:	$Zn \longrightarrow Zn^{++} - 2\,e^-$	$E^\circ = +0.76$ v
Cathode half-reaction:	$2\,H^+ + 2\,e^- \longrightarrow H_2$	$E^\circ = 0.00$ v
Net cell reaction:	$Zn + 2\,H^+ \longrightarrow Zn^{++} + H_2$	$E^\circ_{cell} = +0.76$ v

Knowing the E°_{cell}, we can now calculate E_{cell} from the Nernst equation.

$$E_{cell} = E^\circ_{cell} - \frac{0.0591}{n} \log Q = +0.76 - \frac{0.0591}{n} \log Q$$

The number of moles of electrons being exchanged during the net cell reaction ($Zn + 2\ H^+ \longrightarrow Zn^{++} + H_2$) is $n = 2$. The Q ratio of the net cell reaction is:

$$Q = \frac{[Zn^{++}][H_2]}{[Zn][H^+]^2} = \frac{0.1 \times 1}{1 \times 1^2} = 10^{-1} \quad \text{Therefore, } \log Q = -1$$

Hence:

$$E_{cell} = +0.76 - \frac{0.0591}{2} \times (-1)$$

$$E_{cell} = +0.76 + 0.03 = +0.79 \text{ volts}$$

Since E_{anode} is chosen to be 0.00 volts, in this case E_{cell} is simply $E_{cathode}$, that is, the desired electrode potential, $E = +0.79$ volts. More directly, we could have used the following expression in which all symbols have their usual meanings and Q is the activity ratio of the half-cell reaction:

$$E_{electrode} = E^\circ_{electrode} - \frac{0.0591}{n} \log Q$$

Substituting the appropriate values in this expression we obtain

$$E_{electrode} = +0.76 - \frac{0.0591}{2} \times \log \frac{[Zn^{++}]}{[Zn]}$$

$$= +0.76 - \frac{0.0591}{2} \times (-1) = 0.76 + 0.03 = +0.79 \text{ volts}$$

22-8 Concentration Cells

As we have just seen, the electrode potential of a given couple varies with the relative concentrations of the oxidized and reduced forms of the couple in the electrolyte. It is therefore possible to construct energy cells in which the half-cells differ *only in their ion concentrations.* Such a kind of cell is called a *concentration cell.* An example is a cell that consists of a zinc half-cell with a Zn^{++} ion concentration of 1 M, and a zinc half-cell with a Zn^{++} ion concentration of 0.1 M. We can determine the direction of the electron flow and the voltage of this combined cell by calculating, according to the Nernst equation, the potential of each electrode and then using the values thus obtained to calculate the electromotive force of the combined cell. For the standard zinc half-cell, as we know,

$$E_{Zn,Zn^{++}(1.0M)} = E^\circ_{Zn,Zn^{++}} = +0.76 \text{ v (standard electrode potential)}$$

For the non-standard zinc half-cell,

$$E_{Zn,Zn^{++}(0.1M)} = E^\circ_{Zn,Zn^{++}} - \frac{0.0591}{n} \log \frac{[Zn^{++}]}{[Zn]}$$

$$E_{Zn,Zn^{++}(0.1M)} = E^\circ_{Zn,Zn^{++}} - \frac{0.0591}{2} \times \log \frac{0.1}{1}$$

$$= +0.76 - 0.03 \times (-1)$$

$$= 0.76 + 0.03 = +0.79 \text{ volts}$$

As we have learned, the electrode with the larger positive potential—Zn,Zn^{++} (0.1 M), $E = +0.79$ v—is the anode of the combined cell. So the net cell reaction of the combined cell—Zn,Zn^{++} (0.1 M) – Zn,Zn^{++} (1.0 M)—is:

Anode half-reac:	$Zn \longrightarrow Zn^{++}\ (0.1\ M) + 2\ e^-$	$E_{anode} = +0.79$ v
Cathode half-reac:	$Zn^{++}\ (1.0\ M) + 2\ e^- \longrightarrow Zn$	$E_{cathode} = -0.76$ v
Net cell reac:	$Zn^{++}\ (1.0\ M) \longrightarrow Zn^{++}\ (0.1\ M)$	$E_{cell} = +0.03$ v

Thus, the electromotive force calculated for this combined cell, Zn,Zn^{++} (0.1 *M*)—Zn,Zn^{++} (1.0 *M*), is +0.03 v.

When we close the switch and the current flows between the two half-cells, the net cell reaction, which results from the formation of Zn^{++} ions at the anode and the plating out of an equal number of Zn^{++} ions at the cathode, is essentially a "transfer" of Zn^{++} ions from the more concentrated solution to the less concentrated solution. Consequently, as the cell operates, the concentration of the anode solution (initially 0.1 *M*) gradually increases, whereas the concentration of the cathode solution (initially 1.0 *M*) gradually decreases—and the difference between the concentrations of the two half-cells decreases. Hence, as the cell operates, the voltage of the concentration cell gradually decreases and finally becomes zero when the two half-cells attain the same concentration of Zn^{++} ions.

Let us now calculate the maximum quantity of energy per mole-reaction that can be obtained from the operation of this particular concentration cell: Zn,Zn^{++} (0.1 *M*)—Zn,Zn^{++} (1.0 *M*) at 25°C. Let us assume that the anode solution consists of 1,000 liters of 0.1 *M* Zn^{++} solution (a total of 100 moles of Zn^{++} ions), and that the cathode solution consists similarly of 1,000 liters of 1 *M* Zn^{++} solution (a total of 1,000 moles of Zn^{++} ions). We let the cell operate for such a period of time that 1 mole of Zn^{++} ions forms at the anode ($Zn \longrightarrow Zn^{++} + 2\,e^-$); during this time 2 moles of electrons (2 × 96,500 coulombs) pass through the external circuit from the anode to the cathode, where 1 mole of Zn will plate out at the cathode ($Zn^{++} + 2\,e^- \longrightarrow Zn$). The net electrochemical reaction consists, therefore, of the transfer of 1 mole of Zn^{++} ions from the more concentrated solution (the cathode) to the less concentrated solution (the anode). The total number of moles of Zn^{++} ions in the anode solution will now be 101. That is, the concentration of the anode solution has changed from 0.1000 mole/l. to 0.1010 mole/l. At the cathode, the total number of moles of Zn^{++} ions in solution is now 999, and the concentration of the cathode solution has changed from 1.000 mole/l. to 0.999 mole/l. Thus we can represent the electrochemical reaction also as follows:

Initial State		*Final State*
Anode sol: 1000 l. 0.1000 mole/l.	transfer of 2 moles of electrons through ⟶ external circuit from anode to cathode	Anode sol: 1000 l. 0.1010 mole/l.
Cathode sol: 1000 l. 1.000 mole/l.		Cathode sol: 1000 l. 0.999 mole/l.

As you can verify by applying the Nernst equation, the voltage of the cell is almost the same in the initial state as in the final state, because the "transfer" of 1 mole of Zn^{++} ions from the cathode to the anode results only in a very small change of the concentrations of the Zn^{++} ions in the two half-cells. Thus, the voltage of the concentration cell remains constant at about 0.03 v throughout the electrochemical reaction. We can then calculate the electrical energy made available by 1 mole-(cell) reaction:

$$\text{electrical energy} = nFE = 2 \times 96{,}500 \text{ coulombs} \times 0.03 \text{ volts} = 5{,}990 \text{ coulombs} \times \text{volts}$$

And the corresponding free energy change, ΔG, per mole-(cell) reaction is:

$$\Delta G = -23.06 \times nE = -23.06 \times 2 \times 0.06 = -2.77 \text{ kcal}$$

We know from our discussion in Chapter 17 that the free energy change of any reaction at constant temperature and pressure is itself the difference of two independent energy terms, ΔH and $T\,\Delta S$, that is $\Delta G = \Delta H - T\,\Delta S$. For the particular reaction considered, the transfer of 1 mole of Zn^{++} ions (more accurately 1 mole each of Zn^{++} and $SO_4^{=}$ ions) from the more concentrated solution (1.000 mole/l.) to the less concentrated solution (0.100 mole/l.), the enthalpy change, ΔH, is with good approximation the heat evolved in the dilution of 1,000 liters of $ZnSO_4$ solution from 1.000 mole/l. to 0.999 mole/l., minus the heat absorbed in concentrating 1,000 liters of

$ZnSO_4$ solution from 0.1000 mole/l. to 0.1010 mole/l. Since the changes in concentrations of the two solutions are very small, the heat evolved in the dilution process and that absorbed in the concentration process are both small, and very nearly compensate each other. Thus ΔH for the transformation considered is virtually zero, and $\Delta G \cong -T\,\Delta S$. The tendency of the two $ZnSO_4$ solutions of different concentrations to approach the same intermediate concentration when brought into contact, either directly (by diffusion) or in an electrochemical system, is therefore the principal driving force of this cell reaction. Since our concentration cell operates at the standard temperature of 25°C (298°K) we have:

$$\Delta G \cong -T\,\Delta S$$
$$\Delta S = -\Delta G/T = -(-2.77 \text{ kcal/mole-reaction})/298 \text{ deg} = 9.3 \text{ cal/mole-reaction} \times \text{deg}$$

In general, the increase of entropy, which results whenever two solutions at different concentrations mix (partially or completely), is the chief factor responsible for the operation of concentration energy cells.

22-9 Limitations on the Use of Standard Half-Cell Potentials

According to the principles outlined in this chapter, we can use the $E°$ values to predict whether a given oxidation-reduction reaction has the capacity to take place spontaneously as written, under the specified conditions of temperature, concentrations, and pressure. In many cases a reaction which should be spontaneous on the basis of the $E°$ values does indeed occur as predicted. In some cases, however a reaction that can be spontaneous does not actually take place to any appreciable extent under the specified set of conditions. For example, from the oxidation potentials of the couples Al,Al^{+++} ($E° = +1.66$ v) and H_2,H^+ (10^{-7} M; $E = +0.41$ v), we would predict that Al metal is capable of displacing H_2 gas from water in a neutral solution.* And yet it is an experimental fact that aluminum metal does *not* react to any noticeable extent with H_2O to liberate H_2 gas. This experimental fact is an indication that standard half-cell voltages are of limited use, and reminds us of the importance of recognizing *other* factors that may affect the feasibility of chemical reactions.

First, remember that an $E°$ value represents only a *tendency* of the indicated chemical reaction to take place when the solution has an ion concentration of 1 M. In other words, an $E°$ value calls our attention to a natural tendency or driving force that *could* cause the indicated reaction to take place. If any conditions arise to thwart that tendency, however, the reaction will not actually occur. The reason that Al metal does not react to any appreciable extent with water is that the reaction stops when the surface atoms of the Al metal have been converted to aluminum oxide. The oxide forms a tight film which prevents further contact between the Al and the H_2O.

On the other hand, when an aluminum amalgam (an *amalgam* is an alloy of a metal with mercury) is brought into contact with water, H_2 gas is evolved. Apparently, the mercury interferes with the adhesion of the film of aluminum oxide to the surface of the aluminum and thereby permits the aluminum to continue to come into contact with the water.

Furthermore, an $E°$ value tells us nothing about the *rate* at which H_2 is evolved. For example, on the basis of its $E°$ value, we might predict that a given half-cell will liberate H_2 from water to form a basic solution, but then find through actual experiment that the reaction occurs so slowly that the products of the reaction are hardly detectable. Thus, although we can usually state whether a chemical reaction will tend to take place, we cannot always predict its speed (see Chapter 26).

* Remember that a neutral solution has a H^+ concentration of 10^{-7} mole/l.

Exercises

22-1 For each of the following, (a) draw a sketch illustrating the half-cell, and (b) write the half-cell equilibrium reaction: (1) Zn,Zn^{++}; (2) Cu,Cu^{++}; (3) H_2,H^+; (4) Mn^{++},MnO_4^- (in the presence of H^+ ions); (5) Fe^{++},Fe^{+++}; (6) Cl^-,Cl_2.

22-2 (a) What physical and chemical processes take place when we connect a standard zinc half-cell and a standard copper half-cell to form a combined cell, Zn,Zn^{++}—Cu,Cu^{++}? (b) What is the function of the salt bridge (or porous partition) through which the solutions of the two half-cells are brought into contact?

22-3 What do we mean by the term "electromotive force" of a cell? And how do we measure such an electromotive force?

22-4 If we connect the two electrodes of an energy cell through an external circuit, does the voltage of the cell (a) remain constant at the initial value, (b) increase, or (c) decrease, as time passes?

22-5 For each of the following standard cells, give (a) a pictorial representation of the complete cell, (b) the flow of electrons in the external circuit, (c) the anode and cathode half-cell reactions that take place, (d) the equation for the net cell reaction, and (e) the electromotive force of the cell (using Table 22-1).

1. Al,Al^{+++} and Ag,Ag^+
2. Al,Al^{+++} and Fe,Fe^{++}
3. Cr^{++},Cr^{+++} and Cu,Cu^{++}
4. Ag,Ag^+ and Fe^{++},Fe^{+++}
5. Cr^{++},Cr^{+++} and Fe^{++},Fe^{+++}
6. Zn,Zn^{++} and Ag,Ag^+

22-6 For the following cell, give (a) the anode and cathode half-cell reactions, (b) the equation for the net cell reaction, and (c) the $E°$ value of the cell: A platinum electrode in one half-cell containing Fe^{+++} (1 *M*) and Fe^{++} (1 *M*), and a tin electrode in the other half-cell containing Sn^{++} (1 *M*).

22-7 On the basis of the $E°$ values for the following *hypothetical* metal half-cells, predict which would react with 1 *M* hydrochloric acid: A,A^+; $E° = +1.1$ v; B,B^{++}; $E° = -1.2$ v; C,C^+; $E° = +2.5$ v.

22-8 The $E°$ values of a hypothetical metal M are as follows: $M = M^+ + 1\,e^-$; $E° = +0.32$ v; $M^+ = M^{++} + 1\,e^-$; $E° = -0.25$ v. (a) Can metal M dissolve in an aqueous solution containing 1 *M* H^+ ions to produce H_2 gas? (b) If so, is the M^+ or the M^{++} ion produced? Explain your answer.

22-9 A metal M ($M = M^+ + e^-$; $E° = -1.6$ v) is dipped into an aqueous solution containing 1 *M* H^+ ions. Can H_2 gas be evolved? Explain your answer.

22-10 A metal M ($M = M^{++} + 2\,e^-$; $E° = +0.84$ v) is placed in separate 1 molar aqueous solutions containing each of the following: (a) R^{++} ($R = R^{++} + 2\,e^-$; $E° = -1.6$ v). (b) L^+ ($L = L^+ + e^-$; $E° = +1.3$ v). (c) T^{+++} ($T = T^{+++} + 3\,e^-$; $E° = -2.4$ v). (d) H^+ (1 *M*). (e) H_2O. In each case indicate whether or not a reaction can take place, and explain your answer. (Write equations for the reactions that can take place.)

22-11 In one beaker Ag metal is added to a 1 *M* Fe^{+++} ion solution. In another beaker 1 *M* Ag^+ ions and 1 *M* Fe^{++} ions are mixed. What reaction can take place in each case?

22-12 A 1 *M* $Fe(NO_3)_2$ solution is added to a 1 *M* $AgNO_3$ solution. Predict the reaction that might occur and justify your answer.

22-13 Classify solutions containing 1 *M* ions of the following two sets in order of oxidizing power (list the best oxidizing agent first): (a) (1) Cu^{++}, (2) Zn^{++}, (3) Na^+, (4) Al^{+++}, (5) Ag^+. (b) (1) Fe^{+++}, (2) Cl_2, (3) Br_2, (4) MnO_4^-, (5) HNO_3.

22-14 Classify the following metals in order of their reducing power (list the best reducing agent first): (1) Cu, (2) Na, (3) Zn, (4) Al, (5) Ag.

22-15 Given these half-cell equations: $Ag = Ag^+ + e^-$; $E° = -0.80$ v and $Ag + I^- = AgI + e^-$; $E° = +0.15$ v: (a) Does silver metal, Ag, dissolve in a 1 *M* H^+ solution to liberate H_2 gas? (b) Does silver metal dissolve in a 1 *M* H^+ solution containing 1 *M* I^- to liberate H_2 gas? Explain your answers. (c) If some silver metal were placed in a solution of hydriodic acid ($H^+ + I^-$), would you expect a reaction to take place? Explain your answer.

PROBLEMS

22-1 On the basis of the standard potentials listed in Table 22-1, calculate the voltages of standard cells made up of the following pairs of half-cells: (a) Al,Al^{+++} and Cu,Cu^{++}, (b) Al,Al^{+++} and Zn,Zn^{++}, (c) Ag,Ag^{+} and Cu,Cu^{++}.

22-2 On the basis of the $E°$ values of the following half-cells (given in parentheses in volts), choose the two that, connected appropriately to form a cell, would yield (a) the highest positive voltage, and (b) the lowest positive voltage: Zn,Zn^{++} (+0.76 v); Mg,Mg^{++} (+2.37 v); Cu,Cu^{++} (−0.34 v); Fe,Fe^{++} (+0.44 v); Ag,Ag^{+} (−0.80 v); Cr,Cr^{+++} (+0.74 v).

22-3 (a) Write the equation and give the potential for the reaction that takes place when the following standard half-cells are connected: $Fe = Fe^{++} + 2\,e^-$; $E° = +0.44$ v, and $Fe^{+++} + e^- = Fe^{++}$; $E° = +0.77$ v. (b) Assume that we want to reduce a solution of Fe^{+++} ($FeCl_3$) as completely as possible to Fe^{++} ($FeCl_2$). What would be the best method?

22-4 A combined cell is made by connecting a half-cell composed of Zn metal immersed in a solution of Zn^{++} ions at a concentration less than 1 *M*, and a half-cell of Cu metal in a solution of Cu^{++} ions at a concentration greater than 1 *M*. Would the potential of the cell be equal to, less than, or greater than +1.10 v? Explain your answer, using Le Chatelier's principle.

22-5 Use the Nernst equation to calculate the voltage of the combined cell in Problem 22-4 when the Zn^{++} ion concentration is 10.0 *M* and the Cu^{++} ion concentration is 0.0001 *M*.

22-6 Calculate the voltages of the cells in Problem 22-1 under the following conditions: (a) $[Al^{+++}] = 10^{-6}\,M$, $[Cu^{++}] = 10^{-1}\,M$; (b) $[Al^{+++}] = 10^{-3}\,M$, $[Zn^{++}] = 10^{-1}\,M$; (c) $[Ag^{+}] = [Cu^{++}] = 10^{-2}\,M$.

ELECTROCHEMISTRY: II. ELECTROLYSIS

23

In the previous chapter we used oxidation potentials to predict whether a given reaction resulting from the combination of any two half-cell reactions has the capacity to occur spontaneously. As we know, the reaction *can* occur if the E value for the combined cell reaction is positive ($\Delta G_{\text{reaction}}$ is negative). Conversely, if the E value for the combined cell is negative ($\Delta G_{\text{reaction}}$ is positive), the reaction cannot occur spontaneously as written; it requires the addition of energy. By supplying electrical energy to the system it is often possible to force a non-spontaneous reaction to occur—the reaction is then called an *electrolytic* reaction. In this chapter we shall first describe some typical electrolytic reactions, explaining them on the basis of E values, and then we shall consider the quantitative laws of electrolysis—Faraday's Laws.

23-1 General Definitions

ELECTROLYTIC SOLUTIONS

If we consider their behavior under the effect of an electric field—a gradient of electrical potential—we can classify liquids, in particular solutions, into two groups: (1) those that contain only covalent molecules, and (2) those that contain ions (the ions either having been present in an original ionic solid, or having resulted from the reaction of a covalent solute with a polar solvent). As we shall now see, liquids that contain ions can undergo the process of *electrolysis* and are "conductors" of an electric current. These liquids are called *electrolytes;* for solutions, the term commonly used is *electrolytic solutions.* On the other hand, liquids (solutions) that contain only molecules do not undergo electrolysis and are not capable of conducting an electric current; they are called *non-electrolytes* (*non-electrolytic solutions*).

In the following sections we shall discuss in detail the processes by which an electric current "passes through" an electrolyte. First it will be useful to recall briefly how an electric current is conducted through a metal (p. 183). The electrons involved in metallic bonding are relatively free to shift about among neighboring atoms, so if a difference of potential is applied across two parts of a piece of metal these "metallic" electrons migrate toward the positively charged region by moving successively from the orbitals of one atom to those of a neighbor. Thus the "flow" of an electric current through a metal consists of the migration of electrons, and metals are said to conduct an electric current *electronically.*

ELECTROLYTIC REACTIONS. In the previous chapter we saw that the values of the oxidation potentials permit us to predict whether or not a given oxidant is strong enough to react spontaneously with a given reductant, under specified experimental conditions. We also saw that for spontaneous oxidation-reduction reactions ($\Delta G_{\text{reaction}}$ is negative) the maximum voltage obtainable when the reaction is carried out in an electrochemical cell, under reversible conditions, can be calculated from the values of the electrode potentials of the oxidant and of the reductant: $E_{\text{cell}} = E_{\text{anode}} + E_{\text{cathode}}$. From the value of E_{cell}, we can then calculate the maximum quantity of useful work energy, $\Delta G_{\text{reaction}}$, that the system can supply to the surroundings for each mole-reaction which occurs under the specified conditions:

$$\Delta G = -nFE = -23.06\, nE$$

where n is the number of moles of electrons involved in the balanced oxidation-reduction reaction, ΔG is expressed in kcal/mole-eqn and E is expressed in volts.

On the other hand, for oxidation-reduction reactions that are not spontaneous ($\Delta G_{\text{reaction}}$ is positive; E_{cell} is negative) we must supply energy to the system if we wish the reaction to take place.

Let us now consider several examples of non-spontaneous reactions, which can be made to take place if electrical energy is supplied to the system under suitable experimental conditions. Such reactions are generally called *electrolytic reactions,* and the experimental set-up in which they occur is called an *electrolytic cell.* For electrolytic reactions the values of the electrode potentials permit us to predict not only the *products* which may form, but also the minimum voltage that must be supplied to the system to force the reaction to occur. In the following sections we shall make use of the half-reactions and $E°$ values listed in Table 22-1 (p. 478).

23-2 Electrolysis in Aqueous Solutions

ELECTROLYSIS OF A WATER SOLUTION OF HYDROGEN CHLORIDE

In the experimental device called an electrolytic cell, shown in Fig. 23-1, an aqueous solution of hydrogen ions and chloride ions (1 *M* hydrochloric acid) is placed between two graphite plates, the *electrodes,* and joined by metallic wires to the terminals of a battery. The circuit is equipped with a switch, and with a light bulb which glows when an electric current flows through the circuit. Let us assume that at the beginning of the experiment the switch is open, so that only one of the two graphite plates is connected to the battery. Under these conditions no chemical changes are observed at either of the electrodes, and the bulb fails to glow, indicating that no current passes through the circuit. If we now close the switch, important changes begin to take place; gas bubbles form at the surfaces of each of the electrodes and the bulb glows. The bubbles formed at the electrode connected with the negative terminal of the battery (the negative electrode of the electrolytic cell) consists of hydrogen gas, H_2; those formed at the electrode connected with the positive terminal of the battery (the positive electrode of the cell) consist of chlorine gas, Cl_2. If we open the switch again, the lamp instantaneously goes out and the chemical reactions at the electrodes —the formation of the gas bubbles—stop.

What chemical changes are forced to take place at the electrodes when these are connected to a source of electrical energy, the battery? And how can we explain these changes on the basis of what we have learned in the previous chapters about electrode potentials and the free energies of reaction? To find an answer to these questions, we may start from the observation that *chemical changes occur at the electrodes only when the light bulb glows, that is, when an electric current is passing through the circuit.* We have seen that an electric current in a metallic conductor is a flow of electrons; in our closed circuit the electrons flow *out* from the negative terminal of the battery and back *into* the positive terminal of the battery. In the closed circuit the electrons can find their way from the battery to one graphite electrode and from the other graphite electrode back to the battery, for all these parts of the circuit consist of electronic conductors—metal wires and graphite plates (graphite is an electronic conductor). But how do the electrons manage to "travel" from the negative electrode, across the hydrochloric acid solution, to the positive electrode? As we shall see, some chemical reaction takes place at the negative electrode to remove electrons from the graphite plate, and some other reaction takes place at the positive electrode to supply electrons to that graphite plate.

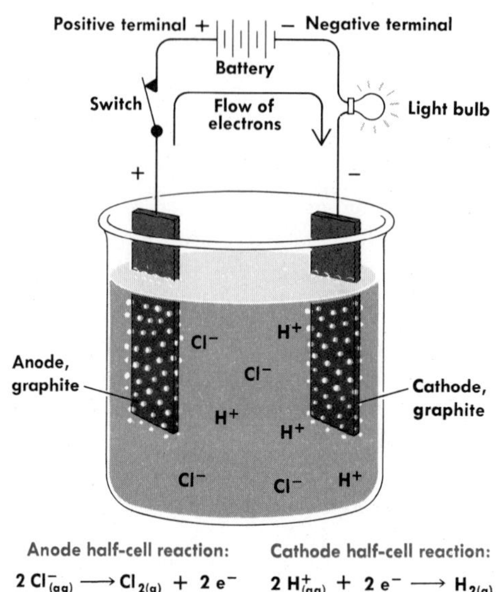

FIGURE 23-1 The electrolysis of a water solution of 1 *M* hydrochloric acid (hydrogen ions and chloride ions).

As we have seen, the net result of the reaction at the negative electrode is the evolution of hydrogen gas, H_2, whereas the reaction at the positive electrode results in the evolution of chlorine gas, Cl_2. Experimentally we find that if we let the current pass through the circuit for a certain period of time, the number of moles of $H_{2(g)}$ evolved at the negative electrode is equal to the number of moles of $Cl_{2(g)}$ evolved at the positive electrode. So the net reaction which occurs in the system when an electric current passes through it may be represented as:

$$\underset{1\ M\ \text{hydrochloric acid}}{2\,H^+_{(aq)} + 2\,Cl^-_{(aq)}} \xrightarrow[\text{energy}]{\text{electrical}} \underset{\substack{\text{at negative}\\ \text{electrode}}}{H_{2(g)}} + \underset{\substack{\text{at positive}\\ \text{electrode}}}{Cl_{2(g)}}$$

As this equation shows, the net result of the chemical reactions which take place at the electrodes is the decomposition of the (1 *M*) hydrochloric acid solution to form $H_{2(g)}$ (at the negative electrode) and $Cl_{2(g)}$ (at the positive electrode). The reaction is called *electrolysis.* We have mentioned previously that, the instant the switch is opened and the current ceases to flow in the system, the decomposition—the electrolysis—stops. This means that the electrolysis is not in fact a spontaneous process, since it takes place only when electrical energy is supplied to the system from the battery.

Let us now consider in more detail what takes place during the electrolysis of a water solution of hydrogen chloride.

MIGRATION OF THE IONS IN SOLUTION. When the switch is open, the positive $H^+_{(aq)}$ and the negative $Cl^-_{(aq)}$ ions present in this hydrochloric acid solution are in continuous, random movement. (Their randomly directed velocities are of the order of 10^4 cm/sec at room temperature.) As soon as the switch is closed, the graphite electrode connected to the negative terminal of the battery becomes negatively charged, the graphite electrode connected to the positive terminal of the battery becomes positively charged, and the positive and negative ions in the solution begin to move non-randomly because of the attraction of the charged electrodes. The positively charged hydrated hydrogen ions, $H^+_{(aq)}$, tend to migrate toward the negative electrode, and the negatively charged hydrated chloride ions, $Cl^-_{(aq)}$, tend to migrate toward the positive electrode. This directed motion of the ions toward the oppositely charged electrode is very slow because the migration is opposed by the frequent collisions with the surrounding water molecules. Even though the migration of the ions toward the oppositely charged electrode is slow, there are so many ions (6.02×10^{23} H^+ ions and 6.02×10^{23} Cl^- ions) in each liter of a 1 *M* solution of $HCl_{(aq)}$ that the number of ions present in the vicinity of each electrode is sufficient to produce a noticeable reaction, the evolution of gas bubbles.

THE REACTION AT THE POSITIVE ELECTRODE, THE ANODE. Under the influence of the voltage applied by the battery, the negatively charged hydrated chloride ions, $Cl^-_{(aq)}$, migrate toward the positively charged graphite plate. When one of these ions comes into contact with the graphite plate, or approaches it very closely, it gives up an electron to the plate and becomes a neutral chlorine atom:

$$Cl^-_{(aq)} \longrightarrow Cl + e^-$$

Under the influence of the potential difference generated by the battery, the electrons (given up to the electrode by the Cl^- ions which have oxidized to Cl atoms) flow from the electrode, through the metallic wires of the circuit, to the positive terminal of the battery. The chlorine atoms formed at the graphite plate in turn combine to form diatomic molecules:

$$2\ Cl \longrightarrow Cl_2$$

When the solution around the electrode has become saturated with chlorine gas, the Cl_2 molecules begin to collect in the form of gas bubbles, which rise to the surface. The complete oxidation half-reaction which takes place at the positive electrode can then be written as:

$$2\ Cl^-_{(aq)} \longrightarrow Cl_{2(g)} + 2\ e^-$$

Thus, at each instant during the electrolysis, hydrated chloride ions, $Cl^-_{(aq)}$, are oxidized at the positively charged electrode to form chlorine gas, $Cl_{2(g)}$, while other hydrated chloride ions arrive at the electrode as they migrate through the solution under the influence of the difference of potential generated by the battery.

Since the term *anode is used to indicate an electrode at which an oxidation reaction takes place,* then the graphite plate where the oxidation of the $Cl^-_{(aq)}$ ions to $Cl_{2(g)}$ molecules occurs is the anode of the electrolytic cell. In general, *in any electrolytic system the anode is the positively charged electrode.*

THE REACTION AT THE NEGATIVE ELECTRODE, THE CATHODE. Each of the positive ions, $H^+_{(aq)}$, in contact with or very near to the cathode takes on 1 electron from the negatively charged graphite plate to form a hydrogen atom:

$$H^+_{(aq)} + 1\ e^- \longrightarrow H$$

The hydrogen atoms, in turn, combine to form diatomic H_2 molecules, which escape as bubbles of hydrogen gas:

$$2\ H \longrightarrow H_{2(g)}$$

The complete reduction half-reaction which takes place at the negative electrode may be written as follows:

$$2\ H^+_{(aq)} + 2\ e^- \longrightarrow H_{2(g)}$$

Thus, at each instant during the electrolysis, hydrated hydrogen ions, $H^+_{(aq)}$, are reduced at the negative electrode, forming hydrogen gas, $H_{2(g)}$; at the same time, other hydrated hydrogen ions arrive at the negative electrode as they migrate through the solution under the influence of the difference of potential applied by the battery.

The formation of hydrogen gas from hydrogen ions is a reduction reaction, and the graphite plate at which such a *reduction reaction occurs is the cathode of the electrolytic cell.* In general, *in any electrolytic system the cathode is the negatively charged electrode.*

Remembering that the half-reaction for a reduction process is obtained by reversing the direction of the couple as written in Table 22-1, we have:

Anode oxidation half-reaction:	$2\ Cl^- \longrightarrow Cl_2 + 2\ e^-$	$E° = -1.36$ v
Cathode reduction half-reaction:	$2\ H^+ + 2\ e^- \longrightarrow H_2$	$E° = 0.00$ v
Net electrolytic reaction:	$2\ H^+ + 2\ Cl^- \xrightarrow[\text{energy}]{\text{electrical}} H_2 + Cl_2$	$E°_{cell} = -1.36$ v

or:

$$2\ HCl_{(aq)} \xrightarrow[\text{energy}]{\text{electrical}} H_{2(g)} + Cl_{2(g)}$$

The negative sign of the reaction potential ($E°_{cell} = -1.36$ v) means that the free energy change for the net reaction, under the specified conditions, is positive ($\Delta G° = -nFE°$). Hence the reaction does not have the capacity to occur spontaneously as written; rather, the reverse reaction—the combination of $H_{2(g)}$ and $Cl_{2(g)}$ in the presence of water to form a solution of hydrochloric acid—will tend to be spontaneous.

In order to force the reaction $2\ HCl_{(aq)} \longrightarrow H_{2(g)} + Cl_{2(g)}$ to take place, we have to supply a sufficient quantity of energy to the system, by applying electrical energy at an appropriate opposing voltage. Under equilibrium conditions, if all reactants and products are present, with activity equal to 1, it would require a potential of at least +1.36 volts to make the reaction proceed from left to right. In fact, a somewhat greater voltage is required to overcome the internal resistance of the cell and push the reaction to the right. Thus, the value of 1.36 volts is the theoretical voltage that has to be exceeded in order to accomplish our purpose. With a platinum cathode the voltage actually required is 1.48 v, and with a nickel cathode it is 1.60 v.

ELECTROLYSIS OF AN AQUEOUS SOLUTION OF NICKEL(II) CHLORIDE

Now let us discuss in detail what happens during the electrolysis of an aqueous 1 *M* solution of nickel(II) chloride, $Ni^{++}(Cl^-)_2$, in an electrolytic cell of the kind shown schematically in Fig. 23-2.

When the switch is closed and the electrical circuit is complete, bubbles of a greenish-yellow gas (chlorine, $Cl_{2(g)}$) appear at the anode—the platinum plate attached to the positive terminal of the battery. Simultaneously, the cathode—the platinum plate attached to the negative terminal of the battery—becomes coated by a bright film (metallic nickel, $Ni_{(s)}$). Also, the light bulb inserted in the circuit lights up, indicating that current is flowing through the circuit. If we keep the current flowing for a long enough time, we notice that the greenish color of the nickel(II) chloride solution becomes lighter and lighter until it finally disappears. The color changes because almost all the hydrated Ni^{++} ions, which are green in color, have been removed from the solution and have been deposited as a metallic nickel coating on the cathode. This decomposition of a solution of nickel chloride, under the effect of an applied voltage, to form chlorine gas, $Cl_{2(g)}$, and metallic nickel $Ni_{(s)}$, is another example of electrolysis.

What would have happened if we had opened the switch, and thus stopped applying a difference of potential between the platinum plates, before the electrolysis had run to completion? The formation of gas bubbles at the anode and the deposition of nickel metal on the cathode would have ceased immediately. Again, we observe the following facts during the electrolysis of an aqueous solution of nickel(II) chloride:

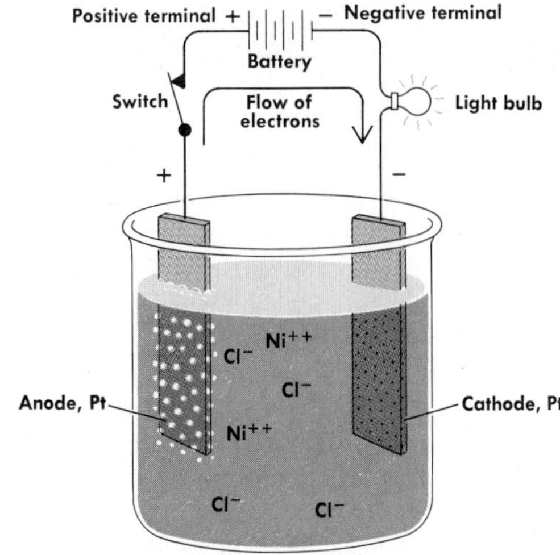

FIGURE 23-2 The electrolysis of a water solution of 1 *M* $NiCl_2$.

1. Electrical energy is necessary for the chemical reactions to take place, and these reactions take place at the regions of contact between electrodes and solution.
2. The formation of a gas at one electrode and of a metallic coating on the other electrode occur simultaneously, even though the electrodes are widely separated.
3. During the electrolysis an electric current flows through the circuit, that is, the aqueous solution of $NiCl_2$ acts as an "apparent" conductor of electricity.

Let us now consider in more detail the reactions that occur at the electrodes when these are connected with the terminals of a battery having sufficiently high voltage.

THE REACTION AT THE ANODE. OXIDATION PROCESS. As in the previous example of the electrolysis of 1 *M* hydrochloric acid, the reaction at the positively charged plate is the oxidation of hydrated chloride ions to chlorine gas:

$$2\,Cl^-_{(aq)} \longrightarrow 2\,Cl_{(\text{on anode})} + 2\,e^-$$
$$2\,Cl_{(\text{on anode})} \longrightarrow Cl_{2\,(g)}$$

THE REACTION AT THE CATHODE. REDUCTION PROCESS. When one of the dipositive hydrated nickel(II) ions, $Ni^{++}_{(aq)}$, comes into contact with the cathode, or moves very close to it, it takes on two electrons from the platinum plate to form a neutral nickel atom:

$$Ni^{++}_{(aq)} + 2\,e^- \longrightarrow Ni_{(s)}$$

We know that this is a reduction reaction, for each nickel(II) ion takes on two electrons to form a neutral nickel atom. The nickel atoms thus formed are then deposited on the cathode as a layer of metallic nickel—that is, they plate out. In general, in any kind of electrolytic system, when a positively charged metal ion is removed from solution by plating out at the negatively charged electrode, this electrode is the cathode of the electrolytic cell. We sometimes say that in an electrolytic process, metal ions are *discharged* at the cathode, because they lose their positive charge by taking on electrons from the negative plate.

SUMMARY OF ELECTROLYSIS OF AN AQUEOUS SOLUTION OF $NiCl_2$

1. The hydrated nickel(II) ions in solution migrate to the cathode, where each $Ni^{++}_{(aq)}$ ion takes on two electrons to form a neutral nickel atom. Metallic nickel is formed and plates out on the cathode. Thus, reduction of the nickel(II) ions takes place at the cathode:

$$Ni^{++}_{(aq)} + 2\ e^- \longrightarrow Ni_{(s)}$$

2. The hydrated chloride ions in solution, $Cl^-_{(aq)}$, migrate to the anode, where each ion loses one electron to form a neutral chlorine atom. The chlorine atoms then combine to form diatomic molecules, which escape from the solution as bubbles of gas. Thus, oxidation of the chloride ions takes place at the anode:

$$2\ Cl^-_{(aq)} \longrightarrow Cl_{2(g)} + 2\ e^-$$

3. As the nickel(II) ions take on electrons at the cathode, the chloride ions at the anode simultaneously give up electrons. For each nickel(II) ion that takes on two electrons to form metallic nickel, two chloride ions each give up one electron to form two chlorine atoms. Thus, the oxidation reaction at the anode and the reduction reaction at the cathode occur *simultaneously* and involve the same (total) number of electrons. Using Table 22-1 we can express the net result of these simultaneous reactions as follows:

Anode oxidation half-reaction:	$2\ Cl^-_{(aq)} \longrightarrow Cl_{2(g)} + 2\ e^-$	$E° = -1.36$ v
Cathode reduction half-reaction:	$Ni^{++}_{(aq)} + 2\ e^- \longrightarrow Ni_{(s)}$	$E° = -0.24$ v
Net electrolytic reaction:	$Ni^{++}_{(aq)} + 2\ Cl^-_{(aq)} \xrightarrow[\text{energy}]{\text{electrical}} Ni_{(s)} + Cl_{2(g)}$	$E°_{cell} = -1.60$ v

The negative sign of the reaction potential, $E_{cell} = -1.60$ v, tells us that the reaction is not spontaneous under the specified conditions, ($\Delta G°$ is positive). So to force the reaction to take place we must supply energy to the system, by applying a voltage slightly greater than 1.60 volts.

ILLUSTRATIVE EXAMPLES

Using the oxidation potentials below indicate whether reactions 1 and 2 below can take place spontaneously as written. In each case indicate also: (a) the total cell voltage, if the reaction takes place spontaneously (in a combined energy cell); and (b) the minimum voltage that needs to be applied if electrical energy must be supplied to force the reaction to occur (in an electrolytic cell).

Reaction	*Couple*	*E°*
1. $2\ Fe^{+++} + Tl^+ \longrightarrow 2\ Fe^{++} + Tl^{+++}$	Fe^{++}, Fe^{+++}	-0.77 v
	Tl^+, Tl^{+++}	-1.25 v
2. $Cd_{(s)} + Sn^{+4} \longrightarrow Cd^{++} + Sn^{+2}$	Cd, Cd^{++}	$+0.40$ v
	Sn^{++}, Sn^{+4}	-0.13 v

SOLUTION FOR REACTION 1. List first the couple with the more positive (or less negative) $E°$ value; then reverse the equation for the other half-reaction, which becomes the reduction half-reaction; and add:

$2\ Fe^{++}$	$= 2\ Fe^{+++} + 2\ e^-$	$E° = -0.77$ v
$Tl^{+++} + 2\ e^-$	$= Tl^+$	$E° = +1.25$ v
$2\ Fe^{++} + Tl^{+++}$	$= 2\ Fe^{+++} + Tl^+$	$E°_{cell} = +0.48$ v

The positive value of E_{cell} ($+0.48$ v) tells us that this reaction *as written* can take place spontaneously, and that in order for the *desired reverse reaction* to take place we must supply electrical energy to the system. Thus, an opposing voltage greater than +0.48 v must be applied to the electrodes to obtain the desired reaction.

$$2\,Fe^{+++} + Tl^{+} \xrightarrow[\text{energy}]{\text{electrical}} 2\,Fe^{++} + Tl^{+++}$$

SOLUTION FOR REACTION 2. The two half-equations for the half-reactions involved are:

$$\begin{array}{lll} Cd & = Cd^{++} + 2\,e^{-} & E^\circ = +0.40\text{ v} \\ Sn^{+4} + 2\,e^{-} & = Sn^{++} & E^\circ = +0.13\text{ v} \\ \hline Cd + Sn^{+4} & = Cd^{++} + Sn^{++} & E^\circ_{cell} = +0.53\text{ v} \end{array}$$

The positive value of E°_{cell} (+0.53 v) tells us that the reaction can take place spontaneously as written (in a combined energy cell).

23-3 Electrolysis Involving Water

In the electrolysis of the two aqueous solutions we have just discussed—hydrogen chloride and nickel(II) chloride—both the negative ions and the positive ions of the solute are discharged at the electrodes. In many aqueous electrolytic solutions, however, we find that only *one* kind of ion of the solute—either the positive ion or the negative ion—is discharged. In these cases the solvent itself, water, undergoes electrolysis at the other electrode. Let us consider some examples.

ELECTROLYSIS OF AN AQUEOUS SOLUTION OF SODIUM CHLORIDE

When a 1 *M* aqueous solution of sodium chloride, Na^+Cl^-, is electrolyzed between graphite electrodes, Cl_2 gas is evolved at the anode, H_2 gas is evolved at the cathode; the solution becomes basic. The total equation for the reaction is:

$$2\,Na^{+}_{(aq)} + 2\,Cl^{-}_{(aq)} + 2\,H_2O_{(l)} \xrightarrow[\text{energy}]{\text{electrical}} H_{2(g)} + Cl_{2(g)} + 2\,Na^{+}_{(aq)} + 2\,OH^{-}_{(aq)}$$

And, if we cancel the $Na^{+}_{(aq)}$ ions that do not undergo reaction, we have simply:

$$2\,Cl^{-}_{(aq)} + 2\,H_2O_{(l)} \xrightarrow[\text{energy}]{\text{electrical}} H_{2(g)} + Cl_{2(g)} + 2\,OH^{-}_{(aq)}$$

To understand the difference between this net reaction and that involving nickel(II) chloride, consider the oxidation potentials of the couples in the table below (see Table 22-1 for complete half-reactions). The minimum voltage which must be applied for the electrolytic separation of $Cl_{2(g)}$ and $Ni_{(s)}$ from a 1 *M* solution of $NiCl_2$ in water ($[Ni^{++}_{(aq)}] = 1\,M$, $[Cl^{-}_{(aq)}] = 2\,M$) is $-(-1.34^{*} - 0.24) = +1.58$ volts, whereas the minimum voltage required for the separation of $Cl_{2(g)}$ and $H_{2(g)}$ from this same (virtually neutral) solution ($[Cl^{-}_{(aq)}] = 2\,M$, $[H^{+}_{(aq)}] = 10^{-7}\,M$) is $-(-1.34 - 0.41) = +1.75$ volts. In the absence of other complicating factors, the reaction requiring the lower applied voltage (+1.60 v) is the one that we expect to occur when the cell is operated. Accordingly, under the specified conditions of concentration, temperature and pressure, nickel metal, $Ni_{(s)}$, rather than hydrogen gas, $H_{2(g)}$, is the principal product at the cathode in the electrolysis of a neutral nickel(II)

$Na_{(s)}$, $Na^{+}_{(aq)}$ (1 M)	$E^\circ = +2.71$ v
$H_{2(g)}$, $H^{+}_{(aq)}$ (10^{-7} M); $H_2O_{(l)}$, $OH^{-}_{(aq)}$ (10^{-7} M)	$E = +0.41$ v
$Ni_{(s)}$, $Ni^{++}_{(aq)}$ (1 M)	$E^\circ = +0.24$ v
$H_{2(g)}$, $H^{+}_{(aq)}$ (1 M)	$E^\circ = 0.00$ v
$Cl^{-}_{(aq)}$ (2 M), $Cl_{2(g)}$	$E = -1.34$ v
$Cl^{-}_{(aq)}$ (1 M), $Cl_{2(g)}$	$E^\circ = -1.36$ v

(All couples at 25°C and 1 atm)

* For 2 *M* chloride ion, as expected, the electrode potential is slightly more positive than −1.36 volts.

chloride solution. On the other hand, in a neutral 1 molar solution of sodium chloride, the voltage $(-(-0.41 - 1.36) = +1.77$ volts) required to evolve $H_{2(g)}$ at the cathode and $Cl_{2(g)}$ at the anode is lower than the voltage $(-(-2.71 - 1.36) = +4.07$ volts) which would be required to form $Na_{(s)}$ at the cathode and $Cl_{2(g)}$ at the anode. That is to say, the voltage (+0.41 v) required to reduce H^+ ions in (neutral) water to H_2 gas is lower than the voltage required to reduce sodium ions, $Na^+{}_{(aq)}$ to Na ($E° = +2.71$). Hence the half-reaction at the cathode is: $H^+ + e^- \longrightarrow$ H (on cathode). The H atoms thus formed on the cathode join together, as expected, to form H_2 molecules which then escape as bubbles of hydrogen gas: 2 H (on cathode) $\longrightarrow H_{2(g)}$.

Thus the net cathode half-reaction can be written as:

$$1. \quad 2\ H^+{}_{(aq)} + 2\ e^- \longrightarrow H_{2(g)}$$

Since in neutral solution the concentration of H_2O molecules is so much higher than that of H^+ ions, we can also write the net cathode half-reaction in the equivalent, but more appropriate form:

$$2. \quad 2\ H_2O_{(l)} + 2\ e^- \longrightarrow H_{2(g)} + 2\ OH^-{}_{(aq)}$$

Notice that equation 2 differs from equation 1 only in that it includes the ionization of water:

$$\begin{array}{rcl} 2\ H_2O_{(l)} & \longrightarrow & 2\ H^+{}_{(aq)} + 2\ OH^-{}_{(aq)} \\ 2\ H^+{}_{(aq)} + 2\ e^- & \longrightarrow & H_{2(g)} \\ \hline 2\ H_2O_{(l)} + 2\ e^- & \longrightarrow & H_{2(g)} \quad + 2\ OH^-{}_{(aq)} \end{array}$$

The ionization of water is not an electrochemical process, so the two half-reactions (1) and (2) are equivalent, and *have the same potential under the same set of conditions.* When we consider acidic solutions, we usually write equation (1) as the electrode half-reaction, whereas when we consider neutral or basic solutions we prefer to use equation (2). Table 23-1 summarizes these and other important considerations concerning the electrolysis of the species of water at different pH conditions.

In the electrolysis of an aqueous solution of NaCl, in addition to the release of H_2 gas, another fundamental chemical change takes place in the vicinity of the cathode. First, the $Na^+{}_{(aq)}$ ions that migrate toward the cathode begin to accumulate in its vicinity. Second, the $OH^-{}_{(aq)}$ ions that are formed at the cathode also begin to

TABLE 23-1 OXIDATION POTENTIALS FOR H_2, H^+ AND H_2O, O_2 COUPLES IN ACID, NEUTRAL, AND BASIC SOLUTIONS AT 25°C AND 1 ATM

	Half-reaction	*Solution*	*Ox. Pot. (volts)*
Equivalent half-reactions for H_2, H^+ couple	$H_{2(g)} \longrightarrow 2\ H^+{}_{(aq)} + 2\ e^-$ (preferred in acid solutions)	1 M acid: $[H^+] = 1$, $[OH^-] = 10^{-14}$	0.00
	$H_{2(g)} + 2\ OH^-{}_{(aq)} \longrightarrow 2\ H_2O_{(l)} + 2\ e^-$ (preferred in neutral and basic solutions)	Neutral: $[H^+] = [OH^-] = 10^{-7}$	+0.41
		1 M basic: $[H^+] = 10^{-14}$, $[OH^-] = 1$	+0.83
Equivalent half-reactions for H_2O, O_2 couple	$2\ H_2O_{(l)} \longrightarrow O_{2(g)} + 4\ H^+{}_{(aq)} + 4\ e^-$ (preferred in acid and neutral solutions)	1 M acid: $[H^+] = 1$, $[OH^-] = 10^{-14}$	−1.23
	$4\ OH^-{}_{(aq)} \longrightarrow O_{2(g)} + 2\ H_2O_{(l)} + 4\ e^-$ (preferred in basic solutions)	Neutral: $[H^+] = [OH^-] = 10^{-7}$	−0.82
		1 M basic: $[H^+] = 10^{-14}$, $[OH^-] = 1$	−0.40

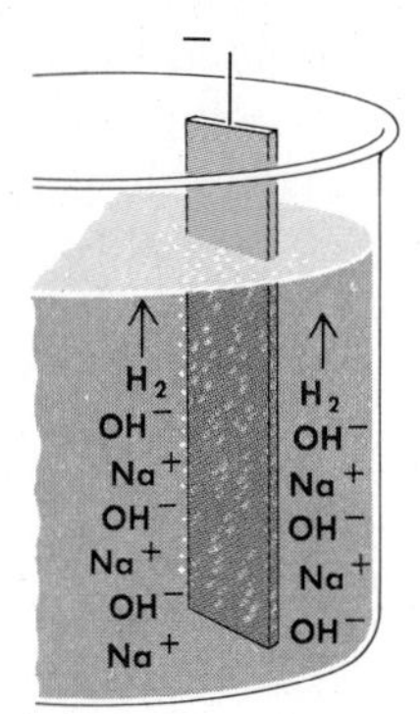

$2\,H_2O + 2\,\bar{e} \longrightarrow H_2 + 2\,OH^-$

FIGURE 23-3 Reaction at the cathode in the electrolysis of an aqueous solution of Na^+ Cl^-.

accumulate in its vicinity, since the electrostatic attraction of the Na^+ ions tends to prevent the OH^- ions from migrating to the positive anode. Thus the solution in the vicinity of the cathode (the cathodic solution) is basic. A strip of red litmus paper immersed in the cathodic solution turns blue, or a drop of the colorless indicator phenolphthalein dropped in the solution near the cathode turns crimson (see Ch. 20), owing to the presence of OH^- ions in excess of neutrality.

Figure 23-3 represents a portion of the electrolytic cell in the vicinity of the cathode, where hydrogen gas, H_2, and hydroxide ions, $OH^-_{(aq)}$ are being produced, while the sodium ions, $Na^+_{(aq)}$, remain unchanged in the solution.

At the anode, the reaction is again the oxidation of the chloride ions and the subsequent formation of chlorine gas, as in the case of the $NiCl_2$ and HCl aqueous solutions.

In each of the three processes we have considered, the electrolysis of aqueous solutions of 1 molar HCl, or 1 molar $NiCl_2$, and 1 molar NaCl, the anodic half-reaction is the oxidation of the chloride ions to chlorine gas:

$$2\,Cl^- \longrightarrow Cl_{2(g)} + 2\,e^- \qquad (E^\circ = -1.36\text{ v})$$

Now, we may ask, why does this oxidation reaction occur, rather than the oxidation of the oxygen atoms of H_2O? In fact, the oxygen of water can be oxidized at the anode of an electrolytic cell—as we shall discuss in detail in the next section—according to the reaction:

$$2\,H_2O_{(l)} \longrightarrow O_{2(g)} + 4\,H^+_{(aq)} + 4\,e^-$$

As shown in Table 23-1, the potential for the oxidation of water is -1.23 v in 1 *M* acid solution and -0.82 v in neutral solution. This means that the oxidation of water, under the equilibrium conditions used to measure *E* values, is energetically less difficult than the oxidation of the chloride ions, and we might therefore expect it to occur. However, since the anodic evolution of O_2 gas on graphite or platinum electrodes has a rather high overvoltage (p. 518), it is the evolution of Cl_2 gas which actually occurs. This is another case in which the value of oxidation potentials—or the value of the free energy of reaction—is not sufficient, alone, to explain the observed behavior. To have a complete explanation of the observed process, we should consider also the *rate* and the mechanism of the reactions.

To summarize: The electrolysis of 1 *M* aqueous solution of sodium chloride, between inert graphite electrodes, can be represented as follows:

Anode half-reac.:	$2\,Cl^-_{(aq)} \longrightarrow Cl_{2(g)} + 2\,e^-$	E°	$= -1.36$ v
Cathode half-reac.:	$2\,H_2O_{(l)} + 2\,e^- \longrightarrow H_{2(g)} + 2\,OH^-_{(aq)}$	E	$= -0.41$ v
Net elec. reac.:	$2\,H_2O_{(l)} + 2\,Cl^-_{(aq)} \xrightarrow[\text{energy}]{\text{electrical}} H_{2(g)} + Cl_{2(g)} + 2\,OH^-_{(aq)}$	E_{cell}	$= -1.77$ v

The negative sign of the reaction potential ($E = -1.77$) tells us that electrical energy must be supplied to the system to cause the chemical reaction to take place as written. The voltage to be applied in order to force the reaction to occur must be greater than $+1.77$ volts, under the conditions we have specified.

THE CATHODIC REDUCTION OF WATER IN NEUTRAL AND BASIC SOLUTIONS

Table 23-1 gives the value of the oxidation potential of the H_2,H^+ couple in neutral solution. This potential is important because its permits us to predict which of the possible cathodic reduction reactions—the reduction of the cations of the solute, or the reduction of the solvent, water—is favored energetically. As an exercise, let us see how we could use the Nernst equation (p. 497) to calculate this potential.

The electrode potential for the standard H_2,H^+ couple in 1 *M* acidic solution is: $E^\circ = 0.00$ volts. The number of moles of electrons in the oxidation half-equation, $H_{2(g)} \longrightarrow 2\ H^+_{(aq)} + 2\ e^-$, is: $n = 2$. In a neutral solution the concentration of hydrogen ions is only 1×10^{-7} *M*; hence the *Q* term in the Nernst equation will be:

$$Q = \frac{[H^+]^2}{[H_2]} = \frac{[10^{-7}]^2}{1} = 10^{-14}$$

By substituting these values into the Nernst equation, we obtain the electrode potential for the H_2,H^+ couple in neutral solution:

$$\begin{aligned} E &= E^\circ - \frac{0.0591}{n} \times \log Q \\ &= 0.00 - \frac{0.0591}{2} \times (-14) \\ &= 0.00 + 0.414 \cong +0.41\ \text{v} \end{aligned}$$

Thus we may write:

$$H_{2(g)} = 2\ H^+_{(aq)} + 2\ e^-; \qquad E_{\text{neutral}} = +0.41\ \text{v}$$

We may now ask ourselves what is the source of the hydrogen ions in a neutral aqueous solution. We know that a neutral solution contains relatively few* hydrogen ions. We must remember, however, that if these $H^+_{(aq)}$ ions are reduced at the cathode, they are immediately replaced by more $H^+_{(aq)}$ ions which come from the ionization of more water molecules, to maintain the equilibrium:

$$H_2O_{(l)} \rightleftharpoons H^+_{(aq)} + OH^-_{(aq)}$$

When hydrogen ions are removed from the system, the equilibrium reaction is shifted to the right in accordance with Le Chateliers' principle. Notice that when the equation proceeds to the right, hydroxide ions are also produced. Therefore by adding the ionization equation, $H_2O_{(l)} = H^+_{(aq)} + OH^-_{(aq)}$, to the reduction half-equation, $2\ H^+_{(aq)} + 2\ e^- = H_{2(g)}$, we can write the following half-reaction, which better describes the final result of the cathodic reduction of water in certain electrolytic cells:

$$\begin{aligned} 2\ H^+_{(aq)} + 2\ e^- &= H_{2(g)} \\ 2\ H_2O_{(l)} &= 2\ H^+_{(aq)} + 2\ OH^-_{(aq)} \\ \hline 2\ H_2O_{(l)} + 2\ e^- &= H_{2(g)} + 2\ OH^-_{(aq)} \end{aligned}$$

This final equation expresses the change that occurs when hydrogen gas, H_2, is produced at the cathode of a cell during the electrolysis of a neutral aqueous solution. The value of the oxidation potential of this equation is the same as that we calculated from the Nernst equation, since of course the dissociation of water does not contribute to the value of the potential. So we may write

$$2\ H_2O_{(l)} + 2\ e^- = H_{2(g)} + 2\ OH^-_{(aq)} \qquad E_{\text{neutral}} = +0.41\ \text{v}$$

If we calculate in a similar manner the value of the oxidation potential of the H_2,H^+ couple in 1 molar basic solution, where $[OH^-] = 1$ and $[H^+] = 10^{-14}$, we obtain the potential value, $E_{\text{basic}} = +0.83$ v, as listed in Table 23-1.

* Of course, the absolute number of $H^+_{(aq)}$ in 1 liter of neutral aqueous solution is quite large: $10^{-7} \times 6.02 \times 10^{23} = 6.02 \times 10^{16}$ $H^+_{(aq)}$ ions per liter. The number of $H^+_{(aq)}$ ions is only small if compared to that of the H_2O molecules: 1 liter of liquid water $\cong$ 55.5 moles of H_2O molecules $= 55.5 \times 6.02 \times 10^{23} \cong 3 \times 10^{25}$ H_2O molecules.

THE ANODIC OXIDATION OF WATER IN ACID, NEUTRAL, AND BASIC SOLUTION

In the H_2O molecule, the H atoms have an oxidation number of +1, the maximum possible oxidation number for hydrogen, and therefore they cannot undergo further oxidation. On the other hand, the oxygen atom of H_2O has an oxidation number of −2, and so can be oxidized to elemental oxygen. Thus, when an aqueous solution is electrolyzed, the water molecules—or more precisely, the O atoms of the H_2O molecules—may undergo anodic oxidation. The equation for the anodic oxidation of H_2O can be written in either of the two following forms:

$$1.\quad 2\,H_2O_{(l)} \longrightarrow O_{2(g)} + 4\,H^+_{(aq)} + 4\,e^-$$
$$2.\quad 4\,OH^-_{(aq)} \longrightarrow O_{2(g)} + 2\,H_2O_{(l)} + 4\,e^-$$

Equations 1 and 2 differ from one another only in that 2 is obtained from 1 by adding the equation for the combination of 4 H^+ ions with 4 OH^- ions to give 4 H_2O molecules;

$$\begin{array}{lrcl} 1. & 2\,H_2O_{(l)} & \longrightarrow & O_{2(g)} + 4\,H^+_{(aq)} + 4\,e^- \\ & 4\,H^+_{(aq)} + 4\,OH^-_{(aq)} & \longrightarrow & 4\,H_2O_{(l)} \\ \hline 2. & 4\,OH^-_{(aq)} & \longrightarrow & O_{2(g)} + 2\,H_2O_{(l)} + 4\,e^- \end{array}$$

Since, as we have just discussed in the preceding section, the ionization of water is not an electrochemical reaction, equations 1 and 2 above are equivalent electrochemically and have the same oxidation potential, provided the temperature, pressure and concentration of H^+ ions (or OH^- ions) in solution are the same. The values of the potential for the anodic oxidation of water are given in Table 23-1 for 1 molar acid solutions, neutral solutions, and 1 molar basic solutions (at 25°C and 1 atm). We see that the oxidation of water becomes less and less difficult as the solution passes from acid to neutral to basic. This is in agreement with the application of Le Chatelier's principle to this equilibrium reaction, written, for example, as

$$4\,OH^-_{(aq)} \rightleftharpoons O_{(2)g} + 2\,H_2O_{(l)} + 4\,e^-$$

ELECTROLYSIS OF A SOLUTION OF SULFURIC ACID IN WATER

In an electrolytic cell with inert (platinum) electrodes, we place an aqueous solution of sulfuric acid, H_2SO_4, which contains hydrated H^+, HSO_4^-, and $SO_4^=$ ions, and of course H_2O molecules. If we apply a sufficiently high voltage, we observe that hydrogen gas, H_2, is evolved at the cathode and that oxygen gas, O_2, is evolved at the anode. The number of moles of H_2 is twice the number of moles of O_2 produced in any given length of time. We also find experimentally that the volume of the solution decreases, while the total quantity of H_2SO_4 in solution remains constant, hence the acidity of the solution slowly but gradually increases as the electrolysis proceeds. Furthermore, the anodic solution is at all times somewhat more acidic than the cathodic solution. How can we explain these experimental observations?

At the cathode the reaction consists of the reduction of the H^+ ions, similar to the reduction of the H^+ ions in hydrochloric acid, or in any other aqueous solution containing a moderately high concentration of H^+ ions:

$$2\,H^+_{(aq)} + 2\,e^- \longrightarrow H_{2(g)}$$

When the hydrogen ion concentration for this solution of H_2SO_4 is $[H^+] = 1\,M$, the potential for the cathodic reduction is 0.00 v.

At the anode, oxygen gas is evolved, as follows:

$$2\,H_2O_{(l)} \longrightarrow O_{2(g)} + 4\,H^+_{(aq)} + 4\,e^-$$

In this reaction 2 molecules of water give up 4 electrons to the positively charged platinum plate to form 1 oxygen molecule, O_2, and 4 hydrated hydrogen ions, 4 H^+. The standard electrode potential for this reaction is $E^\circ = -1.23$ v (see Table 23-1). The H^+ ions formed at the anode tend to migrate away from it, toward the negatively charged cathode. However, as long as the electrolysis is in progress, there is always a relatively higher concentration of H^+ in the vicinity of the anode, because the attraction of the negative HSO_4^- and $SO_4^=$ ions, which migrate to the anode and accumulate there, retard the diffusion of the H^+ ions.

The reaction for the electrolysis of a water solution of H_2SO_4 can be written as:

Anode half-reac.:	$2\,H_2O_{(l)} \longrightarrow O_{2(g)} + 4\,H^+_{(aq)} + 4\,e^-$	E°	$= -1.23$ v
Cathode half-reac.:	$4\,H^+_{(aq)} + 4\,e^- \longrightarrow 2\,H_{2(g)}$	E°	$= 0.00$ v
Net elec. reac.:	$4\,H^+_{(aq)} + 2\,H_2O_{(l)} \xrightarrow[\text{energy}]{\text{electrical}} 2\,H_{2(g)} + O_{2(g)} + 4\,H^+_{(aq)}$	E°_{cell}	$= -1.23$ v

Again, the negative value of E°_{cell} tells us that (electrical) energy must be added to the system to force the desired chemical reaction to take place. The voltage that must be actually applied to cause the electrolysis of water is appreciably higher than the theoretical value of +1.23 v, approaching +1.60 v. One important reason why the required voltage is higher than the theoretical voltage is that during the electrolysis the solution is not uniform, because the concentration of H_2SO_4 (actually H^+, HSO_4^- and $SO_4^=$) is greater around the anode than around the cathode. But when the current is turned off, these ions diffuse toward the regions where their concentration is lower, restoring the uniformity of the solution. Thus, at all moments during electrolysis the solution as a whole is electrically neutral, because the number of electrons given up by the H_2O molecules to the anode is equal at every instant to the number of electrons taken on from the cathode by the $H^+_{(aq)}$ ions. Also, for every 4 H^+ ions reduced at the cathode, 4 H^+ ions are formed at the anode. Consequently there is no net change in the number of H^+ ions in the solution as a result of the electrolysis, and the H^+ ions need not appear in the equation for the electrolytic reaction.

The electrolysis of a water solution of H_2SO_4 then consists essentially of the decomposition of water to form $O_{2(g)}$ (at the anode) and $H_{2(g)}$ (at the cathode). For simplicity, the equation of the process may be written as:

$$2\,H_2O_{(l)} \xrightarrow[\text{electrical energy}]{H_2SO_4} 2\,H_{2(g)} + O_{2(g)}$$

The fact that some water (the solvent) is decomposed during the electrolysis explains the observed change in acidity (increase in the concentration of H_2SO_4).

ELECTROLYSIS OF AN AQUEOUS SOLUTION OF Na_2SO_4

On the basis of what we have learned about the electrolysis of aqueous solutions of NaCl and H_2SO_4, we can now predict that the electrolysis of a solution of Na_2SO_4, which is neutral and contains Na^+ and $SO_4^=$ ions in addition to water molecules, will involve the following reactions.

REACTION AT THE ANODE. OXIDATION PROCESS. Water molecules are oxidized to form oxygen gas and hydrated hydrogen ions:

$$2\,H_2O_{(l)} \longrightarrow O_{2(g)} + 4\,H^+_{(aq)} + 4\,e^- \qquad E = -0.82\text{ v}$$

REACTION AT THE CATHODE. REDUCTION PROCESS. Water molecules are reduced to form hydrogen gas and hydrated OH^- ions:

$$2\,H_2O + 2\,e^- \longrightarrow H_{2(g)} + 2\,OH^-_{(aq)} \qquad E = -0.41\text{ v}$$

Since the number of electrons given up by the reactants to the anode must be equal to the number of electrons taken on by the reactants at the cathode, the complete reaction for this electrolysis is:

$$6\,H_2O_{(l)} \xrightarrow[\text{energy}]{\text{electrical}} 2\,H_{2(g)} + O_{2(g)} + 4\,H^+_{(aq)} + 4\,OH^-_{(aq)} \qquad E_{cell} = -0.82 - 0.41 = -1.23\text{ v}$$

The anode half-reaction and the cathode half-reaction take place simultaneously, so each time a H^+ ion is formed at the anode an OH^- ion is formed at the cathode, and the over-all electroneutrality of the solution is maintained. However, during electrolysis the solution in the vicinity of the cathode is basic, because the diffusion of the OH^- ions away from the cathode is retarded by the attraction of the Na^+ ions accumulated around it. (Recall that the Na^+ ions migrate toward the cathode but are not reduced there.) Similarly, the diffusion of the H^+ ions formed at the anode is retarded by the attraction of the $SO_4^=$ ions that accumulate in the vicinity of the anode (the $SO_4^=$ ions migrate toward the positive electrode, but do not discharge there). Consequently, the solution in the vicinity of the anode is acidic during the electrolysis. When the electrolysis is interrupted by opening the switch, however, all ions accumulated near the electrodes diffuse throughout the solution, which becomes again uniform. Then the H^+ and OH^- ions formed in the anodic and cathodic half-reactions combine to form H_2O molecules ($4\,H^+ + 4\,OH^- \longrightarrow 4\,H_2O$). The *net* reaction for the electrolysis of an aqueous solution of Na_2SO_4 is therefore:

$$2\,H_2O \xrightarrow[\text{electrical energy}]{Na_2SO_4} 2\,H_{2(g)} + O_{2(g)}$$

The electrolytic decomposition of water is not limited to solutions of sodium sulfate or sulfuric (phosphoric, boric, and nitric) acid in water, but is a general reaction for a large number of ionic compounds dissolved in water. For example, none of the monopositive alkali-metal ions (Li^+, Na^+, K^+, Rb^+, and Cs^+) or of the dipositive alkaline-earth ions (Ca^{++}, Sr^{++}, and Ba^{++}) are reduced at the cathode during an electrolysis in aqueous solution; instead, water molecules are reduced. Similarly many common oxoanions—for example, $SO_4^=$, $PO_4^{\equiv}$, NO_3^- and ClO_4^-—when present in an aqueous solution, are not oxidized at the anode during electrolysis; instead, water molecules are oxidized. Consequently, we can use the following generalized equation to represent the electrolysis, between inert electrodes, of aqueous solutions of salts such as $Ca(NO_3)_2$, $NaNO_3$, $KClO_4$, Na_3PO_4, $CsNO_3$, $Ba(NO_3)_2$, K_2SO_4, and many others, containing the cations and anions just mentioned:

$$2\,H_2O_{(l)} \xrightarrow[\text{electrical energy}]{\text{"salt"}} 2\,H_{2(g)} + O_{2(g)}$$

ELECTROLYSIS OF A 1 MOLAR AQUEOUS SOLUTION OF SODIUM HYDROXIDE

A 1 molar aqueous solution of sodium hydroxide contains the ions Na^+ and OH^-, each at a concentration of 1 mole per liter, and water molecules, H_2O.

THE REACTION AT THE ANODE. OXIDATION PROCESS. The oxygen of water is oxidized to form molecular oxygen, O_2. Since the solution is basic, we generally write the oxidation of water in the form involving the OH^- ions as the reactants. The value of the oxidation potential is given in Table 23-1.

$$4\,OH^- \longrightarrow O_{2(g)} + 2\,H_2O + 4\,e^- \qquad E_{basic} = -0.40\text{ v}$$

This reaction is similar to that which occurs at the anode in the electrolysis of a 1 molar solution of Na_2SO_4, but the reaction potential is less negative.

THE REACTION AT THE CATHODE. REDUCTION PROCESS. At the cathode, water molecules take on electrons to form hydrogen gas and hydroxide ions, as we have seen in the electrolysis of NaCl and Na_2SO_4 solutions. However, the potential of this half-reaction is more negative in 1 molar NaOH solution, which is basic, than it is in 1 molar solutions of NaCl or Na_2SO_4, which are neutral. From Table 23-1 we have:

$$2\,H_2O_{(l)} + 2\,e^- \longrightarrow H_{2(g)} + 2\,OH^- \qquad E_{basic} = -0.83\text{ v}$$

As always, the reaction representing the electrolytic process is the sum of the reactions at the anode and cathode:

Anode half-reaction: $4\,OH^- \longrightarrow O_2 + 2\,H_2O + 4\,e^-$ $\qquad E_{anode} = -0.40$ v

Cathode half-reaction: $4\,H_2O_{(l)} + 4\,e^- \longrightarrow 2\,H_2 + 4\,OH^-$ $\qquad E_{cathode} = -0.83$ v

Electrolytic reaction: $4\,H_2O_{(l)} + 4\,OH^-_{(aq)} \longrightarrow 2\,H_{2(g)} + O_{2(g)} + 4\,OH^-_{(aq)} + 2\,H_2O_{(l)}$ $\qquad E_{cell} = -1.23$ v

It is interesting that the value of this reaction potential is $E = -1.23$ v, the same value as the reaction potential for the electrolysis of a 1 molar acid solution of H_2SO_4, or of a 1 molar neutral solution of NaCl or Na_2SO_4. Of course, the net reaction equation is in this case, as in the other cases, simply the electrolysis of water:

$$2\,H_2O_{(l)} \xrightarrow[\text{electrical energy}]{\text{NaOH}} 2\,H_{2(g)} + O_{2(g)}$$

It is to be expected, therefore, that the potential required for this reaction, if carried out under reversible conditions, is independent of the pH of the solution—since as we know $\Delta G = -nFE$, and ΔG depends only on the initial state (H_2O liquid) and the final state (H_2 gas and O_2 gas) both at 1 atm and 25°C. It is true that the potential for the anode half-reaction depends on the pH of the solution, as shown in Table 23-1, and so does the potential of the cathode half-reaction, but their sum—the net reaction potential—remains unchanged.

OVERVOLTAGE

We learned in Chapter 22 that the oxidation potential of a given couple is the electromotive force of the combined cell composed of that couple joined to the standard H_2,H^+ couple. The electromotive force is measured when the oxidized and reduced form of each couple are in equilibrium, that is, when no electrons are flowing through the system. This is done, as we have seen, by using a potentiometer (p. 482), so that the EMF of the cell is exactly counterbalanced by an applied voltage provided by a reference battery. The E value of a given couple, therefore, refers to this couple under equilibrium conditions and holds for oxidation-reduction reactions that take place reversibly. For actual electrochemical processes, which are carried out under non-reversible conditions, the E value represents only a theoretical limiting value—the maximum voltage which can be obtained in an energy cell from a spontaneous reaction, or the minimum voltage which has to be applied to an electrolytic cell to bring about a non-spontaneous reaction. In practice, therefore, the voltage obtainable from an energy cell is less than the E value of the cell. Conversely, the voltage needed for electrolysis is greater than the E value of the reaction considered; the more the reactions at the electrodes depart from equilibrium conditions (reversibility), the greater is the extra voltage required to bring about the desired electrolytic reaction.

The difference between the theoretical E value of an oxidation-reduction process and the voltage needed in practice to bring about such a process in an electrolytic cell is generally called *overvoltage.* Many factors are responsible for the departure of electrode reactions from reversibility, two important considerations being ionic concentration (very high or low) in solution, and the nature and surface conditions of the electrodes. Depending on the reaction considered and on the experimental conditions, the overvoltage may vary from very small, to moderate, to very high. For example, the overvoltage for the reduction of $H^+_{(aq)}$ ions to form $H_{2(g)}$ at the surface of a platinum black electrode is only about 0.02 v, that is, +0.02 volts rather than 0.00 volts are required to reduce $H^+_{(aq)}$ to $H_{2(g)}$ (at 25°C, 1 atm, and $[H^+] = 1$ molar). On the other hand, for this same reaction at the same temperature, pressure, and concentration, +1.1 volts are required if the electrode consists of liquid mercury. Thus, we say that the cathodic evolution of hydrogen gas has negligible overvoltage (0.02 v) on a platinum black cathode, but a high overvoltage (1.10 v) on a mercury cathode.

23-4 Electrolysis Involving Active Electrodes

We have considered many examples of electrolytic reactions in which the electrodes themselves are inert—that is, they do not enter into chemical reaction with the ions of the solution, but serve only as a suitable medium for the transfer of electrons to or from the reactants in solution. Thus, in the electrolysis between platinum electrodes of aqueous solutions of HCl or NaCl or NaOH, one electrode (the cathode) simply serves to transfer electrons from the battery to ions or molecules in the solution, and the other electrode (the anode) simply serves to transfer electrons from ions or molecules in the solution to the battery. In some electrolytic processes, however, the electrodes themselves undergo a chemical reaction. We shall now consider two important examples.

ELECTROLYSIS WITH A MERCURY CATHODE

A few pages back, we found that the electrolysis of a water solution of sodium chloride between inert graphite electrodes produces H_2 gas at the cathode and Cl_2 gas at the anode. If we substitute a mercury cathode for the graphite cathode, however, sodium ions, Na^+, rather than hydrogen ions, H^+, are reduced at the cathode, and sodium atoms, Na, are formed. What factors determine this difference in the two electrolytic processes?

One is that a higher voltage, +1.1 volts, is required in practice to reduce H^+ ions at a mercury cathode than at a graphite cathode. In other words, H_2 gas has an appreciable overvoltage on a mercury cathode and consequently the reduction of H^+ ions to form H_2 on a mercury cathode becomes energetically more difficult than it is on a graphite or platinum black cathode. The second and very important factor is that sodium metal reacts with mercury metal to form an amalgam which does not react with water as long as a sufficient voltage is applied. The formation of this amalgam is a spontaneous, exothermic reaction:

$$x\ Na_{(s)} + y\ Hg_{(l)} \longrightarrow Na_xHg_{y(s)}$$

Because of the large negative value of ΔH for this reaction at 25°C and 1 atm (a favorable energy term), the reduction of $Na^+{}_{(aq)}$ ions at the mercury cathode, to form an amalgam, is energetically less difficult than the reduction of water molecules to form $H_{2(g)}$ and $OH^-{}_{(aq)}$ ions.

ELECTROLYSIS OF A $CuSO_4$ SOLUTION BETWEEN COPPER ELECTRODES

Let us consider another example, the electrolysis of a 1 molar aqueous solution of copper(II) sulfate, $CuSO_4$, between two *copper* electrodes. If we apply a sufficient voltage to these electrodes, so that current flows through the circuit, we observe that the copper anode gradually dissolves while at the cathode copper metal plates out of solution. For any interval of time considered, the loss of weight of the copper anode equals the gain of weight of the copper cathode. We can understand why this process takes place, rather than the electrolysis of water as for a solution of Na_2SO_4 between platinum electrodes, if we again consider the voltage required for each reaction.

THE REACTION AT THE ANODE. At the anode we might expect the oxidation of H_2O to form O_2 gas and $H^+{}_{(aq)}$ ions ($E_{neutral} = -0.82$ v), as in the electrolysis of Na_2SO_4. However, the oxidation of the copper metal itself to form Cu^{++} ions which then pass into solution is energetically less difficult under the specified conditions, and the following half-reaction occurs:

$$Cu_{(s)} \longrightarrow Cu^{++}{}_{(aq)} + 2\ e^- \qquad E^\circ = -0.34\ v$$

THE REACTION AT THE CATHODE. The copper(II) ions in solution are reduced at the copper cathode:

$$Cu^{++}{}_{(aq)} + 2\ e^- \longrightarrow Cu_{(s)} \qquad E^\circ = +\ 0.34\ v$$

Thus metallic copper is deposited on the surface of the copper cathode, just as metallic nickel is deposited on a platinum cathode in the electrolysis of a $NiCl_2$ solution (p. 509). The E° value of this half-reaction shows that the reduction of $Cu^{++}{}_{(aq)}$ ions to Cu metal ($E^\circ = +0.34$ v) is energetically less difficult, under the specified conditions of concentration, than the reduction of H_2O molecules to form $H_{2(g)}$ and OH^- ($E = -0.41$ v in neutral solution). Hence the reduction of $Cu^{++}{}_{(aq)}$ will occur, rather than that of H_2O. Thus, during the electrolysis of a solution of $CuSO_4$ between copper electrodes the following reactions take place: at the anode, Cu atoms lose electrons and enter the solution as $Cu^{++}{}_{(aq)}$ ions, and simultaneously at the cathode $Cu^{++}{}_{(aq)}$ ions take on electrons and are discharged as copper atoms. The net result of these simultaneous reactions is that copper metal is transferred from the anode to the cathode, while the original concentration of $Cu^{++}{}_{(aq)}$ ions in the solution remains constant. In general, the ions of all metals whose oxidation potentials are more negative than that of hydrogen under similar conditions—for example Cu^{++} and Ag^+ ions—are more likely to be reduced at the cathode of an electrolytic cell than are the water molecules. If more than one kind of reducible ion is present (e.g., both Cu^{++} and Ag^+), the ion of the metal which has the greater negative oxidation potential (Ag^+ in this case) is reduced preferentially.

23-5 Summary of the Electrolysis of Solutions

For convenience, we can summarize the electrolysis of solutions under the following headings.

THE FLOW OF ELECTRONS OUTSIDE THE SOLUTION. Outside the solution, the electrons flow from the negative terminal of the battery to the electrode of the cell connected to this terminal (the cathode), and from the other electrode of the cell (the anode) back to the positive terminal of the battery.

THE FLOW OF IONS WITHIN THE SOLUTION. Within the solution the positive ions tend to migrate toward the cathode, and the negative ions tend to migrate toward the anode. In some cases the attraction of the ions of one sign which accumulate in the vicinity of an electrode may impede the movement of oppositely charged ions toward the other electrode.

THE CONDUCTIVITY OF THE SOLUTION. During an electrolytic process, there is a continuous flow of electrons in the metallic circuit outside the electrolytic cell, from the cathode to the anode. Within the electrolytic cell, electrons are given up to one electrode (the anode) by ions or molecules of the solution in contact with it, while an equal number of electrons is simultaneously taken on from the cathode by ions or molecules of the solutions in contact with it. And the ions which react at each electrode are continuously replaced by other ions arriving at the electrode both by migration under the influence of the electric field of the electrodes themselves, and by diffusion (random movement) through the solution. Thus *the "electrical conductivity" of a solution arises from the cathode and anode reactions and also from the migration and diffusion of ions through the solution.*

THE REACTION AT THE CATHODE. An accumulation of electrons builds up on the cathode since it is connected to the negative terminal of the battery. During electrolysis, therefore, the reaction that takes place removes these electrons. In other words, a reduction reaction must occur at the cathode. Surrounding the negatively charged electrode are positive ions that have migrated through the solution and neutral water molecules. If the potential for the reduction of the metal ions is lower than the potential for the reduction of water under the same conditions, the positive ions can take on electrons and be discharged. Alternatively, if the reduction of water is energetically less difficult, the water molecules can take on electrons to form H_2 gas and OH^- ions. Or, if the potentials of these two reduction reactions are close in value, both reactions may take place simultaneously. These reactions can be represented as follows:

$$M^{++} + 2\ e^- \longrightarrow M$$
$$2\ H_2O + 2\ e^- \longrightarrow H_2 + 2\ OH^-$$

Which reaction will predominate depends on: (1) the tendency of the metal ions to be reduced compared with the tendency of the water molecules to be reduced, (2) the relative concentrations of the metal ions and the water molecules, and (3) the nature of the cathode (mercury or platinum, for example).

THE REACTION AT THE ANODE. Since the positive ions or molecules in the solution take on electrons from the cathode, some reaction must take place at the anode to give up an equal number of electrons, thus completing the flow back to the battery. In other words, an oxidation reaction must take place at the anode. Surrounding the positively charged anode are negative ions that have migrated through the solution and neutral water molecules. The following reactions are possible at the anode: (1) electrons may be given up by the negative ions in solution to form neutral atoms, (2) water molecules may be oxidized to produce oxygen gas and hydrogen ions, and (3) if the anode is a reactive metal, atoms of the anode may give up electrons and enter the solution as positive ions. Which of these reactions will occur, or predominate, depends again on the relative values of their potentials, under the specified experimental conditions. The reaction requiring the lower applied potential (the reaction energetically least difficult) is the one that will preferentially take place. Only reactions (1) and (2) take place in the presence of inert electrodes. Reaction (3) occurs only if the metallic anode is reactive. These three reactions can be represented by the following equations, where X^- represents a halide ion, and M represents a reactive metal anode:

1. $2\ X^- \longrightarrow X_2 + 2\ e^-$
2. $2\ H_2O \longrightarrow O_2 + 4\ H^+ + 4\ e^-$
3. $M \longrightarrow M^{++} + 2\ e^-$

In some cases it is possible that two of these reactions, or all three, may take place simultaneously, depending on the concentration of the solution surrounding the anode and on the other experimental conditions.

23-6 Electrolysis of Molten Ionic Compounds

In the electrolytic cell schematically shown in Fig. 23-4, solid sodium chloride is placed between two (unreactive) graphite electrodes, and the electrodes are joined by a metallic conductor connected to a switch, a battery, and a light bulb. When the switch is closed, the light bulb fails to glow even if the applied voltage is quite high, indicating that no current is flowing through the circuit. Clearly, solid sodium chloride is a non-conductor of electricity. In fact, as we know, in the crystalline state the ions that make up this compound are not free to migrate, nor are there mobile electrons to conduct an electric current. *In general, dry ionic solids are rather good insulators.* But if we heat the solid sodium chloride sufficiently, it becomes *molten* (at 801°C), and then important changes take place under the influence of an applied voltage. When we close the switch the lamp glows brightly and we observe the formation of bubbles of Cl_2 gas at the anode and molten sodium metal at the cathode. For any period of time we may consider, the number of moles of Cl_2 gas formed at the anode is equal to one-half the number of moles of Na metal formed at the cathode. So the net result of the reaction is the decomposition—the electrolysis—of molten sodium chloride to form Na metal and Cl_2 gas:

$$2\ NaCl_{(l)} \xrightarrow[\text{current}]{\text{electric}} 2\ Na_{(l)} + Cl_{2(g)}$$

The explanation of the electrolysis of molten sodium chloride is similar to that of the electrolysis of an ionic compound in solution, except that there are no water molecules present so the reactions at the electrodes involve only the ions of the compound. Molten sodium chloride contains positive sodium ions, Na^+, and negative chloride ions, Cl^-, which move about with considerable freedom. Under the influence of the electric field generated by the oppositely charged electrodes, the positive ions, Na^+, tend to migrate to the negative electrode where they are reduced to Na metal, and the negative ions, Cl^-, tend to migrate to the positive electrode where they are oxidized to Cl_2 gas. The electrolysis of molten sodium chloride is used commercially to obtain metallic sodium (see Chapter 30).

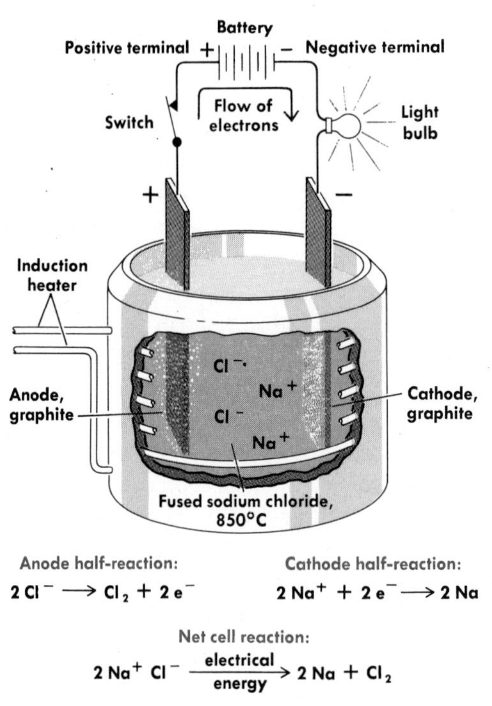

FIGURE 23-4 The electrolysis of molten sodium chloride.

REACTION AT THE ANODE. OXIDATION PROCESS. At the positive electrode the Cl^- ions are reduced to form chlorine atoms, Cl. Thus, $Cl^- \longrightarrow Cl$ (on anode) $+ e^-$. These neutral chlorine atoms then combine to form stable diatomic molecules of chlorine, Cl_2, which escape as gas bubbles: $2\ Cl$ (on anode) $\longrightarrow Cl_2$.

REACTION AT THE CATHODE. REDUCTION PROCESS. The Na^+ ions take on electrons from the negative electrode to form atoms of sodium metal: $Na^+ + e^- \longrightarrow Na$. As some positive Na^+ ions are reduced to Na metal at the cathode, more positive Na^+ ions migrate in from the surrounding melt to replace them. The net cell reaction is then obtained as usual by adding the two electrode half-reactions:

$$\begin{array}{lll} \textit{Anode half-reaction:} & 2\ Cl^- & \longrightarrow Cl_2 + 2\ e^- \\ \textit{Cathode half-reaction:} & 2\ Na^+ + 2\ e^- & \longrightarrow 2\ Na \\ \hline \textit{Net cell reaction:} & 2\ Na^+ + 2\ Cl^- & \xrightarrow[\text{energy}]{\text{electrical}} 2\ Na + Cl_2 \end{array}$$

Thus, the electrolysis of molten sodium chloride, Na^+Cl^-, between inert electrodes forms molten sodium metal at the cathode and chlorine gas at the anode. Again, as for the electrolysis of solutions, the instant the current is turned off, the decomposition stops. In other words, the decomposition is not spontaneous and in fact requires electrical energy.

23-7 The Amount of Current and the Quantity of Material Deposited

So far in this chapter, we have been considering in a descriptive way the electrolysis of compounds in water solution or in the molten state. We have described the chemical reactions that take place at the electrodes and the movement of ions in a solution.

Now we shall investigate the *quantitative* relationship between the amount of current that is "passed through" an electrolytic solution and the weights of material that is oxidized and reduced at the electrodes. For example, what quantity of electricity is required to form 1 mole of metallic silver, Ag, from the electrolysis of a solution of silver nitrate, $AgNO_3$? This reduction reaction is expressed as follows:

Cathode half-reaction: $Ag^+_{(aq)} + 1\ e^- \longrightarrow Ag_{(s)}$

$Ag^+_{(aq)}$	$1\ e^-$	$Ag_{(s)}$
1 mole Ag^+ ion (6.02×10^{23} ions)	1 mole electrons (6.02×10^{23} electrons)	1 mole Ag atoms (6.02×10^{23} atoms)

One mole of silver nitrate, $Ag^+NO_3^-$, contains 6.02×10^{23} silver ions; since each Ag^+ ion requires one electron to be reduced to an atom of metallic silver, Ag, 6.02×10^{23} electrons are required to reduce *all* (6.02×10^{23}) the Ag^+ ions present in one mole of silver nitrate to atoms of metallic silver. These electrons must be supplied to the cathode, where the reduction of the Ag^+ ions takes place. As we know, the quantity of electrical charge in 1 mole of electrons—6.02×10^{23} electrons—is called a *faraday.**

MEASURING ELECTRICAL CURRENT UNITS

We already know that a current of electricity is a flow of electrons—the greater the rate at which the electrons flow, the greater the current. For example, consider two metal wires, A and B, through which different currents are flowing, the current in A being twice that in B. During a given period of time the number of electrons passing through A is twice the number of electrons passing through B. In other words, the *total* number of electrons that pass through a wire depends on *both* the current *and* the time during which the current flows. Thus the flow of electrons through a wire is somewhat analogous to the flow of water through a pipe. For example, the *total* quantity of water flowing through a pipe depends on *both* (1) the *rate* at which the water flows *and* (2) the *length of time it flows.* This quantity of water may be expressed in gallons, grams, milliliters, or in any other convenient unit. For comparison with electrical flow expressed in number of moles of electrons, a convenient unit in which to express the flow of water is the number of moles of molecules. If water flows through a pipe at the rate of 1 mole (18.016 g or about 18 ml) per second, then the number of moles that flow through in 10 hours may be calculated as follows:

$$\frac{1 \text{ mole of molecules}}{1 \cancel{\text{sec}}} \times \frac{60 \cancel{\text{sec}}}{1 \cancel{\text{min}}} \times \frac{60 \cancel{\text{min}}}{1 \cancel{\text{hr}}} \times 10 \cancel{\text{hr}}$$
$$= 3.6 \times 10^4 \text{ moles of molecules (about 650 liters)}$$

Similarly, if electrons flow through a wire at the rate of 1 mole of electrons per second, then the number of electrons that flow through in 10 hours is:

$$\frac{1 \text{ mole of electrons}}{1 \cancel{\text{sec}}} \times \frac{60 \cancel{\text{sec}}}{1 \cancel{\text{min}}} \times \frac{60 \cancel{\text{min}}}{1 \cancel{\text{hr}}} \times 10 \cancel{\text{hr}}$$
$$= 3.6 \times 10^4 \text{ moles of electrons} = 3.6 \times 10^4 \text{ faraday}$$

* The faraday is often also defined, on an experimental basis, as the quantity of electricity needed to deposit 6.02×10^{23} atoms (107.88 g) of metallic silver.

Thus, if we know the number of electrons that pass through a wire in a second, we can easily calculate the total number of electrons (that is, the quantity of electricity) that pass through the wire in any given time period.

The customary unit for expressing quantities of electricity is the *coulomb.* One faraday—that is, the quantity of electricity in 1 mole of electrons—is equal to 96,500* coulombs. The coulomb unit was named in honor of a French scientist, Charles Coulomb (1736–1806), who in 1785 obtained direct experimental confirmation of the law of force between electric charges. The faraday unit was named for an Englishman, Michael Faraday (1791–1867), who made the first quantitative study of electrolysis in 1832 and devised the names *ion, anode,* and *cathode.* The *rate* of flow of electricity is commonly expressed in units of *ampere* (amp), named after a French mathematician and physicist, André Marie Ampère (1775–1836). One ampere represents a rate of flow of 1 coulomb per second. Thus, the number of electrons equal to 1 coulomb can be calculated as follows:

$$\frac{1 \text{ mole of electrons}}{96{,}500 \text{ coulombs}} = \frac{6.02 \times 10^{23} \text{ electrons}}{96.5 \times 10^{3} \text{ coulombs}} = \frac{6.24 \times 10^{18} \text{ electrons}}{1 \text{ coulomb}}$$

The rate of flow of electricity is usually measured by means of an instrument called an *ammeter.* A reading of 1 amp means that in every second 1 coulomb, or 6.24×10^{18} electrons, are passing through the circuit.

LAWS OF FARADAY

In 1832 Faraday discovered two laws of fundamental importance concerning the relationship between the quantity of electricity "passed through" a solution and the quantity of material formed at the electrodes.

Faraday's first law of electrolysis states: *The weights of substances formed at an electrode during electrolysis are directly proportional to the quantity of electricity that passes through the electrolyte solution* (or melt). For example, if 1 mole of electrons (6.02×10^{23} electrons) deposits 107.88 g of silver (1 mole), then 2 moles of electrons ($2 \times 6.02 \times 10^{23}$ electrons) will deposit 2×107.88 g of silver (2 mole), and $\frac{1}{2}$ mole of electrons ($\frac{1}{2} \times 6.02 \times 10^{23}$ electrons) will deposit $\frac{1}{2} \times 107.88$ g of silver ($\frac{1}{2}$ mole), and so on.

Faraday's second law of electrolysis states: *The weights of different substances formed by the passage of the same quantity of electricity are proportional to the equivalent weight of each substance.*

In this case the equivalent weight is defined as the formula weight (atomic weight in the case of elements) divided by the number of electrons involved in the electrolysis per each formula of substance. Here is an illustration. If a given amount of electricity causes 22.99 g (1 eq wt) of sodium metal, Na, to form in the electrolysis of molten Na^+Cl^-, this same quantity of electricity will also cause $63.54/2 = 31.77$ g (1 eq wt) of copper metal, Cu, to form from a solution containing Cu^{++} ions; $26.98/3 = 8.99$ g (1 eq wt) of aluminum metal, Al, from a melt of Al_2O_3 containing Al^{+++} ions, and $106.4/6 = 17.73$ g of $NaClO_3$ from a solution of NaCl, according to the reaction: $NaCl + 3\ H_2O \longrightarrow NaClO_3 + 6\ H^+ + 6\ e^-$.

ILLUSTRATIVE PROBLEMS

PROBLEM. Calculate the number of coulombs of electricity that pass through a circuit when 5.0 amp flow for 2.0 hours.

* The latest most accurate value of the Faraday is 96,490 (±2.4) coulombs, but we shall round it off to 96,500 coulombs, and express it as 9.65×10^3 coulombs.

SOLUTION.

$$5.0 \text{ amp} \times \frac{60 \text{ sec}}{1 \cancel{\text{min}}} \times \frac{60 \cancel{\text{min}}}{1 \cancel{\text{hr}}} \times 2.0 \cancel{\text{hr}} = 3.6 \times 10^4 \text{ amp sec} = 3.6 \times 10^4 \text{ coulombs}$$

PROBLEM. Calculate the weight of copper deposited by the flow of 24,125 coulombs of electricity through a solution of copper(II) sulfate.

SOLUTION.

$$\frac{63.54}{2} = \text{eq wt of copper in copper(II) sulfate, } CuSO_4$$

$$\frac{\frac{63.54}{2} \text{ g Cu}}{9.65 \times 10^4 \cancel{\text{coulombs}}} \times 24{,}125 \cancel{\text{coulombs}} = 7.94 \text{ g Cu}$$

PROBLEM. Calculate the number of coulombs required to liberate (a) 22.4 l. of H_2 at 0°C and 1 atm, (b) 44.8 l. of O_2 at 0°C and 1 atm, (c) 27.42 g of Fe from a Fe^{+++} ion solution.

SOLUTION. One faraday, 9.65×10^4 coulombs, liberates 1.00 eq wt of an element. (a) One equivalent weight of hydrogen is 1.01 g, and at 0°C and 1 atm, 1.01 g of hydrogen gas occupies a volume of:

$$\frac{22.4 \text{ l. } H_2}{2.02 \cancel{\text{g } H_2}} \times 1.01 \cancel{\text{g } H_2} = 11.2 \text{ l. } H_2$$

$$\frac{9.65 \times 10^4 \text{ coulombs}}{11.2 \cancel{\text{l. } H_2}} \times 22.4 \cancel{\text{l. } H_2} = 1.93 \times 10^5 \text{ coulombs}$$

(b) One equivalent weight of oxygen is 8.00 g, and at 0°C and 1 atm, 8.00 g of oxygen occupy a volume of:

$$\frac{22.4 \text{ l. } O_2}{32.0 \cancel{\text{g } O_2}} \times 8.00 \cancel{\text{g } O_2} = 5.60 \text{ l. } O_2$$

$$\frac{9.65 \times 10^4 \text{ coulombs}}{5.60 \cancel{\text{l. } O_2}} \times 44.8 \cancel{\text{l. } O_2} = 7.72 \times 10^5 \text{ coulombs}$$

(c) One gram equivalent weight of Fe in a Fe^{+++} solution is $\frac{55.85 \text{ g}}{3}$.

$$\frac{9.65 \times 10^4 \text{ coulombs}}{\frac{55.85 \cancel{\text{g}}}{3}} \times 27.42 \cancel{\text{g}} = 1.45 \times 10^5 \text{ coulombs}$$

PROBLEM. A current of 0.40 amp flows for 2.5 hr through a solution of (a) $NiCl_2$, (b) H_2SO_4. Calculate the weight or volumes at 0°C and 1 atm of the products formed at the electrodes.

SOLUTION.

$$0.40 \text{ amp} \times 2.5 \cancel{\text{hr}} \times \frac{60 \cancel{\text{min}}}{1 \cancel{\text{hr}}} \times \frac{60 \text{ sec}}{1 \cancel{\text{min}}} = 3.6 \times 10^3 \text{ coulombs}$$

Nickel metal is deposited at the cathode.

(a)

$$\frac{58.71}{2} \text{ g Ni} = \text{equivalent weight of Ni in } NiCl_2 \text{ solution.}$$

$$\frac{\frac{58.71}{2} \text{ g Ni}}{9.65 \times 10^4 \cancel{\text{coulombs}}} \times 3.6 \times 10^3 \cancel{\text{coulombs}} = 1.10 \text{ g Ni}$$

Chlorine gas is liberated at the anode.

The equivalent weight of chlorine, 35.46 g, occupies a volume of 11.2 l. at 0°C and 1 atm.

$$\frac{11.2 \text{ l. } Cl_2}{9.65 \times 10^4 \cancel{\text{coulombs}}} \times 3.6 \times 10^3 \cancel{\text{coulombs}} = 0.418 \text{ l. } Cl_2 \text{ (at 0°C and 1 atm)}$$

(b) H_2 gas is liberated at the cathode.

$$\frac{11.2 \text{ l. } H_2}{9.65 \times 10^4 \text{ coulombs}} \times 3.6 \times 10^3 \text{ coulombs} = 0.418 \text{ l. } H_2 \text{ (at } 0°\text{C and 1 atm)}$$

O_2 gas is liberated at the anode.

$$\frac{5.60 \text{ l. } O_2}{9.65 \times 10^4 \text{ coulombs}} \times 3.6 \times 10^3 \text{ coulombs} = 0.209 \text{ l. } O_2 \text{ (at } 0°\text{C and 1 atm)}$$

Exercises

23-1 Explain the difference between the conduction of an electric current in a metal wire and in an electrolytic cell.

23-2 (a) What individual species are present in (1) solid sugar, (2) solid sodium chloride? (b) Solid sugar is a non-conductor of electric current and solid sodium chloride is in effect a non-conductor of electric current. Explain why *molten* sugar is a non-conductor of electric current, but *molten* sodium chloride is an excellent conductor.

23-3 Hydrogen chloride gas is dissolved in water and the resulting solution is electrolyzed between inert electrodes. (a) Explain any visible changes that take place at the electrodes during the electrolysis. (b) Explain by equations the reactions that take place at the anode and cathode. (c) Explain the electrode reactions. (d) Write the net equation of the electrolysis.

23-4 Explain by equations: (a) the cathode reaction, (b) the anode reaction, and (c) the net reaction, of the electrolysis of a water solution of sodium sulfate between inert electrodes. (d) Explain any changes in acidity or basicity at the electrodes.

23-5 An aqueous solution of nickel(II) sulfate is electrolyzed under standard conditions between inert electrodes. Use Table 22-1 to arrive at the following: (a) the anode half-reaction; (b) the cathode half-reaction; (c) the net equation for the electrolytic reaction; (d) the minimum voltage which would have to be applied in order that electrolysis may occur.

23-6 An aqueous solution of nickel(II) chloride is made 1 molar in hydrogen ions, H^+, by the addition of a strong acid and electrolyzed between inert electrodes. What would you expect the principal product at the cathode to be? Explain your answer.

23-7 A water solution of copper(II) bromide is electrolyzed between inert electrodes. Explain (a) the flow of electrons outside the solution, (b) the migration of ions within the solution, (c) the reactions at the electrodes, and (d) the net reaction of the electrolysis.

23-8 A solution of sodium hydroxide is electrolyzed between inert electrodes. (a) Write equations for the oxidation and reduction reactions that take place at the electrodes. (b) Give the net reaction of the electrolysis.

23-9 A water solution of copper(II) sulfate is electrolyzed between copper electrodes. (a) Write equations for the oxidation and reduction reactions that take place. (b) What is the over-all effect of the electrolysis? (c) Compare and contrast this electrolysis with the electrolysis of a copper(II) sulfate solution employing inert platinum electrodes.

23-10 *Molten* potassium chloride is electrolyzed between inert platinum electrodes. Explain (a) the flow of electrons outside the electrolytic cell, (b) the migration of ions within the electrolyte, (c) the reactions of the electrodes. Write the equation for the electrolysis.

23-11 Explain (a) the migration of ions in molten sodium bromide, and (b) the reactions at the cathode and anode when *molten* sodium bromide is electrolyzed between inert electrodes.

Problems

23-1 An electric current passing through a solution of $CuSO_4$ liberates 15.9 g of metallic copper. How many grams of silver can be liberated by the same amount of current?

PROBLEMS

23-2 When an aqueous solution of $ZnSO_4$ is electrolyzed, the following reaction takes place: $2\ ZnSO_4 + 2\ H_2O \longrightarrow 2\ Zn + 2\ H_2SO_4 + O_2$. If 13 g of zinc are plated out, what weight of oxygen gas is liberated simultaneously? What volume of oxygen, measured at 25°C and 1 atm, is evolved?

23-3 Two faradays of electricity are passed through a dilute solution of H_2SO_4. Calculate the weights of the materials produced at the anode and cathode, assuming that both electrodes are inert.

23-4 How many coulombs of electricity are (a) involved when 0.40 amp flows for 2.0 hr, (b) required to liberate 11.2 l. of H_2 gas at 25°C and 1 atm, (c) required to liberate 11.2 l. of O_2 gas at 25°C and 1 atm, (d) required to liberate 22.4 l. of Cl_2 at 25°C and 1 atm, (e) required to deposit 0.10 mole of Ag, (f) required to deposit 1.0 mole of Fe from (1) a Fe^{++} solution and (2) a Fe^{+++} solution?

23-5 A solution of copper(II) sulfate is electrolyzed between inert electrodes. (a) How many minutes must a current of 2.6 amp flow to deposit 6.0 g of Cu metal? (b) What current must flow for 1.5 hr to deposit 4.8 g of Cu metal?

23-6 If an electric current, flowing for a certain time, plates out 5.4 g of silver from a solution of $AgNO_3$, how many grams of lead will the same current deposit during an equal time period from a solution of lead nitrate, $Pb(NO_3)_2$?

23-7 Equal quantities of electricity are passed successively through (a) molten aluminum chloride, (b) dilute sulfuric acid, (c) hydrochloric acid, and (d) an aqueous solution of copper(II) sulfate. If 11.2 l. of chlorine at 25°C and 1 atm are liberated from solution (a), calculate the grams of hydrogen evolved from solution (b), the volume of hydrogen at 25°C and 1 atm evolved from solution (c), and the grams of copper plated out from solution (d).

23-7 Equal quantities of electricity are passed successively through (a) molten aluminum chloride, (b) dilute sulfuric acid, (c) hydrochloric acid, and (d) an aqueous solution of copper(II) sulfate. If 11.2 l. of chlorine at 25°C and 1 atm are liberated from solution (a), calculate the grams of hydrogen evolved from solution (b), the volume of hydrogen at 25°C and 1 atm evolved from solution (c), and the grams of copper plated out from solution (d).

23-8 A current of 0.040 amp passed for a given time through a solution of silver nitrate deposits 0.16 g of silver. Calculate the volume of H_2 at 25°C and 1 atm that would be liberated from an aqueous KCl solution by the same quantity of electricity.

23-9 In the electrolysis of an aqueous solution of copper(II) sulfate, what weight of copper is deposited at the cathode if 11.2 l. of oxygen at 25°C and 1 atm are evolved at the anode?

23-10 How many liters of (a) H_2, (b) O_2, at 782 torr and 20°C, are liberated by 0.60 amp flowing for 2.1 hr through a dilute aqueous solution of H_2SO_4?

EQUILIBRIUM: I

24

In the preceding chapters, we have often referred to systems in a state of equilibrium. We have seen that any system, in which a physical process or a chemical reaction can occur spontaneously, tends to change itself so as to approach a final state of equilibrium. And we have seen that a system is in equilibrium when its free energy—its capacity to do useful work—has the minimum value possible under the specified conditions. Familiar examples of spontaneous transformations that reach a state of equilibrium are the transfer of heat from a warmer object to a colder object, the effusion of a gas from a container under high pressure when a valve is opened, and the ionization of a weak acid such as acetic acid in aqueous solution.

Now we want to look at equilibrium more systematically. In this chapter we shall consider chemical equilibrium in a qualitative way, focusing on several examples. In the next chapter we shall study the quantitative laws that govern chemical equilibrium.

24-1 Equilibrium in Chemical Reactions

Let us consider a specific example of a reaction that proceeds spontaneously until the system reaches equilibrium conditions. A mixture of 1 mole of H_2 gas and 1 mole of I_2 gas in a closed container of fixed volume at a definite temperature (a temperature high enough to insure that all the iodine is in the gaseous state) reacts to form the gas HI. As soon as a sufficient concentration of HI gas has built up, the reverse reaction—the decomposition of $HI_{(g)}$ to form $H_{2(g)}$ and $I_{2(g)}$—also begins. In effect, two reactions are taking place *at the same time* in our system:

$$H_{2(g)} + I_{2(g)} \longrightarrow 2\ HI_{(g)}$$
$$2\ HI_{(g)} \longrightarrow H_{2(g)} + I_{2(g)}$$

It is customary to represent two such reactions by means of a single equation with arrows pointing in both directions:

$$H_{2(g)} + I_{2(g)} \rightleftharpoons 2\ HI_{(g)}$$

Eventually the system will attain a state of equilibrium in which the concentrations of $H_{2(g)}$, $I_{2(g)}$, and $HI_{(g)}$ will each reach a constant, definite value for these particular experimental conditions, and the concentration of each substance will remain constant indefinitely. *Whenever a constant concentration is reached for each substance involved in a reaction, the system is in a state of equilibrium.* A particular state of equilibrium, determined by a particular set of conditions, is known as a *position* of equilibrium.

Suppose that we had started with 2 moles of $HI_{(g)}$ instead of 1 mole of $H_{2(g)}$ and $I_{2(g)}$. If we used a container of the same fixed volume and at the same temperature, we would find when equilibrium is established this system also consists of the same gases, H_2, I_2 and HI, present in the same concentrations as in the first case. Thus, the same final state of equilibrium is attained whether we start out with an initial state consisting of 1 mole of $H_{2(g)}$ and 1 mole of $I_{2(g)}$, or consisting of 2 moles of $HI_{(g)}$ (given the same total volume and at the same temperature).

Although the concentration of each substance in the equilibrium mixture remains constant, even after equilibrium is established, both reactions ($H_2 + I_2 \longrightarrow 2\ HI$, and $2\ HI \longrightarrow H_2 + I_2$) continue to take place. But the rate at which H_2 reacts with I_2 to form HI is exactly equal to the rate at which HI reacts to form H_2 and I_2. So the quantities of H_2, I_2, and HI used up in any interval of time are *exactly equal* to the quantities re-formed in the same interval of time, and there is no *net* change of the individual concentrations. Thus, we see that chemical equilibrium has a dynamic character—that is, in a system in chemical equilibrium both the forward and the reverse reactions are equally permitted and occur at the same rate. We have already met a similar situation in the equilibrium between solute and solvent in saturated solutions or the equilibrium between a metal plate and a solution of its cations in an open-circuit half-cell.

If we change in some way the conditions of a system in chemical equilibrium, the system will automatically adjust itself to the new situation and will establish a *new* position of equilibrium. The concentrations of reactants and products will be different, but they will remain constant so long as the new conditions remain unchanged. When a system passes from one state of equilibrium to another, as a result of a change in conditions, we say it has "shifted its position of equilibrium."

24-2 Principle of Le Chatelier

If we know the position of equilibrium for a chemical system under a specified set of conditions (concentrations, temperature, and pressure), we can estimate qualitatively, even without experimentation, the new equilibrium position that will result from any specific change in the conditions. To determine such shifts, we use the *principle of Le Chatelier*, named after the French scientist Henri Louis Le Chatelier (1850–1936). From his studies of thermodynamics, Le Chatelier formulated this very general principle: *If we change the conditions under which a system exists in equilibrium, the system will shift its equilibrium position in a way that will reduce in part the effect of the imposed (applied) change.* Here is another way of stating Le Chatelier's principle: If we add or remove either some of a substance (or substances) or some energy in any form from a system which is in equilibrium and the equilibrium of the system is thereby disturbed, the system will spontaneously readjust itself by shifting its equilibrium in the direction that will tend to offset in part the imposed disturbance. Le Chatelier's principle, which we have already encountered in Chapter 23, is very helpful in predicting qualitatively the effect of various changes of conditions on the equilibrium state of a certain system. We shall now consider in detail some of the most common applications of Le Chatelier's principle.

THE EFFECT OF CONCENTRATION CHANGES ON EQUILIBRIUM

When a system is in equilibrium at a specified temperature and pressure, the concentration of each component of the system has a fixed constant value. Le Chatelier's principle tells us that if we *add* to a system in equilibrium a certain amount of one of the components so that its concentration *increases* above its initial equilibrium value, the system will undergo that reaction or change of state which results in a subsequent *decrease* of the concentration of that component. Conversely, if we *remove* one of the components so that its concentration *decreases* below its original equilibrium value, the system undergoes that reaction or change of state which results in a subsequent *increase* of the concentration of that component. As an illustration, let us consider the reaction between carbon dioxide gas and hydrogen gas that produces water vapor and carbon monoxide gas:

$$CO_{2(g)} + H_{2(g)} \rightleftharpoons H_2O_{(g)} + CO_{(g)}$$

Assume that we have a closed cylinder containing these four gases at equilibrium at a constant temperature and pressure. Now we suddenly introduce additional CO_2 into the cylinder, thereby increasing its concentration. Le Chatelier's principle tells us that the system will change in such a way as to remove some of the added CO_2. The only way that some CO_2 can be removed from the closed container is by reacting chemically with H_2 to form H_2O and CO, as shown above by the equation for the forward reaction. Thus, as a result of adding more CO_2, the concentration of H_2 is decreased and the concentration of H_2O and CO is increased, and a new position of equilibrium is established. That is, at the new equilibrium position, more of the H_2 will have reacted with CO_2 to produce H_2O and CO than at the original equilibrium position.

At the new position of equilibrium, then, we would expect to find (and, indeed, we do find by experiment) that: (1) The quantity of the H_2 is less than it was at the original equilibrium position because more H_2 will have reacted with the CO_2. (2) The quantity of CO_2 present is greater than the initial quantity, simply because we have added more CO_2 to the cylinder. But the increase in the quantity of CO_2 is less than the amount we actually added, because some of it has reacted with the H_2. (3) The quantity of both the H_2O and the CO has increased.

When a system shifts the position of its equilibrium in response to a change in conditions, we usually say that the shift has been either "to the left" or "to the right" with regard to the chemical equation that describes the system. In this example, $CO_{2(g)} + H_{2(g)} \rightleftharpoons H_2O_{(g)} + CO_{(g)}$, the introduction of additional CO_2 into the system increases the concentration of the products, H_2O and CO, which are written at the right of the equation. Consequently, this change in equilibrium position is described as a "shift to the right."

Now, what happens if we remove some of the water from the cylinder, for example by means of a dehydrating agent such as P_4O_{10}? The system will readjust itself so as to replace part of the water that has been removed, and more CO_2 will then react with H_2 to form H_2O—and more CO, of course—as shown by the forward equation $CO_2 + H_2 \longrightarrow H_2O + CO$. At the new position of equilibrium there will be a higher concentration of CO, and a lower concentration of CO_2 and H_2 (and, of course, a lower concentration of H_2O) than in the original equilibrium system. Here, again we find that the equilibrium has shifted to the right. We can say, then, that either *an increase in the concentration of one of the reactants or a decrease in the concentration of one of the products will shift the equilibrium to the right.* Conversely, either *a decrease in the concentration of one of the reactants or an increase in the concentration of one of the products will shift the equilibrium to the left.*

THE EFFECT OF TEMPERATURE CHANGES ON EQUILIBRIUM

Temperature is one condition that affects the position of the equilibrium of most systems. Consequently, a change in temperature, caused either by supplying heat to the system, or by removing it, generally leads to a shift in the equilibrium position.

Le Chatelier's principle tells us that if a system is in equilibrium at a certain temperature, supplying heat to the system—that is, raising its temperature—will favor that reaction or change in state which is accompanied by the *absorption* of heat. Conversely, a *lowering* of the temperature will favor that reaction or change in state which is accompanied by the *evolution* of heat. That is, an increase in temperature will favor the endothermic process, whereas a decrease in temperature will favor the exothermic process.

EFFECT OF TEMPERATURE CHANGES ON SOLUBILITY

As a first illustrative example, let us consider the recrystallization of a salt, a process we have already discussed in Chapter 18. If we consider a salt such as potassium nitrate, $K^+NO_3^-$, the dissolution process is endothermic:

$$\text{Salt}_{(s)} \xrightleftharpoons{\text{excess water}} \text{Salt}_{(aq)} \quad \begin{cases} \Delta H \text{ forward process} = \text{positive} \\ \Delta H \text{ reverse process} = \text{negative} \end{cases}$$

In this case Le Chatelier's principle tells us that if we have a saturated (equilibrium) solution of the salt in water at a given temperature, a rise in temperature favors further dissolution of the salt, since such a process is accompanied by the absorption of heat. Conversely, cooling will favor the formation of some crystals of the salt because the crystallization process is exothermic. Thus, the solubility of this salt must increase with increasing temperature. You will recall that this is indeed the case for potassium nitrate, $K^+NO_3^-$ (Fig. 18-4, p. 409). And, as we have seen, the most common method for recrystallizing a salt whose solubility increases with increasing temperature is to dissolve the salt in a solvent at a high temperature and then to cool the solution until crystals of the salt separate.

EFFECT OF TEMPERATURE CHANGES ON CHEMICAL EQUILIBRIUM

In a chemical reaction that involves an enthalpy change, we can shift the position of the equilibrium either by adding heat to or by removing heat from the system. Take the equilibrium of carbon monoxide, oxygen, and carbon dioxide in the gaseous state at a specified constant temperature:

$$2\ CO_{(g)} + O_{2(g)} \rightleftharpoons 2\ CO_{2(g)} \quad \begin{cases} \Delta H_{\text{forward reaction}} = \text{negative} \\ \Delta H_{\text{reverse reaction}} = \text{positive} \end{cases}$$

At this temperature a certain constant concentration of all three substances, CO, O_2 and CO_2, will be present at equilibrium. If we withdraw heat energy and maintain the system at this new lower temperature, the system will readjust itself so as to offset the loss of heat energy. More of the CO and O_2 molecules will react to form more CO_2 molecules, thus liberating heat since the forward reaction is exothermic ($2\ CO + O_2 \longrightarrow 2\ CO_2$; $\Delta H =$ negative). In other words, by lowering the temperature, we shift the original position of the equilibrium to the right, until a new position of equilibrium is established.

If, on the other hand, we supply heat and maintain the system at the new higher temperature, the system will tend to do what it can to remove some of the added heat energy. More CO_2 molecules will decompose to form more CO and O_2 molecules, thus taking on heat energy because the reverse reaction is endothermic ($2\ CO + O_2 \longleftarrow 2\ CO_2$; ΔH = positive). In short, the original position of the equilibrium is shifted to the left, and a new position of equilibrium is established.

EFFECT OF PRESSURE CHANGES ON EQUILIBRIUM

In general, for any reaction in which a shift in the equilibrium position of the system produces a change in volume, an alteration in pressure will bring about a shift in the equilibrium.

As an illustration, let us consider the effect of a change in pressure on the equilibrium of gaseous NO_2 with gaseous N_2O_4, the equation for which is $2\ NO_2 \rightleftharpoons N_2O_4$. We'll assume that an equilibrium mixture of NO_2 and N_2O_4 is enclosed in a cylindrical vessel closed by a movable piston, under a pressure of 1 atm and at a constant temperature. If we increase the pressure by decreasing the volume of the container, the system will tend to do what it can to reduce the increased pressure. Since, according to the above equation, for every *two* molecules of NO_2 that react only *one* molecule of N_2O_4 is produced, the total number of molecules in the container is reduced as some of the molecules of NO_2 are converted into molecules of N_2O_4. And, consequently, the pressure is reduced. Thus, the effect of increasing the pressure on the system by decreasing the volume is partly offset by the equilibrium shift to the right.

Another interesting example of the effect of pressure on equilibrium is provided by the melting of ice. When equilibrium is established between ice and water at 1 atm pressure, the temperature is 0°C. As we learned in Chapter 10, solid ice and liquid water can co-exist in equilibrium at 1 atm *only* when the temperature is 0°C:

$$\text{ice} \underset{1\text{ atm}}{\overset{0^\circ\text{C}}{\rightleftharpoons}} \text{water} \quad \begin{cases} \Delta H_{\text{forward process}} = \text{positive} \\ \Delta H_{\text{reverse process}} = \text{negative} \end{cases}$$

The principle of Le Chatelier enables us to predict what will happen if we increase the pressure on the mixture to, say, 100 atm and insulate the system to prevent loss or gain of heat. The volume of water is slightly smaller than the volume of an equal weight of ice—that is, water has a slightly greater density than ice. Consequently, an increase in pressure will cause some of the ice to change to water, because the system tends to offset the increased pressure by forming more of the component that has less volume. But ice requires heat to melt, and this heat is taken on from the ice-water mixture itself; consequently, the temperature of the mixture falls, and a new position of equilibrium is established at the new temperature. This lower temperature is the equilibrium temperature of ice and water—or the melting point of ice—at 100 atm pressure. Here we have an explanation of why the melting point of ice at 100 atm is slightly lower than 0°C, shown in Fig. 10-20, p. 189.

24-3 The Role of a Catalyst in Equilibrium

In the preceding reactions we have considered examples of systems that attain equilibrium—by themselves—within a time period sufficiently slow to be suitable for experimental observation. But, as we have observed several times in the earlier chapters, equilibrium is not always reached within a conveniently short time. A system may approach equilibrium so slowly that no detectable change is observed. In such cases, we can generally shorten the time required to attain equilibrium by introducing into the system an appropriate catalyst, which simply serves to decrease the time interval between the start of the reaction and the establishment of equilibrium. With or without the catalyst, however, the system finally reaches the *same position of equilibrium*, that is, the catalyst does *not* shift the position of equilibrium. Clearly, then, a catalyst must have the same effect on *both* the forward reaction and the reverse reaction involved in the equilibrium.

Here is a specific example of a reversible reaction that reaches equilibrium with or without a catalyst. Acetic acid, CH_3COOH, and ethyl alcohol, C_2H_5OH, react to form ethyl acetate, $CH_3COOC_2H_5$, and water, H_2O. Conversely, $CH_3COOC_2H_5$ and H_2O react to form CH_3COOH and C_2H_5OH. Regardless of which pair of compounds is mixed, within a very short time all four substances will be present in the solution. And finally the system will achieve equilibrium.

$$CH_3COOH + C_2H_5OH \rightleftharpoons CH_3COOC_2H_5 + H_2O$$

In the absence of a catalyst, this reversible reaction achieves equilibrium only after several days. But the addition of a small quantity of HCl to the mixture produces H^+ ions which catalyze the reaction and enable it to reach equilibrium in just a few hours. At equilibrium, however, the same proportions of the four compounds are present whether or not a catalyst is present in the mixture.

24-4 Ionization Equilibria Involving Weak Acids and Bases

As we found in Chapter 20, in aqueous solutions weak acids and bases dissociate only slightly into their ions. For example, when a weak acid of the general formula HA is dissolved in water, a certain portion of the HA molecules dissociate into hydrated H^+ ions and hydrated A^- ions; and equilibrium is established: $HA \rightleftharpoons H^+ + A^-$. A weak acid of the general formula HA in an aqueous solution, then, consists mostly of undissociated HA molecules and relatively few H^+ and A^- ions.

THE ACETIC ACID EQUILIBRIUM

Acetic acid is a familiar example of a weak acid. It ionizes only slightly in aqueous solution, giving rise to an equilibrium between the covalent hydrogen acetate molecules, CH_3COOH, and the H^+ and CH_3COO^- ions: $CH_3COOH \rightleftharpoons H^+ + CH_3COO^-$. For example, when 0.1 mole of hydrogen acetate, CH_3COOH, is dissolved in 1 l. of an aqueous solution to yield a 0.1 molar solution of acetic acid, only about 1.3 per cent of the CH_3COOH molecules are ionized into H^+ ions and CH_3COO^- ions; the remaining 98.7 per cent exist at equilibrium as undissociated CH_3COOH molecules. We can obtain this same equilibrium solution if we start with the products of the ionization, H^+ ions and CH_3COO^- ions. For example, we can use a solution of a strong acid to provide the H^+ ions, and a soluble metal acetate salt to provide the CH_3COO^- ions. As we know, a solution of hydrochloric acid (a strong acid) contains essentially only H^+ ions and Cl^- ions, and a solution of sodium acetate (a strong electrolyte) contains essentially only Na^+ ions and CH_3COO^- ions. When these two solutions are mixed, four different ions—Na^+, Cl^-, H^+, and CH_3COO^-—will be briefly present with high concentrations in the resulting solution. The Na^+ ions and the Cl^- ions have little tendency to combine, because NaCl is a strong electrolyte (it dissociates completely). But since acetic acid is a weak acid, a reaction will take place in solution between the H^+ ions supplied by the hydrochloric acid, and the CH_3COO^- ions supplied by the sodium acetate, to form covalent CH_3COOH molecules. The net equilibrium reaction that takes place when the hydrochloric acid solution and the sodium acetate solution are mixed is:

$$H^+ + \cancel{Cl^-} + \cancel{Na^+} + CH_3COO^- \rightleftharpoons CH_3COOH + \cancel{Na^+} + \cancel{Cl^-}$$

In other words, the equilibrium achieved by a solution of CH_3COOH in water is exactly the same as the equilibrium achieved by a mixture of an aqueous solution of $H^+ + Cl^-$ ions with a solution of $Na^+ + CH_3COO^-$ ions:

$$1. \quad CH_3COOH \rightleftharpoons H^+ + CH_3COO^-$$

$$2. \quad H^+ + CH_3COO^- \rightleftharpoons CH_3COOH$$

Notice that in the first, the reaction approaches equilibrium from the direction of its covalent molecules, whereas in the second, it approaches equilibrium from the direction of its ions.

EQUILIBRIUM SHIFTS IN SOLUTIONS OF WEAK ACIDS

How can we shift the position of equilibrium in solutions of acetic acid and other weak acids? The principle of Le Chatelier applies here as well as in other chemical reactions at equilibrium.

THE EFFECT OF CONCENTRATION CHANGES ON EQUILIBRIUM

Assume that we have an aqueous solution of acetic acid in a state of equilibrium: $CH_3COOH \rightleftharpoons H^+ + CH_3COO^-$. Now we add a small amount of solid $CH_3COO^-Na^+$, a strong electrolyte that dissociates completely into Na^+ ions and CH_3COO^- ions. The Na^+ ions have only a very minor effect on the equilibrium of the acetic acid solution, as we shall learn in the next chapter. But the presence of the added CH_3COO^- ions markedly affects the position of the ionization equilibrium of acetic acid, for they react with the H^+ ions in the solution to form undissociated CH_3COOH molecules. On the basis of Le Chatelier's principle, an increase in the concentration of the CH_3COO^- ions favors the reverse reaction, $CH_3COOH \longleftarrow H^+ + CH_3COO^-$, because this reaction results in a subsequent decrease of the amount of the added CH_3COO^- ions. Thus, the system adjusts itself to the presence of the $CH_3COO^-Na^+$ by shifting its position of equilibrium. Once the new equilibrium has been established, we can confirm experimentally that the concentration of CH_3COOH molecules has increased and the concentration of H^+ ions has decreased. In this example, we see that the addition of sodium acetate to a solution of acetic acid causes the H^+ ion concentration to decrease. Sodium acetate provides the same ion, CH_3COO^-, as is formed by the ionization of acetic acid itself.

$$CH_3COOH \rightleftharpoons H^+ + CH_3COO^-$$

Because the same CH_3COO^- ion is added to the solution, the equilibrium is shifted to the left and the H^+ ion concentration is reduced. Generally, the addition of a common ion will cause a shift in the equilibrium of a weak acid or of any weak electrolyte. This effect is generally known as the *common-ion effect.*

Here is another example of a common-ion effect. We start from the same aqueous solution of acetic acid at equilibrium, but this time we add a small amount of hydrochloric acid, a strong electrolyte that ionizes almost completely into H^+ ions and Cl^- ions. The Cl^- ions have only a very minor effect on the equilibrium. The H^+ ions from the hydrochloric acid, however, react to a large extent with some of the CH_3COO^- ions in solution to form additional CH_3COOH molecules. On the basis of Le Chatelier's principle, an increase in the concentration of the H^+ ions favors the reverse reaction, $CH_3COOH \longleftarrow H^+ + CH_3COO^-$, because it results in a subsequent decrease of the amount of the H^+ ions added. As a result, when the new position of equilibrium is established, the concentration of the CH_3COOH molecules has increased slightly, and the concentration of the CH_3COO^- ions has decreased by an equal amount. The final concentration of the H^+ ions has increased, because only a part of the H^+ ions from the HCl has reacted with the CH_3COO^- ions to form CH_3COOH molecules.

We can add CH_3COO^- *indirectly* to a solution of acetic acid at equilibrium by the following method. Add a few drops of NaOH to a solution of acetic acid, just enough to neutralize part of the acid. When the NaOH is added, the CH_3COOH molecules neutralize the added OH^- ions to form H_2O molecules and CH_3COO^- ions:

$$CH_3COOH + \cancel{Na^+} + OH^- \longrightarrow H_2O + \cancel{Na^+} + CH_3COO^-$$

This is a neutralization reaction. We can disregard the effect of the Na^+ ions on the equilibrium dissociation of acetic acid, but the CH_3COO^- ions have a marked effect, for some of them combine with H^+ ions and thereby reduce the H^+ ion concentration. This is still another instance of the common-ion effect. Notice that this example is essentially the same as the addition of $CH_3COO^-Na^+$ to an acetic acid solution at equilibrium.

EQUILIBRIA INVOLVING WEAK BASES

When ammonia gas, NH_3, is dissolved in water, a certain proportion of the hydrated NH_3 molecules form a coordinate covalent bond with a proton from a H_2O molecule, and the following equilibrium is established:

$$NH_{3(aq)} + H_2O_{(l)} \rightleftharpoons NH^+_{4(aq)} + OH^-_{(aq)}$$

If 1 mole of NH_3 gas is dissolved in 1 l. of aqueous solution, about 0.004 mole of NH_3 molecules ionize (react with water), so that about 0.004 mole of $NH_4{}^+$ ions, and about 0.004 mole of OH^- ions are present at equilibrium. In water, then, ammonia, NH_3, ionizes only 0.4 per cent, that is, it behaves as a weak base.

The principles that apply to equilibrium shifts in solutions of weak acids also apply to solutions of weak bases. Let us see what happens when we add a substance that yields $NH_4{}^+$ or OH^- ions to an equilibrium solution of aqueous ammonia. The addition of any other strong base, for example, NaOH, increases the concentration of OH^- ions in the solution. From Le Chatelier's principle, an increase in the concentration of OH^- ions favors the reverse reaction, $NH_3 + H_2O \longleftarrow NH_4{}^+ + OH^-$, because this reaction results in a subsequent decrease of the OH^- ions. Thus, some of these OH^- ions react with the $NH_4{}^+$ that is present in the solution to form molecules of ammonia, NH_3, and water, H_2O. As a result, the concentration of NH_3 molecules is increased, and the concentration of $NH_4{}^+$ ions is decreased. That is, the system has shifted its equilibrium to the left in response to altered concentration conditions.

Similarly, we can predict the effect that the addition or removal of $NH_4{}^+$ ions will have on an equilibrium solution of ammonia. For example, the addition of the soluble salt, ammonium chloride, $NH_4{}^+Cl^-$, will shift the equilibrium to the left, because some of the added $NH_4{}^+$ ions combine with OH^- ions of the base to form more ammonia molecules, NH_3, and water, H_2O.

In our discussion of the ionization of weak acids, we found that the same position of equilibrium could be achieved either by dissolving the acid in water or by mixing solutions containing the ions of the acid. The same holds true for solutions of weak bases. For example, if we mix a solution of 1 mole of solid Na^+OH^- dissolved in 0.5 l. of water with a solution of 1 mole of $NH_4{}^+Cl^-$ dissolved in 0.5 l. of water, the resulting solution (1 mole Na^+OH^- and 1 mole $NH_4{}^+Cl^-$ in 1 l. of solution) contains, in addition to the Na^+ ions and Cl^- ions, an equilibrium solution of ammonia:

$$\cancel{Na^+} + OH^- + NH_4{}^+ + \cancel{Cl^-} \rightleftharpoons NH_3 + H_2O + \cancel{Na^+} + \cancel{Cl^-}$$

Thus, neglecting the effects of the Na^+ ions and Cl^- ions, we can say that the solution consists of 0.996 mole NH_3, 0.004 mole $NH_4{}^+$ ions, and 0.004 mole OH^- ions. This is the same as the 1 M solution of ammonia described above, which was formed by dissolving gaseous NH_3 molecules in water.

WEAK SALTS

Weak salts ionize only slightly in water solution. Although, as a rule, soluble salts ionize completely in solution (are strong electrolytes), there are exceptions. Mercury(II) chloride, $HgCl_2$, for example, is very soluble in H_2O but is ionized only slightly, as is shown by the fact that an aqueous solution of $HgCl_2$ is a very poor conductor of electric current. Such a solution contains a high proportion of $HgCl_2$ molecules in equilibrium with a small proportion of $HgCl^+$ ions, Hg^{++} ions, and Cl^- ions. The equilibrium in an aqueous solution of $HgCl_2$ is represented by the following:

$$HgCl_{2(aq)} \rightleftharpoons HgCl^+{}_{(aq)} + Cl^-{}_{(aq)} \rightleftharpoons Hg^{++}{}_{(aq)} + 2\ Cl^-{}_{(aq)}$$

As we have said, the extent of ionization is very small—that is, the position of the equilibrium is far to the left. We can express this condition briefly by saying that $HgCl_2$ is a weak salt (a weak electrolyte).

Lead(II) acetate, $Pb(CH_3COO)_2$, is another example of a weak salt. Lead(II) acetate, in fact, is soluble in water, but solutions are poor conductors of the electric current—an indication that $Pb(CH_3COO)_2$ ionizes only slightly. A solution of lead(II) acetate contains a high proportion of undissociated $Pb(CH_3COO)_2$ molecules in equilibrium with a small proportion of $Pb(CH_3COO)^+$ ions, Pb^{++} ions, and CH_3COO^- ions. The equilibrium which again is far to the left is represented by the following:

$$Pb(CH_3COO)_2 \rightleftharpoons Pb(CH_3COO)^+ + CH_3COO^- \rightleftharpoons Pb^{++} + 2\ CH_3COO^-$$

24-5 Equilibrium between Solid and Solution

We know that a solution of a solid in a liquid is saturated when an equilibrium exists between the solid solute and the solute in solution. Thus, a saturated solution is a system at equilibrium, and we can predict its behavior to imposed changes on the basis of Le Chatelier's principle. We have already discussed the effect of temperature changes on solubility. Now we shall consider the effect of common-ion concentration on the solubility of ionic solids—an effect which is very important in understanding many simple reactions.

In a saturated solution of an ionic solid which is in equilibrium with an excess of the solid, ions are continually leaving the solid to go into solution while at the same time ions are leaving the solution and being deposited on the ionic solid. In the case of an ionic compound of the general formula M^+X^-, the solubility equilibrium is:

$$M^+X^-{}_{(s)} \underset{}{\overset{\text{water}}{\rightleftharpoons}} M^+{}_{(aq)} + X^-{}_{(aq)}$$

As we saw earlier, this equilibrium is established only when solid solute is in contact with the solution; but the actual quantity of solid present, which could be very small or very large, has no effect on the equilibrium.

If we add to the saturated solution of the M^+X^- salt another substance which yields either M^+ or X^- ions—that is, if we increase the concentration of either of these ions—the system will automatically adjust itself to the new situation. And we can predict the position of the new state of equilibrium on the basis of Le Chatelier's principle. For example, if to a saturated solution of M^+X^- we add a substance that yields M^+ ions, the principle tells us, the reverse reaction, $M^+X^-{}_{(s)} \longleftarrow M^+ + X^-$, occurs—because this now "removes" some of the added M^+ ions from solution, and thus tends to lessen the imposed change. Consequently additional $M^+X^-{}_{(s)}$ will be formed by the further reaction between M^+ and X^- ions, and will precipitate out of solution. Thus, the solubility of M^+X^- in water is decreased by the addition of M^+ ions to the solution. And if we add to the saturated solution of M^+X^- a substance that provides X^- ions, again the reverse reaction, $M^+X^-{}_{(s)} \longleftarrow M^+{}_{(aq)} + X^-{}_{(aq)}$ occurs, because this reaction will "remove" from the solution some X^- ions, and thus will tend to lessen the imposed change. Consequently more $M^+X^-{}_{(s)}$ crystallizes from solution and its solubility is decreased.

What happens if we remove some of the M^+ ions from the saturated solution of M^+X^- in pure water? Once again Le Chatelier's principle tells us that an imposed decrease in the concentration of the M^+ ions (one of the components of the equilibrium) favors the forward reaction, $M^+X^-_{(s)} \longrightarrow M^+ + X^-$, since the reaction produces this component, and hence tends to restore the original concentration. So, some additional solid M^+X^- dissolves to produce more M^+ ions (and more X^- ions, of course), and the solubility equilibrium shifts to the right (the solubility increases). Let us now consider some specific examples of changes in solubility resulting from the addition of a substance that furnishes a common ion.

THE SODIUM CHLORIDE EQUILIBRIUM. Consider first the solubility equilibrium in a saturated aqueous solution of sodium chloride: $Na^+Cl^-_{(s)} \rightleftharpoons Na^+_{(aq)} + Cl^-_{(aq)}$. What would be the effect of adding some concentrated hydrochloric acid, which yields a high concentration of H^+ ions and Cl^- ions (a common ion) to the saturated solution of NaCl? The concentration of the Cl^- ions is increased, causing the solubility equilibrium to shift to the left. Thus, $NaCl_{(s)}$ precipitates out of solution. Even in a moderately concentrated but still *unsaturated* solution of NaCl, the addition of a sufficient quantity of hydrochloric acid will increase the Cl^- ion concentration enough to precipitate some solid NaCl.

THE CALCIUM SULFATE EQUILIBRIUM. As another example, consider the equilibrium in a saturated solution of the slightly soluble calcium sulfate: $Ca^{++}SO^{=}_{4(s)} \rightleftharpoons Ca^{++}_{(aq)} + SO^{=}_{4(aq)}$. If we add to the saturated solution even a relatively small amount of a soluble salt that yields the common ion, $SO_4^{=}$ (a salt such as Na_2SO_4, for example), some solid $CaSO_4$ crystallizes from solution. And if we add to the saturated solution even a relatively small amount of a soluble salt that yields the common ion, Ca^{++} ($CaCl_2$, for example), again some solid $CaSO_4$ crystallizes from solution. Thus, as the principle of Le Chatelier predicts, the solubility of a slightly soluble salt depends on the concentration of *each ion* and is very sensitive to the addition of even small quantities of a common ion from a foreign substance.

In our discussions of solutions of weak acids and of weak bases, we found that the same equilibrium solution could be obtained either by dissolving covalent molecules of the acid or base in water, or by mixing solutions containing the ions. A somewhat similar condition holds for the preparation of saturated solutions of slightly soluble salts in water—we can either dissolve the slightly soluble salt in water, or mix solutions containing the ions of the salt. For example, we can obtain a saturated solution of $CaSO_4$ in water either by dissolving this solid in water, or by mixing two solutions, one containing Ca^{++} ions (and anions) and the other solution containing $SO_4^{=}$ ions (and cations). For example, if we add a solution of a soluble calcium salt, such as $CaCl_2$, to a solution of a soluble sulfate, such as Na_2SO_4, a white precipitate of solid $CaSO_4$ will form:

$$Ca^{++}_{(aq)} + \cancel{2Cl^-}_{(aq)} + \cancel{2Na^+}_{(aq)} + SO^{=}_{4(aq)} \rightleftharpoons Ca^{++}SO^{=}_{4(s)} + \cancel{2Na^+}_{(aq)} + \cancel{2Cl^-}_{(aq)}$$

Except for the minor secondary effects of the Na^+ ions and the Cl^- ions in the solution, the same equilibrium condition exists here as in a saturated $CaSO_4$ solution formed by dissolving pure $CaSO_{4(s)}$ in water.

EFFECT OF THE FORMATION OF COMPLEX IONS ON SOLUBILITY EQUILIBRIA

THE SILVER CHLORIDE EQUILIBRIUM. We have seen that a salt can be *precipitated* from a saturated solution when we increase the concentration of one of its ions. Conversely, a salt can be *dissolved* by decreasing the concentration of one of its ions. When an excess of slightly soluble silver chloride, AgCl, is in contact with its saturated solution, the following equilibrium is established: $Ag^+Cl^-_{(s)} \rightleftharpoons Ag^+_{(aq)} + Cl^-_{(aq)}$.

Let us now see what happens if we add some ammonia to this saturated solution. The NH_3 molecules unite with some of the Ag^+ ions to form the soluble complex ion, $[Ag(NH_3)_2]^+$. Thus, the addition of ammonia disturbs the solubility equilibrium of silver chloride by removing Ag^+ ions from solution, to form the stable complex ion

$[Ag(NH_3)_2]^+$. Consequently the concentration of Ag^+ ions in solution decreases, and further dissolution of $Ag^+Cl^-_{(s)}$ will occur: $Ag^+Cl^- \longrightarrow Ag^+ + Cl^-$. If we add sufficient NH_3, all solid AgCl will finally dissolve. The effect of NH_3 on the equilibrium between solid Ag^+Cl^- and its ions in solution, Ag^+ and Cl^-, is shown as follows:

$$\begin{array}{lcl} Ag^+Cl^- & \rightleftharpoons & Ag^+ + Cl^- \\ & & \quad + \\ & & 2\ NH_3 \rightleftharpoons [Ag(NH_3)_2]^+ \end{array}$$

That is to say, the dissolution of solid (insoluble) Ag^+Cl^- in an aqueous ammonia solution can be represented as the chemical reaction:

$$Ag^+Cl^-_{(s)} + 2\ NH_{3(aq)} \longrightarrow [Ag(NH_3)_2]^+_{(aq)} + Cl^-_{(aq)}$$

The fact that $AgCl_{(s)}$ dissolves in aqueous ammonia according to the above equation tells us that the complex salt $[Ag(NH_3)_2]^+Cl^-_{(s)}$ must be very soluble in water—as indeed is the case. In the formation of the complex $[Ag(NH_3)_2]^+$ ion, each of two NH_3 molecules donates its lone electron pair to the Ag^+ ion, to form a co-ordinate covalent bond. As we shall learn in Chapter 33, the formation of a complex ion in solution is in fact an equilibrium reaction:

$$Ag^+ + 2\!:\!NH_3 \rightleftharpoons [H_3N\!\rightarrow\!Ag\!\leftarrow\!NH_3]^+$$

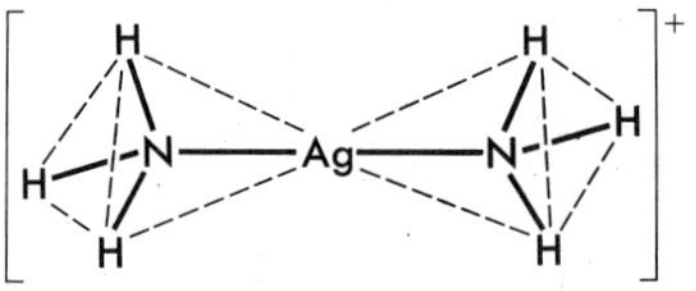

Thus the process by which solid AgCl is dissolved by an ammonia solution can be reversed—the solid AgCl may be re-formed by the addition of a strong acid solution, such as nitric acid. Since in solution the $[Ag(NH_3)_2]^+$ ion is in equilibrium with its components, Ag^+ and NH_3, Le Chatelier's principle tells us that the addition of H^+ ions, which react with NH_3 to form the NH_4^+, decreases the concentration of the NH_3 molecules in the solution and consequently favors the forward reaction, $Ag(NH_3)_2^+ \longrightarrow Ag^+ + 2\ NH_3$. Here is the net chemical equation representing the reaction of a strong acid with a solution of the diamminesilver(I) ion:

$$\begin{array}{lcl} [Ag(NH_3)_2]^+_{(aq)} + 2\ H^+_{(aq)} & \rightleftharpoons & Ag^+_{(aq)} + 2\ NH^+_{4(aq)} \\ [H_3N\!\rightarrow\!Ag\!\leftarrow\!NH_3]^+ + 2\ H^+ & \rightleftharpoons & Ag^+ \quad + 2\ [H\!\leftarrow\!NH_3]^+ \end{array}$$

When the $[Ag(NH_3)_2]^+$ ion breaks up in the presence of an excess of H^+ ions, the nitrogen atom of each NH_3 molecule donates its lone pair to a proton, H^+, forming a NH_4^+ ion. Thus, the co-ordinate covalent bond between each NH_3 molecule and the Ag^+ ion in the complex ion $[Ag(NH_3)_2]^+$ is broken, and a new co-ordinate covalent bond between the central N atom of each NH_3 and a H^+ ion is formed in each NH_4^+ ion. The Ag^+ ions then recombine with the Cl^- ions, to form solid AgCl, and we are back again at the original state of solubility equilibrium of AgCl.

Here is a general equation illustrating the effect of the H^+ ion in shifting the positions of equilibrium of the silver chloride ammonia system.

$$[Ag(NH_3)_2]^+_{(aq)} + Cl^-_{(aq)} + H^+_{(aq)} \rightleftharpoons NH^+_{4(aq)} + Ag^+_{(aq)} + Cl^-_{(aq)} \rightleftharpoons Ag^+Cl^-_{(s)}$$
$$\xrightarrow{\qquad\qquad\qquad H^+ \qquad\qquad\qquad}$$

THE MERCURY(II) IODIDE EQUILIBRIUM. Assume we have a saturated solution of mercury(II) iodide, HgI_2, in contact with excess solid HgI_2. Mercury(II) iodide, which is only slightly soluble in water, is far more soluble in a solution of KI, even though this salt supplies a common ion, I^-. The explanation is that the excess of I^- ions from the KI react with the HgI_2 to form the very stable complex ion $[HgI_4]^=$. The net reaction is written as:

$$HgI_{2(s)} + \cancel{2K^+}_{(aq)} + 2\ I^-_{(aq)} \rightleftharpoons \cancel{2K^+}_{(aq)} + [HgI_4]^=_{(aq)}$$

Again, the fact that $HgI_{2(s)}$ dissolves in a solution containing I^- ions, according to the above equation, tells us that the complex salt $K_2[HgI_4]$ must be very soluble in water—and in fact it is so. In the formation of the complex $[HgI_4]^=$ ion, each of two I^- ions donates a lone pair of electrons to the central Hg atom of the HgI_2 molecule, forming a co-ordinate bond. The $[HgI_4]^=$ complex ion is tetrahedral, with the Hg^{++} ion at the center and a I^- ion at each of the four corners. The central Hg^{++} ion has a $(5)d^{10}$ closed shell electronic configuration, and the four bond pairs (one bond pair from each I^- ion) arrange themselves tetrahedrally about the central Hg^{++}.

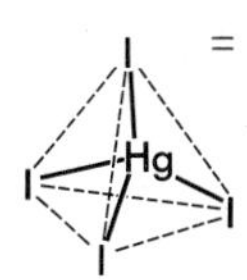

THE ZINC HYDROXIDE EQUILIBRIUM. Here is still another example in which the solubility of a slightly soluble salt is increased by the formation of a complex ion. Assume that we have a saturated solution of slightly soluble zinc(II) hydroxide, $Zn(OH)_2$, in contact with excess solid $Zn(OH)_2$. If to this saturated solution we add a strong base—for example, sodium hydroxide—the OH^- ions supplied by the Na^+OH^- react with the solid $Zn(OH)_2$ to form a complex ion, $[Zn(OH)_4]^=_{(aq)}$. If we add enough Na^+OH^-, all the solid $Zn(OH)_2$ dissolves, according to the net equation:

$$Zn(OH)_{2(s)} + \cancel{2\,Na^+}_{(aq)} + 2\,OH^-_{(aq)} \longrightarrow \cancel{2\,Na^+}_{(aq)} + [Zn(OH)_4]^=_{(aq)}$$

In general, the formation of hydroxo complexes explains why many insoluble metal hydroxides are soluble in "an excess of basic solution." Besides $Zn(OH)_2$, other common examples are $Al(OH)_3$ and $Sn(OH)_2$.

24-6 Solubility of Salts in Acids

Certain slightly soluble salts of weak acids dissolve readily when a strong acid is added to the solution.

THE BARIUM CARBONATE EQUILIBRIUM. Barium carbonate, $BaCO_3$, a salt of the weak acid H_2CO_3, is only very slightly soluble in water, but it readily dissolves when HCl is added to the solution. The following equations summarize the equilibria that exist in solutions of $BaCO_3$ alone, and in the presence of added H^+ ions.

1. Solid $BaCO_3$ alone in pure water. The equilibrium position is far to the left (relatively few ions in solution).

$$BaCO_{3(s)} \xrightleftharpoons{\text{pure water}} Ba^{++}_{(aq)} + CO_3^={}_{(aq)}$$

2. When HCl is added, each of the $CO_3^=$ ions in solution takes on two H^+ ions to form the weak acid, H_2CO_3. The equilibrium position is far to the right.

$$2\,H^+_{(aq)} + CO_3^={}_{(aq)} \xrightleftharpoons{H^+_{(aq)}} H_2CO_{3(aq)}$$

3. The H_2CO_3 molecules then break down into H_2O and CO_2, the latter escaping from the solution as a gas. The equilibrium position is far to the right, because the solubility of carbon dioxide in water at ordinary pressure is small.

$$H_2CO_{3(aq)} \rightleftharpoons H_2O_{(l)} + CO_{2(g)}$$

4. The $CO_3^=$ ions are continuously removed from the solution, forming gaseous CO_2, and, as Le Chatelier's principle predicts, the solubility equilibrium is shifted to the right. If we continue to add HCl, the H^+ ions keep removing the $CO_3^=$ ions, to form H_2O and CO_2, and finally complete solution of the $BaCO_{3(s)}$ takes place. The equilibrium equations representing these changes may be combined as:

$$\left.\begin{array}{r} BaCO_{3(s)} \rightleftharpoons Ba^{++}_{(aq)} + CO_3^={}_{(aq)} \\ + \\ 2\,H^+_{(aq)} \end{array}\right\} H_2CO_{3(aq)} \rightleftharpoons H_2O_{(l)} + CO_{2(g)}$$

And the net ionic reaction is:

$$BaCO_{3(s)} + 2\,H^+_{(aq)} \longrightarrow Ba^{++}_{(aq)} + H_2O_{(l)} + CO_{2(g)}$$

This reaction occurs not only with $BaCO_3$ and hydrochloric acid, HCl, but also in general with all metal carbonates and all strong acids, and explains why all metal carbonates, and in general all slightly soluble salts of weak acids dissolve readily in solutions of (appropriate) stronger acids. Of course, if we wish to bring the metal ion in solution, we must use a strong acid whose anion does not itself form an insoluble salt with the metal cation. Otherwise, we only change the insoluble carbonate to another insoluble salt. For example, if we treat $BaCO_3$ with a solution of sulfuric acid, the net reaction is:

$$BaCO_{3(s)} + 2\,H^+_{(aq)} + SO^=_{4(aq)} \longrightarrow BaSO_{4(s)} + CO_{2(g)} + H_2O_{(l)}$$

SOLUBILITY OF SLIGHTLY SOLUBLE SALT, M^+A^-, IN ACIDS

In order for an acid to dissolve a slightly soluble salt, two independent requirements must be satisfied. First, the solvent acid must be stronger than the acid corresponding to the anion of the slightly soluble salt. Second, the anion of the solvent acid must form a soluble salt with the cation of the salt to be dissolved. In the following discussion, we shall assume that this latter requirement is always satisfied. Thus, any slightly soluble salt, M^+A^-, will dissolve in any acid stronger than the acid HA, provided the concentration of A^- ions furnished by the saturated solution of M^+A^- is not too low. If the concentration of A^- ions is too low, the salt M^+A^- will not dissolve in an acid even if this acid is stronger than HA.

If a slightly soluble salt, M^+A^-, of a weak acid, HA, dissolves in a solution of a strong acid, the H^+ ions from the strong acid react with the anions, A^-, of the salt to form molecules of the weak acid:

$$MA_{(s)} \rightleftharpoons M^+_{(aq)} + A^-_{(aq)} \qquad \text{and} \qquad H^+_{(aq)} + A^-_{(aq)} \rightleftharpoons HA_{(aq)}$$

If, at a given temperature, the reaction with the H^+ ions sufficiently lowers the concentration of the anion, A^-, the solution will no longer be saturated with respect to the $M^+A^-_{(s)}$ salt. Consequently, more of the salt will dissolve. And if enough strong acid is present so that the concentration of A^- continues to remain sufficiently low, all the $M^+A^-_{(s)}$ salt will eventually dissolve.

What we have just said holds for salts of weak acids. The solubility of a slightly soluble salt of a *strong* acid, is not, as a rule, increased by the presence of another strong acid. The slightly soluble salt $BaSO_4$, for example, is not soluble in a HCl solution. The H^+ ions from the HCl solution do join with a large proportion of the $SO_4^=$ anions of the salt, forming HSO_4^- ions, but the concentration of $SO_4^=$ ions in solution remains appreciably high. Consequently, no additional $SO_4^=$ ions are drawn into solution from the solid $BaSO_4$, and the solubility of the salt is not increased. Just how great a H^+ concentration we need to bring about the solution of a slightly soluble metal salt, MA, depends on two factors:

1. The solubility of the salt, MA, in water, that is, its tendency to dissolve, forming $M^+_{(aq)}$ and $A^-_{(aq)}$ ions.
2. The strength of the weak acid HA formed by the reaction of the hydrogen ion, H^+, with the anion $A^-_{(aq)}$.

The more soluble the salt, the more opportunity there is for the H^+ ions from the added strong acid to form HA. And, consequently, the greater will be the effect of the H^+ ions on the solubility of the slightly soluble salt. Conversely, the greater the tendency for the HA to dissociate into H^+ and A^- ions, the smaller the effect of the added H^+ ions on the solubility of the slightly soluble salt, M^+A^-.

THE SEPARATION OF SLIGHTLY SOLUBLE SALTS: $CaCO_3$ AND CaC_2O_4. What practical use can we make of this information? Suppose we have a mixture of two slightly soluble salts, solid calcium carbonate, $CaCO_3$, and solid calcium oxalate, CaC_2O_4, and we want to bring about the solution of all the $CaCO_3$ but not of the CaC_2O_4. We may take advantage, for example, of the fact that acetic acid, CH_3COOH, is a stronger acid than carbonic acid, H_2CO_3, but weaker than oxalic acid, $H_2C_2O_4$ (or

TABLE 24-1 METHODS OF SHIFTING EQUILIBRIUM

Method	*Example*
1. Formation of a precipitate.	$Ag^+ + \cancel{NO_3^-} + \cancel{H^+} + Cl^- \rightleftharpoons AgCl + \cancel{H^+} + \cancel{NO_3^-}$ $\cancel{2\,Na^+} + SO_4^= + Ca^{++} + \cancel{2\,Cl^-} \rightleftharpoons CaSO_4 + \cancel{2\,Na^+} + \cancel{2\,Cl^-}$
2. Formation of weakly ionized compounds.	$H^+ + \cancel{NO_3^-} + \cancel{K^+} + OH^- \rightleftharpoons H_2O + \cancel{K^+} + \cancel{NO_3^-}$ $H^+ + \cancel{Cl^-} + \cancel{2\,Na^+} + CO_3^= \rightleftharpoons HCO_3^- + \cancel{2\,Na^+} + \cancel{Cl^-}$
3. Formation of complex ion.	$AgCl + 2\,NH_3 \rightleftharpoons Ag(NH_3)_2^+ + Cl^-$ $Zn(OH)_2 + \cancel{2\,K^+} + 2\,OH^- \rightleftharpoons Zn(OH)_4^= + \cancel{2\,K^+}$
4. Formation of volatile compound.	$\cancel{2\,Na^+} + CO_3^= + 2\,H^+ + \cancel{2\,Cl^-} \rightleftharpoons$ $\cancel{2\,Na^+} + \cancel{2\,Cl^-} + H_2CO_3 \rightleftharpoons H_2O + CO_2\uparrow$
5. Oxidation-reduction.	$3\,S^= + 2\,NO_3^- + 8\,H^+ \rightleftharpoons 3\,S + 2\,NO + 4\,H_2O$ $Zn + Cu^{++} + \cancel{SO_4^=} \rightleftharpoons Cu + Zn^{++} + \cancel{SO_4^=}$ $Cl_2 + \cancel{2\,Na^+} + 2\,Br^- \rightleftharpoons Br_2 + \cancel{2\,Na^+} + 2\,Cl^-$

HOOC—COOH). If we add water to the mixture of the two solid salts, $CaCO_3$ and CaC_2O_4, we will obtain a saturated solution, in which the ions of each dissolved salt are in equilibrium with the undissolved solid. But if we add a solution of acetic acid, CH_3COOH, the solid $CaCO_3$ dissolves whereas the solid CaC_2O_4 does *not*. Thus, we can separate the two salts by treating the mixture with a solution of acetic acid. We could not use a solution of hydrochloric acid for this purpose, however, because HCl is a stronger acid than either H_2CO_3 or $H_2C_2O_4$ and therefore *both* the salts would then dissolve.

SOLUBILITY BEHAVIOR. The following generalizations concerning the solubility of compounds in water are useful:

1. The metal nitrates, acetates, and chlorates are soluble. There are, however, exceptions, such as basic nitrates and basic acetates.
2. The metal chlorides, bromides, and iodides are soluble. Exceptions are Ag(I), Pb(II), and Hg(I) salts, and a few basic salts such as BiOCl and SbOCl.
3. The metal sulfates—except for $CaSO_4$, $SrSO_4$, $BaSO_4$, Ag_2SO_4, $PbSO_4$, and Hg_2SO_4—are soluble.
4. The common salts and hydroxides of sodium, potassium, and ammonium are soluble. Notable exceptions are K_2PtCl_6 and $KClO_4$.
5. The hydroxides and sulfides of calcium, strontium, and barium are moderately soluble. Most other hydroxides and sulfides are insoluble.

24-7 Summary of Methods of Shifting Equilibrium

Various methods of shifting the position of equilibrium in chemical systems at constant conditions of temperature and pressure are summarized in Table 24-1.

Exercises

24-1 Consider a chemical reaction represented by the general equation: $2\,A + B_2 \rightleftharpoons 2\,AB$. (a) Define equilibrium for this reaction. (b) Has all reaction stopped at equilibrium? Explain your answer in detail. (c) Explain the meaning of "a shift in the position of equilibrium."

24-2 Discuss the effect (if any) on the position of the equilibrium of (a) lowering the temperature, (b) adding nitrogen, for the following reactions:

1. $N_{2(g)} + 3\,H_{2(g)} \rightleftharpoons 2\,NH_{3(g)}$ ΔH = positive
2. $N_{2(g)} + O_{2(g)} \rightleftharpoons 2\,NO_{(g)}$ ΔH = positive
3. $4\,NH_{3(g)} + 5\,O_{2(g)} \rightleftharpoons 4\,NO_{(g)} + 6\,H_2O_{(g)}$ ΔH = positive

24-3 What is the effect on the equilibria in 24-2 of: (a) increasing the pressure, (b) adding a catalyst, (c) adding Kr gas?

24-4 (a) Water is formed when pressure is applied to ice at a constant temperature. Explain this transformation in terms of Le Chatelier's principle. (b) Carbon tetrachloride contracts when it freezes. If the pressure is increased, will the freezing point of this liquid be raised or lowered? Explain. (c) Sodium sulfate is more soluble in water at low temperatures than at high temperatures. When this salt is dissolved in water, is heat liberated or absorbed? Explain.

24-5 Consider the following equilibrium reaction:

$$H_{2(g)} + Cl_{2(g)} \rightleftharpoons 2\,HCl_{(g)} \qquad \Delta H = \text{negative}$$

Explain the effect of: (a) increasing the concentration of (1) H_2, (2) Cl_2; (b) increasing the pressure; (c) decreasing the temperature; (d) adding a catalyst.

24-6 An acid with the general formula, HA, is a weak acid. (a) Write the equation to represent the equilibrium present in an aqueous solution of this acid. (b) Explain the effect on the ionization equilibrium (if any) of the addition of each of the following: (1) HCl, (2) NaA, (3) KOH, (4) KCl, (5) H_2O.

24-7 Compare (a) the electrical conductivity, (b) the effect on litmus paper, and (c) the reaction with metallic Mg, of 1 mole of CH_3COOH in 1 l. of solution, and of 1 mole of HCl in 1 l. of solution. Explain your answer.

24-8 A solution of the hypothetical salt NaX is basic. A solution of the hypothetical salt NaY is neutral. Compare aqueous solutions of the hypothetical acids HX and HY in regard to (a) electrical conductivity, (b) effect on litmus paper, (c) freezing point of equimolar aqueous solutions, (d) rate of reaction with Zn metal, (e) quantity of H_2 gas evolved by reaction of 1 mole of Zn with excess acid.

24-9 (a) Compare aqueous solutions of 0.1 *M* NH_3 and 0.1 *M* NaOH in regard to (1) conductivity, (2) effect on litmus paper, (3) freezing point, (4) acidity or basicity of the resulting solution when 0.1 mole of gaseous HCl is bubbled through 1 l. of each solution. (b) Compare the reaction (if any) of Zn metal with concentrated aqueous solutions of NH_3 and NaOH. Explain your answer.

24-10 If any reaction takes place between the following pairs of reactants, complete the equation and explain your answer. If no reaction takes place, write N.R.

(a) $Ca(CH_3COO)_2 + HCl \longrightarrow$
(b) $NH_4Cl + KOH \longrightarrow$
(c) $NaNO_2 + H_2SO_4 \longrightarrow$
(d) $Na_2CO_3 + H_3PO_4 \longrightarrow$
(e) $KNO_3 + Na_2SO_4 \longrightarrow$
(f) $NaHSO_3 + HCl \longrightarrow$
(g) $BaCO_3 + HCl \longrightarrow$
(h) $Ca(OH)_2 + HCl \longrightarrow$
(i) $Ba(NO_3)_2 + H_2SO_4 \longrightarrow$
(j) $BaSO_4 + CH_3COOH \longrightarrow$

24-11 Nitrous acid, HNO_2, is a weak acid. (a) Explain the meaning of this statement. (b) Write the equilibrium equation for an aqueous solution of this acid. (c) If a solution of H_2SO_4 and a solution of KNO_2 are mixed, will any reaction take place? Explain. (d) Is a solution of $NaNO_2$ acidic, basic, or neutral? Explain.

24-12 (a) Gaseous NH_3 is passed into water in beaker A. Solid NaOH is dissolved in water in beaker B. Solid NH_4Cl is dissolved in water in beaker C. What ion is present in the solutions in both beaker A and beaker B? (b) What ion is present in the solutions in both beaker A and beaker C? (c) What substance is present in the solution in beaker A that is not present in the solution in either beaker B or beaker C?

24-13 A 0.1 *M* solution of NaQ is more basic than a 0.1 *M* solution of NaR. Is the acid HQ weaker or stronger than the acid HR? Explain your answer.

24-14 Beakers *A*, *B*, *C*, and *D* contain equal volumes of 0.1 *M* CH_3COOH. To beaker *A* is added 0.01 mole CH_3COONH_4; to beaker *B* is added 0.01 mole NH_3; to beaker *C* is added 0.01 mole HCl; nothing is added to beaker *D*. Compare the solutions in *A*, *B*, *C*, and *D* in respect to (a) H^+ ion concentration, (b) CH_3COO^- ion concentration.

24-15 Explain how mixtures of the following pairs of substances, all insoluble in water, may be separated from one another: (a) $BaSO_4$ and $BaSO_3$, (b) $CaSO_4$ and $CaCO_3$.

EQUILIBRIUM: II

25

In the preceding chapter we used the principle of Le Chatelier to describe, in a qualitative way, the effect of changing conditions on the equilibrium of chemical reactions. In this chapter we shall focus our attention on two other matters: the concentrations of the reactants and of the products present in a chemical system at equilibrium, and *the quantitative changes that occur in the system when the concentrations of the reactants and products are varied at a constant temperature.* First, we shall state the *approximate quantitative relationship that exists between the concentration of the reactants and the concentration of the products at equilibrium at a certain specified temperature.* Then we shall compare the experimental data for some chemical systems at equilibrium with the calculated data to see just how closely the quantitative concentration-relationship agrees with the observed facts.

We shall also see that this quantitative concentration-relationship is related to the standard free energy change of the reaction, ΔG°. Finally, we shall discuss how the actual free energy change of the reaction at non-standard conditions, ΔG, depends on the actual concentrations of all the reactants and products.

25-1 Reactants and Products in a System at Equilibrium

EQUATION FOR EQUILIBRIUM REACTION

Here is a generalized equation for the state of equilibrium of any reversible chemical reaction involving two reactants and two products:

$$a\,A + b\,B \rightleftharpoons c\,C + d\,D$$

In this equation the small italic letters represent the coefficients of the reactants and products indicated by the capital letters. Let us apply this generalized equation to a particular case: the equilibrium reaction between (reactants) acetic acid, CH_3COOH, and ethyl alcohol, C_2H_5OH, and (products) ethyl acetate, $CH_3COOC_2H_5$, and water, H_2O.

$$\begin{array}{lllll} a\ A & + b\ B & \rightleftharpoons c\ C & + d\ D \\ 1\ CH_3COOH & + 1\ C_2H_5OH & \rightleftharpoons 1\ CH_3COOC_2H_5 & + 1\ H_2O \end{array}$$

Here the coefficients *a*, *b*, *c*, and *d* are all equal to 1. Another example is the equilibrium involving hydrogen, H_2, iodine, I_2, and hydrogen iodide, HI:

$$\begin{array}{lll} a\,A & + b\,B & \rightleftharpoons c\,C \\ 1\ H_2 & + 1\ I_2 & \rightleftharpoons 2\ HI \end{array}$$

In this case the coefficient $a = 1$, $b = 1$, and $c = 2$. A third example is the equilibrium reaction between acetic acid molecules, CH_3COOH, (hydrated) hydrogen ions, H^+, and (hydrated) acetate ions, CH_3COO^-, in aqueous solution (a, c, d, all $= 1$):

$$\begin{array}{lll} a\ A & \rightleftharpoons c\ C & + d\ D \\ 1\ CH_3COOH & \rightleftharpoons 1\ H^+ & + 1\ CH_3COO^- \end{array}$$

THE LAW OF MASS ACTION

Experiments show that an approximate quantitative relationship (often exact to two significant figures) exists between the concentration of the reactants and the concentration of the products in the generalized reaction at equilibrium:

Generalized equation: $a\,A + b\,B \rightleftharpoons c\,C + d\,D$

Quantitative relationship: $\dfrac{[C]^c \times [D]^d}{[A]^a \times [B]^b} = \text{equilibrium quotient} = K$

This relationship is known as the Law of Mass Action, or the Law of Guldberg and Waage, who were the first to announce the law in full in 1866.

Each capital letter in brackets represents the equilibrium concentration, expressed in moles/liter, of the substance for which it stands. For example, [C] represents the concentration at equilibrium of product C in moles/liter. Similarly, [D], [A], and [B] represent the respective equilibrium concentrations, in moles/liter, of product D, reactant A, and reactant B.

Notice that the concentrations of the products appear in the numerator of the expression whereas the concentrations of the reactants appear in the denominator. The coefficients in the generalized equation now appear as exponents indicating the power to which the concentration of each substance at equilibrium must be raised to satisfy the mathematical relationship.

The *equilibrium quotient, K*, represents a numerical value that is approximately constant for any given chemical system at equilibrium at a given, constant temperature. For this reason the equilibrium quotient is generally called the *equilibrium constant*. The value of *K* is different for different chemical reactions at equilibrium, and even for the same chemical reaction at different temperatures. But it is nearly constant for any given chemical reaction at a fixed temperature, regardless of the actual concentrations of the substances involved in the equilibrium. As we shall see, equilibrium constants are very useful because they show how far an indicated chemical reaction can proceed as written at the specified temperature—assuming we start with the pure reactants. The larger the value of *K*, the greater the extent to which the forward reaction has proceeded when the system has attained equilibrium.

APPLICATION OF THE LAW OF MASS ACTION

Now let us apply this mathematical relationship, the equilibrium expression, to the three equilibrium reactions we mentioned above.

Chemical equation: $CH_3COOH_{(l)} + C_2H_5OH_{(l)} \rightleftharpoons CH_3COOC_2H_{5(l)} + H_2O_{(l)}$

Equilibrium expression: $$\frac{[CH_3COOC_2H_5]^1 \times [H_2O]^1}{[CH_3COOH]^1 \times [C_2H_5OH]^1} = K$$

Here $[CH_3COOC_2H_5]^1$ represents the concentration of $CH_3COOC_2H_5$, ethyl acetate, in moles/liter, raised to the first power, since the coefficient of $CH_3COOC_2H_5$ in the chemical equation is 1. Similarly, for the other components, each of the concentrations—$[H_2O]$, $[CH_3COOH]$, and $[C_2H_5OH]$—is raised to the power 1, in keeping with the coefficients in the chemical equation. Notice that in writing this equilibrium constant, *K*, we have omitted the subscripts (l) after the formulas of the reactants and products. In general, the subscripts (aq), (s), (l), and (g) are omitted, for the sake of simplicity, from the expressions of the equilibrium constants.

Chemical equation: $H_{2(g)} + I_{2(g)} \rightleftharpoons 2\,HI_{(g)}$

Equilibrium expression: $$\frac{[HI]^2}{[H_2]^1 \times [I_2]^1} = K$$

We can read this expression as follows: "The concentration in moles/liter of HI, squared, divided by the product of the concentration in moles/l. of H_2 and the concentration in moles/l. of I_2, equals the equilibrium constant, *K*."

Chemical equation: $CH_3COOH_{(aq)} \rightleftharpoons H^+{}_{(aq)} + CH_3COO^-{}_{(aq)}$

Equilibrium expression: $$\frac{[H^+]^1 \times [CH_3COO^-]^1}{[CH_3COOH]^1} = K$$

This reads: "The concentration in moles/liter of the H^+ ions, multiplied by the concentration in moles/liter of the CH_3COO^- ions, divided by the concentration in moles/liter of the CH_3COOH molecules, equals the constant, *K*."

EXPERIMENTAL DATA FOR THE EQUILIBRIUM: $H_{2(g)} + I_{2(g)} \rightleftharpoons 2\,HI_{(g)}$

Let us turn now to some experimental data that have actually been obtained for the equilibrium reaction of hydrogen gas with iodine gas to produce hydrogen iodide gas (net equation: $H_{2(g)} + I_{2(g)} \rightleftharpoons 2\,HI_{(g)}$). Since a very simple procedure was used in these experiments, the data are not highly accurate, yet they are good enough to show the equilibrium relationship. Known quantities of hydrogen gas and solid iodine were sealed in glass tubes and heated to a constant temperature, 454°C, for several days to insure that equilibrium was established. (At this temperature, hydrogen, iodine, and hydrogen iodide are all gases, so this is an equilibrium reaction in the gas phase.) The mixture was then cooled down quickly to room temperature and the contents were analyzed for HI and I_2; the equilibrium was scarcely disturbed because at room temperature the rate of the reaction is negligible (Chapter 26). The results of these experiments are given in Table 25-1.

By substituting the numerical values of the concentrations of the product and the reactants in the equilibrium expression,

$$\frac{[HI]^2}{[H_2]^1 \times [I_2]^1} = K$$

we can calculate the value of the equilibrium constant. For example, for the first experiment in Table 25-1:

TABLE 25-1 DATA ON EQUILIBRIUM REACTION: $H_{2(g)} + I_{2(g)} \rightleftharpoons 2\,HI_{(g)}$, AT 454°C

Expt.	At Start [H_2] moles/l.	At Start [I_2] moles/l.	At Equilibrium [H_2] moles/l.	At Equilibrium [I_2] moles/l.	At Equilibrium [HI] moles/l.	$\frac{[HI]^2}{[H_2]^1 \times [I_2]^1} = K$ moles/l.
1	1.35	0.493	0.885	0.020	0.945	50.4
2	1.33	0.888	0.535	0.092	1.590	51.4
3	1.35	1.554	0.224	0.426	2.257	53.4
4	1.36	2.413	0.111	1.170	2.502	48.2
						50.8 = average

$$\frac{[0.945]^2}{[0.885]^1 \times [0.020]^1} = 50.4 = K$$

The other equilibrium constants listed in Table 25-1 were calculated in the same way. Notice that the values thus obtained range from 48.2 to 53.4. This lack of agreement is due in part to experimental error. Another source of inaccuracy is the use, in the calculation, of the concentrations of the reactants and products in place of their activities (see p. 555). The average value of the equilibrium constant, $K = 50.8$, means that when equilibrium is attained at 454°C, the product of the concentrations [HI] and [HI] is 50.8 times greater than the product of the concentrations [H_2] and [I_2]. Thus, knowing the initial concentration of the reactants, H_2 and I_2, we can estimate how far they have reacted in each experiment to form HI.

Now let us examine the data of Table 25-1 in terms of Le Chatelier's principle. Table 25-1 (column 2) shows that in each experiment the concentration of H_2 *at the start* is virtually the same, whereas the concentration of I_2 increases gradually from experiment 1 to experiment 4. Thus, in each successive experiment we introduce additional I_2 into the system, and we may regard this additional I_2 as being added to the system of experiment 1 at equilibrium. On the basis of Le Chatelier's principle, we would predict that when additional I_2 is introduced into the system, the concentration of $H_{2(g)}$ will decrease and the concentration of $HI_{(g)}$ will increase compared to that of the original state of equilibrium.

Do the experimental data support this prediction? They do. The "At Equilibrium" section of Table 25-1 shows that, from experiment 1 to experiment 4, the concentration of H_2 decreases from 0.885 to 0.111 mole/l., and the concentration of HI correspondingly increases from 0.945 to 2.502 moles/l.

Another set of data listing only equilibrium values of the same equilibrium reaction at a slightly different temperature is given in Table 25-2. These data were assembled under more carefully controlled experimental conditions, and, consequently, are more reliable. Notice that the individual equilibrium constants are closer to the average than those in Table 25-1.

In the equilibrium quotient of the above example the concentrations are expressed in moles/l. Therefore K is:

$$K = \frac{[HI]^2}{[H_2]^1 \times [I_2]^1} = \frac{\cancel{(moles/l.)^2}}{\cancel{(moles/l.)} \times \cancel{(moles/l.)}}$$

and consequently has no units, i.e. it is dimensionless. However, in many cases K does have units and for clarity and precision it is necessary to state them. For example, for the equilibrium $CH_3COOH \rightleftharpoons H^+ + CH_3COO^-$

$$K = \frac{[H^+][CH_3COO^-]}{[CH_3COOH]}$$

where again each concentration is expressed in moles/l, the units of K are therefore:

TABLE 25-2 DATA ON EQUILIBRIUM REACTION: $H_{2(g)} + I_{2(g)} \rightleftharpoons 2\ HI_{(g)}$, AT 457.7°C

Expt.	At Equilibrium [H_2] moles/l.	[I_2] moles/l.	[HI] moles/l.	$\frac{[HI]^2}{[H_2]^1 \times [I_2]^1} = K$ moles/l.
1	0.0056170	0.0005936	0.012699	48.38
2	0.0045804	0.0009733	0.014858	49.56
3	0.0045669	0.0010577	0.015445	49.40 } 48.88 = average
4	0.0038415	0.0015238	0.016871	48.61
5	0.0016958	0.0016958	0.011807	48.44

$\frac{\text{(moles/l.)} \times \cancel{\text{(moles/l.)}}}{\cancel{\text{(moles/l.)}}}$, that is, moles/l. In all subsequent examples, wherever appropriate, the units of K will be added immediately after its numerical value. Where no units appear, K is dimensionless, as for the equilibrium $H_{2(g)} + I_{2(g)} \rightleftharpoons 2\ HI_{(g)}$.

EXPERIMENTAL DATA FOR THE EQUILIBRIUM: $CH_3COOH_{(aq)} \rightleftharpoons H^+_{(aq)} + CH_3COO^-_{(aq)}$

Now let us apply the Law of Mass Action to an equilibrium reaction in solution—the ionization of acetic acid:

Chemical equation: $CH_3COOH \rightleftharpoons H^+ + CH_3COO^-$

Equilibrium expression: $\frac{[H^+]^1 \times [CH_3COO^-]^1}{[CH_3COOH]^1} = K$

Table 25-3 lists some precise data measured in a series of experiments with very dilute solutions of acetic acid in water. "Total concentration" means the concentration of acetic acid actually introduced into the system—that is, the concentration that the CH_3COOH molecules would have if no ionization were to occur. It is, of course, equal to the concentration of the un-ionized acetic acid molecules, $HC_2H_3O_2$, plus the concentration of the anions, CH_3COO^-, resulting from that portion of the acid which has ionized at equilibrium. If we substitute the numerical values of the concentrations at equilibrium given in experiment 1 in the equilibrium expression, we get

$$\frac{[0.000415]^1 \times [0.000415]^1}{[0.00943]^1} = K = 1.83 \times 10^{-5} \text{ moles/l.}$$

The other values of K listed in the last column were calculated in the same way. This set of experimental data shows that in dilute aqueous solutions of pure acetic acid, K is fairly constant at a given temperature.

TABLE 25-3 DATA ON EQUILIBRIUM REACTION: $CH_3COOH_{(aq)} \rightleftharpoons H^+_{(aq)} + CH_3COO^-_{(aq)}$, AT 25°C

Expt.	At Start Total CH_3COOH Concentration moles/l.	At Equilibrium [H^+] moles/l.	[CH_3COO^-] moles/l.	[CH_3COOH] moles/l.	$\frac{[H^+]^1 \times [CH_3COO^-]^1}{[CH_3COOH]^1} = K$ moles/l.
1	0.00980	0.000415	0.000415	0.00943	1.83×10^{-5}
2	0.00344	0.000240	0.000240	0.00320	1.81×10^{-5} } 1.79×10^{-5} = average
3	0.0013638	0.000148	0.000148	0.001216	1.80×10^{-5}
4	0.0000280	0.0000150	0.0000150	0.0000130	1.73×10^{-5}

Now let us consider the equilibrium for the ionization of acetic acid when we mix a very dilute aqueous solution of acetic acid, CH_3COOH, with an aqueous solution of sodium acetate, CH_3COONa. Both solutions contain the acetate ion, CH_3COO^-, in one case from the partial ionization of acetic acid, in the other from the dissolving of the *ionic* sodium acetate. Table 25-4 gives the results of a series of experiments with a mixture of these two solutions at 25°C, results that illustrate the "common-ion effect." Again, total concentration means the concentration that the acetic acid molecules, CH_3COOH, would have if no ionization were to occur. The equation for the ionization of acetic acid and the equilibrium expression are, of course, the same as in the previous example. Thus, we can similarly calculate the value of K; for example, using the data of experiment 2 in Table 25-4:

$$\frac{[3.84 \times 10^{-4}]^1 \times [0.0100]^1}{[0.190]^1} = K = 2.02 \times 10^{-5} \quad \text{moles/l.}$$

First, notice that the principle of Le Chatelier holds good, because as additional CH_3COO^- ions (from sodium acetate, $CH_3COO^- + Na^+$) are added to the system at equilibrium the reverse reaction, $CH_3COOH \longleftarrow H^+ + CH_3COO^-$, occurs, thus tending to reduce the concentration of the H^+ ions and to increase the concentration of CH_3COOH molecules. In terms of the equilibrium expression $[H^+] \times [CH_3COO^-]/[CH_3COOH]$ the concentrations of H^+, CH_3COO^-, and CH_3COOH spontaneously adjust themselves until the product of the concentrations in the numerator once more balance the concentration in the denominator to give the same value of the equilibrium constant, K. From the data of experiments 1–5 we see that as the quantity of acetate ions, CH_3COO^-, added (as sodium acetate) at the start increases, the equilibrium concentration of the H^+ ions decreases and that of CH_3COOH molecules increases, until again the ratio $[H^+] \times [CH_3COO^-]/[CH_3COOH]$ gives the constant, K.

The K values listed in Table 25-4 vary somewhat more than in preceding examples, but are still within about 10 per cent of the average value. This is about the accuracy of agreement of the K values when the simple equilibrium constant expression is employed for solutions of this kind.

EXPERIMENTAL DATA FOR THE EQUILIBRIUM

$$CH_3COOH_{(l)} + C_2H_5OH_{(l)} \rightleftharpoons CH_3COOC_2H_{5(l)} + H_2O_{(l)}$$

For a final example of equilibrium in solutions, take the reaction of acetic acid, CH_3COOH, with ethyl alcohol, C_2H_5OH, to form ethyl acetate, $CH_3COOC_2H_5$, and water, H_2O:

$$CH_3COOH_{(l)} + C_2H_5OH_{(l)} \rightleftharpoons CH_3COOC_2H_{5(l)} + H_2O_{(l)}$$

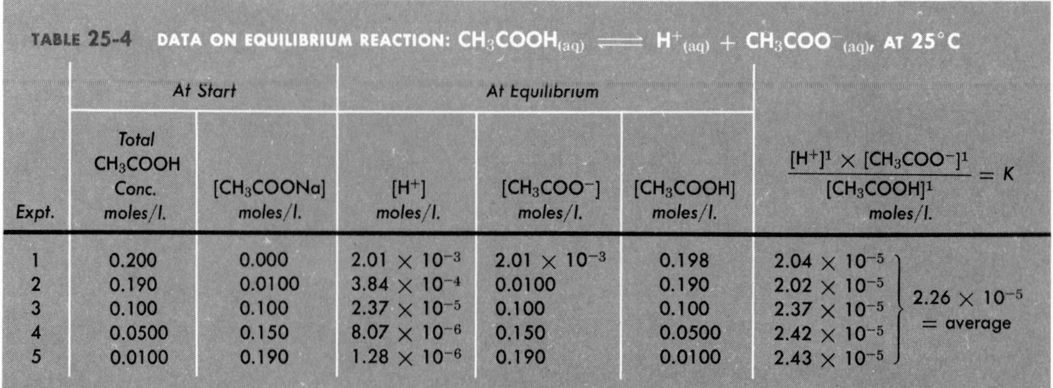

TABLE 25-4 DATA ON EQUILIBRIUM REACTION: $CH_3COOH_{(aq)} \rightleftharpoons H^+_{(aq)} + CH_3COO^-_{(aq)}$, AT 25°C

	At Start		*At Equilibrium*			
Expt.	*Total* CH_3COOH Conc. *moles/l.*	$[CH_3COONa]$ *moles/l.*	$[H^+]$ *moles/l.*	$[CH_3COO^-]$ *moles/l.*	$[CH_3COOH]$ *moles/l.*	$\frac{[H^+]^1 \times [CH_3COO^-]^1}{[CH_3COOH]^1} = K$ *moles/l.*
1	0.200	0.000	2.01×10^{-3}	2.01×10^{-3}	0.198	2.04×10^{-5}
2	0.190	0.0100	3.84×10^{-4}	0.0100	0.190	2.02×10^{-5}
3	0.100	0.100	2.37×10^{-5}	0.100	0.100	2.37×10^{-5}
4	0.0500	0.150	8.07×10^{-6}	0.150	0.0500	2.42×10^{-5}
5	0.0100	0.190	1.28×10^{-6}	0.190	0.0100	2.43×10^{-5}

2.26×10^{-5} = average

This time all the substances involved in the reaction appear as molecules. We use the subscript (l) to indicate that all reactants and products are liquids—actually, completely miscible liquids—but water is not the solvent. In this reaction, H_2O is just one of the products, and its concentration in the system is relatively low.

Chemical equation: $CH_3COOH + C_2H_5OH \rightleftharpoons CH_3COOC_2H_5 + H_2O$

Equilibrium expression: $$\frac{[CH_3COOC_2H_5]^1 \times [H_2O]^1}{[CH_3COOH]^1 \times [C_2H_5OH]^1} = K$$

Substituting the values of experiment 2, Table 25-5, we get:

$$K = \frac{[0.667]^1 \times [0.667]^1}{[0.333]^1 \times [0.333]^1} = 4.00$$

Notice that, as in the reaction $H_2 + I_2 \rightleftharpoons 2\,HI$, K is a pure member, with no units, because the various units involved in the equilibrium expression all cancel out:

$$\frac{\cancel{(moles/l.)} \times \cancel{(moles/l.)}}{\cancel{(moles/l.)} \times \cancel{(moles/l.)}}$$

Table 25-5 gives the data on this equilibrium measured at 25°C.

Again, notice that the system acts in accordance with the principle of Le Chatelier, for as the concentration of C_2H_5OH increases, the concentration of CH_3COOH decreases, and the concentrations of both $CH_3COOC_2H_5$ and H_2O increase. Thus as more C_2H_5OH is added to the above reversible system at equilibrium (experiment 1), the forward reaction, $CH_3COOH + C_2H_5OH \longrightarrow CH_3COOC_2H_5 + H_2O$, occurs; this reduces the amount of CH_3COOH and increases the amounts of $CH_3COOC_2H_5$ and H_2O, until $[CH_3COOC_2H_5] \times [H_2O]/[CH_3COOH] \times [C_2H_5OH]$ again gives the value of the equilibrium constant, K. And, in fact, the values for K listed in the last column of Table 25-5 indicate that the equilibrium quotients are fairly constant throughout all the experiments.

ILLUSTRATIVE EXAMPLES

All these experimental data, then, indicate that the equilibrium quotient, K, of a given reaction at a constant temperature is approximately constant, even though the individual values of both the initial and the equilibrium concentrations of the reactants and products may vary considerably. For any chemical system at equilibrium which is represented as $a\,A + b\,B \rightleftharpoons c\,C + d\,D$, we can use the general equilibrium expression:

$$\frac{[C]^c \times [D]^d}{[A]^a \times [B]^b} = K$$

to calculate the approximate concentration of substances in systems at equilibrium, if we know the initial concentration of the reactants and the value of the equilibrium constant, K. Several examples of this type of calculation follow.

TABLE 25-5 DATA ON EQUIL. REACTION: $CH_3COOH + C_2H_5OH \rightleftharpoons CH_3COOC_2H_5 + H_2O$ AT 25°C

	At Start		At Equilibrium				Equilibrium Constant,
Expt.	$[CH_3COOH]$ moles/l.	$[C_2H_5OH]$ moles/l.	$[CH_3COOH]$ moles/l.	$[C_2H_5OH]$ moles/l.	$[CH_3COOC_2H_5]$ moles/l.	$[H_2O]$ moles/l.	K moles/l.
1	1.00	0.180	0.829	0.0090	0.171	0.171	3.93
2	1.00	1.00	0.333	0.333	0.667	0.667	4.00
3	1.00	2.00	0.142	1.142	0.858	0.858	4.54
4	1.00	8.00	0.034	7.034	0.966	0.966	3.90

4.09 = average

PROBLEM. If 1 mole of H_2 and 1 mole of I_2 in a 1 l. vessel come to equilibrium at 457.7°C, what will be the concentration of each substance at equilibrium? The K value for this equilibrium is 48.9.

SOLUTION. *Chemical equation:* $H_{2(g)} + I_{2(g)} \rightleftharpoons 2\ HI_{(g)}$

Equilibrium expression: $\dfrac{[HI]^2}{[H_2]^1 \times [I_2]^1} = K = 48.9$

The initial concentrations are: $[H_2] = 1$ mole/l., $[I_2] = 1$ mole/l., $[HI] = 0$.

The equilibrium concentrations can be represented in terms of an unknown, x. Let x equal the number of moles of H_2 (in 1 l.) that react with I_2 to form HI. Then the number of moles of H_2 that are left at equilibrium will be the original number of moles present, 1, minus x, the number that have reacted: $1 - x$. Since the chemical equation tells us that the reaction of 1 mole of H_2 uses up 1 mole of I_2, when x moles of H_2 react, x moles of I_2 also must react. Thus, the concentration of I_2 remaining at equilibrium will also be $1 - x$. Since, according to the chemical equation, the reaction of 1 mole of H_2 produces 2 moles of HI, x moles of H_2 will react to produce $2x$ moles of HI at equilibrium. Consequently, the concentration of HI at equilibrium will be $2x$.

Now we can represent the concentrations at the start of the reaction and at equilibrium as follows:

Chemical equation:	H_2 +	I_2 $\rightleftharpoons$	$2\ HI$
Concentration (moles/l.) at start:	1.00	1.00	0
Concentration (moles/l.) at equilibrium:	$1.00 - x$	$1.00 - x$	$2x$

If we substitute the equilibrium concentrations in the equilibrium expression, we have:

$$\frac{[2x]^2}{[1.00 - x]^1 \times [1.00 - x]^1} = 48.9$$

To solve this equation, take the square root of both sides of the equation: $\dfrac{[2x]}{[1.00 - x]} = \sqrt{48.9}$. The $\sqrt{48.9}$ is 6.99, so we have: $2x = 6.99\,[1.00 - x]$ and $2x = 6.99 - 6.99x$. And finally, $8.99x = 6.99$, from which $x = \dfrac{6.99}{8.99} = 0.78$ mole/l. Thus, at equilibrium, the $[H_2] = (1.00 - x) = (1.00 - 0.78) = 0.22$ mole/l. The $[I_2] = (1.00 - x) = (1.00 - 0.78) = 0.22$ mole/l.; and $[HI] = 2.00x = 2.00(0.78) = 1.56$ moles/l.

PROBLEM. Calculate the concentrations of the H^+ ions, the CH_3COO^- ions, and the CH_3COOH molecules present at equilibrium when 0.100 mole of CH_3COOH is dissolved to make exactly 1 l. of aqueous solution. The K value for the ionization of acetic acid in water at 25°C is 1.85×10^{-5}.

SOLUTION. *Chemical equation:* $CH_3COOH_{(aq)} \rightleftharpoons H^+{}_{(aq)} + CH_3COO^-{}_{(aq)}$

The concentrations of the molecules and ions present at the start and at equilibrium are shown below, where x is equal to the number of moles of CH_3COOH that have ionized. For each CH_3COOH molecule that ionizes, one H^+ ion and one CH_3COO^- ion will form. Consequently, if x CH_3COOH molecules ionize, x H^+ ions and x CH_3COO^- ions are formed.

Chemical equation:	CH_3COOH $\rightleftharpoons$	H^+ +	CH_3COO^-
Concentration (moles/l.) at start:	0.100	0	0
Concentration (moles/l.) at equilibrium:	$0.100 - x$	x	x

Concentration at the start represents an assumed condition in which all the acetic acid is present as undissociated CH_3COOH molecules.

Equilibrium expression: $\dfrac{[H^+]^1 \times [CH_3COO^-]^1}{[CH_3COOH]^1} = 1.85 \times 10^{-5}$ (moles/l.)

If we substitute the equilibrium concentrations in the equilibrium expression, we have:

$$\frac{[x]^1 \times [x]^1}{[0.100 - x]^1} = 1.85 \times 10^{-5}$$

$$x^2 = 1.85 \times 10^{-5}(0.100 - x)$$

$$x^2 = (1.85 \times 10^{-6}) - (1.85 \times 10^{-5}\,x)$$

$$x^2 + (1.85 \times 10^{-5}\,x) - (1.85 \times 10^{-6}) = 0$$

Solving this quadratic equation, we get:

$$x = \frac{0.0026}{2} = 1.3 \times 10^{-3} = H^+ \text{ ion concentration in moles/l.}$$

Thus, at equilibrium, the concentrations of both the H^+ ions and the CH_3COO^- ions are 1.3×10^{-3} moles/l., and the concentration of the undissociated CH_3COOH molecules is $(0.100 - 0.0013) = 0.099$ mole/l.

We could have solved this problem just as correctly by the following simpler method. Notice that the value of x, 0.0013 (or 1.3×10^{-3}) is small in comparison with 0.1, so that $0.100 - 0.0013 = 0.0987$, which is approximately equal to 0.100. Therefore, if in the calculation we replace $(0.100 - x)$ by 0.100, we are actually replacing 0.0987 by 0.100. Let us calculate the H^+ concentration, replacing $(0.100 - x)$ by 0.100, and see what happens when we ignore x in the $[0.100 - x]$ term. The equilibrium expression is:

$$\frac{[x]^1 \times [x]^1}{[0.100 - x]^1} = 1.85 \times 10^{-5}$$

If we neglect x in the denominator, we have

$$\frac{[x]^1 \times [x]^1}{[0.100]^1} = 1.85 \times 10^{-5} \quad \text{and} \quad x^2 = (1.85 \times 10^{-5}) \times 0.100$$

From which: $x = 1.4 \times 10^{-3} = H^+$ ion concentration in moles/l.

Thus the value of x obtained in both calculations is the same to one decimal place. As a general rule, for weak acids having a K value of about 10^{-4} (moles/l.) or less, the value $(0.100 - x)$ may be taken as equal to 0.100.

PROBLEM. Cyanic acid, HCNO, is a weak acid; its K value is 2.00×10^{-4} (moles/l.). Calculate the concentration of H^+ ions at equilibrium in a 0.10 M solution.

SOLUTION. *Chemical equation:* $HCNO_{(aq)} \rightleftharpoons H^+{}_{(aq)} + CNO^-{}_{(aq)}$

For each molecule of HCNO that ionizes, one H^+ ion and one CNO^- ion will form. Thus, if x moles of HCNO ionize, x moles of H^+ ions and x moles of CNO^- ions will be formed.

Chemical equation:	HCNO $\rightleftharpoons$	H^+ +	CNO^-
Concentration (moles/l.) at start:	0.10	0	0
Concentration (moles/l.) at equilibrium:	$0.10 - x$	x	x

Equilibrium expression:

$$\frac{[H^+]^1 \times [CNO^-]^1}{[HCNO]^1} = K$$

Substituting the concentration (moles/l.) of H^+, CNO^-, and HCNO, at equilibrium, we get

$$\frac{[x]^1 \times [x]^1}{[0.10 - x]^1} = 2.0 \times 10^{-4} \text{ (moles/l.)}$$

Since K is small (approx. 10^{-4}), it is reasonable to assume that the value of $(0.10 - x)$ is nearly equal to 0.10; thus x may be omitted:

$$\frac{(x)(x)}{(0.10)} = 2.0 \times 10^{-4}$$

$$x^2 = 2.0 \times 10^{-5} = 20 \times 10^{-6}$$

$$x = \sqrt{20 \times 10^{-6}} = 4.5 \times 10^{-3}$$

$$x = 4.5 \times 10^{-3} = H^+ \text{ concentration in moles/l.}$$

As a check on our assumption note that $0.10 - 0.0045 = 0.10$.

PROBLEM. A solution is made by dissolving exactly 0.1 mole of acetic acid, CH_3COOH, and exactly 0.2 mole of sodium acetate, CH_3COONa in exactly 1 l. of solution. Calculate the H^+ ion concentration in this solution at equilibrium. The K value for the ionization of acetic acid in aqueous solution at 25°C is 1.85×10^{-5}.

SOLUTION. *Chemical equation:* $CH_3COOH \rightleftharpoons H^+ + CH_3COO^-$

The CH_3COOH ionizes slightly in water, and the undissociated CH_3COOH molecules are in equilibrium with the H^+ ions and the CH_3COO^- ions. Na^+ and additional CH_3COO^- ions are also present, resulting from the solution of the solid CH_3COONa. In the equilibrium reaction between the H^+ ions and the CH_3COO^- ions, the H^+ ions can combine with the CH_3COO^- ions that come from either the CH_3COOH or the CH_3COONa. Therefore, the concentration of CH_3COO^- ions in the equilibrium expression must include CH_3COO^- ions from *both* sources. Only relatively few CH_3COO^- ions are formed by the ionization of CH_3COOH, since acetic acid is a weak acid and dissociates only slightly. A relatively high concentration of CH_3COO^- ions is formed from CH_3COONa, because it is an ionic salt that dissociates almost 100 per cent.

Assume that at equilibrium x moles of CH_3COOH ionize. Then, at equilibrium, the CH_3COOH concentration is $0.1 - x$, the H^+ ion concentration is x, and the CH_3COO^- ion concentration is $(x + 0.2)$ the x is from ionization of CH_3COOH, and the 0.2 from dissociation of CH_3COONa.

	CH_3COOH	$\rightleftharpoons H^+$	$+ CH_3COO^-$
Chemical equation:	CH_3COOH	H^+	CH_3COO^-
Concentration (moles/l.) at start (assuming all CH_3COOH to be un-ionized):	0.1	0	0.2
Concentration (moles/l.) at equilibrium:	$0.1 - x$	x	$x + 0.2^a$

(^{a} from 100% dissociated (0.2 *M*) $CH_3COO^-Na^+$)

Equilibrium expression:

$$\frac{[H^+]^1 \times [CH_3COO^-]^1}{[CH_3COOH]^1} = 1.85 \times 10^{-5} \text{ (moles/l.)}$$

Substituting the equilibrium concentrations in the equilibrium expression, we have

$$\frac{[x]^1 \times [x + 0.2]^1}{[0.1 - x]^1} = 1.85 \times 10^{-5}$$

Since x is small compared to 0.1, and to 0.2, $(0.1 - x)$ may be taken to be approximately equal to 0.1 and $(0.2 - x)$ approximately equal to 0.2. Hence:

$$\frac{(x) \times (0.2)}{(0.1)} = 1.85 \times 10^{-5} \quad \text{and} \quad x = 0.93 \times 10^{-5} = H^+ \text{ ion concentration in moles/l.}$$

PROBLEM. To 500 ml of a 0.20 *M* solution of ammonia in water, $NH_3 + H_2O$, 500 ml of a 0.10 *M* solution of NH_4Cl are added. Calculate the OH^- ion concentration in the resulting solution at equilibrium.* The *K* value for the reaction $NH_3 + H_2O \rightleftharpoons NH_4^+ + OH^-$ is 3.2×10^{-7} at 18°C.

SOLUTION. When the two solutions are mixed, the total concentrations in the resulting solution are:

$$[NH_3] = 0.20\ M \times \frac{500 \text{ ml}}{1000 \text{ ml}} = 0.10\ M$$

$$[NH_4Cl] = 0.10\ M \times \frac{500 \text{ ml}}{1000 \text{ ml}} = 0.050\ M$$

Let x represent the number of moles of NH_3 that react according to the equilibrium equation below. Thus, x will also represent the OH^- ion concentration at equilibrium. The equilibrium equation and the concentrations of the constituents at the start and at equilibrium are as follows:

Chemical equation:	$NH_3 + H_2O$	$\rightleftharpoons NH_4^+$	$+ OH^-$
Concentration (moles/l.) at start (assuming all NH_3 to be unreacted):	0.10	0	0
Concentration (moles/l.) at equilibrium:	$(0.10 - x)$	$(0.050^a + x)$	x

(^{a} from 100% dissociated (0.050 *M*) $NH_4^+Cl^-$)

Equilibrium expression:

$$\frac{[NH_4^+]^1 \times [OH^-]^1}{[NH_3]^1 \times [H_2O]^1} = K$$

* As we learned in Chapter 18, when two or more different solutions or liquids are mixed, the total volume of the mixture does not always equal exactly the sum of the individual volumes. For simplicity, however, we shall assume that the volume of the mixture is the same as the sum of the individual volumes.

Substituting the equilibrium concentrations in the equilibrium expression, we have:

$$\frac{[0.050 + x]^1 \times [x]^1}{[0.10 - x]^1 \times [56]} = 3.2 \times 10^{-7}$$

In the terms $(0.050 + x)$ and $(0.10 - x)$, x may be neglected:

$$\frac{(0.050) \times (x)}{(0.10) \times (56)} = 3.2 \times 10^{-7}; \text{ and } x = 3.6 \times 10^{-5} = [OH^-] \text{ moles/l.}$$

We could have solved the problem also in the following manner. Since the concentrations of the solutes (NH_3 and NH_4Cl) are small, the concentration of the solvent (water) is approximately the same as in pure water, 56 moles/l. Also, the concentration of water does not change significantly as a result of the reactions, even though the concentration of that solute which reacts with water does change. For this reason, it is generally convenient to incorporate the (approximately constant) value of the concentration of water into the value of K. In this case, for example, we have:

$$\frac{[NH_4]^1 \times [OH^-]^1}{[NH_3]^1} = [H_2O]^1 \times K = 56 \times 3.2 \times 10^{-7} = 1.8 \times 10^{-5} \text{ mole/l.}$$

We then proceed to solve the problem as outlined above, using this "simplified" value of K. In general, whenever we consider an equilibrium reaction in aqueous solution, and water itself is either a reactant or a product, it is customary to express the equilibrium by a simplified equation not involving water, and to use a value of the equilibrium constant that includes the constant factor arising from the concentration of water.

PROBLEM. To 500 ml of a 0.6 M solution of CH_3COOH, 0.2 mole of solid NaOH are added. Calculate the H^+ ion concentration in the resulting solution, assuming that no change in volume takes place. The K of ionization for CH_3COOH in aqueous solution = 1.8×10^{-5} moles/l. at 18°C.

SOLUTION. In 500 ml of 0.6 M CH_3COOH there are present: 0.5 l. $\times$ 0.6 mole/l. = 0.3 mole of CH_3COOH. Since we have more moles of acid (0.3) than we have moles of base (0.2), all the base, NaOH, is neutralized by part of the acid, CH_3COOH, producing the salt, CH_3COONa (and H_2O):

$$CH_3COOH + NaOH \longrightarrow CH_3COONa + H_2O$$

Of the 0.3 mole of CH_3COOH, 0.2 mole is neutralized by 0.2 mole of NaOH, producing 0.2 mole CH_3COONa. Thus, after neutralization, the resulting 0.5-l. solution contains 0.3 − 0.2 = 0.1 mole of CH_3COOH and 0.2 mole of CH_3COONa. The concentrations, in moles/l., of the CH_3COOH and the CH_3COONa follow:

$$\text{Concentration at start of } CH_3COOH = \frac{0.1 \text{ mole}}{0.5 \text{ l.}} = 0.2\ M$$

$$\text{Concentration at start of } CH_3COONa = \frac{0.2 \text{ mole}}{0.5 \text{ l.}} = 0.4\ M$$

Let x equal H^+ ion concentration at equilibrium:

Chemical equation:	CH_3COOH $\rightleftharpoons$	H^+ +	CH_3COO^-
Concentration (moles/l.) at start (assuming all CH_3COOH to be un-ionized):	0.2	0	0.4^a
Concentration (moles/l.) at equilibrium:	$(0.2 - x)$	x	$(0.4^a + x)$

(^{a} from 100% dissociated (0.4 M) $CH_3COO^-Na^+$)

Equilibrium expression:
$$\frac{[H^+]^1 \times [CH_3COO^-]^1}{[CH_3COOH]^1} = 1.8 \times 10^{-5} \text{ (moles/l.)}$$

$$\frac{(x) \times (0.4 + x)}{(0.2 - x)} = 1.8 \times 10^{-5}$$

As a first approximation, the value of x may be omitted in both the terms $(0.4 + x)$ and $(0.2 - x)$:

$$\frac{(x) \times (0.4)}{0.2} = 1.8 \times 10^{-5}$$

$$x = 0.9 \times 10^{-5} = H^+ \text{ ion concentration in moles/l.}$$

Note that our approximation is acceptable:

$$0.4 + 0.9 \times 10^{-5} = 0.4; \text{ and } 0.2 - 0.9 \times 10^{-5} = 0.2.$$

THE EFFECT OF CONCENTRATION ON EQUILIBRIUM CONSTANTS

We have seen that the equilibrium quotient, K, is approximately a constant for gaseous reactions and for reactions in very dilute solutions. It can be shown that K would be truly constant, at any specified constant temperature, only for equilibrium reactions in ideal gaseous systems where there are no van der Waals intermolecular interactions, and where the volume occupied by the gas molecules is negligible compared with the total available volume. For equilibrium reactions in solution, we would expect the equilibrium quotient to approach a truly constant value, the more the solutions behave ideally. In other words, the equilibrium quotient is truly an equilibrium constant only when the secondary effects created by the attractive forces between particles are negligible. For example, consider a very dilute solution formed by dissolving a weak acid, such as acetic acid, in water; when we introduce the equilibrium concentrations of the ions and the un-ionized molecules in the equilibrium expression, we obtain a value for the equilibrium quotient that is virtually constant. This is so because in a very dilute solution of a weak acid in water, the ions are very far apart (since the acid is weak, only a relatively small portion of its molecules are dissociated into ions; moreover, the solution is very dilute). Consequently, the oppositely charged ions exert very little electrostatic attraction on one another. But as we keep increasing the amount of the weak acid dissolved in water, even though the number of ions is still relatively small (because, after all, the acid is weak), it becomes more probable that the oppositely charged ions will come together and hence begin to exert more and more electrostatic attraction on one another. Under these conditions the values of the equilibrium quotient are different from one another and from the value for the very dilute solution first discussed. For example, we have seen (Table 25-3) that, for very dilute water solutions of acetic acid, from about 0.000028 to 0.01 M, the K value is very close to a constant value, 1.8×10^{-5} moles/l. At a concentration of 1 M, however, K is 1.4×10^{-5} moles/l. The equilibrium quotient value does not necessarily decrease, as the concentration of the solution increases; in fact, in some cases it increases.

THE EFFECT OF FOREIGN IONS ON EQUILIBRIUM CONSTANTS

Ions present in a solution which are different from those involved in the equilibrium reaction itself are often called "foreign ions." We saw above that the concentrations of the particles involved in the equilibrium reaction have an effect on the value of K, owing to attractive forces among the particles. Foreign ions in a solution of a weak electrolyte such as acetic acid also exert attractive forces for the particles involved in the equilibrium reaction. And consequently, the value of K for all weak electrolytes is affected by the presence of foreign ions. For example, the value of K for acetic acid is changed by the addition of a salt such as KCl. In a 0.1 M water solution of KCl, the K value for 0.1 M acetic acid is 2.9×10^{-5} moles/l., whereas in a 0.1 M solution of acetic acid in the absence of KCl, the K value is about 1.8×10^{-5} moles/l. And the greater the charge on the foreign ions, the greater the effect. For example, the change in K for a given concentration of acetic acid is greater in the presence of a $Ca^{++}(Cl^-)_2$ solution than in the presence of a K^+Cl^- solution of equal normality. This difference in effect results from the greater charge of the Ca^{++} ion than of the K^+ ion.

ACTIVITY

We have seen in the preceding sections that, for a system consisting of real gases and real solutions, the value of the equilibrium quotient, K, at a constant temperature depends somewhat on the concentrations of the substances in equilibrium as well as on the presence of foreign substances. In other words, for real systems the equilibrium quotient, expressed in terms of molar concentrations, is not truly a constant and the Law of Mass Action is obeyed only as a first approximation. We could, however, obtain a truly constant value of K by multiplying the concentration of each substance that appears in the equilibrium expression by an appropriate correction factor. This correction factor, called the "activity coefficient," takes into account the various effects that cause the substance considered to depart from its ideal behavior. Thus, if the molar concentration of a given substance is multiplied by its activity coefficient, we obtain the "effective or active concentration," or the *activity* of that substance in the system. The activity, indicated by the symbol **a**, is therefore expressed as:

$$\mathbf{a} = \text{activity coefficient} \times \text{molar concentration}$$

If we write the equilibrium expression for our usual general equation, $a\,\mathrm{A} + b\,\mathrm{B} \rightleftharpoons c\,\mathrm{C} + d\,\mathrm{D}$, in terms of the activity of each reactant and product, then the resulting value of K (indicated as $K_{\mathbf{a}}$) is truly constant at a constant temperature:

$$\frac{(\mathbf{a}_\mathrm{C})^c \times (\mathbf{a}_\mathrm{D})^d}{(\mathbf{a}_\mathrm{A})^a \times (\mathbf{a}_\mathrm{B})^b} = K_{\mathbf{a}} = \text{constant}$$

For any system, the difference between the value of the true equilibrium constant, $K_{\mathbf{a}}$, and the value of the equilibrium quotient expressed in terms of molar concentrations, K, is a measure of the system's departure from ideal behavior. The activity coefficient, and hence the activity, of a substance present at a certain molar concentration in a given system can be determined experimentally—for example, by comparing the experimental values of freezing point depressions, $\Delta T_{\mathrm{f.p.}}$, or boiling point elevation, $\Delta T_{\mathrm{b.p.}}$, or osmotic pressure, π, of solutions with the calculated values assuming ideal behavior (Chapter 19). Or we can determine activities from solubility values (see page 557) or from electromotive forces (see pages 481–485 and page 565). Generally, determining the activity of each substance present in a system consisting of several components is not a simple task. As a first approximation, therefore, we usually write the equilibrium expression simply in terms of the molar concentration. The value of the equilibrium quotient, K, is somewhat different from the true value of the equilibrium constant, $K_{\mathbf{a}}$, at the same temperature, but it is sufficiently accurate for most of the calculations in which we are interested.

25-2 Solutions with Constant H^+ Ion (and OH^- Ion) Concentration—Buffer Solutions

Sometimes it is desirable to have a solution that is able to maintain a nearly constant H^+ ion concentration—that is, a constant pH value—when relatively small amounts of H^+ ions or OH^- ions are added. Such a solution, called a *buffer solution,* has a "reserve power" to maintain an approximately constant H^+ ion concentration. Buffer solutions are simply solutions containing a mixture of a weak Bronsted acid (a weak proton donor) and its conjugate base (a proton acceptor).

An example of a buffer solution is an aqueous solution that is 1 *M* in acetic acid and 1 *M* in sodium acetate. If HCl is added to this solution, the H^+ ions of this strong acid will join with CH_3COO^- ions (the Bronsted base) from the sodium acetate present in solution to form undissociated CH_3COOH molecules. The equilibrium quotient for the reaction: $H^+ + CH_3COO^-_{(\text{Bronsted base})} \rightleftharpoons CH_3COOH_{(\text{Bronsted acid})}$ remains constant, and the added H^+ ions are removed. If NaOH is added to the solution, an equilibrium is established between the added OH^- ions and the undissociated acetic acid molecules:

$$CH_3COOH + OH^- \rightleftharpoons CH_3COO^- + H_2O$$

This, as we found in Chapter 20, represents the competition for the proton of two different Bronsted bases—the OH^- ion and the CH_3COO^- molecule. And since the OH^- ion is a better proton acceptor (a stronger Bronsted base) than the CH_3COO^- ion, the equilibrium is shifted far to the right. In effect, therefore, the added OH^- ions are "removed."

Thus, the addition of a small amount of a strong acid to a buffer solution produces no *appreciable* increase in the H^+ ion concentration. And the addition of a small amount of a strong base produces no *appreciable* increase in the OH^- ion concentration.

Another example of a buffer solution is a solution of aqueous ammonia and ammonium chloride (in this case, NH_3 is the Bronsted base and NH_4^+ the Bronsted acid of the buffer solution). When small amounts of either a strong acid such as HCl or a strong base such as NaOH are added, the OH^- ion concentration, and hence also the H^+ ion concentration, of this solution remain essentially constant. In this solution, there is an equilibrium among NH_3 molecules, NH_4^+ ions, and OH^- ions; the concentration of the NH_3 molecules and that of the NH_4^+ ions are high relative to the concentration of the OH^- ions, because the presence of the common ion, NH_4^+ (from NH_4Cl), shifts the equilibrium far to the left:

$$NH_3 + H_2O \rightleftharpoons NH_4^+ + OH^-$$

When HCl is added, the OH^- ions (Bronsted base) will accept these extra H^+ ions to form NH_4^+ ions (Bronsted acid). When, on the other hand, NaOH is added, the NH_4^+ (Bronsted acid) will give up a proton to the added OH^- ions, to form additional NH_3 molecules (Bronsted base).

A buffer solution can be prepared by mixing any weak Bronsted acid with approximately an equivalent amount of its conjugate base. In addition to those mentioned above, the following are commonly used buffer solutions: (a) $NaHCO_3$ + Na_2CO_3 (here HCO_3^- is the Bronsted acid and $CO_3^=$ is its conjugate base), and (b) NaH_2PO_4 and Na_2HPO_4 (here $H_2PO_4^-$ is the Bronsted acid and $HPO_4^=$ its conjugate base).

Buffer solutions are used to control the H^+ ion (or OH^- ion) concentration of aqueous solutions when a change of pH is undesirable. For example, if we pass H_2S gas into an aqueous solution of $ZnCl_2$, the following equilibrium reaction occurs:

$$H_2S_{(aq)} + Zn^{++}_{(aq)} + \cancel{2\,Cl^-_{(aq)}} \rightleftharpoons ZnS_{(s)} + 2\,H^+_{(aq)} + \cancel{2\,Cl^-_{(aq)}}$$

As this reaction shows, H^+ ions are also formed as products; thus, as the H^+ ion concentration increases, precipitation of ZnS is prevented. And in fact, Zn^{++} ions are not completely precipitated by H_2S from a neutral solution of a Zn(II) salt alone. But if we pass H_2S gas into an aqueous solution of $ZnCl_2$ containing an excess of $CH_3COO^-Na^+$, *all* the Zn^{++} ions precipitate as ZnS, as shown by the following sequence of equilibrium reactions:

$$H_2S_{(aq)} + Zn^{++}_{(aq)} + \cancel{2\,Cl^-_{(aq)}} \rightleftharpoons ZnS_{(s)} + 2\,H^+_{(aq)} + \cancel{2\,Cl^-_{(aq)}}$$

$$+$$

$$2\,CH_3COO^-_{(aq)} + 2\,Na^+_{(aq)}$$

$$\updownarrow$$

$$2\,CH_3COOH_{(aq)}$$

Notice that the H^+ ions produced react with the CH_3COO^- ions to form CH_3COOH molecules and that the solution now contains a buffer of acetic acid and sodium acetate.

ILLUSTRATIVE EXAMPLES

PROBLEM. In 1.0 l. of a buffer solution of 0.10 *M* CH_3COOH and 0.10 *M* CH_3COONa, we dissolve 0.01 mole of HCl gas. Assume that there is no change in the volume of the resulting solution. (a) Calculate the H^+ ion concentration *before* the HCl gas is added. (b) Calculate the H^+ ion concentration *after* the HCl gas is added.

SOLUTION. (a) As we have seen before (p. 552), the H^+ ion concentration of the original buffer solution may be calculated as follows:

$$\frac{[H^+]^1 \times [CH_3COO^-]^1}{[CH_3COOH]^1} = 1.8 \times 10^{-5} \text{ (moles/l.)}$$

$$\frac{(x) \times (0.10 + x)}{(0.10 - x)} = 1.8 \times 10^{-5}$$

Assuming that x is negligible in comparison with 0.10, we have x = H^+ ion concentration of original buffer solution = 1.8×10^{-5} (moles/l.). (b) Let y equal the number of moles of HCl that react with CH_3COO^- ions to form CH_3COOH.

Chemical equation:

$$CH_3COOH \rightleftharpoons H^+ + CH_3COO^-$$

Concentration at start:

$$(0.10 - 1.8 \times 10^{-5}) \quad (0.01 + 1.8 \times 10^{-5}) \quad (0.10 + 1.8 \times 10^{-5})$$

Concentration at equilibrium:

$$(0.10 - 1.8 \times 10^{-5} + y) \quad (0.01 - y + 1.8 \times 10^{-5}) \quad (0.10 + 1.8 \times 10^{-5} - y)$$

Since 1.8×10^{-5} is negligible added to or subtracted from 0.10 and 0.01, we have the following concentrations at equilibrium:

$$CH_3COOH \rightleftharpoons H^+ + CH_3COO^-$$

$$(0.10 + y) \quad (0.01 - y) \quad (0.10 - y)$$

$$\frac{[H^+]^1 \times [CH_3COO^-]^1}{[CH_3COOH]^1} = 1.8 \times 10^{-5}$$

$$\frac{(0.01 - y) \times (0.10 - y)}{(0.10 + y)} = 1.8 \times 10^{-5}$$

Solving the equation, we get $y = 0.0099 = 9.9 \times 10^{-3}$

The calculation shows that 0.0099 mole of the added 0.01 mole of HCl has reacted with CH_3COO^- ions to form molecular CH_3COOH. The effective increase in the H^+ ion concentration, therefore, is only (0.010 – 0.0099) = 0.001. In other words, the addition of 0.01 mole of this strong acid (HCl) has increased the H^+ ion concentration of the buffer solution by only a negligible amount, 1×10^{-3} moles/l. The added H^+ ions have been 99 per cent neutralized by the CH_3COO^- ions in the buffer solution.

25-3 Equilibrium Between an Ionic Solid and Its Saturated Solution—Solubility Product

In saturated solutions of both soluble and slightly soluble salts, equilibrium exists between the crystalline solid and the ions of the salt in solution at any given temperature. But only in the case of saturated solutions of very slightly soluble salts, where the concentrations of the ions are sufficiently low, can we calculate changes in the concentrations of the ions at equilibrium resulting from the effects of common ions.

First, we shall state the approximate quantitative relationship that exists between the concentrations of the ions at equilibrium in saturated solutions of very slightly soluble ionic salts. Then we shall examine some experimental data to show how closely the quantitative relationship agrees with the observed facts.

Here is a generalized equation that represents the equilibrium reaction existing in a saturated solution of a slightly soluble ionic salt of formula A_2B_3:

$$A_2B_{3(s)} \rightleftharpoons 2\,A^{+++}{}_{(aq)} + 3\,B^{=}{}_{(aq)}$$

The equilibrium expression for the above reaction at a constant temperature is:

$$\frac{[A^{+++}]^2 \times [B^{=}]^3}{[A_2B_3]^1} = K_1$$

The effective concentration (activity) of a solid is always the same regardless of the amount of solid present. Thus, in the equilibrium expression above, the concentration of solid A_2B_3 will be a constant. For this reason the term $[A_2B_3]_{(s)}$ can be replaced by a constant, K_2, giving:

$$\frac{[A^{+++}]^2 \times [B^=]^3}{K_2} = K_1$$

Rearrangement gives: $$[A^{+++}]^2 \times [B^=]^3 = K_1 \times K_2$$

The product of two constants, $K_1 \times K_2$, may be expressed as a third constant, K_{sp}:

$$[A^{+++}]^2 \times [B^=]^3 = K_{sp}$$

In this simplified equilibrium expression, which we often call "solubility expression," the brackets represent as usual the equilibrium concentration expressed in moles/liter. We can read this expression as follows: "The concentration in moles/l. of the A^{+++} ion, raised to the second power, multiplied by the concentration in moles/l. of the $B^=$ ion, raised to the third power, equals a constant, K_{sp}, called the *solubility product* of the A_2B_3 salt."

In general, for any saturated solution of a slightly soluble ionic compound, we raise the concentration of each ion in solution to a power equal to the coefficient of that ion in the ionic dissociation equation, and then multiply one concentration by the other; the product obtained is called the solubility product of the ionic compound. The solubility product has a numerical value that is approximately constant for any slightly soluble ionic salt present in a saturated solution at a specified, constant temperature.

Now let us apply the solubility expression to a slightly soluble ionic compound of the general formula MX_2. Consider a saturated aqueous solution in which the slightly soluble compound $MX_{2(s)}$ is in equilibrium with its ions, $M^{++}_{(aq)}$ and $X^-_{(aq)}$:

Chemical equation: $MX_{2(s)} \rightleftharpoons M^{++}_{(aq)} + X^-_{(aq)} + X^-_{(aq)}$
Or, simply: $MX_2 \rightleftharpoons M^{++} + 2\,X^-$

Solubility expression: $[M^{++}]^1 \times [X^-]^1 \times [X^-]^1 = K_{sp}$ of MX_2
Or, simply: $[M^{++}]^1 \times [X^-]^2 = K_{sp}$ of MX_2

The K_{sp} of MX_2 is the product of the concentrations (in moles/l.) of all the ions present in the solution, each concentration raised to a power equal to the coefficient of the ion in the chemical equation. If the concentrations are expressed in other units, the numerical value of K_{sp} will be different, which emphasizes the importance of attaching units to K values and K_{sp} values (as stated on p. 546). For instance, the units of K_{sp} in the above case are $(\text{moles/l.})^1 \times (\text{moles/l.})^2 = (\text{moles/l.})^3$. Here are some examples of the solubility expression as applied to the slightly soluble salts, silver chloride, AgCl; barium sulfate, $BaSO_4$; and lead chloride, $PbCl_2$.

1. *Chemical equation:* $AgCl \rightleftharpoons Ag^+ + Cl^-$
   Solubility expression: $[Ag^+]^1 \times [Cl^-]^1 = K_{sp}$ of AgCl (moles/l.)^2

2. *Chemical equation:* $BaSO_4 \rightleftharpoons Ba^{++} + SO_4^=$
   Solubility expression: $[Ba^{++}]^1 \times [SO_4^=]^1 = K_{sp}$ of $BaSO_4$ (moles/l.)^2

3. *Chemical equation:* $PbCl_2 \rightleftharpoons Pb^{++} + 2\,Cl^-$
   Solubility expression: $[Pb^{++}]^1 \times [Cl^-]^2 = K_{sp}$ of $PbCl_2$ (moles/l.)^3

THE EFFECT OF COMMON IONS ON EQUILIBRIUM CONSTANTS

Let us examine some experimental data on the solubility of a slightly soluble salt in pure water and in solutions containing a common ion. Table 25-6 presents the data assembled from a series of experiments on the solubility of slightly soluble thallium(I) chloride, TlCl, in pure water and in aqueous soutions of potassium chloride, KCl, at various concentrations at 25°C. The solubility of TlCl was determined by adding an excess of solid TlCl either to pure water (experiment 1) or to aqueous solutions containing a known concentration of KCl. In each case the components were analyzed after the system had reached equilibrium.

The data in Table 25-6 show that as the concentration of KCl increases from experiment 1 ([KCl] = 0) to experiment 4, the solubility of TlCl decreases. On the basis of Le Chatelier's principle, we would predict that when additional Cl^- ions are added to a saturated solution of TlCl in water at equilibrium, $TlCl \rightleftharpoons Tl^+ + Cl^-$, some additional TlCl would precipitate—as is the case.

By substituting in the solubility expression the numerical values for the concentrations in moles/l. of the Tl^+ and Cl^- ions, we can calculate the value of the solubility product, K_{sp}, for TlCl in water at 25°C.

Chemical equation: $TlCl \rightleftharpoons Tl^+ + Cl^-$
Solubility expression: $[Tl^+]^1 \times [Cl^-]^1 = K_{sp}$

Using, for example, the data for experiment 2, we have:

$$[Tl^+]^1 \times [Cl^-]^1 = K_{sp}$$
$$[8.69 \times 10^{-3}]^1 \times [33.69 \times 10^{-3}]^1 = 2.93 \times 10^{-4} \quad (\text{moles/l.})^2$$

The other values for K_{sp} listed in the last column of Table 25-6 were calculated in the same way. The K_{sp} values vary quite a bit from pure water to 0.1 *M* KCl. Nevertheless, calculations made on the assumption that the K_{sp} is a constant are useful, for they enable us to calculate the *approximate* solubilities of slightly soluble soutions containing common ions.

EFFECT OF IONS ON K_{sp} VALUES

When a very slightly soluble ionic compound is dissolved in water to form a saturated solution, the concentrations of the positive and negative ions are very low. Consequently, the ions are so far apart that they exert almost no electrostatic attraction on one another. When an appreciable concentration of a soluble salt is added to a saturated solution of a very slightly soluble salt, certain effects become important, effects that arise from the attractive forces between the ions of the very slightly soluble salt and the "foreign ions" of the added soluble salt. So, the K_{sp} value in the presence of foreign ions differs somewhat from the K_{sp} value for pure water. The details of the action of foreign ions with ions involved in the reversible reaction are fairly complicated, and their effect on the value of the K_{sp} is difficult to explain. But the important point is, they *do* affect the value of the K_{sp}.

As an illustration, consider the following experimental data on the K_{sp} of TlCl in (1) water, and in the presence of a water solution of (2) KNO_3 and (3) K_2SO_4, salts that do not have an ion in common with TlCl. At 25°C, the solubility of TlCl in pure water is 16.07×10^{-3} mole/l., and its K_{sp} value is 2.58×10^{-4} (mole/l.)^2 (see Table

TABLE 25-6 SOLUBILITY OF TlCl IN PURE WATER AND IN AQUEOUS SOLUTIONS OF KCl AT 25°C

Expt.	*Concentration of KCl (moles/l.)*	*Solubility of TlCl (moles/l.)*	*Concentration of Tl^+ (moles/l.)*	*Concentration of Cl^- (moles/l.)*	$[Ti^+]^1 \times [Cl^-]^1 = K_{sp}$ *(moles/l.)^2*	
1	0.000 (pure water)	16.07×10^{-3}	16.07×10^{-3}	16.07×10^{-3}	2.58×10^{-4}	
2	25.0×10^{-3}	8.69×10^{-3}	8.69×10^{-3}	33.69×10^{-3}	2.93×10^{-4}	3.23×10^{-4}
3	50.0×10^{-3}	5.90×10^{-3}	5.90×10^{-3}	55.90×10^{-3}	3.30×10^{-4}	= average
4	100×10^{-3}	3.96×10^{-3}	3.96×10^{-3}	103.96×10^{-3}	4.12×10^{-4}	

25-6). In an aqueous solution containing 50×10^{-3} mole/l. of KNO_3, the solubility of TlCl is 18.26×10^{-3} mole/l., and its K_{sp} value is 3.33×10^{-4} (mole/l.)^2. In an aqueous solution containing 25×10^{-3} mole/l. of K_2SO_4, the solubility of TlCl is 19.42×10^{-3} mole/l., and its K_{sp} value is 3.77×10^{-4} (mole/l.)^2. In these examples, the K_{sp} value increases with concentration—in certain other cases, however, the K_{sp} value decreases.

ILLUSTRATIVE EXAMPLES

PROBLEM. 100 ml of water will dissolve 1.0×10^{-5} mole of lead sulfate, $PbSO_4$, at 25°C. Calculate the K_{sp} of $PbSO_4$ in pure water at this temperature.

SOLUTION. The concentration of $PbSO_4$ in moles/l. is:

$$1.0 \times 10^{-5} \text{ mole}/0.1 \text{ l.} = 1.0 \times 10^{-4} \text{ mole/l.}$$

Chemical equation: $PbSO_4 \rightleftharpoons Pb^{++} + SO_4^{=}$

Concentration (moles/l.) at equilibrium: 1.0×10^{-4} $\quad$ 1.0×10^{-4}

Solubility expression: $[Pb^{++}]^1 \times [SO_4^{=}]^1 = K_{sp}$

$$[1.0 \times 10^{-4}]^1 \times [1.0 \times 10^{-4}]^1 = K_{sp} = 1 \times 10^{-8} \quad \text{(mole/l.)}^2$$

PROBLEM. Calculate the solubility of $Cd(OH)_2$ in (a) moles/l., (b) grams/l. The K_{sp} of $Cd(OH)_2 = 1.2 \times 10^{-14}$ (mole/l.)^3. The formula wt. of $Cd(OH)_2 = 146.42$.

SOLUTION. (a) Let x equal the solubility of $Cd(OH)_2$ in moles/l. Then the concentration in moles/l. of Cd^{++} ions in also x. And the concentration of OH^- ions is $2x$, because each $Cd(OH)_2$ that dissolves provides one Cd^{++} ion and two OH^- ions.

Chemical equation: $Cd(OH)_2 \rightleftharpoons Cd^{++} + 2\,OH^-$

Concentration (moles/l.) at equilibrium: x $\quad$ $2x$

Solubility expression: $[Cd^{++}]^1 \times [OH^-]^2 = K_{sp} = 1.2 \times 10^{-14}$ (mole/l.)^3

$$[x]^1 \times [2x]^2 = 1.2 \times 10^{-14}$$

$$4x^3 = 1.2 \times 10^{-14} = 12 \times 10^{-15}$$

$$x^3 = 3.0 \times 10^{-15}$$

$$x = 1.4 \times 10^{-5} \text{ mole/l. of } Cd(OH)_2$$

(b) 1.4×10^{-5} mole/l. $\times$ 146.42 g/mole $= 2.1 \times 10^{-3}$ g/l. of $Cd(OH)_2$

PROBLEM. A saturated solution is prepared by dissolving pure Ag_2SO_4 in 400 ml of water. If the K_{sp} of $Ag_2SO_4 = 1.2 \times 10^{-5}$ (mole/l.)^3, calculate the number of grams of Ag_2SO_4 that dissolve. Formula wt. $Ag_2SO_4 = 311.83$.

SOLUTION. Let x equal the concentration in moles/l. of $SO_4^{=}$ at equilibrium. Then $2x$ must equal the concentration in moles/l. of Ag^+, because each Ag_2SO_4 that dissolves produces one $SO_4^{=}$ ion and two Ag^+ ions.

Chemical equation: $Ag_2SO_4 \rightleftharpoons 2\,Ag^+ + 1\,SO_4^{=}$

Concentration (moles/l.) at equilibrium: $2x$ $\quad$ x

Solubility expression: $[Ag^+]^2 \times [SO_4^{=}]^1 = 1.2 \times 10^{-5}$ (mole/l.)^3

$$(2x)^2 \times x^1 = 1.2 \times 10^{-5}$$

$$4x^3 = 1.2 \times 10^{-5}$$

$$x^3 = 0.30 \times 10^{-5} = 3.0 \times 10^{-6}$$

$$x = 1.4 \times 10^{-2} = \text{conc. of } SO_4^{=} \text{ ions in mole/l.}$$

Thus, the number of moles of Ag_2SO_4 that dissolve in 1 l. of water is also 1.4×10^{-2}. The number of grams of Ag_2SO_4 that dissolve in 0.400 l. of water is:

$$\frac{1.4 \times 10^{-2}\ \cancel{\text{mole}}}{1\ \cancel{\text{l.}}} \times \frac{311.83\text{ g}}{\cancel{\text{mole}}} \times 0.400\ \cancel{\text{l.}} = 1.7\text{ g}$$

PROBLEM. To a 1.0 l. saturated solution of AgCl is added enough NaCl so that the final concentration of Cl^- ions in solution after the AgCl solid has precipitated is 0.10 *M*.

Calculate (a) the concentration of Ag^+ ions remaining in solution, (b) the number of moles of AgCl that precipitated. The K_{sp} of AgCl = 1.2×10^{-10} (mole/l.)^2.

SOLUTION. (a) The final concentration of Cl^- ions is 0.10 mole/l. Let x equal the final concentration of Ag^+ ion in moles/l.

Chemical equation: $AgCl \rightleftharpoons Ag^+ + Cl^-$

Concentration (moles/l.) at equilibrium: $x \quad 0.10$

Solubility expression:

$$[Ag^+]^1 \times [Cl^-]^1 = K_{sp} = 1.2 \times 10^{-10}$$

$$[x]^1 \times [0.10]^1 = 1.2 \times 10^{-10} \quad \text{(mole/l.)}^2$$

$$x = \frac{1.2 \times 10^{-10}}{0.10} = 1.2 \times 10^{-9} \text{ mole/l. of } Ag^+$$

(b) We must calculate the Ag^+ ion concentration in a saturated solution in pure water. Let x equal the concentration of Ag^+ ions in moles/l. Then x also equals the concentration of Cl^- ions in moles/l.

Chemical equation: $AgCl \rightleftharpoons Ag^+ + Cl^-$

Concentration (moles/l.) at equilibrium: $x \quad x$

Solubility expression:

$$[Ag^+]^1 \times [Cl^-]^1 = 1.2 \times 10^{-10} \quad \text{(mole/l.)}^2$$

$$[x]^1 \times [x]^1 = 1.2 \times 10^{-10}$$

$$x^2 = 1.2 \times 10^{-10}$$

$$x = 1.1 \times 10^{-5} \text{ mole/l. of } Ag^+ \text{ ions in pure water.}$$

The number of moles of Ag^+ ions that precipitated as AgCl is equal to the number of moles of Ag^+ ions present in the saturated water solution (1.1×10^{-5}) minus the number of moles of Ag^+ ions left in the saturated solution containing excess Cl^- ions (1.2×10^{-9}). Thus, ($1.1 \times 10^{-5} - 1.2 \times 10^{-9}$) = 1.1×10^{-5}. This means that "almost all" the Ag^+ ions were removed. Consequently, 1.1×10^{-5} mole of solid AgCl was precipitated.

25-4 Selective Precipitation

In a saturated solution of a slightly soluble ionic salt, the product of the concentrations of the ions, each raised to the power indicated in the chemical equation for equilibrium, is, as we have seen, *equal to* the K_{sp} value of the salt. If in a solution of a slightly soluble salt, the product of the concentrations of the ions each raised to the appropriate power is *less than* the K_{sp} of the salt, the solution is unsaturated. If the product of the concentrations of the ions each raised to the appropriate power *exceeds* the K_{sp} value of the slightly soluble salt, the solution is supersaturated and precipitation will be likely. By applying these general considerations, we can control the concentration of a solution so as to avoid or bring about the precipitation of a certain slightly soluble ionic compound.

SELECTIVE PRECIPITATION BY CONTROL OF H^+ ION CONCENTRATION

By regulating the H^+ ion concentration of a solution, we can sometimes control the order in which various salts, with slightly different solubility products, precipitate out of the solution. Here is an example of this kind of controlled precipitation. We have an aqueous solution containing barium chloride, $BaCl_2$, and strontium chloride, $SrCl_2$. If we add enough of a 0.5 *M* solution of sodium chromate, Na_2CrO_4, to the solution, both the barium chromate, $BaCrO_4$, and the strontium chromate, $SrCrO_4$, will precipitate.

$$\cancel{2\,Na^+_{(aq)}} + CrO^{=}_{4(aq)} + Ba^{++}_{(aq)} + \cancel{2\,Cl^-_{(aq)}} \rightleftharpoons BaCrO_{4(s)} + \cancel{2\,Na^+_{(aq)}} + \cancel{2\,Cl^-_{(aq)}}$$

$$K_{sp} \text{ of } BaCrO_4 = 1.0 \times 10^{-10} \quad \text{(mole/l.)}^2$$

$$\cancel{2\,Na^+_{(aq)}} + CrO^{=}_{4(aq)} + Sr^{++}_{(aq)} + \cancel{2\,Cl^-_{(aq)}} \rightleftharpoons SrCrO_{4(s)} + \cancel{2\,Na^+_{(aq)}} + \cancel{2\,Cl^-_{(aq)}}$$

$$K_{sp} \text{ of } SrCrO_4 = 3.6 \times 10^{-5} \quad \text{(mole/l.)}^2$$

In each case the $CrO_4^{=}$ ion concentration is high enough so that the K_{sp} values of $BaCrO_4$ and $SrCrO_4$ are exceeded, and both salts are precipitated.

Now suppose we have an aqueous solution of $BaCl_2$ and $SrCl_2$ containing enough acetic acid to make it 6 *M* with respect to acetic acid. If we add 0.5 *M* Na_2CrO_4 to this solution, no precipitate of either $BaCrO_4$ or $SrCrO_4$ forms. The explanation is as follows. The $CrO_4^{=}$ ion is a stronger Lewis base (better electron-pair donor) than the CH_3COO^- ion. Hence, the $CrO_4^{=}$ ions will accept H^+ ions from the acetic acid to form $HCrO_4^-$ ions:

$$\begin{array}{ccc} CH_3COOH & \rightleftharpoons & H^+ + CH_3COO^- \\ & & + \\ & & CrO_4^{=} \\ & & \downarrow\uparrow \\ & & HCrO_4^- \end{array}$$

At equilibrium, in the presence of 6 *M* acetic acid, the concentration of $CrO_4^{=}$ ions is so low that the product of the concentrations of the Ba^{++} ions and the $CrO_4^{=}$ ions, and the product of the concentrations of the Sr^{++} and the $CrO_4^{=}$ ions, both fall below their K_{sp} values. In other words, the solution is now unsaturated and precipitation does not occur. If we add a solution of ammonium acetate, $CH_3COO^-NH_4^+$, drop by drop, we find that the $BaCrO_4$ precipitates, but that the more soluble $SrCrO_4$ remains in solution! This is so because when we increase the supply of the CH_3COO^- ions by adding $CH_3COO^-NH_4^+$, some of the $HCrO_4^-$ ions join with the CH_3COO^- ions to form CH_3COOH molecules and $CrO_4^{=}$ ions:

$$HCrO_4^- + CH_3COO^- \rightleftharpoons CH_3COOH + CrO_4^{=}$$

Thus the $CrO_4^{=}$ ion concentration increases. As we continue to add the $CH_3COO^-NH_4^+$, drop by drop, we reach a point where the $CrO_4^{=}$ ion concentration is increased sufficiently to exceed the K_{sp} value of the less soluble $BaCrO_4$. In other words, just the right quantity of $CH_3COO^-NH_4^+$ will increase the $CrO_4^{=}$ ion concentration to the value required for the precipitation of the less soluble $BaCrO_4$, but that quantity will not be enough to increase the $CrO_4^{=}$ ion concentration sufficiently to precipitate the more soluble $SrCrO_4$.

25-5 Thermodynamical Aspects of Equilibrium and Free Energy Change

Let us consider again the general equilibrium reaction

$$\underset{\text{(reactants)}}{a\,A + b\,B} \;\underset{\text{reverse reaction}}{\overset{\text{forward reaction}}{\rightleftharpoons}}\; \underset{\text{(products)}}{c\,C + d\,D}$$

We have seen that at any given temperature the state of equilibrium of the system corresponds to:

$$\frac{[C]^c \times [D]^d}{[A]^a \times [B]^b} = K$$

This state of equilibrium can be reached either by starting with the reactants A and B alone, or with the products C and D alone, or with a mixture containing any three or all four of the substances. For any non-equilibrium system consisting of A, B, C, and D, we can write a *reaction quotient, Q*, which is expressed in terms of the molar concentration of each of the reactants and products present in the system:

$$\textit{Reaction quotient:}\quad \frac{[C]^c \times [D]^d}{[A]^a \times [B]^b} = Q_{\text{non-equilibrium}}$$

If in the initial state of the system, or at any other moment, *the reaction quotient, Q, is less than the equilibrium constant, K,* the reactants A and B can proceed to form the products C and D, that is, the *net forward reaction* can proceed until equilibrium is established. Conversely, if in the initial state of the system, or at any other moment, *the reaction quotient, Q, is greater than the equilibrium, K,* then some of the products, C and D, will react to form the reactants, A and B, that is, *the net reverse reaction* can proceed until equilibrium is established.

Now, we know that the criterion that determines whether a certain reaction can proceed under specified conditions is the free energy change, ΔG, for that reaction. If ΔG is negative, that is, if the free energy of the system decreases in passing from the initial state to the final state, the reaction can proceed spontaneously. It follows that, for any system consisting initially of a non-equilibrium mixture of A, B, C, and D, the value of the free energy change, ΔG, must be related to the value of the reaction quotient, Q, and to the value of the equilibrium constant, K. In fact, as we have just seen, the forward reaction, $a\,\mathrm{A} + b\,\mathrm{B} \longrightarrow c\,\mathrm{C} + d\,\mathrm{D}$, is permitted ($\Delta G_{\text{forward reaction}}$ is negative) when Q is smaller than K. Conversely, if Q is greater than K, then the reverse reaction $a\,\mathrm{A} + b\,\mathrm{B} \longleftarrow c\,\mathrm{C} + d\,\mathrm{D}$ is permitted ($\Delta G_{\text{reverse reaction}}$ is negative). Thus, whenever Q is different from K, the system can react spontaneously. The reaction can proceed in that direction which corresponds to a decrease in free energy, until equilibrium is established and the reaction quotient, Q, becomes equal to the equilibrium constant, K.

When the concentrations of the reactants and products have the values required to satisfy the specified value of K, then the system is at equilibrium, and $\Delta G_{\text{reaction}} = 0$. For a system in equilibrium under a specified set of conditions, the free energy has its minimum value. Hence, the system does not have the capacity to undergo any further *net change* spontaneously, and any displacement from the position of equilibrium requires that energy be supplied to the system from the surroundings. Notice the phrase "net change," meaning a macroscopically observable change, such as a change of concentration, temperature, or pressure. Actually, as we know, in a system at equilibrium both the forward and the reverse reactions occur continuously, but they occur at the same rate, so that there is no net change.

RELATIONSHIP BETWEEN $\Delta G_{\text{reaction}}$ AND REACTION QUOTIENT, Q

In the preceding section, we concluded in a qualitative manner that there must be a relationship between the value of the free energy change of a reaction and the equilibrium constant of the reaction. The quantitative expression that links these quantities is:

$$1.\quad \Delta G_{\text{reaction}} = \Delta G^\circ_{\text{reaction}} + RT \ln Q$$

(As usual, R is the ideal gas constant, T is the absolute temperature at which the reaction takes place, and ΔG° is the free energy change of the reaction when each of the reactants and products has an activity = 1.) By introducing in expression (1) the conversion factor from natural to base 10 logarithm ($\ln Y = 2.303 \log Y$), we obtain the following expression for the $\Delta G_{\text{reaction}}$, in kcal/mole-equation:

$$2.\quad \Delta G_{\text{reaction}} = \Delta G^\circ_{\text{reaction}} + 2.303 \times RT \times \log Q$$

At equilibrium, $Q = K$ and, as we have seen, $\Delta G = 0$. Expression 1 then becomes:

$$0 = \Delta G^\circ_{\text{reaction}} + RT \ln K$$

and

$$3.\quad \Delta G^\circ_{\text{reaction}} = -RT \ln K$$

$$4.\quad \Delta G^\circ_{\text{reaction}} = -2.303\, RT \log K$$

Expressions 3 and 4 tell us that the standard free energy change, ΔG°, for a reaction is directly proportional to the absolute temperature, T, and is also directly proportional to the logarithm of the equilibrium constant, K, at that same temperature. If now we substitute in expression 1 the value of $\Delta G°$ given by expression 3, we obtain the general relationship that links together the values of the free energy change, ΔG, of the equilibrium constant, K, and of the reaction quotient, Q, for any given system at constant temperature, when the concentrations of the reactants and products are different from those obtained at equilibrium as well as from those of the standard state.

$$\Delta G_{\text{reaction}} = -RT \ln K + RT \ln Q = RT(\ln Q - \ln K)$$

$$5.\ \Delta G_{\text{reaction}} = RT \ln \frac{Q}{K}$$

Also,

$$6.\ \Delta G_{\text{reaction}} = 2.303\ RT \log \frac{Q}{K}$$

These general expressions, 5 and 6, permit us to calculate the free energy change for any reaction at constant temperature, if we know the value of the concentrations (more correctly, activities) of each of the substances involved in the equilibrium reaction, and either the equilibrium constant, K, or the standard free energy change, $\Delta G°$, of the reaction.

THE VALUE OF K AND THE EXTENT OF REACTION

The expression $\Delta G° = -2.303\ RT \log K$ is of basic importance for it permits us to calculate the standard free energy change for a reaction at a certain temperature, if we can determine experimentally the value of the equilibrium constant for that reaction at that same temperature. And from this calculated value of $\Delta G°$—and the value of $\Delta H°$, which can be determined independently—we can calculate the standard entropy change, $\Delta S°$, that accompanies the reaction—a quantity which is generally quite difficult to estimate directly:

$$\Delta G° = \Delta H° - T\,\Delta S°, \text{ and } \Delta S° = (\Delta H° - \Delta G°)/T$$

Conversely, let us consider that we know $\Delta G°$ for a certain reaction at a given temperature, for example, from tabulated values of $\Delta G°_{\text{form}}$ or from the values of standard cell voltages, $E°$. We can then calculate the equilibrium constant, K, and predict to what extent a reaction can proceed at the specified temperature, if we start with a system in which each of the reactants and products is in its standard state (activity = 1).

A number of useful generalizations can be drawn from the fact that the equilibrium constant, K, and the free energy change, $\Delta G°$, for a chemical reaction at constant temperature, T, are related by the simple expression, $\Delta G° = -2.303\ RT \log K$. Since $\Delta G°$ is directly proportional, not to K itself, but to $\log K$, even a small change of $\Delta G°$ means a relatively large change of K. This fact is illustrated in Table 25-7. As this table shows, a change of $\Delta G°$ from about -5.5 kcal/mole-eqn to about $+5.5$ kcal/mole-eqn, (that is, a total change of about 10 kcal/mole-eqn) means a change from $K = 10^4$ (equilibrium almost completely shifted to the right) to $K = 10^{-4}$ (equilibrium almost completely shifted to the left). Thus, we see that when the magnitude of $\Delta G°$ is of the order of 10 or more kcal/mole-eqn, the reaction can either proceed virtually to completion (if $\Delta G°$ is negative) or does not have the capacity to proceed to any appre-

TABLE 25-7 RELATIONSHIP BETWEEN K AND $\Delta G°$, AT 25°C

K	$\Delta G°$ (kcal/mole)
0.0001	5.45
0.001	4.09
0.01	2.73
0.1	1.36
1	0
10	−1.36
100	−2.73
1000	−4.09
10,000	−5.45

ciable extent (if $\Delta G°$ is positive). But when the magnitude of $\Delta G°$ is between -10 and $+10$ kcal/mole-eqn, the system at equilibrium will consist of reactants as well as products. In other words, we may expect to have "equilibrium mixtures" of reactants and products at the final state of the reaction in all cases where the magnitude of $\Delta G°$ is between $+10$ kcal/mole-eqn and -10 kcal/mole-eqn.

Notice that if we know the value of $\Delta G°$ for a reaction, we can always calculate very easily the value of K. On the other hand, calculating from the value of K the extent to which the reaction has proceeded from a specified initial state is generally a rather complicated task, except for the simplest kinds of reactions. Thus, we can readily calculate the relative values of the concentrations of the reactants and products from the value of K if the reaction is of the type A $\longrightarrow$ B, or A $\longrightarrow$ 2 B. But for more complicated reactions, for example 2 A $\longrightarrow$ 3 B + C, the calculation becomes very involved.

Here are some examples. Consider first the reaction A $\longrightarrow$ B (an example is the isomerization of normal butane to *iso*-butane, shown in the margin). In this case, if $\Delta G° = 0$, then $K = 1$, and at equilibrium [A] = [B]. Thus if we started with a system consisting of pure A, at equilibrium 50 per cent of it will have transformed into B. And if $\Delta G° = -1$ and $K = 10$, then at equilibrium [B] = 10 [A]. That is, the concentration of B is 10 times greater than the concentration of A. And if the initial state again consisted of pure A, we can express the concentration of A at equilibrium as $1 - x$ and the concentration of B as x. We then have $[A] = 1 - x$, $[B] = x$, and $[B] = 10\ [A]$. Hence, $x = 10(1 - x)$, $x = 10 - 10x$, $x = 10/11$, and $[A] = 1 - 10/11 = 1/11$. That is, about 90.9 per cent of the initial A has transformed into B. For a system initially consisting of pure A we can calculate in a similar manner the extent of reaction for the different values of $\Delta G°$ listed in Table 25-7.

Normal Butane

$$CH_3—CH_2—CH_2—CH_3$$
$$\rightleftharpoons$$
$$CH_3—CH(CH_3)—CH_3$$

iso-butane

Let us now try to carry out a similar calculation for another very simple reaction, the dissociation A $\longrightarrow$ 2 B. An example would be the dissociation of iodine molecules into iodine atoms: $I_{2(s)} \longrightarrow 2\ I_{(g)}$. Let us start again with $\Delta G° = 0$ and $K = 1$. At equilibrium, $[A] = [B]^2$. Thus, if the initial concentration of A is 1 mole/l., and the extent of A dissociated at equilibrium is indicated as x, we have, at equilibrium, $[A] = 1 - x$, and $[B] = 2x$. Hence, $1 - x = 4x^2$. For this equation we have two solutions, $x = 0.359$ and $x = -0.609$, of which only the first has a physical significance. Thus, at equilibrium, 35.9 per cent of the original A has dissociated. Now if $\Delta G° = -1$ and $K = 10$, at equilibrium $10[A] = [B]^2$, or $10(1 - x) = 4x^2$; the two solutions are $x = 0.768$ and $x = -3.27$. In this case, at equilibrium, 76.8 per cent of the original A is dissociated. And similarly for the other values of $\Delta G°$ listed in Table 25-7.

Finally, let us consider a reaction of the type 2 A $\longrightarrow$ 3 B + C (for example, $2\ NH_3 \longrightarrow 3\ H_2 + N_2$). Again, if initially we start off with pure A, at equilibrium we can indicate the concentrations as $[A] = 1 - 2x$, $[B] = 3x$, and $[C] = x$. To find the extent to which the reaction has proceeded from the initial state, we must solve the following expression: $(1 - 2x)^2 = (3x)^3x$. Only by making a number of approximations can we obtain the value of x from this expression.

STANDARD VOLTAGES AND EQUILIBRIUM CONSTANTS

In Chapter 22 we learned the relationship between the standard free energy change, $\Delta G°$, of an oxidation-reduction reaction at constant temperature, and the standard voltage, $E°$, of the energy cell in which such a reaction takes place under reversible conditions. At 25°C, the relationship is:

$$1.\quad \Delta G° = -nFE° = -23.06\ nE°$$

where $\Delta G°$ is expressed in kcal/mole-eqn, $E°$ is expressed in volts, and n is the number of moles of electrons exchanged between the oxidant and the reductant in the balanced oxidation-reduction equation. Now, as we have seen in a preceding section,

ΔG° is related to the equilibrium constant by the expression $\Delta G^\circ = -RT \ln K$, or

$$2.\ \Delta G^\circ = -2.303\ RT \log K$$

By combining 1 and 2, we obtain a new expression that relates the standard voltage, E°, of a reaction at 25°C to the equilibrium constant, K, of that reaction at 25°C:

$$3.\ -nFE^\circ = -RT \ln K$$

$$E^\circ = \frac{RT}{nF} \ln K = 2.303 \times \frac{RT}{nF} \log K. \text{ Thus, } E^\circ = \frac{0.0591}{n} \log K, \text{ at } 25^\circ\text{C.}$$

Or, we can solve expression 3 ($-nFE^\circ = -RT \ln K$) to obtain log K:

$$2.303 \log K = \frac{nF}{RT} E^\circ$$

$$\log K = \frac{nF}{2.303 \times RT} E^\circ = \frac{n}{0.0591} E^\circ$$

Thus, if we know E° we can calculate the equilibrium constant of the oxidation-reduction reaction, and *vice versa*. As an illustration, consider the reaction:

$$Fe_{(s)} + Cd^{++}{}_{(aq)}\ (1\ M) \rightleftharpoons Fe^{++}{}_{(aq)}\ (1\ M) + Cd_{(s)} \qquad E^\circ = 0.040 \text{ volts}$$

The equilibrium constant for this reaction is:

$$K = \frac{[Fe^{++}{}_{(aq)}][Cd_{(s)}]}{[Cd^{++}{}_{(aq)}][Fe_{(s)}]}$$

Because the activities of pure, solid Fe metal and Cd metal are constant and equal to unity, this expression can be written as

$$K = \frac{[Fe^{++}{}_{(aq)}]}{[Cd^{++}{}_{(aq)}]} \quad \text{or simply,} \quad K = \frac{[Fe^{++}]}{[Cd^{++}]}.$$

$$\log K = \frac{nE^\circ}{0.0591} = \frac{2 \times 0.40}{0.0591} = 1.35 \quad \text{and} \quad K = 22.6$$

Thus, at equilibrium the concentration of Fe^{++} is 22.6 times greater than that of Cd^{++}, and we would obtain this ratio whether we start with pure $Fe_{(s)}$ and a 1 M solution of Cd^{++} ions, or with pure $Cd_{(s)}$ and a 1 M solution of Fe^{++} ions.

RELATIONSHIP BETWEEN THE NON-STANDARD VOLTAGE, E, THE EQUILIBRIUM CONSTANT, K, AND THE REACTION QUOTIENT, Q

Now let us go one step further and explore the relationship between the equilibrium constant of the oxidation-reduction reaction and the voltage of an energy cell in which one or more of the species involved in the reaction is present in the system at a non-standard concentration. We know in general that for a non-standard cell at 25°C, $\Delta G = -nFE$ (where, as usual, n is the number of moles of electrons involved in the balanced oxidation-reduction equation, ΔG is expressed in kcal/mole-eqn, and E is expressed in volts). We also know that $\Delta G = \Delta G^\circ + RT \ln Q$. Hence, combining these two expressions, we obtain:

$$-nFE = \Delta G^\circ + RT \ln Q$$

Substituting in this expression the value of $\Delta G^\circ = -nFE^\circ$, we get for an oxidation-reduction reaction at 25°C:

$$-nFE = -nFE^\circ + RT \ln Q$$

$$E = E^\circ - \frac{RT}{nF} \ln Q$$

$$E = E^\circ - \frac{0.0591}{n} \log Q$$

This last expression, you will recall, is the *Nernst equation,* which we used in Chapter 22 to calculate the voltage of a non-standard cell (or a non-standard half-cell) from the values of the standard voltage, $E°$, and the concentrations of the reductant and of the oxidant in the system. As an illustration, consider again the reaction which takes place in the $Fe_{(s)},Fe^{++};Cd_{(s)},Cd^{++}$ cell mentioned earlier, for which $E° = 0.04$ volts. For this cell, we found that the equilibrium constant, K, was equal to 22.6. Now let us examine the effect of varying the concentration of Cd^{++} and Fe^{++}. If $[Fe^{++}] = 0.10\ M$ and $[Cd^{++}] = 1.0\ M$, then, from $E = E° - \frac{0.0591}{n} \log Q$

$$E = 0.04 \text{ volts} - \frac{0.0591}{2} \log \frac{0.10}{1.0} = 0.04 + .03 = 0.07 \text{ volts}$$

and we see that under these conditions, the voltage is greater than the standard voltage. If, on the other hand, $[Fe^{++}] = 1.0\ M$ and $[Cd^{++}] = 0.10\ M$

$$E = 0.04 \text{ volts} - \frac{0.0591}{2} \log \frac{1.0}{0.10} = 0.01 \text{ volts}$$

and the voltage is less than the standard voltage.

If we substitute the ratio of the equilibrium concentrations of Fe^{++} and Cd^{++} ions, $[Fe^{++}]/[Cd^{++}]$, into the expression, we get:

$$E = 0.04 \text{ volts} - \frac{0.0591}{2} \log \frac{22.6}{1} = 0.04 \text{ volts} - 0.04 \text{ volts} = 0.0 \text{ volts.}$$

From these examples, we see that when the reaction quotient, Q, is less than 1, the observed voltage is greater than the standard voltage, and when it is greater than 1, the voltage is less than the standard voltage. Also, when the reaction quotient, Q, is equal to the equilibrium constant, K, the cell is in equilibrium and the voltage is zero.

Exercises

25-1 State the Law of Mass Action. Write the equilibrium expression and specify the dimensions of the equilibrium constant, K, for each of the following:
(a) $H_2 + I_2 \rightleftharpoons 2\ HI$
(b) $2\ SO_2 + O_2 \rightleftharpoons 2\ SO_3$
(c) $N_2 + O_2 \rightleftharpoons 2\ NO$
(d) $N_2 + 3\ H_2 \rightleftharpoons 2\ NH_3$
(e) $HNO_2 \rightleftharpoons H^+ + NO_2^-$
(f) $NH_3 + H_2O \rightleftharpoons NH_4^+ + OH^-$

25-2 Silver chloride, AgCl, is slightly soluble. (a) Write the equilibrium present in a saturated solution. (b) What happens to this equilibrium if ammonia solution is added? (c) It is desirable to precipitate *pure* AgCl from a solution containing NaCl and Na_2CO_3. To do this, would you add (1) a solution of $AgNO_3$, or (2) a solution of $AgNO_3$ containing some nitric acid? Explain your answer.

25-3 ZnS is insoluble. (a) When H_2S is passed into a $ZnCl_2$ solution, only a very slight precipitate of ZnS forms. If H_2S is passed into a $ZnCl_2$ solution containing a little NaOH, however, a large precipitate of ZnS forms. Explain. (b) If H_2S is passed into an aqueous solution of $Zn(CH_3COO)_2$, would you expect a slight or a large precipitate of ZnS to form? Explain. (Hint: CH_3COOH is a weak acid.)

25-4 Magnesium hydroxide, $Mg(OH)_2$, is an insoluble compound. (a) Write the equilibrium that is present in a saturated solution. (b) Predict and explain the effect that the addition of each of the following will have on the solution: (1) NaOH, (2) HCl, (3) NH_4Cl, (4) KOH, (5) KNO_3.

25-5 Explain how each of the following pairs of substances may be separated: (a) $CaCO_3$ and $CaSO_4$, (b) $CaCO_3$ and CaC_2O_4, (c) CuS and HgS, (d) $Ca_3(PO_4)_2$ and $CaCO_3$, (e) $BaCrO_4$ and $SrCrO_4$, (f) AgCl and $PbCl_2$, (g) $Ca(HCO_3)_2$ and $CaCO_3$, (h) $Zn(OH)_2$ and $Cu(OH)_2$.

Problems

25-1 (a) Consider the reaction: $2\ A + B \rightleftharpoons A_2B$ at a given constant temperature. At the start of the experiment, 2 moles of A and 2 moles of B are present in a 1 l.

flask. When equilibrium is established, 0.5 mole of A_2B is present. Calculate the numerical value of the equilibrium constant and specify its dimensions. (b) Given: the equilibrium reaction $X + Y \rightleftharpoons Z$; $\Delta H = -10.0$ kcal/mole-eqn at a given temperature, T. (1) Does the value of the equilibrium constant increase or decrease as the temperature is raised? Explain. (2) If 5 moles of Y are put into the flask at the start of the reaction, and if 2 moles are present when equilibrium is established at the temperature, T, how many moles of X have reacted? Calculate the amount of heat evolved.

25-2 (a) A solution is made by adding 500 ml of 1.0 M CH_3COONa to 500 ml of 1.0 M CH_3COOH. Calculate the H^+ ion concentration of the resulting solution. (K $CH_3COOH = 1.8 \times 10^{-5}$ mole/l. at 25°C.) (b) A solution is made by dissolving 0.10 mole of NH_3 and 0.10 mole of NaOH in 1.0 l. of solution. Calculate the OH^- ion concentration. (K $[NH_4^+][OH^-]/[NH_3] = 1.8 \times 10^{-5}$ mole/l. at 25°C).

25-3 Calculate the H^+ ion concentration of the following solutions: (a) 0.0010 N HCl, (b) 0.010 N H_2SO_4, (c) 0.0010 N NaOH, (d) 0.0010 N CH_3COOH, (e) 0.0010 N ammonia.

25-4 To a 1.0 l. solution containing 0.40 mole of CH_3COOH, 0.20 mole of solid NaOH is added. Calculate the H^+ ion concentration of the resulting solution.

25-5 To a solution containing 250 ml of a 0.10 M KOH, 250 ml of 0.40 M CH_3COOH are added. Calculate the H^+ ion concentration of the resulting solution.

25-6 The solubility of $CaSO_4$ in water is 0.015 mole/l. (a) To a 500 ml 0.20 M $Ca(NO_3)_2$ solution are added 500 ml of 0.20 M H_2SO_4. Calculate the number of moles of $CaSO_4$ that will be precipitated. (b) Calculate the number of moles of $CaSO_4$ that will precipitate when 50 ml of 0.40 M H_2SO_4 are added to 100 ml of 0.20 M $CaCl_2$.

25-7 The concentration of $SO_4^{=}$ ions in a solution is 0.020 M. Calculate the maximum concentration of Ba^{++} ions that may be present without causing $BaSO_4$ to precipitate (K_{sp} $BaSO_4 = 1 \times 10^{-10}$ (mole/l.)^2).

25-8 How many moles of AgBr can dissolve in (a) 1.0 l. of water, (b) 1.0 l. of a 1 M HBr solution, (c) 0.50 l. of water containing 10.29 g of NaBr (K_{sp} AgBr $= 3.5 \times 10^{-13}$ mole/l.)^2.

25-9 How many grams of Ag_2CrO_4 can dissolve in 100 ml of a solution containing 0.10 M Na_2CrO_4? The K_{sp} of $Ag_2CrO_4 = 9 \times 10^{-12}$ (mole/l.)^2.

25-10 For the reaction, $C_{(s,gr)} + \frac{1}{2} O_{2(g)} \rightleftharpoons CO_{(g)}$, $\Delta G° = -32.8$ kcal/mole-eqn at 25°C. Calculate the ratio of the concentrations (mole/l.) of CO gas and O_2 gas in equilibrium at 25°C in the presence of an excess of solid carbon (graphite).

25-11 Consider the isomerization of normal butane to isobutane at 25°C:

$$CH_3{-}CH_2{-}CH_2{-}CH_{3(g)} \longrightarrow CH_3{-}\underset{\displaystyle CH_3}{\underset{|}{CH}}{-}CH_{3(g)} \qquad K = 2.5.$$

Calculate:

(a) the percentage of conversion of normal butane to isobutane, (b) the $\Delta G°$ value of the forward isomerization reaction. (c) Would you expect the entropy change of this reaction to be large, small, or very small? (d) On the basis of your answers to (b) and (c), is the $\Delta H°$ value for the forward reaction negative or positive? (d) In which direction will the equilibrium be shifted if the temperature is raised?

25-12 Using the values of Table 25-7, (a) carefully construct a graph showing how $\Delta G°$ is related to K at 25°C. Use this graph to find rapidly the appropriate values of $\Delta G°$ for the following reactions at 25°C:

$H_2S_{(aq)} \rightleftharpoons H^+_{(aq)} + HS^-_{(aq)}$ $\qquad K = 1.0 \times 10^{-7}$ mole/l.

$HCN_{(aq)} \rightleftharpoons H^+_{(aq)} + CN^-_{(aq)}$ $\qquad K = 5.0 \times 10^{-10}$ mole/l.

$CH_3COOH_{(aq)} \rightleftharpoons H^+_{(aq)} + CH_3COO^-_{(aq)}$ $\qquad K = 1.8 \times 10^{-5}$ mole/l.

25-13 The value of $\Delta G°$ for a reaction $A + B \rightleftharpoons 2\,C$ is -5.0 kcal/mole-eqn (for the forward reaction) at 25°C. (a) If the initial system consists of 1.0 mole of A and 1 mole of B, to what extent (approximately) will the reaction proceed at 25°C to form C? (b) If the initial system consists of 1.0 mole of C, to what extent (approximately) will the reaction proceed at 25°C to form A + B?

25-14 Calculate the ratio of the concentrations (in moles/l.) of Zn^{++} and Pb^{++} ions in equilibrium with each other and with their respective metals, $Zn_{(s)}$ and $Pb_{(s)}$ at 25°C, knowing that the emf of the Zn,Zn^{++}-Pb,Pb^{++} combined standard cell is $E° = +0.64$ volts.

RATES AND MECHANISMS OF CHEMICAL REACTIONS

26

In Chapter 17 we saw that if we know the change in free energy, ΔG, that accompanies a reaction we can predict whether or not the reaction can occur spontaneously. If the change in free energy for a given reaction of a specified system has a negative value, then we know that the reaction can occur spontaneously and, under appropriate conditions, can produce useful work. Also, we saw in Chapter 25 that for spontaneous reactions the value of ΔG actually determines whether the reactions, under a given set of conditions, can react completely to yield the products, or whether a state of equilibrium can be reached in which reactions and products coexist in somewhat comparable concentrations. However, these considerations of the free energy change of a reaction can only tell us whether and to what extent a reaction *can* occur, not *how* or *how fast* a thermodynamically favorable (spontaneous) reaction proceeds. It is very important to know the rate at which a certain chemical process occurs, and a branch of science called chemical kinetics (from a Greek word meaning study of motion) deals with this significant area.

The importance of chemical kinetics is twofold. On the one hand, it is one of the most useful sources of information on *how* chemical reactions occur—that is, on the mechanism of chemical reactions—one of the most interesting problems in modern chemistry. On the other hand, a knowledge of reaction rates is essential to the success of industrial chemical processes; it lets chemists select the conditions of a reaction so as to obtain the optimum rate under the most economical conditions.

26-1 General Considerations on the Rate of Chemical Reactions

The rate at which chemical reactions take place varies within exceedingly wide limits. At one extreme, there are reactions which, even though thermodynamically favorable, occur so very slowly that for all practical purposes it is as if they did not occur at all. At the other extreme, there are extremely fast reactions that require less than, say, 10^{-7} sec to proceed to completion (to reach equilibrium). And in between these two extremes, there is a very large number of important reactions which occur at intermediate rates and require say from 10^{-3} sec to several days to reach a state of equilibrium. Let us look at some examples.

EXTREMELY FAST REACTIONS. The neutralization of any strong acid by any strong base in aqueous solution is one of the fastest reactions known. In fact, the neutralization of a strong acid—for example, a 0.10 *M* solution of hydrochloric acid—by a strong base—for example, a 0.10 *M* solution of sodium hydroxide—occurs just as rapidly as the two solutions become mixed, which requires at least 10^{-3} sec. And it is known from experimental data that if it were possible to mix the reactants instantaneously, the reaction $H^+_{(aq)} + OH^-_{(aq)} \rightarrow H_2O$ would be 99 per cent complete in less than 10^{-7} sec.

In general, reactions which involve combinations of oppositely charged ions in aqueous solution are very fast, although not as fast as the acid-base neutralization reaction. Sometimes the reaction between the oppositely charged ions in solution may produce an insoluble compound. For example, when aqueous solutions of sodium chloride, $Na^+_{(aq)} + Cl^-_{(aq)}$, and silver nitrate, $Ag^+_{(aq)} + NO^-_{3(aq)}$, are mixed, the insoluble silver chloride, AgCl, precipitates rapidly. Similarly, whenever solutions containing $Ba^{++}_{(aq)}$ ions and $SO^{=}_{4(aq)}$ ions are mixed under ordinary conditions, barium sulfate, $BaSO_4$ begins to precipitate as rapidly as the solutions are brought together. However, the precipitation of AgCl and $BaSO_4$—and in general the precipitation of any ionic solid formed by mixing solutions of the oppositely charged ions —always requires a certain time, because a very large number of ions must come together and arrange themselves in the regular three-dimensional array of the crystal lattice in order to form even a very small particle of the ionic solid. And, as we know, we can often obtain a supersaturated solution of an ionic solid (rate of precipitation = zero).

Other extremely fast reactions are those that involve atoms or groups of atoms having unpaired electrons. An example is the combination of gaseous iodine atoms to form gaseous iodine molecules, $2\ I_{(g)} \longrightarrow I_{2(g)}$, which is complete within about 10^{-6} sec at room temperature.

REACTIONS THAT OCCUR AT A MODERATE RATE. Many of the reactions that we have studied in earlier chapters proceed at a moderate rate. The reactions of electropositive metals with acids (p. 92), for example, take minutes or hours to run to completion, and so does the reaction of some of the more electropositive metals with water or steam to form the hydroxide or the oxide of the metal and H_2 gas (p. 91). The reversible decomposition of gaseous hydrogen iodide $2\ HI_{(g)} \rightleftharpoons H_{2(g)} + I_{2(g)}$ at 500°C requires less than five minutes to reach equilibrium. The reversible reaction $CH_3COOH_{(l)} + C_2H_5OH_{(l)} \rightleftharpoons CH_3COOC_2H_{5(l)} + H_2O_{(l)}$ at room temperature, described in Chapter 25, is another example of a reaction that occurs at a moderate rate.

REACTIONS THAT DO NOT OCCUR AT AN APPRECIABLE RATE AT ROOM TEMPERATURE. Many chemical reactions do not occur to a detectable extent at room temperature even though they may be thermodynamically favorable ($\Delta G_{\text{reaction}}$ is negative). For example, gasoline, natural gas, and coal do not burn in air at room temperature, *unless they are ignited by a match, a spark, or in some other way.* But, if gasoline vapor is mixed with air in the cylinder of an engine and then is sparked, it burns explosively, and if coal is heated, it readily reacts with the oxygen in the air. The combustion of both gasoline and coal produces a great quantity of heat (ΔH has a large negative value), and once started, it keeps going spontaneously until all the gasoline or coal is burned, or until all the oxygen available has been used up. Similarly, we know that the reaction of hydrogen gas, $H_{2(g)}$, with oxygen gas, $O_{2(g)}$, to form liquid water, $H_2O_{(l)}$, is energetically very favorable, because the ΔG of the reaction has a (large) negative value:

$$H_{2(g)} + \tfrac{1}{2}\,O_{2(g)} \longrightarrow H_2O_{(l)} \qquad \begin{cases} \Delta H_{298^\circ} = -68.3 \text{ kcal/mole } H_2O_{(l)} \\ \Delta G_{298^\circ} = -56.7 \text{ kcal/mole } H_2O_{(l)} \end{cases}$$

Thus, the reaction has the capacity to occur spontaneously. However, if we mix pure H_2 gas with pure O_2 gas, in a clean quartz flask at room temperature, no reaction occurs and the system can be kept for an extremely long time without a trace of water being produced. In fact, it has been calculated indirectly that it would require more than 10^{10} years (more than the age of the solar system!) for half of the initial $H_{2(g)}$ and $O_{2(g)}$ molecules to combine at room temperature to form $H_2O_{(l)}$. But if we place in the flask a minute amount of appropriately prepared platinum powder, the H_2 and O_2 immediately and completely combine to produce H_2O, releasing a great deal of heat in the process. We may conclude that in all these examples the reactions proceed too slowly at room temperature to be detected, but can be speeded up in various ways—by a rise in temperature, by an electrical spark, by the presence of an appropriate foreign substance (catalyst).

As a general rule, we may say that most familiar reactions of organic compounds (as well as some reaction of inorganic compounds) are kinetically controlled. That is, the fact that these reactions do or do not occur under a given set of conditions is dependent upon their rate, and not upon their free energy change. The vital importance of this fact will be evident if you recall that for most organic substances the combustion at ordinary temperature and pressure is thermodynamically very favorable. In fact, almost all organic substances have the capacity to burn at room temperature in the presence of air, but do not do so because they are kinetically inert.

VARIATIONS IN RATES OF REACTIONS. We have seen many times in the past chapters that different combinations of substances react at different rates, even though the reactions themselves may be of the same general type. For example, when heated in air magnesium metal oxidizes more rapidly than iron metal; sodium metal reacts very rapidly with water whereas zinc metal appears not to. It is also important to realize that the rate at which the *same* reactants produce the *same* products may differ greatly from one set of experimental conditions to another. For example, iron metal oxidizes far more rapidly in pure oxygen than in air (which contains only about 20 per cent of oxygen); moreover, a sample of finely divided iron is oxidized by either air or oxygen much faster than a single large piece of iron. A given mixture of H_2 gas and I_2 gas will react to form HI far more rapidly at a higher temperature—say 400°C than at a lower temperature—say 200°C. And the hydrolysis of ethyl acetate, $CH_3COOC_2H_5$, in acidic aqueous solution will occur twice as rapidly if the hydrogen ion concentration is doubled. The purpose of all these examples is simply to give you some idea of how widely the rate of chemical reactions may vary, not only from one reaction to another, but also for the same reaction under different conditions.

INERT AND LABILE COMPOUNDS. We have seen that the rates at which compounds react, under comparable conditions, vary within extremely wide limits. Obviously, a clear-cut classification of compounds according to the speed at which they react is not possible. It is common, however, to call *inert* a substance which reacts slowly, or not at all, even though it has the capacity to react ($\Delta G_{\text{reaction}}$ is negative). The term *labile* is used to mean the opposite of inert—that is, a substance which reacts fast. *Inert* and *labile* are only relative terms, and do not give us a quantative indication of the actual speed at which a substance reacts. Furthermore, a substance may be inert under some conditions (for example, at a low temperature) but labile under different conditions (for example, at a high temperature).

26-2 Kinetic Studies of Reactions

THE RATE OF A REACTION

The *rate of a reaction* is generally defined as *the speed at which the reactants are transformed into the products at any selected instant, under a specified set of experimental conditions.* That is, the rate of a reaction is the speed of the net conversion of the reactants into the products. As a general rule, for a system which reacts at constant temperature and pressure, the rate of reaction is not constant in time. In most cases, the rate has its maximum value at the beginning of the reaction—when the reactants have just been mixed—then gradually decreases and finally becomes zero when the system reaches a state of equilibrium. There are also many reactions which start slowly, accelerate to a maximum rate, and then decrease gradually until equilibrium is reached. In this final state of equilibrium, the system may be composed of: (a) almost entirely the products, if the reaction has proceeded virtually to completion, (b) almost entirely the reactants, if virtually no reaction has occurred, or (c) a mixture of the reactants and products in some fixed relative concentrations between the limits of (a) and (b).

The rate of a reaction generally depends on the concentration(s) of one or more of the reactants and sometimes also of one or more of the products. Therefore, the first step in the kinetic study of a reaction consists of determining which are the reactants and products whose concentrations influence the reaction rate at a given temperature. The next step is to establish how the rate of reaction depends on the concentration of these species involved—that is, the so-called "rate-concentration dependence" of the reaction. Finally, it is generally important to determine how the reaction varies with the temperature, under constant conditions of concentration.

THE EXPERIMENTAL DETERMINATION OF THE RATE OF A REACTION

In general, we can determine experimentally the rate-concentration dependence of a reaction by measuring how the concentrations of the reactants and products vary with time as the reaction proceeds from an initial state to a final state of equilibrium. For reactions which are relatively slow—for example, reactions which require a few seconds to a few days to reach equilibrium—the variation of concentration with time can be determined by measuring, at short time intervals and under fixed experimental conditions, the concentration(s) of one or more of the reactants still remaining, or the concentration(s) of one or more of the products formed, or preferably both.

In each case, of course, we have to use an appropriate method to measure the desired concentrations. For example, we may simply titrate one or more of the components of the system, or if any of the components has a typical absorption spectrum, we can follow the intensity of the absorption (spectrophotometric analysis). When a reaction involves ionic species, it may be possible to follow its rate by determining how the electrical conductivity of the solution changes with time. Or, the quantity of heat evolved or absorbed in the reaction up to a certain instant can be taken as a measure of the extent to which the reaction has proceeded. All these methods, and some others, are applicable provided the reaction is slow enough so that there is no appreciable activity during the time required for the concentration measurement. Also, the time required for mixing the reagents, which is about of the order of 10^{-3} sec by usual procedures, must of course be very small with respect to the duration of the reaction itself.

VERY FAST REACTIONS. When reactions are very fast, special techniques are used to determine the rate. For reactions which are complete in about 10^{-2} to 10^{-3} sec, the so-called "flow system" can be used. In this method, the reactants are mixed together in a specially designed vessel, from which they flow at a known speed along a tube; the concentrations (of the reactants, or products, or both) are then determined at various positions along the flow tube, each position corresponding to a known time interval. For reactions which reach equilibrium in less than 10^{-3} sec, a different approach is adopted, because the time required to mix the reactants would be longer than that required for the reactants to reach equilibrium. In this case, we start off with a system which is already in equilibrium and we abruptly disturb the equilibrium—for example, by suddenly changing the pressure or the temperature, or by flashing the system with light of an appropriate frequency (energy)—in short, by suddenly supplying a certain quantity of radiation energy to the system. When the equilibrium of the system is thus suddenly disturbed, we know that the system will react and achieve a new equilibrium position. The rate at which the new equilibrium is attained can then be determined by using high-speed spectrophotometric recorders. By this technique chemists can now measure reaction times of less than one millionth of a second (10^{-6} sec).

OTHER FACTORS INFLUENCING REACTION RATES. After we have determined the rate-concentration dependence of a reaction under a specified set of experimental conditions, the next step is to determine how the rate of the reaction is influenced by changes in these experimental conditions, such as temperature, pressure, particle size of the solid reagents, and the presence of foreign substances.

It is very important from both a theoretical and practical viewpoint to know how the rate of a reaction depends on any one, or all, of the factors mentioned above. From the theoretical viewpoint, this knowledge helps us to gain an insight into how the reactants are transformed into the products. From a practical viewpoint, a knowledge of the reaction rate enables us to carry out a certain chemical process under a set of conditions appropriately chosen to produce the desired fast, or slow, rate of reaction.

HOMOGENEOUS AND HETEROGENEOUS REACTIONS

At this point it becomes convenient to classify chemical reactions into two general groups, *homogeneous* and *heterogeneous.* When all the reactants and products are present in the same physical phase—for example, when all are gases or all are present in solution—and when the reaction rate is unaffected by any change in the nature and surface area of any solid in contact with the system, then the reaction is *homogeneous.* When, on the other hand, one or more of the reactants or products are present in different physical phases, the reaction is *heterogeneous.* We also consider as heterogeneous any reaction in which the reactants and products are all in one phase, but the rate of reaction depends on the nature and surface area of any solid (including the walls of the vessel) with which the system is in contact. A familiar example of a heterogeneous reaction is the combustion of carbon, $C_{(s)}$, with oxygen, O_2, gas to yield carbon dioxide, CO_2, gas.

For any given *homogeneous* reaction, the rate depends in a consistently reproducible manner on only two factors, the temperature and the concentration of one (or more) of the reactants. The rate of a reaction can then be expressed fairly simply as a function of the temperature and concentration(s), and is typical for any homogeneous reaction under a specified set of conditions. For *heterogeneous* systems, the rate depends not only on the temperature and on the concentrations of the gaseous or liquid reactants, but also on how finely subdivided and efficiently mixed the reactants are. And since the degree of subdivision of the reactants and the efficiency of their mixing are not easy to control and reproduce exactly, the rate of a heterogeneous reaction may not be readily reproducible from one experiment to another. Also, it is usually very difficult to express in a reasonably simple form the dependence of the reaction rate of all these factors.

For these reasons, it is convenient to consider separately the kinetic study of homogeneous and heterogeneous reactions, although, as we shall see, the theoretical explanation for the speed at which both types of reactions proceeds is the same. Here we shall first consider in detail homogeneous reactions in gaseous systems, then extend our conclusions to homogeneous reactions in liquid systems, and finally to heterogeneous reactions.

26-3 Homogeneous Reactions

MOLECULAR COLLISIONS LEADING TO REACTIONS IN GASEOUS SYSTEMS

In order to understand that the rate of a reaction varies markedly with the reaction conditions, we must consider in some detail how the molecules of the reactants actually come to react. Because, as we know, the molecules of substances in the gaseous state are relatively independent of one another, it is easier to visualize reactions between gaseous species than reactions between species in solution, or even more so, in heterogeneous systems. Thus, we shall use gaseous systems as examples in our discussion of the various factors that influence reaction rates. But what we shall learn about reactions in gaseous systems holds, in general, also for reactions in solution, as well as for heterogeneous reactions.

Let us focus our attention on a simple reaction involving two (or more) different substances. Before two different substances can react with one another, their molecules must come close enough to one another to interact—in effect, the molecules must virtually collide. So for a thermodynamically favorable reaction (ΔG is negative), any change in experimental conditions that increases the number of collisions between the molecules also increases the rate at which the reaction occurs. But there is another condition that must be met before a thermodynamically favorable reaction may actually take place: the molecules of the reactants, in addition to colliding, must also be *in a suitable condition to react.* We shall explain later on what this requirement means. Here we wish to emphasize that for almost all reactions that occur at moderate speed *not all the collisions between the molecules of the reactants actually result in reaction.* An example is the decomposition at high temperature of molecules of HI gas into molecules of H_2 and I_2 gas:

$$2\,HI_{(g)} \longrightarrow H_{2(g)} + I_{2(g)}$$

It is reasonable to assume that in order for HI to decompose into H_2 and I_2, two molecules of HI must collide, so that the hydrogen atoms and also the iodine atoms of the two HI molecules can come close enough to react and form H_2 and I_2. On the basis of the kinetic molecular theory, we can calculate that the collision rate between the HI molecules, at room temperature and atmospheric pressure, is extremely high (about 10^{28} collisions every second for each cm^3 of gas). And of course, the collision rate would be even greater at higher temperatures, because, as we know, the velocity of gas molecules increases as the temperature rises. If then every collision between two HI molecules actually resulted in the chemical reaction which produces H_2 and I_2, the HI would decompose at an extremely fast rate. In fact, since one mole is 6.02×10^{23} molecules, 10^{28} fruitful molecular collisions would bring about the dissociation of about $10^{28}/6 \times 10^{23} \cong 2 \times 10^4$ moles of HI per second and per one cm^3 of gas! On the other hand, if only one collision in many, many collisions resulted in the decomposition of HI, the reaction would be slower, and if for some reason none of the collisions resulted in dissociation, of course no reaction would occur at all. The experimentally observed rate for the dissociation of HI gas is very slow at room temperature, and even at high temperatures is very much slower than it would be if every collision between two HI molecules actually resulted in a reaction. This means that the number of HI molecules that actually react during each second is far smaller than the number of HI molecules which collide. Thus, only an extremely small percentage of the colliding molecules are for some reason in a suitable condition to react.

From these considerations it follows that the rate of a chemical reaction depends on at least two factors: (1) *the frequency of the collisions*, and (2) *the chance that the colliding molecules are in a suitable condition to undergo chemical reaction.* We can therefore influence (increase or decrease) the rate of a chemical reaction by varying (increasing or decreasing) the frequency with which the molecules of the reactants collide. But if none (or very few) of the collisions results in a reaction in the first place, increasing the number of collisions *alone* will not speed up the reaction appreciably, and we will have to try somehow to bring the colliding molecules to a condition more suitable to reaction.

Just what constitutes this "suitable condition"?

ENERGY OF THE MOLECULES OF THE REACTANTS

A factor which determines whether the individual molecules of a reactant are in a suitable condition to react is the *energy* possessed by the individual molecules. We know that the *average internal energy* of a gas has a constant value, and that in general this energy consists of thermal energy (kinetic translational, kinetic rotational, and vibrational energy) and of chemical bond energy. If we consider fairly simple mono-, di-, and tri-atomic gases, as a first approximation we need take into account only the translational kinetic energy to explain why only an extremely small fraction of the colliding molecules react. At a given temperature, we know that the individual molecules of a gas do not all possess the same kinetic energy—in fact, the kinetic energy, $\frac{1}{2}mv^2$, varies widely from one molecule to another, as does the individual velocity, v, of the molecules. In our discussion of the kinetic theory of gases, we have shown graphically (Fig. 9-13) the distribution of the molecular velocities in a gas. Now, since the translational kinetic energy depends on the velocity as indicated by the expression K.E. $= \frac{1}{2}mv^2$, the distribution of the kinetic energies will also follow a similar pattern, as shown in Fig. 26-1. This energy-distribution diagram can be interpreted in a way strictly analogous to that discussed for the velocity-distribution diagram: each point of the curve represents the probability that a given molecule has exactly the specified energy and indicates the number of molecules out of every 100 total molecules with that particular energy value. If we consider any two energy values, E_a and E_b, the area under the curve between E_a and E_b represents the number of molecules out of every 100 total molecules which have an energy within E_a and E_b. The kinetic energy-distribution curve shows that the majority of the molecules have kinetic energies in the region of the average value, but that there are always some molecules that have very low, and some that have very high kinetic energies.

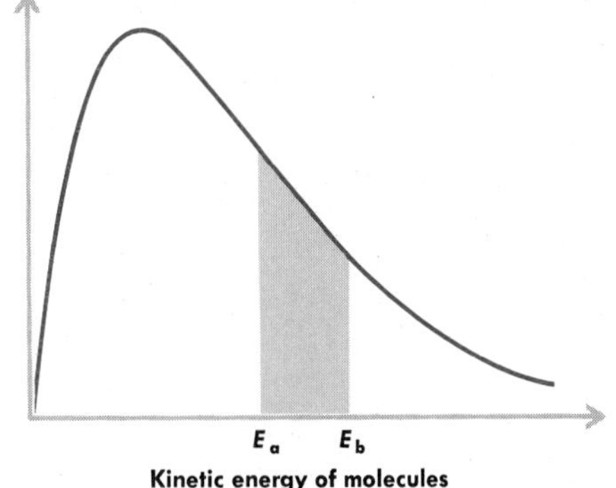

FIGURE 26-1 Energy distribution among gas molecules at a given temperature.

ACTIVATION ENERGY

The distribution of energy among the molecules of a gas explains why not all collisions between molecules of the reactants are fruitful. In fact, only those molecules can react which collide with an energy high enough to bring about the bond rearrangements (bond-breaking of reactants, and bond-making of products, or both) which constitute the reaction. When molecules of the reactants collide with less energy than required by these bond rearrangements, the molecules simply bounce apart.

We may in general assume that any chemical reaction, AB + C $\longrightarrow$ A + BC, occurs via the formation of an intermediate substance [ABC], which then rearranges itself to form the products A and BC:

$$\text{AB} + \text{C} \longrightarrow [\text{ABC}] \longrightarrow \text{A} + \text{BC}$$

The intermediate substance, [ABC], formed when an AB molecule and a C molecule collide with enough energy to react, is called the *activated* complex. In the formation of this activated complex, as the A—B bond is being broken, the B—C bond is being formed simultaneously, so that in the activated complex, which we can represent as [A--B--C], there is a *partial bond* between A and B, as well as another partial bond between B and C. As the term "activated complex" implies, the species [ABC] has a higher potential energy than the AB and C molecules from which it is formed, and than the A and BC molecules formed from it. Figure 26-2 represents graphically how the potential energy varies as one AB molecule comes together with a C molecule, first to form the activated complex [ABC], and then the final products, a molecule of BC and a molecule of A. We see that the potential energy rises sharply from the two isolated reactants, AB + C, to the [ABC] complex, and then gradually decreases as the [ABC] complex rearranges to form the products, A + BC. We can visualize the difference of potential energy as resulting from the greater vibrational motions of the atoms in the [ABC] complex with respect to both the reactants, AB + C, and the products, A + BC. In order to react, the AB and C molecules must not only come together, but must also be able to overcome the potential-energy barrier for the formation of the activated complex.

Thus we have visualized the energy requirement for a single reaction event—the fruitful encounter of one AB molecule with one C molecule to form [ABC]. Now let

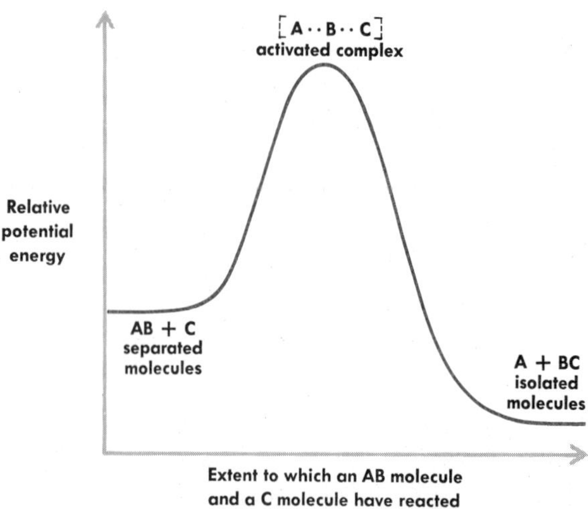

FIGURE 26-2 Potential energy barrier for the formation of an activated complex.

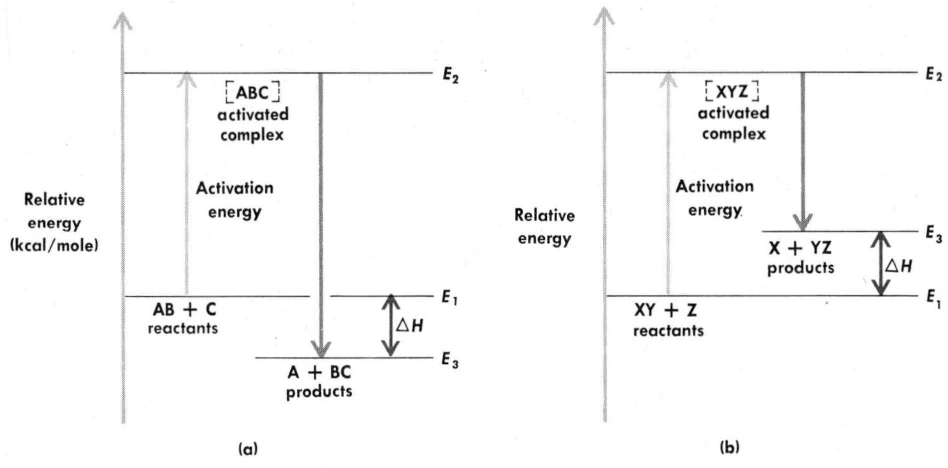

FIGURE 26-3 Energy diagram of reactions at constant T and P. (a) Exothermic reaction: AB + C ⟶ [ABC] ⟶ A + BC. (b) Endothermic reaction: XY + Z ⟶ [XYZ] ⟶ X + YZ.

us apply similar considerations to a (macroscopic) system consisting of an extremely large number of AB and C molecules. For such a system composed of an extremely large number of AB molecules and C molecules, we can represent the reaction

$$\text{AB} + \text{C} \longrightarrow \text{A} + \text{BC}$$

in terms of the energy (for example, internal energy, E) of the reactants, of the activated complex, and of the products—as shown in Fig. 26-3. In this diagram we plot the sum, E_1, of the average internal energies of the reactants, AB + C, the internal energy, E_2, of the activated complex [ABC], and the sum of the average internal energies, E_3, of the products, A + BC. The diagram shows that the energy, E_2, of the activated complex [ABC] is higher than the *average* energy, E_1, of the reactants from which it is formed, so the question arises, how can the colliding molecules AB and C react to form [ABC]? The explanation can be obtained from the energy distribution curve (Fig. 26-1) discussed above.

A collision between AB and C will result in the formation of [ABC] *only when the sum of the energies of the reactants (AB + C) is greater than the energy of the activated complex.* Thus the activated complex can be formed when either AB or C, or both, has an energy so much higher than their respective average energies that the energy sum equals or exceeds the energy of the activated complex [ABC]. For example, any AB molecule with energy higher than E_2 can react upon collision with any C molecule (however low its energy might be), and any C molecule with energy higher than E_2 will react with any AB molecule however low its energy. Similarly, any AB molecule and any C molecule whose combined energies are equal to or higher than E_2 can react upon collision. So when we say that the colliding molecules of the reactants do not have enough energy to bring about a reaction, we actually mean that they do not have enough energy to form the activated complex first. In general, because of the energy distribution, only a *fraction* of the reactant molecules which collide in a given instant will have enough energy to form the activated complex (when *they collide with the proper orientation,* as we shall discuss later). Thus, the more molecules there are with sufficient energy to react, the faster the reaction.

The difference between the energy, E_2, of the activated complex and the sum, E_1, of the average energies of the molecules of the reactants is called the *activation energy,* and may be represented as ΔE_{act}. The activation energy, ΔE_{act}, then represents the quantity of energy which is in excess of the average that the molecules of the reactants must possess to form the activated complex. It should be pointed out here that, in order for the reaction to take place when molecules of the reactants collide, their kinetic energies must be converted in part to the appropriate potential energy. For example, a particular combination of bond vibrations may need to be activated for the desired reaction to occur. Whether this conversion of kinetic energy into potential energy can take place before the molecules of the reactants come apart or transfer their energy to another molecule in a subsequent collision is another important factor which affects reaction rates.

As a general rule, we may say that for a reaction which can take place under different conditions (for example, with or without a catalyst) at a given temperature, the lower the activation energy, the higher the fraction of colliding reactant molecules which can actually react, and the greater the rate of the reaction.

Once the activated complex is formed, it may revert to the reactants or it may form the products. If the activated complex $[ABC]$ reforms the reactants, $AB + C$, a quantity of energy equal on the average to the activation energy is released and hence there is no *net* heat effect. When, on the other hand, the activated complex $[ABC]$ rearranges to form the products, $A + BC$, a quantity of heat energy is released which, depending on the reaction considered, may on the average be greater than the activation energy (exothermic reaction, Fig. 26-3(a)), or less than the activation energy (endothermic reaction, Fig. 26-3(b)).

For reactions that occur at constant temperature and pressure, and involve no volume change, the type of energy diagram shown in Fig. 26-3(a) and (b) also indicates the heat, q, released or absorbed in the reaction. Under these conditions, $q = \Delta E = \Delta H$ (because the pressure-volume work, $P\,\Delta V$, is zero) and the diagrams of Fig. 26-3 become the familiar enthalpy diagrams, showing the enthalpy of activation ($\Delta H_{\text{act}} = \Delta E_{\text{act}}$) as well as the enthalpy change of the reaction, $\Delta H_{\text{reaction}}$. Notice that the difference $E_3 - E_1$ represents the positive or negative value of the enthalpy change, $\Delta H_{\text{reaction}}$, but has nothing to do with the *rate* of the reaction, which depends on the activation energy, $\Delta E_{\text{act}} = E_2 - E_1$.

Now let us see how we can use an energy diagram of this sort for a specific reaction, for example, the reaction between hydrogen gas, H_2 and iodine gas, I_2, to form hydrogen iodide gas:

$$H_{2(g)} + I_{2(g)} \longrightarrow [H_2I_2]_{(g)} \longrightarrow 2\,HI_{(g)} \qquad \Delta H = -3.0 \text{ kcal/mole } HI_{(g)} \text{ at } 25^\circ\text{C and 1 atm}$$

This reaction is exothermic ($\Delta H = -3.0$ kcal/mole $HI_{(g)}$), yet it is necessary to supply some heat in order to speed it up, because a collision between a H_2 molecule and a I_2 molecule will form the activated complex only if the sum of the energies of the colliding molecules is at least as great as the energy of the intermediate activated complex $[H_2I_2]$. In this case the energy of the activated complex (Fig. 26-4) is much higher than the sum of the average energies of the H_2 and I_2 molecules (the activation energy for the reaction is +40.8 kcal/mole), which explains why the reaction is slow. Figure 26-4 shows also that the reverse reaction, the decomposition of gaseous hydrogen iodide,

FIGURE 26-4 Formation of $HI_{(g)}$ from $H_{2(g)}$ and $I_{2(g)}$ at constant *T* and *P*.

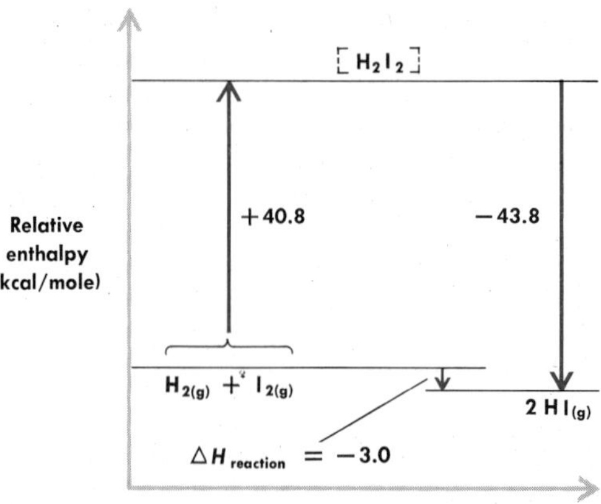

$2\ HI_{(g)} \longrightarrow [H_2I_2]_{(g)} \longrightarrow H_{2(g)} + I_{2(g)}$, is endothermic ($\Delta H = +3.0$ kcal/mole $HI_{(g)}$) and that the activation energy for this decomposition or reverse reaction is therefore $(+40.8 + 3.0) = +43.8$ kcal/mole. Because the activation energy of the reverse reaction is higher than that for the forward reaction, HI decomposes to H_2 and I_2 at room temperature even more slowly.

We know that, whether we start only with HI or with a mixture of H_2 and I_2, the final state of the reaction will be a state of equilibrium in which H_2, I_2, and HI co-exist in constant concentrations. At equilibrium, the rate at which HI is formed from I_2 and H_2 equals the rate at which HI decomposes to form H_2 and I_2.

THE STERIC FACTOR IN MOLECULAR COLLISIONS

We have mentioned that two molecules can react only if they collide with sufficient energy and with the proper orientation to form the activated complex. To better visualize what we mean by proper orientation, let us consider once more the decomposition of HI molecules into H_2 and I_2 molecules. Assume that two molecules of HI collide with enough energy to react. The formation of the activated complex $[H_2I_2]$ and its rearrangement into the products, $H_2 + I_2$, may be thought to occur by the following three successive steps (Fig. 26-5).

1. A high-energy HI molecule is about to collide with another high-energy HI molecule in proper alignment for reaction.

2. Upon collision, an intermediate activated complex is formed, in which one H atom is linked partially both with the other H atom and with an I atom. Once the activated complex $[H_2I_2]$ is formed, it may revert to the original reactants, 2 HI, or it may rearrange itself to form the products.

3. The activated complex $[H_2I_2]$ rearranges to form the products. As the original two H—I bonds are broken, a new H—H bond (H_2 molecule) is formed simultaneously, together with two isolated I atoms. In turn, these two I atoms may combine to form an I_2 molecule, because iodine atoms and diatomic iodine molecules are in equilibrium, $2\ I \rightleftharpoons I_2$, at the temperature at which reaction occurs.

H H
| |
I I

[H---H
| |
I I]

H—H
+
I + I
⇅
I—I

This series of steps is summarized as follows:

$$HI + HI \rightleftharpoons \left[\begin{array}{c} H\text{---}I \\ \vdots \quad \vdots \\ H\text{---}I \end{array}\right] \rightleftharpoons H_2 + 2I$$
$$2I \rightleftharpoons I_2$$

In order for the activated complex to be formed when two high-energy HI molecules collide, these molecules must be so oriented with respect to each other that the two H atoms can make contact, thus forming a sort of H—H bond. If two high-energy HI molecules collide with an unfavorable orientation, so that the two H atoms are not close enough to form the partial H—H bond, the HI molecules will simply bounce off, even though their energy may be sufficient to bring about the formation of the $[H_2I_2]$ complex. In other words, whether two colliding molecules actually react depends not only on their energy, but also on their relative orientation in space. This is generally called the *steric factor* in the molecular collision. Of all the colliding molecules

FIGURE 26-5 Schematic representation of the reaction, $2\ HI \rightleftharpoons H_2 + I_2$.

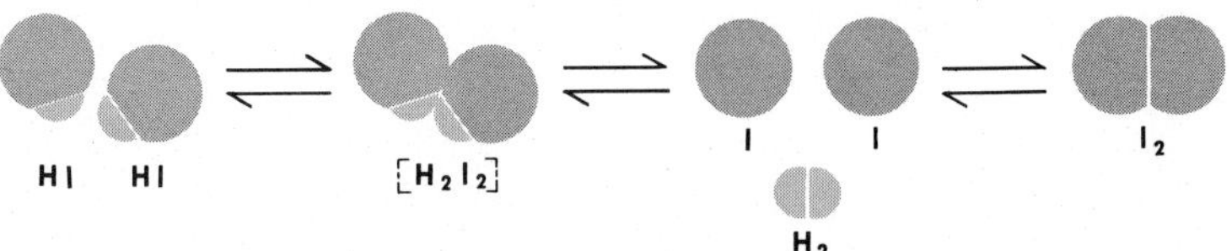

which have sufficient energy to react, only a fraction—those with the proper orientation—finally bring about the formation of the activated complex. For the decomposition of HI, this fraction is about 20 per cent of the total colliding molecules. For complicated molecules, the figure may be much smaller, on the order of a few per cent or less.

Similar general considerations apply to the formation of gaseous HI from gaseous H_2 and I_2. This reaction follows a reverse sequence of the steps considered above. First, an I_2 molecule dissociates into two isolated I atoms. Then *two* I atoms collide with a H_2 molecule to form the activated complex $\lceil H_2I_2 \rceil$, which may rearrange to yield two HI molecules. When the rate at which the activated complex decomposes to the products is equal to the rate at which the activated complex decomposes to the reactants, the forward and reverse reactions are in a state of dynamic equilibrium.

THE STERIC FACTOR AND THE ENTROPY OF ACTIVATION. We may notice that when two (or more) substances come together to form an activated complex, there is a change in the number of particles as well as in their freedom of motion—that is to say—a change of entropy. The steric factor in molecular collisions is indeed a measure of the entropy change which accompanies the formation of the activated complex from the reactants, that is, of the $\Delta S_{\text{activation}}$ of the reaction.

These considerations indicate that, if we wish to have a more complete picture of the factors determining the rate of a reaction, we must take into account not only the activation energy, which we have seen is a heat energy term, but also the activation entropy. In fact, it is the free energy change, ΔG, which determines whether a certain reaction has or does not have the capacity to take place spontaneously. Thus, it is the free energy of activation, $\Delta G_{\text{activation}} = \Delta G_{\text{activated complex}} - \Delta G_{\text{reactants}}$, which determines what fraction of the reactants has the capacity to form the activated complex and consequently determines the rate of the reaction. For reactions at constant temperature and pressure, $\Delta G_{\text{activation}} = \Delta H_{\text{activation}} - T\,\Delta S_{\text{activation}}$; hence the difference in entropy between the activated complex and the reactants also plays a significant role in reaction rates. We shall see later that the effect of $\Delta S_{\text{activation}}$ is especially important for catalyzed reactions (p. 591). In general, it is difficult to determine the value of either $\Delta G_{\text{activation}}$ or $\Delta S_{\text{activation}}$ for a reaction; this is why we usually speak only of the activation energy, whose value can be determined experimentally by measuring how the reaction rate varies with the temperature.

THE EFFECT OF TEMPERATURE ON REACTION RATE

In addition to the steric factor just considered, we have seen that the rate of a reaction between gaseous molecules depends on (1) the frequency with which the molecules collide, and (2) the fraction of colliding molecules that possess enough energy to react. These two factors are directly affected by one of the conditions under which the reaction is taking place—namely, the *temperature.*

A rise in temperature increases the frequency with which the molecules collide, and this contributes to some extent to increasing the reaction rate. However, this effect is not substantial, because a temperature rise of 10°C, for example, will increase the frequency of collisions of gaseous molecules by only about 2 per cent at ordinary temperatures; and we know that only a very minute fraction of these additional colliding molecules actually react. Far more important is the fact that a rise in temperature increases the proportion of molecules that will have sufficient energy to react. Consequently, the higher the temperature, the higher the proportion of colliding molecules that actually react with one another and the higher the rate of the reaction.

The increase in the number of high-energy molecules produced by an increase in temperature from t_1 to t_2 is shown by the energy-distribution curves in Fig. 26-6. Assume that the energy required for a molecule to form the activated complex is E_{act}. The molecules that possess (at least) this amount of energy are represented by area A

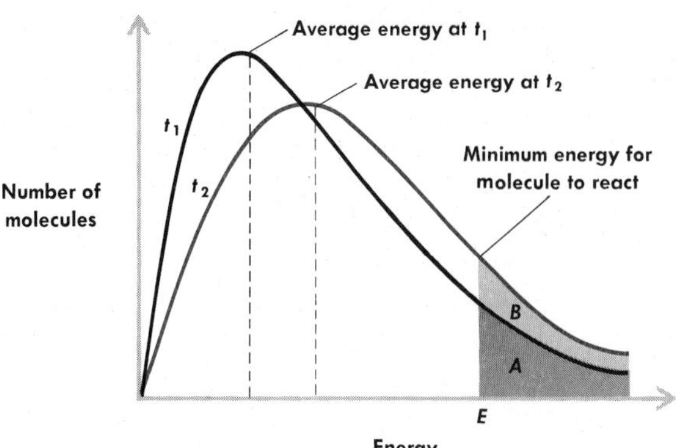

FIGURE 26-6 Energy distribution among molecules, at a lower temperature, t_1, and at a higher temperature, t_2.

for the lower temperature, t_1, and by area B for the higher temperature, t_2. Thus when we increase the temperature of the gas from t_1 to t_2, the fraction of molecules with at least an energy E_{act} increases markedly, as shown in the diagram. The experimental observation that the rate of a reaction increases significantly when the temperature is increased even slightly supports the concept of activation energy which we have discussed above.

As an example of how the rate of a reaction increases with a rise in temperature, let us consider again the thermal decomposition of gaseous $HI_{(g)}$ into $H_{2(g)}$ and $I_{2(g)}$ (the latter in equilibrium with isolated $I_{(g)}$ atoms). We find experimentally that the dissociation at 400°C is about 250 times faster than it is at 300°C, and at 500°C it is about 25,000 times faster than at 300°C. And if we increase the temperature by only 10°C, say from 500°C to 510°C, we find that the decomposition rate of the HI almost doubles. This sharp increase in the rate of decomposition shows that as the temperature is raised the fraction of colliding molecules having enough energy to react must have increased markedly! For example, if at 500°C only one out of every 100,000 collisions between HI molecules results in a chemical change during a given period of time, at 510°C 2 out of every 100,000 collisions between HI molecules results in a chemical reaction.

THE EFFECT OF CONCENTRATION ON REACTION RATE

As long as the temperature of a given reaction system remains constant, the proportion of molecules with sufficient energy to react chemically will remain fixed. How can we then increase the reaction rate without raising the temperature or introducing a catalyst? The only way is to alter another factor that controls the reaction rate—namely, the frequency of collisions. Since at constant temperature the frequency of collision between the molecules of a system depends on the number of molecules present in a given volume, the rate of a chemical reaction must depend on the *concentration of (one or more of) the reacting molecules.* As an illustration, consider how the concentration of HI influences the rate of its dissociation to form the products H_2 and I_2, as described in the following experiments.

In the first experiment we place in a vessel of fixed volume and at constant temperature (sufficiently high to give a convenient reaction rate) a known number (moles) of $HI_{(g)}$ molecules. After a relatively short time, so that the amount of HI which has dissociated is very small compared with the total amount of HI still present, we analyze a sample of the reaction mixture. That is, we determine the extent to which $HI_{(g)}$ has disappeared and $H_{2(g)}$ and $I_{2(g)}$ have formed. We then repeat the experiment, this time placing in the vessel twice as many molecules of $HI_{(g)}$ as in the first experiment and again analyze a sample of the mixture after the same short time interval. We find now that the extent of the reaction is four times as great as in the first experiment. Since the vessel has a fixed volume, the concentration of $HI_{(g)}$ in the second experiment is twice that in the first experiment; thus, if at constant volume and temperature we double the concentration of $HI_{(g)}$, we increase four-fold the rate of its dissociation to form $H_{2(g)}$ and $I_{2(g)}$. A further experiment shows that if we increase the concentration of $HI_{(g)}$ three times, the rate of reaction increases nine times.

The above observations show that the initial rate of the dissociation of HI to H_2 and I_2 is directly proportional to the initial concentration of the HI molecules multiplied by the initial concentration of HI molecules. Also, at any moment during the reaction the rate of dissociation of HI is directly proportional to the second power of the concentration of HI molecules still present in the system. If [HI] represents, as usual, the concentration of HI in mole/liter at a given moment, we can state that the rate of dissociation of HI is proportional to [HI] $\times$ [HI] or to $[HI]^2$. And if we introduce a proportionality constant, k_1, we can express this relationship as

$$\text{Rate of dissociation of HI} = k_1[\text{HI}]^2$$

Now let us consider the reverse reaction, the combination of $H_{2(gas)}$ with $I_{2(gas)}$ to form HI gas: $H_{2(g)} + I_{2(g)} \longrightarrow 2\ HI_{(g)}$. Again let us determine the rate-concentration dependence of this reaction by a series of experiments analogous to those described for the dissociation of HI. In the first experiment we introduce into the vessel of fixed volume and at constant temperature equal numbers of moles of H_2 and I_2. After a very short time interval, so that the amounts of H_2 and I_2 which have reacted are very small as compared with their total amounts still present in the system, we analyze a sample of the mixture and determine the extent to which H_2 and I_2 have combined to form HI. In the second experiment the number of H_2 moles is doubled, but the number of I_2 moles remains the same. We find that after the same short time interval, the extent of the reaction between H_2 and I_2 is twice as great as in the first experiment. An additional experiment shows that if we keep the molar concentration of H_2 constant but double the molar concentration of I_2, again we double the rate of the reaction. And if we double the molar concentration of *both* the H_2 and I_2, the reaction rate increases four-fold.

We conclude from these experimental data that the rate of combination of H_2 and I_2 to form HI is, at any moment during the reaction, directly proportional to the (total) molar concentration of hydrogen multiplied by the (total) molar concentration of iodine present in the system at the moment considered. And if we introduce a proportionality constant, k_2, we can write:

$$\text{Rate of combination of } H_2 \text{ with } I_2 = k_2 \times [\text{hydrogen}] \times [\text{iodine}]$$

Let us now see how we can attempt to relate this observed rate-concentration dependence to the possible path(s) by which the reaction may be thought to take place. When we mix hydrogen gas and iodine gas and find that they react to form gaseous hydrogen iodide, we can think of several likely paths—or mechanisms—by which the reaction may take place. One such likely mechanism is the collision of a H_2 molecule with an I_2 molecule to form an intermediate activated complex $[H_2I_2]$, which then decomposes to produce two HI molecules. To visualize how the observed rate-concentration relationship may result from this mechanism, let us consider a very tiny volume, and assume that at first this volume contains just two molecules of H_2 and two molecules of I_2 (Fig. 26-7, experiment 1). Since each of the two H_2 molecules can collide with each of the two I_2 molecules, there are four possible distinct collisions between a H_2 molecule and an I_2 molecule, as shown by the dashed lines. Thus, the number of possible collisions in a given time is equal to the product of the numbers of each kind of molecule present, $2 \times 2 = 4$. In the second experiment we double the number of H_2 molecules in the same tiny volume. Since there are two I_2 molecules, each of the four H_2 moles has two chances of colliding with an I_2 molecule. Thus, the total number of possible collisions between a H_2 molecule and an I_2 molecule in a given time is $4 \times 2 = 8$. In experi-

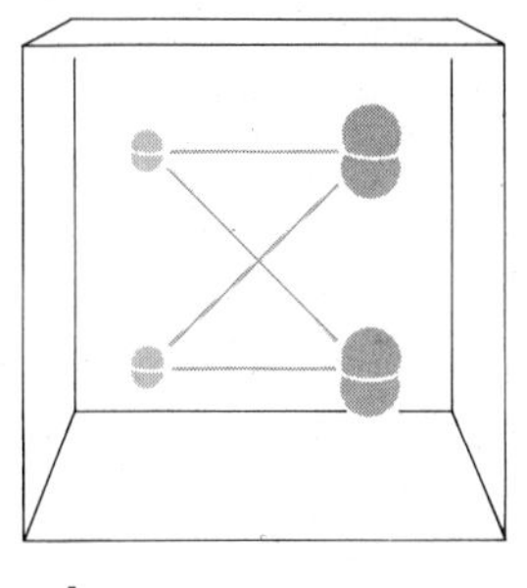
1

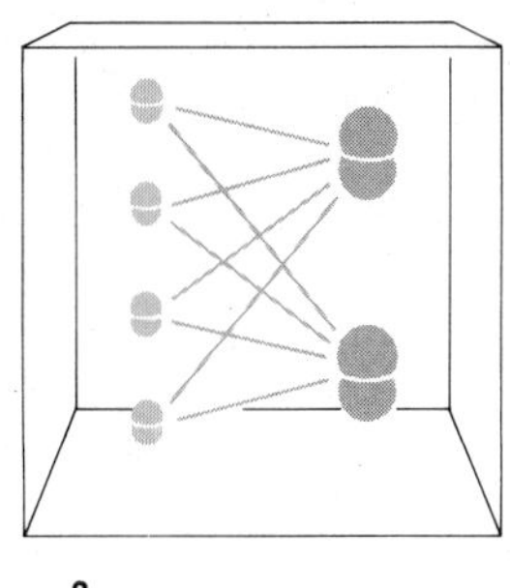
2

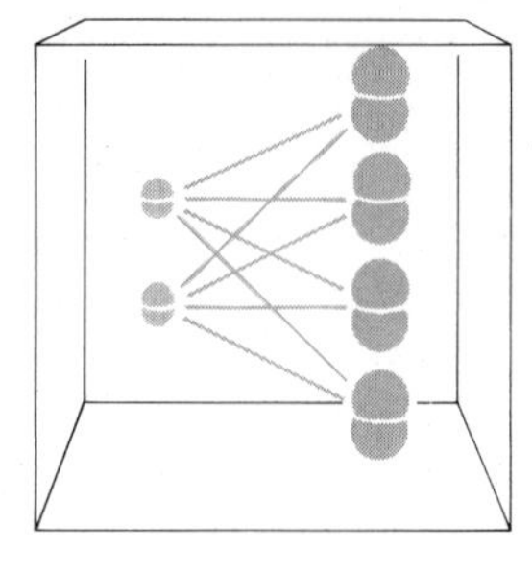
3

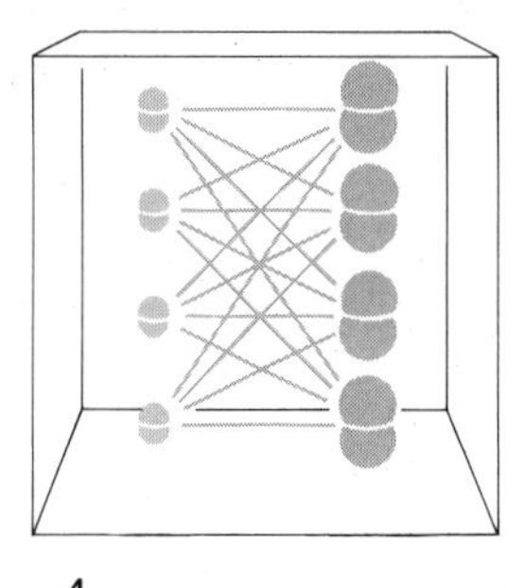
4

FIGURE 26-7 Chances of collision between H_2 and I_2 molecules.

ment 3 we double the number of I_2 molecules—that is, we double the concentration of I_2—and restore the H_2 concentration to what it was originally. Now the chance that any one of the four I_2 molecules will collide with any one of the two H_2 molecules in a given time is $4 \times 2 = 8$. Finally, in experiment 4, the concentration of *both* the H_2 and I_2 is doubled, so that each of the four H_2 molecules has four chances of colliding with one of the four I_2 molecules. Thus, the total chance of collision between a H_2 molecule and an I_2 molecule in a given time is $4 \times 4 = 16$. Thus we see that the number of collisions between molecules of H_2 and I_2 is proportional to the product: the concentration of H_2 multiplied by the concentration of I_2. The experimental observation that the rate of reaction is proportional to the total concentration of hydrogen multiplied by the total concentration of iodine is therefore consistent with the mechanism we have assumed—the collision of one H_2 molecule with one I_2 molecule.

The collision of a H_2 molecule with an I_2 molecule is not, however, the only plausible mechanism through which the formation of hydrogen iodide from hydrogen and iodine may be thought to take place. We know that the dissociation of gaseous iodine molecules, I_2, into gaseous iodine atoms, I, begins at a rather low temperature. So, at the moderately high temperature at which the experiment is conducted, we must consider that part or all of the iodine introduced into the vessel may be present as an equilibrium mixture of diatomic molecules and isolated atoms: $I_{2(g)} \rightleftharpoons 2\ I_{(g)}$. Notice that we would not expect a similar equilibrium for hydrogen, because the dissociation of H_2 molecules begins to set in only at very high temperatures (p. 99). There is, then, another likely mechanism by which HI may be formed —namely, the collision of one H_2 molecule with two I atoms simultaneously, to form again the intermediate activated complex $[H_2I_2]$. This mechanism would still be consistent with the observed rate-concentration dependence, provided the total concentration of iodine atoms, [I], is very small relative to the concentration of the iodine molecules, $[I_2]$. Thus, there are at least two different mechanisms which explain equally well the observed rate-concentration dependence under these conditions of moderately high temperature and ordinary pressure. Clearly, we need additional experimental evidence, of a different kind, to decide whether one of these two mechanisms—and if so, which one—really represents how gaseous hydrogen iodide is formed from hydrogen gas and iodine gas.

REACTIONS IN SOLUTION

We have discussed the chief factors which influence the rate of reactions in gaseous systems—the frequency with which the molecules of the reactants collide, their average energy, their relative orientations in the collision. These same factors also determine the rate of reactions in homogeneous liquid systems, and particularly in solution, but the significance of the factors themselves is somewhat different. We know that in the gaseous state the molecules move freely at extremely high speeds, and are almost independent of one another except at the instant in which they collide. Furthermore, in the gas phase the duration of each collision is extremely short, so molecules that collide with insufficient energy or with unsuitable orientation, or that do not have time to convert their kinetic energy into the required potential vibrational energy, will bounce apart without reacting.

In the liquid phase, on the other hand, each particle is closely surrounded by, and interacts relatively strongly with, a number of neighbors. Each particle is in ceaseless motion, and so are its neighbors; but as a particle moves it remains at all times closely surrounded by the same average number of neighbors, even though the neighbors themselves may shift and change. As a consequence of these strong interactions among neighbors, which are characteristic of the liquid state, the actual speed at which a particle (molecule or ion) moves in solution is much less than the speed at which a gas molecule moves at the same temperature. If we consider a reaction in solution involving two solutes A and B, the frequency with which a particle of A and a particle of B come close enough to react is much less than it would be if these particles were gaseous and free to move in the same volume at the same temperature. However, when the A and B particles do come together in solution, they remain in close contact for a relatively long time interval, because the surrounding layers of solvent molecules now act as a "cage" and serve to prevent the A and B particles from separating again. Thus even if at first in their encounter the A and B particles are not properly oriented or do not have sufficient energy to react, they may still have a chance to shift to a more favorable orientation or to acquire the necessary energy from the surrounding solvent molecules, before finally coming apart. In other words, even though the frequency of the encounters of A with B is much higher in the gas than in the liquid phase, the chance that an encounter may be fruitful is much greater in the liquid than in the gas phase. These two opposing factors almost completely compensate for each other.

Another important difference between reactions in gaseous and liquid systems is that the gaseous molecules depend chiefly on collision with other gaseous molecules both to acquire the necessary energy to react and to give up their excess energy after reaction has occurred. In solution, on the other hand, the particles can transfer energy simply by contact with the surrounding solvent molecules, so that the collisions between the reactants lose importance as a means of energy transfer. Finally, we must always be aware of the fact that in solution each solute particle (molecule or ion) is closely associated with a number of solvent molecules. And these solvent molecules very often play a fundamental role in the actual path of the reaction, although they do not appear in the net reaction equation.

26-4 The Mechanism of Reactions

THE ORDER OF A REACTION. As we have seen, we can determine by experiments that the rate of the reaction between H_2 and I_2 to form HI is, at any moment, directly proportional to the product of the total concentration of hydrogen and the total concentration of iodine present at that moment in the system: reaction rate $= k[H_2][I_2]$. We sometimes express this experimental result by saying that the reaction of H_2 and I_2 is of the *first order* with respect to hydrogen because the concentration of H_2 appears once—that is, with an exponent equal to 1—in the rate-concentration equation. Similarly, we say that the reaction is of the *first order* with respect to iodine because the concentration of I_2 also appears with an exponent equal to 1 in the rate-concentration expression. We may also say that the over-all order of the reaction is 2, or that *the reaction is of the second order,* meaning that the sum of the exponents of all concentration terms which appear in the rate expression is $1 + 1 = 2$. As we know, the experimental fact that the rate of the reaction is directly proportional to the concentrations of both the reactants, H_2 and I_2, is consistent with at least two distinct *mechanisms* which may be *assumed* to explain the reaction: (a) the collision of one $H_{2(g)}$ molecule with one $I_{2(g)}$ molecule, and (b) the collision of one $H_{2(g)}$ molecule with two $I_{(g)}$ atoms. If the reaction of H_2 and I_2 proceeded by a mechanism *completely different* from any one of these two assumed, the rate of the reaction probably would *not* be directly proportional to the product of the concentration of H_2 by the concentration of I_2 (the reaction probably would *not* be of the second order). Thus, the experimentally determined order of this reaction permits us to say that the assumed mechanisms are reasonable and *possible* for this reaction. However, the order of the reaction alone—or more specifically, the dependence of the reaction rate on the concentration(s) of the reactant(s) and of the products can only *suggest* one or more possible reaction mechanisms.

THE PROPOSED MECHANISM. In general, before we can propose a possible mechanism for a reaction, we must establish the experimental facts concerning its rate, often under different sets of conditions. Only after we have accurately determined by experiments how the rate of a given reaction depends on the concentration of one or more of the reactants (rate-concentration dependence), may we attempt to *propose* a *possible* mechanism for the reaction. We must also keep in mind that the rate-concentration dependence gives only an indication of the possible mechanism of a reaction, and that other experimental findings, in particular the isolation and identification of intermediates, are necessary to support the proposed mechanism. A proposed mechanism may be considered correct only when it is consistent with all the known facts concerning the reaction. If a proposed mechanism is found to be inconsistent with a fact observed in a subsequent experiment, then the mechanism is incorrect and must be modified to account for the new evidence, or it may have to be discarded. *It is not possible to prove a certain mechanism,* and even after much research and study a mechanism ultimately remains only a likely possibility.

In fact, there are only relatively few types of reactions where the detailed mechanisms are firmly established. Among these are the substitution and addition reactions of organic compounds, the reactions of square planar complexes, and a number of reactions in solutions. Although they are seemingly more simple, gas phase reactions usually have a very complicated mechanism, because gaseous molecules usually transfer energy by direct collision with one another, whereas molecules in solution can acquire the desired energy, or get rid of any undesired excess energy, by transfer with the neighboring solvent molecules. Also, many gaseous reactions involve surface catalysis. One of the most studied of the mechanisms of gas phase reactions is that of the dissociation of $HI_{(g)}$ to form $H_{2(g)}$ and $I_{2(g)}$. This is one of the reasons why we use this reaction so often as an example in our discussion of reaction kinetics. As we have already discussed, in this reaction the mechanism of formation of the activated complex $\lceil H_2I_2 \rfloor$ is believed to consist of the collision of two $HI_{(g)}$ molecules. For the reaction of hydrogen and iodine to form hydrogen iodide, the mechanism was long believed to be the collision of one H_2 molecule with one I_2 molecule; only recently has new evidence indicated that the reaction actually proceeds by the collision of one $H_{2(g)}$ molecule with *two* $I_{(g)}$ atoms resulting from the previous dissociation of the $I_{2(g)}$ molecule.

It is generally possible to determine experimentally how the rate of a reaction depends on the concentration of the reactants. The dependence may be of a simple type, as for the decomposition of HI, or it may be more complex. We can define the order of a reaction only when the rate-concentration dependence is simple enough, and the rate is proportional to integral power(s) of the concentration(s) of the reactant(s). For example, if for a given chemical reaction involving two reactants, A and B, we find that the rate is proportional to the concentration of A multiplied by the concentration of B to the second power, we may write the rate-concentration dependence as: *Rate of reaction of* A *with* $B = k[A] \times [B]^2$, and we may express this by saying that this reaction is *third-order* (first-order with respect to A and second-order with respect to B). Again, the order of the reaction is given by the sum of the exponents of the concentrations which appear in the rate expression $k[A] \times [B]^2$. The exponent of [A] is 1, the exponent of $[B]^2$ is 2, and their sum is 3 (third-order reaction). We may infer that a possible mechanism for the reaction between A and B is the collision of one A molecule with two B molecules: $A + 2\ B \longrightarrow [AB_2] \longrightarrow$ products. Notice that we have arrived at this possible mechanism without even considering the stoichiometric equation for the reaction of A and B.

An actual reaction which reveals a third order rate-concentration dependence is that of NO gas with O_2 gas to form two molecules of NO_2 gas: rate of reaction of NO with $O_2 = k\,[NO]^2 \times [O_2]$. We may infer from this experimental result that the reaction involves the collision of *two* molecules of NO with *one* molecule of O_2 to form an activated complex $[(NO)_2O_2]$, which then rearranges to form two molecules of NO_2. It is now believed that this reaction actually occurs via this trimolecular collision mechanism. Notice, however, that we can *propose* this as a possible mechanism only on the basis of the experimental kinetic data. The fact that the reaction equation, $2\ NO + O_2 \longrightarrow 2\ NO_2$, agrees with the proposed mechanism is purely coincidental.

NET EQUATION AND MECHANISM. We must always be aware that the *net* equation of a reaction does not give any indication of the mechanism by which the reaction proceeds. This becomes obvious when we consider a complicated reaction, such as the oxidation of the bromide ion, Br^-, to bromine, Br_2, by the permanganate ion, MnO_4^-, in acidic (H^+) aqueous solution, as represented by the net ionic equation:

$$2\ MnO_4^- + 10\ Br^- + 16\ H^+ \longrightarrow 2\ Mn^{++} + 5\ Br_2 + 8\ H_2O$$

Obviously, this reaction will not occur through the most unlikely simultaneous encounter of 28 ions ($2\ MnO_{4(aq)}^-$, $10\ Br^-_{(aq)}$, and $16\ H^+_{(aq)}$); rather, the reaction will proceed through a sequence of simple steps, each involving either the dissociation of a single species, or the encounter of two, or at the most, three species. The sum of all these simple intermediate steps then results in the net reaction equation. A stoichiometric chemical equation of the sort that we customarily use states only the *initial reactants* and the *final products;* it tells us nothing about the steps by which the reaction actually proceeds, nor about the *short-lived intermediate species* which may be formed during these intermediate steps. And yet almost all chemical reactions proceed by at least a few, and often, many intermediate steps.

CHAIN REACTIONS—MECHANISM OF COMBINATION OF HYDROGEN AND BROMINE

Now let us consider the reaction of H_2 gas with Br_2 gas to produce HBr gas, which has the same stoichiometry as the reaction of $H_{2(g)}$ with $I_{2(g)}$ to produce $HI_{(g)}$. Here are the stoichiometric equations that we ordinarily use to represent these reactions:

$$H_{2(g)} + Br_{2(g)} \longrightarrow 2\ HBr_{(g)} \quad \text{and} \quad H_{2(g)} + I_{2(g)} \longrightarrow 2\ HI_{(g)}$$

It would be incorrect to assume that both reactions proceed by the same mechanism, simply because their stoichiometric equations are the same. In fact, as we shall now see, the reaction of $H_{2(g)}$ with $Br_{2(g)}$ proceeds by a mechanism entirely different from that of the reaction of $H_{2(g)}$ with $I_{2(g)}$.

To determine how the rate of the reaction, $H_{2(g)} + Br_{2(g)} \longrightarrow 2\ HBr_{(g)}$ depends on the concentrations of the reactants, we can perform the usual series of experiments. We first determine at a constant temperature and volume the rate at which these gases combine when their concentrations are equal at the start of the experiment. We then repeat the experiment, keeping constant the concentration of H_2, but doubling the concentration of Br_2. We find that doubling the concentration of Br_2 does *not* double the rate of the reaction. In fact, the rate of the reaction only increases by a factor about equal to the square root of 2 ($\sqrt{2}$). And if we increase three-fold the concentration of Br_2, while keeping that of H_2 constant, we find that the rate of the reaction increases by a factor about equal to $\sqrt{3}$. On the other hand, if we keep the concentration of Br_2 constant and double the concentration of H_2, we find that the rate almost doubles, and if we increase three-fold the concentration of H_2 the rate almost triples. We would also find, by measuring the rate in the presence of various amounts of added HBr, that the conversion of H_2 and Br_2 to HBr becomes slower as HBr is added. Thus for this reaction the rate-concentration dependence is different from, and much more complicated than, that for the reaction of H_2 and I_2 to form HI. These experimental results indicate that the mechanism of the reaction of H_2 with Br_2 *cannot* be explained simply on the basis of collisions between H_2 molecules and Br_2 molecules, as for the apparently similar reaction of H_2 with I_2. The reaction between H_2 and Br_2 is believed to be a *chain reaction,* taking place by the three following steps:

		ΔH (kcal/mole-equation)	Activation Energy (kcal/mole-equation)	
1.	$:\ddot{Br}:\ddot{Br}: \longrightarrow :\ddot{Br}\cdot + \cdot\ddot{Br}:$	+53.4	—	chain-initiation step
2.	$:\ddot{Br}\cdot + H:H \longrightarrow H:\ddot{Br}: + \cdot H$	+16.40	+17.6	chain-propagation steps
3.	$H\cdot + :\ddot{Br}:\ddot{Br}: \longrightarrow H:\ddot{Br}: + \cdot\ddot{Br}:$	−40.0	+38.8	chain-propagation steps

Step 1 consists of the dissociation of a Br_2 molecule into its constituent Br atoms, and is called the *chain-initiation* step. Step 2 consists of the reaction of a Br atom (formed in step 1) with a H_2 molecule, resulting in the formation of a HBr molecule and a H atom. Step 3 consists of the reaction of an isolated H atom (formed in step 2) with a Br_2 molecule to form a HBr molecule and an isolated Br atom. This Br atom in turn reacts with a H_2 molecule according to step 2, and so forth. Steps 2 and 3 repeat themselves over and over again, because the product of one of these steps is the reactant of the other step. These repeated alternating steps constitute a *chain reaction* which keeps going without step 1 being repeated, and are called *chain-propagation* steps. The chain reaction can be terminated by any one of the following *chain-termination* steps: (a) a H atom collides with another H atom and a H_2 molecule is reformed, $H\cdot + .H \longrightarrow H_2$, (b) a Br atom collides with another Br atom and a Br_2 molecule is reformed, $Br\cdot + \cdot Br \longrightarrow Br_2$, (c) a Br atom and a H atom collide to form HBr, $H\cdot + \cdot Br \longrightarrow HBr$, or (d) either a Br atom or a H atom collide with a molecule of a foreign substance to form a product which does not participate in the chain reaction. In a system which reacts via a chain mechanism, innumerable chain reactions proceed simultaneously, and during each second innumerable chains are started while others are terminated. Thus, the reaction between H_2 and Br_2 proceeds via a sequence of innumerable simultaneous chains, until all the H_2 or all the Br_2, or both, are converted to HBr.

Another reaction which can take place in the system, one that becomes more and more likely as the concentration of the product, HBr, increases, is: $H + HBr \longrightarrow Br + H_2$. Although this reaction does not break the chain, it consumes the desired product, HBr, and hence is called a *chain retardation* step.

Thus we see that such a seemingly simple reaction as $H_2 + Br_2 \longrightarrow 2\ HBr$, actually involves several steps, with the formation of several intermediate substances, even though these are not shown by the net equation of this reaction.

MECHANISM OF OXIDATION-REDUCTION REACTIONS

We have seen that the equation for an oxidation-reduction reaction may be balanced in a number of ways, without requiring any knowledge of the actual path by which the reaction takes place. In the formal process of balancing oxidation-reduction equations we often speak of electron(s) "transferred from one reactant (the reductant) to another (the oxidant)." If we consider the mechanism of oxidation-reduction reactions, however, we find that many reactions do actually occur by the direct transfer of an electron from the reductant to the oxidant, but many others follow a more complicated path, involving the formation of an activated intermediate in which the oxidant and the reductant are linked together by bridging atoms or groups. Red-ox reactions which proceed via a bridged intermediate usually result not only in a change of oxidation state but also in the transfer of an atom or group of atoms from one reactant to the other.

An example of a reaction which is believed to proceed by direct electron transfer is the oxidation of the $[Fe^{+2}(CN)_6]^{-4}$ complex ion by the $[Fe^{+3}(CN)_6]^{-3}$ complex ion:

$$\underbrace{[Fe^{+2}(CN)_6]^{-4} + [Fe^{+3}(CN)_6]^{-3}}_{\text{electron transfer}} \rightleftharpoons \underbrace{[Fe^{+3}(CN)_6]^{-3} + [Fe^{+2}(CN)_6]^{-4}}_{\text{electron transfer}}$$

If we mix a solution containing the reductant $[Fe^{+2}(CN)_6]^{-4}$ ion with a solution containing the oxidant $[Fe^{+3}(CN)_6]^{-3}$ ion—one of which, say $[Fe^{+2}(CN)_6]^{-4}$, has been labeled with a radioactive isotope of iron, $\overset{*}{Fe}$—we observe that the radioactivity becomes distributed very rapidly between the $[Fe^{+2}(CN)_6]^{-4}$ and the $[Fe^{+3}(CN)_6]^{+3}$ species. We can easily determine the rate of this "radioactive exchange reaction" because the Fe(II) complex and the Fe(III) complex differ markedly in some of their chemical properties and can be readily separated. On the other hand, if we study the rate at which the free cyanide ion in solution, CN^-, exchanges with the CN^- attached to iron in either complex, $[Fe^{+2}(CN)_6]^{-4}$ or $[Fe^{+3}(CN)_6]^{-3}$, we find that this "cyanide exchange reaction" is extremely slow. We also find that the CN^- attached to iron in these complexes does not exchange with H_2O molecules of the solvent water. Thus the high rate of the radioactive exchange reaction simply indicates that the red-ox reaction

$$[\overset{*}{Fe}{}^{+2}(CN)_6]^{-4} + [Fe^{+3}(CN)_6]^{-3} \longrightarrow [\overset{*}{Fe}{}^{+3}(CN)_6]^{-3} + [Fe^{+2}(CN)_6]^{-4}$$

occurs by the direct transfer of an electron from the labeled Fe(II) of $[Fe^{+3}(CN)_6]^{-4}$ to the Fe(III) of $[Fe^{+3}(CN)_6]^{-3}$, without appreciably disrupting the coordination sphere of either complex.

An example of a red-ox reaction which is believed to take place via a bridged intermediate is the oxidation of sulfur dioxide, SO_2, by the chlorate ion, ClO_3^-, in water solution, to form sulfate, $SO_4^=$, chlorate, ClO_2^-, and H^+ ions:

$$S^{+4}O_2 + Cl^{+5}O_3^- + H_2O \longrightarrow S^{+6}O_4^= + Cl^{+3}O_2^- + 2\,H^+$$

In this reaction, SO_2 is the reductant and the ClO_3^- ion is the oxidant, and the transfer of one oxygen atom from the ClO_3^- ion to SO_2, as shown:

$$SO_2 + ClO_3^- \longrightarrow [O_2S{-}OClO_2]^- \longrightarrow SO_3 + ClO_2^-$$

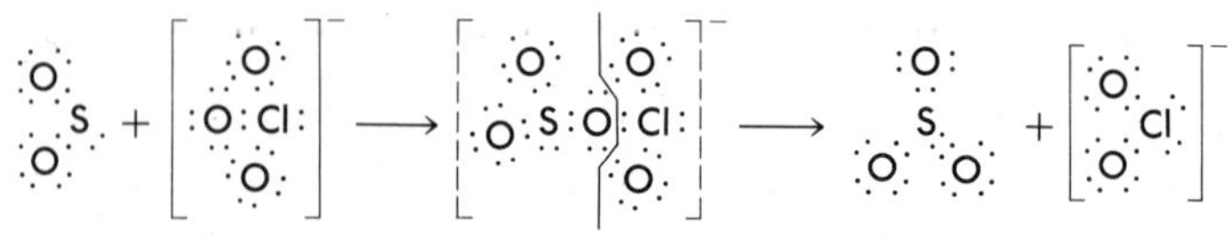

In the presence of H_2O the SO_3 formed reacts to give $S^{+6}O_4^=$ and $2\,H^+$.

26-5 The Effect of Light on Reaction Rate

Certain chemical reactions proceed quite rapidly when the reactants are exposed to light, whereas they do not take place at an appreciable rate—at the same temperature—when the reactants are kept in the dark. Reactions of this sort, which require light to proceed, are called *photochemical* reactions. Many photochemical reactions are quite familiar—the darkening of a photographic film when it is exposed to light, the slow fading of dyed fabrics in the presence of sunlight, and the photosynthetic process in plants, by which carbon dioxide and water of the atmosphere, in the presence of chlorophyll, are changed into carbohydrates and oxygen. The branch of chemistry that deals with photochemical reactions is known as *photochemistry.*

Light is a form of energy, and when a molecule or a polyatomic ion absorbs light, its energy increases; the molecule or ion may be excited rotationally, vibrationally, or electronically, or sometimes one or more of the covalent bonds that hold the molecule or ion together may break. This bond-breaking gives rise to the formation of atoms, or groups of atoms, which have one unpaired electron each and are called free radicals. In fact, we may define a *free radical* as a chemical entity which has one (or more) unpaired electrons and can exist long enough to take part in a distinguishable step of a chemical reaction. Here are two general schematic examples of bond-breaking reactions leading to the formation of free radicals:

$$A{:}BC \longrightarrow A^{\cdot} + .BC \quad \text{and} \quad AB{:}CD \longrightarrow AB^{\cdot} + .CD$$

So the absorption of light by a molecule may cause it to decompose into fragments (free radicals) extremely more reactive than the original molecule. When this is the case, the sequence of reaction steps leading to the final products involves these free radicals (even though they may exist only temporarily in the reaction system) rather than the original molecules of the reactants.

As an example of a photochemical reaction involving free radicals, consider the reaction of H_2 gas with Cl_2 gas to form HCl gas. If pure H_2 gas and pure Cl_2 gas are mixed together in a clean quartz vessel in the dark, no detectable reaction occurs, even though the formation of $HCl_{(g)}$ from $H_{2(g)}$ and $Cl_{2(g)}$ is thermodynamically favorable ($\Delta G = -22.8$ kcal/mole HCl at 25°, 1 atm). However, if we expose the $H_2 + Cl_2$ mixture to light, the reaction proceeds very rapidly with the evolution of heat ($\Delta H = -22.1$ kcal/mole HCl at 25°, 1 atm). And if the light is very intense, the reaction proceeds so very rapidly that the sudden evolution of this large quantity of heat, and the consequent sudden expansion of the gas, may give rise to an explosion.

Let us now consider what happens when a mixture of gaseous H_2 and Cl_2 molecules is exposed to light. Since hydrogen is a colorless gas, we know that its molecules do not absorb visible light; chlorine, on the other hand, is a yellow-green gas and this indicates that the Cl_2 molecules are capable of absorbing visible light. When a Cl_2 molecule absorbs light energy, it passes to a higher-energy (excited) state—and if the energy of this excited state is sufficiently high, the Cl—Cl bond of the Cl_2 molecule may break to form two Cl atoms. Remember that in order to dissociate a Cl_2 molecule into its two atoms, a relatively large quantity of energy, $\Delta H = +57.8$ kcal/mole Cl_2, must be supplied. The decomposition of Cl_2 molecules by absorption of light energy, $h\nu$, is illustrated by the following equation:

$$Cl_2 \xrightarrow[h\nu]{\text{energy}} Cl + Cl \quad \text{or} \quad :\ddot{\underset{..}{Cl}}:\ddot{\underset{..}{Cl}}: \xrightarrow[h\nu]{\text{energy}} :\ddot{\underset{..}{Cl}}^{\cdot} + .\ddot{\underset{..}{Cl}}: \qquad (1)$$

Here the symbol $h\nu$ stands for a quantity of radiation energy known as a *photon; h* is Planck's constant* (6.6×10^{-27} erg $\times$ sec) and ν is the frequency of the absorbed light. When a Cl_2 molecule absorbs a photon of sufficiently high energy, the Cl_2 molecule becomes so energetic that it dissociates into two Cl atoms. Since the energy of a system consisting of 2 moles of Cl atoms is higher than that of a system of 1 mole of Cl_2 molecules by as much as 57.8 kcal, the chlorine atoms are more reactive than the chlorine molecule and thus may undergo reactions which would have too high an

* This is a universal and fundamental constant which is connected with the Quantum Theory of the German physicist Max Planck (1858–1947).

activation energy for Cl_2 molecules. Notice also that an isolated chlorine atom (radical) has one unpaired electron, whereas in the covalent Cl_2 molecule each chlorine atom

has a noble-gas electron configuration. Consequently, chlorine atoms, $:\ddot{\mathrm{Cl}}\cdot$, may react via different pathways from chlorine molecules $:\ddot{\mathrm{Cl}}:\ddot{\mathrm{Cl}}:$. In fact, it is these Cl atoms, present temporarily in chlorine gas exposed to light, which in the presence of hydrogen gas are responsible for the formation of HCl, by the following chain reaction:

	ΔH (kcal/mole-equation)	Activation Energy (kcal/mole-equation)	
1. $Cl_2 \xrightarrow{\text{light energy}} 2\,Cl$	$+57.8$	—	chain-initiation step
2. $Cl + H_2 \longrightarrow HCl + H$	$+1.1$	$+6.7$	chain-propagation step
3. $H + Cl_2 \longrightarrow HCl + Cl$	-45.0	$+2.0$	chain-propagation step

A chain reaction of this sort, in which initiation step 1 involves the absorption of a photon of appropriate energy is called a *photochemical chain reaction.* The chain reaction is eventually broken when a Cl atom collides with another Cl atom, absorbed on the wall of the reaction vessel, to re-form a Cl_2 molecule. The chain reaction may also be interrupted when a Cl atom reacts with some impurity present in the system to form a product which no longer contributes to maintaining the chain reaction. Such a chain-terminating step is, for example, the reaction of a Cl atom with an oxygen molecule, O_2 (which is itself a sort of "double" free radical, having two unpaired electrons) to form chlorine dioxide gas: $Cl + O_2 \longrightarrow ClO_2$.

In the complete absence of oxygen and other impurities, the only important chain-terminating step is the recombination of the two Cl atoms absorbed on the surface of the vessel; chain-propagating steps 2 and 3 repeat on the average about 100,000 times before the chain is interrupted. The average number of molecules which react as a result of the absorption of one single photon, $h\nu$, is called the *quantum yield* of the photochemical reaction. For this reaction, the quantum yield is therefore about 100,000.

26-6 Kinetics of Heterogeneous Reactions

We have so far discussed the kinetics and mechanism of homogeneous reactions, reactions which occur in only one physical phase, gaseous or liquid. The factors which determine the rates of heterogeneous reactions are again the same ones that we have considered in detail for homogeneous reactions. That is, the reaction will occur when molecules of the reactants come into contact with sufficient energy and suitable orientations to react. In homogeneous reactions, as we have seen, the frequency with which the reactant molecules come close enough to interact depends only on the temperature and on the concentration of the reactants. In heterogeneous reactions, however, the molecules of reactants in different physical phases can come close enough to react only at the surface of contact between the phases. Therefore, the larger a surface of contact, the greater the chance that the molecules of the reactants may come together, and therefore the faster the reaction. The speed at which the molecules of the reactants arrive at the contact surface, and the speed at which the molecules of the products leave it, is also important in determining the rate of the heterogeneous reaction. In fact, if the molecules of the products do not leave the surface of contact but remain there, they soon form a film which may prevent additional reactant molecules from making contact and reacting. Thus the speed of a heterogeneous reaction is very often determined by the extent to which the reactants actually come into contact—that is to say, by such factors as the degree of subdivision of the reactants and the efficiency of their mixing.

In general, as we have seen earlier in many examples, the rate of heterogeneous reactions increases as the reactants become more finely subdivided and more thoroughly mixed. And of course the rates of heterogeneous reactions also increase with an increase in the temperature and concentration of the reactants, just as does the rate of homogeneous reaction. For example, the rate at which a solid dissolves in a liquid increases as the solid becomes more and more finely divided (Ch. 18). Similarly, the reaction between a metal and an acid becomes faster and faster the more finely the metal is divided (p. 96). The study of the kinetics and mechanism of heterogeneous reactions follows the same general lines we have discussed for homogeneous reactions. However, in addition to the temperature and concentration, the kinetic study must also take into account additional factors concerning the degree of division of the reagents, their mixing, and their diffusion. Thus a complete study of the rate of a heterogeneous reaction is often very complicated experimentally, and is also difficult to interpret in terms of a possible mechanism. Consequently, less is known in general about the mechanisms of heterogeneous than of homogeneous reactions.

Of reactions in which all the reactants appearing in the net equation belong to the same physical phase, all are not truly homogeneous from the point of view of their reaction mechanisms. In fact, the rate of many reactions between gases depends not only on the type, but also on the size and even the shape of any solid surface with which the gases are in contact. This surface may simply be the walls of a containing vessel or a specially prepared solid (a catalyst) intentionally introduced into the reaction mixture. This dependence of the reaction rate on the type and area of a solid surface in contact with the gaseous system indicates that some step(s) of the reaction can involve species that are absorbed on the solid surface and therefore no longer belong to the (homogeneous) gaseous system. Whenever we observe this dependence of the rate of the reaction between gases (or liquids) on the presence of a solid surface, we say that the surface acts as a catalyst in the reaction. In section 26-7 we shall consider the phenomenon of catalysis in some detail.

26-7 The Effect of a Catalyst on Reaction Rate

We have seen that we can speed up a chemical reaction by increasing both the frequency with which the molecules collide and the fraction of molecules which possess the required energy to react. And we have found that this increase in speed can be brought about either by raising the temperature or increasing the concentration of one or more of the reactants, or both. An additional way to speed up a chemical reaction is to add a *catalyst*—a substance that increases the rate at which a chemical reaction takes place, although it itself does not undergo a permanent chemical change as a result of the reaction and therefore does not appear in the net reaction equation. The phenomenon by which such a substance, often present only in relatively minute amounts, increases the rate of a reaction is called *catalysis.*

Just as we have considered separately the rates of reactions in homogeneous and heterogeneous systems, it is now convenient to distinguish between *homogeneous* catalysis and *heterogeneous* or (*surface*) catalysis. When the reactants, the products, and the catalyst are all present in the same physical phase—for example, when all are present as gases or in aqueous solution—the catalysis is homogeneous. On the other hand, when the reactants, the products and the catalyst do not all belong to the same physical phase—for example, when the reactants and products are gases but the catalyst is a solid—the catalysis is heterogeneous.

HOMOGENEOUS CATALYSIS

As a specific example of homogeneous catalysis, consider the oxidation of sulfur dioxide gas, SO_2, with oxygen gas, O_2, to produce sulfur trioxide gas, SO_3, according to the reversible reaction:

$$SO_{2(g)} + \frac{1}{2}O_{2(g)} \rightleftharpoons SO_{3(g)} \quad \begin{cases} \Delta H = -23.49 \text{ kcal/mole } SO_{3(g)} \\ \Delta G = -16.91 \text{ kcal/mole } SO_{3(g)} \end{cases}$$

As the large negative value of the change in free energy, ΔG, indicates, the oxidation of SO_2 to SO_3 by oxygen is thermodynamically favorable. And in fact, at room temperature the *equilibrium* of this reversible reaction lies almost completely to the right. In the absence of a catalyst, however, the activation energy of the reaction is so high that the rate of the reaction is immeasurably slow. In other words, at room temperature a mixture of pure $SO_{2(g)}$ and pure $O_{2(g)}$ alone does not react to any appreciable extent to produce $SO_{3(g)}$. If now we add to the gaseous mixture of SO_2 and O_2 some nitric oxide gas, NO, the rate of oxidation of SO_2 to SO_3 measurably increases. The catalytic action of NO very likely stems from its ability to be rapidly oxidized by O_2 to NO_2, which then can rapidly oxidize SO_2 to SO_3 while being reduced to re-form NO. Thus NO catalyzes the oxidation of SO_2 to SO_3 by actually participating in the oxidation process, through the following intermediate steps:

1. $NO + \frac{1}{2}O_2 \longrightarrow NO_2$
2. $NO_2 + SO_2 \longrightarrow SO_3 + NO$

We see that NO acts as a catalyst by providing a new pathway, steps 1 and 2, through which the oxidation of SO_2 to SO_3 can proceed more rapidly. This catalytic reaction is the basis of the lead-chamber process (Ch. 28) for the industrial production of sulfuric acid, H_2SO_4.

A typical example of homogeneous catalysis in solution is the hydrolysis of an ester such as ethyl acetate, $CH_3COOC_2H_5$, by an excess of water, H_2O, in the presence of an acid, $H^+_{(aq)}$, according to the reversible equation:

$$CH_3COOC_2H_{5(l)} + H_2O_{(l)} \xrightleftharpoons{H^+_{(aq)}} CH_3COOH_{(l)} + C_2H_5OH_{(l)}$$

Although $H^+_{(aq)}$ does not appear in the net equation, the presence of an acid greatly increases the rate at which $CH_3COOC_2H_5$ is hydrolyzed by excess H_2O. The fact that $H^+_{(aq)}$ actually participates in some intermediate step of the hydrolysis is shown by the fact that the rate of the reaction is directly proportional to the concentration of $H^+_{(aq)}$. Thus a strong acid is a more effective catalyst than a weak acid (at the same total concentration) and indeed this catalytic activity of an acid may be taken as a measure of its acid strength. In general, acids and bases are the most important classes of substances that exert a powerful catalytic action in aqueous solution.

HETEROGENEOUS OR SURFACE CATALYSIS

In an earlier chapter we discussed an example of heterogeneous catalysis which can be readily set up in the laboratory. We have seen (p. 73) that the thermal decomposition of solid $KClO_3$ to solid KCl and O_2 gas is catalyzed by a small quantity of solid MnO_2. In fact, when $KClO_3$ alone is heated to its melting point, it decomposes slowly to KCl and O_2 gas, but when we add some solid MnO_2 to the molten salt at the same temperature, the rate at which O_2 gas is evolved markedly increases. Both the reactant, $KClO_3$, and the products, KCl and O_2, are the same whether or not the MnO_2 catalyst is present; but the catalyst, without being consumed itself or undergoing a permanent chemical change, has shortened the time required for the reaction to occur.

Another example of heterogeneous catalysis that we have already encountered is the reaction between hydrogen gas, H_2, and oxygen gas, O_2, at room temperature in the presence of activated platinum, to form liquid water, H_2O. At room temperature H_2 gas does not react perceptibly with O_2 gas to produce H_2O although the reaction is thermodynamically favorable ($\Delta G = -56.7$ kcal/mole). But if we add to the mixture of H_2 and O_2 some finely divided platinum metal (obtained, for example, by heating a platinum (II) salt adsorbed on a porous carrier), the reaction proceeds rapidly and heat energy is evolved ($\Delta H = -63.3$ kcal/mole). On the other hand, a highly polished piece of platinum would have no appreciable effect on the speed of the reaction. We may conclude that the reaction between H_2 and O_2 is speeded up on contact with the platinum surface—and we may consider this to be an example of *surface catalysis*. Obviously, both the type of the platinum surface and its area have a direct and fundamental influence on the rate of the reaction. How can we explain the catalytic action of the platinum surface for this reaction?

Consider that at first we have only H_2 gas in the presence of our active platinum surface. We find experimentally that an appreciable amount of hydrogen is adsorbed by the platinum, just as is the case of the metal palladium (p. 98), and that the adsorption process is exothermic. Thus, when the gaseous H_2 molecules become adsorbed on the platinum surface, energy is released as a result of the strong Pt—H interactions (bond-formation process). This energy is not sufficient to completely dissociate the H—H bond of the adsorbed H_2 molecule (which would require 104.2 kcal/mole H_2), but can promote the electrons of the bonded hydrogen atoms to a higher energy state. These pairs of loosely bonded, higher-energy H atoms (H···H), linked to the platinum atoms on the surface of the metal and also somewhat beneath it, can then react more readily with gaseous O_2 molecules than can hydrogen gas in its ordinary gaseous molecular form, H_2. The active platinum surface lowers the free energy of activation for the reaction of H_2 with O_2 molecules by raising the energy of the adsorbed hydrogen. In other words, the platinum surface acts as a catalyst because it provides an energetically more favorable path by which the reaction can take place. In a similar manner, finely divided active platinum acts as a catalyst not only for the reaction $2\,H_2 + O_2 \longrightarrow 2\,H_2O$, but also for a large number of other reactions involving H_2 gas. It is important to note that the total free energy change for the reaction is the same, under the same conditions of temperature and pressure, with or without the catalyst. The catalyst merely serves to lower the free energy of the intermediate complex of the reaction, as illustrated in Fig. 26-8.

In surface catalysis, the chemical reaction is speeded up on the surface of a solid catalyst, so the extent to which the reaction is increased—the efficiency of the catalysis—depends largely on how much surface of the catalyst is exposed to the reactants. For this reason, the catalysts used in surface reactions are always finely divided (powder, mesh, porous briquets) to insure the greatest possible area of contact with the reactants (gas or liquids).

FIGURE 26-8 (a) Free-energy diagram of the reaction AB + C $\longrightarrow$ A + BC, with and without a catalyst. (b) Energy distribution curve for the reactants. The purple shaded area shows the *increase* in the number of molecules which have sufficient energy to react, due to the catalyst.

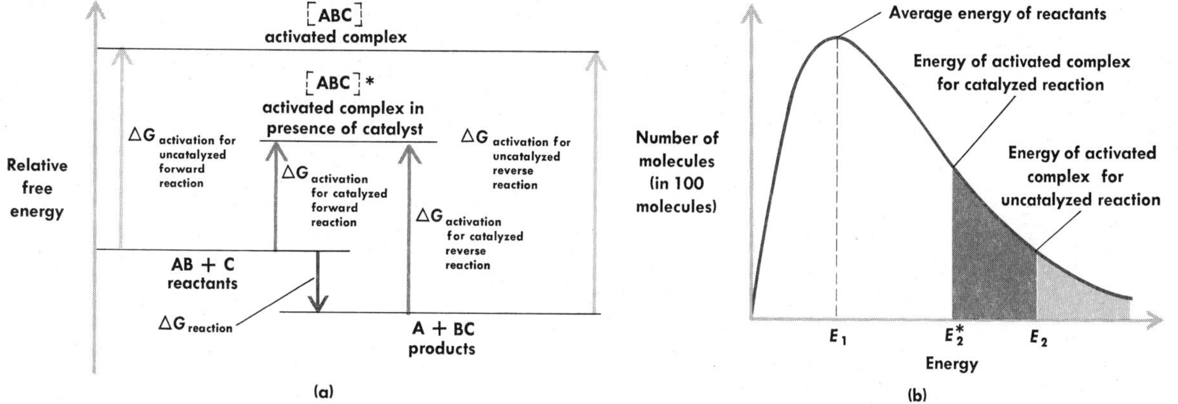

Another important factor in surface catalysis is the state of the surface of the catalyst. The ability of the surface to activate the molecules of the reactants is generally due to the presence of imperfections in the crystal lattice of the exposed surface. Such imperfections—holes in the lattice, traces of impurities, stresses and irregularities of various origin—enable the catalyst to adsorb the reactant molecules much more easily than would a perfectly regular crystal lattice. Hence the appropriate preparation of the catalyst is of fundamental importance for optimum efficiency.

Notice finally that by adsorbing one or more of the reactants on its surface, a heterogeneous catalyst increases the local concentration of the reactant(s), and this factor, too, helps to accelerate the reaction.

Heterogeneous catalysis is widely applied in most large-scale industrial chemical processes. The Haber process for the manufacture of NH_3 gas from N_2 gas and H_2 gas uses a mixed-metal catalyst, usually iron with small amounts of potassium and aluminum oxides. The extremely large quantities of the NH_3 thus produced are used in the manufacture of other chemicals, such as those contained in fertilizers. In the Ostwald process for preparing NO gas via the oxidation of NH_3 gas by O_2 gas, a platinum gauze serves as the catalyst; the NO that is obtained is used directly in the preparation of nitric acid, HNO_3. And the nitric acid is indispensable in the manufacture of such widely used materials as lacquers, fertilizers, dynamite, and many organic materials.

Platinum catalysts are used extensively in the reaction of SO_2 gas with O_2 gas to form SO_3 gas in the contact process for the manufacture of sulfuric acid, H_2SO_4. Other catalysts such as Al_2O_3 and $AlCl_3$ are used to convert the heavy, less volatile molecules of hydrocarbons present in petroleum into the lighter, more volatile hydrocarbon molecules that are suitable for use as gasoline. The catalysts permit this conversion to occur at a much lower temperature than would otherwise be possible, and the widespread use of catalysts of this sort has almost doubled the quantity of gasoline that can be obtained economically by the "cracking" of petroleum.

Liquid vegetable oils are converted into solid fats by catalytic hydrogenation. Huge quantities of low-cost cotton-seed oil and cocoanut oil, for example, are treated under pressure with H_2 gas in the presence of colloidal nickel as the catalyst to produce more useful and valuable shortenings, such as oleomargarine.

ENZYME CATALYSIS

Catalysts also plays an important role in biochemistry, for most of the chemical processes which maintain life and growth of both plants and animals require the presence of appropriate organic compounds as catalysts. In fact, catalysts are even more vital to biological processes than to industrial ones, because in a biological system we are not free to change to any extent such rate-determining factors as the temperature and the concentrations of the reactants.

The complicated sequences of reactions which occur in biological systems all proceed sufficiently rapidly at relatively low temperatures and under conditions of relatively low concentrations owing to the presence of efficient catalysts. This biological type of catalysis was first recognized and studied in the fermentation of sugar by yeast; the catalyst which could be extracted from the yeast was called *enzyme* (from the Greek: *in yeast*). The term "enzyme" is now used for all catalytic substances which function in plant and in animal cells. The majority of enzymes are essentially very large protein molecules with molecular weights on the order of several hundred thousand, often present as colloidal particles in the aqeuous solutions which are the media of biological reactions. Enzymes exhibit extremely marked, as well as specific catalytic activity. For example, the decomposition of hydrogen peroxide, H_2O_2, has an activation energy of about 18 kcal/mole; in the presence of such an effective heterogeneous catalyst as finely divided platinum metal the activation energy is

12 kcal/mole, but in the presence of the enzyme catalyst the activation energy is only about 5 kcal/mole. Another example that further illustrates the remarkable activity of enzyme catalysis is the reaction $H_{2(g)} + 3\ H_{2(g)} \longrightarrow 2\ NH_{3(g)}$, which in nature occurs smoothly at room temperature and atmospheric pressure, in the presence of an appropriate enzyme (Ch. 29). The industrial catalytic synthesis of ammonia with a mixed-metal catalyst (Haber process) requires, on the other hand, very drastic conditions (400 atm pressure and a temperature of 500°).

ACTIVATION ENERGY FOR CATALYZED REACTIONS

As we already mentioned in a previous chapter, a catalyst cannot increase the rate of a reversible reaction beyond the rate that corresponds to equilibrium, for it accelerates equally both the forward and the reverse reactions. Thus, a catalyst does not alter the position of equilibrium for a reversible reaction, but only shortens the time required for the reacting system to attain equilibrium under a given set of conditions.

A catalyst increases the rate of a chemical reaction by providing a new and energetically more favorable pathway through which the reactants can be transformed into the products. This means that the pathway followed in a catalyzed reaction involves an intermediate (activated) complex of lower *free energy* than the intermediate complex of the uncatalyzed reaction; in other words, the *free energy of activation* of the catalyzed reaction is lower than that of the uncatalyzed reaction. Now the free energy of the intermediate complex may be lowered either because its enthalpy is lowered or because its entropy is increased relative to that of the uncatalyzed intermediate. Thus, the catalyst may act in two ways—by lowering the enthalpy of activation (formation of bonds between catalyst and reactants) and also by increasing the entropy of activation, that is, the freedom of rotation-vibration and the possible configurations of the intermediate complex. Thus a substance may act as a catalyst by bringing the reactants together in a more favorable orientation than they would adopt without the catalyst.

In accordance with these considerations, it has been found that in all catalyzed reactions the intermediate complex actually involves the catalyst as well as one or more of the reactants. When the intermediate complex decomposes to give the products, the catalyst is then regenerated. Thus we see that a catalyst may be considered to be both a reactant and a product in the catalyzed reaction.

The free energy relationships for the general reaction $AB + C \longrightarrow A + BC$ are represented schematically in Fig. 26-8, where $[ABC]$ is the activated complex in the absence of a catalyst, and $[ABC]^*$ is the activated complex in the presence of a catalyst. Of course, if the activated complex of the catalyzed reaction has a lower free energy than the activated complex of the uncatalyzed reaction, a larger fraction of the molecules of the reactants will have sufficient energy to form this activated $[ABC]^*$ catalyzed complex, and the rate of the reaction will consequently be greater.

THE PRODUCTION OF DIFFERENT PRODUCTS BY USE OF DIFFERENT CATALYSTS. A given set of reactants may sometimes yield a certain set of products in the presence of one catalyst and a different set of products in the presence of another catalyst. For example, carbon monoxide gas, CO, reacts with H_2 gas in the presence of a (solid) catalytic mixture of ZnO and Cr_2O_3 to produce gaseous methyl alcohol, CH_3OH:

$$CO_{(g)} + 2\ H_{2(g)} \xrightarrow{ZnO,\ Cr_2O_3} CH_3OH_{(g)} \begin{cases} \Delta H = -21.7\ \text{kcal/mole}\ CH_3OH_{(g)} \\ \Delta G = -5.9\ \text{kcal/mole}\ CH_3OH_{(g)} \end{cases}$$

In the presence of finely divided nickel, however, quite a different reaction takes place, producing methane, CH_4, and water, H_2O:

$$CO_{(g)} + 3\ H_{2(g)} \xrightarrow{Ni} CH_{4(g)} + H_2O_{(g)} \begin{cases} \Delta H = -49.3\ \text{kcal/mole}\ CH_{4(g)} \\ \Delta G = -33.3\ \text{kcal/mole}\ CH_{4(g)} \end{cases}$$

This means that a mixture of CO and H_2 is actually capable of undergoing (at least) these two different reactions, both extremely slow in the absence of a catalyst. One catalyst speeds up one of the reactions, and the other catalyst speeds up the other. Thus, through an appropriate choice of catalyst, we can sometimes control the products that can be obtained from given reactants.

Here is another example of how catalysis might not only speed up a reaction but also produce a different product. In the absence of a catalyst, ammonia will burn in oxygen to give nitrogen:

$$2\ NH_3 + \tfrac{3}{2}\ O_2 = N_2 + 3\ H_2O$$

But in the presence of a platinum gauze as the catalyst (Ostwald process) the following alternative reaction takes place preferentially:

$$2\ NH_3 + \tfrac{5}{2}\ O_2 = 2\ NO + 3\ H_2O$$

This platinum-catalyzed combustion of NH_3 is very important, as it represents one of the two main steps in the manufacture of nitric acid (Chapter 29).

INHIBITORS. Some reactions are slowed down considerably by the presence of even very minute quantities of certain foreign substances called *inhibitors*. For example, as we saw in an earlier chapter (Ch. 11), sodium pyrophosphate, $Na_4P_2O_7$, acts as an inhibitor for the decomposition reaction of hydrogen peroxide, $H_2O_2 \longrightarrow \frac{1}{2}\ O_2 + H_2O$. Similarly, lead tetraethyl, $Pb(C_2H_5)_4$, a common "antiknock" agent for gasoline, is an inhibitor which slows down the explosion rate of gasoline vapor in the cylinder of an automobile engine, and thus produces smoother engine operation.

Many inhibitors operate by deactivating a catalyst of the undesired reaction. In the example considered above, $Na_2P_2O_7$ slows down the decomposition of H_2O_2 because it forms a relatively stable and inactive complex with the traces of Fe^{3+}, a common impurity, which would otherwise catalyze the decomposition reaction. In chain reactions, on the other hand, the inhibitors generally serve to capture the free radicals which propagate the reaction and provide an additional step by which a chain reaction can be terminated. This will result in a drastic reduction of the chain length and hence a much slower reaction rate.

Exercises

26-1 Give an example of a chemical reaction that occurs: (a) extremely fast, (b) at a moderate rate (at room temperature), (c) extremely slowly at room temperature but quickly at high temperature.

26-2 List the most important factors which influence the rate of a reaction.

26-3 Describe briefly the procedure used experimentally to determine the rate-concentration dependence of a reaction at a given temperature.

26-4 Why is it important that we should know the rates of reactions, and the manner in which the rates depend on the experimental conditions?

26-5 Define in your own words (a) a homogeneous reaction, (b) a heterogeneous reaction.

26-6 If two gases are capable of reacting chemically, why is it that all the molecules do not react instantaneously as soon as the gases are mixed?

26-7 Sketch a curve showing the energy distribution among the molecules of a sample of a gas assumed to behave ideally.

26-8 Explain why the rate of a reaction increases more rapidly with an increase in temperature than does the frequency of molecular collisions.

26-9 Explain in your own words the meaning of the terms (a) activated complex, (b) activation energy.

26-10 Not all the collisions between the molecules of the reactants having enough energy to react actually result in the formation of an activated complex. Explain.

26-11 What is the "steric factor" in molecular collisions? Illustrate with an example.

26-12 In the reaction $X_2 + Y_2 \longrightarrow 2\ XY$ ($\Delta H = -P$ kcal/mole), heat energy must be added to initiate the reaction, even though the reaction itself is exothermic. By means of an energy diagram, indicate (a) the relative energy levels of the reactants, (b) the relative energy of the activated state, (c) the relative energy of the product, (d) the activation energy, (e) the heat of the reaction.

26-13 Supply the same information for the following endothermic reaction: $M + Y_2 \longrightarrow MY_2$ ($\Delta H = +R$ kcal/mole). The activation energy for this reaction is greater than R kcal/mole.

26-14 The following reactions are both exothermic: (a) $AC + D_2 \longrightarrow AD + CD$; (b) $G_2 + H_2 \longrightarrow 2\ GH$. Reaction (a) has a higher activation energy and a higher heat of reaction than reaction (b). On the same graph sketch the energy diagrams of these systems.

26-15 How can we double the rate of reaction of H_2 with I_2 without changing the temperature?

26-16 The initial rate of reaction of H_2 with I_2 to form HI is proportional to the initial (total) concentration of the H_2 multiplied by the initial (total) concentration of the I_2. On the basis of this experimental observation, what can we conclude about the possible mechanisms of this reaction?

26-17 Define in your own words the *order of a reaction* and illustrate with several examples.

26-18 Discuss to what extent the order of a reaction may be used to establish the reaction mechanism. Illustrate with several examples.

26-19 In the reaction $M_2 + Q_2 \longrightarrow 2\ MQ$, the molecules M:M and Q:Q react chemically via a mechanism that involves the dissociation of M:M to M atoms by the absorption of light energy. Write a series of equations describing this chain reaction and indicate (a) the chain-initiation step, (b) the chain-propagation steps, and (c) one or more likely chain-termination steps.

26-20 What is a "free radical"? Give some examples.

26-21 Which are the two main kinds of mechanisms by which oxidation-reduction reactions take place?

26-22 Give an example of an oxidation-reduction reaction which occurs by: (a) electron transfer, (b) group transfer.

26-23 Define the term *catalysis* and illustrate with several examples.

26-24 Discuss an example of (a) homogeneous catalysis and (b) heterogeneous catalysis.

26-25 Explain the role of a catalyst in chemical reactions in regard to (a) the change in the rate of the reaction, (b) the effect on the equilibrium position of the reaction, and (c) the effect on the activation energy. Illustrate with an energy diagram.

26-26 What is an inhibitor, and on what principle does it operate? Illustrate with one example.

Problems

26-1 The initial rate of reaction of an equal number of H_2 molecules and I_2 molecules at a definite temperature in a given volume is x(mole/sec). If at the same temperature and volume the concentration of the H_2 molecules is doubled and the concentration of the I_2 molecules is tripled, what does the rate of reaction become?

26-2 The initial rate of change of NO_2 to N_2O_4 at a certain temperature and 76 cm of Hg pressure is x moles per minute. What would be the initial rate of disappearance of NO_2 at the same temperature but at 7.6 cm of Hg pressure?

26-3 The initial rate of decomposition of a certain weight of HI molecules to form H_2 and I_2 in a given volume is x molecules per second. If the temperature is kept constant, at what initial rate would the same weight of HI decompose at constant temperature but in double the volume?

THE HALOGENS: THE GROUP VIIB ELEMENTS. THE NOBLE GASES: GROUP 0

			VIIB	0
				He
C	N	O	F	Ne
Si	P	S	Cl	Ar
Ge	As	Se	Br	Kr
Sn	Sb	Te	I	Xe
Pb	Bi	Po	At	Rn

Here and in several later chapters, we will discuss various elements that resemble one another in chemical and physical properties and that are members of the same groups of the Periodic Table. As we consider the properties and reactions of these families of elements, we will see that the experimental data of descriptive chemistry can be classified and correlated according to the theoretical principles discussed in the previous chapters.

Theoretical chemistry has not as yet been developed to the point where we can acquire a well-rounded knowledge of the science from a study of principles *alone*. Chemistry still rests on a foundation of experimental facts, and we must become familiar with at least the most significant of these facts before we can develop any real understanding of the science of chemistry. Theory, however, permits the chemist to correlate and explain most of the known experimental facts, and it often enables him to predict the behavior of chemical substances.

In this chapter we shall discuss primarily the chemistry of the halogens—the elements of Group VIIB of the Periodic Table. We shall also consider briefly the noble gases—the elements of Group 0—which immediately follow the halogens.

Stable State at 25°, 1 atm	VIIB
pale-yellow gas	F
green-yellow gas	Cl
red-brown liquid	Br
dark crystals	I
	At

The elements of the halogen family—fluorine, F; chlorine, Cl; bromine, Br; iodine, I; and astatine, At—exhibit many similarities in physical and chemical characteristics, and their properties vary gradually, from fluorine to chlorine to bromine to iodine. However, the lightest element, fluorine ($2s^2\ 2p^5$), differs markedly from the other halogens in some of its properties and iodine ($5s^2\ 5p^5$) shows some properties that the others lack. We shall observe this same pattern—that an element of the $n = 2$ Series, and an element of the $n = 5$ Series differ somewhat in behavior from the other elements—in our study of several other families. The heaviest halogen astatine, At, occurs in nature only in barely detectable quantities as a product of the decay of certain radioactive series. Consequently, we shall not discuss it.

Since the halogens are the first family to be considered in our study of the descriptive chemistry of the elements, we shall give them a more extended treatment than the other families. For, once we have established a systematic approach to the experimental facts known about the halogens, it will be easier to approach the other groups of elements in a similarly logical manner.

27-1 General Characteristics of the Halogens

The electron configurations of the halogens are given in Table 27-1, together with a number of their physical properties. The relative sizes of the halogen atoms, which depend on their electron configurations (as we discussed in Chapter 13, p. 254), are particularly useful in correlating and explaining many of their physical and chemical properties. Notice that the greatest difference in atomic size exists between the first member of the family, fluorine, and second member, chlorine; the fluorine atom ($1s^2, 2s^2\,2p^5$) is smaller than might be expected, because its outermost 7 electrons are shielded from the attraction of the positive nucleus only by the $1s^2$ electron shell. The other halogen atoms have, in addition to these two inner electrons, complete shells containing 8 or 18 electrons, which act as a more effective shield in reducing the attraction of the nucleus for the 7 outermost electrons—the s^2p^5 valence electrons.

STABILITY OF THE HALOGEN MOLECULES TOWARDS DISSOCIATION INTO ATOMS

As we know, at ordinary temperatures the halogens exist as covalent diatomic molecules, F_2, Cl_2, Br_2 and I_2, in which each atom attains a stable eight-electron outer configuration similar to that of the next noble gas. The heats of dissociation, ΔH_{diss}, of the diatomic gaseous halogen molecules into gaseous atoms at 25° C and 1 atm, are shown in the diagram, along with their free energies of dissociation, ΔG_{diss}. The high positive value of ΔH_{diss} for the $X_{2(g)}$ molecules, which may be taken as a measure of the strength of the covalent bond, indicates that the gaseous halogen molecules, at room temperature, are remarkably stable with respect to disso-

TABLE 27-1 PROPERTIES OF THE HALOGENS (GROUPS VIIB ELEMENTS)

Element	Outer Electron Config.	Atomic Weight	Atomic Radius A	Ionic Radius A	Melting Point °C	ΔH_{fusion} kcal/mole	Boiling Point °C	$\Delta H_{vaporiz.}$ kcal/mole	$\Delta H_{subl.}$ kcal/mole	Ioniz. Energy	Electron Affinity	Electro-negativity (Pauling)
$_9F$	$2s^2\,2p^5$	18.9984	0.64	1.36	−218	0.37	−188	1.51	[a]	401.54[b] 17.4[c]	82.99[b] 3.6[c]	4.0
$_{17}Cl$	$3s^2\,3p^5$	35.453	0.99	1.81	−101	1.53	−34	4.88	6.03	278.75 13.0	86.44 3.7	3.0
$_{35}Br$	$4s^2\,4p^5$	79.909	1.14	1.95	−7.3	2.52	58.8	7.34	10.00	272.9 11.8	81.37 3.5	2.8
$_{53}I$	$5s^2\,5p^5$	126.9044	1.33	2.16	113.6	3.74	183	10.39	14.88	270.66 10.4	73.77 3.2	2.5

[a] No experimental value available.
[b] In kcal/mole.
[c] In electron volts (e.v.).

$X_{2(g)} \longrightarrow X_{(g)} + X_{(g)}$		
(kcal/mole 25 C, 1 atm)		
	ΔH_{diss}	ΔG_{diss}
F_2	+36.6	+28.4
Cl_2	+58.0	+50.4
Br_2	+46.1	+38.7
I_2	+36.1	+29.0

ciation into their gaseous atoms. In fact, the large positive ΔH_{diss} term, which in each case is *unfavorable* to dissociation, more than compensates for the *positive* $T\,\Delta S_{diss}$ energy term, which is *favorable* to dissociation. At room temperature the resulting value of the free energy change, for the dissociation reaction, $\Delta G_{diss} = \Delta H_{diss} - T\,\Delta S_{diss}$ is positive, and therefore the halogen molecules do not have the capacity to decompose spontaneously to form their atoms. At higher temperatures, however, the favorable $T\,\Delta S$ term, which is proportional to the (absolute) temperature T, becomes relatively more and more important. The iodine molecules, I_2, which has the lowest ΔH_{diss}, dissociates at the lowest temperature.

The regularly decreasing values of the ΔH_{diss} in the series Cl_2, Br_2, and I_2 (excluding F_2) show that the stability of the covalent bond in these diatomic molecules decreases regularly as the size of the atoms increases. This is so because, other factors being equal, in the smaller atoms the nuclear charge is less effectively shielded and exerts a greater attraction on the bond electron pair. The F_2 molecule is out of line, as shown by its low heat of dissociation, because the size of the F atoms is so small that the repulsion between the outer lone pairs of the two bonded atoms more than counterbalances the increase in the effective nuclear charge.

PHYSICAL STATES

The melting points and the boiling points of the halogens (Table 27-1) increase regularly from fluorine to iodine. As the sizes of the atoms in the halogen molecules increase, the electron clouds of the molecules become larger and more polarizable, that is, more easily deformed (see p. 145), and consequently the van der Waals intermolecular attractions become stronger. In general, for any given family of elements the van der Waals attractions increase as the size of the electron cloud increases. Additional evidence for the increase of the van der Waals attractions with increasing atomic number is provided by the regular increase in the heats of fusion and vaporization (Table 27-1) of the halogens.

At room temperature and 1 atm pressure, fluorine is a pale-yellow gas; chlorine is a green-yellow gas; bromine is a reddish-brown liquid; and iodine is a dark-purple, almost black, solid. The different physical states of the halogens at the same temperature and pressure are explained by the different strengths of the van der Waals attractions between the halogen molecules. In solid iodine, the diatomic I_2 molecules are held together in a crystal lattice by van der Waals forces which are strong enough to overcome the thermal motion of the molecules. In liquid bromine, the van der Waals attractions are too weak to give rise to an ordered three-dimensional arrangement of Br_2 molecules—a crystal—but they are strong enough to result in molecular cohesion and the liquid state. However, if the temperature is decreased to $-7.3°C$, crystalline bromine is formed, with the same crystal form as solid iodine. A comparison (Table 27-1) of the heat of sublimation of iodine, I_2, with that of bromine, Br_2, also reveals that the van der Waals forces are stronger in solid iodine than in solid bromine. Chlorine and fluorine exist as gases at room temperature because the van der Waals intermolecular attractions are too weak to overcome the kinetic energy of the molecules.

OCCURRENCE IN NATURE

The forms in which an element occurs in nature are of practical importance because they generally determine what we start with in preparing the pure element and its compounds. The chemical and physical forms in which the element appears in nature also often give an indication of its chemical and physical properties.

For example, the fact that the noble metals, Au, Ag, and Pt, often exist in nature as free elements is an indication that they are very unreactive. On the other hand, the alkali metals, Li, Na, K, Rb, and Cs, are never found in nature as free elements because, as we know, they are strongly electropositive and therefore extremely reactive to water and oxygen. Similarly, since chlorine occurs most commonly in nature as ionic NaCl, we know that chlorine must be a very electronegative element and that in the manufacture of chlorine and its compounds, NaCl is frequently the starting material.

FLUORINE. Fluorine always occurs in nature in chemical combination with other elements, as in the following rather widely distributed minerals: fluorspar, CaF_2; fluorapatite, $CaF_2 \cdot 3\ Ca_3(PO_4)_2$; and cryolite, Na_3AlF_6. Fluorine is the second most abundant halogen.

CHLORINE. Chlorine, the most abundant halogen, also occurs in nature only in compounds. Sea water contains about 2.5 per cent by weight of sodium chloride, together with smaller amounts of other dissolved salts. The sodium chloride in sea water accumulates through the washing action of ground water, which extracts small amounts of this salt from land deposits and carries it in solution to the seas. Deposits of crystalline sodium chloride are widely distributed across the continents and are sometimes mined as rock salt. When the deposits are too deep for easy mining, the sodium chloride is pumped to the surface as a concentrated water solution, called brine. The vast concentrations of sodium chloride present in the Great Salt Lake in Utah and in the Dead Sea result from the evaporation of water from these bodies, which have no natural outlets. Other water-soluble chlorine compounds that occur in nature are KCl, $MgCl_2$, and $CaCl_2$. An insoluble compound, silver chloride, AgCl, occurs in nature as a mineral called horn silver.

BROMINE. Bromine is far less abundant than chlorine or fluorine. It occurs in the form of soluble bromides, NaBr, KBr, and $MgBr_2$, in small quantities in sea water and in brine wells, especially in Michigan and in Stassfurt, Germany.

IODINE. Iodine is even less abundant in nature than bromine. The principal sources of iodine are Chilean deposits of sodium nitrate, $NaNO_3$, which contain as impurities small amounts of the compounds sodium iodate, $NaIO_3$, and sodium periodate, $NaIO_4$. Sodium and potassium iodides occur in minute quantities in sea water, and in relatively high concentrations in the brine associated with certain petroleum wells in California. These wells are the chief source of iodine in the United States. Another important source is the sodium iodide and potassium iodide present in various marine plants, such as seaweed.

27-2 Preparation of the Halogens

As we have seen, the most abundant halogen-containing compounds in nature are salts in which the halogens are present as negative ions. Consequently, both the laboratory and industrial methods of preparing the free halogens involve the oxidation of the halide ion, X^-, to the free halogen element, X_2. This oxidation may be carried out for all the halogens by electrolytic methods, and for all the halogens except fluorine by the use of the appropriate oxidants.

ELECTROLYTIC METHODS

FLUORINE, F_2. Fluorine can be prepared commercially and in the laboratory by the electrolysis of fused potassium hydrogen fluoride, KHF_2, at a temperature of about 250°C (mp of KHF_2 = 239°C), between graphite electrodes. Gaseous fluorine, F_2, is produced at the anode, and gaseous hydrogen, H_2, is produced at the cathode. The net process is, therefore, the electrolysis of ionized hydrogen fluoride *in the liquid but anhydrous state:*

$$2\ HF_{(l)} \longrightarrow H_{2(g)} + F_{2(g)}$$

The potassium ions, K^+, present in the starting material KHF_2, do not participate in the reaction because, as we know, a higher potential is required for the reduction of the K^+ ions to K metal that for the reduction of the H^+ ions to $H_{2(g)}$ (p. 491). However, the presence in the electrolyte of potassium ions and hydrogen fluoride ions (from the dissolved salt $K^+(HF_2^-)$) is essential, because pure liquid hydrogen fluoride is not sufficiently ionized to conduct an electric current, and consequently by itself does not undergo electrolysis. The complete equation for the electrolytic process is:

$$2\ KHF_{2(fused)} \xrightarrow[\text{energy}]{\text{electrical}} F_{2(g)} + H_{2(g)} + 2\ KF_{(fused)}$$

All traces of moisture must be excluded from this reaction, for fluorine, F_2, reacts very vigorously with water to form oxygen and hydrogen fluoride. The electrolysis is carried out in an electrically heated copper vessel. The compact layer of insoluble copper(II) fluoride, CuF_2, that forms on the surface of the copper vessel at the beginning of the process, protects the vessel from further attack by the extremely reactive fluorine gas. Fluorine gas is very reactive and must be handled with extreme care.

Fluorine gas is also prepared commercially by a slight variation of the method just described—the electrolysis of anhydrous liquid hydrogen fluoride, with potassium hydrogen fluoride, KHF_2, dissolved in the liquid. Again, the KHF_2 is added to impart conductivity to the electrolyte. In principle, this reaction is similar to the electrolysis of H_2O by the addition of an electrolyte such as KOH or $KHSO_4$, discussed in Chapter 23. The $E°$ value for the half-reactions listed below explain why the electrolytic preparation of fluorine requires rigorously anhydrous conditions, and why we cannot obtain fluorine from the electrolysis of a water solution of a soluble metal fluoride, such as NaF. The electrolysis of such a solution in fact yields H_2 gas and O_2 gas.

$$2\ H_2O = O_2 + 4\ H^+ + 4\ e^- \qquad E° = -1.23\ v$$

$$2\ F^- = F_2 + 2\ e^- \qquad E° = -2.85\ v$$

$$Na = Na^+ + e^- \qquad E° = +2.71\ v$$

$$H_2 = 2\ H^+\ (10^{-7}\ M) + 2\ e^- \qquad E° = +0.41\ v$$

These $E°$ values show that it is easier to oxidize H_2O ($E° = -1.23$ v) than it is to oxidize the F^- ion to F_2, ($E° = -2.85$ v).* Also it is easier to reduce the H^+ ion of H_2O to H_2 than it is to reduce the Na^+ ion to the sodium atom Na.

Notice that fluorine, the strongest of all oxidants (the F^-,F_2 couple has the largest negative potential, $E° = -2.85$, of all couples) can be prepared by electrolytic oxidation of compounds containing F^- ions, but not by chemical oxidation with other substances.

CHLORINE, Cl_2. Most commercial chlorine is prepared by the electrolytic oxidation of the chloride ion in a NaCl solution. This process was discussed in Chapter 23, p. 511; the complete equation for the reaction is:

$$2\ NaCl + 2\ H_2O \xrightarrow[\text{energy}]{\text{electrical}} \underset{\text{at anode}}{Cl_2} + 2\ NaOH + \underset{\text{at cathode}}{H_2}$$

The other products of the electrolysis—the sodium hydroxide solution and the hydrogen gas—are useful by-products. The electrolytic cell used in this process is designed in such a way that the anode and cathode compartments are separated. This arrangement prevents both the reaction of the Cl_2 gas with the H_2 gas to form HCl gas (which could take place explosively) and the reaction of the Cl_2 gas with the NaOH solution to form the compounds NaCl and NaClO (see p. 615).

BROMINE, Br_2, AND IODINE, I_2. These halogens can be obtained by the same electrolytic method used for Cl_2, but in practice they are prepared by chemical methods.

* Consequently, from an aqueous solution containing F^- ions, gaseous oxygen is liberated before the F^- ions can be oxidized.

CHEMICAL METHODS

All the halogens, except fluorine, can be prepared by treating the corresponding halide ion with an appropriate oxidant. The general reaction is expressed by the following schematic oxidation-reduction equation, where X^- represents the halide ion and X_2 the halogen molecule:

$$\underset{\text{reductant}}{2\,X^-} + \text{oxidant} \longrightarrow \underset{\text{oxidation product}}{X_2} + \text{reduction product}$$

CHLORINE. Some oxidants that are appropriate for the preparation of Cl_2 by oxidation of the Cl^- ion are listed in Table 27-2, together with their reduction products. When any of these oxidants is mixed with a solution containing the Cl^- ions and an appropriate concentration of the H^+ ions, the products are Cl_2, the reduction product of the oxidant, and H_2O. Following is a specific example.

TABLE 27-2 SOME OXIDANTS AND THEIR REDUCTION PRODUCTS

Oxidant		Reduction Product
$MnO_2 + H^+$	$\longrightarrow$	$Mn^{++} + H_2O$
$MnO_4^- + H^+$	$\longrightarrow$	$Mn^{++} + H_2O$
$Cr_2O_7^{=} + H^+$	$\longrightarrow$	$Cr^{+++} + H_2O$
$PbO_2 + H^+$	$\longrightarrow$	$Pb^{++} + H_2O$

PREPARATION OF Cl_2 BY THE OXIDATION OF HCl WITH MnO_2. When a concentrated hydrochloric acid solution, which contains Cl^- and H^+ ions, is added to solid manganese dioxide, MnO_2, the products are Cl_2 gas, water, and a solution of manganese(II) chloride which contains Mn^{++} and Cl^- ions:

$$MnO_{2(s)} + 4\,HCl_{(aq)} \longrightarrow Cl_{2(g)} + MnCl_{2(aq)} + 2\,H_2O_{(l)}$$

The complete balanced ionic equation, and the net ionic equation for this reaction are:

$$MnO_{2(s)} + 4\,H^+_{(aq)} + 4\,Cl^-_{(aq)} \longrightarrow Cl_{2(g)} + Mn^{++}_{(aq)} + 2\,Cl^-_{(aq)} + 2\,H_2O_{(l)}$$

$$\underset{\text{oxidizing agent}}{MnO_{2(s)}} + 4\,H^+_{(aq)} + \underset{\text{reducing agent}}{2\,Cl^-_{(aq)}} \longrightarrow \underset{\text{oxidation product}}{Cl_{2(g)}} + \underset{\text{reduction product}}{Mn^{++}_{(aq)}} + 2\,H_2O_{(l)}$$

We see by comparison of the complete and net ionic equations that only two of the four Cl^- ions are oxidized to form one molecule of chlorine gas, Cl_2; the other two Cl^- ions remain unchanged and serve to electrically neutralize the double positive charge of the Mn^{++} ion. In place of the concentrated HCl solution, we can also use for this reaction a mixture of sodium chloride, NaCl (which supplies the Cl^- ions), and concentrated H_2SO_4 (which supplies the H^+ ions). The balanced, complete ionic and net equations are:

$$2\,Na^+_{(aq)} + 2\,Cl^-_{(aq)} + 4\,H^+_{(aq)} + 2\,SO^{=}_{4(aq)} + MnO_{2(s)} \longrightarrow Cl_{2(g)} + Mn^{++}_{(aq)} + 2\,Na^+_{(aq)} + 2\,SO^{=}_{4(aq)} + 2\,H_2O_{(l)}$$

$$MnO_{2(s)} + 4\,H^+_{(aq)} + 2\,Cl^-_{(aq)} \longrightarrow Cl_{2(g)} + Mn^{++}_{(aq)} + 2\,H_2O_{(l)}$$

Thus we see that the net ionic equation of the red-ox process is the same whether we start with concentrated HCl or with a mixture of NaCl and concentrated H_2SO_4. In a similar manner, balanced equations can be written for the oxidation of the Cl^- ion in the presence of H^+ ions by the other oxidizing agents listed in Table 27-2.

In the laboratory, Cl_2 is usually prepared with the apparatus shown schematically in Fig. 27-1. Solid MnO_2 is covered with concentrated HCl, and the mixture is gently warmed. The evolved Cl_2, which is about $2\frac{1}{2}$ times heavier than air, is collected by the upward displacement of air.

BROMINE AND IODINE. As we shall explain in the next section, it is easier to oxidize the iodide ion, I^-, and the bromide ion, Br^-, to the corresponding elements, I_2 and Br_2, than it is to oxidize the smaller chloride ion, Cl^-, to Cl_2. Thus, any of the

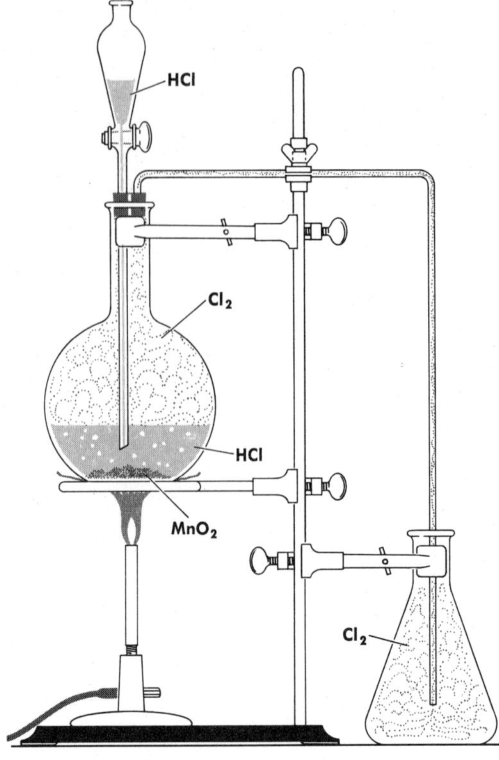

FIGURE 27-1 Laboratory preparation of $Cl_{2(g)}$ by oxidation of $HCl_{(aq)}$ with $MnO_{2(s)}$.

oxidizing agents already discussed in connection with Cl_2 can be used for the preparation of Br_2 and I_2. For example, the reaction of aqueous HBr with MnO_2 forms Br_2, evolved as a vapor from the hot reaction mixture, together with $MnBr_2$ and H_2O:

$$MnO_{2(s)} + 4\ HBr_{(aq)} \longrightarrow Br_{2(g)} + MnBr_{2(aq)} + 2\ H_2O_{(l)}$$

As in the preparation of Cl_2, a mixture of the sodium halide and H_2SO_4 can be used in place of the halogen acid:

$$2\ NaBr_{(aq)} + 2\ H_2SO_{4(aq)} + MnO_{2(s)} \longrightarrow Br_{2(g)} + MnSO_{4(aq)} + Na_2SO_{4(aq)} + 2\ H_2O_{(l)}$$

Similar reactions take place with the corresponding iodide compounds.

As we would expect, some oxidizing agents that are incapable of oxidizing the Cl^- ion are quite capable of oxidizing the Br^- and I^- ions—concentrated sulfuric acid, H_2SO_4, is an example. Weaker oxidizing agents—such as the $Fe^{+++}{}_{(aq)}$ and $Cu^{++}{}_{(aq)}$ ions—are capable of oxidizing only the I^- ion. For example, a 1 *M* solution of iron(III) nitrate, $Fe(NO_3)_3$, has no effect on 1 *M* solutions of either Br^- or Cl^- ions but it reacts with a 1 *M* solution of HI to produce I_2 and Fe^{++} ions:

$$2\ Fe(NO_3)_{3(aq)} + 2\ HI_{(aq)} \longrightarrow I_{2(aq)} + 2\ Fe(NO_3)_{2(aq)} + 2\ HNO_{3(aq)}$$

27-3 Chemical Properties of the Halogens and Oxidation Potentials

In Chapter 22 we learned how to use the standard oxidation potentials, $E°$, of half-cell reactions to predict which oxidation-reduction reactions can take place spontaneously. Thus, the oxidants which can be used in the preparation of each of the halogens, under specified experimental conditions, can be related to the $E°$ values of the halide ion–halogen couples, listed in Table 27-3. (This table also lists the $E°$ values of some other couples which we shall use in this section.) We know that, if all reactants have the standard concentration (1 *M*), or more accurately, an activity equal to unity, the oxidized form of any couple can oxidize the reduced form of any other couple that has a more positive $E°$ value. Since F_2 is the strongest oxidant listed, with $E° = -2.85$ v, we can conclude that no other of these oxidants can oxidize the F^- ion to F_2, as long as the reactants all have standard concentrations.* The oxidants in the list which can oxidize Cl^- ion to Cl_2 are those whose $E°$ values are more negative than

* You might think that, by appropriately changing the concentrations of the reactants, the (non-standard) oxidation potential of the couples involved could be so modified as to make the chemical oxidation of F^- to F_2 possible. This is not the case, however, because the effect of non-standard concentrations is relatively minor and can overcome only small differences of $E°$ values.

-1.40—the $E°$ value of the Cl^-,Cl_2 couple. Thus, we can conclude that $PbO_{2(s)}$ ($E° = -1.46$ v), $MnO^-_{4(aq)}$ ($E° = -1.51$ v), and $HClO_{(aq)}$ ($E° = -1.63$ v) in the presence of $H^+_{(aq)}$ ions can oxidize the $Cl^-_{(aq)}$ ion to $Cl_{2(aq)}$. Similarly, all oxidants in the list that have an $E°$ value more negative than -1.09 can oxidize the $Br^-_{(aq)}$ ion to $Br_{2(aq)}$. And all oxidants in the list can oxidize the $I^-_{(aq)}$ ion to $I_{2(aq)}$, because all have an oxidation potential more negative than -0.62 v. These conclusions, of course, hold rigorously only when all reactants in solution have 1 *M* concentration (more correctly, an activity = 1), but they can also serve as guidelines for reactions under non-standard conditions. As an example, let us consider how we can use the $E°$ values in Table 27-3 to arrive at the conclusions that the Cl^- ion can be oxidized to Cl_2 by the MnO_4^- ion in the presence of H^+ ions.

THE OXIDATION OF Cl^- IONS BY MnO_4^- IONS. The half-cell reaction,

$$Mn^{++}_{(aq)} + 4\,H_2O_{(l)} = MnO^-_{4(aq)} + 8\,H^+_{(aq)} + 5\,e^- \qquad E° = -1.51 \text{ v}$$

has a more negative $E°$ value than the half-cell reaction,

$$2\,Cl^-_{(aq)} = Cl_{2(aq)} + 2\,e^- \qquad E° = -1.40 \text{ v}$$

If therefore we were to connect the two couples to form a combined standard cell, the Cl^-,Cl_2 half-cell would be the *anode* and the Mn,MnO_4^- half cell would be the cathode of the combined cell:

Anode half-reaction:	$2\,Cl^- = Cl_2 + 2\,e^-$	$E° = -1.40$ v
Cathode half-reaction:	$MnO_4^- + 8\,H^+ + 5\,e^- = Mn^{++} + 4\,H_2O$	$E° = +1.51$ v

To equalize the number of electrons given up at the anode and the number of electrons taken on at the cathode, we multiply the anode half-equation by 5 and the cathode half-equation by 2 (notice that the $E°$ values are not changed; see Chapter 22, p. 492).

TABLE 27-3 STANDARD OXIDATION POTENTIALS OF HALOGEN COUPLES AND OF SOME OTHER COUPLES*

Half-Reaction	Standard Oxidation Potential, $E°$ (volt)
$2\,I^- = I_2 + 2\,e^-$	−0.62
$Fe^{++} = Fe^{+++} + e^-$	−0.77
$2\,Br^- = Br_2 + 2\,e^-$	−1.09
$Mn^{++} + 2\,H_2O = MnO_2 + 4\,H^+ + 2\,e^-$	−1.23
$2\,Cr^{+++} + 7\,H_2O = Cr_2O_7^= + 14\,H^+ + 6\,e^-$	−1.33
$2\,Cl^- = Cl_{2(aq)} + 2\,e^-$	−1.40
$Pb^{++} + 2\,H_2O = PbO_2 + 4\,H^+ + 2\,e^-$	−1.46
$Mn^{++} + 4\,H_2O = MnO_4^- + 8\,H^+ + 5\,e^-$	−1.51
$\frac{1}{2}\,Cl_{2(aq)} + H_2O = HClO + H^+ + e^-$	−1.63
$PbSO_4 + 2\,H_2O = PbO_2 + SO_4^= + 4\,H^+ + 2\,e^-$	−1.69
$2\,F^- = F_2 + 2\,e^-$	−2.85

*A complete listing of standard oxidation potentials is given in the Appendix, Tables I and II.

Anode:	$10\ Cl^- = 5\ Cl_2 + 10\ e^-$	$E° = -1.40$ v
Cathode:	$2\ MnO_4^- + 16\ H^+ + 10\ e^- = 2\ Mn^{++} + 8\ H_2O$	$E° = +1.51$ v

Adding these two half-reactions, we obtain the balanced net ionic equation of the desired reaction, which is the reaction of the standard Cl^-,Cl_2—Mn^{++},MnO_4^- combined cell.

$$2\ MnO_4^- + 16\ H^+ + 10\ Cl^- \longrightarrow 2\ Mn^{++} + 8\ H_2O + 5\ Cl_2 \qquad E° = +0.11\ v$$

Notice that the voltage of this cell, $E° = +0.11$ volts, is positive. And a positive potential, as we learned in Chapter 22, means a negative $\Delta G_{reaction}$—or, in other words, the reaction can occur sopntaneously with release of energy. Thus the $E°$ value of $+0.11$ v is a measure of the tendency of this oxidation-reduction reaction to take place under the specified conditions of concentration, temperature, and pressure.

The same principles are involved in working out the $E°$ values for the oxidation-reduction reactions of the permanganate couple, Mn^{++},MnO_4^- with the Br^-,Br_2 couple, and with the I^-,I_2 couple. These two couples also have less-negative $E°$ values than the Mn^{++},MnO_4^- couple and also a less-negative $E°$ value than the Cl^-,Cl_2 couple. As we would expect, the Br^- ion is more easily oxidized by MnO_4^- than the Cl^- ion, and the I^- ion more easily than the Br^- ion. The relative tendency of the Cl^-, Br^-, and I^- ions to be oxidized by permanganate in acid solution is expressed quantitatively by the algebraic difference between the $E°$ value for the acid permanganate couple and the $E°$ value for each of the halide ion–halogen couples. These values are: $+1.51 - 0.62 = +0.89$ v for the I^- ion; $+1.51 - 1.09 = +0.42$ v for the Br^- ion; and $+1.51 - 1.40 = +0.11$ v for the Cl^- ion.

EXAMPLES OF DIFFERENT RED-OX PROPERTIES OF THE HALOGENS. The oxidation potentials of the halide ion–halogen couples reflect the gradual change in chemical properties from one halogen element to the next, and they are very helpful in predicting certain chemical reactions. For example, we can predict that chlorine, Cl_2, will oxidize the bromide ion, Br^-, to bromine, Br_2:

$$Cl_2 + 2\ Br^- \longrightarrow 2\ Cl^- + Br_2$$

Furthermore, we can understand why, of all the halide ions, only the iodide ion, I^-, can be oxidized by the hydrated iron(III) ion, $Fe^{+++}{}_{(aq)}$. Thus we can explain, on the basis of the $E°$ values, why Fe^{+++} ions can exist in solutions containing F^-, Cl^-, and Br^- ions, but cannot exist in solutions containing I^- ions:

$$Fe^{+++}{}_{(aq)} + I^-{}_{(aq)} \longrightarrow Fe^{++}{}_{(aq)} + \tfrac{1}{2}\ I_{2(aq)}$$

Conversely, F_2, Cl_2, and Br_2 can all oxidize the iron(II) ion, Fe^{++}, to the iron(III) ion, Fe^{+++}, but I_2 can not do so. The equation for the reaction of Fe^{++} with Br_2, is:

$$\tfrac{1}{2}\ Br_2 + Fe^{++} \longrightarrow Br^- + Fe^{+++}$$

Before concluding this section, it is interesting to point out that the oxidation of I^- to I_2 by hydrated Fe^{+++} ions occurs with such salts as $Fe(NO_3)_3$ and $Fe_2(SO_4)_3$ in water solution, that is, with the hydrated Fe^{+++} ion, $[Fe(H_2O)_6]^{+++}$ (see Chapter 33). But if we add to this $Fe^{+++}{}_{(aq)}$ solution an excess of fluoride ions, F^-, the oxidation of I^- ions to iodine, I_2, no longer takes place. This is so because the F^- ions react with the $[Fe(H_2O)_6]^{+++}$ ion to form the very stable complex $[FeF_6]^{\equiv}$.

$$[Fe(H_2O)_6]^{+++} + 6\ F^- \longrightarrow [FeF_6]^{\equiv} + 6\ H_2O$$

The $[FeF_6]^{\equiv}$ complex ion is not as good an oxidizing agent as $[Fe(H_2O)_6]^{+++}$ is, and in fact the $E°$ value for the $[Fe(H_2O)_6]^{++}$, $[FeF_6]^{\equiv}$ couple is more negative than that of the I^-,I_2 couple.

The following oxidation-reduction couples have very nearly the same oxidation potential value:

$$Mn^{++} + 2\,H_2O = MnO_2 + 4\,H^+ + 2\,e^- \qquad E° = -1.23\ v$$
$$2\,Cl^- = Cl_{2(g)} + 2\,e^- \qquad E° = -1.40\ v$$

And it is an experimental fact that in an acid solution manganese dioxide, MnO_2, will oxidize the Cl^- to Cl_2. We have here an illustration of the effect of *concentration* on potential values. As we know, the $E°$ values are defined for systems in which all reactants and products are present with an activity of 1—in this case, a system in which the Cl^-, Mn^{++}, and H^+ ions are at a 1 M concentration, and solid MnO_2 as well as Cl_2 gas are at 1 atm pressure. If we increase the concentration of the H^+ ion (for example, by adding an excess of hydrochloric acid, $H^+ + Cl^-$), the oxidizing power of the couple Mn^{++},MnO_2 assumes a value more negative than -1.23. And if we decrease the pressure of Cl_2 below 1 atm pressure, the oxidizing power of the couple Cl^-,Cl_2 assumes a value less negative than -1.40. We can calculate approximately these changes of oxidation potential due to non-standard activities by means of the Nernst equation (see Chapter 22). $E = E°\ (-0.0591/n) \log Q$ (where n is the number of electrons appearing in the half-equation and Q is the activity ratio for the half reaction). For example, the oxidation potential of the half-reaction $Mn^{++} + 2\,H_2O \longrightarrow MnO_2 + 4\,H^+ + 2\,e^-$, in a solution containing 0.1 mole/liter of Mn^{++} ions and 5 moles/liter of H^+ ions would have the following oxidation potential:

$$E = E° - \frac{0.0591}{n} \log Q$$

$$E = -1.23 - \frac{0.0591}{4} \log \frac{[MnO_2] \times [H^+]^4}{[Mn^{++}] \times [H_2O]^2}$$

$$= -1.23 - \frac{0.0591}{4} \log \frac{[1] \times [5]^4}{[0.1] \times [1]^2} = -1.23 - 0.0148 \log 6.25 \times 10^3$$

$$= -1.23 - 0.0148 \times (3 + 0.796) = -1.29$$

In fact, if we increase the concentration of the H^+ ions by adding hydrochloric acid, and if we reduce the pressure of the $Cl_{2(g)}$ by heating so that $Cl_{2(g)}$ escapes, the oxidation of Cl^- ions by MnO_2 proceeds virtually to completion. In general, changing the relative concentrations of the oxidized and the reduced forms of a half-cell always affects to some extent the potential of the half-cell. Very marked concentration changes, and hence marked changes in oxidation potentials, are often caused by (1) the formation and precipitation of insoluble compounds, (2) the production and evolution of gases from the solution, and (3) the formation of complex ions in solution (to be discussed in Chapter 33).

27-4 General Reactions of the Halogens

The halogens are highly reactive elements, for they are good oxidizing agents —as we have just seen their standard oxidation potentials are highly negative. Therefore they have the capacity to react spontaneously not only with those elements which have positive standard oxidation potentials—the electropositive metals—but also with elements which have a negative standard oxidation potential—the noble metals and the non-metals. In all cases, whether a halogen has the capacity to react spontaneously with a given element (under specified experimental conditions of concentration, temperature, and pressure) depends on the value of the free energy change of the reaction, $\Delta G_{reaction}$. When $\Delta G_{reaction}$ is negative, then the reaction can occur spontaneously and the products are thermodynamically stable. If we know both the enthalpy change, ΔH, and the entropy change, ΔS, for a certain reaction at a temperature T and constant pressure, we can predict whether or not the reaction can occur spontaneously from the fundamental equation, $\Delta G = \Delta H - T\,\Delta S$. Alternatively, we can make use of the relationship $\Delta G = -nFE$, which relates the free energy change to the reaction potential. In general, the reaction potential, E, can be estimated for non-standard conditions from the E° value (given, for example, in Tables I and II in the Appendix) and Le Chatelier's principle; more precisely it can be calculated by means of the Nernst equation. A positive reaction potential means a negative free energy change—that is, a spontaneous reaction. Thus we may use either the value of ΔG or the value of E, whichever is more readily accessible, to predict whether a certain reaction of a halogen, as of any element, has the capacity to occur spontaneously as written under a specified set of conditions.

Of course, the above considerations refer only to the *capacity* of a halogen to react spontaneously with other substances, and bear no relationship to the *rate* at which the reaction, if thermodynamically favorable, does actually occur. Thus, a halogen may not appear to react with a certain substance under a certain set of conditions —even though the reactions may have a negative ΔG (a positive E value)—because of the very slow reaction rate. We have already discussed a typical example, the reaction of $Cl_{2(g)}$, with $H_{2(g)}$ to form $HCl_{(g)}$ (Chapter 26, p. 589). In studying the chemistry of the halogens—as well as of any other elements—we must keep always in mind that two independent requirements must be satisfied for a reaction to occur spontaneously at a convenient speed: (1) the reaction must be thermodynamically favorable ($\Delta G < 0$, $E > 0$), and (2) its activation energy must be relatively low so that the rate of reaction may be appreciable. In short, the reaction must be both thermodynamically favorable and kinetically feasible.

REACTIONS OF HALOGENS WITH METALS. Fluorine, the most reactive chemical substance known, reacts rapidly with all the metals, evolving heat in the process; the metal fluorides thus formed are stable at room temperature. Chlorine also reacts directly with all the metals to form metal halides, but the reactions are generally less exothermic and slower than with fluorine. Bromine and iodine react with all the metals except some of the noble metals.

THE REACTION OF HALOGENS WITH NON-METALS

Fluorine reacts directly with all the non-metals and also with the noble gases krypton, Kr, and xenon, Xe. The reaction of chlorine with most of the non-metals parallels that of fluorine, but again is generally less exothermic and also slower than for fluorine. And chlorine fails to react directly with carbon, oxygen, nitrogen, and the noble gases. As we would expect, bromine and iodine, which are less reactive than the more electronegative fluorine and chlorine, combine directly with fewer non-metals.

THE REACTION OF HALOGENS WITH HYDROGEN. As we have already learned, the gaseous halogens react with hydrogen gas to form the gaseous covalent hydrogen halides: $H_{2(g)} + X_{2(g)} \longrightarrow 2\ HX_{(g)}$. The reaction becomes less exothermic as the size of the halogen atom increases; the ΔH values of this reaction (in kcal/mole HX) are: HF, -64.2; HCl, -22.1; HBr, -8.7; HI, $+6.2$, all at 25° and 1 atm. A detailed discussion of the enthalpy diagram for this reaction was given in Chapter 16, p. 345.

The reaction of the various halogens with hydrogen also differs widely in terms of kinetics. Fluorine and hydrogen react very rapidly, even at the temperature of liquid air, -185°C. Chlorine and hydrogen at ordinary temperatures and in the absence of light or of a catalyst do not react at a detectable rate. However, if we add a catalyst or illuminate the mixture with a bright light, the reaction proceeds rapidly. We have studied the mechanism of the light-catalyzed reaction as a typical example of photochemistry in Chapter 26. The reaction of bromine with hydrogen in the absence of a catalyst or light can be initiated at a lower temperature than that of chlorine—that is, the activation energy is lower—even though the quantity of heat liberated in the reaction is less. The *mechanism* of this reaction was also discussed in Chapter 26, as a typical example of a *self-initiated chain-reaction.* And for the equilibrium system, $H_{2(g)} + I_{2(g)} \rightleftharpoons 2\ HI_{(g)}$, the mechanisms of both the forward and the reverse reactions have been discussed in Chapter 26, and the equilibrium constant was discussed in Chapter 25.

THE REACTION OF HALOGENS WITH COMPOUNDS

The halogens also show their strong oxidizing properties in their reactions with various compounds. For example, even I_2, the weakest oxidizing halogen, reacts with H_2S, forming HI and elementary sulfur: $H_2S + I_2 \longrightarrow 2\ HI + S$.

In general, the halogens react with compounds containing hydrogen and a non-metal to form the hydrogen halide and the free non-metal. The free non-metal, in turn, may react with more of the halogen to form its halide. Hydrogen sulfide, H_2S, for example, reacts with chlorine as follows:

$$H_2S + Cl_2 \longrightarrow 2\ HCl + S \qquad 2\ S + Cl_2 \longrightarrow S_2Cl_2$$

All hydrocarbons burn in chlorine to form HCl and free carbon. For benzene, C_6H_6, the equation is: $C_6H_6 + 3\ Cl_2 \longrightarrow 6\ HCl + 6\ C$.

We shall discuss some other reactions of the halogens with saturated and unsaturated hydrocarbons in Chapter 36, where we consider organic compounds.

One of the most common reactions of the halogens is the oxidation of an element, in the form of its halide, from a lower oxidation state to a higher oxidation state. This reaction occurs with metals as well as non-metals. For example:

$$2\ \overset{+2}{Fe}Cl_2 + Cl_2 \longrightarrow 2\ \overset{+3}{Fe}Cl_3$$

$$\overset{+3}{P}Cl_3 + Cl_2 \longrightarrow \overset{+5}{P}Cl_5$$

Table 27-4 summarizes some important reactions of the halogens.

TABLE 27-4 SOME IMPORTANT REACTIONS OF HALOGENS ($X_2 = F_2, Cl_2, Br_2,$ OR I_2)

General Equations		Remarks
X_2 + reducing agent $X_2 + 2\ X'^-$	$\longrightarrow 2\ X^-$ + oxidation product $\longrightarrow X'_2 + 2\ X^-$	$F_2 > Cl_2 > Br_2 > I_2$ F_2 replaces Cl_2, replaces Br_2, replaces I_2
$nX_2 + 2\ M$	$\longrightarrow 2\ MX_n$	With almost all metals, M
$X_2 + H_2$	$\longrightarrow 2\ HX$	ΔH reaction: $F_2 > Cl_2 > Br_2 > I_2$
$3\ X_2 + 2\ P$	$\longrightarrow 2\ PX_3$	Using excess P
$X_2 + PX_3$ $5\ X_2 + 2\ P$	$\longrightarrow PX_5$ $\longrightarrow 2\ PX_5$	All halogens except I_2
$X_2 + H_2S$	$\longrightarrow 2\ HX + S$	$-\Delta H$ reaction: $F_2 > Cl_2 > Br_2 > I_2$
$X_2 + X'_2$	$\longrightarrow 2\ XX'$*	All except I_2 with F_2
$X_2 + H_2O$	$\longrightarrow H^+ + X^- + HOX$	All except F_2
$X_2 + H_2O$	$\longrightarrow 2\ H^+ + 2\ X^- + O_2$	$-\Delta H$ reaction: $F_2 > Cl_2 > Br_2 > I_2$

* $X'_2 = F_2, Cl_2, Br_2, I_2$ but $X'_2 \neq X_2$.

27-5 The Hydrogen Halides

PREPARATION OF THE HYDROGEN HALIDES

HYDROGEN FLUORIDE, HF. A mixture of H_2 and F_2 reacts spontaneously and rapidly to form HF, but too violently to provide a suitable means of preparation. The most common method of preparing HF is based on the action of concentrated sulfuric acid on a metal fluoride, such as CaF_2. When the reactants are heated, the volatile HF gas passes off, and during the reaction the high-boiling, non-volatile sulfuric acid remains in the reaction flask with the insoluble $CaSO_4$:

$$CaF_{2(s)} + H_2SO_{4(l)} \longrightarrow 2\ HF_{(g)} + CaSO_{4(s)}$$

Pure anhydrous hydrogen fluoride may also be prepared by heating potassium hydrogen fluoride, KHF_2: $KHF_{2(s)} \longrightarrow HF_{(g)} + KF_{(s)}$.

Hydrogen fluoride attacks glass (it reacts with silica, SiO_2, one of the chief constituents of glass) and most of the common metals. However, copper, steel, lead, and platinum are not attacked by HF, and in fact copper is used to construct the apparatus for the preparation of HF described above. Liquid anhydrous hydrogen fluoride is available commercially in steel cylinders. Plastic coated vessels are used to package the corrosive aqueous solutions of hydrogen fluoride (hydrofluoric acid), and beakers or flasks made of polyethylene, an almost unbreakable hydrocarbon polymer that is inert to HF as well as to most chemical reagents, are used in the laboratory when handling hydrofluoric acid.

HYDROGEN CHLORIDE, HCl. Hydrogen chloride is usually prepared in the laboratory by the action of concentrated sulfuric acid on NaCl. The rate of the reaction can be accelerated by warming the reaction mixture. Gaseous hydrogen chloride, HCl, and solid sodium hydrogen sulfate, $NaHSO_4$, are the first products:

$$NaCl + H_2SO_4 \longrightarrow HCl + NaHSO_4$$

If the $NaHSO_4$ is mixed with additional NaCl and the mixture is heated to about 500°C, further reaction takes place to produce Na_2SO_4 and additional HCl gas:

$$NaCl + NaHSO_4 \longrightarrow HCl + Na_2SO_4$$

Hydrogen chloride is prepared commercially chiefly by the catalytized reaction of H_2 with Cl_2, these gases having been obtained as by-products from the electrolysis of aqueous sodium chloride to produce sodium hydroxide.

HYDROGEN BROMIDE, HBr, AND HYDROGEN IODIDE, HI. Hydrogen bromide, HBr, and hydrogen iodide, HI, are commonly prepared by the reaction of a soluble metal bromide or iodide with liquid, non-volatile, non-oxidizing phosphoric acid, H_3PO_4:

$$NaBr + H_3PO_4 \longrightarrow HBr + NaH_2PO_4$$
$$NaI + H_3PO_4 \longrightarrow HI + NaH_2PO_4$$

Hydrogen bromide and hydrogen iodide are evolved as gases from the heated liquid reaction mixture. Sulfuric acid, especially if it is hot and concentrated, cannot be used for the preparation of HBr or HI from their salts, because the more readily oxidizable Br^- and I^- ions are oxidized to the free halogens while the oxidizing agent, H_2SO_4, is reduced to SO_2. For example:

$$2\ HBr + H_2SO_4 \longrightarrow Br_2 + SO_2 + 2\ H_2O$$

PROPERTIES OF THE HYDROGEN HALIDES, HX

The anhydrous hydrogen halides are colorless gases, highly irritating to the mucous membranes, with a disagreeable, pungent odor. The pure covalent liquids obtained by condensing the gases at low temperature are non-conductors of electricity; they have about the same low electrical conductivity as water. All the hydrogen halide gases are extremely soluble in water, and the dissolution reaction is accompanied by the evolution of a large quantity of heat. Because of their great tendency to dissolve in water, the gaseous or liquid hydrogen halides "fume" in moist air—that is, they cause some of the atmospheric moisture to condense, forming a fog of tiny droplets of the solution of the hydrogen halide.

Anhydrous hydrogen fluoride differs in many of its properties from the other hydrogen halides, more than would be expected solely on the basis of its lighter molecular weight and smaller size. That is to say, HF is anomalous with respect to the other hydrogen halides just as water, H_2O, is anomalous with respect to hydrogen sulfide, H_2S, and hydrogen selenide, H_2Se. For example, the boiling point of hydrogen fluoride is exceptionally high; HF boils at $+20°C$, HCl at $-85°C$, HBr at $-67°C$, and HI at $-51°C$. (Remember that the boiling point of water, $100°C$, is also exceptionally high in comparison with those of H_2S, $-61.8°C$, and H_2Se, $-42°C$.) Earlier (p. 194), we learned that the unusual properties of water arise from the strong hydrogen bonds between H_2O molecules. The anomalous properties of HF can also be attributed to the strong hydrogen bonds between HF molecules. The F atom is the most electronegative of all atoms (p. 315) and is very small in size; the HF molecule is therefore highly polar, $\overset{\delta+}{H}-\overset{\delta-}{F}$. The partial positive charge on the hydrogen atom of one HF molecule is attracted by the partial negative charge on the fluorine atom of a nearby HF molecule, and a strong hydrogen bond results, which joins these two HF molecules together to form a dimer, $(HF)_2$ or H_2F_2, as shown in the margin. In this dimer the terminal H atom, which is not already hydrogen-bonded, can further attract a F atom of a neighboring HF molecule. Similarly, the terminal F atom of the H_2F_2 dimer can form a hydrogen bond with a H atom of another adjacent HF molecule—and the process can be repeated to form polymeric species consisting of n molecules of HF linked together by hydrogen bonding, $(HF)_n$. A portion of such a polymer, which has a zig-zag structure because of the strong lone-pair–lone-pair repulsion on the F atoms, is shown below. Unlike water, which exhibits hydrogen bonding only in the condensed (solid and liquid) states, hydrogen fluoride shows hydrogen bonding even in the gaseous state. However, as the temperature and hence the kinetic energy of the molecules is increased, the extent of the hydrogen bonding decreases. For example, at room temperature as many as six HF molecules may be held together as a unit, $(HF)_6$, whereas at about $100°C$, almost only single HF molecules exist.

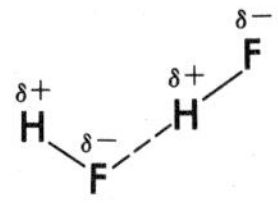

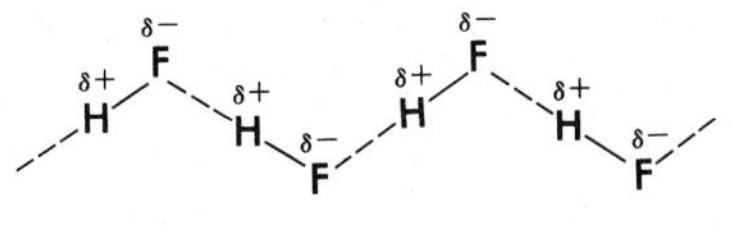

δ+ H, δ− F, δ+ H, δ− F

δ− F, δ+ H, δ+ H, δ− F, δ− F, δ+ H, δ+ H, δ− F

The Cl, Br, and I atoms in the molecules HCl, HBr, and HI are much less electronegative and much larger in size than the F atom. Consequently, no appreciable hydrogen bonds form between molecules of HCl, HBr, and HI.

THE ACID STRENGTHS OF HYDROGEN HALIDES IN AQUEOUS SOLUTION

The electrical conductivity of dilute aqueous solutions of hydrogen fluoride is much lower than that of aqueous solutions of the other hydrogen halides at the same molar concentration. Also, the acidity of a dilute aqueous solution of HF is lower than that of equimolar solutions of the other hydrogen halides. These two experimental observations indicate that HF in dilute aqueous solution is a much weaker acid—that is, much less ionized to form $H^+{}_{(aq)}$ ions—than are HCl, HBr and HI. To understand this difference in acid strength let us consider the ionization equilibrium of the hydrogen halides in water:

$$HX_{(aq)} \rightleftharpoons H^+{}_{(aq)} + X^-{}_{(aq)} \qquad K_{ioniz} = \frac{[H^+][X^-]}{[HX]}$$

As we have seen in Chapter 25, the equilibrium constant of this reaction, K_{ioniz}, and its standard free energy change, $\Delta G^\circ_{\text{ioniz}}$, are related by the expression: $\Delta G^\circ_{\text{ioniz}} = -2.303\,RT \log K_{\text{ioniz}}$. That is, at 25°C and 1 atm the value of the equilibrium constant is determined by the value of $\Delta G^\circ_{\text{ioniz}}$ as shown in Table 25–7, p. 564. In turn $\Delta G^\circ_{\text{ioniz}}$ is given by the expression $\Delta G^\circ_{\text{ioniz}} = \Delta H^\circ_{\text{ioniz}} - T\,\Delta S^\circ_{\text{ioniz}}$. Since the entropy change for the ionization reaction, $\Delta S^\circ_{\text{ioniz}}$, will be about the same for HF, HCl, HBr, and HI, the value of $\Delta G^\circ_{\text{ioniz}}$ for these acids can be considered to run parallel to the value of $\Delta H^\circ_{\text{ioniz}}$. Hence, the larger the negative value of $\Delta H^\circ_{\text{ioniz}}$, the larger will be the value of the equilibrium constant of the ionization reaction—that is, the stronger will be the acid.

To evaluate the trend of $\Delta H^\circ_{\text{ioniz}}$ for HF, HCl, HBr, and HI, we may consider the ionization reaction $HX_{(aq)} \longrightarrow H^+_{(aq)} + X^-_{(aq)}$, to occur by the following series of (imaginary) steps, as shown in the enthalpy diagram of Fig. 27-2(a):

1. $HX_{(aq)} \longrightarrow HX_{(g)} + \text{water}$ — ΔH_1 (positive) $= -(\Delta H_{\text{soln}}$ of $HX_{(g)})$
2. $HX_{(g)} \longrightarrow H_{(g)} + X_{(g)}$ — ΔH_2 (positive) $=$ H—X bond energy
3. $H_{(g)} \longrightarrow H^+_{(g)} + e^-$ — ΔH_3 (positive) $=$ ionization energy of H
4. $H^+_{(g)} + \text{water} \longrightarrow H^+_{(aq)}$ — ΔH_4 (negative) $= \Delta H_{\text{hydr}}$ of H^+
5. $X_{(g)} + e^- \longrightarrow X^-_{(g)}$ — ΔH_5 (negative) $= -$(electron affinity of X)
6. $X^-_{(g)} + \text{water} \longrightarrow X^-_{(aq)}$ — ΔH_6 (negative) $= \Delta H_{\text{hydr}}$ of X^-

The value of ΔH_1 is small and very similar for the various hydrogen halides, as shown by their experimentally determined heats of solution in a non-ionizing solvent such as benzene. Also, ΔH_3 and ΔH_4 are the same for all hydrogen halides. Thus the terms which determine the different values of ΔH_{ioniz} for the four halogen halides are ΔH_2, ΔH_5, and ΔH_6 (Fig. 27-2(a) and (b)). Ultimately, the relative acid strength of the halogen acids in aqueous solution can be related directly to three factors—the H—X bond strength, the electron affinity of X, and the hydration energy of the X^- ion. For example, the difference in hydration energy (32.3 kcal/mole) between F^- and Cl^- favors the ionization of HF over HCl, almost exactly counterbalancing the difference in

FIGURE 27-2 The ionization of hydrogen halides in water. (a) Generalized enthalpy diagram. (b) Trends in hydration energies, bond energies, and electron affinities.

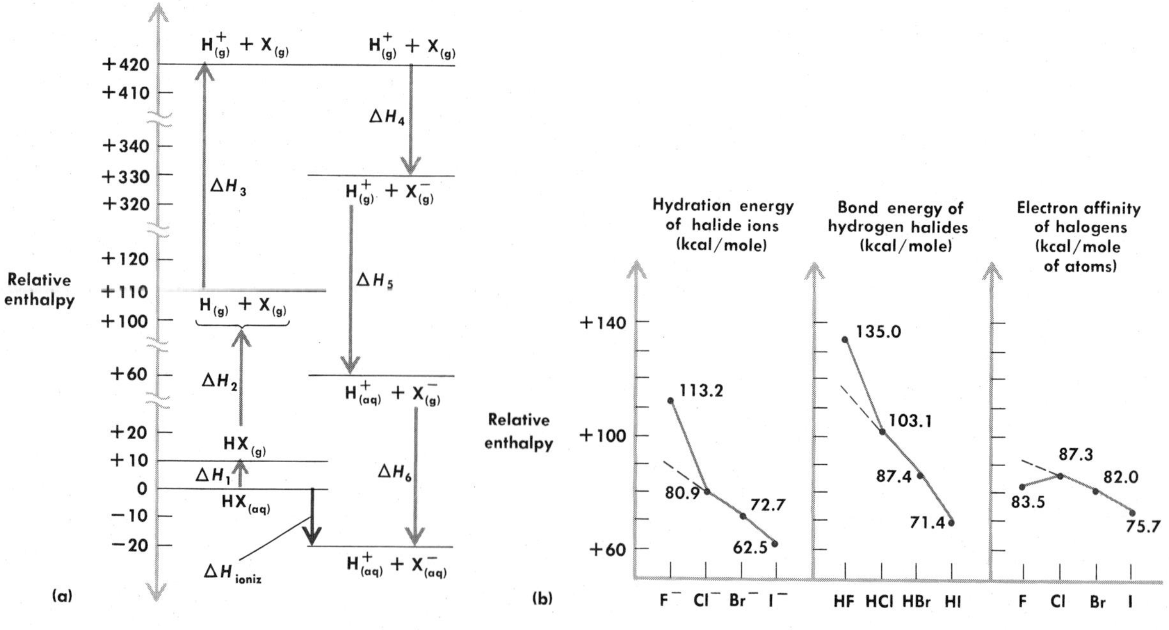

bond strength (31.9 kcal/mole), which favors the dissociation of HCl over HF. So the relatively small difference in electron affinity (3.8 kcal/mole) between F and Cl favoring the dissociation of HCl over that of HF finally explains why in dilute aqueous solution HCl is a stronger acid than HF. (Recall that even a relatively small change of $\Delta H°$, and hence $\Delta G°$, means a large change of the equilibrium constant, $K_{ioniz.}$) Could this acidity trend be reversed under a different set of conditions? The above considerations suggest that if we can increase in some way the solvation energy of the fluoride ion, we may be able to reverse the acidity trend. And indeed, in a very concentrated solution HF becomes a stronger acid than one of HCl does because the large number of undissociated HF molecules solvate the F^- ions (and H^+ ions) better than H_2O molecules. We may say that in a concentrated solution HF is a very strong acid because the solution contains essentially $[HF_2]^-$ ions rather than $F^-(H_2O)_y$ ions. The $[HF_2]^-$ ions are held together by very strong hydrogen bonds (stronger than the F^--to-H_2O bonds in $F^-(H_2O)_y$), so the formation of $[HF_2]^-$ ions increases enormously the solvation energy of F^- and thus favors the ionization of HF.

Aqueous hydrogen fluoride differs somewhat from the other aqueous hydrogen halides not only in its acidity but also in its reactions. For example, aqueous hydrogen fluoride is the only hydrogen halide that reacts with SiO_2 (and with the other chief constituents of glass, $CaSiO_3$ and Na_2SiO_3) to evolve the volatile gas silicon tetrafluoride, SiF_4:

$$4\ HF + SiO_2 \longrightarrow SiF_{4(g)} + 2\ H_2O$$

ANALYTICAL PROPERTIES OF THE HALIDE IONS

The metal fluorides are often quite different in their solubility from the other metal halides. For example, the chlorides, bromides, and iodides of the alkaline-earth metal ions are soluble in water, but the fluorides are insoluble. More specifically, CaF_2 is only very slightly soluble in water, but $CaCl_2$, $CaBr_2$, and CaI_2 are very soluble. On the other hand, silver fluoride, AgF, is very soluble in water, whereas AgCl, AgBr, and AgI are practically insoluble. The solubility relationships of these salts can be understood on the basis of the energetics of the dissolution reactions as discussed in Chapter 18 (p. 397). We commonly take advantage of the varying solubilities of the silver halides to detect the presence (qualitative analysis) and determine the amount (quantitative analysis) of the halide ions in solutions and compounds.

The most convenient method for the quantitative determination of I_2, which has the lowest oxidation potential of all the halogens, is to titrate its solution with a solution of sodium thiosulfate, $Na_2S_2O_3$. The I_2 oxidizes the thiosulfate ion to the tetrathionate ion, $S_4O_6^=$:

$$I_2 + \cancel{4\ Na^+} + 2\ S_2O_3^= \longrightarrow \cancel{4\ Na^+} + 2\ I^- + S_4O_6^=$$

The end-point of the titration is indicated when a starch-solution indicator loses its deep-blue color, which is due to a [starch-I_2] complex, and becomes colorless.

27-6 Oxides and Oxoacids of the Halogens

OXIDES OF THE HALOGENS

The halogens form a series of binary compounds with oxygen, called in general, the halogen oxides. The halogen atoms in these compounds exhibit the oxidation states: +1, +4, +6, +7. The known halogen oxides, which are prepared by indirect methods rather than by the direct combination of the elements, are listed in Table 27-5. These compounds are named according to the rules given in Chapter 5, p. 58—that is, their composition is indicated by means of Greek numerical prefixes. They are either very volatile liquids or gases.

TABLE 27-5 OXIDES OF THE HALOGENS*

Halogen	+1	+4	+5	+6	+7
F	F_2O	—	—	—	—
Cl	Cl_2O	ClO_2	—	Cl_2O_6	Cl_2O_7
Br	Br_2O	BrO_2	—	—	—
I	*	I_2O_4	I_2O_5	—	—

(Column heading over +1 to +7: Oxidation Number)

* Dashes indicate that the compounds are unknown.

OXOACIDS OF THE HALOGENS AND THEIR SALTS

The general formula of the oxoacids of the halogens is HXO_x, where $x = 1$ to 4. In all cases, the H atom is linked covalently to an oxygen atom, which in turn is covalently bonded to the halogen atom. Thus, as we have already seen in Chapter 20, the general formula of these halogen oxoacids can also be written as $XO_m(OH)_{(l)}$ where $m = 0$, 1, 2, or 3. When these oxoacids are dissolved in water, they ionize, to a larger or smaller extent, to form the hydrated proton $H^+{}_{(aq)}$, and the hydrated anion $(XO_mO)^-{}_{(aq)}$. In Chapter 20 we discussed how the tendency of the oxoacids of chlorine towards ionization in water—that is, their acid strength—varies with the oxidation number of the central Cl atom, or, (which is the same) with the number of (O_m) atoms in the formula $ClO_m(OH)_{(l)}$.

The formulas of the halogen oxoacids and of the corresponding oxoanions are listed in Table 27-6, which also gives the stereochemistry of the anion. We see that all these compounds have the stereochemistry expected on the basis of the number of bond pairs and lone pairs associated with the central atom, as we discussed in Chapter 14. Table 27-6 shows that no oxoacids of fluorine are known, and that only chlorine forms a complete series of oxoacids and oxosalts, with all odd oxidation states from +1 to +7. In the following pages, we shall chiefly discuss the chemical behavior of the oxoacids and oxoanions of chlorine; the corresponding compounds of bromine and iodine have similar behavior except for some differences in their oxidizing-reducing ability.

TABLE 27-6 OXOACIDS AND OXOANIONS OF THE HALOGENS*

Acid	Anion	Halogen	Ox. No. of X	C.N. of X	E.P.C.N.† of X	Stereochemistry of Anion, XO_m^-
HXO or X(OH)	XO^- hypohalite	Cl, Br, I	+1	1	4	linear
HXO_2 or XO(OH)	XO_2^- halite	Cl	+3	2	4	bent
HXO_3 or $XO_2(OH)$	XO_3^- halate	Cl, Br, I	+5	3	4	pyramidal
HXO_4 or $XO_3(OH)$	XO_4^- perhalate	Cl, Br, I	+7	4	4	tetrahedral

* These compounds are named according to the rules given in Chapter 5.
† Electron-Pair Coordination Number (see Chapter 14).

THE Cl_2–H_2O REACTION. Chlorine gas is somewhat soluble in water; at room temperature 1 volume of the gas at 1 atm pressure dissolves in about $2\frac{1}{2}$ volumes of water. The resulting solution, called *chlorine water*, has the odor, color, and chemical properties of chlorine gas. But the solution also has chemical properties of its own; these properties result from reactions that take place between the chlorine and the water. When chlorine gas, Cl_2, is dissolved in water at ordinary temperatures and in the absence of strong light, the following equilibrium is established:

$$Cl_2 + H_2O \rightleftharpoons HOCl + HCl$$

At 25°C and 1 atm pressure of chlorine gas, the saturated equilibrium solution contains about 50 per cent of its chlorine in the form of Cl_2 molecules, and the remaining 50 per cent is equally divided between HCl and HOCl. Thus chlorine water contains free Cl_2 molecules and therefore has the odor and color of chlorine. The solution also contains partially ionized HOCl (a weak acid) and fully ionized HCl, and therefore behaves as an acidic solution. If we want to shift the equilibrium reaction of chlorine water to the right, we can do so easily by adding a base, for example NaOH. The added OH^- ions react with the H^+ ions resulting from the complete ionization of the HCl, and by the partial ionization of the HClO, to form un-ionized H_2O molecules. As the HCl and HClO are "removed" by reaction with the base, the equilibrium shifts to the right so that the addition of sufficient NaOH produces a solution containing only NaOCl, NaCl, and H_2O. That is to say, Cl_2 gas reacts with the OH^- ions of a strong base, such as NaOH, to form a mixture of *hypochlorite* and chloride:

$$Cl_2 + \cancel{2\,Na^+} + 2\,OH^- \longrightarrow \cancel{2\,Na^+} + Cl^- + OCl^- + H_2O$$

The concentration of HOCl in the room-temperature equilibrium mixture of chlorine water, $Cl_2 + H_2O \rightleftharpoons HOCl + HCl$, can be increased by adding $AgNO_3$. The Ag^+ ions remove the Cl^- ions by forming insoluble AgCl and thus shift the equilibrium to the right. (The resulting solution also contains H^+ and NO_3^- ions, that is, ionized nitric acid, HNO_3.)

$$HCl_{(aq)} + AgNO_{3(aq)} \longrightarrow AgCl_{(s)} + HNO_{3(aq)}$$

To obtain a solution containing only HOCl, we can add solid mercury(II) oxide, HgO, to the equilibrium mixture of chlorine water, for the insoluble basic oxide HgO reacts with the H^+ ions of HCl to form $HgCl_2$ and H_2O. The $HgCl_2$ in turn precipitates as the insoluble compound $HgO \cdot HgCl_2$, while the very weak acid HClO remains undissociated in solution.

$$2\,Cl_{2(aq)} + H_2O_{(l)} + 2\,HgO_{(s)} \longrightarrow 2\,HOCl_{(aq)} + HgO \cdot HgCl_{2(s)}$$

The reaction of Br_2 and I_2 with water at room temperature in the absence of light is similar to that of Cl_2, even though the extent of reactions differs markedly. At equilibrium, less than 50 per cent of the bromine, Br_2, reacts with the water to form HBr and HOBr. In the case of iodine little or no reaction with water takes place and the dissolved iodine remains essentially in the form of I_2 molecules. On the other hand, the reaction of F_2 with water is quite different. The F^-,F_2 couple has such a large negative oxidation potential that fluorine gas, F_2, reacts vigorously and almost explosively with water to form HF and O_2.

$$2\,F_{2(g)} + 2\,H_2O_{(l)} \longrightarrow 4\,HF_{(aq)} + O_{2(g)}$$

ACTION OF Cl_2 ON STRONG BASIC SOLUTIONS AT HIGH TEMPERATURE. When Cl_2 gas is passed into a hot concentrated basic solution—for example, a solution of potassium hydroxide, KOH, at about 70°C—the oxidation products formed are not the same as in the reaction at room temperature. The oxidized chlorine compound formed in this case is $KClO_3$ rather than $KClO$:

$$3\ Cl_2 + 6\ KOH \longrightarrow KClO_3 + 5\ KCl + 3\ H_2O$$

The $KClO_3$, which is only slightly soluble in cold water, may be easily separated from the KCl by cooling the solution. The compounds $KBrO_3$ and KIO_3 may be obtained by means of similar reactions.

OXIDATION POTENTIALS OF THE OXOACIDS OF CHLORINE

The anions of the oxoacids of the halogens are strong oxidizing agents. Table 27-7 lists the relevant standard oxidation potentials. These $E°$ values indicate that in acid solution all the oxoacids of chlorine (whether completely ionized or not) have oxidation-potential values more negative than -0.82 v, and are therefore sufficiently powerful oxidants to liberate oxygen from pure water ($[H^+] = 10^{-7}$). It follows, therefore, that aqueous solutions of the anions of these acids, in the presence of H^+ ions, are unstable. However, at room temperature and in the absence of a catalyst these oxoacids decompose water very slowly, so that their aqueous solutions can be stored for a fairly long time without appreciable decomposition.

Notice in Table 27-7 that the oxidizing power of the oxoanions of chlorine increases as the number of oxygen atoms present decreases. In fact, all the oxoanions of chlorine, except ClO_4^-, can oxidize the Cl^- ions to Cl_2 in the presence of H^+ ions. The hypochlorite ion, ClO^-, is the most powerful oxidant in this list; in fact, a very convenient method of preparing Cl_2 makes use of the salt CaCl(ClO), commonly called "bleaching powder." When this solid compound is treated with an acid, Cl_2 is vigorously evolved, even in the cold, by the mutual oxidation of the Cl^- ion and reduction of the ClO^- ion in the presence of H^+ ions:

Oxidation half-reaction: $2\ Cl^- \longrightarrow Cl_{2(g)} + 2\ e^-$

Reduction half-reaction: $2\ ClO^- + 4\ H^+ + 2\ e^- \longrightarrow Cl_{2(g)} + 2\ H_2O$

Net reaction: $2\ Cl^- + 2\ ClO^- + 4\ H^+ \longrightarrow 2\ Cl_{2(g)} + 2\ H_2O$

This method of preparing Cl_2 has the advantage of producing only the desired product, Cl_2, along with H_2O, from both the oxidizing and the reducing agents.

TABLE 27-7 STANDARD OXIDATION POTENTIALS OF THE OXOACIDS OF CHLORINE

Half-Cell Reaction	*E°*
$2\ H_2O = O_2 + 4\ H^+\ (10^{-7}\ M) + 4\ e^-$ (water)	-0.82
$2\ H_2O = O_2 + 4\ H^+ + 4\ e^-$ (1 M acid)	-1.23
$\frac{1}{2}Cl_2 + 4\ H_2O = ClO_4^- + 8\ H^+ + 7\ e^-$	-1.34
$Cl^- = \frac{1}{2}Cl_2 + 1\ e^-$	-1.40
$\frac{1}{2}Cl_2 + 3\ H_2O = ClO_3^- + 6\ H^+ + 5\ e^-$	-1.47
$\frac{1}{2}Cl_2 + 2\ H_2O = HClO_2 + 3\ H^+ + 3\ e^-$	-1.63
$\frac{1}{2}Cl_2 + H_2O = HClO + H^+ + e^-$	-1.62

A method for predicting chemical reactions by graphically combining oxidation potentials into diagrams was introduced in 1938 by Professor Wendell M. Latimer (1893–1957) of the University of California. This system is based on the principle, discussed extensively in Chapters 17 and 22, that a chemical reaction will occur spontaneously, under a specified set of experimental conditions, in the direction which corresponds to a negative change of the free energy ($\Delta G < 0$) or to a positive reaction potential ($E > 0$). The advantage of oxidation-reduction diagrams is that they show at a glance what particular oxidation reactions can occur spontaneously, even for elements which can exist in more than two oxidation states. Before we apply the Latimer diagram method to chlorine—an element which exists in many oxidation states—let us see how it may be applied to a few simple cases.

The Latimer oxidation-reduction diagram relates ions, atoms, or molecules in which an element exists in different oxidation states, and gives the numerical values of the standard oxidation potentials, $E°$, for the various pairs of oxidation states (couples). Remember that the $E°$ values refer to couples in which all ions have 1 M concentration (more correctly, an activity = 1), and are measured against the standard H_2,H^+ couple, where H_2 gas is at a pressure of 1 atm and the H^+ ion has 1 M concentration. For reactions in basic media, $E°_{basic}$ values are used. These are measured against a H_2,H^+ couple where H_2 is again at a pressure of 1 atm but the H^+ ion concentration is 10^{-14} M (OH^- ion concentration = 1 M).

THE LATIMER OXIDATION-REDUCTION DIAGRAM OF IRON

As an example of how we use a Latimer oxidation-reduction diagram, often called simply a potential diagram, let us look at three of the known oxidation states of the element iron, Fe, Fe^{++}, and Fe^{+++}, and at the $E°$ values of the Fe,Fe^{++} couple, and of the Fe^{++},Fe^{+++} couple. The potential diagram represents schematically the $E°$ values of the half-reactions written in full at the right:

Latimer Oxidation-Reduction Diagram

Ox. No.: 0 +2 +3

Fe —— +0.47 —— Fe^{++} —— −0.77 —— Fe^{+++}

$$Fe \longrightarrow Fe^{++} + 2\,e^- \qquad E° = +0.47\ v$$
$$(H_2 \longrightarrow 2\,H^+ + 2\,e^- \qquad E° = 0.00\ v)$$
$$Fe^{++} \longrightarrow Fe^{+++} + e^- \qquad E° = -0.77\ v$$

Notice that in going from left to right in the potential diagram, the oxidation state of the element increases. The values shown in the lines joining the oxidation states are the $E°$ volts for the connected pairs of oxidation states. The $E°$ value for the Fe,Fe^{++} couple is +0.47; the $E°$ value for the Fe^{++},Fe^{+++} couple is −0.77. In a potential diagram a plus sign of $E°$ means that when the ions are at 1 M concentration at 25°C, the change from the lower oxidation state to the higher oxidation state, Fe^{++} —+0.47— Fe—the oxidation reaction—can occur spontaneously in the presence of 1 M H^+ and H_2 gas at 1 atm. A minus sign means that under the same conditions the change from the higher oxidation state to the lower oxidation state, Fe^{+++} —−0.77— Fe^{++}—the reduction reaction—can take place spontaneously.

The same information we have obtained above from the Latimer oxidation-reduction diagram could also be derived from a similar diagram showing the standard *free energy* change, $\Delta G°$, of each oxidation reaction instead of the $E°$ value. Since $\Delta G° = -nFE°$, the Latimer potential diagram and the *Latimer free energy diagram* are, of course, equivalent. For iron, at 25°C and 1 atm and with each ionic species at 1 M concentration (more accurately, activity = 1) we have:

Latimer Free Energy Diagram

Ox. No.: 0 +2 +3

Fe —(−21.7 kcal/mole)— Fe^{++} —(+17.7 kcal/mole)— Fe^{+++}

Fe	$\longrightarrow$	$Fe^{++} + 2e^-$	$\Delta G° = -21.7$ kcal/mole-eqn
(H_2	$\longrightarrow$	$2H^+ + 2e^-$	$\Delta G° = 0.00$ kcal/mole-eqn)
Fe^{++}	$\longrightarrow$	$Fe^{+++} + e^-$	$\Delta G° = +17.7$ kcal/mole-eqn

Again, the diagram tells us that the oxidation of Fe metal to Fe^{++} is thermodynamically permitted ($\Delta G°$ is negative, -21.7 kcal/mole) in the presence of 1-molar H^+ ions, 1-molar Fe^{++} ions, and H_2 gas at 1 atm and 25°C. On the other hand, the positive value of $\Delta G°$ (+17.7 kcal/mole) for the change $Fe^{++} \longrightarrow Fe^{+++} + e^-$, tells us that the oxidation of Fe^{++} to Fe^{+++} cannot take place spontaneously under the same conditions. Rather, the reduction of Fe^{+++} to Fe^{++} by $H_{2(g)}$ is the thermodynamically permitted reaction ($\Delta G° = -17.7$ kcal/mole). In practice we do not observe any appreciable reaction when treating a Fe^{+++} salt (1-molar) with H_2 gas (1 atm and 25°C) in the presence of 1-molar H^+ ions and 1 molar Fe^{++} ions because of the very slow *rate* of the spontaneous reaction $Fe^{+++} + \frac{1}{2} H_{2(g)} \longrightarrow Fe^{++} + H^+$.

In the Latimer oxidation-reduction diagram above, the +0.47 value in the line which connects Fe with Fe^{++}, Fe—+0.47—Fe^{++}, tells us that iron metal, Fe, has a tendency to react with 1 *M* H^+ ions in a 1 *M* solution of Fe^{++} ions to form H_2 gas at 1 atm pressure and (additional) Fe^{++} ions. In the same potential diagram, the −0.77 value in the line connecting Fe^{++} with Fe^{+++}, Fe^{++}—−0.77—Fe^{+++}, means that H^+ ions at 1 *M* concentration will not oxidize Fe^{++} ions at 1 *M* concentration to Fe^{+++} ions at 1 *M* concentration. In fact, the minus value (−0.77) tells us that the *reverse* reaction has the capacity to take place spontaneously—that is, H_2 gas at 1 atm pressure in the presence of 1 *M* H^+ ions can reduce Fe^{+++} ions at a 1 *M* concentration to Fe^{++} ions at a 1 *M* concentration, forming (additional) H^+ ions as the other product.

In summary: The potential diagram tells us that iron metal, Fe, will dissolve in 1 *M* H^+ ions to form Fe^{++} ions, and that the Fe^{++} ions will not be oxidized by 1 *M* H^+ ions to Fe^{+++} ions. This same information, of course, could have been obtained directly from the half-cell reactions and corresponding $E°$ values listed to the right of the Latimer oxidation-reduction diagram of iron. The advantage of the simpler Latimer oxidation-reduction diagram is evident: the spontaneous direction of a reaction is indicated by the relative $E°$ values—and in this diagram they are shown by the curved arrows:

Fe —+0.47— Fe^{++} —−0.77— Fe^{+++}

THE LATIMER OXIDATION-REDUCTION DIAGRAM FOR COPPER. The potential diagram for copper is as follows:

Ox. No.: 0 +1 +2

Cu —−0.52— Cu^+ —−0.16— Cu^{++}

(H_2	$\longrightarrow$	$2H^+ + 2e^-$	$E° = 0.00$ v)
Cu^+	$\longrightarrow$	$Cu^{++} + e^-$	$E° = -0.16$ v
Cu	$\longrightarrow$	$Cu^+ + e^-$	$E° = -0.52$ v

The negative value, −0.52, between the line connecting Cu with Cu^+ tells us that Cu does not have the capacity to be oxidized spontaneously to Cu^+ ions by 1 *M* H^+ ions, under the conditions specified by the $E°$ value. Remember if there is *no* tendency for a forward reaction to take place, the *reverse* reaction *does* tend to take place. In this example, Cu^+ can be reduced to Cu by H_2 at 1 atm pressure in the presence of 1 *M* H^+ ions. Similarly, the negative value −0.16 tells us that Cu^+ does not have the capacity to be oxidized to Cu^{++} by H^+ ions, under the conditions specified by the $E°$ value.

Now consider this reaction: $2\,Cu^+ \longrightarrow Cu + Cu^{++}$. In this reaction a Cu^+ ion can go to Cu only if another Cu^+ ion goes to Cu^{++} ion. Now the potential diagram

Cu—-0.52—Cu^+ tells us that the tendency for Cu^+ to go to Cu is expressed numerically as a reaction potential of $+0.52$ volts. Similarly, the potential diagram, Cu^+—-0.16—Cu^{++}, tells us that the reaction potential opposing the conversion of Cu^+ to Cu^{++} is -0.16 volts. Since the favorable reaction potential ($Cu^+ \longrightarrow Cu$, $+0.52$) is greater than the unfavorable reaction potential ($Cu^+ \longrightarrow Cu^{++}$, -0.16), Cu^+ ions are able to disproportionate spontaneously to form Cu and Cu^{++}:

$$2\,Cu^+ \longrightarrow Cu + Cu^{++}$$

(Recall that a reaction in which a substance undergoes self-oxidation–reduction is called a *disproportionation* reaction, and the substance is said to *disproportionate.*)

Sometimes a given oxidation state of an element in a potential diagram is joined to more than two other oxidation states. For example, the Latimer oxidation-potential diagram of copper is often given as follows:

$$\underbrace{Cu \text{---} {-0.52} \text{---} Cu^+ \text{---} {-0.16} \text{---} Cu^{++}}_{-0.34}$$

The negative value in the potential diagram Cu—-0.34—Cu^{++} tells us that Cu^{++} ions at 1 *M* concentration can be reduced to Cu by H_2 gas at 1 atm pressure in the presence of 1 *M* H^+ ions. It also tells us, of course, that copper metal, Cu, does not dissolve in 1 *M* H^+ ions to form Cu^{++}.

MUTUAL OXIDATION-REDUCTION REACTIONS OF THE SPECIES IN A POTENTIAL DIAGRAM

Consider that we have three different oxidation states, A, B, and C of the same element. If these three states can be connected in a Latimer potential diagram, then they have the capacity to undergo a mutual oxidation-reduction reaction, and the following two cases are possible (A, B, and C being arranged in order of increasing oxidation number from left to right).

1. The potential value written on the right-hand side of the diagram is *more* positive than that written on the left-hand side: For example:

A—$+1.0$—B—$+1.5$—C or A—-1.2—B—$+1.6$—C or A—-1.7—B—-1.1—C

In each case, the tendency of B to go to A is greater than the tendency of C to go to B, and the intermediate oxidation state B spontaneously disproportionates to A and C:

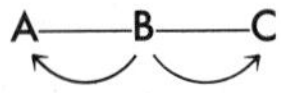

A ⟵ B ⟶ C

In fact if we add together the potential value on the right with its sign as written (since we consider the reaction (B $\longrightarrow$ C) and the potential value on the left *with its sign changed* (since we consider the reaction B $\longrightarrow$ A), we obtain a positive value for the over-all reaction potential. And, as we know, a positive $E°$ value means that the reaction can take place spontaneously under the specified conditions.

2. The potential value written on the right-hand side of the diagram is *less* positive than that on the left-hand side. For example:

A—$+0.6$—B—$+0.4$—C or A—$+1.4$—B—-2.0—C or A—-0.5—B—-1.6—C

In each case A and C have the capacity to react spontaneously with each other to form the entity of intermediate oxidation state, B. In fact, if we add the potential on the left with its sign as written (reaction A $\longrightarrow$ B) and the potential on the right with the sign changed (reaction C $\longrightarrow$ B), we obtain a positive potential value for the over-all reaction:

A ⟶ B ⟵ C

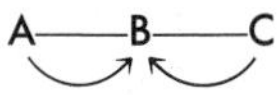

By keeping these generalizations in mind, we can understand and remember more easily the chemical behavior and relative stability of the compounds of those elements —such as the halogens—which exhibit more than two oxidation states.

POTENTIAL DIAGRAM OF CHLORINE IN ACIDIC SOLUTION

The oxidation states of chlorine are -1, 0, $+1$, $+3$, $+5$, and $+7$. (We shall not consider here the $+4$ oxidation state which appears only in gaseous ClO_2.) The following potential diagram is useful in correlating the more important chemical properties of chlorine in acidic solution:

$$\overset{-1}{Cl^-} \text{—} {-1.40} \text{—} \overset{0}{Cl_2} \text{—} {-1.62} \text{—} \overset{+1}{HClO} \text{—} {-1.64} \text{—} \overset{+3}{HClO_2} \text{—} {-1.21} \text{—} \overset{+5}{ClO_3^-} \text{—} {-1.19} \text{—} \overset{+7}{ClO_4^-}$$

$$Cl_2 \text{ —— } {-1.47} \text{ —— } ClO_3^-$$

First, notice that Cl_2 gas has a strong tendency to go to Cl^- ions, as indicated by the negative value -1.40, $Cl^-\text{—}{-1.40}\text{—}Cl_2$. Therefore, Cl_2 readily takes on electrons to form Cl^- ions, and is a strong oxidant in 1 *M* acid solution. Also, since the potential (-1.62) for the change $Cl_2 \longrightarrow HClO$ is *less positive* (or *more negative*) than the potential (-1.40) for the change $Cl^- \longrightarrow Cl_2$, the Cl_2 does *not* disproportionate to Cl^- and HClO in acid solution. Rather, if Cl^- and HClO are brought together in the presence of H^+ ions, they can react with each other to give Cl_2 (this is an example of case 2 discussed in the previous section).

The negative value of the oxidation potential of Cl^- to Cl_2 (-1.40) is more negative than that of the H_2O,O_2 couple (-1.23). Consequently, Cl_2 in acid solution has the capacity to react spontaneously with H_2O, liberating O_2, although the rate of this reaction is very slow.

Here is the Latimer oxidation-reduction diagram for chlorine in the three oxidation states $+1$, $+3$, and $+5$:

$$HClO\text{—}{-1.64}\text{—}HClO_2\text{—}{-1.21}\text{—}ClO_3^-$$

The potential (-1.21) for the conversion $HClO_2 \longrightarrow ClO_3^-$ is *more positive* (or *less negative*) than the potential (-1.64) for the change $HClO \longrightarrow HClO_2$. Hence, as in case 1 considered in the previous section, $HClO_2$ is capable of disproportionation to HClO and ClO_3^-.

The following Latimer *free energy* diagram can be used similarly to arrive at the same conclusions:

$$\overset{+1}{HClO} \xrightarrow[\text{kcal/mole}]{+75.6} \overset{+3}{HClO_2} \xrightarrow[\text{kcal/mole}]{+55.8} \overset{+5}{ClO_3^-}$$

This Latimer free energy diagram tells us that $HClO_2$ can disproportionate to HClO and ClO_3^-, because the $\Delta G°$ for the disproportionation reaction is negative: $-75.6 + 55.8 = -19.8$ kcal/mole.

Now let us consider the partial Latimer oxidation-potential diagram for chlorine in the three oxidation states $+3$, $+5$ and $+7$:

$$HClO_2\text{—}{-1.21}\text{—}ClO_3^-\text{—}{-1.19}\text{—}ClO_4^-.$$

This diagram tells us that ClO_3^- is able to disproportionate to $HClO_2$ and ClO_4^-. (The *rate* of this self-oxidation-reduction reaction, however, is slow under most conditions.)

From the entire potential diagram of chlorine we also see that both HClO (-1.62) and $HClO_2$ (-1.64) are sufficiently strong oxidizing agents to liberate oxygen from water (-1.23). Also, both these acids have a more negative oxidation potential than that of Cl^-, Cl_2 ($E° = -1.40$), and thus can oxidize Cl^- to Cl_2; the reduction product of the HClO and $HClO_2$ is also Cl_2. Finally, we see that the ClO_3^- ion can disproportionate to Cl_2 and ClO_4^- (compare -1.47 with -1.19), but this reaction is slow under most conditions.

LATIMER POTENTIAL DIAGRAM OF CHLORINE IN BASIC SOLUTION. The following Latimer oxidation-potential diagram summarizes the chlorine potentials in basic solution:

$$\overset{-1}{Cl^-} \xrightarrow{-1.40} \overset{0}{Cl_2} \xrightarrow{-0.40} \overset{+1}{ClO^-} \xrightarrow{-0.66} \overset{+3}{ClO_2^-} \xrightarrow{-0.33} \overset{+5}{ClO_3^-} \xrightarrow{-0.17} \overset{+7}{ClO_4^-}$$

$$Cl^- \xrightarrow{-0.89} ClO^- \qquad ClO^- \xrightarrow{-0.50} ClO_3^-$$

The partial potential diagram, $Cl^- \text{---} {-1.40} \text{---} Cl_2 \text{---} {-0.40} \text{---} ClO^-$, tells us that Cl_2 in basic solution has a strong tendency to disproportionate, because the potential for the reduction of Cl_2 to Cl^- ($+1.40$) is more positive than the potential to be overcome (-0.40) for the oxidation of Cl_2 to ClO^-. Similarly, the potential diagram, $Cl^- \text{---} {-0.89} \text{---} ClO^- \text{---} {-0.50} \text{---} ClO_3^-$, tells us that ClO^- is capable of reducing itself to Cl^- while oxidizing itself to ClO_3^-. That is to say, ClO^- is able to disproportionate to Cl^- and ClO_3^-.

27-8 The Noble Gases and Their Compounds

The elements known as the *noble gases*—helium, He; neon, Ne; argon, Ar; krypton, Kr; xenon, Xe; and radon, Rn—belong to Group 0 of the Periodic Table, as we have seen in Chapter 12. It is appropriate, however, to include a description of this group of elements in a chapter devoted to the halogens, because fluorine is the only element known to enter into direct chemical combination with the two heavier noble gases, xenon, Xe, and krypton, Kr, to form stable compounds.

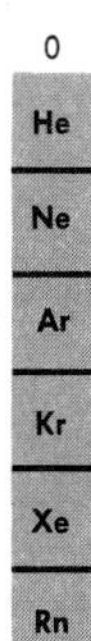

The noble gases occur in nature as minor constituents of the atmosphere. The first indication of the existence of the noble gases was reported by the English chemist Cavendish in 1784. He observed that after he repeatedly sparked air with an excess of oxygen in the presence of alkali (which absorbed the nitrogen oxides thus formed, as well as the originally present carbon dioxide), and then removed the unreacted excess of oxygen, there was always the same residual volume of gas—about $\frac{1}{120}$ of the initial volume of air. In 1894 two other English scientists, Ramsay and Lord Rayleigh, isolated the first known noble gas—the most abundant noble gas in air—and named it argon, Ar (meaning the lazy one) because all their efforts to react it with other chemicals were unsuccessful. The next noble gas they isolated, helium, He, was obtained in 1895 by heating a uranium ore, so that the gas trapped in its cavities was released (the gas was there as a product of the radioactive decay of uranium. Helium was known to exist in the chromosphere of the sun (hence its name) from spectroscopic data 27 years previous to its being isolated on earth. Within six years after the discovery of helium by Ramsay and Lord Rayleigh all the other noble gases were isolated and characterized. For the next 60 years it was the general belief, accepted by the majority of chemists, that the noble gases were incapable of forming normal chemical compounds; all attempts made during this time to prepare compounds of the noble gases had failed. It was not until 1962 that the English chemist Neil Bartlett succeeded in forming the first true chemical compound of a noble gas, the yellow crystalline solid salt, $Xe^+[PtF_6]^-$, by the reaction of xenon gas, Xe, with platinum hexafluoride vapor, PtF_6. Since the discovery of this first compound of a noble gas, a great deal of work has been done to investigate the experimental techniques suitable for the preparation of noble gas compounds and to explain their stability and type of bonding on the basis of theoretical considerations. These studies have shown that, given the appropriate experimental conditions, several compounds of the noble gases can be isolated—and that they are stable at ordinary conditions if the free energy of their formation reaction is negative, $\Delta G_{formation} < 0$. The compounds of the noble gases, like all chemical compounds, obey the rules of thermodynamic stability discussed in Chapter 17.

GENERAL CHARACTERISTICS

The atoms of the noble gases have complete valence shells; helium has a $1s^2$ electron configuration, and each of the other noble gases has an outer s^2p^6 electron configuration (octet). The noble gases exist as monoatomic molecules; some of their most important physical properties are given in Table 27-8. As this table shows, the noble gases have low boiling points (helium has the lowest b.p. of any substance) and low heats of vaporization, both of which increase regularly as their atomic numbers increase. These properties, as well as the monoatomic character of the molecules, can be explained on the basis that only weak van der Waals forces exist between the atoms of the noble gases. The regular increase in boiling point, heat of vaporization, and solubility in water as we go down the family from helium to xenon, can be related to the increasing size of their molecules (atoms). In fact, the larger its electron cloud, the more polarizable a molecule becomes, and the stronger are the van der Waals attractions of these molecules with one another as well as with other molecules—for example, with polar water molecules.

CHEMICAL PROPERTIES. The chemical properties of the noble gases—as in general those of all elements—can be explained on the basis of their electron configurations, their ionization potentials, and their promotion energies to the lowest valency states. As expected, the ionization potentials of the noble gases decrease regularly with atomic number, as do their promotion energies. On the basis of ionization potentials, we might predict that if any noble gas will react and form a compound in which it is present as a monopositive ion, then the larger atoms would be the more likely to react. Similarly, on the basis of the promotion energies listed in Table 27-8, we would expect the tendency of a noble gas to form compounds by sharing electron pairs with other atoms to increase as the atomic number increases. And, in fact, only the three heaviest members of the family—Kr, Xe, and Rn—are known at present to enter into chemical reactions.

REACTION OF NOBLE GASES WITH FLUORINE

The simplest known reaction of a noble gas is that which occurs between xenon and fluorine when a mixture of these gases, in a 1:5 (xenon:fluorine) mole ratio, is heated in a nickel vessel to 400°C. Under these conditions xenon reacts com-

TABLE 27-8 SOME PROPERTIES OF THE NOBLE GASES

Element	Outer Electron Config.	Atomic Weight	Boiling Point °C	$\Delta H_{vaporiz}$ kcal/mole	Solubility in water[a]	First Ioniz. Energy[b]	Second Ioniz. Energy[b]	Promotion Energy[b] to Lowest Valency State[c]	
$_{2}He$	$1s^2$	4.0026	−268.9	0.022	8.61	576.2 24.59	1254.8 54.40	$(1s^1,2s^1)$	392.0 19.8
$_{10}Ne$	$2s^2\,2p^6$	20.183	−246.1	0.44	10.5	497.3 21.56	947.3 41.07	$(2s^2\,2p^5,3s^1)$	382.9 16.6
$_{18}Ar$	$3s^2\,3p^6$	39.948	−185.9	1.50	33.6	363.5 15.76	637.1 27.62	$(3s^2\,3p^5,4s^1)$	265.3 11.5
$_{36}Kr$	$4s^2\,4p^6$	83.80	−153.4	2.31	59.4	322.9 14.00	566.5 24.56	$(4s^2\,4p^5,5s^1)$	228.3 9.9
$_{54}Xe$	$5s^2\,5p^6$	131.30	−108.1	3.27	108.1	279.8 12.13	489.2 21.21	$(5s^2\,5p^5,6s^1)$	191.9 8.3
$_{86}Rn$	$6s^2\,6p^6$	(222)	−62.0	4.3	—	248.0 10.75	— —	$(6s^2\,6p^5,7s^1)$	156.8 6.8

[a] cm^3 of gas in 1000 g of water at 25° and 1 atm.
[b] Upper figure in kcal/mole, lower figure in electron volts.
[c] The electronic configuration of the valency state is given in parentheses.

pletely to form a colorless crystalline compound of formula XeF_4, xenon tetrafluoride:

$$Xe_{(g)} + 2\ F_{2(g)} \longrightarrow XeF_{4(g)}$$

Xenon also reacts directly with fluorine gas to form colorless crystals of xenon difluoride, XeF_2:

$$Xe_{(g)} + F_{2(g)} \longrightarrow XeF_{2(s)}$$

This compound can be obtained by quickly passing the reaction mixture through a tube cooled at $-50°C$, so that solid XeF_2 separates out before it can further react with additional F_2 to form XeF_4:

$$XeF_{2(s)} + F_{2(g)} \longrightarrow XeF_{4(g)}$$

If a fluorine-xenon mixture with a mole ratio of about 20:1 is heated at a higher temperature (about 700°C) and under a high pressure (about 200 atm) a different compound—the colorless, solid xenon hexafluoride, XeF_6—is produced:

$$Xe_{(g)} + 3\ F_{(g)} \xrightarrow[\text{high press}]{\text{high temp}} XeF_{6(s)}$$

The compond XeF_6 reacts rapidly with quartz—which is a form of silica, SiO_2—to form a colorless liquid, xenon oxotetrafluoride, $XeOF_4$:

$$2\ XeF_{6(s)} + SiO_{2(s)} \longrightarrow 2\ XeOF_{4(l)} + SiF_{4(g)}$$

Thus we see that xenon reacts directly with the most electronegative of all elements, fluorine, to produce XeF_2, XeF_4 or XeF_6 depending on the experimental conditions.

No compounds have been reported to arise from the direct or indirect reaction of helium, neon, and argon with fluorine. However, a mixture of F_2 and Kr, when either irradiated at a low pressure or submitted to an electric discharge at low temperature ($-150°C$), reacts to form the colorless, crystalline solid, krypton difluoride, KrF_2:

$$Kr_{(g)} + F_{2(g)} \xrightarrow[\text{electric discharge}]{h\nu,\text{ or}} KrF_{2(s)}$$

OXYGEN COMPOUNDS OF XENON. Oxygen gas does not react directly with xenon, but several compounds of xenon with oxygen can be prepared by reaction of the fluorine compounds with oygen-containing compounds, for example water.

$$XeF_6 + H_2O \longrightarrow XeOF_4 + 2\ HF$$

(Notice that this reaction is similar to that written above for XeF_6 and SiO_2.) The reaction of XeF_6 with water can proceed further, giving as the final product xenon trioxide, XeO_3, a thermodynamically unstable compound which has explosive properties comparable to those of trinitrotoluene (T.N.T.).

$$XeF_6 + 3\ H_2O \longrightarrow XeO_3 + 6\ HF$$

All the known compounds of xenon (as well as the few known compounds of krypton), contain fluorine, or oxygen, or both. The formulas of some additional compounds of xenon follow: $CsXeF_7$, $XeOF_2$, $XeOF_4$, $Xe(OH)_6$, and Ba_3XeO_6.

STABILITY OF AND BONDING IN XENON COMPOUNDS

Let us take xenon tetrafluoride, XeF_4, and follow through the "anatomy" of its formation reaction at standard conditions (25°C and 1 atm), as we outlined in Chapter 17.

$$Xe_{(g)} + F_{2(g)} \longrightarrow XeF_{4(s)} \quad \begin{cases} \Delta H^\circ_{\text{form}} = -60 \text{ kcal/mole-eqn} \\ \Delta S^\circ_{\text{form}} = -102 \text{ cal/deg} \times \text{mole-eqn} \end{cases}$$

Thus we have:

$$\Delta G^\circ_{form} = \Delta H^\circ - T\Delta S^\circ = -60 - [298 \times (-102 \times 10^{-3})] = -60 + 31$$
$$= -29 \text{ kcal/mole-eqn}$$

The negative value of ΔG°_{form} (−29 kcal/mole-equation) tells us that at 25°C and 1 atm the formation of xenon tetrafluoride, XeF_4, by direct union of xenon gas, Xe, and fluorine gas, F_2, has the capacity to take place spontaneously. Hence solid XeF_4 at room temperature is stable with respect to dissociation into its elements, even though it may have the capacity to undergo reaction with other substances—water, for example. From the values of ΔH°_{form} and ΔS°_{form} given above, we see that the free energy of formation of XeF_4 is favorable ($\Delta G^\circ_{form} < 0$), because the large favorable enthalpy term ($\Delta H^\circ = -60$ kcal/mole-equation) overcomes the unfavorable entropy term ($\Delta S^\circ = -102$ cal/deg × mole-equation). At higher temperatures, XeF_4 becomes unstable because the unfavorable $T\,\Delta S$ term—which increases proportionally to the absolute temperature T—finally becomes predominant over the favorable ΔH term. Thus, the fact that XeF_4 is prepared—as was said above—by the synthesis of $Xe_{(g)}$ and $F_{2(g)}$ at 400°C, simply reflects the need to obtain a convenient reaction *rate* (an increase in temperature does not influence favorably the tendency of the reaction to take place).

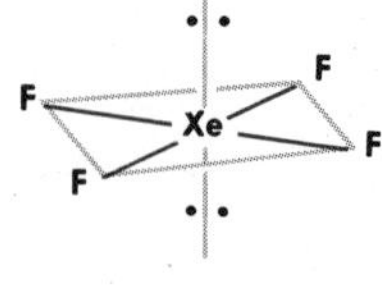

Let us now consider the electronic changes brought about by the above reaction. One reactant, xenon gas, is composed of monoatomic molecules (outer electron configuration, $5s^2\,5p^6$) which interact only by very weak van der Waals forces—as we know from Chapter 9, p. 144, the energy of induced dipole–induced dipole interactions is about 1 to 3 kcal/mole. The other reactant, fluorine gas, consists of diatomic molecules, with the 2 F atoms joined by a strong covalent bond resulting from the overlap of a $2p$ orbital from each F atom (F—F bond energy = 37.0 kcal/mole). The product, solid xenon tetrafluoride, XeF_4, consists of covalent XeF_4 molecules held together in a crystal lattice by fairly strong van der Waals forces. Each XeF_4 molecule has a planar stereochemistry, which is in agreement with the number of bond pairs (four) and lone pairs (two) surrounding the central atom—as shown by the accompanying diagram. Notice that XeF_4 is isoelectronic and has the same stereochemistry as the square planar ICl_4^- ion.

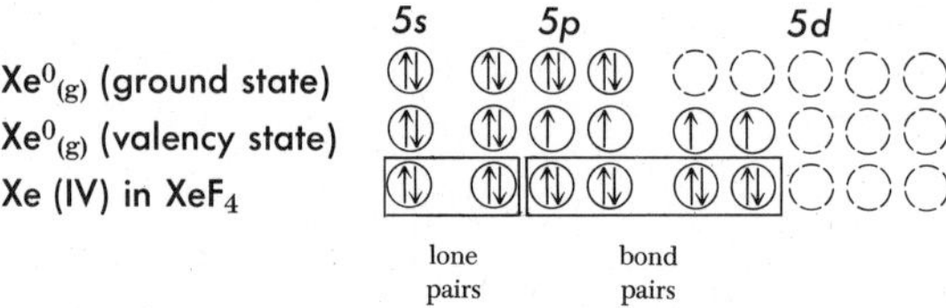

Exercises

27-1 (a) List the atoms of the halogens in order of increasing size. (b) Write the electron configurations of the halogen atoms: $_9F$, $_{17}Cl$, $_{35}Br$, $_{53}I$. (c) Explain the increasing size of the halogen atoms on the basis of their electronic configurations. (d) List the halogens, X_2, in order of increasing stability toward dissociation into their component atoms (least stable first). (e) On the basis of van der Waals forces, explain the difference in physical states between F_2 and I_2. (f) List the halogens in order of increasing melting point. (g) The halogens, except I_2, do not occur free in nature. Explain. (h) Which of the known halogens: 1. cannot be prepared by the electrolysis of an aqueous solution of its metallic halide? 2. is the darkest in color? 3. does not form oxygen acids? 4. forms the most stable hydrogen halide? 5. is the best reducing agent? 6. is purified by sublimation? 7. is obtained on a commercial scale from sea water? 8. is a reddish-brown gas? 9. as a gas, weighs the most per liter?

EXERCISES

27-2 (a) Indicate the two general methods whereby the halide ions, Cl^-, Br^-, and I^-, may be oxidized to the free halogen. (b) Why is it not possible to prepare fluorine by the electrolysis of an aqueous solution of a metal fluoride. Explain. (c) How is fluorine prepared? Give equations. (d) Mention the special features involved in the preparation of fluorine.

27-3 Give equations for an electrolytic and a chemical method used to prepare Cl_2, Br_2, and I_2.

27-4 Write an equation showing the electrolysis of a sodium chloride solution. What commercial products may be synthesized from the other products of the electrolysis? Write equations.

27-5 Explain by equations the reactions, if any, which take place in the following: (a) Cl_2 is passed into an aqueous solution of NaBr. (b) I_2 is added to an aqueous solution of KCl. (c) Br_2 is added to an aqueous solution of KI.

27-6 Complete and balance the following expressions, indicating the oxidizing agent, the reducing agent, the oxidation product, and the reduction product:

(a) $MnO_2 + HCl \longrightarrow$ (c) $KMnO_4 + KBr + H_2SO_4 \longrightarrow$
(b) $KMnO_4 + HI \longrightarrow$ (d) $K_2Cr_2O_7 + NaCl + H_2SO_4 \longrightarrow$

27-7 Write equations for the reactions of chlorine with:
Metals: copper, zinc, sodium, antimony.
Non-metals: phosphorus, hydrogen.

27-8 If a reaction takes place, complete and balance the following expressions. If no reaction takes place, write N.R.

(a) $Fe + Cl_2$ (d) $FeBr_2 + Br_2$ (g) $I_2 + H_2S$
(b) $Fe + Br_2$ (e) $CaCl_2 + NaBr$ (h) $Cl_2 + AgNO_3$
(c) $FeCl_2 + Cl_2$ (f) $F_2 + H_2$ (i) $CaF_2 + H_2SO_4$ + heat

27-9 (a) Write an equation showing the equilibrium that exists when Cl_2 is passed into water. (b) Dry chlorine will not bleach but chlorine in water will. Explain.

27-10 Cl_2 gas is bubbled into each of the following aqueous solutions. If a reaction takes place, write the equation for it. If no reaction takes place, write N.R. (a) $AgNO_3$, (b) Na_2CO_3, (c) Na_2S, (d) $Ca(OH)_2$.

27-11 Using Br_2 as one of the starting materials, explain how you could prepare: (a) $ZnBr_2$, (b) $KBrO_3$, (c) HBr, (d) AgBr, (e) PBr_3. Give equations.

27-12 (a) List the important uses of chlorine. (b) Describe and give equations for detecting the ions Cl^-, Br^-, and I^-.

27-13 (a) Write equations to illustrate the preparation of gaseous HCl, using concentrated H_2SO_4 as one of the reactants. (b) Can gaseous HBr and HI be so prepared? Explain. (c) What reagent may be substituted for H_2SO_4 to prepare HBr and HI? Write equations. (d) Explain the roles played by H_2SO_4 and H_3PO_4 in their reaction with metal halides to produce the free halogen.

27-14 What is the observed trend in the acid strength of the aqueous hydrogen halides? What are the factors that determine such a trend?

27-15 (a) Name the hydrogen halide that is most stable toward decomposition into the free elements. Explain your answer. (b) Are aqueous solutions of NaCl, NaBr, and NaI acidic, basic, or neutral? Explain your answer.

27-16 (a) Write equations for the reaction of Br_2 with (1) cold NaOH solution, (2) hot NaOH solution. (b) Write an equation for the disproportionation of KClO.

27-17 Write the formulas and names of four different oxides of the halogens.

27-18 Name the following compounds and indicate the oxidation number of the halogen in each case: (a) $KBrO_3$, (b) $NaClO_2$, (c) $HBrO_2$, (d) Cl_2O_7, (e) HIO, (f) $Ba(BrO_3)_2$, (g) $Ca(IO_4)_2$, (h) $Ca(OCl)_2$, (i) HIO_4.

27-19 Write the formulas for the following compounds and indicate the oxidation number of the halogen in each case: (a) hypobromous acid, (b) zinc chlorite, (c) copper(II) chlorate, (d) aluminum periodate, (e) cadmium hypochlorite, (f) bromic acid, (g) iodic acid, (h) periodic acid. (i) Is periodic acid a strong or a weak acid? Explain your answer.

27-20 Justify writing the formula of hydrogen perchlorate as $ClO_3(OH)$ (rather than $HClO_4$), but the perchlorate ion as ClO_4^-.

27-21 A water solution of NaCl does not react with a water solution of NaOCl. But if we add a few drops of diluted sulfuric acid, H_2SO_4, to the solution Cl_2, gas is rapidly evolved. Explain.

27-22 Using the (Latimer) oxidation-reduction diagram for chlorine compounds in 1 M H^+ solution, given on p. 620, (a) complete the following reactions if they can occur spontaneously. (b) Explain *why* they can occur spontaneously. If a reaction cannot occur spontaneously, write N.R.

(1) $Cl^- + HClO \longrightarrow$ (4) $ClO_3^- + ClO_3^- \longrightarrow$
(2) $HClO + ClO_3^- \longrightarrow$ (5) $Cl^- + ClO_3^- \longrightarrow$
(3) $HClO_2 + ClO_4^- \longrightarrow$ (6) $\longrightarrow HClO + ClO_3^-$
(c) Make a few statements generalizing the possible type of oxidation-reduction reactions of (1) Cl^-, (2) ClO_4^-, (3) HClO.

27-23 Using the (Latimer) oxidation-reduction diagram for chlorine compounds in basic solution ($[OH^-] = 1\ M$), given on p. 621, complete the following reactions if they occur spontaneously and explain *why* they occur spontaneously. If a reaction does not occur spontaneously, write N.R.
(1) $Cl^- + ClO^- \longrightarrow$; (2) $Cl_2 + ClO_2^- \longrightarrow$; (3) $Cl_2 + Cl_2 \longrightarrow$.

27-24 Using the following partial oxidation-reduction diagrams, indicate whether disproportionation will take place. If so, write the ion which disproportionates.
(a) $HClO_2 \text{---} {-1.21} \text{---} ClO_3^- \text{---} {-1.19} \text{---} ClO_4^-$
(b) $Cl^- \text{---} {-1.40} \text{---} Cl_2 \text{---} {-0.40} \text{---} ClO^-$
(c) $Fe^0 \text{---} {+0.44} \text{---} Fe^{++} \text{---} {-0.77} \text{---} Fe^{+++}$
(d) $HClO \text{---} {-1.64} \text{---} HClO_2 \text{---} {-1.21} \text{---} ClO_3^-$

27-25 Why is the $E°$ value for the couple $I^- \text{---} {-0.53}\ v \text{---} I_2$ independent of the hydrogen-ion concentration?

THE OXYGEN-SULFUR FAMILY: THE GROUP VIB ELEMENTS

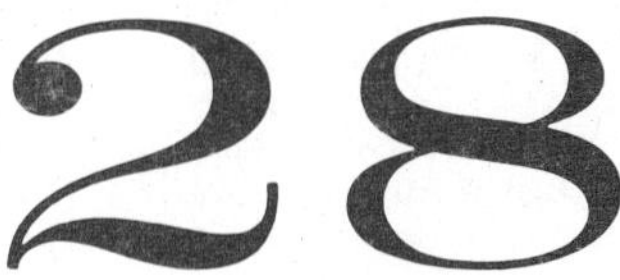

		VIB		He
C	N	O	F	Ne
Si	P	S	Cl	Ar
Ge	As	Se	Br	Kr
Sn	Sb	Te	I	Xe
Pb	Bi	Po	At	Rn

The elements of Group VIB of the Periodic Table—oxygen, O; sulfur, S; selenium, Se; tellurium, Te; and polonium, Po—are closely related to one another, though not to the same extent as are the halogens. In this chapter we shall discuss the resemblances and differences among the members of this family, and we shall study in some detail the chemistry of sulfur. We already discussed the chemistry of oxygen in Chapter 6, and the other elements of this family are not of sufficient importance to warrant lengthy consideration here.

28-1 General Characteristics

The first member of Group VIB, the nonmetal oxygen, is highly electronegative and differs appreciably from the other members in its physical and chemical properties. The next three elements—sulfur, selenium, and tellurium—resemble one another fairly closely, and their properties vary gradually with increasing atomic number. The last member of the group, polonium, is essentially metallic in its properties. As the atomic weight increases in this family—as in all the B families of the Periodic Table—the electropositive character of the element also increases, as shown by the decreasing values of the first ionization energy in Table 28-1. Thus, oxygen and sulfur are distinctly non-metals; selenium and especially tellurium exhibit some metallic properties; and polonium is distinctly a metal.

Table 28-1 lists some of the physical properties of the elements of the oxygen-sulfur family.

Stable State at 25°C, 1 atm	VIB
colorless gas	O
yellow crystals	S
gray solid	Se
gray solid	Te
gray solid	Po

The highly unstable element polonium is omitted, because the values of many of its physical properties have not been measured.

All the atoms of the Group VIB elements have a ns^2np^4 outer electron configuration—that is, two electrons less than the atoms of the noble gases. Therefore, we would expect the Group VIB elements to be present in their ionic compounds as dinegative ions with a noble-gas-like electron configuration. In fact, all atoms of Group VIB, which we represent in general as Y, form dinegative ions, $Y^=$, but their tendency to do so decreases as the added electrons enter higher energy levels in the order: $O > S > Se > Te > Po$. Because of their electron configurations, the atoms of all elements of the oxygen-sulfur family are able to form covalent compounds of the general formula YA_z by sharing at least two—and possibly more—electron pairs with atoms of other elements. In fact, all elements of this family form, for example, dihydrides—H_2O, H_2S, H_2Se, H_2Te—which are similar to one another in electron configuration and in stereochemistry, (they are all bent molecules, like H_2O) even though they differ markedly in their properties. The extent to which these hydrides ionize in water ($H_2Y_{(aq)} \rightleftharpoons H^+_{(aq)} + HY^-_{(aq)}$) depends—as with the hydrogen halides—on the balance of several factors, the main ones being the strength of the H—Y covalent bond, and the hydration energy of the HY^- ion. (The $Y^=$ ion is present only in very small concentration, as we shall discuss.) In this series of hydrides, the major factor is the H—Y bond strength which, as we discussed in Chapter 15, p. 314, decreases as the electronegativity of Y decreases. Thus the degree of dissociation increases markedly, in the order $H_2O < H_2S < H_2Se < H_2Te$, as a result of the marked decrease in electronegativity from oxygen to tellurium.

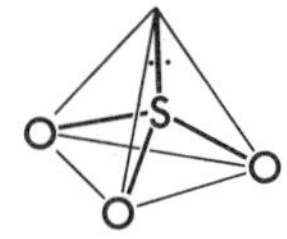

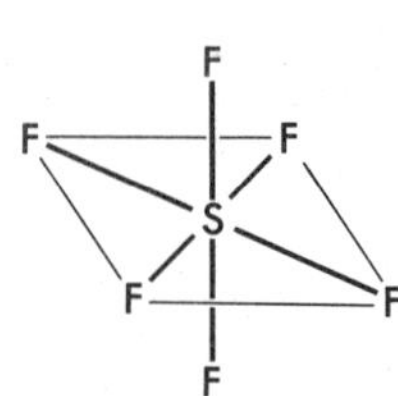

With the exception of oxygen, which in its covalent compounds generally forms only two strong covalent bonds, all other members of the family form covalent compounds in which they share 3, 4, or 6 electron pairs with other atoms. The resulting compounds, YA_3, YA_4, and YA_6, have in all cases the stereochemistry expected on the basis of the number of lone pairs and bond pairs associated with the central Y atom. Thus, the YA_2 compounds with 2 bond pairs and 2 lone pairs are angular (examples are H_2O and SO_2); the YA_3 compounds with 3 bond pairs and 1 lone pair are pyramidal (examples are OH_3^+ and $SO_3^=$); the YA_4 compounds with 4 bond pairs and no lone pairs are tetrahedral ($SO_4^=$ and $SeCl_4$); and the YA_6 compounds with 6 bond pairs and no lone pairs are octahedral (SF_6 and $Te(OH)_6$).

PHYSICAL STATES

At room temperature oxygen is a colorless gas; sulfur is a yellow, odorless solid; selenium, tellurium, and polonium are grayish solids. The differences in the physical state of the elements of this family arise, not as in the halogen family

TABLE 28-1 PROPERTIES OF THE OXYGEN-SULFUR FAMILY (GROUP VIB ELEMENTS)

Element	Outer Electron Config.	Atomic Weight	Atomic Radius A	Ionic Radius A	Melting Point °C	ΔH_{fusion} kcal/mole	Boiling Point °C	$\Delta H_{vaporiz.}$ kcal/mole	First Ioniz. Energy*	Electro-negativity (Pauling)	$\Delta H_{atomiz.}$ kcal/mole
$_8O$	$2s^22p^4$	16.00	0.74	1.40	−218.4	53	−182.96	814	13.62 314	3.5	59.6
$_{16}S$	$3s^23p^4$	32.06	1.04	1.84	112.8 (α) 118.95 (β)	293	444.6	2,520	10.36 239	2.5	69.6
$_{34}Se$	$4s^24p^4$	78.96	1.14	1.98	217.4	1,250	684.8	5,100	9.75 225	2.4	49.7
$_{52}Te$	$5s^25p^4$	127.60	1.37	2.21	452	4,280	1,087	11,900	9.01 208	2.1	44.8

* For each element the top value is in e.v./mole of gaseous atoms, and the lower value in kcal/mole of gaseous atoms.

from the differences in atomic weight and hence in polarizability, but from differences of structure and bonding. At 25°C and 1 atm, oxygen gas is composed of diatomic molecules, O_2. The O_2 molecule has a rather unusual structure. Each oxygen atom shares with its partner oxygen atom a pair of electrons in a σ bonding orbital, as well as two unpaired electrons, each occupying an equal-energy π bonding orbital, and, in addition, each O atom has 2 lone pairs of electrons. Under the same conditions of temperature and pressure, solid sulfur consists of S_8 molecules held together in a crystal lattice by van der Waals forces. Within each S_8 molecule, each S atom is linked to 2 adjacent S atoms by 2 covalent single bonds. The S_8 molecule has a puckered ring structure—that is, not all the S atoms are coplanar, as shown in the diagram. (The S_8 ring is puckered because of the repulsion between the 2 lone pairs on each sulfur atom.) At 25°C and 1 atm, the stable solid form of selenium and of tellurium consists of infinite chains of selenium atoms, Se_n or tellurium atoms, Te_n, each atom linked to its two neighbors by covalent bonding. Because of the lone-pair–lone-pair repulsion on each Se or Te atom, these chains have zig-zag configurations, with a bond angle of about 105° for selenium and one of about 102° for tellurium. It is possible, under special conditions, to obtain an unstable form of sulfur—called plastic sulfur—in which each S atom is joined to two neighbors in infinite zig-zag chains—similar, that is, to the stable forms of selenium and tellurium. Also, it is possible, under appropriate conditions, to obtain selenium as a red (unstable) solid consisting of puckered Se_8 rings, similar to the stable form of sulfur.

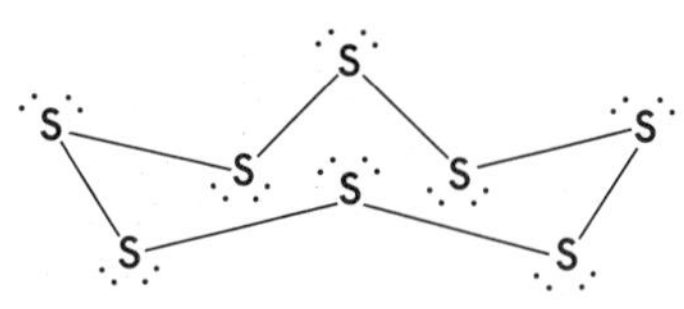

Thus, there is a gradual variation in the structure of the Group VIB elements at ordinary temperature: Oxygen as stable O_2 molecules (in the unstable form, ozone, O_3, 3 atoms of oxygen are joined together, p. 86); sulfur as stable S_8 molecules and unstable S_n chains; selenium as stable Se_n chains and unstable Se_8 molecules; and tellurium only as chains, Te_n. This variation in structure indicates that for the elements of Group VIB, the tendency of like atoms to form covalent bonds with one another (catenation) increases with increasing atomic number. So oxygen has the least, and tellurium the greatest tendency toward catenation. It is important to keep this concept in mind, since it helps us understand some differences in the chemistries of sulfur and oxygen—for example, why there are no oxygen species corresponding to the polysulfides, $S_n^{=}$, and the thiosulfate ion, $S_2O_3^{=}$.

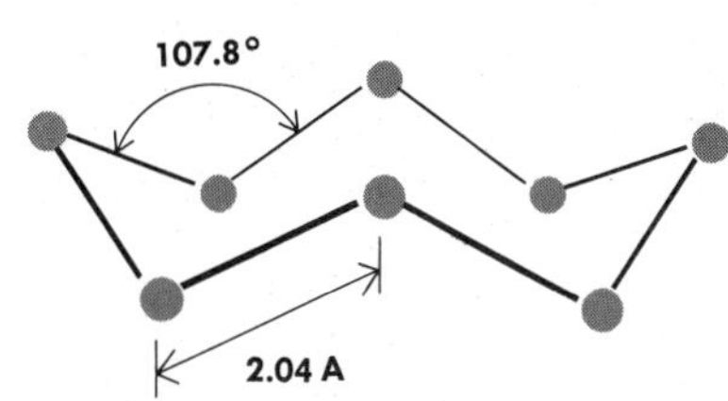

PHYSICAL STATES OF SULFUR

Sulfur can exist as a number of different forms in the solid, liquid, and gaseous states.

SOLID SULFUR. Several crystalline modifications exist. The crystalline rhombic form, which is stable at room temperature, is yellow and has a density of 2.07 g/cm³. If a sample of this rhombic sulfur is heated and maintained at a temperature a little less than 100°C, the rhombic crystals change to a monoclinic form. At room temperature monoclinic sulfur is pale yellow and has a density of 1.96 g/cm³. Both rhombic and monoclinic sulfur are composed of S_8 ring molecules, but these are arranged in different patterns in the crystal lattice. The transition from the rhombic form to the monoclinic form occurs at 95.5°C:

$$S_{(\text{rhombic})} \xrightleftharpoons{95.5^\circ\text{C}} S_{(\text{monoclinic})} \qquad \Delta H = +0.76 \text{ kcal/mole}$$

The fact that heat is absorbed in this transition indicates that the monoclinic form has the higher energy. At 95.5°C the rhombic and monoclinic forms are in equilibrium, and hence have the same vapor pressure and the same solubility in a given solvent. The *rate* of transition from one form to the other is so slow that monoclinic sulfur can exist at a temperature below 95.5°C for several days, but will eventually change into the rhombic form. Similarly, rhombic sulfur can exist above 95.5°C for some time before it changes completely into the monoclinic form. When a sample of molten sulfur (m.p. of sulfur = 112.8°C) solidifies at any temperature above 95.5°C, beautiful needle-shaped crystals of the monoclinic sulfur are formed. But if the molten sulfur is undercooled and then permitted to solidify below 95.5°C, crystals of rhombic sulfur appear. Both rhombic and monoclinic sulfur are insoluble in water but soluble in carbon disulfide, CS_2; in sulfur monochloride, S_2Cl_2, and in certain organic solvents such as benzene. At room temperature, however, the monoclinic form is about 1.3 times more soluble in any solvent than the rhombic form; about 50 g of rhombic sulfur will dissolve in 100 g of CS_2 at room temperature. If we dissolve a sample of either form of sulfur in CS_2, and then evaporate the solvent (b.p. of CS_2 = 46.3°C at 1 atm), crystals of rhombic sulfur will be deposited. In solvents such as carbon disulfide or benzene, sulfur is present as solvated S_8 ring molecules:

$$S_{8(\text{rhombic crystals})} + \text{solvent} \longrightarrow S_{8(\text{solvated})} \qquad \Delta H = +5.2 \text{ kcal/mole } S_8$$

LIQUID SULFUR. If any form of solid sulfur is heated slightly above the melting point of the monoclinic form, 119°C, a clear, yellow, mobile liquid results. Above 160°C, liquid sulfur consists chiefly of long, open-ended zig-zag chain molecules. If this liquid sulfur is suddenly chilled—by pouring it into cold water, for example—a soft, sticky, rubber-like material forms, which is called *plastic sulfur.* This material contains long chains of sulfur atoms, coiled up as shown schematically in the accompanying figure. The elasticity of this form of sulfur, like the elasticity of rubber, results from the uncoiling of the chains under tension and their recoiling when the tension is released. Plastic sulfur, which is not stable at room temperature, slowly changes to granular, brittle rhombic crystals (S_8 ring molecules).

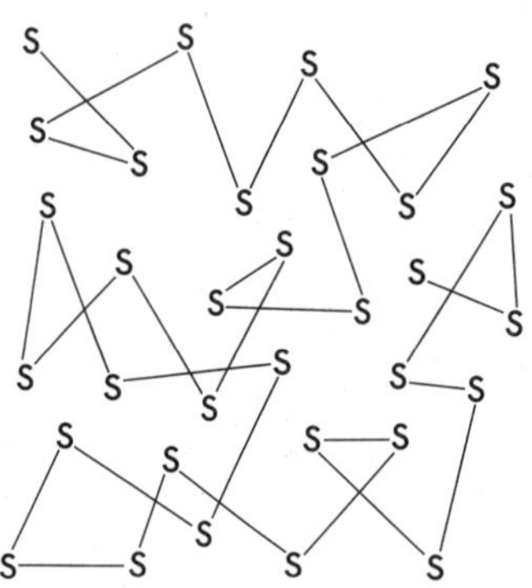

If the temperature of liquid sulfur is increased further, the yellow liquid gradually darkens; above 160°C its mobility decreases, until at about 200°C it becomes a gummy, brown, semi-solid substance. If we raise the temperature well above 200°C, the sulfur again increases in fluidity, until at the boiling point, 444.6°C, it is an almost-black, mobile liquid. An explanation of these changes is that the sulfur atoms may join together in several different geometric arrangements.

VAPOR STATE. At the boiling point, 444.6°C, liquid sulfur is composed of molecules, S_n, in both the cyclic ring form and in the chain form. At the boiling point, the liquid is in equilibrium with sulfur vapor, which contains mostly cyclic S_8 molecules and is red in color. As the temperature of the vapor is increased above the boiling point, the S_8 molecules dissociate into S_2 molecules, and the color of the vapor gradually changes to yellow. At very high temperatures, about 2,000°C, the S_2 molecules dissociate to some extent into the gaseous monoatomic atoms:

$$S_{2(g)} \xrightleftharpoons{2{,}000^\circ\text{C}} 2\,S_{(g)} \qquad \Delta H = +103 \text{ kcal/mole } S_2$$

28-2 Occurrence in Nature

Sulfur occurs in nature in both the free state and the combined state. Much of the world's sulfur supply comes from deposits of native sulfur. Very large quantities of the element are also obtained from the processing of petroleum and natural gases, which always contain sulfur compounds as impurities. Sulfur in the combined state occurs in the following common sulfide minerals: galena, PbS; pyrite, FeS_2; chalcopyrite, $CuFeS_2$; cinnabar, HgS; and argentite, Ag_2S. Deposits of gypsum, $CaSO_4 \cdot 2\ H_2O$, are also of economic importance. Sulfur also occurs in the combined state in many organic substances.

Selenium and tellurium are usually found in the -2 oxidation state, in the form of selenides and tellurides, which are often very similar to the corresponding sulfides.

SULFUR MINING

The deposits of sulfur in Texas and Louisiana lie 100 to 2,000 feet below the surface of the earth, sealed beneath layers of clay and limestone. To extract the mineral, a shaft is drilled and three concentric pipes are lowered into the deposit. The outer pipe carries down superheated steam at about 160°C to melt the sulfur. Simultaneously, hot air under a pressure of about 35 atm is passed down through the innermost pipe. The air mixes with the molten sulfur and forces a frothy mixture of steam, water, sulfur, and air up through the space between the outer and middle pipes to the surface. This mixture, which is about 95 per cent sulfur, is collected in vats, where the sulfur gradually solidifies.

THE PREPARATION OF SULFUR. Naturally occurring impure sulfure can be purified by sublimation, since solid sulfur is easily sublimed and the sulfur vapor is easily condensed. Sulfur prepared in this manner is known as "flowers of sulfur." The element can also be prepared by reduction of the vast quantities of sulfur dioxide, SO_2, that are formed in the industrial production of metals from their sulfides—CuS and Zns, for example. The SO_2 is reduced to elemental sulfur by passing it over white-hot coke at 1,100°C. Once started, this process may be run continuously without supplying energy because the reaction is exothermic:

$$SO_2 + C \longrightarrow CO_2 + S \qquad \Delta H = \text{negative value}$$

28-3 The Chemical Properties of Sulfur

The principal oxidation states of sulfur are even-numbered: -2, 0, $+4$, and $+6$; some important examples are listed in Table 28-2. A knowledge of the oxidation states of sulfur is helpful in remembering the possible chemical reactions of its compounds. For example, in any chemical reaction of the $S^=$ ion, the oxidation number

TABLE 28-2 FORMULAS AND NAMES OF SOME IMPORTANT SULFUR COMPOUNDS

Oxidation State			
-2	0	$+4$	$+6$
H_2S (Hydrogen sulfide)	S_8 (Sulfur) (S_6,S_4,S_2,S)	SO_2 (Sulfur dioxide)	SO_3 (Sulfur trioxide)
HS^- (Hydrogen sulfide ion)		$SO_3^=$ (Sulfite ion)	$SO_4^=$ (Sulfate ion)
$S^=$ (Sulfide ion)		HSO_3^- (Hydrogen sulfite ion)	HSO_4^- (Hydrogen sulfate ion)
		H_2SO_3 (Sulfurous acid)	H_2SO_4 (Sulfuric acid)

of sulfur must either remain unchanged or increase. That is, the $S^=$ can be oxidized, but not reduced. On the other hand, in any given chemical reaction of the $SO_4^=$ ion, the oxidation number of sulfur must either remain unchanged or *decrease.* That is, the $SO_4^=$ can be reduced, but it cannot be oxidized. Elemental sulfur, S_8, and the sulfur compounds with intermediate oxidation states—SO_2, H_2SO_3, and HSO_3^-, for example—can undergo a change in oxidation number to *either* a lower or a higher state—that is, they can be either reduced, or oxidized, or both, depending on the conditions.

OXIDATION STATE OF −2

PREPARATION OF HYDROGEN SULFIDE, H_2S. The best way to prepare hydrogen sulfide gas in the laboratory is through the action of non-oxidizing acids, such as HCl, on a solid, insoluble metal sulfide such as FeS:

$$FeS_{(s)} + 2\ HCl_{(aq)} \longrightarrow H_2S_{(g)} + FeCl_{2(aq)}$$

The H_2S obtained by this method often contains some H_2, because the sulfide has metallic Fe impurities. The gases H_2Se and H_2Te may be prepared in the same way from a metal selenide and telluride, respectively. Pure H_2S can be prepared by direct synthesis from its elements at elevated temperatures: $H_{2(g)} + S_{(g)} \rightleftharpoons H_2S_{(g)}$. When this gaseous equilibrium mixture is cooled below −60°C, H_2S condenses as a liquid and can be separated from both the unreacted solid sulfur and the unreacted gaseous H_2. The liquid H_2S can then be vaporized to yield a pure product. Similarly, Se will react directly with H_2 at high temperatures to form H_2Se. The direct synthesis of H_2Te has not been reported.

PROPERTIES OF H_2S. Hydrogen sulfide is a colorless, malodorous gas (b.p. = −61.80°C); in fact, it is what gives rotten eggs their offensive smell. This gas is very poisonous and great caution should be exercised in using it in the laboratory. Even small concentrations may be enough to paralyze the nerve centers that control respiration. The concentration of H_2S in the air necessary to produce a detectable odor is extremely small and such low concentrations are not very toxic. But since the gas may gradually dull the sense of smell, dangerous or even fatal concentrations sometimes build up insidiously. Gaseous H_2S is stable at room temperature; it is slightly soluble in water, but it may be completely expelled by boiling the soution. Hydrogen sulfide is often stored and shipped in liquid form in steel cylinders under pressure.

Hydrogen sulfide, H_2S, has an electron configuration and stereochemistry similar to that of water (hydrogen oxide), H_2O. The two hydrogen atoms are covalently bonded to the central sulfur atom with an H—S—H bond angle of 92° (compare the H—O—H bond angle of 105°). Because of the lower electronegativity of the S atom as compared with the O atom, the H_2S molecules are much less polar than the H_2O molecules, and they exert on one another only weak van der Waals forces instead of the relatively strong electrostatic forces that produce the hydrogen bonding in water. As we discussed in Chapter 11, p. 197, it is this difference in the strength of the intermolecular bonds that accounts for the marked differences in some of the physical properties of H_2O and H_2S, for example, their melting and boiling points and their heats of fusion and vaporization (see Table 28-3).

TABLE 28-3 SOME PROPERTIES OF THE HYDRIDES OF THE GROUP VIB ELEMENTS

Hydride	M.P., °C	$\Delta H_{fus.}$ kcal/mole	B.P., °C	$\Delta H_{vaporiz.}$ kcal/mole	ΔH°_{form} kcal/mole	ΔG°_{form} kcal/mole
H_2O	0.00	+1.44	100.00	+98.2	−68.4	−56.7
H_2S	−85.5	+0.59	−60.80	+4.46	−4.8	−7.9
H_2Se	−64.0	+1.57	−42.0	+4.75	+20.5	+17.1
H_2Te	−51.0	—	−1.8	+5.55	+36.9	+33.1

CHEMICAL REACTIONS OF H_2S AND OF THE HS^- AND $S^=$ IONS. At temperatures near 250°C, hydrogen sulfide gas burns with a blue flame in the presence of an excess of oxygen to form sulfur dioxide and water:

$$2\ H_2S_{(g)} + 3\ O_{2(g)} \longrightarrow 2\ SO_{2(g)} + 2\ H_2O_{(g)}$$

When H_2S is burned in a limited amount of oxygen, however, the oxidation products are sulfur and water:

$$2\ H_2S_{(g)} + O_{2(g)} \longrightarrow 2\ S_{(g)} + 2\ H_2O_{(g)}$$

The gaseous sulfur thus formed will condense on any cool object that is placed near the flame.

AQUEOUS SOLUTIONS OF H_2S. Gaseous H_2S is slightly soluble in water, forming a saturated solution which is approximately 0.1 *M* at room temperature and 1 atm pressure. In aqueous solution, H_2S behaves like an extremely weak diabasic acid. The first step in the ionization process produces hydrated hydrogen ions, H^+, and hydrated hydrogen sulfide ions, HS^-:

$$H_2S \rightleftharpoons H^+ + HS^- \qquad K_1 = \frac{[H^+]^1 \times [HS^-]^1}{[H_2S]^1} = 9 \times 10^{-8}\ \text{mole/l.}$$

A very small number of these HS^- ions, in turn, ionize further to form additional hydrated H^+ ions and hydrated $S^=$ ions:

$$HS^- \rightleftharpoons H^+ + S^= \qquad K_2 = \frac{[H^+]^1 \times [S^=]^1}{[HS^-]^1} = 1.2 \times 10^{-15}\ \text{mole/l.}$$

As the values of the equilibrium constant for the first and second ionization of H_2S indicate, a liter of a saturated solution of H_2S in water at room temperature and 1 atm pressure of H_2S (which is approximately 0.1 *M* in total H_2S) contains slightly less than 0.1 mole of H_2S molecules, approximately 1×10^{-4} mole of H^+ ions, 1×10^{-4} mole of HS^- ions, and 1×10^{-15} mole of $S^=$ ions. Thus, a solution of H_2S in water consists essentially of H_2S molecules in equilibrium with some H^+ ions and HS^- ions, (at approximately equal concentrations) and few $S^=$ ions. The two ionization steps can be combined to give the total ionization equation of H_2S:

$$H_2S \rightleftharpoons 2\ H^+ + S^= \qquad K_3 = \frac{[H^+]^2 \times [S^=]^1}{[H_2S]^1} = 1.1 \times 10^{-22}\ (\text{mole/l.})^2$$

In a saturated H_2S solution at 25°C and 1 atm, the concentration of H_2S molecules—about 0.1 *M*—remains constant at this value as long as the solution is in equilibrium with H_2S gas. Thus $[H_2S]$ may be taken as 0.1 mole/l., and from the equilibrium expression K_3 we obtain:

$$K_3 = \frac{[H^+]^2 \times [S^=]}{[H_2S]} = \frac{[H^+]^2 \times [S^=]}{[0.1]} = 1.1 \times 10^{-22}\ (\text{mole/l.})^2$$

and

$$[H^+]^2 \times [S^=] = 1.1 \times 10^{-23}\ (\text{mole/l.})$$

As this expression tells us, the $S^=$ ion concentration of the solution can be adjusted by regulating the H^+ ion concentration. For example, the addition of H^+ ions from a strong acid to a saturated solution of H_2S markedly lowers the concentrations of both the $S^=$ ion and the HS^- ion (common-ion effect). And since undissociated H_2S molecules are produced in the reaction, and the original solution was already saturated with H_2S molecules, some hydrogen sulfide is evolved as a gas. Conversely, the removal of H^+ ions by the addition of a base (OH^- ions) appreciably increases the concentration of both the HS^- and $S^=$ ions, and hence additional H_2S gas can now dissolve.

HYDROLYSIS OF SOLUBLE METAL SULFIDES. The alkali and alkaline-earth metal ions form water-soluble ionic sulfides. When dissolved in water, these sulfides first give hydrated metal ions and hydrated $S^=$ ions. But the $S^=$ ion is a good proton acceptor (a good Bronsted base, p. 452) and, in fact, we have seen above that in aqueous solution at ordinary temperature the product $[H^+]^2 \times [S^=]$ cannot exceed the value of about 10^{-23}. Hence the hydrated $S^=$ ions formed in dissolving the metal sulfides react with the H^+ ions of water ($[H^+] \cong 10^{-7}$) to form chiefly HS^- ions. This reaction, which ties up the H^+ ions present in water, upsets the originally existing balance between $[H^+]$ and $[OH^-]$, and the solution becomes basic. Thus, all soluble metal sulfides hydrolyze in water to form HS^-, OH^-, and of course hydrated M^{+n} metal ions (we discussed hydrolysis in general in Chapter 20). The soluble sulfides of metal ions that form insoluble hydroxides, such as Al^{+++}, Cr^{+++}, and Mg^{++}, completely hydrolyze in water, precipitating the hydroxides and evolving H_2S gas. Here is the equation for the reaction of Al_2S_3 with water:

$$Al_2S_{3(s)} + 6\ H_2O_{(l)} \longrightarrow 2\ Al(OH)_{3(s)} + 3\ H_2S_{(g)}$$

H_2S **AS A PRECIPITATING AGENT.** Many metal ions form sulfides that are insoluble in varying degrees, as is indicated by their solubility products, K_{sp}. Therefore we can separate two different metal ions from the same solution by first adjusting conditions so that only one metal sulfide precipitates, filtering off this precipitate, and then readjusting conditions so that the other metal sulfide precipitates.

Suppose we have a solution containing Cu^{++} and Zn^{++} ions in approximately equal concentrations and that we wish to separate them. Both copper(II) sulfide and zinc(II) sulfide are only slightly soluble in water, but CuS ($K_{sp} = 1 \times 10^{-48}$) is much less soluble than ZnS ($K_{sp} = 8 \times 10^{-25}$). If we control the $S^=$ ion concentration of the solution so that the $[M^{++}] \times [S^=]$ product is greater than the K_{sp} for CuS but less than the K_{sp} for ZnS, then only CuS will precipitate.

As we saw before, we can vary the $S^=$ concentration in a water solution of hydrogen sulfide simply by altering the acidity (the H^+ ion concentration) of the solution. If the H^+ concentration is high (we can make it so by adding a strong acid, such as HCl), the concentration of $S^=$ will be extremely low. Experiments have shown that in a saturated solution of H_2S (at 25°C and 1 atm $H_2S_{(g)}$ pressure) also containing 0.3 mole/l. of HCl, the $S^=$ ion concentration is just high enough to precipitate a sulfide such as CuS with a very small K_{sp}, whereas the $[S^=]$ is too low to precipitate a sulfide such as ZnS with a higher K_{sp}. Hence, if we add to the solution containing Cu^{++} ions and Zn^{++} ions enough HCl solution to make it 0.3 *M* in H^+ ions, and then we saturate it with H_2S gas at 1 atm, only CuS will precipitate. By filtering the mixture we can then separate the Zn^{++} ions still in solution from the insoluble CuS.

TEST FOR H_2S. The characteristic reaction of H_2S with metal ions is commonly used as a test for its presence. For example, when H_2S gas is passed over a strip of filter paper impregnated with white $Pb(CH_3COO)_2$, black PbS forms. Also, the gas H_2S may be readily detected by its odor.

REDUCING PROPERTIES OF H_2S. In acid solutions H_2S is a powerful reductant since its oxidation to elemental sulfur has an oxidation potential only slightly more negative than that of the H_2, H^+ couple.

$$H_2S = S + 2\ H^+ + 2\ e^- \qquad E^\circ = -0.140$$

Consequently, H_2S can be oxidized by a number of oxidants; I_2 and the Fe^{+++} ion, for example, oxidize H_2S to S, quantitatively (and rapidly). And of course H_2S is oxidized by such strong oxidants as concentrated nitric acid, HNO_3, and the permanganate ion, MnO_4^-, in acid solution. Even oxygen from the air dissolved in the solution will oxidize H_2S to S. Although the sulfur atom of H_2S, which has an oxidation number of -2, is a good reductant, the hydrogen atoms, which have an oxidation number of $+1$, can occasionally act as oxidants toward metals. For example, the small quantities of H_2S in the air will tarnish the surface of metallic silver (and other metals).

$$2\ Ag_{(s)} + H_2S_{(g)} \longrightarrow Ag_2S_{(s)} + H_{2(g)}$$

Notice that in this reaction the oxidation state of the sulfur remains unchanged, whereas the oxidation state of the hydrogen decreases from +1 to 0, and that of silver increases from 0 to +1. In this respect, the reaction is similar to that of an electropositive metal, such as zinc, with an acid such as HCl. We could have predicted that H_2S gas has the capacity to react spontaneously with metallic silver to form H_2 gas and solid silver sulfide, AgS, from the standard free energy change of the reaction ($\Delta G^\circ_{reaction}$). This can be calculated, as outlined in Chapter 17.

$$2\ Ag_{(s)} + H_2S_{(g)} \longrightarrow Ag_2S_{(s)} + H_{2(g)}$$

$$\Delta G^\circ_{form} = 0 \quad -7.9 \quad -9.6 \quad 0 \quad \text{(kcal/mole)}$$

$$\Delta G^\circ_{reaction} = \Delta G^\circ_{form} \text{ of products} - \Delta G^\circ_{form} \text{ of reactants}$$

$$\Delta G^\circ_{reaction} = -9.6 - (-7.9) = -1.7 \text{ kcal/mole-eqn}$$

Thus when each of the reactants and products is in its standard state at 25°C and 1 atm, the reaction can take place spontaneously because the free energy of the system decreases as the reaction proceeds ($\Delta G^\circ_{reaction}$ is negative).

FORMATION OF POLYSULFIDES. When elemental sulfur is boiled with a solution of a soluble sulfide, such as the sulfides of the alkali metals or the alkaine-earth metals, polysulfide ions are formed. The resulting solutions are yellow to dark red in color. The composition of the polysulfide ions formed, $S_2^=$, $S_3^=$ . . . $S_n^=$, depends on the concentration of the soluble sulfide and the amount of sulfur added:

Equilibrium present among all ions:

$$S + S^= \rightleftharpoons S_2^= \quad \text{(disulfide ion)}$$

$$2\ S + S^= \rightleftharpoons S_3^= \quad \text{(trisulfide ion)}$$

$$3\ S + S^= \rightleftharpoons S_4^= \quad \text{(tetrasulfide ion)}$$

$$nS + S^= \rightleftharpoons S^=_{(n+1)} \quad ((n+1) \text{ sulfide ion})$$

Compositions up to $n = 5$ are definitely known.

As we learned earlier, sulfur atoms have a strong tendency to form covalent links among themselves (catenation). It is the relatively high stability of the sulfur-to-sulfur links that is responsible for the existence of polysulfides:

$$[:\ddot{S}:\ddot{S}:]^= \qquad [S_3]^= \qquad [S_4]^=$$

All polysulfides decompose in acid solutions to reform $S^=$ ion—or more appropriately, HS^- ions and H_2S molecules—together with elemental sulfur.

OXIDATION STATE OF +4

In the +4 oxidation state sulfur forms the important compounds sulfur dioxide, SO_2, sulfurous acid, H_2SO_3, and the sulfites.

PREPARATION OF SO_2. Sulfur dioxide is usually obtained by burning sulfur in air or in oxygen; the resulting gas in both cases contains a certain amount (3.6 per cent) of SO_3. If the sulfur is burned in air, the resulting gas also contains N_2 and the other gases commonly present in air.

Sulfur dioxide is also obtained as a by-product of the oxidation of metal sulfides at high temperatures, a step in preparing metals from their ores. The equation for this type of reaction, with zinc blende, ZnS, as an example of the ore, is:

$$2\ ZnS_{(s)} + 3\ O_{2(g)} \longrightarrow 2\ SO_{2(g)} + 2\ ZnO_{(s)}$$

In the laboratory SO_2 can be prepared by adding a dilute solution of a strong acid, such as H_2SO_4, or HCl, drop by drop, to a solution of an alkali-metal hydrogen sulfite, $MHSO_3$, or an alkali-metal sulfite, M_2SO_3:

$$H_2SO_{4(l)} + 2\ NaHSO_{3(aq)} \longrightarrow 2\ SO_{2(g)} + Na_2SO_{4(aq)} + 2\ H_2O_{(l)}$$

$$2\ HCl_{(aq)} + Na_2SO_{3(aq)} \longrightarrow SO_{2(g)} + 2\ NaCl_{(aq)} + H_2O_{(l)}$$

The SO_2 gas that is liberated can be dried by bubbling it through concentrated H_2SO_4. Relatively pure SO_2 is also prepared by the oxidation of copper metal with hot concentrated H_2SO_4, as will be discussed later.

PROPERTIES OF SO_2. SO_2 is a colorless gas that is extremely stable toward decomposition, as is indicated by the high values of its standard enthalpy and standard free energy of formation:

$$S_{(g)} + O_{2(g)} \longrightarrow SO_{2(g)} \quad \begin{cases} \Delta H^\circ_{form} = -71.0 \text{ kcal/mole} \\ \Delta G^\circ_{form} = -71.8 \text{ kcal/mole} \end{cases}$$

Temperatures of over 2,000°C are required to bring about any detectable decomposition of SO_2 into its elements. In the vapor state sulfur dioxide exists as individual SO_2 molecules, which have an angular shape, with an O—S—O angle of 119.5°. This bond angle is almost identical in value to that observed for the bond angles (120°) of trigonal planar molecules. Two of the contributing electronic structures of SO_2, I and II, are shown in the margin. In these structures the S atom forms a σ bond with each of the two O atoms. In addition, the S atom forms a resonating π bond, and has a lone electron pair. Thus, on the basis of our rules for the stereochemistry of compounds, we would indeed expect the SO_2 molecule to be angular with a 120° bond angle.

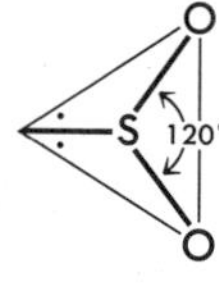

Sulfur dioxide gas is a little more than twice as dense as air ($\frac{64}{29}$). It has a characteristic choking odor and can easily be liquefied into a colorless heavy liquid at room temperature by a pressure of about 5 atm. The ease with which it can be liquefied makes it especially useful as a refrigerant. It is shipped and stored in the liquid state in metal cylinders.

USES OF SO_2. Large quantities of SO_2 are used to produce SO_3 for the preparation of sulfuric acid. It is also used as an effective yet mild bleaching agent for paper, straw, wool, and silk. The gas is often used as a fumigant to destroy bacteria and molds. Both its bleaching action and its bactericidal action are useful in the preservation of dried fruits.

SULFUROUS ACID. Sulfur dioxide gas readily dissolves in water to form a solution of sulfurous acid, H_2SO_3, a weak, dibasic acid. Thus, SO_2 is the anhydride of H_2SO_3. If SO_2 gas at 1 atm pressure and room temperature is passed into water to form sulfurous acid, the resulting saturated solution is approximately 1.4 *M*. In a water solution of sulfurous acid the following equilibria exist:

$$SO_{2(aq)} + H_2O_{(l)} \rightleftharpoons H_2SO_{3(aq)} \rightleftharpoons H^+_{(aq)} + HSO^-_{3(aq)}$$
$$\downarrow\uparrow$$
$$H^+_{(aq)} + SO^=_{3(aq)}$$

Thus, some hydrated SO_2 is present at equilibrium in the solution of H_2SO_3. Because of this equilibrium, solutions of H_2SO_3 are unstable at room temperature in an open container, and gradually evolve gaseous SO_2. As always for polybasic acids, the second ionization of H_2SO_3 occurs to a far smaller extent than the first ionization, so the concentration of $SO_3^=$ ions is much smaller than the concentration of HSO_3^- ions. The ionization constants, K_1 and K_2, for the two successive ionization reactions of sulfurous acids are:

$$H_2SO_3 \rightleftharpoons H^+ + HSO_3^- \qquad K_1 = \frac{[H^+] \times [HSO_3^-]}{[H_2SO_3]} = 1.25 \times 10^{-2} \text{ mole/l.}$$

$$HSO_3^- \rightleftharpoons H^+ + SO_3^= \qquad K_2 = \frac{[H^+] \times [SO_3^=]}{[HSO_3^-]} = 5.6 \times 10^{-8} \text{ mole/l.}$$

Thus, H_2SO_3 ($K_1 = 1.25 \times 10^{-2}$ mole/l.) is a stronger acid than either CH_3COOH ($K = 1.8 \times 10^{-5}$ mole/l.) or H_2CO_3 ($K_1 = 4.3 \times 10^{-7}$ mole/l.). It is possible to prepare either the hydrogen sulfite salts (acid salts) or the normal sulfites of alkali-metal ions by passing the appropriate amount of SO_2 into an aqueous solution of an alkali-metal carbonate (or hydroxide):

$$K_2CO_3 + 2\ SO_2 + H_2O \longrightarrow 2\ KHSO_3 + CO_2$$
$$K_2CO_3 + SO_2 \longrightarrow K_2SO_3 + CO_2$$

OXIDIZING-REDUCING PROPERTIES OF SULFUROUS ACID AND SULFITES. Although solutions of sulfur dioxide and of sulfites may, in principle, act both as oxidants and as reductants, most of the useful reactions of these sulfur componds are based on their reducing action. The oxidation-potential value of the sulfite-sulfate couple is -0.17 v:

$$H_2SO_3 + H_2O = SO_4^{=} + 4\ H^+ + 2\ e^- \qquad E° = -0.17\ \text{v}$$

This means that oxidants with an $E°$ value more negative than -0.17 can oxidize the sulfite ion to the sulfate ion. Examples are the slow oxidation of sulfurous acid and sulfite solutions by oxygen from the air (H_2O,O_2 couple, $E° = -1.23$ v):

$$2\ H_2SO_3 + O_2 \longrightarrow 2\ H_2SO_4$$

and the reactions with chlorine gas (Cl^-,Cl_2 couple, $E° = -1.40$ v) and with permanganate (Mn^{++},MnO_4^- couple, $E° = -1.51$ v) in acid solution:

$$Cl_2 + H_2SO_3 + H_2O \longrightarrow H_2SO_4 + 2\ HCl$$
$$2\ KMnO_4 + 5\ H_2SO_3 \longrightarrow 2\ H_2SO_4 + 2\ MnSO_4 + K_2SO_4 + 3\ H_2O$$

An example of a reaction in which sulfurous acid acts as an oxidant is the oxidation of H_2S to elemental sulfur (H_2S,S couple, $E° = +0.14$ v):

$$H_2\overset{+4}{S}O_3 + 2\ H_2\overset{-2}{S} \longrightarrow 3\ \overset{0}{S} + 3\ H_2O$$

OXIDATION STATE OF +6

PREPARATION OF SULFUR TRIOXIDE, SO_3. The oxidation of SO_2 to SO_3 with oxygen of the air at ordinary temperature and pressure is a thermodynamically favorable reaction because the large negative enthalpy term (favorable to spontaneity) more than outweighs the negative entropy term (unfavorable to spontaneity).

$$SO_{2(g)} + \tfrac{1}{2}\ O_{2(g)} \longrightarrow SO_{3(g)} \quad \text{at } 25°\text{C, 1 atm} \begin{cases} \Delta H = -23.4\ \text{kcal/mole-eqn} \\ \Delta S = -24.7\ \text{cal/deg} \times \text{mole-eqn} \\ \Delta G = -16.7\ \text{kcal/mole-eqn} \end{cases}$$

The entropy of the system decreases because the number of gas molecules decreases. In the presence of a catalyst such as finely divided platinum, the reaction is rapid, and achieves an equilibrium that strongly favors the formation of SO_3. But the spontaneous reaction only takes place very slowly because of a very high activation energy. The oxidation of SO_2 to SO_3 is important from a practical viewpoint, for it is the first step in the most common industrial process for the preparation of sulfuric acid. At low temperatures, the equilibrium *position* of $SO_{2(g)} + \frac{1}{2}\ O_{2(g)} \rightleftharpoons SO_{3(g)}$, is far to the right—that is to say, it is very favorable to the production of SO_3, but the *rate* at which the equilibrium is attained is very slow. As the temperature is increased, the *rate* of reaction is greatly increased, but at the same time the position of the *equilibrium* is displaced toward the left—that is, it becomes less and less favorable to the production of SO_3, because the unfavorable $T\,\Delta S$ term increases proportionally to the absolute temperature, T. In order to bring about the best possible yield of SO_3 within a reasonable length of time, in the commercial process a mixture of SO_2 and air is passed over a solid catalyst—commonly divanadium pentoxide, V_2O_5, or finely divided platinum—at temperatures of 400–500°C. The SO_2 used in this process must be very pure, because even small amounts of impurities, especially compounds of arsenic, such as As_2O_3, render the catalyst ineffective. In practice, although V_2O_5 is not as efficient, it is very much cheaper and less easily poisoned than platinum and so is almost exclusively used as the catalyst.

STRUCTURE OF SO_3. At temperatures higher than ordinary, sulfur trioxide is a gas consisting of SO_3 molecules. Below 30° it condenses to a colorless solid—more rapidly if traces of moisture are present. The gaseous SO_3 molecule has a trigonal planar stereochemistry, with 120° O—S—O bond angles. As for the SO_2 molecule, this stereochemistry is explained on the basis of the 3 equivalent contributing electronic structures (I, II, III) shown in the margin. Each of the S—O bonds in SO_3 has one-third of a double-($\sigma + \pi$) bond character. In the solid state, the individual SO_3 molecules bind together through oxygen bridges to form either trimers, in the form of puckered rings, $(SO_3)_3$, or polymers, in the form of infinite zig-zag chains, $(SO_3)_n$. The solid consisting of ring, $(SO_3)_3$, molecules has different properties (for example, a lower vaporization temperature) than the solid consisting of chains, $(SO_3)_n$. In both solid forms, each S atom is bonded to four O atoms in a tetrahedral arrangement: the S atom of each SO_3 unit acts as an electron-pair acceptor and an O atom of each SO_3 unit acts as an electron-pair donor.

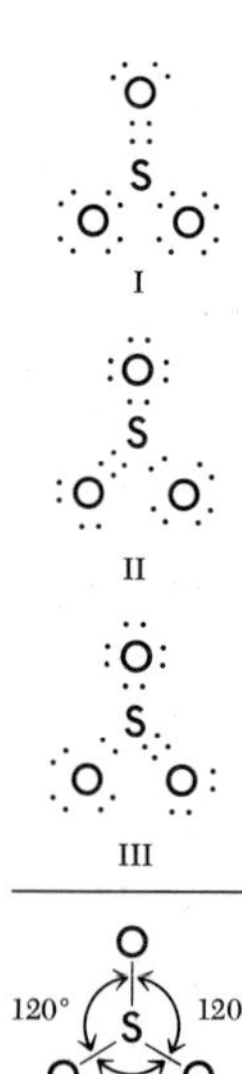

REACTIONS OF SO_3. Sulfur trioxide is an acidic oxide. It reacts readily with basic oxides to form sulfates. The electron-dot representation of the reaction of SO_3 with the basic oxide BaO follows:

$$Ba^{++}:\ddot{O}:^{=} + SO_3 \longrightarrow Ba^{++} + [SO_4]^{=}$$

In this reaction, the oxide ion acts as an electron-pair donor, and the sulfur atom acts as an electron-pair acceptor.

Sulfur trioxide reacts readily with the water vapor in the air to form "white fumes" that consist of tiny droplets of sulfuric acid solution (compare the behavior of gaseous hydrogen halides, p. 611). With liquid water, SO_3 reacts very violently, almost explosively, because the heat involved in the reaction, $SO_3 + H_2O \longrightarrow H_2SO_4$, is so large that it causes the vaporization of some of the water. For this reason it is not convenient to absorb SO_3 gas directly into water. Rather, SO_3 is passed into a solution of concentrated H_2SO_4, where it reacts smoothly with the small quantity of water present to form 100 per cent H_2SO_4. If an excess of SO_3 is passed through the concentrated sulfuric acid, a solution of SO_3 in 100 per cent H_2SO_4 is obtained—the so-called "fuming sulfuric acid."

THE INDUSTRIAL PREPARATION OF SULFURIC ACID, H_2SO_4

Two widely used industrial processes for the preparation of sulfuric acid, H_2SO_4, are the *contact process* and the *lead-chamber process*.

CONTACT PROCESS. The first step in the contact process involves the catalytic oxidation of SO_2 with O_2 to form SO_3. As discussed before, these gases react when they come into contact on the surface of a solid catalyst (either platinum, or vanadium(V) oxide), hence the name "contact" process. The gaseous SO_3 thus obtained is absorbed, as we said above, into a solution of concentrated H_2SO_4 to form fuming sulfuric acid. This is then treated with water to convert the dissolved SO_3 into H_2SO_4. The contact process is used when a pure, concentrated sulfuric acid is the desired product.

LEAD-CHAMBER PROCESS. In this process, which has slowly evolved over a period of 200 years and is still in use, the reactions take place in lead chambers. Sulfur dioxide gas, SO_2, mixed with an excess of air or oxygen and a relatively small quantity of nitrogen oxide, NO, is passed through a series of large lead-lined reaction chambers, where water is added in the form of fine warm spray.

In the lead chambers several concurrent reactions take place, some in the gaseous phase and some in the liquid condensed at the bottom of the chambers. In the gaseous phase the chief reaction is the catalytic oxidation of SO_2 to SO_3 by O_2 in the presence of NO, which we discussed in Chapter 25 as an example of homogeneous catalysis:

$$NO_{(g)} + \tfrac{1}{2}O_{2(g)} \xrightarrow{\text{fast}} NO_{2(g)}$$
$$SO_{2(g)} + NO_{2(g)} \longrightarrow SO_{3(g)} + NO_{(g)}$$

The reactions that occur in the liquid phase or between the gaseous and liquid phase are rather complex, but all again consist of the oxidation of S(IV) compounds to S(VI) compounds by the N(III) and N(IV) compounds formed in the rapid spontaneous oxidation of N(II) by oxygen. At the end of the process, practically all the initial SO_2 is transformed into H_2SO_4, and most of the nitrogen oxide, NO, used as the catalyst is recovered unchanged and recycled to continue the process.

The acid produced by this lead-chamber process is approximately a 77 per cent solution of H_2SO_4. When pyrite, FeS_2, is used as the source of the SO_2, the sulfuric acid contains small amounts of impurities, but these are not harmful in many industrial applications—the manufacture of fertilizers, for example. The inner wall of the reaction chambers are exposed to the action of highly corrosive substances such as SO_3, H_2SO_4, and the oxides of nitrogen in the presence of moisture and at relatively high temperature. Lead is used as a protective lining because it reacts with H_2SO_4 to form a compact, tenacious layer of insoluble lead sulfate $PbSO_4$, which protects the walls from further attack.

PROPERTIES OF SULFURIC ACID. Ordinary concentrated sulfuric acid contains about 97 per cent H_2SO_4. Pure (100 per cent) covalent H_2SO_4 (anhydrous sulfuric acid) is a colorless, oily liquid almost twice as heavy as water (density at 25°C = 1.8 g/ml³), which at 10.37°C solidifies to colorless crystals. Pure liquid sulfuric acid consists of covalent H_2SO_4 molecules, in which the central S atom is tetrahedrally surrounded by 4 O atoms and the S—O—H bonds form an angle because of the repulsion of lone pairs on the O atom. Considerable hydrogen bonding exists between the H_2SO_4 molecules in the liquid. When heated to its boiling point, 290°C, the liquid partially decomposes to SO_3 and H_2O; the SO_3 passes off more rapidly than the water. The boiling point of the remaining solution increases and reaches a maximum value of 317°C when the composition is 98.54 per cent H_2SO_4. If the temperature is maintained at this level, additional SO_3 and H_2O are lost. But now they are lost in the same proportions, and the composition of the liquid remains constant. On the other hand, a sulfuric acid solution that contains *less* than 98.54 per cent H_2SO_4 loses H_2O faster than it loses SO_3 until it attains this 98.54 per cent composition.

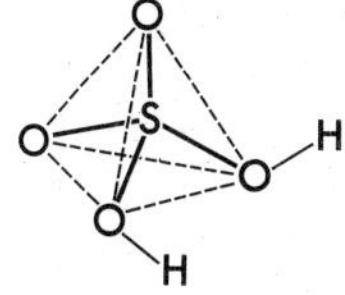

We have already mentioned the formation of the so-called "fuming sulfuric acid," or *oleum*. When H_2SO_4 and SO_3 are mixed in a 1:1 mole ratio, pyrosulfuric acid, $H_2S_2O_7$, is formed. Both acids lose SO_3 when they are heated.

Concentrated sulfuric acid dissolves in water with the evolution of a large quantity of heat, most of which arises from the very high hydration energy of the H^+ ions ($\Delta H_{hydr} = -267.9$ kcal/mole H^+) formed in the ionization reaction of H_2SO_4.

$$H_2SO_{4(l)} + H_2O_{(l)}\ (55.5\text{ moles}) \longrightarrow H_2SO_{4(aq)}\ (1\ M)$$
$$\Delta H_{soln} = -17.5\text{ kcal/mole } H_2SO_4 \text{ at } 25°C$$

The safest way to prepare aqueous solutions of H_2SO_4 is to pour the acid very carefully and slowly into the water. The heavier H_2SO_4 sinks down through the water, and the heat liberated is distributed throughout the entire solution. If we fail to take this precaution, and inadvertently add the water to the H_2SO_4, the lighter water remains near the surface and more of the heat is liberated primarily in one spot. As a result, local boiling takes place, and the acid solution spatters violently.

IONIZATION OF H_2SO_4. Sulfuric acid is a dibasic acid. In dilute solutions the first ionization is almost complete:

$$H_2SO_4 \longrightarrow H^+ + HSO_4^- \qquad K_1 = \text{very large}$$

As usual for polybasic acids, the second ionization takes place only to a smaller, though still appreciable, extent.

$$HSO_4^- \rightleftharpoons H^+ + SO_4^= \qquad K_2 = \frac{[H^+] \times [SO_4^=]}{[HSO_4^-]} = 3.5 \times 10^{-2} \text{ mole/l.}$$

For example, a 0.1 *M* solution of H_2SO_4 contains about 10 per cent $SO_4^=$ ions. This decreased tendency of the second ionization, $HSO_4^- \rightleftharpoons H^+ + SO_4^=$, to occur in comparison to the first ionization, $H_2SO_4 \longrightarrow H^+ + HSO_4^-$, has an important consequence. Moderately concentrated H_2SO_4 solutions contain a relatively high proportion of HSO_4^- ions and a relatively low proportion of $SO_4^=$ ions, whereas dilute solutions contain a greater proportion of $SO_4^=$ ions and a correspondingly smaller proportion of HSO_4^- ions. Because at different concentrations different proportions of HSO_4^- ions and $SO_4^=$ ions are present in solution, it is possible to prepare, by combination with positive ions, M^+, either the hydrogen sulfates, $MHSO_4$, or the normal sulfates, M_2SO_4, depending on the conditions.

ACID SALTS OF SULFURIC ACID. The metal hydrogen sulfates, for example $NaHSO_4$, can be prepared by bringing together the proper amounts of H_2SO_4 with a metal hydroxide:

$$H_2SO_4 + NaOH \longrightarrow NaHSO_4 + H_2O$$

When heated, the metal hydrogen sulfates lose water to form the pyrosulfates, $M_2S_2O_7$. When the pyrosulfates of the alkali metals are heated to still higher temperatures, they lose SO_3 to form the normal sulfates:

$$Na_2S_2O_7 \longrightarrow Na_2SO_4 + SO_3$$

REACTIONS OF CONCENTRATED SULFURIC ACID. We can classify the reactions of concentrated sulfuric acid according to whether they arise from any one of the following 3 properties: (1) Oxidizing ability due to the presence of sulfur in the +6 oxidation state. (2) Dehydrating effect of H_2SO_4. (3) High boiling point of sulfuric acid.

SULFURIC ACID AS AN OXIDANT. We know that metals below hydrogen in the electromotive series do not dissolve in *cold* concentrated or dilute sulfuric acid, or in any other non-oxidizing acid. Some such metals do dissolve in *hot* concentrated sulfuric acid, however, because the hot acid acts as an effective oxidant, itself being reduced to SO_2 gas. No H_2 is evolved in this reaction. From the $E°$ values of the couples involved, we see that the reaction

$$Cu + 2\,H_2SO_4 \longrightarrow CuSO_4 + SO_2 + 2\,H_2O$$

cannot occur spontaneously if each reactant is present in solution at 1 *M* concentration and the temperature is 25°C.

Oxidation half-reaction:	$Cu \longrightarrow Cu^{++} + \cancel{2e^-}$	$E° = -0.34$ v
Reduction half-reaction:	$H_2SO_4 + 2\,H^+ + \cancel{2e^-} \longrightarrow 2\,H_2O + SO_2$	$E° = +0.17$ v
Net oxidation-reduction reaction:	$Cu + H_2SO_4 + 2\,H^+ \longrightarrow Cu^{++} + SO_2 + 2\,H_2O$	$E° = -0.17$ v

This negative reaction potential −0.17 means the reaction cannot occur spontaneously under standard conditions. But in concentrated H_2SO_4, the H^+ ion concentration is much greater than under the conditions adopted to measure $E°$, and Le Chatelier's principle tells us that an increase in $[H^+]$ will cause a marked increase in the potential of the reduction reaction of H_2SO_4. Furthermore, at higher temperature the reduction of H_2SO_4 is more favorable because the two products of the reduction, H_2O and SO_2, are eliminated as gases. So the reaction that cannot take place at room temperature in 1 *M* solution can occur under more drastic conditions. In many reactions in which H_2SO_4 is used as an oxidizing agent, more than one reduction product of the acid is formed, although one predominates. And the product that predominates also depends on the concentration and the temperature of the acid.

DEHYDRATING REACTION OF H_2SO_4. Because of its very marked tendency to combine with water concentrated sulfuric acid is an effective drying agent for moist gases and liquids that do not react chemically with it. Concentrated sulfuric acid can even extract the component elements of water from many compounds that contain covalently bonded hydrogen atoms and oxygen atoms. For example, sugar, $C_{12}H_{22}O_{11}$, is converted largely to carbon by concentrated H_2SO_4:

$$C_{12}H_{22}O_{11} + 11\ H_2SO_4 \longrightarrow 12\ C + 11\ H_2SO_4 \cdot H_2O$$

The charring of wood, starch, and cotton and wool fibers by concentrated H_2SO_4 results from this same dehydrating effect.

REACTIONS ATTRIBUTABLE TO THE HIGH BOILING POINT OF H_2SO_4. The high boiling point of H_2SO_4 means that it may be used to displace acids with lower boiling points, especially HCl and HNO_3. If excess H_2SO_4 is added to a solution of HCl, to a solid chloride, or to a concentrated solution containing Cl^- ions, HCl passes off as a gas, while the excess of the non-volatile H_2SO_4 remains behind. Similar reactions occur with any low-boiling acid or the salt of such an acid.

$$NaCl + H_2SO_4 \longrightarrow NaHSO_4 + HCl$$

TEST FOR THE SULFATE ION. We can detect the presence of both HSO_4^- and the $SO_4^=$ ions in a solution by the addition of Ba^{++} ions. Since the salt, barium sulfate, $BaSO_4$, is highly insoluble ($K_{sp} = 1.0 \times 10^{-10}$ (mole/l.)^2 at 25°C), Ba^{++} ions will yield a white precipitate of $BaSO_4$ even in the presence of a relatively high $[H^+]$.

$$Ba^{++}_{(aq)} + SO^=_{4(aq)} \longrightarrow BaSO_{4(s)}$$

In fact, even though an acid solution will contain chiefly HSO_4^- ions, which do *not* form an insoluble precipitate with Ba^{++}, the concentration of $SO_4^=$ ions is still sufficient to exceed the very small K_{sp} of $BaSO_4$. Once some $BaSO_4$ is formed and precipitates, thus removing $SO_4^=$ ions from the solution, some HSO_4^- ions will dissociate to H^+ and $SO_4^=$, which will in turn precipitate as $BaSO_4$—and so on until all H_2SO_4 originally present in solution (either as H_2SO_4, or HSO_4^-, or $SO_4^=$) will be precipitated as $BaSO_{4(s)}$. Many other anions such as the $SO_3^=$ and $CO_3^=$ ions also give white precipitates with the Ba^{++} ion in neutral solution. But we can distinguish between $BaSO_4$ and $BaSO_3$ or $BaCO_3$ by adding a strong acid, such as HCl. The $BaSO_4$ precipitate persists, but the $BaSO_3$ or $BaCO_3$ dissolves in the presence of H^+ ions, forming HSO_3^- or HCO_3^-, which are weaker acids than HSO_4^-.

SULFUR HEXAFLUORIDE

Sulfur combines directly with F_2 to form gaseous sulfur hexafluoride, SF_6, with the liberation of a large quantity of heat. (Se and Te react similarly.)

$$S_{(s)} + 3\ F_{2(g)} \longrightarrow SF_{6(g)} \qquad \begin{cases} \Delta H^\circ_{\text{form}} = -246.0\ \text{kcal/mole} \\ \Delta G^\circ_{\text{form}} = -222.0\ \text{kcal/mole} \end{cases}$$

As the large negative value of the standard free energy of formation indicates, SF_6 is an extremely stable gas. In fact, it can be heated to very high temperatures without decomposing into its elements. Also, at ordinary temperatures, SF_6 does not react with other substances—for example, it is not attacked by Cl_2 or O_2 or H_2. The electron configuration and octahedral stereochemistry of the covalent SF_6 molecule have been discussed in Chapters 14, and 15.

THE THIO ACIDS

The thiosulfate ion (the Greek prefix "thio" means sulfur), usually written as $S_2O_3^=$, has an electronic and structural arrangement very similar to that of the $SO_4^=$ ion, except that one oxygen atom of the tetrahedral sulfate ion is replaced by a sulfur atom. The most common thiosulfate, $Na_2S_2O_3$, is prepared by boiling sulfur with a solution of sodium sulfite Na_2SO_3:

$$2\,Na^+_{(aq)} + SO_{3(aq)}^{=} + S_{(s)} \longrightarrow 2\,Na^+_{(aq)} + S_2O_{3(aq)}^{=}$$

In the thiosulfate ion the central S atom is assigned an oxidation number of +6 (as in the isostructural $SO_4^=$ ion), and the other sulfur atom is assigned an oxidation number of −2 (as is each O atom in $SO_4^=$). The *average* oxidation state of sulfur in $S_2O_3^=$ is therefore +2.

The free acid, $H_2S_2O_3$, is not stable at room temperature. If a solution of $Na_2S_2O_3$, for example, is treated with a dilute solution of a strong acid, the liberated $H_2S_2O_3$ immediately decomposes to H_2SO_3 and free sulfur, which precipitates.

$$\cancel{2\,Na^+} + S_2O_3^= + 2\,H^+ \longrightarrow \cancel{2\,Na^+} + [H_2S_2O_3] \longrightarrow S + SO_2 + H_2O$$

Neutral and alkaline aqueous solutions of the $S_2O_3^=$ ion, as well as the solid alkaline and alkaline earth thiosulfates, are stable with respect to this self-oxidation-reduction reaction. However, the $S_2O_3^=$ ion is an effective reducing agent, as we shall discuss in the following section.

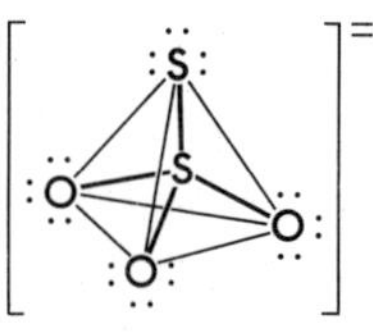

Sodium thiosulfate, $Na_2S_2O_3 \cdot 5\,H_2O$, (commercially called "hypo") is extensively used in the development of photographic films. An aqueous solution of $Na_2S_2O_3$ reacts with the AgBr still present in the exposed film, to form soluble complex salts of the type $Na[Ag(S_2O_3)]$ and $Na_3[Ag(S_2O_3)_2]$. The net reactions are:

$$AgBr_{(s)} + S_2O_{3(aq)}^{=} \longrightarrow [Ag(S_2O_3)]^-_{(aq)} + Br^-_{(aq)}$$
$$AgBr_{(s)} + 2\,S_2O_{3(aq)}^{=} \longrightarrow [Ag(S_2O_3)_2]^{\equiv}_{(aq)} + Br^-_{(aq)}$$

28-4 Latimer Oxidation-Potential Diagram of Sulfur

IN ACID SOLUTION

The following Latimer potential diagram, which shows some of the more important sulfur compounds as they exist in acid solutions, is helpful in correlating the behavior of sulfur compounds.

$$\overset{-2}{H_2S} \;\text{—}-0.14\text{—}\; \overset{0}{S} \;\text{—}-0.50\text{—}\; \overset{+2}{S_2O_3^=} \;\text{—}-0.40\text{—}\; \overset{+4}{H_2SO_3} \;\text{—}-0.17\text{—}\; \overset{+6}{SO_4^=}$$

$$S_2O_3^= \;\text{—}-0.08\text{—}\; \overset{+2\frac{1}{2}}{S_4O_6^=} \;\text{—}-0.51\text{—}\; H_2SO_3 \qquad S \;\text{—}-0.45\text{—}\; H_2SO_3$$

The small negative value of the potential for the couple H_2S—−0.14—S indicates that H_2S is a fairly good reductant, and that it can be oxidized to free S even by weak oxidants—in fact, by all oxidants whose oxidation potential is more negative than −0.14 volts. The $S_2O_3^=$ ion (average oxidation number of sulfur, +2) has a marked tendency to be oxidized to the $S_4O_6^=$ ion (average oxidation number of sulfur, $+2\frac{1}{2}$), as is indicated again by the small negative value of the oxidation potential, $S_2O_3^=$—−0.08—$S_4O_6^=$. With a mild oxidant such as iodine ($2\,S_2O_3^= + I_2 \longrightarrow S_4O_6^= + 2\,I^-$), the oxidation is rapid and quantitative and is used for the analytical determination of iodine. However, the formation of the $S_4O_6^=$ ion occurs only when the $S_2O_3^=$ ion is treated with a weak oxidant, since stronger oxidants convert the $S_4O_6^=$ ion to H_2SO_3 acid : $S_4O_6^=$—−0.51—H_2SO_3. The oxidation of $S_2O_3^=$ to $S_4O_6^=$ is particularly interesting from the structural viewpoint because it involves the formation of a S—S bond between the two S^{-2} atoms of the two $S_2O_3^=$ ions (notice that the S^{+6} of the $S_2O_3^=$ ions do not undergo any direct electronic change in going to $S_4O_6^=$):

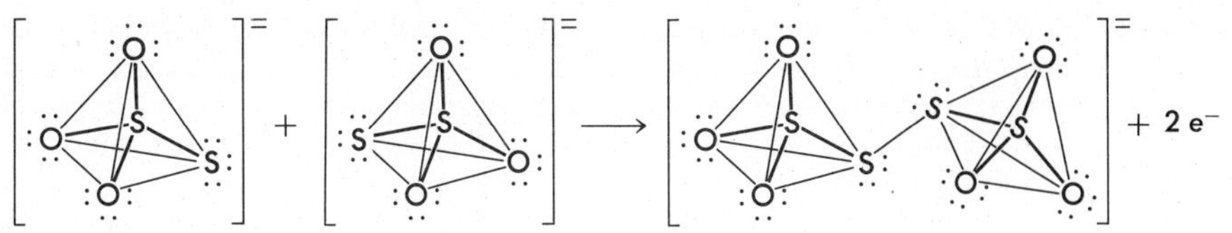

Again, the low oxidation potential of this reaction is indicative of the tendency of sulfur atoms to catenate. In fact, we see from the potential diagram that the oxidation of $S_2O_3^{=}$ to $SO_3^{=}$, which would involve a completely different path, is more difficult, as shown by the higher negative value of the oxidation potential, $S_2O_3^{=} \text{—} {-0.40} \text{—} SO_3^{=}$.

The Latimer potential diagram also tells us that, since the potential for the oxidation of $S_2O_3^{=}$ to H_2SO_3 is more positive (actually less negative) than that for the oxidation of S to $S_2O_3^{=}$, $S \text{—} {-0.50} \text{—} S_2O_3^{=} \text{—} {-0.40} \text{—} H_2SO_3^{=}$, the $S_2O_3^{=}$ ion in acid solution can disproportionate into free S and H_2SO_3.

The following Latimer oxidation-potential diagram shows some of the more important sulfur compounds as they exist in basic solutions, together with their $E°$ relationships:

$$\overset{-2}{S^{=}} \xrightarrow{+0.51} \overset{0}{S} \xrightarrow{+0.74} \overset{+3}{S_2O_3^{=}} \xrightarrow{+0.58} \overset{+4}{SO_3^{=}} \xrightarrow{+0.98} \overset{+6}{SO_4^{=}}$$

$$S \xrightarrow{+0.66} SO_3^{=} \qquad S^{=} \xrightarrow{+0.59} SO_3^{=}$$

In basic solution, elemental sulfur is a poor oxidant, $S^{=} \text{—} {+0.51} \text{—} S$, but even so it is a better oxidant than the $S_2O_3^{=}$ ion, $S \text{—} {+0.74} \text{—} S_2O_3^{=}$. Thus, S can disproportionate to $S^{=}$ and $S_2O_3^{=}$ ions in the presence of OH^- ions.

Let us compare the $E°$ values of sulfur compounds in the acid-solution diagram and the basic-solution diagram. The $S^{=}$ ion in basic solution is much more easily oxidized to sulfur than is H_2S in acid solution. In other words, the $S^{=}$ ion in basic solution is a better reductant: $S^{=} \text{—} {+0.51} \text{—} S$, than is H_2S in acid solution: $H_2S \text{—} {-0.14} \text{—} S$. On the other hand, the $SO_4^{=}$ ion is a better oxidant in acid solution than in basic solution (compare -0.17 with $+0.98$), and H_2SO_3 is a better oxidant in acid solution than is the $SO_3^{=}$ ion in basic solution.

Exercises

28-1 Compare the members of the oxygen-sulfur family in regard to (a) electronic configurations, (b) the tendency to form dinegative ions, (c) melting and boiling points and heats of vaporization, (d) enthalpy and free energy of formation, (e) electronegativity.

28-2 A sample of solid sulfur is heated gradually to its boiling point. Describe the physical changes that take place and explain them in terms of structural units.

28-3 Explain the relatively high values of boiling point, heat of vaporization, and heat of formation of H_2O compared with those of H_2S. Briefly mention the properties of H_2Se and H_2Te in your explanation.

28-4 Compare the acid dissociation of H_2O, H_2S, H_2Se, and H_2Te in aqueous solution and explain.

28-5 List the principal oxidation states of sulfur, together with the formulas and names of some of its oxides, acids, and salts.

28-6 A solution of H_2S in water can act as (a) a weak acid, (b) a dibasic acid, (c) a reducing agent, (d) a reagent useful in qualitative analysis. Write chemical equations to illustrate each of these properties.

28-7 H_2S passed into a neutral solution of $NiSO_4$ does not precipitate NiS, but H_2S passed into a solution of $CuSO_4$ does precipitate CuS. Suggest an explanation.

28-8 H_2S passed into a solution of $MnSO_4$ does not precipitate MnS, but H_2S passed into a solution of $MnSO_4$ containing some NH_3 does precipitate MnS. Explain.

28-9 (a) H_2S passed into an aqueous solution of $ZnCl_2$ produces a slight (or no) precipitate of ZnS, but H_2S passed into the same solution containing ammonium acetate $(NH_4^+)(CH_3COO^-)$ produces a copious precipitate of ZnS. Suggest an explanation. (b) What zinc salt would produce a copious precipitate of ZnS when H_2S is passed into its solution?

28-10 (a) Write an equation to show the equilibrium present in an aqueous solution of H_2S. (b) Indicate approximately the relative concentrations of all molecules and ions present in this solution. (c) List three compounds which when added to this solution would (1) increase the $S^=$ ion concentration, (2) decrease the $S^=$ ion concentration.

28-11 Complete and balance: (a) $H_2S + O_2 \longrightarrow$ (b) $H_2S + I_2 \longrightarrow$ (c) $H_2S + FeCl_3 \longrightarrow$ (d) $H_2S + HNO_3 \longrightarrow$

28-12 Using each of the following, (a) S, (b) $Ca(HSO_3)_2$, (c) Na_2SO_3, (d) FeS, (e) conc. H_2SO_4, as one of the reactants, write equations to illustrate the preparation of SO_2.

28-13 On the basis of four entirely different properties, show that H_2SO_3 is a weak acid.

28-14 (a) List the equilibria present in an aqueous solution of H_2SO_3. (b) State the approximate relative concentrations of all molecules and ions present in this solution. (c) List three compounds which, added to this solution, would (1) increase the $SO_3^=$ ion concentration, (2) decrease the $SO_3^=$ ion concentration.

28-15 A water solution of SO_2 can act as (a) a dibasic acid, (b) an oxidizing agent, (c) a reducing agent. Write chemical equations to illustrate these properties.

28-16 Write the equation for the reaction of H_2S with SO_2 to illustrate the reducing property of the former and the oxidizing property of the latter.

28-17 Starting with SO_2 gas and KOH solution, explain how you would prepare (a) $KHSO_3$, (b) K_2SO_3.

28-18 In the reaction of SO_2 with O_2 to produce SO_3, discuss the factors that influence the position of the equilibrium, and the rate at which such equilibrium is attained.

28-19 What property of concentrated H_2SO_4 makes it: (a) Capable of dissolving metallic copper? (b) Useful in preparing HCl from NaCl? (c) Useful in removing moisture from gases? (d) Write equations for the reactions that take place in (a) and (b).

28-20 Compare aqueous solutions of H_2SO_3 and H_2SO_4 in as many ways as possible. Give equations where possible.

28-21 Write equations for the chief reactions which result in the formation of H_2SO_4 in the lead chamber process.

28-22 Explain how the following pairs of substances may be distinguished: (a) A water-soluble white solid, Na_2SO_3, and a water-soluble white solid, Na_2SO_4. (b) A water-insoluble white solid, $BaSO_3$, and an insoluble white solid, $BaSO_4$. (c) A water-soluble white solid, Na_2SO_3, and a water-soluble white solid, $Na_2S_2O_3$.

28-23 Complete and balance the following expressions:

(a) $Na_2SO_3 + S \longrightarrow$ (d) H_2SO_4 (conc.) + Zn $\longrightarrow$
(b) $NaHSO_4 + BaCl_2 \longrightarrow$ (e) H_2SO_4 (dil.) + Zn $\longrightarrow$
(c) H_2SO_4 (conc.) + Cu $\longrightarrow$ (f) $BaSO_3 + H_2SO_4 \longrightarrow$

28-24 Given: $H_2S \overset{-0.14}{—} S \overset{-0.50}{—} S_2O_3^= \overset{-0.40}{—} H_2SO_3 \overset{-0.17}{—} SO_4^=$. (a) List all species that disproportionate, giving products. (b) Write a balanced net ionic equation for the reaction of $S_2O_3^=$ with H_2S. (c) Give the $E°$ for this reaction.

28-25 Refer to the Latimer oxidation-potential diagram of sulfur in acid solution given in Section 28-4 on page 642.

(a) Complete the following reactions if they occur spontaneously and explain *why* they occur spontaneously. If a reaction does not occur spontaneously (requires energy), write N.R.

(1) $H_2S + S_2O_3^= \longrightarrow$ (5) $H_2S + MnO_4^- \longrightarrow$
(2) $S + H_2SO_3 \longrightarrow$ (6) $S_2O_3^= + S_2O_3^= \longrightarrow$
(3) $S_2O_3^= + H_2SO_3 \longrightarrow$ (7) $H_2SO_3 + H_2SO_3 \longrightarrow$
(4) $S_4O_6^= + SO_4^= \longrightarrow$ (8) $H_2S + SO_4^= \longrightarrow$

(b) What species, if any, listed in the potential diagram can react spontaneously to form the products: (1) $\longrightarrow S + H_2SO_3$ (2) $\longrightarrow SO_4^= + S$

(c) Make three statements generalizing the chemistry of the possible type of reactions of (1) H_2S, (2) $SO_4^=$, (3) H_2SO_3.

THE NITROGEN FAMILY: THE GROUP VB ELEMENTS

	VB			He
C	N	O	F	Ne
Si	P	S	Cl	Ar
Ge	As	Se	Br	Kr
Sn	Sb	Te	I	Xe
Pb	Bi	Po	At	Rn

Stable State at 25°, 1 atm	VB
colorless gas	N
black crystals	P
silvery-gray crystals	As
silvery-white crystals	Sb
light gray metal	Bi

The Group VB elements, the nitrogen family—nitrogen, N; phosphorus, P; arsenic, As; antimony, Sb; and bismuth, Bi—exhibit certain characteristic similarities, but also show appreciable differences. As in the case of the Group VIB elements, this change in properties is not regular throughout the family; the greatest difference exists between the first two members, nitrogen and phosphorus. We shall consider the chemistry of nitrogen first, then that of phosphorus, and finally the chemistry of arsenic, antimony, and bismuth together.

29-1 Group Relationships

Some of the important physical properties of the Group VB elements are listed in Table 29-1. Notice that for each element the outer electron configuration is $ns^2\ np^3$. The boiling points of the Group VB elements increase with increasing atomic weight. There is a pronounced decrease in electronegativity from N to Bi, the largest decrease occurring from the first to the second member of the family, as in Group VIB and Group VIIB. All the elements, however, with the possible exception of Bi, are somewhat electronegative (non-metallic), and hence tend to form covalent compounds with other non-metals. Only the smallest and most electronegative element of Group VB, nitrogen, shows any tendency to form monoatomic negative ions, and then only in its reactions with the most electropositive elements, such as the alkali and alkaline-earth metals. The resulting compounds—such as sodium nitride, Na_3N and cal-

TABLE 29-1 SOME PROPERTIES OF THE NITROGEN FAMILY (GROUP VB ELEMENTS)

Element	Outer Electron Config.	Atomic Weight	Atomic Radius A	Melting Point °C	Boiling Point °C	First Ioniz. Energy[a]	Electro-negativity (Pauling)	$\Delta H_{atomiz.}$ (kcal/mole of atoms)
${}_{7}N$	$2s^22p^3$	14.01	0.74	−210	−196	14.55 335	3.0	113.0
${}_{15}P$	$3s^23p^3$	30.98	1.10	44 (white)	280 (white)	10.98 242	2.1	79.8
${}_{33}As$	$4s^24p^3$	74.91	1.21	814[b]	610 Sublimes	10.5 226	2.0	72.4
${}_{51}Sb$	$5s^25p^3$	121.76	1.41	631	1380	8.64 199	1.8	63.2
${}_{83}Bi$	$6s^26p^3$	209.00	1.52	271	1560	8.0 184	—	49.5

[a] For each element the top value is in e.v./mole of gaseous atoms and the lower value in kcal/mole of gaseous atoms.
[b] At 36 atm pressure.

cium nitride, Ca_3N_2—have an essentially ionic character, containing the trinegative nitride ion, $N^{\equiv}$, with a neon-like electron configuration.

In the covalent compounds of nitrogen, the total number of valence electrons around the nitrogen core is never more than 8, since only the $2s$ and $2p$ orbitals are available. The other elements of this family, however, can accommodate more than 8 valence electrons by utilizing their *nd* orbitals. For example, phosphorus, in addition to forming PH_3 and PCl_3 which correspond to the nitrogen compounds NH_3 and NCl_3, forms compounds of the formula PCl_5 and PF_5. In this respect, nitrogen behaves like oxygen, the first element of Group VIB, and phosphorus behaves like sulfur, the second element of Group VIB.

29-2 Nitrogen

OCCURRENCE AND PHYSICAL PROPERTIES

Gaseous nitrogen, N_2, constitutes about 78 per cent by volume of the atmosphere. This almost unlimited reservoir is a convenient source of starting material for the commercial preparation of nitrogen compounds. In addition, combined nitrogen occurs to some extent naturally in minerals; for example sodium nitrate, $NaNO_3$, exists in large quantities in Chile. The soil, especially in fertile regions, usually contains combined nitrogen in the form of nitrates, nitrites, and ammonium compounds. Finally, the tissues of all living organisms, both animal and vegetable, contain combined nitrogen in compounds known as proteins.

At ordinary conditions nitrogen is a colorless, odorless, and tasteless gas. Nitrogen is only slightly soluble in water, with which it does not react. Other physical properties of nitrogen are listed in Table 29-1.

ELEMENTARY NITROGEN. Elementary nitrogen exists as diatomic molecules, N_2, in which the two N atoms are linked by a triple covalent bond (a σ and two π bonds), as shown by the electron-dot formula, :N:::N: (compare the electron-dot formula of corresponding elements O_2, Group VI, and F_2, Group VII). The dissociation energy of the N_2 molecule is extremely high—the highest known of any homonuclear diatomic molecule—indicating that the nitrogen-to-nitrogen link must be a multiple bond—compare the dissociation energy of the corresponding elements O_2 (119 kcal/mole) of Group VI and F_2 (37 kcal/mole) of Group VII.

$$N_{2(g)} \longrightarrow 2\,N_{(g)} \qquad \Delta H_{diss} = 226 \text{ kcal/mole of } N_{2(g)} \text{ at } 25°\text{C and 1 atm}$$

This very high dissociation energy accounts for many of the chemical properties of nitrogen. For example, it accounts for the general lack of chemical reactivity of nitrogen gas and for the instability of many nitrogen compounds, which even at ordinary temperatures tend to decompose to form the element $N_{2(g)}$. The most important reactions of elemental nitrogen, N_2, are the direct combination with hydrogen, H_2, to form ammonia, NH_3, and with oxygen, O_2, to form nitric oxide, NO. We shall discuss these reactions in detail later. Nitrogen also reacts with certain electropositive metals to form nitrides. At temperatures of 300–500°C the alkaline-earth metals (Mg, Ca, Sr, and Ba) and the alkali metal Li combine rapidly with N_2 to form ionic nitrides such as Mg_3N_2, Ca_3N_2, and Li_3N.

PREPARATION

LABORATORY METHODS. Pure nitrogen can be conveniently prepared in the laboratory by the careful thermal decomposition of ammonium nitrite, NH_4NO_2. In practice, since solid NH_4NO_2 is too unstable to be stored, the reaction is carried out by mixing aqueous solutions of NH_4Cl and $NaNO_2$, and gently warming the mixture. The net ionic equation for this reaction is:

$$\overset{-3}{N}H^+_{4(aq)} + \overset{+3}{N}O^-_{2(aq)} \longrightarrow \overset{0}{N}_{2(g)} + 2\,H_2O_{(l)}$$

Nitrogen, N_2, can also be prepared by heating dry, solid $(NH_4)_2Cr_2O_7$:

$$(\overset{-3}{N}H_4)_2\overset{+6}{Cr}_2O_7 \longrightarrow \overset{0}{N}_2\uparrow + \overset{+3}{Cr}_2O_3 + 4\,H_2O$$

Here is an important word of caution, however: The above reactions should be carried out only with very small quantities of reactants, for the thermal decomposition of some NH_4^+ salts with oxidizing anions may take place with explosive violence.

COMMERCIAL METHODS. Nitrogen gas containing argon and a small percentage of oxygen is prepared commercially by the fractional distillation of liquid air (p. 76). This commercial nitrogen is usually stored and shipped as a gas under pressure in steel cylinders. When oxygen-free nitrogen is required, the oxygen can be removed by passing the commercial nitrogen over hot copper mesh, or through aqueous ammonia containing finely divided suspended copper metal, or through chromium(II) salt solutions. Nitrogen prepared from the air has a slightly higher (0.5%) density than nitrogen prepared from the decomposition of nitrogen-containing compounds. It was this small but constant difference that prompted Rayleigh and Ramsey in 1895 to investigate the reason for it and ultimately led to their discovery of the noble gases (p. 621).

USE OF NITROGEN

The most important commercial use of nitrogen is in the production of NH_3, which in turn is used in the manufacture of fertilizers, nitric acid, and other nitrogen compounds. Nitrogen is also used to provide an inert atmosphere in certain metallurgical and chemical processes, and in general in all cases where the presence of atmospheric oxygen may cause unwanted oxidation processes. For example, meats and vegetables kept in a nitrogen atmosphere at the appropriate temperature and humidity maintain their freshness much longer than they do in air. Also, the life of automobile tires can be appreciably lengthened by filling them with nitrogen rather than air, thus preventing the corrosive oxidation of the inner rubber walls by the O_2 molecules at the high pressure and temperature that normally develops inside the running tires.

29-3 Nitrogen Compounds

In its compounds nitrogen exhibits oxidation states from −3 to +5. Some of the more important compounds of nitrogen are listed in Table 29-2. A few compounds are also known in which nitrogen exhibits a fractional *average* oxidation number. In HN_3, hydrazoic acid, for example, nitrogen has an average oxidation number of $-\frac{1}{3}$.

OXIDATION STATE OF −3

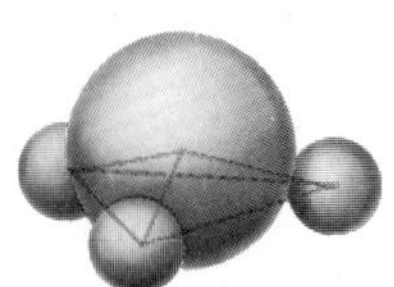

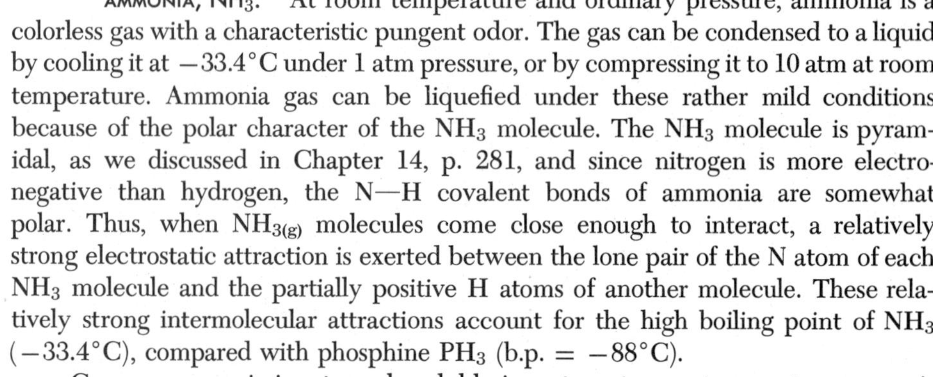

AMMONIA, NH_3. At room temperature and ordinary pressure, ammonia is a colorless gas with a characteristic pungent odor. The gas can be condensed to a liquid by cooling it at −33.4°C under 1 atm pressure, or by compressing it to 10 atm at room temperature. Ammonia gas can be liquefied under these rather mild conditions because of the polar character of the NH_3 molecule. The NH_3 molecule is pyramidal, as we discussed in Chapter 14, p. 281, and since nitrogen is more electronegative than hydrogen, the N—H covalent bonds of ammonia are somewhat polar. Thus, when $NH_{3(g)}$ molecules come close enough to interact, a relatively strong electrostatic attraction is exerted between the lone pair of the N atom of each NH_3 molecule and the partially positive H atoms of another molecule. These relatively strong intermolecular attractions account for the high boiling point of NH_3 (−33.4°C), compared with phosphine PH_3 (b.p. = −88°C).

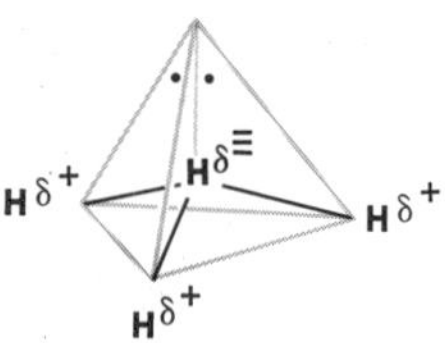

Gaseous ammonia is extremely soluble in water; at room temperature approximately 700 volumes of NH_3 gas must be dissolved in 1 volume of water to form a saturated solution in equilibrium with the gas above it. The great solubility of ammonia in water is due to hydration and ionization reactions which we shall discuss later.

THE LABORATORY PREPARATION OF AMMONIA. A convenient way of preparing pure NH_3 gas in the laboratory is to heat an ammonium salt, such as NH_4Cl, with a concentrated solution of a strong base, such as KOH:

$$NH_4Cl_{(s)} + KOH_{(aq)} \longrightarrow NH_{3(g)} + H_2O_{(l)} + KCl_{(aq)}$$

We use a concentrated solution of KOH because the product, NH_3, is much less soluble in such a solution than it is in water. Ammonia can also be prepared by gently warming a concentrated solution of NH_3 in water, a method that produces a steady stream of NH_3 gas. In both methods of preparation, the moist ammonia gas that is produced can be dried simply by passing it over a dehydrating substance that will not react with it—solid KOH, for example.

THE COMMERCIAL PREPARATION OF AMMONIA. The two most important methods for the commercial preparation of ammonia are the synthetic, or Haber, process, and the cyanamide process. Large quantities of NH_3 are also obtained as a by-product in

TABLE 29-2 SOME IMPORTANT COMPOUNDS OF NITROGEN AND THEIR OXIDATION STATES

Ox. No. of Nitrogen	−3	0	+1	+2	+3	+4	+5
Formula and Name	NH_3, ammonia	N_2	N_2O dinitrogen oxide	NO nitrogen oxide	N_2O_3 dinitrogen trioxide	NO_2 nitrogen dioxide	N_2O_5 dinitrogen pentoxide
	NH_4Cl, ammonium chloride				HNO_2 nitrous acid	N_2O_4 dinitrogen tetroxide	HNO_3 nitric acid
	$NaNH_2$, sodium amide				NO_2^- nitrite ion		NO_3^- nitrate ion

the production of coke, which involves heating coal in the absence of oxygen until all volatile materials have been distilled or sublimed.

The Haber process. This process is named after a German scientist, Fritz Haber, who worked it out in 1915–16 and received the Noble Prize for this work in 1918. This process is a good example of the interplay of thermodynamic and kinetic factors that determine the feasibility of chemical reactions. At 25°C and 1 atm, H_2 gas and N_2 gas can form NH_3, because the favorable enthalpy term, ΔH, outweighs the unfavorable $T\,\Delta S$ term (ΔS is negative because the number of moles of gas decreases from 4 to 2).

$$N_{2(g)} + 3\,H_{2(g)} \rightleftharpoons 2\,NH_{3(g)} \quad \begin{cases} \Delta H^\circ = -22.0 \text{ kcal/mole-eqn} \\ \Delta S^\circ = -47.4 \text{ cal/deg} \times \text{mole-eqn} \end{cases}$$

$$\Delta G^\circ = \Delta H^\circ - T\,\Delta S^\circ = -8.0 \text{ kcal/mole-eqn}$$

A mixture of these gases *in equilibrium* at room temperature therefore would contain appreciable quantities of NH_3. However, at room temperature the rate at which equilibrium is attained is so slow that for all practical purposes no reaction takes place. Increasing the temperature, will, as we know, increase the rate of reaction, but, on the other hand, it will decrease the concentration of NH_3 present in the equilibrium mixture. In fact, a rise in temperature increases the value of the unfavorable $T\,\Delta S$ term as compared to that of the favorable ΔH term, and ΔG gradually approaches zero. In practice, the synthesis of NH_3 from N_2 and H_2 is carried out at temperatures of 450–600°C, in the presence of a catalyst (usually iron with small amounts of potassium and aluminum oxides) and high pressure (in the range of 200–600 atm). The high pressure helps, according to the principle of Le Chatelier, because the volume of the system decreases as the reaction proceeds to the right. The use of high pressure demands that the reaction take place in strong-walled steel containers.

CHEMICAL PROPERTIES AND REACTIONS OF AMMONIA. We can classify most of the chemical reactions of ammonia into two groups: (1) those related to the electron-pair donor (Lewis-base) properties of NH_3, and (2) those involving the oxidation of NH_3, in which nitrogen has its lowest oxidation number, -3. For example, the reactions of NH_3 with electron-pair acceptors, such as the H^+ ion, the BF_3 molecule, and many metal ions—occur by virtue of the availability of the lone pair on the nitrogen atom of NH_3, and essentially consist of the formation of a coordinate covalent bond:

$$NH_{3(aq)} + H^+{}_{(aq)} \longrightarrow [NH_4]^+{}_{(aq)}$$
$$NH_3 + BF_3 \longrightarrow [H_3N \rightarrow BF_3]$$
$$2\,NH_{3(aq)} + Ag^+{}_{(aq)} \longrightarrow [Ag(NH_3)_2]^+{}_{(aq)}$$

The equilibrium that exists in an aqueous solution of ammonia and the weakly basic properties of such a solution ($K = 1.8 \times 10^{-5}$ mole/l.) were discussed in Chapter 20.

As we have seen above, NH_3 at room temperature is stable with respect to decomposition into N_2 and H_2 ($\Delta G^\circ_{form} = -4.0$ kcal/mole NH_3); however, when mixed with oxygen (or air), ammonia tends to undergo spontaneous oxidation, forming water and either NO or N_2, or both. At 25°C and 1 atm, we have:

1. $$2\,NH_{3(g)} + \tfrac{3}{2}\,O_{2(g)} \longrightarrow N_{2(g)} + 3\,H_2O_{(l)} \quad \begin{cases} \Delta H^\circ = -182.9 \text{ kcal/mole-eqn} \\ \Delta G^\circ = -162.7 \text{ kcal/mole-eqn} \end{cases}$$

2. $$2\,NH_{3(g)} + \tfrac{5}{2}\,O_{2(g)} \longrightarrow 2\,NO_{(g)} + 3\,H_2O_{(l)} \quad \begin{cases} \Delta H^\circ = -139.7 \text{ kcal/mole-eqn} \\ \Delta G^\circ = -120.7 \text{ kcal/mole-eqn} \end{cases}$$

As the ΔG° values show, both reactions are thermodynamically favorable, although the one that produces N_2 is *more favorable* than the one that yields NO. At room temperature both reactions take place so very slowly that no detectable amounts of the products are formed, but at temperatures of about 500°C they proceed at an appreciable rate. If, at that temperature, both reactions are allowed to reach equilibrium, a greater amount of N_2 than of NO will form. However, by carrying out the oxidation of NH_3 in the presence of a catalyst of platinum gauze, the reaction of NH_3 with O_2 yields principally NO because the platinum catalyst accelerates reaction 1 more than reaction 2. Therefore, if the aim of the reaction is to produce NO as an intermediate step in the preparation of nitric acid (see p. 654), the mixture of NH_3 and air heated to 500°C is passed very rapidly over the platinum gauze, and the products are then cooled and separated from the reaction mixture before equilibrium has time to be established. Notice that under these conditions the *rate factor* determines the relative quantities of NO and N_2 produced, rather than the free energy factor.

AMMONIUM SALTS. We have seen that ammonia, NH_3, reacts with the H^+ ion to form the ammonium ion, NH_4^+. That is, both gaseous and aqueous ammonia react with strong acids to form ammonium salts. Gaseous NH_3 reacts with gaseous HCl to form solid NH_4Cl, for example. And when NH_3 is passed into aqueous H_2SO_4, it forms $(NH_4)_2SO_4$, which can be crystallized from solution. If HNO_3 is used, the salt NH_4NO_3 can be prepared in the same way.

In crystal structure and solubility, the ammonium salts closely resemble the salts of the alkali metals (see Chapter 30). The size (effective radius) of the tetrahedral NH_4^+ ion, 1.48 A, is the same as that of the Cs^+ ion, and only a little larger than that of the K^+ ion, which has a radius of 1.33 A. Moreover, all three ions have the same charge. With only four notable exceptions—NH_4ClO_4, $(NH_4)_3[Co(NO_2)_6]$, $(NH_4)_2[PtCl_6]$, and $NH_4[B(C_6H_5)_4]$—the ammonium salts are very soluble in water. As we found in an earlier chapter (p. 442), the NH_4^+ ion hydrolyzes very slightly in aqueous solutions to form an equilibrium mixture with $NH_{3(aq)}$ molecules and $H^+_{(aq)}$ ions. Because of this hydrolysis, aqueous solutions of ammonium salts of strong acids—NH_4Cl and NH_4NO_3, for example—are somewhat acidic.

When ammonium salts of non-oxidizing acids are heated, both in the solid state and in solution, they decompose into NH_3 and the acid:

$$NH_4HCO_{3(aq)} \longrightarrow NH_{3(g)} + H_2CO_{3(aq)}$$
$$H_2CO_{3(aq)} \rightleftharpoons CO_{2(g)} + H_2O_{(l)}$$
$$NH_4Cl_{(s)} \longrightarrow NH_{3(g)} + HCl_{(g)}$$

But when ammonium salts of *oxidizing* acids such as $(NH_4)_2Cr_2O_7$ are heated, oxidation products of ammonia are formed. The -3 oxidation state of nitrogen is generally increased to zero (N_2) or to $+1$ (N_2O).

$$(NH_4)_2Cr_2O_7 \longrightarrow Cr_2O_3 + N_2 + 4\,H_2O$$
$$NH_4NO_3 \longrightarrow N_2O + 2\,H_2O$$
$$NH_4NO_2 \longrightarrow N_2 + 2\,H_2O$$

USES OF AMMONIA. The impure NH_3 obtained as a by-product in the preparation of coke from coal is usually dissolved in aqueous solutions of H_2SO_4 and H_3PO_4 to produce $(NH_4)_2SO_4$ or $(NH_4)_3PO_4$, which are widely used in the preparation of agricultural fertilizers. A part of the purer NH_3 formed by the Haber process and the cyanamide process (see below) is also used for this purpose, but a major quantity is used as an intermediate in the preparation of nitric acid (p. 654).

The cyanamide process. The cyanamide process is based on the reaction of N_2 gas with solid calcium carbide, CaC_2, in an electric-arc furnace at 900–1,000°C. The process starts with the decomposition of limestone, $CaCO_3$, and involves the following four independent steps:

1. The limestone, $CaCO_3$, is decomposed at temperatures above 825°C:

$$CaCO_{3(s)} \longrightarrow CaO_{(s)} + CO_{2(g)}$$

2. The CaO is heated with coke (carbon) at 3,000°C in an electric furnace:

$$CaO_{(s)} + 3\ C_{(s)} \longrightarrow CaC_{2(s)} + CO_{(g)}$$

3. Next, the CaC_2 is ground very finely, and mixed with powdered CaF_2, which acts as a catalyst. Then the mixture is heated in the presence of N_2 gas at 900–1,000°C. Under these conditions the N_2 reacts with the CaC_2 to form $CaCN_2$, calcium cyanamide, and carbon:

$$CaC_{2(s)} + N_{2(g)} \longrightarrow CaCN_{2(s)} + C_{(s)}$$

4. Finally, the $CaCN_2$ is treated with steam to form NH_3 and $CaCO_3$:

$$CaCN_{2(s)} + 3\ H_2O_{(g)} \longrightarrow 2\ NH_{3(g)} + CaCO_{3(s)}$$

The $NH_{3(g)}$ can be recycled to step (1).

OXIDATION STATE +1: N_2O

Nitrogen forms several compounds with oxygen. In fact, oxides exist in which nitrogen has all the positive oxidation states, from +1 to +5. Dinitrogen oxide (nitrous oxide), N_2O, in which nitrogen is in the +1 oxidation state, is a colorless, odorless gas, which can be most conveniently prepared by the careful decomposition of molten ammonium nitrate, NH_4NO_3, at temperatures only slightly above its melting point (170°C):

$$NH_4NO_{3(l)} \xrightarrow{170\text{–}200^\circ C} N_2O_{(g)} + 2\ H_2O_{(g)}$$

This reaction must be carried out with caution, because very rapid heating of NH_4NO_3 may result in an explosive reaction that liberates N_2, O_2, and H_2O. The N_2O gas is usually collected over hot water, since it is appreciably soluble in cold water (about 1.5 volumes of gas dissolve in 1 volume of water at room temperature). At low temperatures a crystalline hydrate, $N_2O \cdot 6\ H_2O$, may be obtained from water solutions of N_2O. When heated, this hydrate regenerates pure N_2O.

At room temperature N_2O can decompose spontaneously into its elements, N_2 and O_2, as shown by the positive values of its ΔG°_{form}:

$$2\ N_{2(g)} + O_{2(g)} \longrightarrow 2\ N_2O_{(g)} \qquad \begin{cases} \Delta H^\circ_{form} = +39.4\ \text{kcal/mole-eqn} \\ \Delta G^\circ_{form} = +49.6\ \text{kcal/mole-eqn} \end{cases}$$

Notice that for the formation reaction of N_2O not only is ΔH° unfavorable, but also ΔS° because the number of gas moles of the product is less than the number of moles of the reactants. The compound N_2O persists at room temperature, however, because its *rate* of decomposition is negligible. But above 565°C N_2O decomposes fairly rapidly into N_2 and O_2.

The molecule of N_2O is linear, with the two N atoms joined together by a multiple bond and the O atom in a terminal position. The electronic structure of the molecule is represented as a resonance hybrid involving the two non-equivalent contributing forms I and II. Nitrous oxide is a relatively inert substance; however, materials that burn in air burn even more brightly in N_2O, which readily gives up its oxygen, forming N_2. When N_2O gas is inhaled in controlled low concentrations, it produces a mild hysteria (hence its common name, "laughing gas"). It has useful anesthetic effects. It is also used in the commercial preparation of whipped cream, because of its relative solubility in cream, its non-toxicity, and its ability to retard souring.

:N:::N:Ö:
I

:N::N::O:
II

OXIDATION STATE +2: NO

Nitrogen oxide (nitric oxide), NO, is a colorless gas. We have already discussed its commercial preparation from NH_3 (p. 649). Nitric oxide can also be prepared by direct combination of nitrogen gas and oxygen gas at very high temperature.

At room temperature the reaction is thermodynamically forbidden:

$$\tfrac{1}{2}\,N_{2(g)} + \tfrac{1}{2}\,O_{2(g)} \longrightarrow NO_{(g)} \qquad \Delta G^\circ = +20.7 \text{ kcal/mole-eqn}$$

But since the entropy of the system increases slightly from left to right ($\Delta S^\circ = +2.9$ cal/deg $\times$ mole-eqn), at very high temperature the favorable $T\,\Delta S$ term finally overcomes the unfavorable ΔH term ($\Delta H^\circ = +21.6$ kcal/mole-eqn); then ΔG becomes negative and some NO is formed. Thus, by passing air (20 per cent O_2, 80 per cent N_2) in an electric arc at 3,500°C and rapidly cooling the equilibrium mixture of NO, O_2, and N_2 thus obtained, so that the decomposition of NO is slowed down, a concentration of about 3 or 4 per cent of NO in air at room temperature can be obtained.

In the laboratory NO is prepared in a fairly pure state by the reduction of dilute HNO_3 with copper metal:

$$3\,Cu_{(s)} + 8\,HNO_{3(aq)} \longrightarrow 2\,NO_{(g)} + 3\,Cu(NO_3)_{2(aq)} + 4\,H_2O_{(l)}$$

Since NO is rapidly oxidized to NO_2 by the oxygen of the air, the air originally present in the reaction vessel oxidizes the first portion of the colorless NO produced to brownish-red NO_2. But after all the air originally present in the apparatus has been displaced, the NO formed can be collected pure over water.

The most important reaction of NO is its spontaneous and fairly rapid oxidation by oxygen to form nitrogen dioxide, NO_2. At room temperature the equilibrium is almost completely shifted toward the formation of NO_2:

$$2\,NO_{(g)} + O_{2(g)} \rightleftharpoons 2\,NO_{2(g)} \qquad \begin{cases} \Delta H^\circ = -53.0 \text{ kcal/mole-eqn} \\ \Delta G^\circ = -36.6 \text{ kcal/mole-eqn} \end{cases}$$

As we already discussed, this reaction is an essential step in the preparation of sulfuric acid from SO_2 in the lead chamber process (p. 638).

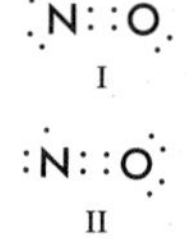

The electronic structure of the NO molecule is explained on the basis of resonance between the two contributing structures, I and II. In contributing structure I, the nitrogen atom has 4 electron pairs in the valence shell, whereas the oxygen atom has 3 electron pairs plus an "odd electron." In contributing structure II, the oxygen atom has 4 electron pairs whereas the nitrogen atom has 3 electron pairs plus an "odd electron." Actually, the odd electron is not confined to a specified orbital of the nitrogen atom or of the oxygen atom, but is *delocalized* over both the oxygen atom and the nitrogen atom. As with most molecules with an odd electron, nitric oxide is paramagnetic.

OXIDATION STATE +3: N_2O_3, NITRITES, AND NITROGEN TRIHALIDES

Dinitrogen trioxide, N_2O_3, is obtained as a blue liquid when a 1:1 molar mixture of NO and NO_2 is condensed at -20°C. The N_2O_3 molecule results from the pairing up of two odd electrons—one on the N atom of NO and one on the N atom of NO_2—to form a covalent N—N bond. In fact, N_2O_3 has the structure shown in the margin. At room temperature and above, N_2O_3 decomposes rapidly to form a gaseous equilibrium mixture consisting chiefly of NO and NO_2:

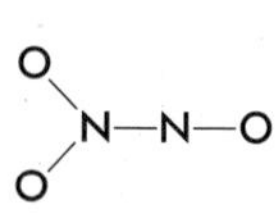

$$N_2O_{3(g)} \rightleftharpoons NO_{(g)} + NO_{2(g)}$$

When this equilibrium mixture is passed into an aqueous basic *solution*, such as KOH, the corresponding metal nitrite is obtained:

$$N_2O_3 + \cancel{2\,K^+} + 2\,OH^- \longrightarrow \cancel{2\,K^+} + 2\,NO_2^- + H_2O$$

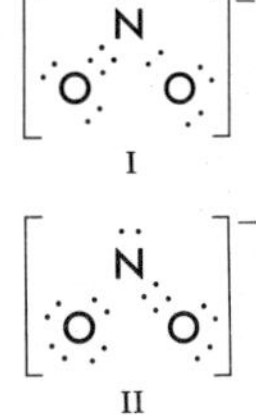

The nitrite ion, NO_2^-, is angular, the O—N—O bond angle being approximately 125°. The two important contributing structures, I, II, of the nitrite ion are shown in the margin.

As we shall discuss in detail later (p. 658), the NO_2^- ion is relatively stable in basic and neutral solutions. However, the corresponding acid, nitrous acid, HNO_2, is very unstable, for it tends to disproportionate to NO and HNO_3. It is a weak acid:

$$HNO_2 \rightleftharpoons H^+ + NO_2^- \qquad K = \frac{[H^+] \times [NO_2^-]}{[HNO_2]} = 6.0 \times 10^{-4} \text{ mole/l.}$$

NITROGEN TRIHALIDES. Nitrogen in the oxidation state +3 forms a series of trihalides—NF_3, NCl_3, and NI_3 are the best known—whose molecules are pyramidal, similar to that of ammonia. At room temperature only NF_3 is stable towards decomposition into nitrogen and fluorine ($\Delta H^\circ_{form} = -26$ kcal/mole) whereas NCl_3 and NI_3 have large positive heats of formation (NCl_3, $\Delta H^\circ_{form} = +55$ kcal/mole) and are explosives. This difference between the very stable NF_3 and the very unstable NCl_3 can be attributed largely to the appreciable difference in electronegativity between F (4.0) and N (3.0) which imparts a dipolar character to the N—F covalent bond and thus increases the bond strength. In NCl_3 the electronegativities of the N atom and of the Cl atom (3.0) are almost identical, and the N—Cl bond is much less strong then the N—F bond. Therefore, in the formation of the trihalides, $N_2 + 3\,X_2 \longrightarrow 2\,NX_3$, only with F is the energy released in forming 3 N—X bonds sufficient to compensate for the energy expended to break the N≡N triple bond and 3 X—X single bonds.

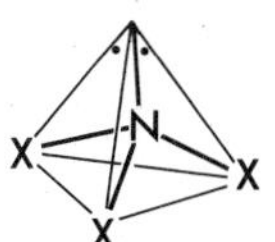

OXIDATION STATE +4: NO_2 AND N_2O_4

We have already mentioned the formation of the reddish-brown gas NO_2 when NO is oxidized by oxygen (above). Nitrogen dioxide, NO_2, can also be prepared in the laboratory by the thermal decomposition of solid lead(II) nitrate:

$$2\,Pb(NO_3)_{2(s)} \longrightarrow 2\,PbO_{(s)} + 4\,NO_{2(g)} + O_{2(g)}$$

The NO_2 molecule is bent, with an O—N—O angle of 134°. Like the molecule of NO, that of NO_2 has an unpaired electron in its valence shell and is therefore paramagnetic. As shown by the 4 important contributing structures, I–IV, of NO_2, given in the margin, the unpaired electron may be pictured as belonging to the N atom as well as to the two O atoms; also, each nitrogen-to-oxygen bond has a partial double-bond character.

I II III IV

At room temperature, reddish-brown NO_2 is always in equilibrium with its dimer, the pale yellow N_2O_4, dinitrogen tetroxide:

$$2\,NO_{2(g)} \rightleftharpoons N_2O_{4(g)} \qquad \Delta H^\circ = -13.9 \text{ kcal/mole-eqn}$$

The reaction is exothermic; that is, ΔH° is favorable to the dimerization of NO_2 to N_2O_4. However, the dimerization results in a decrease in the number of moles of gas —a negative, unfavorable entropy change ($\Delta S^\circ = -41.9$ cal/deg × mole-eqn). The value of ΔG° is still favorable to dimerization ($\Delta G^\circ = \Delta H^\circ - T\,\Delta S^\circ = -1.3$ kcal/mole-eqn at 25° and 1 atm), but so slightly that the dimerization does not proceed to completion and an equilibrium is established. As the temperature decreases this equilibrium is shifted to the right; the liquid and solid forms in which the equilibrium mixture exists at low temperatures are pale yellow, an indication that they are composed substantially of N_2O_4. Conversely, as the temperature rises, the gaseous mixture becomes increasingly brown-red in color, an indication of an increasing concentration of NO_2 molecules. The N_2O_4 molecule is planar, and has the stereochemistry and electronic structure shown in the accompanying figure. Notice that, whereas NO_2 has an unpaired electron and is paramagnetic, N_2O_4 has no unpaired electrons (the two originally unpaired electrons now constitute the N—N covalent bond) and is diamagnetic.

OXIDATION STATE +5: N_2O_5, HNO_3, AND THE NITRATES

DINITROGEN PENTOXIDE, N_2O_5. Dinitrogen pentoxide at room temperature is a white crystalline solid, which is obtained by the dehydration of 100 per cent HNO_3 with P_4O_{10}:

$$4\ HNO_{3(l)} + P_4O_{10(s)} \longrightarrow 2\ N_2O_{5(s)} + 4\ HPO_{3(l)}$$

With water, N_2O_5 immediately reforms nitric acid; thus N_2O_5 is the anhydride of HNO_3. (Only one other of the nitrogen oxides is an acid anhydride—N_2O_3, the anhydride of HNO_2.) Solid N_2O_5 sublimes (at room temperature) and the vapor decomposes (slowly at room temperature, more rapidly at higher temperatures) into NO_2 and O_2:

$$N_2O_{5(s)} \rightleftharpoons 2\ NO_{2(g)} + \tfrac{1}{2}\ O_{2(g)} \qquad \Delta H^\circ = +12.2\ \text{kcal/mole-eqn}$$

The reaction is endothermic (ΔH° is unfavorable), so in this case the increase in entropy resulting from the increased number of gas moles renders the reaction thermodynamically possible. The vapor of dinitrogen pentoxide consists of individual N_2O_5 molecules, which probably have the structure shown in the margin. In the solid state, dinitrogen pentoxide is an ionic compound consisting of linear NO_2^+ cations, $[\,:\!\dot{O}\!=\!N\!=\!\dot{O}\!:\,]^+$, and trigonal planar NO_3^- anions. The NO_2^+ cation is called *nitronium.* This solid dinitrogen pentoxide should be called more appropriately *nitronium nitrate,* $(NO_2)^+(NO_3)^-$.

NITRIC ACID, HNO_3. The most convenient laboratory method for preparing HNO_3 is to heat an alkali-metal nitrate, such as $NaNO_3$, with sulfuric acid, H_2SO_4. The relatively low boiling point of HNO_3 (83°C) compared with that of H_2SO_4 (290°C) makes this reaction feasible:

$$NaNO_{3(s)} + H_2SO_{4(l)} \longrightarrow HNO_{3(g)} + NaHSO_{4(s)}$$

Most commercial nitric acid is obtained from the reaction of gaseous NO_2 with water. The NO_2 is formed by the spontaneous oxidation of NO by oxygen; NO is first obtained from the catalytic oxidation of NH_3:

$$\begin{aligned} &1.\ 4\ NH_3 + 5\ O_2 \longrightarrow 4\ NO + 6\ H_2O \\ &2.\ 2\ NO + O_2 \longrightarrow 2\ NO_2 \\ &3.\ 3\ NO_2 + 2\ H_2O \longrightarrow 2\ HNO_3 + NO \end{aligned}$$

Reactions 1 and 2 have been extensively discussed on pp. 649 and 652, respectively. Reaction 3 is the disproportionation of the N^{+4} of NO_2 to give the N^{+5} of HNO_3 and the N^{+2} of NO. This NO can then be recycled to reaction 2 to form more NO_2, which then reacts with water according to reaction 3, and so on until the conversion to HNO_3 is complete.

THE PHYSICAL PROPERTIES OF NITRIC ACID. Pure 100 per cent nitric acid, HNO_3, is a colorless liquid with a boiling point of 83°C. It freezes to a colorless crystalline solid at −41.59°C. When a dilute aqueous solution of nitric acid is distilled, water is lost preferentially as against the HNO_3, until the concentration of the solution finally reaches 68.4 per cent. At this concentration the solution boils unchanged at 121.9°C, and the composition of the vapor is the same as that of the liquid. Both anhydrous liquid HNO_3 and its aqueous solutions usually become yellowish to yellow-brown if exposed to heat and light, because brownish NO_2 is formed by decomposition of the HNO_3 molecules or of the NO_3^- ions in the presence of H^+ ions:

$$4\ HNO_3 \longrightarrow 4\ NO_2 + O_2 + 2\ H_2O$$

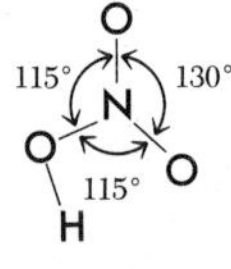

The HNO_3 molecule has the stereochemistry shown in the margin.

THE CHEMICAL PROPERTIES OF NITRIC ACID. Nitric acid exhibits three important sets of chemical properties: (1) acidic properties, (2) oxidizing properties, and (3) nitrating properties.

Acidic properties. Nitric acid is one of the strongest acids known; dilute aqueous solutions are almost completely ionized into H^+ and NO_3^- ions.

Oxidizing properties. Nitric acid—or more precisely the NO_3^- ion in the presence of H^+ ions—can act as an oxidant but not as a reductant (+5 is the highest oxidation state of nitrogen). The reduction products of nitric acid may be nitrogen itself, N_2, or one or more of the nitrogen compounds: N_2O, NO, NH_3, NO_2, for example. The reduction products depend both on the concentration of the nitric acid and on the reductant. As a general rule, the chief reduction product of *concentrated* nitric acid is NO_2, and the chief reduction product of *dilute* nitric acid is NO, but various amounts of other nitrogen products can also be formed.

REACTION OF HNO_3 WITH METALS. Nitric acid can oxidize all but a few metals, such as gold and platinum. Cold concentrated nitric acid, however, attacks some electropositive metals very slowly or only superficially because the oxidation first gives rise to a compact film of insoluble metal oxide, which adheres to the metallic surface and protects it from further attack. This phenomenon is called "passivation"; aluminum, iron, and chromium, for example, become "passive" in contact with cold concentrated nitric acid. These same metals, however, readily dissolve in dilute nitric acid, which although it is not such a strong oxidant it does not produce the protective oxide film.

The reactions of various metals with nitric acid solutions are good examples of the formation of the different reduction products of nitric acid. Metals below H_2 in the electromotive series, such as Cu and Ag, react with *concentrated* nitric acid solutions, giving NO_2 as the main reduction product:

$$Cu + 4\ HNO_3 \longrightarrow Cu(NO_3)_2 + 2\ NO_2 + 2\ H_2O$$

The rate at which concentrated nitric acid reacts with these metals, as well as with others, is often slow at the start. But once the reaction has begun, it proceeds vigorously, because the reaction itself is exothermic and also because the reduction product, NO_2 gas, apparently acts as a catalyst. For this reason, heat is supplied at the beginning of the reaction, although the reaction mixture later requires cooling for smooth operation.

With *dilute* nitric acid solution, Cu and Ag react to yield NO as the principal reduction product:

$$3\ Cu + 8\ HNO_3 \longrightarrow 3\ Cu(NO_3)_2 + 2\ NO + 4\ H_2O$$

The more electropositive metals, such as Zn and Mg, which are better reducing agents than Cu, can under appropriate conditions reduce the N^{+5} of the NO_3^- ion to its lowest possible oxidation number, -3, with formation of the NH_4^+ ion:

$$4\ Zn + 10\ HNO_3 \longrightarrow 4\ Zn(NO_3)_2 + NH_4NO_3 + 3\ H_2O$$

In very dilute solutions, HNO_3 may lose its oxidizing properties completely, and the solution will then act simply as a non-oxidizing acid. For example, 1 or 2 per cent nitric acid reacts with magnesium to liberate H_2 gas:

$$Mg + 2\ H^+ + 2\ NO_3^- \longrightarrow H_2 + Mg^{++} + 2\ NO_3^-$$

THE REACTION OF HNO_3 WITH NON-METALS. Solutions of nitric acid oxidize the non-metals carbon and sulfur to their dioxides:

$$3\ C_{(s)} + 4\ HNO_{3(aq)} \longrightarrow 3\ CO_{2(g)} + 4\ NO_{(g)} + 2\ H_2O_{(l)}$$
$$3\ S_{(s)} + 4\ HNO_{3(aq)} \longrightarrow 3\ SO_{2(g)} + 4\ NO_{(g)} + 2\ H_2O_{(l)}$$

The SO_2 evolved in this reaction may be further oxidized by more HNO_3 to H_2SO_4:

$$S_{(s)} + 2\ HNO_{3(aq)} \longrightarrow H_2SO_{4(aq)} + 2\ NO_{(g)}$$

Concentrated HNO_3 oxidizes elemental phosphorus, P_4, to its highest oxidation state, forming H_3PO_4; the reduction products are a mixture of NO and NO_2:

$$P_{4(s)} + 10\ HNO_{3(aq)} + H_2O_{(l)} \longrightarrow 4\ H_3PO_{4(aq)} + 5\ NO_{(g)} + 5\ NO_{2(g)}$$

AQUA REGIA. Some metals, such as gold and platinum, and certain compounds, such as HgS, are not oxidized even by hot concentrated HNO_3. Such metals and compounds can often be oxidized by a mixture of three parts (by volume) of concentrated HCl and one part of concentrated HNO_3. This mixture is called *aqua regia* (royal water), because it is able to oxidize even the noble metals gold and platinum. The exceptionally strong oxidizing properties of aqua regia result from several concurring factors. First, the solution contains, in addition to the NO_3^- ion, nitrosyl chloride, NOCl, which is a strong oxidant; second, the Cl^- ions from the hydrochloric acid facilitate the oxidation of the metal by converting the metal ions into complex chloro-anions. This combined action may be illustrated by the oxidation of HgS with aqua regia:

$$\begin{array}{ccccc} HgS_{(s)} & \rightleftharpoons & Hg^{++} & + & S^= \\ & & + & & + \\ & & 4\,Cl^- & & 2\,H^+ + NO_3^- \\ & & \downarrow\uparrow & & \downarrow\uparrow \\ & & [HgCl_4]^= & & S + NO_2 + H_2O \end{array}$$

Notice that the Cl^- ions combine with the Hg^{++} ions (whose oxidation number is unchanged) to form the complex chloro-anion $[HgCl_4]^=$, while the NO_3^- ions (in the presence of H^+ ions) oxidize the $S^=$ ions to elemental sulfur. The over-all equation is:

$$3\,HgS_{(s)} + 12\,HCl_{(aq)} + 2\,HNO_{3(aq)} \longrightarrow 6\,H^+_{(aq)} + 3\,[HgCl_4]^=_{(aq)} + 3\,S_{(s)} + 2\,NO_{(g)} + 4\,H_2O_{(l)}$$

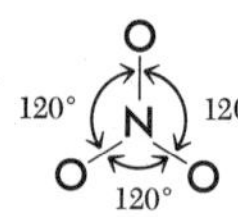

THE NITRATES. The metal nitrates can be prepared by neutralizing metal hydroxides, oxides, or carbonates with nitric acid. The anions present in these compounds—OH^-, $O^=$, $CO_3^=$—react with the hydrogen ions of nitric acid to form water (or water and CO_2 gas in the case of carbonates), thereby leaving only NO_3^- anions in solution. The nitrate salts, $M^{+n}(NO_3)_n^-$, separate when the water is evaporated from the solution.

Most metal nitrates are decomposed by heat. The products of decomposition depend on the nature of the positive ion, and, in the case of metal cations, on the position of the metal in the electromotive series. We have discussed the decomposition of ammonium nitrate, NH_4NO_3 to form N_2O and H_2O (p. 650). The thermal decomposition of the nitrates of the more electropositive metals, such as the alkali-metals and the alkaline-earth metals, yields the corresponding nitrites and oxygen:

$$2\,KNO_{3(s)} \longrightarrow 2\,KNO_{2(s)} + O_{2(g)} \quad \text{and} \quad Mg(NO_3)_{2(s)} \longrightarrow Mg(NO_2)_{2(s)} + O_{2(g)}$$

The nitrates of metals that appear *lower* in the electromotive series, such as $Pb(NO_3)_2$ and $Cu(NO_3)_2$ generally yield the metal oxide together with NO_2 and O_2:

$$2\,Pb(NO_3)_{2(s)} \longrightarrow 2\,PbO_{(s)} + 4\,NO_{2(g)} + O_{2(g)}$$

And the nitrates of metals that appear even lower in the electromotive series, such as $Hg(NO_3)_2$ and $AgNO_3$, produce the free metal together with NO_2 and O_2:

$$Hg(NO_3)_{2(s)} \longrightarrow Hg_{(g)} + 2\,NO_{2(g)} + O_{2(g)}$$

HYDROGEN CYANIDE AND THE METAL CYANIDES

$\left\{\begin{array}{l} H\!:\!:\!CN\!: \\ H\!\equiv\!CN \end{array}\right.$

$[:C\!:\!:\!N:]^-$

Hydrogen cyanide, HCN, is a very low-boiling liquid (b.p. 26°C), so that it can be readily obtained both in a gaseous and in liquid form. Liquid or gaseous HCN is extremely soluble in water; the solution is a very weak acid ($K = 7.2 \times 10^{-10}$ moles/l.) called hydrocyanic acid.

The HCN molecule is linear, and has the electronic structure shown in the margin, with a triple covalent bond between the bonded N and C atoms. The salts of the cyanide anion, vary widely both in structures and properties, depending on the cation. The alkali-metal cyanides, except LiCN, are essentially ionic compounds;

NaCN crystallizes with the rock-salt structure. Since HCN is a very weak acid, the alkali-metal cyanides hydrolyze extensively in water, so that their solutions react as bases: $CN^- + H_2O \rightleftharpoons OH^- + HCN$. Mercury(II) cyanide, $Hg(CN)_2$, consists of covalent molecules with an almost linear stereochemistry, :N≡C—Hg—C≡N:, and silver cyanide, AgCN, is a polymer which contains continuous linear chains ···Ag—C≡N—Ag-C≡N—Ag—C≡N····. The CN^- ion has an unusually strong tendency to coordinate to metal ions; we shall discuss some typical cyano-complexes in Chapter 33. *Hydrogen cyanide, HCN, and the cyanide salts are extremely poisonous. Great caution must be taken in handling all cyanide compounds, because if they enter the body in any way they may cause almost instant death.*

29-4 Oxidation-Potential Diagrams of Nitrogen Compounds

As with the halogens and sulfur, the oxidation potentials of nitrogen in its various oxidation states have different values in acid solutions and in basic solutions. Thus, the oxidation-reduction behavior of nitrogen compounds varies gradually as the H^+ ion concentration varies. The Latimer oxidation-potential diagram of nitrogen in 1 *M* acid solution follows.

In Acid Solution

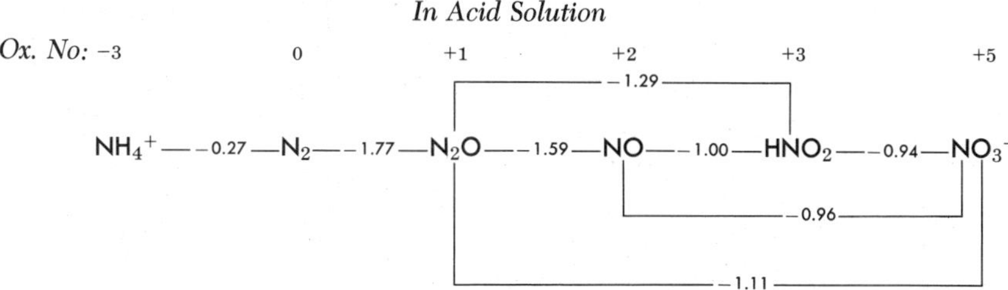

As usual, we can rationalize the observed oxidation-reduction behavior of nitrogen compounds on the basis of the Latimer oxidation-potential diagram. First, the large negative potentials of the three couples N_2O—−1.11—NO_3^-, NO—−1.00—NO_3^-, and HNO_2—−0.94—NO_3^- tell us that the NO_3^- ion in the presence of 1 *M* H^+ ion is a strong oxidant which has almost the same tendency to form N_2O, NO, and HNO_2 as the reduction products. For example, it can oxidize the I^- ion to I_2 ($E° = -0.54$ v), and the Fe^{++} ion to the Fe^{+++} ion ($E° = -0.77$ v).

Second, the oxidation-potential diagram, NO—−1.00—HNO_2—−0.94—NO_3^-, tells us that HNO_2 tends to disproportionate into nitric acid and nitrogen oxide, NO, even though the rate of this reaction is slow in cold dilute solution.

$$3\,HNO_2 \longrightarrow H^+ + NO_3^- + 2\,NO + H_2O$$

You can, as an exercise, construct the Latimer free energy diagram for these three compounds, using the relationship $\Delta G° = -23.06 \times nE°$, and repeat this discussion in terms of free energy changes.

Since the oxidation of HNO_2 to NO_3^- has a high negative $E°$ value (−0.94 v), a couple whose $E°$ value is more negative than −0.94 v is required to bring about this reaction. Such a couple could be, for example, the Mn^{++},MnO_4^- couple in 1 *M* H^+ solution ($E° = -1.51$ v). Also since in 1 *M* H^+ solution the $E°$ value for the Cl^-,Cl_2 couple is −1.40 v and for the Br^-,Br_2 couple it is −1.09 v, both Cl_2 and Br_2 in 1 *M* H^+ solution can oxidize HNO_2 to HNO_3.

The negative potential of the couple, NO—−1.00—HNO_2, indicates that nitrous acid can also act as an oxidant. For example, the Fe^{++} ion ($E°$: Fe^{++},Fe^{+++} = −0.77 v) and the Ti^{++} ion ($E°$: Ti^{++},Ti^{+++} = +0.37 v), are oxidized by HNO_2 to their tripositive states, and NO is the reduction product.

The oxidation-potential diagram for nitrogen in basic solutions ($[OH^-] = 1M$) follows:

In Basic Solution

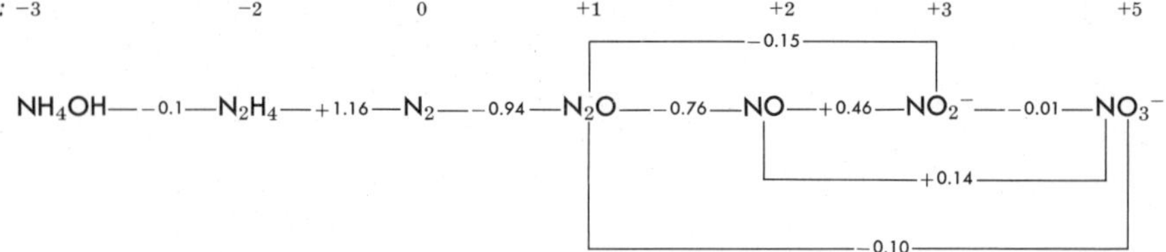

The effect of the concentration of the H^+ ion on the oxidizing ability of the NO_3^- ion becomes strikingly clear when we compare the couple NO_2^-,NO_3^- ($E^\circ_{basic} = -0.01$ v) with the couple HNO_2,NO_3^- in acid solution ($E^\circ = -0.94$ v). The NO_2^-,NO_3^- couple in basic solution is a very poor oxidant, as the very small E°_{basic} value, -0.01 v, indicates, and in fact NO_2^- can be oxidized to NO_3^- by many comparatively weak oxidizing couples with E° values more negative than -0.01 v. Finally, if we consider together both the acid solution and the basic solution Latimer oxidation diagrams we see that any nitrogen compound with an oxidation state intermediate between -3 (NH_3 or NH_4^+) and $+5$ (HNO_3 or NO_3^-) can, under the appropriate pH conditions, act either as an oxidant or as a reductant.

29-5 The Nitrogen Cycle

All living organisms, plant and animal alike, contain nitrogen combined with carbon, nitrogen, and oxygen in proteins. Proteins are organic compounds with a very large molecular weight (they may contain hundreds of N, C, H, and O atoms per molecule) which are essential to life. Animals and most plants must assimilate nitrogen compounds as a source of nitrogen for the formation of proteins, because they are unable to make direct use of the elemental nitrogen, N_2, present in the atmosphere.

There are, however, a few plants of the leguminous family (clover, alfalfa, beans) that have nearly direct access to nitrogen by virtues of a symbiotic (cooperative) relationship with certain bacteria. These bacteria, which are found on the root nodules of the leguminous plants, can absorb elemental nitrogen and combine it with other elements to form compounds that the plants can absorb through their roots and utilize as a source of nitrogen in the synthesis of the proteins. The bacteria that perform this function are called *nitrogen-fixing bacteria.*

A small amount of the nitrogen in the atmosphere is also converted into an assimilable form by the electrical discharges of lightning, which cause the nitrogen and oxygen of the air to combine. The nitrogen oxides ultimately form nitric acid by reaction with atmospheric moisture, and this is carried to the soil by rain.

If all plants had the ability to live in symbiosis with nitrogen-fixing bacteria and if discharges of lightning were more effective, there would be no need for farmers to add assimilable nitrogen, in the form of fertilizer, to the soil. But since this is not so it is fortunate that there is an unlimited supply of nitrogen in the atmosphere from which we can manufacture ammonia and other nitrogen compounds for use in fertilizers. The decay of waste products from animals and the decay of dead plant and animal organisms also yield nitrogen compounds that find their way back to plants for reconversion into proteins. Some of the nitrogen in the decaying material is also converted into free nitrogen, N_2, by other bacteria. In this way, the nitrogen consumed by living plants and animals is returned to the atmosphere. The circulation of nitrogen—from the atmosphere to chemical compounds that can be assimilated by plants, then to plant and animal proteins, and ultimately back to nitrogen compounds or to free nitrogen, N_2—is called the "nitrogen cycle."

Quite apart from their practical usefulness, the nitrogen-fixing bacteria pose one of the most interesting questions of present-day chemistry. Since these bacteria act at ordinary conditions of temperature and pressure, the nitrogen compounds synthesized through their action must be thermodynamically stable with respect to their free elements. The bacteria simply act as a live catalyst—that is, they provide a low-activation-energy path for the reaction of the very inert $:N{\equiv}N:$ molecules with other substances. But what are the kinetically favorable paths that enable the nitrogen-fixing bacteria to catalyze reactions which otherwise require temperatures of the order of 400°–600°C or higher? If we knew the answer to this question, not only could we duplicate these low-activation-energy reactions artificially on an industrial scale, but we would also gain an invaluable insight into the mechanism of reactions involving the N_2 molecule—and possibly a new branch of synthetic chemistry would be opened. Much work is being done on the artifical fixation of nitrogen, and many interesting results have been obtained, but the effective and mild catalytic action of nitrogen-fixing bacteria is not yet understood.

29-6 Phosphorus

In the preceding chapter we found that the atoms of sulfur, the second element of Group VIB, have less tendency to form *multiple* bonds, one to another, than do the atoms of oxygen, the first element of that family. The same relationship holds for the first two members of the nitrogen family, for phosphorus has much less tendency to form such multiple bonds than nitrogen. Thus, in the vapor state nitrogen exists as N_2 molecules, in which the two N atoms are joined by a triple bond, whereas phosphorus exists as P_4 molecules in which each P atom is joined to the other three by a single bond. Also, phosphorus atoms have some tendency to form single bonds with one another (catenation), both in the element and in compounds, but this tendency is not so pronounced as in sulfur. As nitrogen does, phosphorus exists in various oxidation states, but phosphorus compounds generally are not strong oxidants or reductants.

$:N{\equiv}N:$

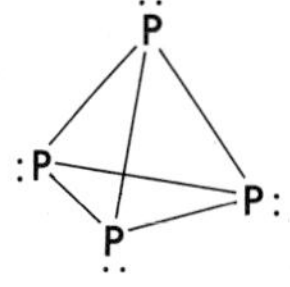

THE OCCURRENCE AND PREPARATION OF PHOSPHORUS

Phosphorus, the twelfth most abundant element, is the only member of Group VB that is never found in the free state in nature. The element occurs principally in the form of phosphates—the simple calcium phosphate, $Ca_3(PO_4)_2$, and the mixed phosphate $CaF_2 \cdot 3\ Ca_3(PO_4)_2$, known as apatite. Phosphorus occurs in all fertile soils; if it is present as a water-soluble compound, it can be absorbed by plants. Phosphorus is an essential element in all living matter, and calcium phosphate, $Ca_3(PO_4)_2$, is the principal constituent of bones (about 60 per cent).

Phosphorus is commonly prepared by a process that starts with the reaction of $Ca_3(PO_4)_2$ or $CaF_2 \cdot 3\ Ca_3(PO_4)_2$ with SiO_2 and coke in an electric-arc furnace at a temperature of 1,450°C. The first stage of the reaction is essentially the displacement from $Ca(PO_4)_2$ of the volatile P_4O_{10} (the anhydride of phosphoric acid) by the nonvolatile SiO_2 (the anhydride of silicic acid):

$$2\ Ca_3(PO_4)_{2(s)} + 6\ SiO_{2(s)} \longrightarrow 6\ CaSiO_{3(s)} + P_4O_{10(g)}$$

The gaseous P_4O_{10} is then reduced as soon as it is formed by the heated coke:

$$P_4O_{10(g)} + 10\ C_{(s)} \longrightarrow P_{4(g)} + 10\ CO_{(g)}$$

At intervals, the $CaSiO_3$ and the excess SiO_2 are removed as slag from the bottom of the electric furnace. The phosphorus vapor is condensed to the liquid state under water, to prevent it from being rapidly oxidized by air. On solidification of the liquid at room temperature, waxy white phosphorus is obtained, which can be further purified by fractional distillation in a vacuum or in an inert atmosphere of nitrogen.

PROPERTIES OF ELEMENTARY PHOSPHORUS

In the solid state, phosphorus exists in various crystalline modifications, thus closely resembling sulfur in this respect.

WHITE OR YELLOW PHOSPHORUS. The condensation of phosphorus vapor at ordinary conditions yields white phosphorus. This form is also referred to as yellow phosphorus, because of the yellowish tinge it rapidly acquires when it is exposed to light. White phosphorus is a soft, waxy solid which is a molecular crystal of P_4 molecules. It melts at 44.2°C and boils at 280°C. It is insoluble in water but is soluble in many organic solvents—for example, carbon disulfide, CS_2, and benzene, C_6H_6. In these solvents it exists as P_4 molecules, as it also does in the vapor state (below 800°C).

White phosphorus ignites spontaneously in air, so it must be stored under water. White phosphorus is the most reactive of all the solid forms of phosphorus. It is extremely toxic and causes serious burns if it comes in contact with the skin. Consequently, extreme care must be exercised in handling it.

RED AND BLACK PHOSPHORUS. When white phosphorus is exposed to light, it changes very slowly to a more stable form called red phosphorus:

$$\text{Phosphorus (white)} \longrightarrow \text{Phosphorus (red)} \qquad \Delta H = -4.4 \text{ kcal/mole of P atoms}$$

The rate at which the white form is converted to the red form can be increased by raising the temperature and by adding a catalyst, such as iodine. Red phosphorus is a covalent crystal consisting of infinite chains of phosphorus atoms. The structure of these chains, however, is not known with certainty. Red phosphorus is much less reactive than white phosphorus—for example, it must be heated to about 260°C before it ignites in air.

The most stable form of phosphorus known is "black phosphorus" obtained by prolonged heating of white phosphorus with copper metal as a catalyst. Black phosphorus consists of layers of P atoms, each bonded to three nearest neighbors as shown in Fig. 29-1. Notice that in white phosphorus the small P_4 molecules are held together by van der Waals forces only, whereas in red and black phosphorus the P-to-P bonds extend throughout the entire covalent crystal. This difference in structure explains why white phosphorus is more volatile, more soluble in all solvents, and more reactive then the other forms.

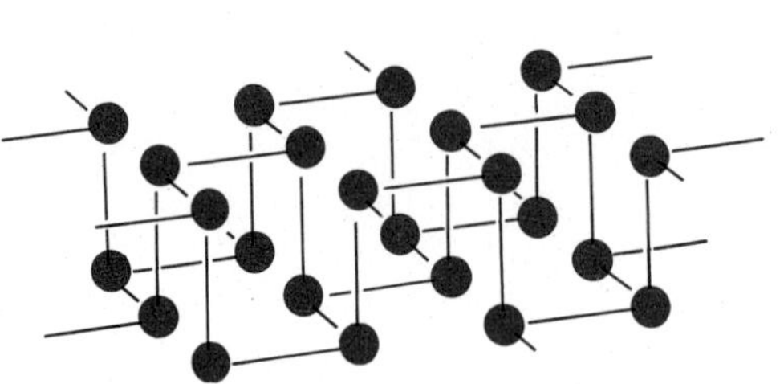

FIGURE 29-1 Structure of black phosphorus.

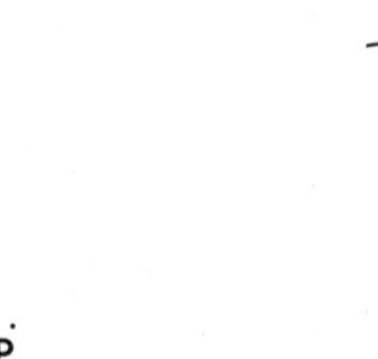

In the gaseous state at temperatures below 800°C, phosphorus consists of tetrahedral P_4 molecules in which each P atom is linked to the other three P atoms by a single covalent bond and also has a lone electron pair, as shown in the margin. In the P_4 molecule the P—P—P bond angles are 60°. At 800°C and above, the P_4 molecules begin to dissociate into P_2 molecules. It is very likely that the electronic structure of P_2 is similar to that of N_2.

:P⁝⁝P:

USES OF PHOSPHORUS

Most of the phosphorus prepared commercially goes into the manufacture of soluble phosphates, especially the sodium and ammonium salts which are employed as fertilizers. The ammonium phosphates are especially useful, for they supply both nitrogen and phosphorus to the soil. Phosphorus is also the starting material in the preparation of many other compounds of commercial importance, for example, P_4S_3, which is used in the manufacture of "strike anywhere" matches.

Phosphine, PH_3, the binary compound of phosphorus and hydrogen which corresponds to ammonia, NH_3, has no commercial importance. The molecule of phosphine, PH_3, like that of ammonia, NH_3, has a pyramidal structure, but the H—P—H bond angle, 94°, is smaller than the H—N—H bond angle, 107°. Also, because the phosphorus atom is larger than the nitrogen atom, the P—H internuclear distance, 1.42 A, in PH_3 is greater than the N—H distance, 1.01 A, in NH_3.

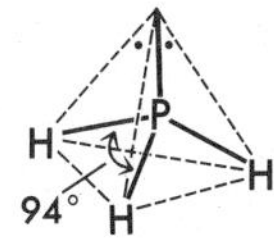

Phosphine is an extremely poisonous, colorless gas that is only moderately soluble in water (in contrast to the extremely soluble NH_3). It is a much weaker Lewis base than ammonia—that is, the phosphorus atom in PH_3 shows far less tendency to donate a pair of electrons to a proton to form $[PH_4]^+$ than the nitrogen atom in NH_3 does in forming $[NH_4]^+$. In fact, phosphine has no basic character in water solution, because the OH^- ion is a much stronger base than the PH_3 molecules. Phosphonium salts can be obtained only under anhydrous conditions. Phosphine gas, PH_3, is prepared in the laboratory by boiling white phosphorus with a solution of a strong base, such as KOH. The soluble hypophosphite ion, $H_2PO_2^-$, is the other product of the disproportionation of phosphorus.

$$P_{4(s)} + \cancel{3\,K^+_{(aq)}} + 3\,OH^-_{(aq)} + 3\,H_2O_{(l)} \longrightarrow PH_{3(g)} + \cancel{3\,K^+_{(aq)}} + 3\,H_2PO^-_{2(aq)}$$

THE PHOSPHORUS HALIDES. Fluorine, chlorine, and bromine combine directly with phosphorus to form compounds of the types PX_3 and PX_5 (X = halogen). Iodine forms PI_3 and P_2I_4.

TRIHALIDES. The trihalides of phosphorus, PX_3, are all pyramidal molecules, similar to phosphine, PH_3, except that the X—P—X bond angle is slightly larger (X—P—X) ≅ 100° versus H—P—H = 94°). The phosphorus trihalides are stable compounds which at room temperature do not have the capacity to decompose into their elements because their ΔG°_{form} is negative (compare the different behavior of the nitrogen halides, except NF_3, p. 653). In the presence of water, all PX_3 compounds hydrolyze completely to phosphorus acid and halogen halide:

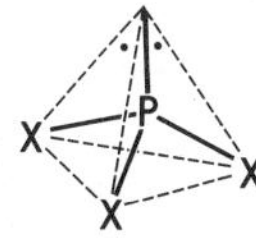

$$PCl_3 + 3\,H_2O \longrightarrow H_3PO_3 + 3\,HCl$$

The phosphorus trihalides, and in particular PF_3 and PCl_3, have a strong tendency to share the lone electron pair on the P atom with a suitable acceptor—usually a transition metal—to form coordination compounds.

PENTAHALIDES. Since P is in Series 3 of the Periodic Table, it has available empty 3*d* orbitals, whose energy is not very much higher than that of the 3*s* and 3*p* orbitals of the valence electrons. This enables phosphorus to expand its valence shell beyond 8 electrons, and to form many compounds with a coordination number greater than 4. (Nitrogen cannot form such compounds because the available empty orbitals 3*s*3*p*3*d*, are all much higher in energy than the 2*s*2*p* orbitals of the valence electrons.) For example, NF_3 does not react with F_2, but PF_3 does:

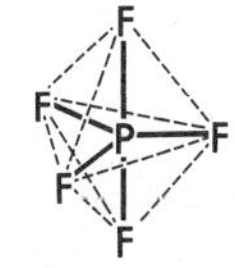

$$PF_3 + F_2 \longrightarrow PF_5$$

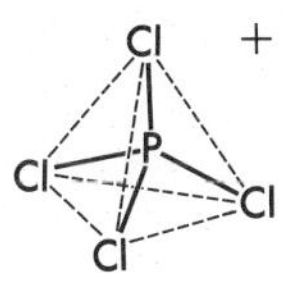

The pentahalides PF_5, PCl_5 and PBr_5 are stable compounds; PI_5 is not known. In the vapor state the phosphorus pentahalides are covalent compounds composed of trigonal bipyramidal PX_5 molecules. In the solid state, however, the pentachloride and pentabromide have different structures. Solid phosphorus pentachloride is ionic and contains positive tetrahedral PCl_4^+ ions and negative octahedral PCl_6^- ions, arranged in a three-dimensional crystal lattice of the CsCl type. Solid phosphorus pentabromide is also ionic, the ions present being the tetrahedral PBr_4^+ cations and Br^- ions. Solid pentabromide has this structure rather than one similar to the penta-

$[PCl_4]^+$

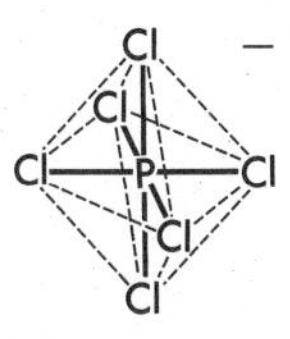

$[PCl_6]^-$

chloride because the Br atoms are larger than the Cl atoms, and six Br atoms cannot fit around the relatively small central P atom.

Partial hydrolysis of the pentahalides of phosphorus yields phosphorus oxyhalides and the hydrogen halide, HX:

$$PCl_5 + H_2O \longrightarrow POCl_3 + 2\ HCl$$

The addition of excess water brings about the hydrolysis of the $POCl_3$ and produces phosphoric acid:

$$POCl_3 + 3\ H_2O \longrightarrow H_3PO_4 + 3\ HCl$$

THE OXIDES OF PHOSPHORUS

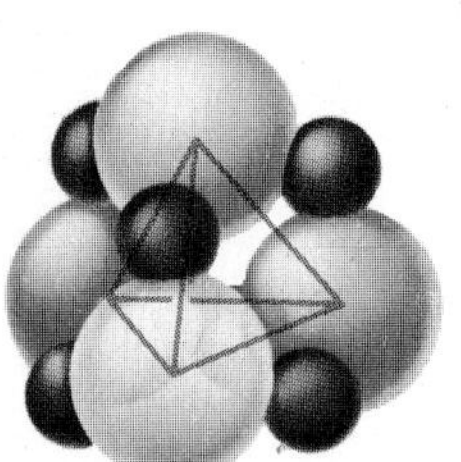

P_4O_6 molecule

P_4O_{10} molecule

Among the common oxides of phosphorus are the compounds P_4O_6 (the anhydride of H_3PO_3) and P_4O_{10} (the anhydride of H_3PO_4).

THE OXIDE P_4O_6. This compound is usually called phosphorus trioxide, but a better name would be phosphorus(III) oxide, or tetraphosphorus hexaoxide. Both in the vapor state and in the solid state, this compound consists of P_4O_6 molcules. In the P_4O_6 molecule each P atom is bonded to 3 O atoms (and in addition has a lone pair), and each O atom is linked to 2 P atoms (and has 2 lone pairs). Thus each O atom forms a bridge between 2 P atoms; there is no direct bonding among the 4 P atoms, or among the 6 O atoms. In P_4O_6, the 4 phosphorus atoms are located at the corners of a tertahedron and each of the 6 oxygen atoms is located just above the mid-point of one of the edges of this tetrahedron. Notice that this structure is consistent with the usual rules about lone-pair–lone-pair and bond-pair–lone-pair repulsion (each P atom forms 3 bonds in a pyramidal arrangement, and each O atom forms 2 bonds in an angular arrangement).

The compound P_4O_6 is a white crystalline solid that melts at 23.8°C and boils without decomposing at 175.4°C; it is very poisonous. It can be obtained only under special conditions, by slowly passing a stream of oxygen-enriched air at reduced pressure over white phosphorus.

THE OXIDE P_4O_{10}. This compound is usually called phosphorus pentoxide, but a better name would be phosphorus(V) oxide, or tetraphosphorus decaoxide. In the vapor and solid state this compound consists of P_4O_{10} molecules. The structure of the P_4O_{10} molecule is similar to that of P_4O_6, except that each P atom has a bonded O atom in place of the lone pair in the apical position. The compound P_4O_{10} is readily formed by burning white or red phosphorus in an excess of air or oxygen:

$$P_4 + 5\ O_2 \longrightarrow P_4O_{10}.$$

THE OXOACIDS OF PHOSPHORUS

Phosphorus forms a number of oxoacids, of which the most important are those of phosphorus(V) and phosphorus(III) (shown in Table 29-3).

THE OXOACIDS OF PHOSPHORUS(V) AND THEIR SALTS. The three oxoacids of phosphorus(V) (Table 29-4) differ from one another in the amount of water combined with phosphorus(V) oxide. The acid formed from the largest amount of water is called *ortho*phosphoric acid. When *one* molecule of water is removed from *one* molecule of orthophosphoric acid, the *meta*phosphoric acid is formed. When *one* molecule of water is removed from *two* molecules of orthophosphoric acid, the *pyro*phosphoric acid is formed. The most important of these acids is H_3PO_4, orthophosphoric acid, often referred to simply as phosphoric acid.

Preparation. Orthophosphoric acid, H_3PO_4, can be prepared in the laboratory by the action of excess water on the pentahalides, PX_5, on the oxyhalides, POX_3, or on the oxide, P_4O_{10}. When a small quantity of water is added to P_4O_{10}, the metaphosphoric acid, $(HPO_3)_n$, is first produced. As more water is added, the pyrophosphoric acid, $H_4P_2O_7$, and finally the orthophosphoric acid, H_3PO_4, are formed.

TABLE 29-3 OXOACIDS OF PHOSPHORUS(V) AND PHOSPHORUS(III)

Ox. No. of Phosphorus	Formula and Name	No. of Replaceable H	Structure
5	H_3PO_4 Orthophosphoric acid	3	
5	$H_4P_2O_7$ Pyrophosphoric acid	4	P—O—P = 134°
5	$(HPO_3)_n$ Metaphosphoric acid	1 n	Probably chains or rings of $\{PO_4\}$ tetrahedra sharing O atoms
3	H_3PO_3 Orthophosphorous acid	2	
1	H_3PO_2 Hypophosphorous acid	1	

$$P_4O_{10} + 2\ H_2O \longrightarrow 4/n\ (HPO_3)_n$$
$$P_4O_{10} + 4\ H_2O \longrightarrow 2\ H_4P_2O_7$$
$$P_4O_{10} + 6\ H_2O \longrightarrow 4\ H_3PO_4$$

Treating P_4O_{10}, $(HPO_3)_n$, or $H_4P_2O_7$ with excess H_2O always produces H_3PO_4, orthophosphoric acid, as the final product. When the H_3PO_4 is heated, some water is lost and either $H_4P_2O_7$ or $(HPO_3)_n$ is produced, depending on the temperature, as indicated above. Metaphosphoric acid, $(HPO_3)_n$ cannot be dehydrated further.

The anhydride P_4O_{10} is an excellent drying agent, whose drying properties persist even after it has absorbed some water, because the mixture of P_4O_{10} and $(HPO_3)_n$ thus formed has only an extremely low vapor pressure of water. Such drying agents as solid $CaCl_2$ and concentrated H_2SO_4, on the other hand, exert an appreciable water vapor pressure after they have absorbed some water. And, in fact, H_2SO_4 can actually be dehydrated to its anhydride by an excess of P_4O_{10}:

$$2\ n\ H_2SO_4 + n\ P_4O_{10} \longrightarrow 4\ (HPO_3)_n + 2\ n\ SO_3$$

In the meta-, pyro-, and ortho-phosphoric acids, each of the hydrogen atoms is covalently bonded to an oxygen atom as an OH group and thus is a "replaceable," or acidic, hydrogen atom. The acid dissociation constants, K, of the ortho- and pyrophosphoric acids are given in Table 29-4. As the K values indicate, there is one strongly ionizable hydrogen atom per each phosphorus atom; the other hydrogen atoms are weakly acidic, as is the rule for polybasic acids. Thus, we can calculate that a 0.1 molar solution of H_3PO_4 ($K_1 = 7.5 \times 10^{-3}$ mole/l.) has H^+ ion and $H_2PO_4^-$ ion concentrations of 0.025 mole/l., corresponding to the ionization of 25 per cent of the

TABLE 29-4 IONIZATION CONSTANTS OF PHOSPHORIC ACIDS

Ionization constant (mole/l.)	Acid	
	$H_4P_2O_7$	H_3PO_4
K_1	$[1.4 \times 10^{-1}]$	$[7.5 \times 10^{-3}]$
K_2	$[1.1 \times 10^{-2}]$	6.2×10^{-8}
K_3	2.9×10^{-7}	5×10^{-13}
K_4	3.6×10^{-9}	—

total acid. Similarly, from the value of the second ionization constant, $K_2 = 6.2 \times 10^{-8}$ mole/l., we calculate that the $HPO_4^{=}$ ion concentration is approximately 6.2×10^{-8} mole/l. And using $K_3 = 5 \times 10^{-13}$ mole/l. for the third ionization constant, we calculate the $PO_4^{\equiv}$ ion concentration as approximately 2×10^{-19} mole/l. Since the $PO_4^{\equiv}$ ion concentration is exceedingly small, phosphate salts containing the $PO_4^{\equiv}$ ion are seldom precipitated from an orthophosphoric acid solution, even when the solubility product of the phosphate salt is very small. The compounds that do precipitate from such solutions usually contain the $H_2PO_4^-$ ion or the $HPO_4^{=}$ ion.

Orthophosphoric acid, H_3PO_4, being a tribasic acid, forms three series of salts: for example, NaH_2PO_4, sodium dihydrogen phosphate; Na_2HPO_4, disodium hydrogen phosphate; and Na_3PO_4, trisodium phosphate. The solubilities of these salts in water decrease in the order $NaH_2PO_4 > Na_2HPO_4 > Na_3PO_4$. In Chapter 20, p. 442, we have discussed the relative acidic and basic character—in the Bronsted sense—of H_3PO_4, $H_2PO_4^-$, $HPO_4^{=}$, and $PO_4^{\equiv}$. Those considerations explain, that as a result of hydrolysis, solutions of NaH_2PO_4 are acidic ($[H^+] > 10^{-7}$), whereas solutions of Na_3PO_4 are basic ($[H^+] < 10^{-7}$).

THE OXOACIDS OF PHOSPHORUS(III) AND THEIR SALTS. Three known phosphorus(III) oxoacids are listed in Table 29-4. The most important—H_3PO_3, *ortho*-phosphorous acid, usually referred to simply as phosphorous acid—can be conveniently prepared by the reaction of PCl_3 with cold water:

$$PCl_3 + 3\,H_2O \longrightarrow H_3PO_3 + 3\,HCl$$

Although H_3PO_3 contains three hydrogen atoms, it is only a dibasic acid, for only two of the H atoms are linked to oxygen atoms and hence ionizable; the third H atom is bonded directly to the central P atom (Table 29-3). The two ionization reactions of H_3PO_3 and the K_1 and K_2 values, follow:

$$H_3PO_3 \rightleftharpoons H^+ + H_2PO_3^- \qquad K_1 = 2 \times 10^{-2}\ \text{mole/l.}$$
$$H_2PO_3^- \rightleftharpoons H^+ + HPO_3^{=} \qquad K_2 = 2 \times 10^{-7}\ \text{mole/l.}$$

The $HPO_3^{=}$ ion cannot ionize further; that is, the $PO_3^{\equiv}$ ion does not exist in aqueous solutions.

HYPOPHOSPHOROUS ACID, H_3PO_2, AND HYPOPHOSPHITES. This acid is a low-melting crystalline solid (m.p. 26°C) and is very soluble in water. As indicated by its structure (Table 29-3), it is a monobasic acid, because only one of its three H atoms belongs to a OH group and is "replaceable." Thus, the hypophosphites have the general formula $M(H_2PO_2)_n$, where n is the positive charge of the metal ion M—for example, NaH_2PO_2 and $Ba(H_2PO_2)_2$. Hypophosphorous acid, H_3PO_2, is a moderately strong acid ($K \simeq 10^{-2}$ mole/l.). We have already seen that the hypophosphite ion, $(H_2PO_2)^-$, is formed together with phosphine, PH_3, by the reaction of white phosphorus with a solution of an alkali-metal hydroxide (p. 661). The free acid can be obtained by treating a solution of $Ba(H_2PO_2)_2$ with the calculated quantity of H_2SO_4, causing the precipitation of insoluble $BaSO_4$ while H_3PO_2 remains in solution.

A COMPARISON OF THE OXOACIDS OF SULFUR, NITROGEN, AND PHOSPHORUS

We can now make some general comparisons among the oxoacids of sulfur, nitrogen, and phosphorus. First, whereas HNO_3 and H_2SO_4 are strong acids, H_3PO_4 is only a moderately strong acid. This behavior is in agreement with the generalizations on the strength of acid of formula $EO_m(OH)_n$, which we discussed in Chapter 20. Second, the oxoacids in which nitrogen and sulfur appear in their highest oxidation state, HNO_3 and H_2SO_4, are effective oxidizing agents; the corresponding oxoacid of phosphorus, H_3PO_4, is not an oxidizing agent. Furthermore, H_2SO_4 and H_3PO_4 have high boiling points, whereas HNO_3 has a low boiling point. Consequently, when a high-boiling, non-oxidizing acid is required, H_3PO_4 is used. When oxidizing action alone is required, HNO_3 is usually used, for it is a stronger oxidizing agent than H_2SO_4 and it usually reacts more rapidly. Sulfuric acid, H_2SO_4, is used when *both* oxidizing properties (at high temperature) *and* a high boiling point are required. Mixtures of these acids are sometimes employed to take advantage of the characteristic properties of each.

OXIDATION-POTENTIAL DIAGRAMS OF PHOSPHORUS

Let us briefly consider the Latimer oxidation-potential diagrams of phosphorus in acid and basic solution, showing some of the more important oxidation states and their $E°$ relationships. Phosphorus and its compounds—except, of course, the compounds of phosphorus(V)—have relatively high positive oxidation potentials,

In Acid Solution

$$\begin{array}{lccccc} \textit{Ox. No:} & -3 & 0 & +1 & +3 & +5 \\ & PH_3 \text{---}{+0.06}\text{---} & P_4 \text{---}{+0.51}\text{---} & H_3PO_2 \text{---}{+0.50}\text{---} & H_3PO_3 \text{---}{+0.28}\text{---} & H_3PO_4 \end{array}$$

$$P_4 \text{ --- } {+0.50} \text{ --- } H_3PO_3$$

an indication of their good reducing properties in acid medium. We would expect, therefore, that an oxidizing agent that is capable of oxidizing phosphine, PH_3, or elemental phosphorus to the next higher oxidation state, H_3PO_2, would also be capable of oxidizing H_3PO_2 first to H_3PO_3 and finally to the highest oxidation state of phosphorus, +5. In fact, phosphorus is easily and rapidly oxidized to H_3PO_4 by 50 per cent aqueous nitric acid solution:

$$P_4 + 20\ HNO_3 \longrightarrow 4\ H_3PO_4 + 20\ NO_2 + 4\ H_2O$$

The oxidation-potential values of the partial diagram,

$$PH_3 \text{---}{+0.06}\text{---} P_4 \text{---}{+0.51}\text{---} H_3PO_2$$

indicate that elementary phoshorus, P_4, can disproportionate into PH_3 and H_3PO_2 in acid solution, although the tendency for this reaction, $P_4 + 6\ H_2O \longrightarrow PH_3 + 3\ H_3PO_2$, to take place is much smaller than in the basic solution.

In Basic Solution

$$\begin{array}{lccccc} \textit{Ox. No:} & -3 & 0 & +1 & +3 & +5 \\ & PH_3 \text{---}{+0.89}\text{---} & P_4 \text{---}{+2.05}\text{---} & H_2PO_2^- \text{---}{+1.57}\text{---} & HPO_3^= \text{---}{+1.12}\text{---} & PO_4^{\equiv} \end{array}$$

The high positive oxidation potentials of phosphorus and phosphorus compounds in basic solution indicate that, again, both the elements and its compounds—except the $PO_4^{\equiv}$ ion—are fairly strong reductants. In basic solution, for example, the hypophosphite ion, $H_2PO_2^-$, can reduce iron(II) hydroxide, $Fe(OH)_2$, to iron, Fe ($E°$ of the Fe,Fe(OH)$_2$ couple = 0.90 v).

29-7 Arsenic, Antimony, and Bismuth

OXIDES AND ACIDS OF ARSENIC, ANTIMONY, AND BISMUTH

Arsenic, antimony, and bismuth form two series of oxides, corresponding to the oxidation states +3, and +5 respectively. The oxides corresponding to the oxidation state +3 have the empirical formula Y_2O_3. The arsenic compound has the molecular formula As_4O_6 both in the solid state (molecular crystal) and in the vapor state. The As_4O_6 molecule is analogous to the P_4O_6 molecule (p. 662). The antimony(III) oxide has the same molecular structure in the vapor, and in one of its solid forms. Another solid form consists of infinite puckered double chains, in which each Sb atom is bonded to 3 O atoms in a pyramidal arrangement, and each O atom is bonded to 2 Sb atoms in an angular arrangement. Bismuth(III) oxide is a solid whose structure is best described as an ionic lattice; it is generally written as Bi_2O_3. The oxide As_4O_6 has both basic and acidic properties (that is, it is amphoteric), although it is slightly more acidic than basic. The oxide Sb_4O_6 is slightly more basic than acidic, and the oxide Bi_2O_3 is definitely basic. The oxide As_4O_6 is slightly soluble in water forming the extremely weak orthoarsenious acid, H_3AsO_3, which, unlike its phosphorus analog, is tribasic:

$$As_4O_6 + 6\,H_2O \rightleftharpoons 4\,H_3AsO_3 \qquad K_1 = 6 \times 10^{-10}\ \text{mole/l.}$$

In basic solutions, As_4O_6 readily dissolves to form the orthoarsenite ion, $As_3O_3^{\equiv}$.

The oxides of arsenic(V) and antimony(V), are well-known compounds of empirical formula As_2O_5 and Sb_2O_5, but we have no definite evidence of the existence of the pure bismuth(V) oxide. The oxide As_4O_{10} is an acidic oxide, which dissolves in water to form H_3AsO_4, orthoarsenic acid, and in alkali to form the orthoarsenate ion, $AsO_4^{\equiv}$. The acid, H_3AsO_4, and the ion, $AsO_4^{\equiv}$, are similar to H_3PO_4 and the $PO_4^{\equiv}$ ion.

HALIDES OF ARSENIC, ANTIMONY, AND BISMUTH

All the halides of arsenic, antimony, and bismuth in the +3 oxidation state are known to exist. The molecules of these compounds in the vapor state, YX_3, have pyramidal structures similar to those of NX_3 and PX_3. The boiling points of the chlorides, MCl_3, increase markedly from nitrogen to bismuth: NCl_3, less than 71°C; PCl_3, 76°C; $AsCl_3$, 130°C; $SbCl_3$, 221°C; and $BiCl_3$, 441°C. This very marked change results not only because the molecular weight increases, but also because as we proceed down the family the element Y becomes more metallic and hence the halides become more ionic in character. All these halides hydrolize in water, as is illustrated by the chlorides:

$$PCl_3 + 3\,H_2O \longrightarrow H_3PO_3 + 3\,HCl$$
$$AsCl_3 + 3\,H_2O \longrightarrow H_3AsO_3 + 3\,HCl$$
$$SbCl_3 + H_2O \rightleftharpoons SbOCl + 2\,HCl$$
$$BiCl_3 + H_2O \rightleftharpoons BiOCl + 2\,HCl$$

The tendency toward hydrolysis of the halides, YX_3, decreases as we move from P to Bi. The hydrolysis of PCl_3 is complete and the hydrolysis of $AsCl_3$ is nearly so. Both $SbCl_3$ and $BiCl_3$, however, hydrolyze only partially to form an equilibrium mixture, as is indicated in the above equations. The last two hydrolysis products—SbOCl, antimony oxochloride; and BiOCl, bismuth oxochloride—are only slightly soluble in water.

Several pentahalides of arsenic and antimony are also known, including AsF_5, SbF_5 and $SbCl_5$. In the vapor state, they consist of trigonal bipyramidal molecules. It is interesting that, unlike PCl_5 (p. 661), $SbCl_5$ maintains this molecular structure even in the solid state.

HYDROGEN COMPOUNDS OF ARSENIC AND ANTIMONY

The hydrogen compounds of arsenic and antimony, analogous to NH_3 and PH_3, are arsine, AsH_3, and stibine, SbH_3. There is some question about the existence of bismuthine, BiH_3. These hydrides can be prepared by the hydrolysis of the compounds Na_3As and Zn_3Sb_2, respectively, but they are unstable towards decomposition into their elements (for AsH_3, $\Delta H^\circ_{\text{form}} = +41.0$ kcal/mole) and oxidize very rapidly in air. The compounds AsH_3 and SbH_3 are almost insoluble in water and they do not form cations similar to NH_4^+ and PH_4^+. Thus, the basicity of the hydrides for the Group VB elements decreases in going down the family from N to Bi.

EXERCISES

29-1 Compare the elements nitrogen, phosphorus, arsenic, antimony, and bismuth with regard to the following: (a) electron configuration, (b) relative covalent radius, (c) relative electronegativity, (d) tendency to form ionic compounds, (e) relative tendency to form multiple bonds. Give examples.

29-2 Write equations for the following reactions: (a) The burning of ammonia in air. (b) The heating of ammonium nitrite. (c) The heating of ammonium nitrate. (d) The heating of ammonium chloride.

29-3 Write equations for the preparation of ammonia from four ammonium salts.

29-4 Explain why the Haber process for the preparation of NH_3 employs (1) temperature, (2) high pressure, (3) a catalyst.

29-5 Under appropriate experimental conditions, ammonia reacts with (a) sodium metal, (b) copper(II) sulfate, (c) silver nitrate, (d) silver chloride, (e) zinc nitrate. Indicate the appropriate conditions and write the equations for the chemical reactions.

29-6 Ammonia, water, and hydrogen fluoride have relatively high boiling points compared with the corresponding compounds: phosphine, hydrogen sulfide, and hydrogen chloride. Explain.

29-7 Is an aqueous solution of the following acidic, basic, or neutral: (a) ammonium chloride, (b) sodium acetate, (c) sodium dihydrogen phosphate? Explain.

29-8 Write equations for the preparation of (a) N_2O, (b) NO, (c) NO_2, (d) N_2O_3.

29-9 Sketch structures of (a) N_2O, (b) NO, (c) NO_2, (d) N_2O_4, (e) HNO_2, (f) NO_2^-, (g) HNO_3, (h) NO_3^-.

29-10 Is NO stable at room temperature in regard to (a) decomposition into $N_2 + O_2$, (b) oxidation with O_2 to give NO_2, (c) hydrolysis in water?

29-11 Compare HNO_2 and HNO_3 in regard to: (a) strength as acids, (b) oxidation state of nitrogen, (c) ability to act as oxidizing and reducing agents, (d) action of their metal salts with water.

29-12 (a) Both HCl and HNO_3 are strong acids. Copper dissolves in HNO_3 but not in HCl. Explain. Write the chemical equation. (b) Mg and Cu react with dilute nitric acid, but different reduction products of HNO_3 are formed. Give products and explain.

29-13 Complete and balance the following expressions:

$Cu + HNO_3$ (dilute) $\longrightarrow$ $\qquad$ $S + HNO_3$ (conc.) $\longrightarrow$

$Cu + HNO_3$ (conc.) $\longrightarrow$ $\qquad$ $NaOH + HNO_3$ (dilute) $\longrightarrow$

$BaO + HNO_3$ (dilute) $\longrightarrow$ $\qquad$ $Pb + HNO_3$ (conc.) $\longrightarrow$

$Zn + HNO_3$ (dilute) $\longrightarrow$ $\qquad$ $CuS + HNO_3$ (dilute) $\longrightarrow$

29-14 Write equations for the reactions that take place when the following compounds are thermally decomposed: (a) NH_4NO_3, (b) NH_4NO_2, (c) $Pb(NO_3)_2$, (d) NH_4Cl, (e) $(NH_4)_2Cr_2O_7$, (f) $(NH_4)_2CO_3$.

29-15 Starting with KNO_2 as one of the reactants, write equations for the preparation of (a) HNO_2, (b) HNO_3, (c) KNO_3.

29-16 Starting with NO as one of the reactants, write equations for the preparation of (a) N_2O, (b) NO_2, (c) N_2O_5, (d) N_2, (e) NH_3.

29-17 Compare the compounds NH_3 and PH_3 in regard to: (a) boiling point, (b) solubility in water, (c) basicity.

29-18 Sketch the structures of: (a) PCl_3, (b) P_4O_6, (c) PF_5, (d) PCl_5 gas and PCl_5 solid, (e) PBr_5 gas and PBr_5 solid. Give a rational reason for the different crystal structures of PCl_5 and PBr_5.

29-19 Write equations for the following: (a) preparation of PCl_3, (b) reaction of PCl_3 with H_2O, (c) preparation of P_4O_{10}, (d) reactions of P_4O_{10} with water.

29-20 Compare ortho-, pyro-, and meta-phosphoric acids in regard to (a) preparation, (b) structure, (c) oxidation state of phosphorus, (d) number of replaceable H atoms, (e) acid strength.

29-21 Briefly compare the elements of group VB in regard to (a) their hydrides YH_3, (b) their oxides in the +3 and +5 oxidation states, (c) their halides.

29-22 Complete and balance the following expressions:

$P + HNO_3$ (conc.) $\longrightarrow$ $\qquad$ $Sb(OH)_3 + HCl$ (conc.) $\longrightarrow$

$P + O_2$ (excess) $\longrightarrow$ $\qquad$ $Sb(OH)_3 + NaOH$ (conc.) $\longrightarrow$

$PH_3 + O_2 \longrightarrow$

29-23 Using any appropriate table for the values of $E°$, write a possible reaction for: (a) hypophosphoric acid acting as a reductant in 1 *M* acid solution, (b) phosphorus acid acting as a reductant in 1 *M* acid solution, (c) the hypophosphite ion acting as a reductant in 1 *M* basic solution.

29-24 Using the Latimer oxidation-potential diagram of nitrogen in acid solution (p. 657), complete the following reactions if they occur spontaneously, and explain *why* they occur spontaneously. If a reaction does not occur spontaneously (requires energy), write N.R.:

(a) $N_2O + HNO_2 \longrightarrow$ (d) $N_2O + N_2O \longrightarrow$
(b) $NH_4^+ + N_2O \longrightarrow$ (e) $NO + NO_3^- \longrightarrow$
(c) $HNO_2 + HNO_2 \longrightarrow$ (f) $N_2 + NO \longrightarrow$

29-25 Using the Latimer oxidation-potential diagram of phosphorus in acid solution (p. 665), complete the following reactions if they occur spontaneously, and explain *why* they occur spontaneously. If a reaction does not occur spontaneously (requires energy) write N.R.: (a) $PH_3 + H_3PO_4$; (b) $P_4 + H_3PO_3$; (c) $P_4 + H_3PO_4$.

29-26 Using the Latimer oxidation-potential diagram of phosphorus in basic solution (p. 665), complete the following reactions if they occur spontaneously, and explain *why* they occur spontaneously. If a reaction does not occur spontaneously (requires energy), write N.R.: (a) $PH_3 + H_2PO_2^-$; (b) $H_2PO_4^- + PO_4^{\equiv}$; (c) $P_4 + P_4$; (d) $P_4 + HPO_3^{=}$.

THE ALKALI METALS: THE GROUP IA ELEMENTS

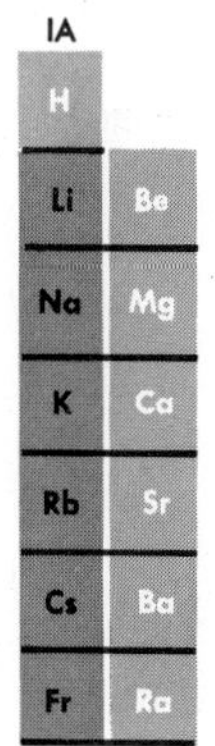

Stable Crystal Structure at 25°C, 1 atm	IA
body-centered cubic	Li
body-centered cubic	Na
body-centered cubic	K
body-centered cubic	Rb
body-centered cubic	Cs
———	Fr

In this chapter, and in several of the following chapters, we shall discuss the chemical and physical properties of the more important groups of metallic elements. Here we shall consider the six elements of Group IA—lithium, Li; sodium, Na; potassium, K; rubidium, Rb; cesium, Cs; and francium, Fr—which constitute the *alkali metal* family. The term Alkali was used by medieval Arabs to indicate the sodium and potassium carbonates obtained from the ashes of plants. In our discussion of the alkali metals, M, we shall stress the chemical properties of their ions, for the chemistry of these compounds is essentially the chemistry of their monopositive ions, M^+.

The heaviest element of Group IA, francium, Fr, is radioactive and does not occur in nature; it has only been obtained artifically. Because of its scarcity and instability, the chemistry of francium has little importance for the beginning student and we shall not discuss it here.

The alkali metals constitute a family of typically metallic elements, and studying them will give us an excellent opportunity—as the halogens did for non-metallic elements—to correlate and rationalize the observed properties and behavior with the theoretical principles discussed in the first part of the book.

30-1 Occurrence and Physical Properties of Alkali Metals

OCCURRENCE. As is characteristic of all very electropositive elements, none of the alkali metals occurs free in nature. The Group IA elements, M, always occur in the form of compounds containing the monopositive ions, M^+. The compounds of sodium and potassium are very abundant in nature, but the compounds of lithium, rubidium, and cesium occur only sparingly. The most common minerals containing alkali metals are mixed oxides or halides. For example, potassium occurs abundantly as the mineral feldspar (K_2O, Al_2O_3, 3 SiO_2); lithium occurs in relatively small amounts as the mineral spodumene (Li_2O, Al_2O_3, 2 SiO_2); rubidium and cesium also occur to a small extent in mixed oxide minerals. The most abundant compound of sodium is sodium chloride, whereas potassium chloride occurs only to a limited extent. Sodium is also found as $NaNO_3$ (Chile nitrate) and $Na_2B_4O_7 \cdot 4\ H_2O$ (borax), and potassium as K_2SO_4 mixed with magnesium and calcium sulfates.

CRYSTAL STRUCTURE AND METALLIC BOND STRENGTH

The atoms of the alkali metals have only one electron in their valence shells—that is, they all have a ns^1 electron configuration (see Table 30-1). At 25°C and 1 atm the alkali metals are all silvery-white solids, whose surface soon tarnishes when exposed to air. The crystal structure of the alkali metals is body-centered cubic, as shown in the margin. In this structure each atom is surrounded by 8 equidistant nearest neighbors arranged at the corners of an imaginary cube, which is also the unit cell of the crystal. The atoms of the alkali metals are held together in the crystal lattice by moderately strong metallic bonds involving the ns^1 valence electrons. The heat of atomization of a metal, ΔH_{atomiz}, represents, as we know, the energy required to transform 1 mole of crystalline metal at 25°C and 1 atm to 1 mole of gaseous atoms: $M_{(s)} \longrightarrow M_{(g)}$, also at 25°C and 1 atm; the ΔH_{atomiz} is therefore a direct measure of the strength of the metallic bond. For the alkali metals, the values of ΔH_{atomiz} listed in Table 30-1 show that the strength of the metallic bonds increases as the size of the metal atom decreases because the closer the atoms are, the better the orbital overlap leading to bonding is.

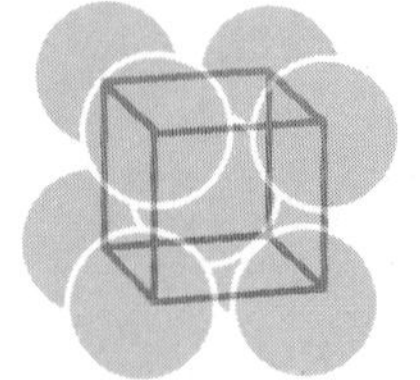

We know that, in general, the weaker the bonds between the atoms of a metal, the lower the melting and boiling points of the metal and the lower its hardness. And in fact, as the size of the atom increases from Li to Cs, the melting point decreases from 180°C for Li to 29°C for Cs, and the boiling point decreases from 1,330°C for Li to 690°C for Cs. (Notice that, except for Li, the alkali metals melt below the boiling point of water.) Similarly, hardness decreases in the family. Lithium is not easily cut with a knife; but with increasing atomic size the metals become increasingly soft—from Na

TABLE 30-1 SOME PROPERTIES OF THE ALKALI METALS (GROUP IA ELEMENTS)

	Outer Electron Config.	Atomic Weight	Atomic (Metallic) Radius[a] A	Density at 20°C g/cm.^{3}	Ionic Radius of M^+ Ion, A	Melting Point °C	ΔH_{fusion} at m.p. (kcal/mole of atoms)	Boiling Point °C	$\Delta H_{vaporiz.}$ at b.p. (kcal/mole)	First Ioniz. Energy[b]	Electro-negativity (Pauling)	$\Delta H_{atomiz.}$ at 25°C, 1 atm (kcal/mole of atoms)
$_3$Li	$2s^1$	6.94	1.52	0.53	0.60	180	0.70	1330	35.3	5.39 124	1.0	38.6
$_{11}$Na	$3s^1$	22.99	1.86	0.97	0.95	98	0.63	892	23.7	5.14 118	0.9	25.9
$_{19}$K	$4s^1$	39.10	2.27	0.86	1.33	63	0.57	760	18.9	4.34 100	0.8	21.3
$_{37}$Rb	$5s^1$	85.49	2.48	1.53	1.48	39	0.53	688	18.1	4.13 96	0.8	19.5
$_{55}$Cs	$6s^1$	132.91	2.63	1.90	1.69	29	0.51	690	17.3	3.89 89	0.7	18.7

[a] Metallic co-ordination number = 8

[b] The top value is in e.v.; the lower value in kcal/mole of gaseous atoms.

to Cs they are easily cut with a knife. The greatest difference in hardness, melting point, and boiling point for two consecutive members of the family is that between Li and Na, as we would expect from the sizes and electron configurations of these elements. The chief difference between Li and the other alkali metals is that the next-to-the-outermost (penultimate) shell of the Li atom has an s^2 electron configuration, whereas the penultimate shell of all the other alkali metals has an s^2p^6 electron configuration.

DENSITY OF THE ALKALI METALS. The alkali metals are "light metals," indeed, the densities of the first three—Li, Na, and K—are less than 1 g/ml, which is lighter than water. From Li to Cs there is a gradual increase in density because in general the greater atomic weight more than compensates for the larger size of the atom. Potassium, however, is out of line since it has a lower density than sodium, which precedes it (Table 30-1). This irregularity is explained by the relatively very large increase in size from sodium to potassium—the increase in atomic radius is 0.18 A from Li to Na, 0.52 A from Na to K, 0.15 A from K to Rb, and 0.19 A from Rb to Cs.

GASEOUS DIATOMIC MOLECULES, M_2, OF ALKALI METALS

Compared to other metals, the alkali metals have relatively low boiling points and consequently relatively high vapor pressures. The vapor of the alkali metals, at a temperature not much higher than the boiling point, consists of diatomic covalent molecules, M_2. The M—M covalent bond is fairly strong, its strength decreasing regularly with increasing atomic size from Li to Cs; we observed this also for the diatomic molecules of the halogens (for the halogens, however, the ΔH_{diss} of F_2 was out of line because of the strong repulsion between the lone pairs of the two very small F atoms).

ΔH_{diss} M_2 molecules (kcal/mole)	
$Li_{2(g)}$	25.0
$Na_{2(g)}$	17.3
$K_{2(g)}$	11.9
$Rb_{(g)}$	10.8
$Cs_{(g)}$	10.4

IONIZATION ENERGY. In Chapter 13, in our general discussion of ionization energies, we found that the ionization energy of an atom depends on two chief factors—effective nuclear charge and size. As the effective nuclear charge of an atom increases, so does the ionization energy; conversely, as the atomic size increases, the ionization energy decreases. Now for the alkali metals, as in general for all *s*-block elements, the effective nuclear charge acting on the ns^1 valence electrons is approximately constant because the underlying shell is a complete $(n-1)s^2(n-1)p^6$ shell. The ionization energy of the alkali metals—that is, the energy required for the process $M_{(g)} \longrightarrow M^+_{(g)} + e^-$—is therefore inversely proportional to the atomic radius (see the accompanying graph). The ionization energies of the alkali metals are the lowest of all the elements and that of Cs is the lowest of all. Notice, however, that even cesium requires a large quantity of energy—89 kcal per 1 mole of Cs atoms—to be ionized. It is only when compared to the energy required to ionize other elements (for example, I.E. (kcal/mole of atoms) = 313 for H, 178 for Cu, 300 for Cl) that the ionization energies of the alkali metals appear to be *relatively* small.

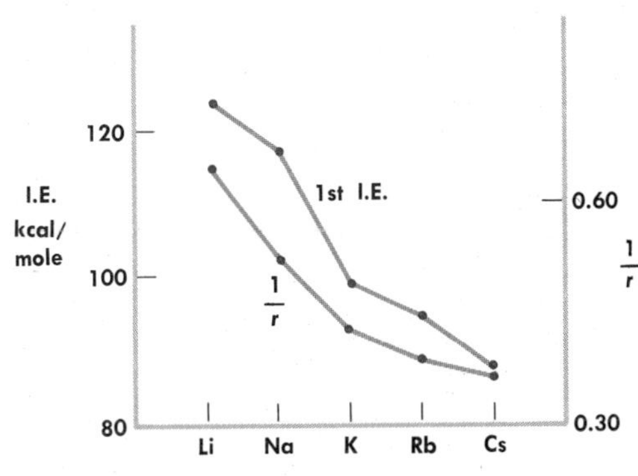

30-2 Preparation of the Alkali Metals

Since the alkali metals, M, occur in nature as compounds containing their monopositive ions, M^+, the preparation of an alkali metal always involves as the fundamental step the reduction of the M^+ ion to the metal atom, M. We can bring this about by electrolyzing an appropriate alkali-metal salt in the molten state, or by having it react with another metal that, under the conditions employed, is a stronger reductant than the alkali metal itself.

ELECTROLYTIC METHOD. Molten alkali-metal *chlorides* are the most satisfactory salts for the electrolytic preparation of pure alkali metals. Metallic sodium, for example, is prepared industrially by the electrolysis of fused sodium chloride, in a method known as the *Downs process.* Pure sodium chloride has a high melting point, 804°C, but a mixture of sodium chloride with a relatively small quantity of calcium chloride, $CaCl_2$, has a lower melting point and is a good electrolyte. In the Downs process, the addition of small quantities of calcium chloride to sodium chloride makes it possible to carry out the electrolytic reaction, more conveniently and economically, at lower temperatures. Sodium metal, Na, is produced at the cathode, chlorine gas, Cl_2, at the anode:

$$2\ Na^+Cl^-_{(l)} \xrightarrow[CaCl_2]{\text{electrical energy}} 2\ Na_{(l)(\text{at cathode})} + Cl_{2(g)(\text{at anode})}$$

The anode is made of graphite, which does not react with chlorine gas even at high temperature, and the cathode is generally made of iron or copper, which resist well the attack by the molten electrolyte and by the alkali metal.

As we have seen (p. 519), sodium can be obtained in the form of an amalgam (a sodium-mercury alloy) by the electrolysis of an aqueous solution of sodium chloride with a mercury cathode. This method, however, is not used for the preparation of sodium metal, because once the amalgam is formed, it is very difficult to separate the sodium metal from the mercury metal.

OTHER METHODS OF PREPARATION. The alkali metals can also be prepared by the reduction at moderately high temperatures of their hydroxides, oxides, sulfides, or carbonates by less electropositive metals, such as Ca, Al, and Mg. For example, Na_2O is reduced to metallic sodium by magnesium metal at a temperature above the boiling point of Na metal and below the boiling point of Mg metal. The more volatile sodium metal escapes as vapor from the reaction mixture, and is then condensed to solid sodium metal under an inert atmosphere:

$$Na_2O_{(s)} + Mg_{(s)} \longrightarrow Na_{2(g)} + MgO_{(s)}$$

Metals such as Ca, Al, or Mg can be used as the reductant in these reduction processes because the free energy change for the reaction, ΔG, is favorable, and furthermore the alkali metal produced is more volatile than the reducing metal. In a similar manner, the favorable difference in the ΔG of formation of sodium chloride and potassium chloride ($\Delta G^\circ_{\text{form}}$, in kcal/mole: $NaCl_{(s)} = -92.2$; $KCl_{(s)} = 97.6$), together with the favorable difference of volatility between the sodium metal (b.p. 883°C) and potassium metal (b.p. 760°C), makes it possible to reduce even potassium chloride by sodium metal to produce metallic potassium:

$$2\ Na_{(s)} + 2\ KCl_{(s)} \longrightarrow 2\ NaCl_{(s)} + K_{2(g)}$$

The lower-boiling potassium vapor, $K_{2(g)}$ can be distilled off and the reaction can be made to go to completion. This method is, in fact, the one used commercially for the production of potassium metal.

30-3 Chemical Properties of the Alkali Metals

THERMODYNAMIC PROPERTIES. The alkali metals are among the most reactive of all elements. They combine directly with most of the non-metals to form ionic compounds in which they are present as monopositive ions, M^+, and they combine directly with many metals to form alloys. The reactions of the alkali metals with the non-metals are generally exothermic, and are accompanied by a negative free energy change.

This means that at ordinary temperatures the binary ionic compounds of the alkali metals, $(M^+)_nX^{-n}$, are stable toward decomposition into their elements. As we saw in the preceding chapter, even gaseous nitrogen, N_2, which is generally so unreactive, combines directly with the alkali metal lithium at only moderately high temperatures, to form the ionic nitride Li_3N. The alkali metals also react with many compounds—H_2O, for example—again showing a great tendency to form ionic compounds that contain the M^+ ions.

KINETIC PROPERTIES. The activation energy for reactions involving the alkali metals is relatively low, so that many reactions take place rapidly even at room temperature. And in general even those reactions whose rate becomes appreciable only at higher temperatures require merely an initial heating. Once the reaction has started, the heat evolved in the reaction itself is sufficient to maintain the temperature required for a fast rate. Actually, even when an initial heating is required to start the reaction, it often becomes necessary to cool off the reacting mixture to prevent the reaction from becoming too violent.

BEHAVIOR IN SOLUTION. We learned earlier that the alkali-metal ions are all strongly hydrated in water solution, and we discussed the structure of these hydrated ions. As we would expect, the hydration energies of the alkali metal ions—shown in the margin—decrease regularly with increasing ionic size. This is so because the attraction of the positive metal ion for the negatively charged oxygen atom of the dipolar H_2O molecules decreases as the charge/radius ratio of the positive ion decreases.

$\Delta H_{hydr.}$ of M^+ (kcal/mole)	
Li^+	−130
Na^+	−104
K^+	−84
Rb^+	−78
Cs^+	−70

Most compounds of the alkali metals are ionic and completely dissociate in water solution, yielding hydrated alkali-metal cations and hydrated anions. Hence, the solution chemistry of the alkali-metal compounds is the chemistry of their hydrated ions (both cations and anions). And since the alkali-metal ions are very stable as the hydrated species in water solution, and have little tendency to undergo further reaction, the solution chemistry of the alkali-metal compounds is for most practical purposes the chemistry of the partner anions. That the alkali-metal ions cannot undergo any oxidation-reduction reaction in water solution under ordinary conditions is indicated by the values of their oxidation potentials, given in the margin. We see that the $E°$ value for the couple M,M^+ is highly positive for all the alkali metals—actually they are the highest in the $E°$ list—and hence the alkali-metal ions cannot be chemically reduced to their element as long as water is present. Notice also that the alkali-metal ions cannot be further oxidized. In fact, the very high value of their second ionization energy (Li, 1,743; Na, 1,090; K, 733 kcal/mole) indicates that the $E°$ value for the couple M^+,M^{++} would be so extremely negative that the M^{++} ion could not exist in the presence of water (it would oxidize H_2O to O_2 and H^+ ions). Let us now consider some important reactions and compounds of the alkali metals.

Couple	$E°$, volts
Li,Li^+	+3.05
Na,Na^+	+2.71
K,K^+	+2.92
Rb,Rb^+	+2.92
Cs,Cs^+	+2.92

OXIDES OF THE ALKALI METALS

The alkali metals combine with oxygen to form oxides of three different classes: the regular oxides or monoxides, M_2O; the peroxides, M_2O_2; and the superoxides, MO_2. In all these compounds the alkali-metal ion is present as the monopositive M^+ ion, and the different formulas arise from differences in the charge and structure of the anion.

STRUCTURE AND REACTIONS OF THE THREE CLASSES OF OXIDES. The *monoxides,* M_2O, contain the monopositive alkali-metal ion, M^+, and the dinegative oxide ion, $O^=$, arranged in a three-dimensional ionic lattice. With the exception of Cs_2O, which has a more complicated structure, all alkali-metal monoxides (Li_2O, Na_2O, K_2O, and Rb_2O) adopt a crystal arrangement of the anti-fluorite type (p. 175), in which each M^+ ion is tetrahedrally surrounded by 4 $O^=$ ions and each $O^=$ ion is surrounded by 8 M^+ ions situated at the corners of a cube. The alkali-metal monoxides, M_2O, are extremely soluble in water, with which they react forming the highly ionized hydroxide $M^+_{(aq)} + OH^-_{(aq)}$ (p. 82).

The alkali-metal *peroxides,* M_2O_2, are again crystalline ionic compounds, containing the monopositive alkali-metal ion, M^+, and the dinegative peroxide, $O_2^=$, in which the two O atoms are joined together by a single covalent bond, as shown in the margin. These peroxides, therefore, can be considered as the salts of the extremely weak acid hydrogen peroxide, H_2O_2. In fact, they react with water to produce H_2O_2 and a solution of the alkali-metal hydroxide. Since concentrated solutions of H_2O_2 are unstable at *room temperature,* when water is added drop by drop to solid sodium peroxide, Na_2O_2, the H_2O_2 that is formed immediately decomposes into O_2 gas and H_2O. This reaction is often used to obtain oxygen gas in the laboratory.

$$\left[:\ddot{\underset{..}{O}}:\ddot{\underset{..}{O}}:\right]^{=}$$

$$Na_2O_{2(s)} + 2\ H_2O_{(l)} \longrightarrow 2\ NaOH_{(aq)} + [H_2O_2] \longrightarrow H_2O_{(l)} + \tfrac{1}{2}\ O_{2(g)}$$

The alkali-metal *superoxides,* MO_2, are ionic compounds containing the monopositive alkali-metal ion, M^+, and the mononegative superoxide ion, $(O_2)^-$, in which the two oxygen atoms are bound by a single covalent bond. The superoxide ion, which contains an unpaired electron and is paramagnetic, has two contributing structures, I and II. The crystal structure of potassium superoxide, $K^+(O_2)^-$, is similar to that of Na^+Cl^-, with the K^+ ions occupying the positions of the Na^+ ions and the $(O_2)^-$ ions occupying the positions of the Cl^- ions. The alkali-metal superoxides, MO_2, can be considered as the salts of the hypothetical, very weak acid HO_2; they decompose in aqueous solution to form the metal hydroxide, together with H_2O_2, and O_2.

$$\left[:\dot{\underset{..}{O}}:\ddot{\underset{..}{O}}:\right]^{-}$$

I

$$\left[:\ddot{\underset{..}{O}}:\dot{\underset{..}{O}}:\right]^{-}$$

II

PREPARATION OF THE ALKALI-METAL OXIDES. Lithium burns in the presence of excess oxygen gas at about 200°C to form lithium monoxide, Li_2O, a white solid:

$$4\ Li + O_2 \longrightarrow 2\ Li_2O$$

In this reaction a trace of lithium peroxide, Li_2O_2, is also formed. In the preparation of Li_2O and of all other alkali-metal oxides, care must be taken to dry and purify the oxygen gas, since the alkali metals as well as their oxides react readily with any water or carbon dioxide that happens to be present.

It is more difficult to prepare the monoxides of the other alkali metals by the direct combustion of the metal because, as the size of the alkali-metal ion increases, the peroxide or superoxide tends to form rather than the monoxide. We can prepare sodium monoxide, Na_2O, by heating Na metal in a limited supply of dry oxygen gas at a temperature of 160–180°C. The monoxides of Na, K, Rb, or Cs can be produced by the reaction of the metal with its corresponding nitrate or hydroxide, in the absence of oxygen. With potassium, for example, these reactions are:

$$5\ K_{(s)} + KNO_{3(s)} \longrightarrow 3\ K_2O_{(s)} + \tfrac{1}{2}\ N_{2(g)}$$

$$2\ K_{(s)} + 2\ KOH_{(s)} \longrightarrow 2\ K_2O_{(s)} + H_{2(g)}$$

The peroxides of all the alkali metals, except Li, can be prepared directly by combustion of the metal in oxygen:

$$2\ M_{(s)} + O_{2(g)} \longrightarrow M_2O_{2(s)}$$

With sodium, this reaction also yields a small amount (about 5 per cent) of sodium superoxide.

A general method of preparation of the alkali-metal superoxides consists of heating the peroxide, M_2O_2, with oxygen under high pressure:

$$M_2O_{2(s)} + O_{2(g)} \xrightarrow[\text{high pressure}]{500^\circ C} 2\ MO_{2(s)}$$

However, only the larger alkali metals, K, Rb, and Cs, react to form the superoxides, KO_2, RbO_2, and CsO_2.

USES OF THE ALKALI-METAL OXIDES. Sodium peroxide, Na_2O_2, a pale-yellow solid, is widely used as an oxidizing agent, and for the preparation of hydrogen peroxide, H_2O_2. Potassium superoxide, KO_2, is used as a source of oxygen in certain types of gas masks. The moisture of the breath reacts with the KO_2 to generate O_2 gas, and the KOH that is produced at the same time absorbs the carbon dioxide, forming solid $KHCO_3$.

THE REACTION OF THE ALKALI METALS WITH H_2O

We saw earlier that water reacts with all the alkali metals to form the alkali-metal ion, M^+, the OH^- ion, and H_2 gas. This reaction is highly exothermic:

$$M_{(s)} + H_2O_{(l)} \longrightarrow M^+_{(aq)} + OH^-_{(aq)} + \tfrac{1}{2} H_{2(g)} \qquad (\Delta H \text{ is very negative})$$

Even though the ΔH of reaction decreases somewhat in going down the alkali-metal family—that is, the reaction is energetically more favorable for Li than for the heavier members—the rate of reaction is slowest with Li and fastest with Cs. When water reacts with K, Rb, or Cs, heat is liberated so fast that the temperature becomes sufficiently high to start the combustion of H_2 gas with O_2 of air, which also is highly exothermic. The large quantity of heat jointly liberated by the two reactions further accelerates both reactions and also causes some of the liquid water to vaporize very suddenly, with the danger of hazardous explosions. When Li reacts with water, on the other hand, the H_2 formed does not ignite because the rate of reaction between Li and H_2O is relatively slow, and the heat given off can be dissipated before the temperature reaches the required ignition value.

ALKALI-METAL HYDROXIDES

SODIUM HYDROXIDE. Sodium hydroxide, NaOH, is a white crystalline, ionic solid composed of Na^+ ions and OH^- ions arranged regularly in a crystal lattice—there is no hydrogen bonding among adjacent OH^- ions in the crystal of Na^+OH^-. Solid sodium hydroxide is very hygroscopic, and when exposed to the air it deliquesces; its solubility in water is unlimited. A large quantity of heat is evolved when NaOH is dissolved in water. For the dissolution of 1 mole of NaOH in sufficient water (about 55.5 moles) to form 1 liter of 1 M solution at 25°C, the ΔH is -10.2 kcal. Solutions of NaOH in water can be dehydrated by heating, since water is volatile and NaOH is not appreciably so, but the process is quite difficult. As water evaporates and the concentration of NaOH in the solution increases, the temperature of the remaining solution gradually increases, until a fluid mass develops which is more appropriately described as a solution of H_2O in molten NaOH. Finally, after all water has evaporated, fused NaOH (m.p. 322°C) is obtained, which, on cooling to room temperature crystallizes. Sodium hydroxide is very stable with respect to decomposition into its elements ($\Delta G^\circ_{\text{form}} = -91.0$ kcal/mole), and it is not decomposed even at red heat. Sodium hydroxide is a very strong base, for in water solution it is completely dissociated into $Na^+_{(aq)}$ ions and $OH^-_{(aq)}$ ions. Concentrated solutions of NaOH are very powerful chemical reagents, reacting with all substances that have an acidic character to form the corresponding salts (and H_2O). For example, solutions of NaOH attack glass and procelain appreciably, for NaOH reacts with SiO_2, an acid anhydride that is one of the main components of glass:

$$2\,Na^+_{(aq)} + 2\,(OH)^-_{(aq)} + SiO_{2(s)} \longrightarrow 2\,Na^+_{(aq)} + SiO^{=}_{3(aq)} + H_2O_{(l)}$$

Sodium hydroxide solutions also dissolve some electropositive metals to form their hydroxo complexes. For example, metallic zinc dissolves in a 1 *M* solution of NaOH:

$$Zn_{(s)} + 2\,OH^-_{(aq)} + 2\,H_2O_{(l)} \longrightarrow [Zn(OH)_4]^{=}_{(aq)} + H_{2(g)}$$

As an exercise, by considering the $E°$ values given in the Appendix, you can verify that this reaction indeed has the tendency to occur spontaneously.

PREPARATION OF NaOH. Very pure sodium hydroxide, NaOH, can be prepared in the laboratory (if you are careful!) by adding very small pieces of sodium metal to water (p. 90). The chief commercial method for preparing sodium hydroxide is based on the electrolysis of an aqueous solution of sodium chloride. The chief problem with this process, (the principle of which has already been explained, in Chapter 23) is to keep separated the products of the electrolysis, NaOH and Cl_2. If allowed to come into contact, they react to produce ClO^- ions at low temperatures and ClO_3^- ions at higher temperatures (p. 615). A unit known as the Castner-Kellner cell has been designed to overcome this difficulty, and to produce a continuous supply of very pure NaOH. This cell has a mercury cathode, a graphite anode, and the electrolyte is a sodium chloride solution. As we discussed in Chapter 23, p. 519, sodium ions rather than H^+ ions are reduced at the mercury cathode, and the resulting sodium atoms alloy with mercury to form a dilute amalgam. The amalgam is then removed to a separate chamber, where it reacts with water to form a dilute sodium hydroxide solution, liberating hydrogen gas. The Cl_2 formed at the graphite anode does not interfere with the formation of the amalgam.

OTHER ALKALI-METAL HYDROXIDES. The hydroxides, KOH, RbOH, and CsOH, closely resemble NaOH in their properties, except that both solubility in water and basic strength increase from NaOH to CsOH with increasing size of the cation. Lithium hydroxide, on the other hand, has somewhat different properties. In solid LiOH there is extensive hydrogen bonding between OH^- ions in the crystal lattice, and the solubility in water is much lower than that of NaOH. Also, LiOH is a weaker base, because the very small Li^+ ion (ionic radius, 0.60 A) has a very high charge/radius ratio and hence tends to keep the OH^- ions attached to itself.

ALKALI-METAL HYDRIDES

At moderately high temperatures, the alkali metals, M, react with H_2 gas to form ionic hydrides, M^+H^-. Molten sodium, for example, reacts with H_2 gas at temperatures between 100° and 400°C to form sodium hydride, Na^+H^-:

$$2\ Na_{(l)} + H_{2(g)} \longrightarrow 2\ NaH_{(s)} \qquad \Delta H = -26.2 \text{ kcal/mole-eqn at } 25°\text{C and 1 atm}$$

As the negative value of ΔH shows, this reaction is exothermic and the high temperature is only required to increase the reaction *rate*. Actually, an increase in temperature is thermodynamically unfavorable to the formation of $Na^+H^-_{(s)}$, because 1 mole of gas disappears in each mole-reaction. The result is a decrease in entropy ($\Delta S < 0$) and hence an unfavorable $T\,\Delta S$ term, which becomes relatively more important as the temperature, T, is increased. In fact, above 400°C, NaH begins to decompose into its elements according to the reverse of the above reaction.

The alkali-metal hydrides are colorless solids with a crystalline structure of the NaCl type. When the molten hydrides are subjected to electrolysis, the metal ion is reduced at the cathode and H_2 gas is evolved at the anode from the oxidation of the hydride ions:

$$2\ Na^+H^-_{(l)} \xrightarrow{\text{electrical energy}} 2\ Na_{(l)(\text{at cathode})} + H_{2(g)(\text{at anode})}$$

The alkali-metal hydrides react rapidly and exothermally with water to form H_2 gas and a solution of the alkali-metal hydroxide:

$$NaH_{(s)} + H_2O_{(l)} \longrightarrow NaOH_{(aq)} + H_{2(g)}$$

This reaction is essentially the union of a hydride ion, H^-, with a proton, H^+, of the water, through a co-ordinate covalent bond (the H^- ion is a stronger Bronsted base than the OH^- ion, see p. 453):

$$\text{H:}^- + \text{H—}\ddot{\text{O}}\text{:H} \longrightarrow \text{H—H} + \text{:}\ddot{\text{O}}\text{:H}^-$$
(base 1) (acid 2) (acid 1) (base 2)

ALKALI-METAL AMIDES

The alkali metals are soluble in liquid ammonia, the resulting blue solutions are good conductors of an electric current, an indication that they contain ionic species. The solutions of alkali metals in ammonia contain the solvated metal ions, $M^+{}_{(solv)}$, and solvated electrons, $e^-{}_{(solv)}$, which are resposible for the blue color of the solution. When the liquid ammonia is evaporated from these solutions under an inert atmosphere, the alkali metal is recovered unchanged. However, if a catalyst—for example, finely divided iron powder—is added to the solution, the alkali metal reacts with ammonia to give the alkali-metal amide and liberating hydrogen gas. The reaction is then parallel to that of the alkali metals with water. For sodium, we have:

$$Na_{(solv)} + NH_{3(l)} \xrightarrow{\text{catalyst}} Na^+{}_{(solv)} + NH_2^-{}_{(solv)} + \tfrac{1}{2}H_{2(g)}$$

A solution of sodium amide in liquid ammonia is a good conductor of electric current, an indication of the ionic nature of this salt. When the liquid ammonia is evaporated, sodium amide is obtained as a white, crystalline, ionic compound containing Na^+ cations and NH_2^- amide anions (see p. 282). In the lattice of $Na^+NH_2^-$, each Na^+ ion is tetrahedrally surrounded by 4 N atoms of the 4 NH_2^- ions, and each NH_2^- ion is tetrahedrally surrounded by 4 Na^+ ions. The alkali-metal amides can also be obtained by reaction of the alkali metals with ammonia gas at high temperatures. For example, sodium metal reacts with ammonia gas at temperatures between 300° and 400°C to form crystalline sodium amide and H_2 gas:

$$2\,Na_{(l)} + 2\,NH_{3(g)} \xrightarrow{300\text{–}400^\circ C} 2\,Na^+(NH_2)^-{}_{(s)} + H_{2(g)}$$

When an alkali-metal amide is added to water, the amide ion, NH_2^-, reacts rapidly and exothermally with the water to produce NH_3 gas; the hydroxide of the metal remains in solution.

$$Na^+NH_2^-{}_{(s)} + H_2O_{(l)} \longrightarrow Na^+{}_{(aq)} + OH^-_{(aq)} + NH_{3(g)}$$

This reaction consists essentially of the sharing of the lone electron pair of the NH_2^- ion (the stronger Bronsted base) with a H atom of water, to form H_2 and OH^- (the weaker Bronsted base):

$$\left[\text{:}\underset{\text{H}}{\ddot{\text{N}}}\text{:H}\right]^- + \text{:}\underset{\text{H}}{\ddot{\text{O}}}\text{:H} \longrightarrow \left[\text{:}\ddot{\text{O}}\text{:H}\right]^- + \text{H:}\underset{\text{H}}{\ddot{\text{N}}}\text{:H}$$
(base 1) (acid 2) (base 2) (acid 1)

ALKALI-METAL HALIDES

All the alkali metals, M, react rapidly and exothermally with all the halogens, X_2, to form the crystalline, ionic alkali-metal halides, M^+X^-:

$$M_{(s)} + \tfrac{1}{2}X_{2(g)} \longrightarrow M^+X^-{}_{(s)} \qquad (\Delta H \text{ is highly negative})$$

We have already discussed a great many matters that bear on these substances. For instance, we have discussed the crystal structures of the metal halides in Chapter 10, p. 171, and their solubility in water in Chapter 18, p. 397, and Chapter 19, p. 425. All alkali-metal halides are soluble in water, and lithium salts and sodium iodide are also soluble in such organic solvents as ethanol, C_2H_5OH, and acetone, CH_3COCH_3. The heats of formation reaction of the alkali-metal halides were considered in detail in Chapter 13, (see Born-Haber cycle, p. 264), and Chapter 16 (see enthalpy diagram, p. 343). Here let us discuss briefly the trends that appear from the values of the heats of formation of the various alkali halides, listed in Table 30-2. First, we see that for the series of halides of each alkali metal, the ΔH_{form} decreases gradually from the fluoride to the iodide. Since the ΔH_{atomiz} of M and the Ionization Energy of M are constant factors for all the halides of the same metal, the differences in ΔH_{form} arise from the differences among the bond strengths of the halogen molecules ($\Delta H_{diss\ of\ X_2}$), the electron affinities of the halogens, and the lattice energies of the salts. The accompanying graph shows that the variations of electron affinity and dissociation energy are relatively minor as compared to the variations of lattice energy. So the trend in the ΔH_{form} of the alkali-metal halides is the same as the trend of their lattice energies, which in turn decrease as the ionic size increases from F^- to I^-.

TABLE 30-2 $\Delta H^\circ_{formation}$ **OF ALKALI-METAL HALIDES, (KCAL/MOLE) AT 25°C**

	Li^+	Na^+	K^+	Rb^+	Cs^+
F^-	146	136	134	131	127
Cl^-	98	98	104	103	106
Br^-	84	86	94	95	94
I^-	65	69	78	78	80

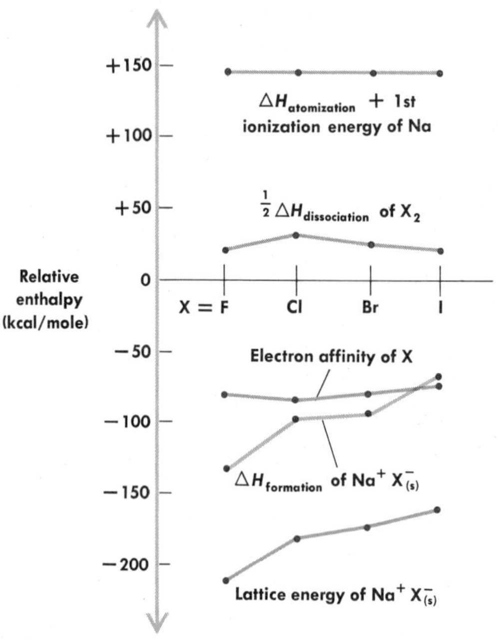

Let us now turn to the trend in ΔH_{form} for the salts of each halide ion with the various alkali-metal ions. Here the constant factors are, for each halogen, the dissociation energy of X_2 and the electron affinity of X, and the determining factors are the heats of atomization of the metal, its ionization energy, and the lattice energy of the salt. As we can see from Table 30-2, the values of the heat of atomization and of the ionization energy of the alkali metals both decrease in the sequence Li, Na, K, Rb, Cs, as the atoms or ions increase in size, and so do the large values of the lattice energy. Therefore if the changes in ionization energy and sublimation energy are dominant, then the heat of formation of a certain halide sale will increase from Li to Cs. This is so for all the halides except for the fluorides. For the fluorides the lattice-energy is the dominant factor, and the heat of formation decreases from Li to Cs.

ALKALI-METAL CARBONATES, M_2CO_3, AND ALKALI-METAL HYDROGEN CARBONATES, $MHCO_3$

The alkali-metal carbonates, M_2CO_3, are soluble ionic compounds that contain the alkali-metal ion, M^+, and the carbonate ion, $CO_3^=$. Since the alkali-metal carbonates are salts of a weak acid, they undergo hydrolysis in aqueous solution:

$$\cancel{2M^+} + CO_3^= + H_2O \rightleftharpoons \cancel{2M^+} + HCO_3^- + OH^-$$

This reaction explains why solutions of the alkali-metal carbonates are basic; a 1 *N* solution of Na_2CO_3, for example, contains OH^- ions in a concentration of about 0.1 *N*. All carbonates and hydrogen carbonates will react with solutions of strong acids to form CO_2 (see Chapter 24, p. 539).

The alkali-metal hydrogen carbonates, $MHCO_3$, are also soluble in water but markedly less so than the corresponding carbonates; their solutions are almost neutral. The alkali-metal hydrogen carbonates are unstable with respect to decomposition by heat. When heated, they produce the alkali-metal carbonate, carbon dioxide, and water:

$$2\ MHCO_{3(s)} \longrightarrow M_2CO_{3(s)} + CO_{2(g)} + H_2O_{(l)}$$

Sodium hydrogen carbonate, $NaHCO_3$, known in the household as "baking soda," is also the chief component of baking powder. Its usefulness in baking is due partly to the decomposition reaction, for when dough is heated in the oven, $NaHCO_3$ decomposes to liberate CO_2 gas (and H_2O). The CO_2 gas thus evolved causes the dough to rise, and gives it the desired lightness.

THE COMMERCIAL PREPARATION OF Na_2CO_3 AND $NaHCO_3$

Sodium carbonate, Na_2CO_3, commercially one of the most important alkali-metal salts, is produced in great quantities. This compound is used directly or indirectly in the manufacture of such widely different substances as glass, soap, sodium hydroxide, drugs, paints, and enamelware.

One important method for preparing Na_2CO_3 is the *Solvay*, or *ammonia*, process, named after a Belgian industrial chemist, Ernest Solvay (1838–1922), who invented it in 1863. In the Solvay process the starting materials are gaseous NH_3, gaseous CO_2, and a saturated aqueous solution of NaCl (brine) at a temperature of 15°C or lower. First, the brine solution is saturated with NH_3 gas, then CO_2 gas is bubbled through it. The CO_2 reacts with the ammonia-saturated water solution to form NH_4^+ and HCO_3^- ions. Since the solution also contains a high concentration of Na^+ ions (from NaCl), the solubility product of the not very soluble $NaHCO_3$ is exceeded; the salt precipitates and is removed by filtration. The net chemical change is:

$$Na^+_{(aq)} + \cancel{Cl^-} + H_2O_{(l)} + NH_{3(aq)} + CO_{2(aq)} \longrightarrow NaHCO_{3(s)} + NH^+_{4(aq)} + \cancel{Cl^-}$$

The rather impure $NaHCO_3$ thus obtained is washed with water and then heated to form sodium carbonate, Na_2CO_3 (the desired product), H_2O, and CO_2 gas, which is recycled to be absorbed into the NH_3-saturated brine solution.

The Solvay process for manufacturing Na_2CO_3 is quite economical because not only can the CO_2 be re-used, but the other expensive starting material, NH_3, can be regenerated by heating the by-product, $NH_4^+Cl^-$, with $Ca(OH)_2$:

$$2\ NH^+_{4(aq)} + \cancel{2\ Cl^-_{(aq)}} + Ca(OH)_{2(s)} \longrightarrow 2\ NH_{3(g)} + Ca^{++}_{(aq)} + \cancel{2\ Cl^-_{(aq)}} + 2\ H_2O_{(l)}$$

Furthermore, both the original CO_2 and the CaO used to make the $Ca(OH)_2$ are obtained by the thermal decomposition of the inexpensive limestone, $CaCO_3$.

$$CaCO_{3(s)} \longrightarrow CaO_{(s)} + CO_{2(g)}$$

THE USES OF ALKALI METALS AND THEIR COMPOUNDS

In order to keep the alkali metals on hand for use in the laboratory, they must be stored under inert liquids such as kerosene and toluene, because, as we have seen, all the alkali metals react spontaneously and at low temperature with the oxygen and moisture of the atmosphere. Large quantities for industrial use are stored in closed tank cars.

All the alkali metals are excellent conductors of heat and electricity. Sodium, which is inexpensive and relatively low-melting (m.p., 98°C), is widely used in industry as a fluid conductor of electricity or heat. Sodium-filled iron pipes, for example, are often employed as conductors of electricity, and liquid sodium is used in airplane and other heavy-duty engines to dissipate the tremendous amounts of heat generated by the fuel combustion.

TABLE 30-3 SUMMARY OF IMPORTANT REACTIONS OF THE ALKALI METALS, M

General Equation	Comments
$2\,M + 2\,H_2O \longrightarrow 2\,M^+ + 2\,OH^- + H_2$	Li slowly; Na, K, Rb, Cs, very fast
$2\,M + X_2 \longrightarrow 2\,M^+X^-$	All alkali metals react violently with all halogens
$4\,M + O_2 \longrightarrow 2\,M_2O$	Li only
$2\,M + O_2 \longrightarrow M_2O_2$	Na only
$M + O_2 \longrightarrow MO_2$	Chiefly K, Rb, Cs
$6\,M + N_2 \longrightarrow 2\,M_3N$	Li only
$2\,M + 2\,NH_{3(g)} \longrightarrow 2\,MNH_2 + H_2$	All alkali metals
$2\,M + 2\,NH_{3(l)} \longrightarrow 2\,MNH_2 + H_2$	All alkali metals in the presence of catalyst—Fe, for example
$2\,M + H_2 \longrightarrow 2\,MH$	All alkali metals yield ionic hydrides

The largest single commercial use of sodium metal is in the manufacture of tetraethyl lead, $Pb(C_2H_5)_4$, which is used as an "anti-knock" agent in gasoline. Sodium is also used in the manufacture of such commercially important compounds as $NaNH_2$, NaCN, Na_2O, and Na_2O_2, and also of many organic chemicals. We have already mentioned the use of sodium to prepare potassium metal from its salts (p. 672). Another important application of sodium metal is in the manufacture of sodium-vapor lamps, which are now widely used in highway lighting. The radiations emitted by these lamps, commonly called "sodium D lines," are very intense and occur in the region of the spectrum to which the human eye is most sensitive. (These radiations are also emitted when any sodium compound is heated in the flame of a bunsen burner, and constitute the familiar bright yellow "sodium light.")

Lithium metal is used to an appreciable extent in the manufacture of special alloys and in the synthesis of certain organic compounds. The other alkali metals have no important commercial use.

Most of the salts of the alkali metals are soluble in water. In fact, when we want to prepare an aqueous solution of a particular anion, often the only salts suitable for the purpose are those of the alkali metals. Because of their high solubility in water and low cost, sodium salts are commonly used in the laboratory and in industry as a source of particular anions. Table 30-3 summarizes the important reactions of the alkali metals.

Exercises

30-1 Write the electron configurations of the alkali metals: $_3Li$, $_{11}Na$, $_{19}K$, $_{37}Rb$, $_{55}Cs$, and $_{87}Fr$.

30-2 Discuss the alkali metals with regard to (a) radii of the atoms, (b) crystal structure, (c) hardness and melting point, (d) strength of metallic bonding.

30-3 Compare the ΔH of atomization, the first ionization energy, and the energy of hydration for all the alkali metals. Discuss the observed trends in the family.

30-4 Describe the general method used for preparing the alkali metals. Give equations.

30-5 (a) Give the empirical as well as the structural formulas for the three different classes of oxides of the alkali metals. Illustrate with examples and names. (b)

Write equations to illustrate the reactions of these different alkali-metal oxides with water.

30-6 Write the general equation for the reaction of alkali metals with water. Why is this reaction explosive in the case of sodium (unless carried out with special precautions) whereas lithium reacts smoothly?

30-7 Describe the physical and chemical properties of sodium hydroxide.

30-8 Describe the one important method for the commercial preparation of sodium hydroxide.

30-9 (a) What is the general method for preparing the alkali-metal hydrides? Illustrate by writing the equation for the preparation of sodium hydride. (b) Contrast the chemical character of the alkali-metal hydrides and the alkali-metal halides. Illustrate by writing the equation for the reaction of sodium hydride with water. (c) Which is the most stable of the alkali-metal hydrides?

EXERCISES

30-10 Write the general equation for the reaction of an alkali metal with gaseous and liquid ammonia. State the conditions required for reaction.

30-11 Outline the preparation of Na_2CO_3 and $NaHCO_3$ by means of the Solvay, or ammonia, process. Give equations.

30-12 With NaCl as one of the starting materials, write equations to illustrate how you would prepare (a) sodium metal, (b) sodium hydroxide, (c) sodium amide, (d) sodium nitrate, (e) sodium peroxide.

30-13 If a reaction takes place when aqueous solutions of the following are mixed, complete the equation and balance. If no reaction takes place, write N.R.

(a) $NaOH + Al_2(SO_4)_3 \longrightarrow$ (d) $NaOH + CuSO_4 \longrightarrow$
(b) $Na_2CO_3 + H_3PO_4 \longrightarrow$ (e) $Na_2CO_3 + Ca(NO_3)_2 \longrightarrow$
(c) $NaOH + H_2SO_4 \longrightarrow$

30-14 Indicate the conditions under which the following will react. Give equations.

(a) $NaOH + Zn + H_2O \longrightarrow$ (c) $NaOH + Br_2 \longrightarrow$
(b) $NaOH + CO_2 \longrightarrow$ (d) $NaHCO_3 + \text{heat} \longrightarrow$

30-15 Which of each of the following pairs of compounds has the greater ionic character? (a) KCl or KI, (b) NaBr or $MgBr_2$, (c) NaCl or CsCl.

30-16 Discuss the observed trends in the heats of formation of the alkali-metal halides. (a) for all the alkali-metal fluorides, (b) for all alkali-metal chlorides, (c) for all halides of lithium, (d) for all halides of cesium.

30-17 State briefly the reasons why ionic $Na^+Cl^-_{(s)}$ is the only product obtained when sodium metal burns in Cl_2 gas.

THE ALKALINE-EARTH METALS: THE GROUP IIA ELEMENTS

31

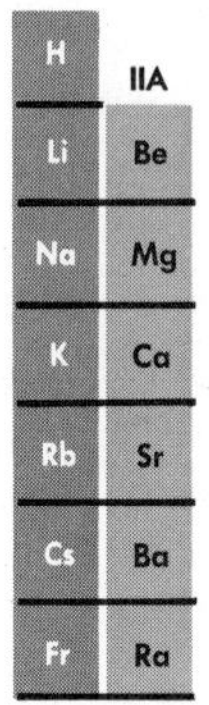

Stable Crystal Structure at 25°C, 1 atm	IIA
hexagonal close-packed	Be
hexagonal close-packed	Mg
face-centered cubic	Ca
face-centered cubic	Sr
body-centered cubic	Ba
———	Ra

In this chapter we shall discuss the elements of Group IIA—beryllium, Be; magnesium, Mg; calcium, Ca; strontium, Sr; barium, Ba—which constitute a closely related family, generally called the alkaline-earth metals. Radium, Ra, the heaviest member of the family, is a strongly radioactive and relatively scarce element, and we shall not discuss its properties here. However, the known properties of radium closely parallel those of its lighter homolog, barium, except—of course—that barium is not radioactive.

31-1 General Characteristics

The elements of Group IIA all have an ns^2 outer electron configuration; they exhibit many similarities to one another and a gradual change in properties as the size of the atoms increases. Some of their important properties are listed in Table 31-1.

STRUCTURE. The alkaline-earth metals all have a gray-white luster when freshly cut, but all except beryllium tarnish rapidly when exposed to air. Beryllium and magnesium have a hexagonal close-packed structure, in which each Mg atom is surrounded by 12 equidistant neighbors, as shown in Figure 31-1 (metallic coordination number = 12); calcium and strontium exist at room temperature in a face-centered cubic structure (metallic coordination number = 12), whereas barium exists in the body-centered cubic structure, as do the alkali metals (metallic coordination number = 8). The Group IIA metals are considerably harder than

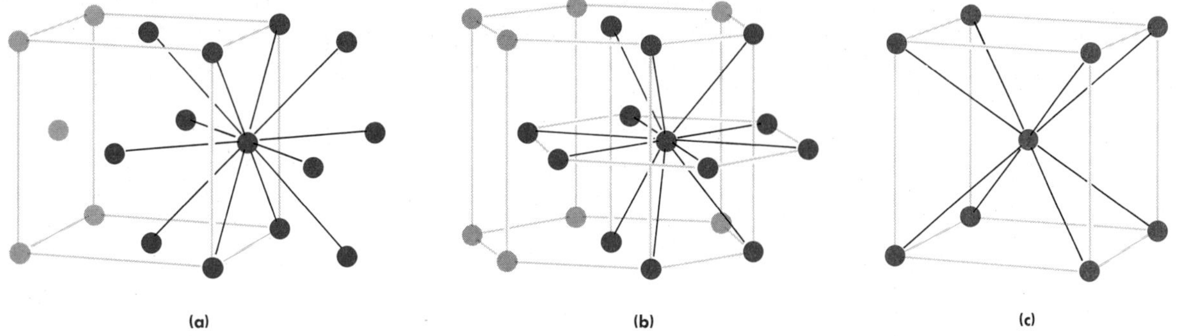

FIGURE 31-1 The three most common metallic structures. (a) Hexagonal close-packed. (b) Cubic close-packed, or face-centered cubic. (c) Body-centered cubic.

the alkali metals. They are good conductors of electricity, and although they are somewhat brittle, they can be hammered and rolled.

DENSITY: MELTING AND BOILING POINTS. The Group IIA metals are appreciably denser than the Group IA metals (compare Tables 31-1 and 30-1). Because of their greater effective nuclear charge, which draws in the outer electron cloud more tightly, the Group IIA atoms are smaller than the corresponding Group IA atoms and can be packed more closely in the crystal lattice. The alkaline-earth metals also have strikingly higher melting and boiling points than the alkali metals, and their heats of atomization are about twice those of the corresponding alkali metals (compare values in Tables 31-1 and 30-1). These properties, together with the greater hardness, indicate that the metallic bonding is much stronger in the alkaline-earth metals than in the alkali metals. This stronger bonding is related chiefly to two factors: (1) The smaller atomic size of Group IIA metals allows the nuclei of the atoms to be closer to one another in the crystal lattice than the nuclei of the Group IA metals are, so that the former share to a greater extent than the latter the valence electrons (greater overlapping of the atomic orbitals). (2) The effective nuclear charge attracting the (bonding) valence electrons is greater in the atoms of the alkaline-earth metals than in the atoms of the alkali metals, because the two ns^2 electrons do not completely screen each other from the nuclear charge (see Chapter 12, p. 241).

TABLE 31-1 SOME PROPERTIES OF THE ALKALINE-EARTH METALS (GROUP IIA) ELEMENTS

	Outer Electron Config.	Atomic Weight	Atomic (Metallic) Radius* A	Ionic Radius of M^{++} Ion, A	Density at 20°C, g/cm³	Melting Point °C	ΔH_{fusion} at m.p. (kcal/mole) of atoms)	Boiling Point, °C	Electro-negativity (Pauling)	ΔH_{atomiz} (at 25°C, 1 atm) (kcal/mole of atoms)
$_4$Be	$2s^2$	9.01	1.12 (12)	0.31	1.85	1280	2.8	2770	1.5	78.2
$_{12}$Mg	$3s^2$	24.31	1.60 (12)	0.65	1.74	650	2.1	1110	1.2	35.3
$_{20}$Ca	$4s^2$	40.08	1.97 (12)	0.99	1.55	838	2.2	1440	1.0	42.2
$_{38}$Sr	$5s^2$	87.62	2.15 (12)	1.13	2.60	768	2.2	1380	1.0	39.1
$_{56}$Ba	$6s^2$	137.34	2.17 (8)	1.35	3.50	714	1.8	1640	0.9	41.7

* The metallic coordination number is given in parentheses.

Another notable difference between the alkali and the alkaline-earth metals is that the latter exist in the vapor state as isolated gaseous atoms, the former as covalent diatomic molecules. We can explain this difference on the basis of the different outer electron configurations of the elements of the two groups. Two atoms of an alkali metal, which in their ground electronic state have an ns^1 outer electron configuration, can form a diatomic molecule simply by sharing their outer ns^1 electrons in a covalent bond. On the other hand, in order for two atoms of an alkaline-earth metal to form a diatomic molecule, both atoms must first be promoted from their ground electronic state ns^2 to an excited state—for example, ns^1np^1—suitable for bond formation. This promotion requires a large quantity of energy (see p. 225), and even the energy that is released in the formation of one or two covalent bonds between the two atoms is insufficient to make the formation of a diatomic molecule energetically favorable.

IONIZATION ENERGIES. Table 31-2 lists the first and second ionization energies of the alkaline-earth metals—that is, the ΔH of the reactions, $M_{(g)} \longrightarrow M^+_{(g)} + e^-$ and $M^+_{(g)} \longrightarrow M^{++}_{(g)} + e^-$—together with their sum. As we would expect, the second ionization energy of each element is much larger than—actually, almost twice as large as—the first ionization energy. This is so, as we know, because other factors being almost equal, more energy is required to remove an electron from a positively charged ion, $M^+_{(g)}$, than from a neutral atom, $M_{(g)}$.

TABLE 31-2 IONIZATION ENERGIES (KCAL/MOLE) OF THE ALKALINE-EARTH METALS

	First Ioniz. Energy	Second Ioniz. Energy	Sum of first and second Ioniz. Energy
Be	+215	+420	+635
Mg	+176	+346	+522
Ca	+141	+274	+415
Sr	+131	+253	+384
Ba	+120	+230	+350

Both the first and the second ionization energies, and hence their sum, gradually decrease in this family with increasing size, because the nuclear attraction on an electron decreases as the distance of the electron from the nucleus increases. Thus the energy required to remove one of the outer electrons of an atom or ion gradually becomes smaller as the atom or ion becomes larger. Similar considerations explain why the first ionization energies of the alkaline-earth metals are so much larger than those of the corresponding alkali metals. For example, the first ionization energy of the beryllium atom, $Be_{(g)}$ (215 kcal/mole; metallic radius, 1.12 A), is almost twice that of the larger lithium atom, $Li_{(g)}$ (124 kcal/mole; metallic radius, 1.52 A), because both outer $2s^2$ electrons of Be experience a stronger nuclear attraction than does the $2s^1$ electron of Li. Not only do we have the size factor to consider, but also, for beryllium, the incomplete screening of the additional nuclear proton by the additional $2s$ electron. Both size decrease and the relative increase in effective nuclear charge contribute to making the removal of one of the $2s^2$ electrons of Be much more difficult than the removal of the $2s^1$ electron of Li.

31-2 Occurrence and Preparation

NATURAL OCCURRENCE

Because all the alkaline-earth metals are highly electropositive, none of them is found free in nature, but they are quite common in many minerals.

BERYLLIUM. Beryllium is a relatively scarce element. Its chief source is the mineral beryl, $Be_3Al_2(SiO_3)_6$, but small amounts of beryllium compounds are also present in various minerals and in silicate rocks.

MAGNESIUM. Magnesium is the sixth most abundant metal in the earth's crust. It occurs in many minerals, in sea water and mineral springs, and in the deposits left by the evaporation of lakes. Some of the important magnesium-containing minerals are spinel, $Mg(AlO_2)_2$; talc, or soapstone, $H_2Mg_3(SiO_3)_4$; asbestos, $CaMg_3(SiO_3)_4$; and olivine, $(Mg,Fe)_2SiO_4$ (the formula $(Mg,Fe)_2SiO_4$ indicates that in this mineral the Mg and Fe ions may be present in varying amounts within the same crystal lattice). The Stassfurt salt beds in Germany contain commercially valuable deposits of magnesite, $MgCO_3$; dolomite, $MgCO_3,CaCO_3$; kieserite, $MgSO_4 \cdot H_2O$; and carnallite, $MgCl_2,KCl \cdot 6\,H_2O$. Small quantities of magnesium are present in most living organisms. Chlorophyll, which is essential to plant life (and which, incidentally, imparts to plants their green color), is a coordination compound in which the Mg^{++} ion is bound to an organic compound.

CALCIUM. The third most abundant of all the metals, calcium, occurs in the minerals gypsum, $CaSO_4 \cdot 2\,H_2O$; anhydrite, $CaSO_4$; fluorite, CaF_2; apatite $CaF_2,3\,Ca_3(PO_4)_2$; and in enormous quantities as dolomite, $MgCO_3,CaCO_3$, and chalk, limestone, and marble which are different forms of $CaCO_3$. Calcium salts occur in most natural waters and are essential components of both plant and animal tissues, and of shells and bones.

STRONTIUM, BARIUM, AND RADIUM. Strontium occurs in strontianite, $SrCO_3$, and in the mineral celestite, $SrSO_4$, so-called because of its sky-blue color, which is due to traces of impurities (pure $SrSO_4$ is colorless). The most common barium mineral is barium sulfate, $BaSO_4$, called barite or heavy spar; barium also occurs as witherite, $BaCO_3$. Radium is present in extremely small amounts in uranium minerals.

PREPARATION

The alkaline-earth metals can be prepared similarly to the alkali metals, with one general difference—the alkaline-earth metal ions, M^{++}, are more easily reduced than the alkali metal ions, M^+. The alkaline-earth metals are commonly obtained by the electrolysis of their fused anhydrous halides, in the presence of some alkali-metal halides which lower the melting point and improve the conductivity of the electrolyte. As an illustration of this general method, we shall describe the electrolytic preparation of magnesium metal. We first obtain magnesium chloride, $MgCl_2$, the halide used in the electrolytic process, from any of several sources. For example, the mineral magnesite, $MgCO_3$, can be thermally decomposed to MgO, which then can be converted to anhydrous $MgCl_2$ by treatment with the gases CO and Cl_2 at high temperatures:

$$MgCO_{3(s)} \longrightarrow MgO_{(s)} + CO_{2(g)}$$
$$MgO_{(s)} + CO_{(g)} + Cl_{2(g)} \longrightarrow MgCl_{2(s)} + CO_{2(g)}$$

The anhydrous magnesium chloride, $MgCl_2$, is then mixed with some NaCl to lower the melting point and to increase the conductivity of the melt; the mixture is electrolyzed in the molten state at 710°C using a graphite anode and an iron cathode. The molten Mg metal formed at the cathode rises to the surface of the molten electrolyte and is collected, while at the anode chlorine gas is liberated:

$$MgCl_{2(l)} \xrightarrow[\text{(NaCl)}]{\text{electrical energy}} Mg_{(l)} + Cl_{2(g)}$$

Magnesium metal can also be prepared by reducing MgO with carbon at high temperatures. The magnesium oxide, MgO, is converted to magnesium metal vapor, $Mg_{(g)}$, by heating it with carbon in an electric furnace at a temperature above 2,000°C:

$$MgO_{(s)} + C_{(s)} \longrightarrow Mg_{(g)} + CO_{(g)}$$

At this high temperature, magnesium vapor distills along with the CO gas. This strongly endothermic reaction is thermodynamically forbidden at low temperatures

($\Delta G^\circ = +103$ kcal/mole-eqn at 25°C), but it becomes permitted at very high temperatures because of the favorable contribution of the $T\,\Delta S$ term. (Notice that the entropy of the system increases because two moles of gas are formed.) To minimize the occurrence of the reverse reaction when the temperature decreases below 2,000°C, the reaction mixture is rapidly quenched by introducing a cold gas, that would not react with either Mg vapor or CO—for example, hydrogen or fuel gas. The Mg vapor condenses to solid Mg, and is then readily separated from the CO remaining as a gas.

Calcium, strontium, and barium can also be prepared in the laboratory by the electrolysis of aqueous solutions of their salts, using a mercury cathode. Again, as for the alkali metals, an amalgam of the alkaline-earth metal rather than hydrogen gas is formed at the cathode. This amalgam is first dried and then heated to vaporize the low-boiling mercury, leaving behind the alkaline-earth metal as a powder. This method is not used industrially, however, for the final product always contains traces of mercury.

Because of the pronounced tendency of barium to react vigorously with oxygen, barium is the most difficult of the alkaline-earth metals to obtain in pure form. It is produced commercially, however, by the reduction of BaO with Al powder at about 1,200°C and under reduced pressure:

$$3\ BaO_{(s)} + 2\ Al_{(s)} \longrightarrow 3\ Ba_{(g)} + Al_2O_{3(s)}$$

Under these conditions barium escapes as vapor from the reaction mixture and can then be condensed in an inert atmosphere to give the pure metal.

31-3 Chemical Properties of the Alkaline-Earth Metals

As we have come to expect, the first element of the family, beryllium, exhibits chemical properties which differ rather markedly from those of the other members. Except for beryllium, the Group IIA metals, M, form essentially ionic compounds in which they are present as dipositive ions, M^{++}. Most beryllium compounds, on the other hand, have appreciable covalent character. All the alkaline-earth metals exhibit only the oxidation number +2 in their compounds.

OXIDATION POTENTIALS

Couple	E° (volts)
Be,Be^{++}	+1.85
Mg,Mg^{++}	+2.37
Ca,Ca^{++}	+2.87
Sr,Sr^{++}	+2.89
Ba,Ba^{++}	+2.91

The alkaline-earth metals are strongly electropositive. Their E° values, shown in the margin, are all highly positive and indicate that the metals are strong reductants, their reducing power increasing gradually from Be to Ba. In fact, all alkaline-earth metals are oxidized to the $M^{++}{}_{(aq)}$ ions by acid solutions and hydrogen is evolved. If the anion of the acid is an oxidant, it too can be reduced together with, or rather than, the H^+ ions—see p. 689 for an example. Because the oxidation potential of each alkaline-earth metal is so highly positive, these metals, like the alkali metals, are also oxidized in the presence of water alone and even in basic solutions. These reactions occur spontaneously because, for the reaction $2\ H_2O \longrightarrow H_2 + 2\ OH^- + 2\ e^-$, the oxidation potential in both neutral solution ($[H^+] = 10^{-7}$, $E = +0.41$ v) and in 1 M basic solution ($[H^+] = 10^{-14}$, $E^\circ_{basic} = +0.83$ v) is less positive than the oxidation potential of the alkaline-earth metal couple, M,M^{++}. The highly positive oxidation potentials of the alkaline-earth metals explain why these metals are generally prepared by "dry" reactions, such as the electrolysis of molten salts or the reduction of the oxide with carbon. The oxidation potentials gradually become more positive from Be to Ba; the greatest differences exist between Be and Mg, and between Mg and Ca, whereas Ca, Sr, and Ba have almost the same oxidation potentials. This trend, together with the analogous trend of the electronegativities, accounts for the similar chemical behaviors of Ca, Sr, and Ba, and can be explained on the basis of the atomic and ionic sizes of these elements. The Be^{++} ion, with 4 nuclear protons and only 2 electrons ($1s^2$), has an extremely small radius, estimated as 0.31 A, and hence the largest charge/radius ratio of all elements of its family. Accordingly, Be^{++} is a very strongly polarizing ion and tends to polarize the surrounding anions or molecules to such an extent that largely covalent bonds result. This effect is somewhat less marked for the Mg^{++} ion, whose radius, 0.65 A, is twice that of Be^{++}, and becomes increasingly weaker as we proceed down the family to the larger Ca^{++}, Sr^{++}, and Ba^{++} ions. Thus Be(II) forms largely covalent bonding; Mg(II) forms ionic bonds with some covalent character; and Ca(II), Sr(II), and Ba(II) form essentially ionic bonding.

HYDRATION ENERGIES

ΔH_{hydr} of M^{++} (kcal/mole)	
Be^{++}	−606
Mg^{++}	−474
Ca^{++}	−395
Sr^{++}	−354
Ba^{++}	−326

As the values given in the margin show, the hydration energies of the alkaline-earth metal ions are much larger than those of the isoelectronic alkali-metal ions (p. 673). The reason is that the alkaline-earth ions are smaller and have a greater positive charge, and consequently exert a much stronger electrostatic attraction on the negative oxygen atom of the polar molecules of water. In fact, the hydration energy of the very small Be^{++} ion is so very large, that all beryllium salts crystallize from solutions as hydrates in which the Be^{++} ion is tetrahedrally surrounded by four O atoms of four H_2O molecules, $[Be(H_2O)_4]^{++}$. And these hydrates cannot be dehydrated simply by heating, because hydrolysis takes place and basic salts of Be(II) are formed. The magnesium ion, Mg^{++}, also has a very high hydration energy, and most of its salts also crystallize from aqueous solutions as hydrates, which hydrolyze rather than dehydrate upon heating. For this reason, all anhydrous salts of Be(II), and many of Mg(II), can be obtained only by anhydrous methods. As the size of the M^{++} ion increases in the alkaline-earth family, however, the polarizing power gradually decreases, so that many salts of Ca^{++}, Sr^{++}, and Ba^{++} crystallize as anhydrous salts from water solutions.

KINETIC PROPERTIES. As a general rule, the rates of similar reactions of the alkaline-earth metals increase gradually down the family, beryllium being the most sluggish and barium the fastest to react under comparable conditions.

Let us now consider some of the more important reactions and compounds of the alkaline-earth metals.

31-4 Compounds of the Alkaline-Earth Metals

OXIDES OF ALKALINE-EARTH METALS

All the alkaline-earth metals, M, can react with oxygen to form white solid metal oxides, MO. The reaction is strongly exothermic:

$$2\ M_{(s)} + O_{2(g)} \longrightarrow 2\ MO_{(s)} \qquad (\Delta H = \text{highly negative})$$

ΔH_{form} (kcal/mole)	
BeO	−146.0
MgO	−143.8
CaO	−151.9
SrO	−141.1
BaO	−133.4

Even though this reaction is strongly favorable thermodynamically, the rate of reaction is very slow at room temperature—especially for the lighter members of the family. But if the temperature is raised until oxidation of the metal begins, the reaction then proceeds rapidly, with the evolution of a very large quantity of heat and, for magnesium, also of light. The familiar magnesium flash is simply the electrically induced instantaneous combustion of a thin magnesium filament in an oxygen atmosphere.

The most commonly used method of preparing the alkaline-earth metal oxides, however, is the thermal decomposition of the corresponding carbonates, MCO_3, which, except for beryllium carbonates, occur in nature.

$$MCO_{3(s)} \longrightarrow MO_{(s)} + CO_{2(g)}$$

All alkaline-earth metal oxides, except BeO, are ionic crystals with the Na^+Cl^- crystalline structure (6:6 crystal coordination). In beryllium oxide, BeO, on the other hand, each Be atom is tetrahedrally surrounded by 4 O atoms, and in turn each O atom is surrounded by 4 Be atoms (4:4 crystal coordination). Thus BeO differs in structure from the oxides of the other members of the alkaline-earth family, for two chief reasons: (1) only 4 O atoms can be accommodated around the very small Be atom, and (2) the 4:4 coordination is compatible with the essentially covalent character of the Be—O bonds—for both the Be atoms and the O atoms have only 4 outer orbitals available for covalent bonding (the one 2*s* and the three 2*p* orbitals).

All the oxides of the alkaline-earth metals have highly negative heats of formation. Consequently, at room temperature these oxides are very stable toward decomposition into their elements. Only at extremely high temperatures—close to 3,000°C or higher—does the $T\Delta S$ energy term, which is favorable to decomposition, finally become sufficiently large to overcome the high ΔH value, which is unfavorable to decomposition. The alkaline-earth metal oxides then begin to dissociate into their elements. Because of their stability to heat, beryllium oxide, BeO (common name, beryllia), and magnesium oxide, MgO (common name, magnesia), are used for the manufacture of refractory bricks for electric furnaces, and of crucibles for some high-temperature industrial processes.

REACTION OF THE ALKALINE-EARTH METAL OXIDES WITH WATER. These oxides, except BeO, readily react with water to form the ionic hydroxides, $M(OH)_2$:

$$MO + H_2O \longrightarrow M(OH)_2 \qquad (\Delta H \text{ is highly negative})$$

The rate of this reaction increases with the size of the metal ion, and also depends on the thermal treatment to which the oxide has been previously submitted. Thus, MgO which has been heated to a very high temperature does not react at all with water.

Solubility (moles/l., at 25°C)	
$Be(OH)_2$	5.0×10^{-9}
$Mg(OH)_2$	3.0×10^{-4}
$Ca(OH)_2$	2.2×10^{-2}
$Sr(OH)_2$	6.5×10^{-2}
$Ba(OH)_2$	2.2×10^{-1}

The metal hydroxides, $M(OH)_2$, are sparingly to moderately soluble in water. Their solubility increases greatly with the size of the metal ion, but even the most soluble hydroxide, $Ba(OH)_2$, is only moderately soluble (see values in margin). The increasing solubility of the hydroxides as we go down the group from Be^{++} to Ba^{++} results principally from the decrease in their lattice energies. As we know, the solubility of an ionic compound depends on the balance between its lattice energy and the sum of the heats of hydration of its ions. For the series of the $M(OH)_2$ hydroxides, both the lattice energy and the heat of hydration decrease with increasing size of the metal ion (the contribution of the ΔH_{hydr} of the OH^- ion being constant). Thus, the increase in solubility from $Be(OH)_2$ to $Ba(OH)_2$ simply reflects the more rapid decrease of the lattice energy compared with the hydration energy.

The basic character of both the oxides, MO, and the hydroxides, $M(OH)_2$, increases as the size of the metal ion increases. Beryllium oxide, BeO, and beryllium hydroxide, $Be(OH)_2$, react with both acids and bases—they are amphoteric. In the reaction of BeO and $Be(OH)_2$ with aqueous solutions of acids, the $[Be(H_2O)_4]^{++}$ complex cation is formed; in the reaction with aqueous solutions of strong bases the complex anion $[Be(OH)_4]^{=}$ is formed. For BeO, the complete equations for these reactions follow:

$$BeO_{(s)} + 2\,H^+_{(aq)} + SO^{=}_{4(aq)} \longrightarrow [Be(H_2O)_4]^{++}_{(aq)} + SO^{=}_{4(aq)}$$
$$BeO_{(s)} + 2\,Na^+_{(aq)} + 2\,OH^-_{(aq)} + H_2O \longrightarrow 2\,Na^+_{(aq)} + [Be(OH)_4]^{=}_{(aq)}$$

The other alkaline-earth metal oxides, MgO, CaO, SrO, and BaO, and their corresponding hydroxides, however, are strongly basic in character, and their basicity increases as the size of the metal ion increases. The hydroxide $Ba(OH)_2$ is the strongest base of the group. These hydroxides react with acids to form the normal salts.

REACTION OF THE ALKALINE-EARTH METALS WITH WATER

We have seen that the alkaline-earth metals have highly positive $E°$ values—that is, they are strong reductants. Accordingly, all alkaline-earth metals are oxidized by water, as well as by acid and alkaline solutions, to form the $M^{++}_{(aq)}$ ions and H_2 gas. Again, as in the case of the alkali metals, if a strongly oxidizing anion is present in the solution—for example, the NO_3^- ion—this anion may be reduced rather than, or together with, the H^+ ions or H_2O molecules. Even though the reaction of all alkaline-earth metals with water is thermodynamically favorable, the rate of reaction is slow for the lighter elements. Thus, beryllium is virtually unaffected by water at ordinary temperatures, but reacts exothermally at higher temperatures. Magnesium undergoes a very slow reaction with cold water, reacts faster at higher temperatures, and reacts vigorously with steam. Calcium reacts sluggishly with water at ordinary temperatures, strontium more rapidly, and barium vigorously. The general equation for the reaction of the alkaline-earth metals with water is:

$$M + 2\,H_2O \longrightarrow M(OH)_2 + H_2 \qquad (\Delta H \text{ is negative})$$

CARBONATES AND HYDROGEN CARBONATES

The carbonates of the alkaline-earth metals are the salts of the weak acid H_2CO_3 and of the hydroxides $M(OH)_2$. As the basicity of the hydroxide increases from $Be(OH)_2$ to $Ba(OH)_2$, the stability towards hydrolysis of the carbonate, MCO_3, markedly increases. Beryllium carbonate, $BeCO_3$, which is the salt of the very weak base $Be(OH)_2$, is so readily hydrolyzed that it cannot be isolated in a pure and anhydrous form, and is only known as a solid mixture with $Be(OH)_2$ or as the tetra-aquo complex salt, $[Be(H_2O)_4]CO_3$—stable in an atomsphere of CO_2.

All the alkaline-earth metal carbonates can be thermally decomposed into the metal oxide and carbon dioxide gas. The temperature at which this decomposition takes place increases as the size of the metal ion increases. $BaCO_3$ must be heated to a very high temperature to bring about its decomposition into BaO and CO_2, while gentle heating decomposes $MgCO_3$ into MgO and CO_2. (We have discussed in Chapter 17, p. 371, the thermodynamic factors involved in the thermal decomposition of $CaCO_3$.)

The carbonates $CaCO_3$, $SrCO_3$, and $BaCO_3$ are formed simply by mixing a water solution containing their metal ions, M^{++}, with a water solution containing $CO_3^=$ ions. The carbonates, which are nearly insoluble, precipitate out of solution as white crystalline powders:

$$M^{++}{}_{(aq)} + CO^=_{3(aq)} \longrightarrow MCO_{3(s)}$$

When a solution of an alkali-metal carbonate—for example, Na_2CO_3, is mixed with a solution of a beryllium salt—for example, $BeSO_4$—or a magnesium salt—say, $MgSO_4$—basic carbonates are precipitated whose composition depends on the concentration of the OH^- ions and the temperature of the solution. The basic beryllium carbonate, for example, has a composition that is variable between $BeCO_3 \cdot 2\,Be(OH)_2$ and $BeCO_3 \cdot 5\,Be(OH)_2$. However, if a solution of a magnesium salt, such as $MgSO_4$, is mixed with a solution of sodium hydrogen carbonate, $NaHCO_3$, saturated with CO_2, the carbonate, $MgCO_3$, is precipitated.

All the alkaline-earth metal carbonates, MCO_3, are soluble in acids, with the evolution of CO_2 gas:

$$MCO_{3(s)} + 2\,H^+{}_{(aq)} \longrightarrow M^{++}{}_{(aq)} + H_2O_{(l)} + CO_{2(g)}$$

The first step of this reaction may be considered to be the formation of the soluble metal-hydrogen carbonate:

$$MCO_{3(s)} + H^+{}_{(aq)} \longrightarrow M^{++}{}_{(aq)} + HCO^-_{3(aq)}$$

This reaction explains how the insoluble carbonates, $MgCO_3$, $CaCO_3$, $SrCO_3$ and $BaCO_3$, which are present in nature as minerals, dissolve in a weakly acid solution such as rain water, which has dissolved CO_2 from the air. This reaction is of the greatest practical importance, for it explains the erosion of carbonate rocks by rain water to form caves and underground rivers, and also accounts for the presence of magnesium and calcium salts in ordinary surface water (see Section 31-5).

When a solution of an alkaline-earth metal hydrogen carbonate is heated, so that the solubility of CO_2 in the water decreases and the solutions lose CO_2, the insoluble carbonates are reprecipitated:

$$M(HCO_3)_{2(aq)} \longrightarrow MCO_{3(s)} + CO_{2(g)} + H_2O_{(l)}$$

This reaction explains such rock formations as the stalactites and stalagmites found in many caves, as well as the formation of the familiar white deposit in hot water boilers fed with normal (hard) water.

SULFATES

The sulfates of the alkaline-earth metals, MSO_4, are white crystalline solids that are remarkably stable to heat. They can be prepared by the action of H_2SO_4 on the metal oxides, hydroxides, or carbonates:

$$MO + H_2SO_4 \longrightarrow MSO_4 + H_2O$$
$$M(OH)_2 + H_2SO_4 \longrightarrow MSO_4 + 2\ H_2O$$
$$MCO_3 + H_2SO_4 \longrightarrow MSO_4 + H_2O + CO_2$$

The solubility in water of the alkaline-earth metal sulfates decreases dramatically in going down the family from Be to Ba. The sulfates of beryllium and magnesium are quite soluble in water, calcium sulfate is only moderately soluble, and strontium and barium sulfates are almost insoluble. The solubility product of $BaSO_4$ is, in fact, so small, $K_{sp} = 1 \times 10^{-10}$ (mole/l.)^2, that Ba^{++} is used as a precipitating agent for the $SO_4^{=}$ ion in quantitative analysis.

The sulfates of Be^{++}, Mg^{++}, and Ca^{++}, crystallize from water in a hydrated form. Beryllium sulfate crystallizes as the tetrahydrate, $BeSO_4 \cdot 4\ H_2O$, which should be more appropriately formulated as $[Be(H_2O)_4]^{++}SO_4^{=}$, since the crystal lattice consists of tetrahedral tetra-aquoberyllium(II) complex cations, $[Be(H_2O)_4]^{++}$, and of tetrahedral $SO_4^{=}$ anions, arranged in a Cs^+Cl^- (body-centered cubic) structure. Magnesium sulfate crystallizes as the 7-hydrate, $MgSO_4 \cdot 7\ H_2O$. Calcium sulfate crystallizes as the dihydrate, $CaSO_4 \cdot 2\ H_2O$, commonly called gypsum. Gypsum, which occurs in large deposits in nature is an important building material. When gypsum is carefully heated so that part of its water is driven off, a powder of formula $(CaSO_4)_2 \cdot H_2O$, known as plaster of Paris, is formed. When water is added to plaster of Paris, gypsum, $CaSO_4 \cdot 2\ H_2O$, is slowly re-formed and the volume of the material increases, forming a hard, white mass. The plaster of Paris is a fine white plaster and is an important constituent of ordinary plaster and cements.

HALIDES

All alkaline-earth metals, M, combine directly and exothermally with the halogens, X_2, to form metal halides, MX_2:

$$M_{(s)} + X_{2(g)} \longrightarrow MX_{2(s)} \qquad (\Delta H \text{ is negative})$$

The character of the metal-to-halogen bonding in the alkaline-earth metal halides varies markedly depending on the metal ion and the halogen. For each metal ion, the ionic character of the bonding gradually *decreases* from the fluoride to the iodide, as the halide ion becomes more and more polarizable with increasing size. For each halide ion, the ionic character of the bonding *increases* from Be^{++} to Ba^{++}, as the charge/radius ratio of the cation decreases. Thus, the halides of the smallest and most polarizing alkaline-earth metal ion, Be^{++}, are largely covalent in character—except for BeF_2, which is essentially ionic because the very small F^- ion is not appreciably polarizable. The halides of the other alkaline-earth metals are essentially ionic and dissolve in water to produce neutral solutions of hydrated M^{++} ions and hydrated halide ions. When the water is evaporated from solutions of the ionic chlorides, for example, the following colorless hydrated salts crystallize: $MgCl_2 \cdot 6\ H_2O$; $CaCl_2 \cdot 6\ H_2O$; and $BaCl_2 \cdot 2\ H_2O$. But when covalent $BeCl_2$ comes into contact with water, it hydrolyzes to form an acidic solution:

$$BeCl_{2(s)} + 2\ H_2O_{(l)} \longrightarrow Be(OH)_{2(s)} + 2\ HCl_{(aq)}$$

Evidence that the character of the alkaline-earth metal chlorides changes from the essentially covalent in $BeCl_2$ to the essentially ionic in $BaCl_2$ is provided by: (1) the poor electrical conductivity of molten $BeCl_2$ as compared with the excellent conductivity of the other molten metal chlorides, and (2) the increase in melting point from the relatively low-melting and volatile $BeCl_2$ to the very high-melting and nonvolatile $BaCl_2$, as shown in the margin.

	M.P. (°C)
$BeCl_2$	405
$MgCl_2$	712
$CaCl_2$	772
$SrCl_2$	872
$BaCl_2$	960

The covalent beryllium halides, $BeCl_2$, $BeBr_2$, and BeI_2, are soluble in many organic solvents, such as methyl alcohol, CH_3OH. For example, $BeCl_2$ dissolves to the extent of 257 g/l. in methyl alcohol at 20°C. Of the other alkaline-earth metal halides, only $MgBr_2$ and MgI_2 are soluble in solvents of this sort. The solubility of beryllium halides in methyl alcohol is again explained on the basis of the strong polarizing ability of the very small Be^{++} ion, which attracts the negatively charged ends of the dipolar solvent molecules so strongly as to form well-defined, soluble complexes—for example, $[Be(CH_3OH)_2Cl_2]$. The energy released in the formation of these stable complexes is the factor which compensates for the loss of lattice energy and imparts solubility to the solid.

HYDRIDES

The hydrides of the Group IIA metals, MH_2, are white solids, considerably ionic in character. Like the alkali metals, the more electropositive alkaline-earth metals Ca, Sr, and Ba react readily with hydrogen gas at elevated temperatures to form the essentially ionic hydrides:

$$M + H_2 \longrightarrow M^{++}(H^-)_2$$

The hydrides BeH_2 and MgH_2 can be prepared only by indirect routes. All the alkaline-earth metal hydrides react readily with water to form the metal hydroxide and hydrogen gas:

$$MH_{2(s)} + 2\ H_2O_{(l)} \longrightarrow M(OH)_{2(s)} + 2\ H_{2(g)}$$

NITRIDES

The alkaline-earth metals, except Be, form ionic nitrides, M_3N_2, containing the metal ion with its normal oxidation number of +2, and the trinegative nitride ion, $N^{\equiv}$. These ionic nitrides are colorless, transparent crystals with high melting points. They can be formed by the direct union of the metal with nitrogen gas at elevated temperatures:

$$3\ M_{(s)} + N_{2(g)} \longrightarrow M_3N_{2(s)}$$

The nitrides of the alkaline-earth metals react with water to form the hydroxide of the metal, $M(OH)_2$ and NH_3:

$$M_3N_2 + 6\ H_2O \longrightarrow 3\ M(OH)_2 + 2\ NH_3$$

SULFIDES

The alkaline-earth metal sulfides can be prepared either by direct union of the elements, or by reduction of the metal sulfate with carbon at high temperature:

$$M + S \longrightarrow MS$$
$$MSO_4 + 2\ C \longrightarrow MS + 2\ CO_2$$

Except for BeS, all these sulfides hydrolyze in water to form $M(OH)_2$ and H_2S:

$$MS + 2\ H_2O \longrightarrow M(OH)_2 + H_2S$$

The reaction is very slow with water, but rapid with aqueous acid solutions:

$$MS + 2\ H^+ \longrightarrow M^{++} + H_2S$$

Except for BeS, all the alkaline-earth metal sulfides have an ionic crystalline structure similar to that of the corresponding monoxides—that is, the Na^+Cl^- structure. The compound BeS has the same structure as zinc-blende, ZnS; each Be atom is surrounded tetrahedrally by 4 S atoms, and each S atom in turn is surrounded tetrahedrally by 4 Be atoms. (Note the similar difference in structure between BeO and the heavier alkaline-earth metal oxides, p. 688.)

31-5 Hard Water and Water Softening

The calcium and magnesium salts dissolved in ordinary tap water are among the salts that react with soap to form a precipitate. Water that contains salts of this sort is called *hard water*. Although soap is a mixture of several compounds of sodium, for simplicity we shall consider it as pure, soluble sodium stearate, $Na^+(C_{17}H_{35}COO)^-$—the sodium salt of stearic acid, $C_{17}H_{35}COOH$. Sodium stearate reacts with divalent metal ions such as Ca^{++}, Mg^{++}, and Fe^{+++} to form insoluble stearates:

$$\cancel{2\ Na^+_{(aq)}} + (C_{17}H_{35}COO)^-_{(aq)} + Ca^{++}_{(aq)} \longrightarrow \{Ca^{++}(C_{17}H_{35}COO^-)_2\}_{(s)} + \cancel{2\ Na^+_{(aq)}}$$

Only after these divalent metal ions have been removed from the water can we work up a rich, soapy lather. To make a lather with hard water, we have to use a great deal of soap, and the harder the water (that is, the higher the concentration of Ca^{++}, Mg^{++}, and Fe^{+++} ions) the more soap we must use.

Water that contains $(HCO_3)^-$ ions along with the Ca^{++} and Mg^{++} ions is said to be *temporarily hard*, for when we boil the water the metal ions are precipitated as normal or basic carbonates. Water is said to be *permanently hard* if, along with the Ca^{++} and Mg^{++} ions, it contains negative ions like $SO_4^{=}$, which do not form insoluble salts with the metal ions when the solution is heated. The most common method by which both "permanent" and "temporary" hardness can be removed from water consists of passing the hard water through an ion-exchanger. An *ion-exchanger* is an insoluble substance, either natural (a mineral) or synthetic (a resin) which has the capacity to bind the objectionable cations, Ca^{++}, Mg^{++}, and Fe^{+++}, replacing them with non-objectionable cations, such as Na^+. A schematic equation to represent this process, commonly called "water-softening," follows:

$$\{Resin \cdot n\ H\}^+_{(s)} + Ca^{++}_{(aq)} \longrightarrow \{Resin \cdot (n-2)H \cdot Ca\}_{(s)} + 2\ H^+_{(aq)}$$

The best ion exchangers are those which remove *all metal cations* present in the water and substitute them with H^+ ions, while also substituting *all anions* present in the water with OH^- ions. The H^+ and OH^- ions thus produced combine to form H_2O—and we obtain water which is free of all dissolved salts. The water thus obtained is said to be *de-ionized*. The use of de-ionized water is becoming more and more common for both industrial and household purposes.

31-6 Uses of the Alkaline-Earth Metals and Their Compounds

Beryllium, which is a light metal, is used extensively in the manufacture of light alloys, such as beryllium-copper and beryllium-nickel. Beryllium-copper alloys, being particularly resistant to salt-water corrosion, are used in the manufacture of marine parts. Beryllium is one of the metals more transparent to X-rays, and consequently is valuable as a window material in X-ray tubes. Beryllium oxide, BeO, is used to make refractory crucibles designed for high-temperature reactions, and is also a component in the coating for fluorescent lamps. The commercial applications of beryllium compounds are limited, however, since these substances are very poisonous.

Magnesium as powder and ribbon finds many uses in flash powders and flash bulbs, military flares, incendiary bombs, and in the industrial synthesis of many organic compounds. Magnesium is used extensively for the preparation of lightweight alloys with a high tensile strength, particularly in the construction of airplane parts, tools, and machine parts. These alloys are often treated with a chromic acid solution to form a surface film of oxide that is resistant to corrosion. Magnesium oxide, MgO, because of its exceedingly high melting point and low reactivity, is valuable as a lining for metallurgical furnaces. A mixture of $Mg(OH)_2$ and $CaCO_3$ is used as an insulating cover for steam and hot-water pipes and boilers. Hydrated magnesium sulfate, $MgSO_4 \cdot 7\,H_2O$, commonly known as Epsom salts, has purgative properties. Magnesium sulfate is also used in the fireproofing of fabrics. A suspension of magnesium hydroxide, $Mg(OH)_2$, in water, commonly known as milk of magnesia, is used medicinally for the treatment of internal acidity. Magnesium hydroxide also serves as a constituent of many toothpastes.

Calcium metal is used to remove oxygen from metal oxides (that is, as a deoxidant) in the manufacture of many important metals, alloys, and special steels. Since calcium hydroxide, $Ca(OH)_2$, is the cheapest source of the hydroxide ion, OH^-, it is used industrially in a number of chemical processes based on reactions with this ion. Calcium carbonate, $CaCO_3$, serves as the source of CaO, which is used in the manufacture of Na_2CO_3 (p. 679), bleaching powder (p. 615), and in the preparation of plaster and mortar. When lime, CaO, is heated to a very high temperature, it gives off a brilliant light, known as "limelight." Years ago light of this sort was used in the theater and elsewhere to provide spotlights—hence its name, and the expression "to be in the limelight."

Strontium and its compounds are very scarce. They find little commercial use, since they have no properties that are significantly different from those of the less expensive calcium and calcium compounds. Barium metal itself finds very little use; however, its oxide, BaO, can be used as a very efficient drying agent that combines not only with the moisture, forming $Ba(OH)_2$, but also with the carbon dioxide in the air, forming $BaCO_3$. Barium sulfate is used as a filler in the manufacture of paints, paper, linoleum, and other materials.

When placed in a flame, the salts of calcium, strontium, and barium produce strikingly brilliant and beautifully colored light: calcium salts, red; strontium salts, crimson; and barium salts, green. For this reason, volatile salts of these elements are used to a limited extent in the manufacture of colored pyrotechnic signals for military purposes, and in fireworks for holiday celebrations. Table 31-3 gives a summary of the important reactions of the metals of Group IIA.

31-7 Explanation for the +2 Oxidation State of Alkaline-Earth Metals in Their Compounds

We have seen that the alkaline-earth metals (Group IIA) exhibit exclusively the +2 oxidation number, and in their ionic compounds they are present as dipositive ions, M^{++}. Why don't the alkaline-earth elements form compounds in the +1 oxidation state? The values of the ionization energies given in Table 31-2 show that only a relatively small quantity of energy is required to ionize a gaseous alkaline-earth metal atom to its monopositive ion, $M_{(g)} \longrightarrow M^+{}_{(g)} + e^-$, whereas a much larger quantity of energy is required to remove an electron from the monopositive ion to form the

TABLE 31-3 SUMMARY OF SOME IMPORTANT REACTIONS OF THE GROUP IIA METALS, M

General Equation	Comments
$M + X_2 \longrightarrow MX_2$ (X = halogen)	All Group IIA metals with all halogens
$2\,M + O_2 \longrightarrow 2\,MO$	All Group IIA metals
$M + O_2 \longrightarrow MO_2$	All Group IIA metals, except Be
$M + 2\,H_2O \longrightarrow M^{++} + 2\,OH^- + H_2$	Be and Mg very slowly with water, but more rapidly with steam. Ca, Sr, and Ba rapidly with cold water
$M + 2\,H^+ \longrightarrow M^{++} + H_2$ ($M + 2\,H^+ + SO_4^= \longrightarrow MSO_{4(s)} + H_2$)	Be slowly, others faster, although formation of insoluble MSO_4, decreases speed of reaction if H_2SO_4 is used
$M + S \longrightarrow MS$	All Group IIA metals
$3\,M + N_2 \longrightarrow M_3N_2$	All Group IIA metals, except Be, at high temperatures
$2\,M + CO_2 \longrightarrow 2\,MO + C$	All Group IIA metals at high temperatures
$3\,M + 2\,NH_3 \longrightarrow M_3N_2 + 3\,H_2$	All Group IIA metals at high temperatures

dipositive ion, $M^+_{(g)} \longrightarrow M^{++}_{(g)} + e^-$. Why then, when calcium metal reacts, for example, with chlorine gas, does the reaction always yield only one product—the ionic crystalline calcium(II) chloride, $\{Ca^{++}(Cl^-)_2\}_{(s)}$—regardless of the mole ratio of calcium to chlorine used in the reaction? Why don't we obtain an ionic $\{Ca^+Cl^-\}_{(s)}$ if we use less chlorine than is required to transform all the calcium metal into $CaCl_2$? And, on the other hand, why do we not obtain $\{Ca^{+++}(Cl^-)_3\}_{(s)}$ if a very large excess of chlorine is used in the reaction mixture?

We may, as a first approximation, disregard the entropy changes involved in the reaction of calcium with chlorine—since the influence of the entropy change is generally small at room temperature wherever large enthalpy values are involved. A simple comparison among the standard heats of formation, $\Delta H^\circ_{\text{form}}$, calculated for the crystalline ionic "CaCl," "$CaCl_2$," and "$CaCl_3$" will then tell us which of these compounds are thermodynamically permitted. As usual, we may consider the reaction of calcium metal with chlorine gas to proceed by a series of steps, each involving its particular enthalpy change. The sum of the ΔH values of all steps will give us the $\Delta H^\circ_{\text{form}}$ of the desired compound:

1.	$Ca_{(s)} \longrightarrow Ca_{(g)}$	$\Delta H_1 = \Delta H_{\text{atomiz}}$ of Ca
2.	$Ca_{(g)} \longrightarrow Ca^{+n}_{(g)} + n\,e^-$	$\Delta H_2 =$ Sum of first n ioniz energies of Ca
3.	$\frac{n}{2}Cl_{2(g)} \longrightarrow n\,Cl_{(g)}$	$\Delta H_3 = \frac{n}{2} \times \Delta H_{\text{dissoc}}$ of Cl_2
4.	$n\,Cl_{(g)} + n\,e^- \longrightarrow n\,Cl^-_{(g)}$	$\Delta H_4 = n \times$ Electron affinity of Cl
5.	$Ca^{+n}_{(g)} + n\,Cl^-_{(g)} \longrightarrow CaCl_{n(s)}$	$\Delta H_5 =$ Lattice energy of salt
	$Ca_{(s)} + \frac{n}{2}Cl_{2(g)} \longrightarrow CaCl_{n(s)}$	$\Delta H_{\text{form}} = \Delta H_1 + \Delta H_2 + \Delta H_3 + \Delta H_4 + \Delta H_5$

Let us carry out the calculation for the three compounds, CaCl, $CaCl_2$, and $CaCl_3$. Of these, only $CaCl_2$ is actually known, so that the value of its crystal lattice energy and its standard heat of formation can be determined experimentally. For CaCl and $CaCl_3$, we can only estimate approximately, by analogy with known compounds,

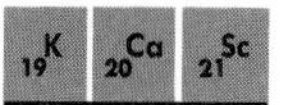

what their lattice energy would be. For example, we may reasonably assume that $Ca^+Cl^-_{(s)}$, if it existed, would have a structure similar to $K^+Cl^-_{(s)}$, because the monopositive $_{20}Ca^+$ ion differs from $_{19}K^+$ only by having one additional nuclear proton and one additional electron, and hence would probably have about the same size. The lattice energy of $K^+Cl^-_{(s)}$ is -167 kcal/mole, so we may estimate that the hypothetical $Ca^+Cl^-_{(s)}$ would also have a lattice energy of about -170 kcal/mole. By a similar reasoning, we may also estimate that the lattice energy of the hypothetical $\{Ca^{+++}(Cl^-)_3\}_{(s)}$ would be about the same as that experimentally determined for the known compound scandium(III) chloride, $\{Sc^{+++}(Cl^-)_3\}_{(s)}$, since the tripositive ion $_{20}Ca^{+++}$ differs from $_{21}Sc^{+++}$ by having one less nuclear proton and one less electron, and hence probably would have a similar size. The lattice energy of $ScCl_{3(s)}$ is -1130 kcal/mole, and we take this value to be also the approximate lattice energy of $CaCl_{3(s)}$. Now we can proceed to calculate the ΔH°_{form} of the ionic compounds $CaCl_{(s)}$, $CaCl_{2(s)}$, and $CaCl_{3(s)}$:

Formula of Ionic Salt	$\{Ca^+Cl^-\}_{(s)}$	$\{Ca^{++}(Cl^-)_2\}_{(s)}$	$\{Ca^{+++}(Cl^-)_3\}_{(s)}$
Ox. No. of Ca, n	$n = 1$	$n = 2$	$n = 3$
$\Delta H_1 = \Delta H_{atomiz}$ of Ca	$+42$	$+42$	$+42$
$\Delta H_2 =$ Total Ioniz. Energy of Ca	$+141$	$(+141 + 274) = +415$	$(+141 + 274 + 1{,}175) = +1{,}590$
$\Delta H_3 = \frac{n}{2} \times \Delta H_{diss}$ of $Cl_{2(g)}$	$[\frac{1}{2}(+58)] = +29$	$[\frac{2}{2}(+58)] = +58$	$[\frac{3}{2}(+58)] = +87$
$\Delta H_4 = n \times$ Electron affinity of Cl	-87	$[2(-87)] = -174$	$[3(-87)] = -261$
$\Delta H_5 =$ Lattice energy of salt	~ -170	-531	$\sim -1{,}130$
ΔH°_{form} of salt	~ -45	-190	$\sim +330$

From this calculation we see that the ΔH°_{form} of ionic $CaCl_{(s)}$ is about -45 kcal/mole, and hence, is favorable to the formation of this compound from its elements. However, ionic $CaCl_{2(s)}$ has an even more negative ΔH°_{form}, -190 kcal/mole, so if ionic $CaCl_{(s)}$ were formed it would have the capacity to disproportionate into $CaCl_{2(s)} + Ca_{(s)}$. In the process, a quantity of heat equal to the difference between the values of ΔH°_{form} for $CaCl_2$ and CaCl would be evolved: $(-190 - (-45)) \cong -145$ kcal/mole. The above calculation also shows that the formation of ionic $CaCl_{3(s)}$ is thermodynamically forbidden, since its ΔH°_{form} has a very large positive value, $+330$ kcal/mole. We must also keep in mind that, in each case, the entropy change, ΔS, is unfavorable to the formation of the compound, because in the reaction a gaseous substance, $Cl_{2(g)}$, reacts to form an ordered ionic chloride; however, the ΔS value is relatively small compared with the ΔH value.

From the above calculation we see that the deciding factor that makes ionic $CaCl_{(s)}$ thermodynamically unstable with respect to ionic $CaCl_{2(s)}$ and $Ca_{(s)}$ is the much larger crystal lattice energy of the latter. The lattice energy of $CaCl_{2(s)}$ is -531 kcal/mole versus only -170 kcal/mole for $CaCl_{(s)}$. On the other hand, for $CaCl_{3(s)}$ the third ionization energy of calcium is such a large unfavorable factor ($Ca^{+2}_{(g)} \longrightarrow Ca^{+3}_{(g)} + 1\,e^-$; $\Delta H = +1{,}175$ kcal/mole) that it is *not* compensated by the greater lattice energy of $CaCl_{3(s)}$. Hence, in this case the total ionization energy, $+1{,}590$ kcal/mole, required to transform $Ca_{(g)} \longrightarrow Ca^{+3}_{(g)} + 3\,e^-$, is the deciding unfavorable factor that makes $CaCl_{3(s)}$ a thermodynamically forbidden compound.

We can now summarize the conditions required for the formation of a particular product—in this case ionic $CaCl_2$—under specified conditions. The ionic $CaCl_{2(s)}$, which has a fluorite type lattice, is formed because: (1) the free energy change for the formation of this ionic compound is more negative than that for any other compound which may be formed from the same reactants, and (2) its rate of formation is faster than the rate of formation of other thermodynamically permitted, but less stable, compounds that may be formed from the same reactants.

Exercises

31-1 Write the electron configurations of the alkaline-earth metals: $_{4}Be$, $_{12}Mg$, $_{20}Ca$, $_{38}Sr$, $_{56}Ba$, $_{88}Ra$.

31-2 Discuss the Group IIA metals in regard to (a) size of atoms and ions, (b) crystal structure, (c) ΔH of atomization, (d) density, melting point, and hardness, (e) ionization energy.

31-3 (a) Describe a general method for the preparation of the alkaline-earth metals; (b) starting with magnesium carbonate, write equations for the preparation of the metal by electrolysis.

31-4 Discuss the alkaline-earth metals in regard to (a) oxidation state, (b) heats of hydration of the M^{++} ions, (c) oxidation potentials of the M,M^{++} couples.

31-5 (a) Other factors being equal, why are the monopositive Group IA metal ions, M^+, and the dipositive Group IIA metal ions, M^{++}, the most stable in regard to reduction to the metal? (b) What statement can be made of Group IA and Group IIA concerning variable oxidation states?

31-6 Discuss the trend of the oxidation potentials of the Group IIA metals with increasing atomic weight from Be to Ba. Which are the energy factors determining the observed trend?

31-7 Compare the alkaline-earth metals in regard to: (a) tendency to form covalent bonding, (b) tendency to form ionic bonding. Explain the observed trends.

31-8 Arrange the following compounds in approximate order of decreasing ionic character (increasing covalent character): $CaCl_2$, CsCl, $CaBr_2$, HCl, NaCl, $BeCl_2$.

31-9 Discuss the oxides, MO, of the alkaline-earth metals in regard to: (a) preparation, (b) crystal structure, (c) character (covalent or ionic) of the metal-to-oxygen bonding.

31-10 (a) Each of the oxides of Group IIA elements is added separately to water. Explain any reactions that may take place. (b) Explain the differences in the solubilities of the Group IIA metal hydroxides, $M(OH)_2$. (c) Which oxide of Group IIA reacts with both acids and bases? Write equations for the reaction of this oxide with an acid and with a base.

31-11 (a) Which Group IIA metal peroxide is unknown? What general method is employed to prepare the peroxides of the other members of this group? (b) Which of the Group IIA metals form superoxides? In this respect how do these metals resemble the Group IA metals?

31-12 The Group IIA metal carbonates that are insoluble in water gradually dissolve when CO_2 is passed into the water. Explain by means of an equation.

31-13 (a) Describe a general method for the preparation of the alkaline-earth metals. (b) Starting with magnesium carbonate, write equations for the preparation of the metal by electrolysis.

31-14 Discuss the halides of the alkaline-earth metals in regard to (a) increasing ionic character of the bonding, (b) obtaining the anhydrous salts, (c) tendency to hydrolyze in water solution.

31-15 Contrast the action of heat on the following. Explain your answers. (a) $MgCl_2 \cdot 6\,H_2O$ and $CaCl_2 \cdot 6\,H_2O$, (b) Na_2CO_3 and $CaCO_3$.

31-16 Write equations for the reaction of water with the following: (a) Ca, (b) SrH_2, (c) SrO, (d) Ca_3N_2, (e) $MgSO_4$, (f) Be, (g) $CaCl_2$, (h) MgO.

31-17 Starting with $BaCO_3$ as one reactant, write equations showing how you would prepare: (a) BaO, (b) Ba, (c) $BaSO_4$, (d) $BaCl_2 \cdot 2\,H_2O$, (e) BaO_2, (f) $Ba(HCO_3)_2$, (g) $Ba(C_2H_3O_2)_2$.

31-18 Explain the meaning of "hard water" and describe the process of "water-softening." Write the general schematic equations for the de-ionization of hard water by means of an ion-exchanger.

31-19 On the basis of the enthalpy factors involved, discuss the reasons why $Ba_{(s)}$ reacts with $F_{2(g)}$ to form exclusively ionic barium(II) fluoride, $Ba^{++}(F^-)_{2(s)}$, even if a very large excess of the strong oxidant, $F_{2(g)}$, is used in the reaction.

THE BORON-ALUMINUM AND CARBON-SILICON FAMILIES: GROUPS IIIB AND IVB ELEMENTS

	IIIB	IVB	
	B	C	N
	Al	Si	P
Zn	Ga	Ge	As
Cd	In	Sn	Sb
Hg	Tl	Pb	Bi

In this chapter we shall consider the elements of the IIIB Group—Boron, B; Aluminum, Al; Gallium, Ga; Indium, In; Thallium, Tl—and of the IVB Group—Carbon, C; Silicon, Si; Germanium, Ge; Tin, Sn; and Lead, Pb. For these elements, as for all elements of the *s* and *p* blocks, the electropositive character increases with increasing atomic weight. We have already discussed this trend both for typical metals such as the alkaline-earth elements of Group IIA and for typical non-metals such as the halogens of Group VIIB. In the IIIB and IVB Groups, this trend is responsible for such a marked change of properties between the lighter and the heavier members of each group that we cannot consider these elements as families. Rather, each element of the boron-aluminum and the carbon-silicon groups—or occasionally a pair of elements—should be considered individually since it has its own particular set of properties. Partly because of their unique behavior and partly because some of the elements of these groups are among the most common and important in nature, the chemistry of Groups IIIB and IVB is varied and extremely interesting.

Stable State at 25°C, 1 atm	IIIB
shiny black crystals	B
silvery-white metal	Al
silvery-white metal	Ga
silvery-white metal	In
silvery-gray metal	Tl

32-1 General Characteristics of the Group IIIB Elements

In Group IIIB the first element, boron, is a solid that exhibits some properties somewhat similar to those of metals, and yet it is not completely metallic; furthermore its chemical behavior has very little in common with that of typical metals.

The second element of Group IIIB, aluminum, is physically a metal, but its oxide has amphoteric properties. And the heavier elements of this group, gallium, indium, and thallium, are all metals with increasingly electropositive character. Since in their ground electronic state all elements of Group IIIB have the same outer electron configuration, $ns^2\ np^1$, this marked variation in property is explained on the basis that as atomic number increases, both the ionization energy and the electronegativity decrease. Again, as for the families of elements we have studied in the preceding chapters, the decrease in ionization energy arises both from an increase in atomic size and from a decrease in the effective nuclear charge acting on the outer electrons. These factors are summarized in Tables 32-1 and 32-2, which also list some other important physical properties of the Group IIIB elements. From Table 32-2 we see that the decrease in the total ionization energy for the reaction $M_{(g)} \longrightarrow M^{+++}{}_{(g)} + 3\ e^-$, in going down Group IIIB, parallels the decrease in the total ionization energy for the reaction $M_{(g)} \longrightarrow Mg^{++}{}_{(g)} + 2\ e^-$, in going down Group IIA, the alkaline-earth metals. (Of course, for each element of Group IIIB, the total ionization energy is greater than that for the corresponding element of Group IIA, since it corresponds to the removal of 3 rather than 2 electrons.) Similarly, the span of electronegativity values is not wider for the elements of Group IIIB than for those of Group IIA, though each element of Group IIIB is more electronegative than the corresponding element of Group IIA. Thus the dramatic change in property from non-metallic to metallic in Group IIIB (and Group IVB) simply parallels the gradual increase of metallic properties along groups IA and IIA, and the gradual decrease of non-metallic properties along groups VIB (oxygen-sulfur family) and VIIB (halogen family). In groups IIIB and IVB we have a change from non-metallic to metallic properties simply because we are in a borderline region of the Periodic Table. For the smaller elements the effective nuclear charge acting on the outer electrons is so strong that these electrons tend to remain associated with their respective nuclei, giving rise to covalent bonding. For the larger elements, on the other hand, the weaker attraction of the nuclear charge for the outer electrons allows electron delocalization in the element itself (metallic state) and the formation of ions in compounds.

32-2 Physical Properties of the Group IIIB Elements

BORON. Pure boron is a black, brittle, crystalline substance, extremely hard (almost as hard as diamond) and extremely high melting (m.p. ~ 2,000°C). It is opaque and highly reflecting, as metals usually are, and it also conducts an electric current electronically. However, the electrical conductivity of boron *increases with increasing temperature, whereas we know that for metals the electrical conductivity always increases with decreasing temperature* (p. 707). Boron, and the other substances whose electrical conductivity increases with increasing temperature, are said to be *semi-conductors* (see Section 32-5). The structure of crystalline boron is a continuous three-dimensional lattice whose building unit is a cluster of 12 B atoms regularly arranged at the corners of an icosahedron (see diagram in margin). Each B atom of each icosahedron is bound not only to 5 B atoms of the same icosahedron, but also to neighboring B atoms of adjacent icosahedrons. The result is an extremely complex network of B atoms, which are not all equivalent in their position and environment. This close-knitted bonding, which extends throughout the crystal, explains why boron resembles diamond in its hardness and high melting point.

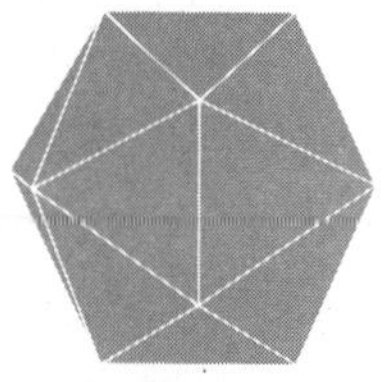
Icosahedron

ALUMINUM. Aluminum has the characteristic physical properties of metals. The clean surface is silvery white (however, when exposed to air the metal has a dull surface because of a thin adherent film of oxide), and is a good conductor of heat as well as an excellent metallic conductor of electric current. In fact, aluminum, because of its low density and low cost is extensively used in the manufacture of electrical conductors.

TABLE 32-1 SOME PROPERTIES OF THE GROUP IIIB ELEMENTS

Element	Outer Electron Config.	Atomic Weight	Atomic Radius A	Ionic Radius M^{+3} Ion, A	Density at 20°C, g/cm³	Melting Point °C	Boiling Point, °C	ΔH_{atomiz} (kcal/mole)
$_5$B	$2s^2 2p^1$	10.81	0.79[a]	(0.20)	2.34	~2000	—	135
$_{13}$Al	$3s^2 3p^1$	26.98	1.43[b] (12)	0.50	2.70	660	2450	78
$_{31}$Ga	$4s^2 4p^1$	69.72	1.35[b] (7)	0.62	5.91	30	2240	65
$_{49}$In	$5s^2 5p^1$	114.82	1.62[b] (12)	0.81	7.31	156	2000	58
$_{81}$Tl	$6s^2 6p^1$	204.37	1.70[b] (12)	0.95	11.85	303	1460	43

[a] Average covalent radius in crystalline boron.
[b] Metallic radius (the number in parentheses represents the metallic coordination number). For Ga, the radius given is the weighed mean for 7 non-equidistant nearest neighbors.

GALLIUM, INDIUM, AND THALLIUM. The three heavier members of Group IIIB have typical metallic properties; in particular, they are metallic conductors of electricity. However, they are unusual in that they have rather low melting points—for example, gallium (m.p. 29.8°C) is a liquid on a warm day. On the other hand, they have relatively high boiling points (Ga, 2,240; In, 2,000; Tl, 1460°C). The temperature range of the liquid state of these metals is therefore extraordinarily wide. Gallium, for example, is a liquid over a range of about 2,000°C. Ga and In are white, and Tl is gray-white; in the solid state they are all rather soft. Thallium, the softest of the three, is softer than lead and can be scratched with a thumbnail. It is interesting to note, (Table 32-1) that the boiling points of Al, Ga, In, and Tl decrease regularly with increasing size (following, as expected, the trend of their heats of atomization) whereas the melting points do not. This irregular trend of the melting points reflects different solid state structures. Aluminum and indium have face-centered cubic lattices, similar to those, for example, of the alkaline-earth metals calcium and strontium, with each metal atom having 12 nearest neighbors. Gallium has a complicated lattice in which each Ga atom has only 7 near

FIGURE 32-1 Comparison of ionization energies of Group IVB elements and other elements.

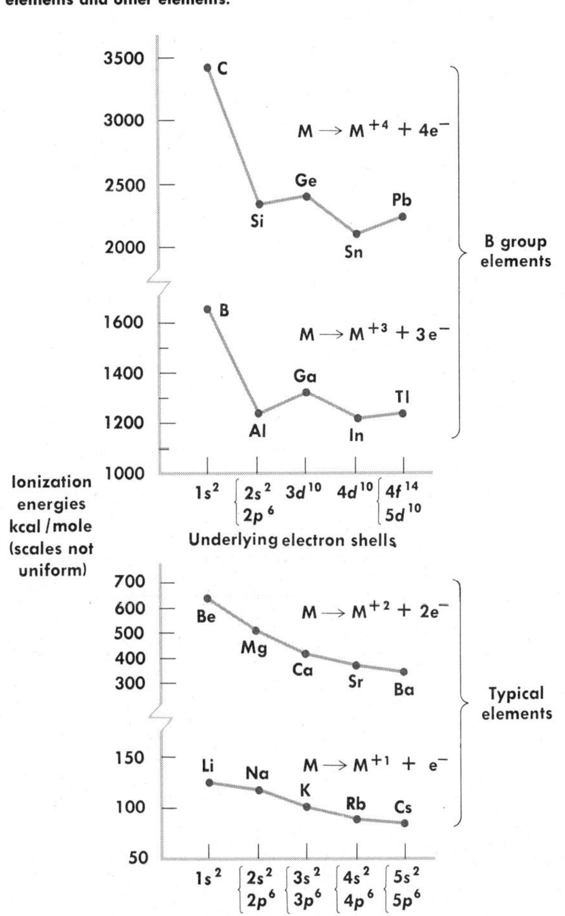

neighbors, and thallium has a hexagonal close-packed structure similar to that of, for example, the alkaline-earth metal magnesium.

IONIZATION ENERGIES

There is an interesting difference between the trend of the total ionization energy for the reaction $M_{(g)} \longrightarrow M^{+3}{}_{(g)} + 3\ e^-$ in Group IIIB and the trend for the reactions $M_{(g)} \longrightarrow M^{+2}{}_{(g)} + 2\ e^-$ in Group IIA, and $M_{(g)} \longrightarrow M^{+}{}_{(g)} + e^-$ in Group IA. We see from Table 32-2 that the total ionization energy for the reaction $M_{(g)} \longrightarrow M^{+3}{}_{(g)} + 3\ e^-$ decreases from B to Al owing to the decrease in size, as expected for elements with a noble-gas type inner shell (s^2 and $s^2\,p^6$, respectively). From Al to Ga, on the other hand, the ionization energy increases because the underlying $3d^{10}$ subshell of Ga is not as effective as a noble-gas type shell in shielding the additional nuclear charge. From Ga to In, the ionization energy again decreases as the size increases, because now both Ga and In have an underlying d^{10} subshell. And the last element of the group, Tl, has a higher ionization energy than the preceding element, In, because the inner $4f^{14}$ subshell of Tl is even less effective in shielding the newly added nuclear charge. The same trend is observed for the sum of the first 4 ionization energies of the elements of Group IVB.

OCCURRENCE

The first member of Group III, boron, B, is a relatively scarce element, whereas the second member, aluminum, Al, is the most plentiful metal in the earth's crust and is the third most abundant of all elements. None of the elements of Group IIIB occurs in nature as the free element. Boron occurs principally in borax, $Na_2B_4O_7 \cdot 10\ H_2O$, and kefnite, $Na_2B_4O_7 \cdot 4\ H_2O$. Boron in very small amounts is essential for plant growth but larger amounts are toxic to plants. Aluminum is widely distributed in nature, especially as a component of various silicates of complex composition. Its chief ore is the hydrated oxide called bauxite, $Al_2O_3 \cdot xH_2O$. Aluminum also occurs in nature as a complex fluoride, Na_3AlF_6, called cryolite. The elements gallium, indium, and thallium, are present in small quantities in the ores of boron and aluminum, as well as in zinc and iron sulfides ores. Commercially, Ga, In, and Tl are often obtained as by-products in the extraction of zinc from zinc blende, ZnS, and of iron from pyrite, FeS_2.

PREPARATION OF THE ELEMENTS

Boron is prepared commercially by reduction of its oxide, B_2O_3, with a strong reductant such as magnesium metal, Mg (or other very electropositive metals

TABLE 32-2 ELECTRONEGATIVITY AND IONIZATION ENERGIES (KCAL/MOLE) OF THE GROUP IIIB ELEMENTS

Element	First Ioniz. Energy	Second Ioniz. Energy	Third Ioniz. Energy	Total Ioniz. Energy for M^{+3} ion	Electronegativity (Pauling)	Oxidation Potential (v) for M,M^+ Couple	Oxidation Potential (v) for M,M^{+3} Couple
B	191	579	880	1,650	2.0	—	+0.73 (calcd)
Al	138	434	658	1,230	1.5	—	+1.66
Ga	138	473	708	1,321	1.6	—	+0.53
In	133	435	646	1,215	1.7	+0.25	+0.34
Tl	141	471	688	1,229	1.8	+0.34	−0.72

such as Al, Ca, Na, and K). The boron thus obtained is amorphous and contaminated with the boride of the reducing metal. Pure crystalline boron is obtained by the reduction of gaseous BCl_3 with H_2 gas at high temperature.

Aluminum is prepared by the electrolysis at 1,000°C of a fused mixture of aluminum oxide, Al_2O_3, containing cryolite, Na_3AlF_6, and small quantities of CaF_2 and NaCl. These ionic compounds are added both to lower the melting point of Al_2O_3 and to increase the electrical conductivity of the melt. The electrodes are made of graphite. At the high temperature of the electrolysis, the oxygen gas evolved at the anode reacts with the graphite to form carbon monoxide gas. This combustion reaction is strongly exothermic, and provides a large portion of the energy required to maintain the necessary high temperature. Molten aluminum is collected at the cathode.

32-3 Chemical Properties of the Group IIIB Elements

COVALENT AND IONIC CHARACTER OF BONDING IN COMPOUNDS. The first member of Group IIIB, boron, has a very small atomic size, and a relatively high effective nuclear charge acting on the three valence electrons, $2s^2\,2p^1$. Hence, boron tends to share its three valence electrons with other atoms in covalent bonds rather than to form ionic compounds containing the tripositive B^{+3} ion. However, the bonding between boron and the more electronegative elements, fluorine, chlorine, and oxygen, has an appreciable ionic character. Aluminum also has some tendency to form covalent compounds, but when combined with the most electronegative elements, fluorine and oxygen, it exists as the tripositive ion, Al^{+++}. The heavier elements, Ga, In, and Tl, show a decreasing tendency to form covalent compounds and an increasing tendency to form ionic compounds—the type of compound depending, in each case, on the difference in electronegativity of the combined elements.

COORDINATION NUMBER. The boron atom can form a maximum of 4 covalent bonds in its covalent compounds, since it has only 4 available low-energy orbitals—the one $2s$ and the three $2p$ oribitals. However, the boron atom itself has only 3 valence electrons ($2s^2\,2p^1$), and hence can form only 3 normal covalent bonds. In all compounds where the B atom forms 4 covalent bonds, one of the bonds is of the coordinate type—the B atom being the electron-pair acceptor and the partner atom the donor.

Boron(III) can achieve its highest electron-pair coordination number, 4, in one of the following ways: (1) by accepting an electron pair in a π coordinate bond from a partner atom in a monomeric molecule—as is the boron trifluoride molecule, BF_3; (2) by accepting an electron pair from a donor ion or molecule in a σ coordinate bond, to form a coordination compound—as in the tetrafluroborate(III) ion, $[BF_4]^-$; and (3) by accepting an electron pair in a σ coordinate bond from a partner atom in a three-dimensional covalent crystal structure—as in boron nitride, $\{BN\}_n$.

Aluminum, like boron, forms a number of compounds in which it has a coordination number of 4, but in other compounds attains a coordination number of 6 by making use of its available $3d$ orbitals. The other elements of this group can also have either C.N. = 4, or C.N. = 6.

STEREOCHEMISTRY. The atoms of the Group IIIB elements have a symmetrical core and 3 valence electrons. Hence, they have a trigonal planar stereochemistry when the C.N. is 3, (for example in $BF_{3(g)}$), a tetrahedral stereochemistry when C.N. = 4 (for example, in $[BF_4]^-$), and an octahedral stereochemistry when C.N. = 6 (for example, in $[AlF_6]^{-3}$).

BINARY COMPOUNDS WITH ELECTRONEGATIVE ELEMENTS

At high temperatures boron and aluminum react directly with the halogens, X_2, to form halides; with oxygen, O_2, to form oxides; with sulfur vapor, S_2, to form sulfides; and with nitrogen, N_2, to form nitrides:

$$2\,M + 3\,X_2 \longrightarrow 2\,MX_3 \qquad 4\,M + 3\,S_2 \longrightarrow 2\,M_2S_3$$
$$4\,M + 3\,O_2 \longrightarrow 2\,M_2O_3 \qquad 2\,M + N_2 \longrightarrow 2\,MN$$

All these compounds have highly negative ΔH°_{form} at 25°C, and are therefore stable at room temperature with respect to decomposition into their elements. Actually, the ΔH°_{form} (257 kcal/mole) of boron trifluoride, BF_3, is one of the highest among simple molecules. However, all these compounds, except the nitrides, hydrolyze rapidly and more or less extensively in the presence of water.

BEHAVIOR IN WATER SOLUTION

The solution chemistry of the Group IIIB elements depends, as for all elements, on three major factors—their oxidation potential to form a given ion, the hydration energy of this ion, and the tendency of the hydrated ion to hydrolyze.

The standard oxidation potentials listed in Table 32-2 indicate that all the elements of Group IIIB can be oxidized to their cations by a 1 M solution of H^+ ions, with the evolution of H_2 gas. Boron, however, does not give a reversible B,B(III) couple, because of the very high activation energy of reactions involving elemental boron; hence the E° value listed for this couple is calculated rather than determined from experiments. Aluminum and gallium react with aqueous acids to form their hydrated tripositive cations, $Al^{+3}{}_{(aq)}$ and $Ga^{+3}{}_{(aq)}$; indium tends to form first the monopositive ion, $In^{+}{}_{(aq)}$, and then the tripositive ion, $In^{+3}{}_{(aq)}$; whereas thallium can form only the monopositive ion, $Tl^{+}{}_{(aq)}$, since the oxidation potential for the Tl,Tl^{+3} couple is negative. Solutions of $Tl^{+3}{}_{(aq)}$ can, of course, be obtained by dissolving metallic thallium in solutions of suitable oxidizing acids. Thus, simply from the values of the standard oxidation potentials, we observe an important variation in the properties of the Group IIIB elements; for B, Al, and Ga, the stable oxidation state in acid and neutral aqueous solution is +3; for In in acid solution both the +1 and +3 oxidation states are possible (as well as the +2 state), but the +3 state is the most stable; for thallium, finally, only the +1 oxidation state is stable in 1 M H^+ solutions of non-oxidizing acids. Thus, the heavier elements of Group IIIB begin to exhibit variable oxidation states, in contrast with the alkali and alkaline-earth elements of Groups IA and IIA, which have one fixed positive oxidation state corresponding to their group number. In particular, the tendency to form compounds in the low oxidation states in Group IIIB increases with increasing size.

We notice from Table 32-2 that the E° value for the reversible M,M^{+3} couple is exceptionally high for aluminum and then decreases regularly from Ga to Tl (B is out of line because the B,B(III) couple is not reversible, and also the $B^{+3}{}_{(aq)}$ ion does not exist as such in solution). We know that for any given couple the E° value depends largely on the balance between an unfavorable enthalpy factor—the ΔH_{atomiz} plus the total ionization energy—and a favorable enthalpy factor—the hydration energy of the ion. Since the unfavorable enthalpy factor (calculated from the data in Tables 32-1 and 32-2) is about the same for the elements of Group IIIB (Al, 1,308; Ga, 1,386; In, 1,273; Tl, 1,272 kcal/mole), the observed decrease in the E° values for the reaction $M_{(s)} \longrightarrow M^{+3}{}_{(aq)} + 3\,e^-$ simply shows that the hydration energy of the M^{+3} ion decreases very markedly from Al^{+3} to Tl^{+3}. And this is what we would expect on the basis of the marked decreases in the charge/radius ratio for these ions, and the consequent decrease in their polarizing ability. In the reaction $Tl_{(s)} \longrightarrow Tl^{+}{}_{(aq)} + e^-$, on the other hand, only one electron is removed from a Tl atom to form a monopositive Tl^+ ion, so that the (unfavorable) ionization energy is much smaller and even the low hydration energy of the Tl^+ ion is sufficient to make the reaction energetically favorable. Of the trivalent cations of Group IIIB, Al^{+3}, Ga^{+3}, In^{+3}, and Tl^{+3}, we would expect the smallest cation, Al^{+3}, to have the greatest tendency to hydrolyze in water solution—and, in fact, this is so. The hydrolysis reaction of the hydrated Al^{+3} ion, $[Al(H_2O)_6]^{+3}$, can be represented schematically by the equation:

$$[Al(H_2O)_6]^{+3} + H_2O \rightleftharpoons [Al(H_2O)_5(OH)]^{+2} + H^+ \cdot H_2O$$

Thus, aqueous solutions of aluminum(III) salts of strong acids—for example, $Al(NO_3)_3$ and $Al_2(SO_4)_3$—are acidic.

32-4 Some Compounds of Group IIIB Elements

A brief survey of some of the more important and common compounds of boron and aluminum will serve to illustrate the properties and trends discussed in the preceding section.

OXIDES. Diboron trioxide, B_2O_3, is a vitreous, tough substance that can be obtained by the slow dehydration of molten boric acid at about 230°C. In the crystalline form—which is obtained with difficulty from the vitreous form—each B atom is tetrahedrally surrounded by four O atoms, in a complicated three-dimensional covalent lattice. The melting point of B_2O_3 is relatively low, 577°C. Aluminum oxide, Al_2O_3, is—in contrast to B_2O_3—an extremely high-melting substance (m.p. 2,045°C) in which the oxygen-to-aluminum bonding is essentially ionic. Its crystal structure (called *corundum* structure from the common name of the crystalline mineral Al_2O_3) consists of a three-dimensional lattice of Al and O atoms having a 6:4 crystal coordination number. That is, each Al is surrounded octahedrally by 6 equidistant O neighbors, and each O is in turn surrounded tetrahedrally by 4 equidistant Al neighbors. Crystalline Al_2O_3 is an extremely stable substance, ($\Delta H^\circ_{form} = -339$ kcal/mole) which finds applications for its high melting point, inertness to reaction, and hardness. Well-formed clear crystals of Al_2O_3, colored red by small quantities (less than 8 per cent) of Cr_2O_3, are called rubies, and find important application in LASER equipment. Both crystalline B_2O_3 and crystalline Al_2O_3 are insoluble in water and aqueous solutions.

HYDROXIDES. The compounds of boron(III) containing OH groups are acidic in character. Boris acid, H_3BO_3 or $B(OH)_3$, which is one of the forms in which boron occurs in nature, is a white, flaky solid whose crystal structure consists of flat layers of H_3BO_3 molecules joined together by hydrogen bonding. Within each H_3BO_3 molecule the B atom is covalently linked to three O atoms in a regular trigonal stereochemistry, and each boron-to-oxygen bond is considered to have $\frac{1}{3}$ double bond character (each B atom forms 3 *sigma* B—O bonds—one to each of the 3 surrounding O atoms—and a *pi* B←O bond which resonates among the 3 possible positions). Adjacent layers are held together in the crystal by relatively weak van der Waals attractions. Boric acid, H_3BO_3, is low melting (m.p. 189°C) and volatile; it is readily soluble in water in which it behaves as a weak acid. The first ionization of boric acid, which is the only one which occurs to an appreciable extent ($K_1 = 6 \times 10^{-10}$ mole/l.) is generally written as:

$$H_3BO_{3(aq)} + H_2O_{(l)} \longrightarrow [B(OH)_4]^-{}_{(aq)} + H^+{}_{(aq)}$$

Aluminum hydroxide, generally written as $Al(OH)_3$, is a gelatinous substance, of formula $Al(OH)_3 \cdot nH_2O$, which dissolves both in acids and bases, that is, it is amphoteric:

$$Al(OH)_{3(s)} + 3\ H^+{}_{(aq)} \longrightarrow Al^{+++}{}_{(aq)} + 3\ H_2O_{(l)}$$
$$Al(OH)_{3(s)} + OH^-{}_{(aq)} \longrightarrow [Al(OH)_4]^-{}_{(aq)}$$

Thus, aluminum hydroxide precipitates from solutions of Al(III) salts when the solution is made slightly basic, but redissolves to form the $[Al(OH)_4]^-$ ion when the OH^- ion concentration increases further.

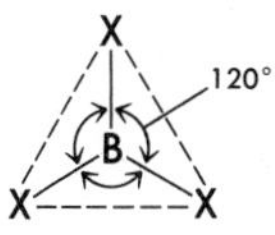

HALIDES. Boron forms three halides, BF_3, BCl_3, BBr_3, which have low melting and boiling points and consist of covalent planar trigonal BX_3 molecules. In the BX_3 molecule, we think of the central B atom as being linked to each of the three

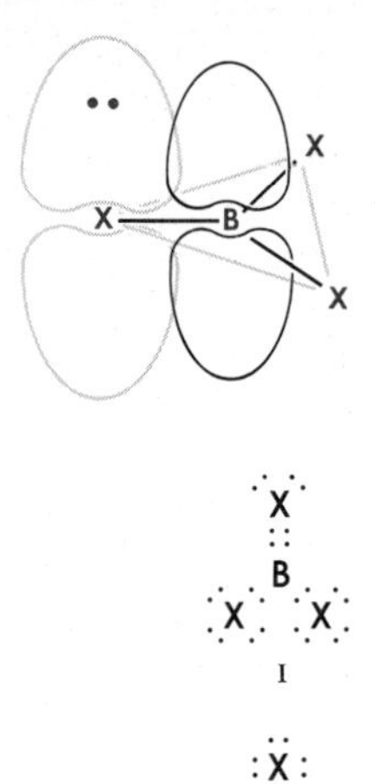

X atoms by a *sigma* B—X covalent bond, involving one of the three $2s\,2p^2$ hybrid orbitals of boron; in addition, the B atom accepts in its vacant $2p$ orbital an electron pair from one of the X atoms, forming a *pi* B←X coordinate bond (see diagram in margin). Since the three X atoms of the BX_3 molecules are all identical, this *pi* B←X bond resonates among the three possible positions, and the electron configuration of BF_3 is represented by the three equivalent contributing structures I, II, and III. Notice that, by forming this resonating π bond, the B atom of BX_3 achieves its maximum electron pair coordination number (E.P.C.N. = 4) and hence the maximum possible stability that can arise from covalent bonds within this monomeric molecule. The central atom of a BX_3 molecule can also attain its maximum and most stable electron pair coordination number, 4, by accepting a pair of electrons from a suitable "outside" donor and forming a coordination compound. Thus, the boron halides are extremely good Lewis acids (electron-pair acceptors) and have a strong tendency to react with Lewis bases. Examples are the reaction of BF_3 with F^-, and NH_3:

I

II

$$BF_3 + F^- \longrightarrow [BF_4]^-$$
$$BF_3 + NH_3 \longrightarrow [F_3B{\leftarrow}NH_3]$$

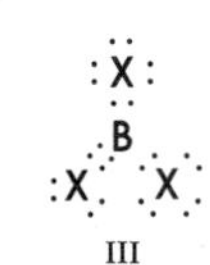

We have already discussed the bonding and stereochemistry of these compounds in Chapter 14 (p. 287) and (p. 288).

The halides of aluminum, AlF_3, $AlCl_3$, $AlBr_3$ and AlI_3, differ in structure from one another depending on the halide present and on the physical state. The fluoride, AlF_3, is a crystalline ionic solid (m.p. 1,040°C), in which each Al^{+3} ion is surrounded octahedrally by 6 F^- ions. The chloride is also an essentially ionic solid, with each Al^{+3} ion surrounded by 6 Cl^- ions. However, aluminum chloride sublimes at only 180°C at 1 atm pressure, and the vapor then consists of dimeric Al_2Cl_6 molecules, in which each of the 2 Al atoms is tetrahedrally surrounded by 4 Cl atoms. Therefore, the 6 Cl atoms of the dimer Al_2Cl_6 molecule are not all equivalent—2 are "bridging chlorines," each bonded to 2 Al atoms, and 4 are "terminal chlorines," each bonded only to one Al atom. (Notice that each of the 2 "bridging chlorines" donates a pair of electrons to one of the Al atoms.) At higher temperature the dimeric Al_2Cl_6 molecules begin to dissociate, and at about 800°C aluminum chloride vapor consists chiefly of $AlCl_3$ monomeric molecules, which would be expected to be planar trigonal. Finally, aluminum bromide and iodide consist of covalent dimeric molecules, Al_2Br_6 and Al_2I_6, not only in the vapor state (like aluminum chloride) but also in the solid state.

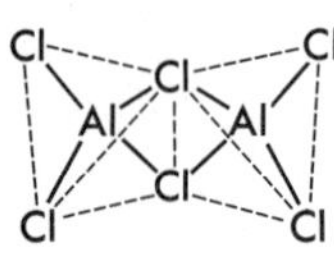

HYDRIDES. Boron forms with hydrogen several binary compounds called boron hydrides, which contain from 2 to 10 B atoms in each molecule. These compounds are all covalent in character and are especially interesting from the structural viewpoint, because they contain a kind of bonding which is known only for some boron compounds. Let us consider the simplest of the boron hydrides, B_2H_6, an unstable colorless liquid ($\Delta H^\circ_{form} = +7$ kcal/mole B_2H_6) which boils at 92.5°C. The B_2H_6 molecule has the stereochemistry shown in the margin. The bonding is explained as follows: each of the 2 B atoms forms a normal covalent bond to each of the 2 H atoms which occupy the terminal positions. In addition, the 2 B atoms share 2 electron pairs with each other and with the 2 H atoms in the bridging positions. And here we see the difficulty of interpreting the bonding present in the B_2H_6 molecule on the basis of the usual valence-bond method. A normal covalent bond requires that an electron pair is shared by the 2 bonded atoms, each having available a suitable orbital—but in B_2H_6 there are only 2 electron pairs to simultaneously join each of the 2 bridging H atoms to both B atoms. Yet some sort of B—H—B bond must be present, or else we would have BH_3 molecules rather than B_2H_6 molecules. We say that a *three-centered bond* joins the 2 B atoms to each of the bridging H atoms; the one electron pair of this B—H—B bond belongs simultaneously to the $1s$ orbital of the H atom and to the available orbitals of the 2 B atoms. The overlap of the orbitals involved in the formation of the 2 three-centered bonds of B_2H_6 is shown schematically in the margin. The molecule B_2H_6 and other boron hydrides are sometimes called "electron-deficient" compounds, to indicate that they do not contain sufficient electrons to account for their bonding in terms of normal electron-pair covalent bonds.

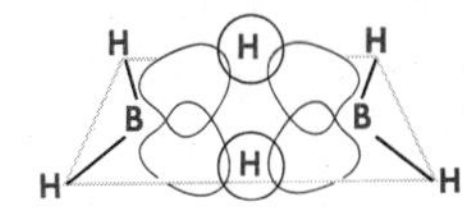

DIAGONAL RELATIONSHIPS

One of the important correlations made by chemists during the early attempts to systematize the behavior of elements is the so-called "diagonal relationship." This relationship simply emphasizes the marked similarity which exists, in certain regions of the Periodic Table, between two elements joined by a diagonal line, downward left to right. For example, the chemistry of Be, the first element of Group II, resembles that of Al, the second element of Group III. A similar likeness exists between the chemistry of Li, the first element of Group I, and Mg, the second element of Group II. The electronegativity of Li (1.0), for example, is comparable to that of Mg (1.2), and Be and Al have the same electronegativity value, 1.5. The similarities of these diagonally located elements arise from the fact that atomic and ionic sizes, as well as effective nuclear charges, increase both as we proceed from left to right across a period and from top to bottom down a group of the Periodic Table. Thus, the ratio of the effective nuclear charge to the atomic radius, which determines the ionization energy, electronegativity, and hydration energy of the ions—in short, the fundamental chemical properties of an element—just happens to have very close values for some pairs of diagonally joined elements.

IA	IIA	IIIB
Li	Be	B
Na	Mg	Al

32-5 General Characteristics of the Group IVB Elements

The variation of physical and chemical properties with increasing atomic number in Group IVB is similar to that in Group IIIB. There is a notable difference, however. Each element of Group IVB has an appreciably higher effective nuclear charge than the corresponding element of Group IIIB, because the additional *np* electron does not completely shield the additional nuclear proton. (As we learned in Chapter 12 in our discussion of the electron configurations of the atoms, the screening ability of electrons decreases in the order *s* electrons $>$ *p* electrons $>$ *d* electrons.) Consequently, the atoms of the Group IVB elements are not appreciably larger than those of the corresponding elements of Group IIIB, but they have higher ionization energies and are more electronegative. The change from non-metallic to metallic properties therefore occurs farther down the group, so tin and lead are the only metals of Group IVB.

Diamond

PHYSICAL PROPERTIES

The outer electron configurations of the atoms of C, Si, Ge, Sn, and Pb —$ns^2\,np^2$—and some of the important physical properties of these elements, are listed in Table 32-3. Ionization energies are shown in Table 32-4.

CARBON. Carbon occurs in two crystalline modifications, diamond and graphite, whose properties, structure, and bonding have already been discussed in Chapter 10, p. 185. An interesting difference between diamond and graphite is that diamond is a non-conductor of electricity at ordinary temperatures (even though it does become a semi-conductor at red heat) whereas graphite is a fair conductor. At ordinary temperature graphite is the stable form of carbon and diamond is the metastable form:

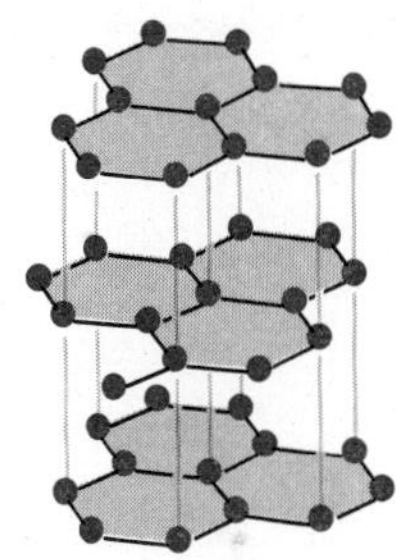
Graphite

$$C_{(\text{diamond})} \longrightarrow C_{(\text{graphite})} \qquad \Delta H = -0.5 \text{ kcal/mole at } 25°\text{C and 1 atm}$$

TABLE 32-3 SOME PROPERTIES OF THE GROUP IVB ELEMENTS

Element	Outer Electron Config.	Atomic Weight	Atomic[a] Radius A	Density at 20°C, g/cm^3	Melting Point °C	Boiling Point °C	ΔH_{atomiz} (kcal/mole of atoms)	Electro-negativity (Pauling)	Oxidation Potential (v) for M,M^{++} Couple
$_6$C	$2s^2\,2p^2$	12.01	0.71[b]	2.26[b]	3730[b]	4830[b]	−171[b]	2.5	—
$_{14}$Si	$3s^2\,3p^2$	28.09	1.18 (4) (covalent)	2.33	1410	2680	−107	1.8	—
$_{32}$Ge	$4s^2\,4p^2$	72.59	1.22 (4) (covalent)	5.32	937	2830	−90	1.8	~0.0
$_{50}$Sn	$5s^2\,5p^2$	118.67	1.40[c] (metallic)	7.30[c]	232[c]	2270[c]	−72[c]	1.8	+0.14
$_{82}$Pb	$6s^2\,6p^2$	207.19	1.75 (12) (metallic)	11.4	327	1730	−46	1.8	+0.13

[a] The number in parentheses represents the crystal coordination number.
[b] Values for graphite.
[c] Values for white tin (metallic structure). The atomic radius is the weighed mean for 6 non-equidistant nearest neighbors.

Stable State at 25°C, 1 atm	IVB
soft gray solid (graphite)	C
shiny hard gray crystals	Si
shiny gray crystals	Ge
silvery-white metal	Sn
silvery-white metal	Pb

At ordinary temperatures the conversion of diamond to graphite does not take place because of an extremely high activation energy; at a temperature of about 1,000°C, however, diamond rapidly converts to graphite.

Charcoal, coke, and carbon black are the more common forms of amorphous carbon. These non-crystalline forms of carbon resemble graphite more than they do diamond. They are relatively soft and considerably less dense than either diamond or graphite. Charcoal is produced by heating wood in the absence of air, while coal, when treated similarly, yields coke. Carbon black is generally made by burning natural gas (chiefly methane, CH_4) in a limited amount of air. Charcoal and carbon black are used in the laboratory and in industry for adsorbing certain gases from gaseous mixtures and certain substances from liquid solution. Large quantities of carbon black are used in the manufacture of automobile tires to improve the resistance of the rubber to abrasion. Graphite is an important constituent of high-temperature lubricants, and because of its electrical conductivity and relatively high chemical inertness it is used to make electrodes for electrolytic processes.

TABLE 32-4 IONIZATION ENERGIES OF GROUP IVB

Element	Underlying Shells and Valence Electrons	Ionization Energies (kcal/mole) 1st	2nd	3rd	4th	Total; M to M^{+4}
$_5$B	$1s^2, 2s^2\,2p^2$	261	563	1,108	1,490	3,422
$_{13}$Al	$2s^2\,2p^6, 3s^2\,3p^2$	188	377	773	1,042	2,381
$_{31}$Ga	$3d^{10}, 4s^2\,4p^2$	187	367	788	1,051	2,394
$_{49}$In	$4d^{10}, 5s^2\,5p^2$	169	335	704	910	2,118
$_{81}$Tl	$4f^{14} 5d^{10}, 6s^2\,6p^2$	171	346	737	972	2,227

SILICON. Crystalline silicon is an opaque, highly reflecting substance which is a semi-conductor of electricity. It is a covalent crystal, with a diamond-like structure in which each Si atom is covalently bonded to 4 other Si atoms in a tetrahedral arrangement. Very pure, single crystals of silicon are used for transistors, rectifiers and solar batteries. Because of its three-dimensional covalent crystal structure, silicon is very hard, with a very high melting point and a large negative value of ΔH_{atomiz}.

GERMANIUM. Germanium, Ge, is a hard, brittle, silvery-white substance with a relatively high melting point (937°C) and boiling point (2,700°C). Crystalline germanium has a diamond-type covalent lattice (tetrahedral) with relatively strong Ge—Ge bonds, as indicated by the large negative value of its ΔH_{atomiz}. Like silicon, germanium is a semi-conductor of electricity, a property that accounts for the major application of this element, its use in transistors and other solid-state electronic devices.

TIN. Tin, like carbon, exists in two allotropic forms—*gray tin,* which has a diamond-like tetrahedral arrangement of Sn atoms, and *white tin,* in which each Sn atom is surrounded by 6 neighbors in a very distorted octahedral arrangement. White tin is the familiar silvery-white form of this element and it is the form stable at room temperature (gray tin $\longrightarrow$ white tin, $\Delta H = +0.6$ kcal/mole at 25°C). White tin has metallic properties—it is malleable and ductile at room temperature, and it has electrical conductivity of the metallic type. Tin has a low melting point for a metal (232°C), but its boiling point is very high (2,270°C); in this respect, tin resembles gallium (diagonal relationship).

LEAD. Lead, when pure, is a soft, white, low-melting metal which has an electrical conductivity less than one-tenth that of copper. Its metallic crystal structure consists of a face-centered cubic arrangement of Pb atoms, each atom having 12 equidistant nearest neighbors.

SEMI-CONDUCTORS. We have seen that carbon in the form of diamond is an electrical insulator at room temperature, whereas silicon and germanium are semi-conductors. The lack of electrical conductivity of diamond at room temperature is explained on the basis that all outer electrons of the carbon atoms are engaged in strong covalent bonds connecting the atoms in a continuous, three-dimensional, covalent lattice. But how do we explain the fact that Si and Ge, which have the same type of crystal structure as diamond, are semi-conductors? And—furthermore—the fact that at high temperatures, diamond itself becomes a semi-conductor?

First of all, when we say that a substance is a semi-conductor, we do not necessarily mean that it is a lesser conductor than metals are. For example, at room temperature, the specific conductivity of the semi-conductor silicon, Si, is about the same as that of the metal nickel, Ni, but for nickel the conductivity decreases with increasing temperature, whereas for silicon it increases. *Semi-conductors are characterized by an electrical conductivity which, unlike metallic conductivity increases with increasing temperature.* This characteristic of semi-conductors helps us to understand how such elements as silicon and germanium can conduct, however weakly, an electric current. Let us consider the case of germanium as an example. At very low temperatures germanium is an extremely poor conductor—it is almost an insulator. This must mean that, at very low temperatures, practically all the valence electrons are localized in the covalent bonds between the Ge atoms, even though a few electrons can break away from these bonds into higher energy levels and become mobile. The electrons that populate these higher energy levels are no longer localized but, similar to the valence electrons of metals, are mobile and can migrate under the influence of an electrical field. As the temperature increases, more and more of the valence electrons of germanium are excited from the localized Ge—Ge covalent bonds to higher energy levels—until finally at room temperature germanium has a sufficient number of mobile electrons to conduct an electric current appreciably. And as the temperature rises even higher, more and more electrons become mobile, and the conductivity increases very markedly. Thus, the difference between metallic and semi-metallic conductors is that in the former, even at low temperatures, there are sufficient mobile electrons to conduct an electric current, and an increase in temperature does not increase the number of mobile electrons. Rather, an increase in temperature decreases the net velocity of migration of the electrons and hence the conductivity, because the increased thermal vibration of the cores of the atoms gives rise to more frequent collisions with the migrating electrons. For semi-conductors, on the other hand, an increase of temperature dramatically increases the number of mobile electrons, thus overshadowing the effect of the more frequent collisions of these electrons with the vibrating cores of the atoms.

We can visualize the phenomenon of semi-conduction as follows. When an electron breaks away from a bond, its former position in the crystal lattice, called the bond site, becomes vacant and is called a ⊕ (plus) hole. Every electron which breaks away from its original bond leaves a ⊕ hole in the crystal. Any given ⊕ hole can be filled by an electron from an adjacent electron-pair bond, and the net result of this displacement of an electron is the movement of a ⊕ hole from one bond site to an adjacent bond site. Consequently, when we apply an electric field to a semi-conductor, both the mobile electrons and the ⊕ holes migrate through the crystal lattice. If a voltage is applied across a piece of Ge, for example, the interstitial electrons migrate toward the positive pole, and the ⊕ holes migrate toward the negative pole.

This picture suggests a simple way to improve the conductivity of Ge—that is, to increase the number of interstitial electrons and hence the number of ⊕ holes in the crystal lattice. To Ge, a Group IV element with 4 valence electrons, we add an extremely small proportion, say one part per million, of a Group V element such as As, which has 5 valence electrons. Each of the relatively few As atoms replaces a Ge atom in the crystal lattice without disturbing the structure of the host germanium lattice. Although an As atom has 5 valence electrons, only 4 of these are used in bonding with the neighboring Ge atoms, because the fundamental lattice structure of germanium involves only 4 bonds for each atom. For each As atom, there is, therefore, one excess electron, which is free to wander throughout the modified crystal lattice. Thus, when a potential is applied, this modified germanium crystal (Ge containing a little As), becomes a better conductor, because the modified crystal contains more mobile electrons than were present in the original pure germanium crystal.

Again, if we add to Ge, a Group IV element, a very small proportion (one part per 10 million) of a Group III element such as indium, In, these relatively few atoms of In replace the corresponding number of Ge atoms in the crystal lattice of the latter. Hence, there will be a ⊕ hole where each In atom is located, because an In atom contains only 3 valence electrons, whereas the Ge atom it replaces contains 4. Again, this modified germanium crystal is a better conductor of electricity than the original germanium crystal, because the modified crystal contains more ⊕ holes. Now let us add *both* excess ⊕ holes and excess electrons to the crystal lattice of the original pure germanium metal by adding *both* In and As. As expected, the resulting modified crystal lattice of germanium conducts the electric current much more easily. In addition, this type of modified germanium crystal containing both a Group III and a Group V element permits the mobile electrons to flow from that part of the crystal which contains an excess of electrons to that part of the crystal which contains an excess of ⊕ holes, but not in the reverse direction. And in this way an alternating current (AC) can be changed (rectified) to a direct current (DC).

OCCURRENCE IN NATURE AND PREPARATION OF THE ELEMENTS

A wide variation exists in the natural abundance of the elements of the IVB group—C, Si, Ge, Sn, Pb. Carbon is not one of the most abundant elements (it is fourteenth in order of abundance), but it is widely distributed throughout the entire world. The carbonate minerals—limestone, marble, and chalk, for example—are all modifications of $CaCO_3$. Wood, coal, peat, natural gas and all petroleum products, and the vast quantity of carbon dioxide in the atmosphere all contain carbon.

Silicon, the most abundant element of this group, is about one-half as plentiful as oxygen, which is the most abundant of all the elements. Silicon occurs in a wide variety of silicates, in clays, and also as pure silica, SiO_2, which exists in a variety of crystalline forms, sand and quartz being the most common. Unlike carbon, which exists free in nature as graphite and diamond, silicon has only been found in the form of its compounds, and always bonded to oxygen. In this respect, silicon is similar to boron. Elemental silicon containing about 2 per cent of various impurities (iron, aluminum, carbon) is prepared by heating SiO_2 at very high temperature with a reducing agent, such as carbon, or with an electropositive metal (Mg, Al):

$$SiO_{2(s)} + 2\ C_{(s)} \longrightarrow Si_{(l)} + 2\ CO_{(g)}$$

The reaction is endothermic ($\Delta H^\circ = +152$ kcal/mole-eqn at 25°C) but since ΔS is favorable (two moles of gas are formed in the reaction), at sufficiently high temperature the reaction becomes thermodynamically permitted. Because silicon has a great tendency to form binary compounds (silicides) with most elements, the preparation of very pure silicon is a laborious and difficult process.

Germanium, Ge, the least abundant of the Group IV elements, is relatively rare. The principal source of germanium is sphalerite, a zinc sulfide (ZnS) ore, which contains only a fraction of 1 per cent of germanium sulfide. The extraction of germanium from its sulfide is carried out by a process similar to that used for lead, which is outlined below.

The only important ore of tin is the oxide SnO_2, cassiterite, from which tin can be obtained by heating the oxide with carbon in a furnace:

$$SnO_2 + 2\ C \xrightarrow{\text{heat}} 2\ CO + Sn \qquad \Delta H^\circ = -86 \text{ kcal/mole-eqn at } 25^\circ C$$

Lead occurs in small quantities in a large variety of minerals such as anglesite, $PbSO_4$; cerussite, $PbCO_3$; and crocoite, $PbCrO_4$. By far the most important ore of lead is the sulfide PbS, galena. Metallic lead is obtained from galena by first roasting the ore in air until it is completely converted to the oxide:

$$2\ PbS + 3\ O_2 \longrightarrow 2\ PbO + 2\ SO_2$$

The oxide is then reduced by heating with carbon:

$$2\ PbO + C \longrightarrow 2\ Pb + CO_2$$

32-6 Chemical Properties of the Group IVB Elements

The outer electron configuration, $ns^2\ np^2$, of the atoms of C, Si, Ge, Sn, and Pb suggests two possible types of compounds for these elements: (1) covalent compounds in which all 4 valence electrons (the $2s$ electrons and the $2p$ electrons) are shared with other atoms as bond pairs; and (2) ionic compounds in which the Group IVB element is present as M^{++} ions, resulting from the removal of only the 2 higher-energy p electrons. Furthermore, we would expect carbon to form a maximum of 4 covalent bonds in its compounds, whereas all other elements, having nd orbitals available, can form up to 6 covalent bonds. The tendency to form ionic compounds containing the M^{+2} ions may be expected to increase down the IVB Group, since the largest elements have the lowest ionization energies as well as the lowest electronegativities. And the occurrence of ionic compounds containing the M^{+4} ions may be considered unlikely for all these elements because of the extremely high ionization energy needed for the reaction $M_{(g)} \longrightarrow M^{+4}{}_{(g)} + 4\ e^-$.

The observed behavior of the Group IVB elements agrees well with the above expectations. The first 3 elements of the Group—C, Sn, and Ge—form only essentially covalent compounds: carbon exhibits coordination numbers 1, 2, 3, and 4; silicon and germanium exhibit coordination numbers 4 and 6 almost exclusively. The two heavier members of the group, tin and lead, form both covalent compounds (C.N. 4 and 6) and ionic compounds containing the ions Sn^{++} and Pb^{++}. The tendency for the s^2 electrons to participate in covalent bonding (by being promoted to higher available empty orbitals) decreases as we go down the group from C to Pb. For this reason the $6s^2$ electron pair of Pb is often called an "inert pair." (A similar "inert pair" also appears in the adjacent elements of the $n = 6$ Periodic Series, Tl of Group IIIB and Bi of Group VB.)

TENDENCY TO CATENATION

The most important chemical property of the first element of Group IVB, carbon, is undoubtedly its ability to form strong covalent bonds with itself, giving rise to compounds containing "chains" of carbon atoms. We saw in Chapter 28 that sulfur has this same ability to some limited extent (as do silicon and germanium), but catenation is indeed a property typical of carbon. The number of known compounds containing from two to thousands of C atoms covalently linked to one another (and also to some other elements, principally hydrogen, oxygen, nitrogen, and phosphorus) very likely exceeds a million, this number is, indeed, continuously increasing, as more compounds are discovered. These carbon compounds, whose varied properties and behavior are of vital importance to life, are called *organic compounds.* For convenience, they are generally the object of separate study and we shall briefly deal with them in Chapter 36. Here we wish to emphasize one important aspect of organic compounds—namely that at room temperature they are generally unstable, from a thermodynamic viewpoint, with respect to combustion in air to form CO_2, H_2O, N_2 and other products. It is only the high activation energy of this combustion reaction which allows organic compounds—and hence life—to exist under the ordinary conditions on earth.

REACTIONS OF THE ELEMENTS. Both carbon and silicon have very high ΔH_{atomiz} (the graphite and diamond structures involve very strong covalent bonds), and therefore reactions involving these elements are characterized by a very high activation energy. Consequently, carbon and silicon are remarkably inert to reaction at room temperature and also at some elevated temperatures, even though the reactions themselves may be thermodynamically favorable. Thus, many carbon compounds are prepared by using methane, CH_4, carbon monoxide, CO, or carbon dioxide, CO_2, as a source of carbon rather than the element itself. Silicon is somewhat less inert than carbon, especially at high temperatures, and the kinetic inertness to reaction decreases further for germanium. Tin and lead have only moderately high activation energies, and many reactions involving these metals occur rapidly at room temperature. Because of this rate effect, we cannot measure a reversible C,C^{+n} couple and hence do not have a value for the oxidation potential of carbon. We know, however, that the reaction, $C_{(s)} + H_2O_{(l)} \longrightarrow CO_{2(g)} + H_{2(g)}$, is thermodynamically forbidden ($\Delta G° = +19$ kcal/mole-eqn at 25°C); therefore we would expect carbon not to be oxidizable by H^+ solutions or by water with liberation of $H_{2(g)}$. In fact, carbon is only oxidized by solutions of very strong oxidants, such as aqua regia.

Silicon can be oxidized by both 1 *M* acid and 1 *M* basic solutions, as well as by pure water:

$$Si + 3\,H_2O \longrightarrow H_2SiO_3 + 4\,H^+ + 4\,e^- \qquad E° = +0.84\text{ v}$$

However, the reaction proceeds rapidly only in basic solution, because the product of the oxidation is then a soluble salt of the $[SiO_4]^{-4}$ ion. Silicon can also be oxidized by solutions containing fluoride ions, which form a complex with Si(IV), as follows:

$$Si_{(s)} + 6\ F^-_{(aq)} \longrightarrow [SiF_6]^{=}_{(aq)} + 4\ e^- \qquad E° = +1.2\ v$$

Germanium, too, has the capacity to be oxidized by acid solutions (Ge,GeO_2 couple, $E° = +0.15$ v), but again for kinetic reasons it does not actually react with solutions of non-oxidizing acids. Tin and lead, on the other hand, react more or less slowly with solutions of non-oxidizing acids, forming the $Sn^{++}_{(aq)}$ and $Pb^{++}_{(aq)}$ ions and liberating hydrogen (Sn,Sn^{++} couple, $E° = +0.14$ v; Pb,Pb^{++} couple, $E° = +0.13$ v).

AQUEOUS-SOLUTION CHEMISTRY OF THE GROUP IVB ELEMENTS

If we do not consider organic compounds, the aqueous-solution chemistry of carbon is almost exclusively the chemistry of hydrated CO_2 (H_2CO_3, HCO_3^-, $CO_3^=$). For silicon, again, the solution chemistry concerns almost exclusively silicon-oxygen compounds—the various forms of silicic acids and silicates—and the same can be said of germanium. Tin and lead are commonly present in aqueous solution as the hydrated Sn^{++} and Pb^{++} ions or as complexes with such anions as OH^-, Cl^-, Br^-, and I^-. We shall now consider some of the most important compounds of these elements.

32-7 Compounds of Carbon

OXIDES. Carbon combines with oxygen to form two oxides: carbon monoxide, CO, and carbon dioxide, CO_2. Both consist of non-associated covalent molecules, and are gases at ordinary conditions. We have already discussed their bonding in Chapters 14 and 15 (pp. 290 and 303), and their thermochemistry in Chapter 16 (p. 343). At temperatures of about 500°C, carbon, whether in excess or not, reacts with oxygen to produce carbon dioxide, CO_2. At higher temperatures (around 1,000°C), a mixture of CO_2 and CO is formed if O_2 is in excess, whereas only CO is formed if C is in excess. Furthermore, if CO_2 is heated with C at about 1,000°C, it reacts to form CO according to the reaction: $CO_2 + C \longrightarrow 2\ CO$.

Carbon monoxide, CO, is a colorless gas (b.p. −190°C) that is almost insoluble in water. It is extensively used as an inexpensive reductant in the high-temperature reduction of many metal oxides (ores) to the metal. For example:

$$Fe_3O_4 + 4\ CO \longrightarrow 3\ Fe + 4\ CO_2$$

Under appropriate conditions, CO combines with many metals to form an interesting class of compounds called *metal carbonyls*. We shall discuss the metal carbonyls in Chapter 33.

Carbon monoxide gas is highly poisonous if inhaled, because it readily combines with the iron present in the hemoglobin of the blood and inhibits its oxygen-carrying capacity. Carbon monoxide is particularly dangerous because, being colorless and odorless, it is not readily detected in the atomsphere.

Carbon dioxide, CO_2, is moderately soluble in water; a saturated solution at room temperature under a 1 atm pressure of CO_2 is 0.3 *M*. Although 99 per cent of the CO_2 molecules present in solution retain their identity, the following equilibrium is established:

$$CO_2 + H_2O \rightleftharpoons H_2CO_3 \rightleftharpoons H^+ + HCO_3^-$$

We have already discussed (see Chapter 20, p. 443), the ionization of the weak carbonic acid, H_2CO_3. Salts of both the hydrogen carbonate ion, HCO_3^-, and of the carbonate ion, $CO_3^=$, exist, and some important examples were mentioned in Chapter 30 (p. 678) and Chapter 31 (p. 689). The alkali-metal carbonates and ammonium carbonate are soluble in water with partial hydrolysis, but all other carbonates are either insoluble or, when added to water, hydrolyze to form insoluble hydroxides or insoluble basic carbonates. All soluble and insoluble carbonate and bicarbonate salts dissolve in solutions of strong acids, liberating CO_2 and forming H_2O:

$$CaCO_3 + 2\ HCl \longrightarrow CaCl_2 + CO_2 + H_2O$$
$$NaHCO_3 + HCl \longrightarrow NaCl + CO_2 + H_2O$$

The $CO_3^{=}$ ion is planar, with a regular trigonal stereochemistry. The 3 contributing electronic structures, I, II, and III, of the $CO_3^{=}$ ion are shown below, together with 2 contributing structures, IV and V, of the HCO_3^- ion:

I II III IV V

$CO_3^{=}$ HCO_3^-

CARBIDES. Carbon combines with the majority of elements, both metals and non-metals, to form binary compounds. Those binary compounds in which the partner element is less electronegative than carbon itself are called *carbides*. Some carbides are prepared by direct combination of carbon with the partner element at high temperature, others are obtained by indirect routes. The carbides exhibit a variety of structures; those of the most electropositive elements are ionic and react with water to form the metal hydroxide and either acetylene, H—C≡C—H, or methane, CH_4. The former are called *acetylides* and among these are the carbides of Li and Ca. The latter are called *methanides*, typical examples being Be_2C and Al_4C_3. The reactions with water are:

$$Li_2C_2 + 2\ H_2O \longrightarrow C_2H_2 + 2\ LiOH$$
$$Be_2C + 4\ H_2O \longrightarrow CH_4 + 2\ Be(OH)_2$$

The crystal structure of the acetylides contains dinegative $(C{\equiv}C)^{=}$ ions arranged in a three-dimensional lattice alternatively with the metal cations. The methanides contain single carbon ions, considered to be C^{-4} ions, that alternate with metal cations in a crystal lattice.

The most important covalent carbide is silicon carbide, SiC. This is a crystalline solid in which each Si atom is covalently bound to 4 C atoms in a tetrahedral arrangement, while in turn each C atom is tetrahedrally bound to 4 Si atoms. Silicon carbide, SiC, is made by the reaction of SiO_2 with C in an electric furnace. It is an extremely stable, very hard, and chemically inert substance, which, because of its hardness is widely used as an abrasive (Carborundum).

CARBON HALIDES. The carbon tetrahalides, CF_4, CCl_4, CBr_4, and CI_4, are covalent compounds consisting of non-associated tetrahedral CX_4 molecules (X = halogen); CF_4 is a gas; CCl_4 and CBr_4 are liquids, and CI_4 is a solid. Carbon tetrafluoride, CF_4, is remarkable in that its intermolecular van der Waals attractions are almost as weak as in the noble gases—that is, CF_4 approaches ideal gas behavior. It is also extremely inert chemically. The other carbon tetrahalides tend to hydrolyze more or less rapidly in water and alkali.

COMPOUNDS OF SILICON. By far the most important and common compounds of silicon involve combination with oxygen. The crystalline compound of formula SiO_2, called silicon dioxide or silica, is a very hard solid and is fairly transparent when pure. Many different crystal modifications of SiO_2 exist, the most common of which is quartz. In each case the structure consists of a regular three-dimensional arrangement of $\{SiO_4\}$ tetrahedral units, joined at their vertices. In this structure, each Si atom is

Silica

tetrahedrally surrounded by 4 O atoms, and each O atom is shared by 2 Si atoms. The various crystal forms of silica differ in the packing of the $\{SiO_4\}$ tetrahedra in the lattice; one of such forms is shown in the illustration on page 712.

Notice the striking difference between carbon dioxide, CO_2, and silicon dioxide, SiO_2. Carbon dioxide is a gas at ordinary temperature and pressure, and at $-78.5°C$ condenses to a soft white solid made up of individual CO_2 molecules held together by van der Waals forces. Silicon dioxide, in contrast, is a very hard crystalline solid that melts at 1,710°C and consists of $\{SiO_4\}$ tetrahedra whose Si and O atoms are bound together by covalent bonds in one giant structure.

Silica is chemically very stable; however, it is readily attacked by hydrogen fluoride to form silicon tetrafluoride, SiF_4 (a colorless gas) and H_2O:

$$SiO_2 + 4\ HF \longrightarrow SiF_4 + 2\ H_2O$$

Silica is also very slowly attacked by strong alkalis, with the formation of soluble silicates:

$$SiO_2 + 2\ NaOH \longrightarrow Na_2SiO_3 + H_2O$$

SILICATES. The silicates are salts of the hypothetical (ortho)silicic acid, H_4SiO_4, and of its various dehydration products, the most important of which is (meta)silicic acid, H_2SiO_3. The silicates are often classified according to the ratio of acid oxide (SiO_2) to basic oxide (CaO, MgO, Al_2O_3) they contain. The ortho-silicate Mg_2SiO_4, for example, can be written as $2\ MgO \cdot SiO_2$, and the ortho-silicate $CaAl_2Si_2O_8$ can be written as $CaO \cdot Al_2O_3 \cdot 2\ SiO_2$. Silicates of various composition occur extensively in nature as rocks and minerals. Cement is a complex aluminum silicate. Glass is fundamentally a vitreous solution of sodium silicate and silica, obtained by melting solid Na_2CO_3 with SiO_2:

$$SiO_2 + Na_2CO_3 \longrightarrow Na_2SiO_3 + CO_2$$

Glasses of different composition can be prepared by varying the ratio of the starting materials, SiO_2 and Na_2CO_3; also, the partial substitution of Na_2CO_3 by oxides such as CaO, PbO, and B_2O_3 yields special glasses.

Although silicates, both those occurring in nature and those obtained industrially, have varied and complicated formulas, all silicate anions consist of tetrahedral $\{SiO_4\}$ units joined together in a variety of ways. When only 2 of the 4 O atoms of each SiO_4 unit are bonded to other Si atoms, a meta-silicate "chain," $(SiO_3{}^=)_n$, or a meta-silicate "ring," $(SiO_3{}^=)_n$, may result. If 3 of the 4 O atoms of each $\{SiO_4\}$ unit are bonded to other Si atoms, a silicate "sheet" may result.

SILICONES. If the non-bridging oxygen atoms of the meta-silicate chain, $(SiO_3{}^=)_n$, are replaced by organic alkyl groups, R—for example, methyl groups, $—CH_3$, compounds of the general formula $\{SiOR_2\}_n$ result. Compounds of this kind are called *silicones*. As we would expect, in silicones, both the Si atoms and the C atoms have a tetrahedral stereochemistry, and the Si—O—Si linkage is bent owing to the lone-pair–lone-pair repulsion on the O atom. The replacement of 2 O atoms of the fundamental SiO_4 group by 2 alkyl groups, R, in silicone imparts to the silicones the lubricating properties characteristic of a hydrocarbon oil. In addition, silicones have the advantage of being very stable compounds, even at high temperatures, because of the strong ···Si—O—Si—O··· bonds, whereas hydrocarbons decompose or burn on strong heating. For these reasons, silicons are widely used as lubricants at high temperatures.

COMPOUNDS OF GERMANIUM. Germanium exhibits two oxidation states, +2 and +4; the latter is the more stable. Germanium is stable toward oxidation by air at ordinary temperature but, when heated, it forms germanium dioxide, GeO_2, a white insoluble solid. Finely divided Ge, when treated with Cl_2 gas, ignites and forms $GeCl_4$, a covalent liquid similar to CCl_4 and $SiCl_4$.

When Ge is placed in dilute or concentrated HCl or in dilute H_2SO_4, no visible reaction occurs even though the oxidation potential of the Ge,Ge^{++} couple is slightly positive ($E° = +0.23$ v). Germanium does, however, react with oxidizing acids such as HNO_3 to form germanium dioxide:

$$3\ Ge + 4\ HNO_3 \longrightarrow 3\ GeO_2 + 4\ NO + 2\ H_2O$$

The insoluble germanium dioxide thus formed is hydrated and a more precise formula for it would be $GeO_2 \cdot xH_2O$. Germanium monoxide, GeO, can be prepared by the reduction of GeO_2 with CO at 900°C, but tends to disproportionate into Ge and the dioxide GeO_2.

TIN AND LEAD. The chemistry of these two elements shows many similarities, except that the oxidation state +2 is more stable for lead than for tin. The Latimer oxidation-potential diagrams of the two metals illustrate this difference:

$$Sn \overset{+0.14}{\text{---}} Sn^{II} \overset{-0.15}{\text{---}} Sn^{IV} \qquad Pb \overset{+0.13}{\text{---}} Pb^{II} \overset{-1.7}{\text{---}} Pb^{IV}$$

Solutions containing Sn(II) are good reducing agents, in fact, oxygen of the air oxidizes solutions of Sn(II) to Sn(IV) unless some metallic Sn is present in contact with the Sn(II) solution. On the other hand, only very strong oxidants can oxidize Pb(II) to Pb(IV) in aqueous solution.

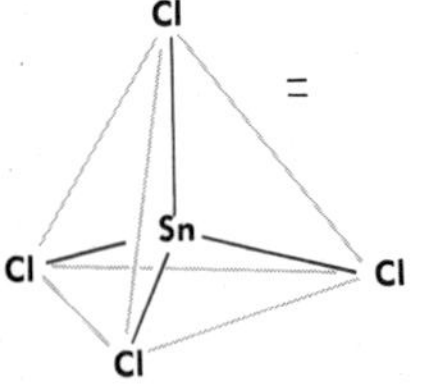

Both Sn and Pb metals can dissolve in 1 *M* solutions of non-oxidizing acids, as their positive $E°$ values indicate. In practice, however, a hot concentrated solution of HCl is necessary to dissolve Sn metal in order to overcome the high overvoltage of H_2 on Sn. The solution thus formed contains Sn(II), not as the $Sn^{++}{}_{(aq)}$ ion but as the chloro-complexes $[SnCl_4]^=$ or $[SnCl_3]^-$ (see structures in margin). Metallic lead does not appreciably dissolve in dilute hydrochloric acid, owing to the formation of an adherent film of insoluble $PbCl_2$ which protects the surface of the metal from further attack. Similarly, Pb is practically insoluble in sulfuric acid (up to 50 per cent concentration) because of the formation of a protective surface layer of insoluble $PbSO_4$. With oxidizing acids, such as concentrated nitric acids, tin and lead react differently. Tin reacts slowly to form the insoluble dioxide, SnO_2; in this case, the Sn(IV) oxidation state results:

$$Sn_{(s)} + 4\ HNO_{3(aq)}\ (\text{hot, conc}) \longrightarrow SnO_{2(s)} + 4\ NO_{2(g)} + 2\ H_2O_{(l)}$$

Even though the insoluble dioxide of Sn(IV) thus formed is written as SnO_2 for simplicity, it is in fact a hydrated dioxide, $SnO_2 \cdot xH_2O$. To get Sn into solution when HNO_3 is used as the oxidizing acid, it is necessary to add a high concentration of Cl^- ions to form the soluble $H_2[SnCl_6{}^=]$ complex acid. Thus, Sn completely dissolves in aqua regia:

$$Sn_{(s)} + 4\ HNO_{3(aq)} + 6\ HCl_{(aq)} \longrightarrow H_2[SnCl_6]_{(aq)} + 4\ NO_{2(g)} + 4\ H_2O_{(l)}$$

Metallic lead, on the other hand, reacts rapidly with HNO_3 to yield soluble Pb(II) nitrate:

$$3\ Pb_{(s)} + 8\ HNO_{3(aq)} \longrightarrow 3\ Pb(NO_3)_{2(aq)} + 2\ NO_{(g)} + 4\ H_2O_{(l)}$$

Solutions containing Sn(II) salts of strong acids are acidic because of the hydrolysis of the hydrated Sn^{++} ions. A 0.1 *M* solution of Sn^{++} hydrolyzes to the extent of about 1 per cent. Thus, solutions of Sn^{++} salts tend to hydrolyze to form insoluble basic salts:

$$Sn^{++}{}_{(aq)} + 2\ Cl^-{}_{(aq)} + H_2O_{(l)} \rightleftharpoons Sn(OH)Cl_{(s)} + H^+{}_{(aq)} + Cl^-{}_{(aq)}$$

The addition of H^+ ions prevents the hydrolysis, whereas the addition of a strong base causes the hydrolysis reaction to proceed further to the right—forming a white hydroxide precipitate, which is usually represented simply as $Sn(OH)_2$.

$$SnOH^+{}_{(aq)} + OH^-{}_{(aq)} \longrightarrow Sn(OH)_{2(s)}$$

If excess OH^- ions are added, the precipitate $Sn(OH)_2$ redissolves to form a complex hydroxo-anion of Sn(II), usually written as $[Sn(OH)_4]^=$.

$$Sn(OH)_{2(s)} + 2\ OH^-_{(aq)} \longrightarrow [Sn(OH)_4]^=_{(aq)}$$

The hydroxide $Sn(OH)_2$ also dissolves in acids to yield the corresponding salts of the Sn^{++} ion; thus, $Sn(OH)_2$ is amphoteric.

Most of the common salts of the Pb^{++} cation, for example the halides $PbCl_2$, $PbBr_2$, and PbI_2, and also PbS, $PbCO_3$, $PbSO_4$, and $PbCrO_4$, are only very slightly soluble in water. Aqueous solutions of soluble Pb^{++} salts are not appreciably hydrolyzed. However, the hydroxide $Pb(OH)_2$ is amphoteric; it reacts with acids to form salts and with excess OH^- ions to form the complex anion $[Pb(OH)_4]^=$.

It is interesting that, although in the solid state the chlorides of Sn(II) and Pb(II) have essentially ionic structures, in the vapor state they consist of individual $SnCl_2$ and $PbCl_2$ covalent molecules. These molecules have an angular shape with a Cl—M—Cl angle smaller than 120°, because the lone-pair–bond-pair repulsion is stronger than the bond-pair–bond-pair repulsion.

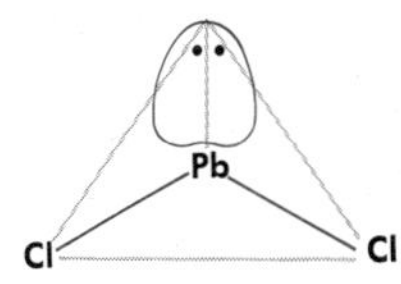

Metallic tin and lead, in the molten state, burn in air to form the oxides of the +4 oxidation state—the yellow SnO_2 and the dark-brown PbO_2. Both these oxides are insoluble in water and other solvents. Under certain conditions, PbO_2 acts as an oxidizing agent. For example:

$$PbO_{2(s)} + 4\ HCl_{(aq)} \longrightarrow Cl_{2(g)} + PbCl_{2(s)} + 2\ H_2O_{(l)}$$

Both Sn(IV) and Pb(IV) form tetrachlorides which consist of tetrahedral covalent molecules, $SnCl_4$ and $PbCl_4$; they are liquids which hydrolyze very readily in the presence of water and moisture.

Lead tetraethyl, $Pb(C_2H_5)_4$, is another compound containing lead in the +4 oxidation state; it is a commercially important compound owing to its "antiknock" properties when added to gasoline. Another important commercial use of lead is in the manufacture of lead storage batteries.

Exercises

32-1 Discuss the elements of Group IIIB—boron, aluminum, gallium, indium and thallium—in regard to: (a) size, (b) ionization energy, (c) heat of atomization, (d) electronegativity. Explain the observed trends in terms of the electron configuration of each element.

32-2 Explain the change from non-metallic to metallic character in going down Group IIIB from boron to thallium. Compare with the behavior of other groups of elements.

32-3 Describe the physical state at ordinary conditions and the structure of the elements (a) boron, (b) aluminum, (c) gallium, (d) indium, (e) thallium.

32-4 Compare in general the compounds of boron and aluminum in regard to their (a) type of bonding, (b) coordination number, (c) stereochemistry.

32-5 What is the most stable oxidation state in water solution for (a) boron, (b) aluminum, (c) gallium, (d) indium, (e) thallium? Explain on the basis of standard oxidation potentials.

32-6 Aluminum metal dissolves in HCl solution but not in concentrated HNO_3 solution. Explain.

32-7 Crystalline boron does not dissolve in water, although for the reaction $2\ B_{(s)} + 3\ H_2O_{(l)} \longrightarrow B_2O_{3(s)} + 3\ H_{2(g)}$, $\Delta G = -103$ kcal/mole-eqn at 25°C and 1 atm. Explain.

32-8 Write an equation for the ionization of boric acid, H_3BO_3, in water. Is H_3BO_3 a weak or strong acid?

32-9 Aluminum hydroxide, $Al(OH)_3$, is amphoteric, whereas $B(OH)_3$ (or H_3BO_3) is an acid: (a) explain, (b) write an equation for the hydrolysis of $Al^{+3}_{(aq)}$ ions in water solution.

32-10 Compare the structures and properties of the oxides of B and Al. Give some examples of practical uses of Al_2O_3.

32-11 Compare the structures of boron and aluminum halides.

32-12 Explain why Al(III) fluoride is an ionic solid, whereas Al(III) bromide is a covalent solid consisting of Al_2Br_6 (dimer "$AlBr_3$") molecules.

32-13 Give examples of boron compounds in which the central B(III) atom has C.N. = 3, and C.N. = 4. Does boron form compounds with C.N. = 5, and C.N. = 6? Explain.

32-14 Give examples of Al(III) compounds with C.N. = 4 and C.N. = 6.

32-15 Discuss the bonding in boron hydride, B_2H_6.

32-16 Write an account of the "diagonal relationship," with special reference to (a) Li and Mg, (b) Be and Al. Given other examples of such a diagonal relationship.

32-17 (a) Explain why diamond and graphite have such widely different physical properties. (b) List some other elements which have a diamond-like structure.

32-18 (a) Explain the meaning of "semi-conductor." (b) Give examples of elements which behave as semi-conductors and show how their conductivity can be increased.

32-19 (a) What does the term "catenation" mean? (b) Why is catenation so very important in the chemistry of carbon?

32-20 Discuss the reactivity of the elements of Group IVB—carbon, silicon, germanium, tin, and lead—in terms of (a) their oxidation potentials, (b) their energy of activation.

32-21 Discuss the elements C, Si, Ge, Sn, and Pb in terms of: (a) ionization energies, (b) ΔH_{atomiz}, (c) electronegativity, (d) more stable oxidation state in solution, (e) type of bonding and coordination number in compounds. Explain your answers.

32-22 Give examples of some compounds of Group IVB elements with (a) oxidation state +2, (b) oxidation state +4, (c) (atom) C.N. = 2, (d) (atom) C.N. = 4, (e) (atom) C.N. = 6.

32-23 To what element is silicon bound in its naturally occurring compounds? Why is SiO_2 so very stable, high-melting, and hard as compared with CO_2, which is a gas?

32-24 Give formulas and sketch the structure of (a) chain silicate, (b) sheet silicate. Which is the most common water-soluble silicate?

32-25 Tin metal dissolves slowly in hydrochloric acid with the evolution of H_2 but does not dissolve in concentrated nitric acid. Explain, and write the formula of the compound formed by each reaction.

32-26 Lead metal dissolves readily in nitric acid, but does not appreciably dissolve in either hydrochloric acid or sulfuric acid of medium concentration. Considering that for the couple Pb,Pb^{++}, $E° = +0.15$ v, explain this behavior.

COORDINATION COMPOUNDS

33

Often, in the course of our discussions, we have encountered many examples of coordination compounds—that is, compounds containing one or more coordinate bonds. Coordination compounds —or "complexes"—are extremely common and include very many familiar substances. The ammonium ion, NH_4^+, is a complex, as are the sulfate ion, $SO_4^=$, the dimeric molecule of gaseous aluminum(III) chloride, Al_2Cl_6, and crystalline silica, SiO_2. In aqueous solutions, all metal ions are present as hydrated ions, and these are, in most cases, well-defined coordination compounds. Even the hydrated proton, H^+, in aqueous solution is best described as a complex—the (hydrated) hydronium ion, $[H_3O]^+_{(aq)}$. Chemical reactions in aqueous solutions therefore involve, to a vast extent, coordination compounds, and we must always keep this in mind when we study the structural, energetic, and kinetic aspects of aqueous chemistry. In a similar manner, the structural properties of solid compounds are also best interpreted in terms of coordination chemistry—especially the compounds of the transition and post-transition elements, which we shall study in the next two chapters. Thus, the study of coordination compounds is not a special topic of chemistry but a general approach to the understanding of chemical phenomena.

Coordination compounds also play an extremely important practical role in all areas of chemistry. In biochemistry, for example, a complex of iron, hemoglobin, is the oxygen-carrying agent of the blood stream; a complex of cobalt, the B_{12}

vitamin, is indispensable to liver functions; and a variety of metal complexes are involved in the digestive hydrolysis of proteins. A magnesium complex, chlorophyll, is the main catalyst in the synthesis of carbohydrates from atmospheric carbon dioxide and water, which takes place in green plants in the presence of sunlight. Many complex ions are also useful in a variety of commercial operations. For example, silver and gold are extracted from their ores by a process involving the formation of the complex ions $[Ag^{I}(CN)_2]^-$ and $[Au^{III}(CN)_4]^-$, which can then be used to deposit electrolytically adherent, thin films of silver and gold from their solutions; nickel metal is purified in industry through the formation and subsequent decomposition of its volatile complex $[Ni(CO)_4]$; and industrial organic chemistry uses very large quantities of coordination compounds as catalysts.

33-1 Definition of Terms

As we learned in Chapter 13, a coordinate bond is an essentially covalent bond in which both electrons of the bond pair are furnished by one of the bonded atoms—the *donor* atom. The other atom, which takes part in the coordinate bond by accepting a share of this donated electron pair, is the *acceptor* atom. A coordinate covalent bond between unlike atoms, A→B, is always dipolar, and often has an appreciable ionic character.

A *coordination compound,* or *complex,* consists of a *central atom* or *ion* bonded by coordinate bonds to a definite number of groups (atoms, molecules, or ions) arranged about it in a definite stereochemistry. Take the complex ion $[Pt(NH_3)_4]^{++}$ as an example. Here the central Pt(II) ion is surrounded by the N atoms of the 4 NH_3 molecules, the Pt(II) ion and the 4 nitrogen atoms lying in the same plane. Each N atom of an ammonia molecule (:NH_3) donates its lone pair to the Pt(II), forming a coordinate bond, and a complex ion results (see diagram). In the complex $[Pt(NH_3)_4]^{++}$ the Pt(II) is the central ion. In general, the central atom or ion of a complex acts as an *electron-pair acceptor.*

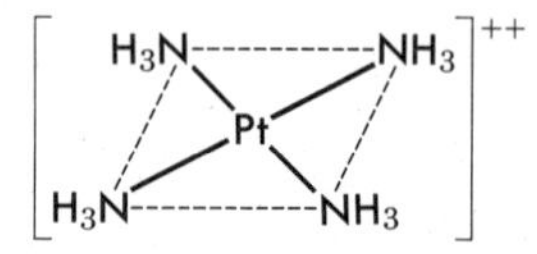

The *coordinating groups,* or *ligands* (from the Latin *ligare,* to bind), are the groups bound to the central atom or ion of the complex. In a ligand, the atom which is attached to the central atom or ion is called the *donor atom,* or the *ligating atom.* For example, in the complex ion $[Pt(NH_3)_4]^{++}$ the NH_3 molecules are the ligands and the N atoms are the donor or ligating atoms. The ligands of a complex act as *electron-pair donors* (Lewis bases), while, as we have said above, the central atom or ion acts as an *electron-pair acceptor* (Lewis acid).

The *coordination number* (C.N.) is the total number of donor atoms coordinated to the central atom or ion. The coordination number is also defined, as we learned in Chapter 13, as the number of *sigma*-bond pairs associated with the central atom or ion of the complex. For $[Pt(NH_3)_4]^{++}$, the coordination number of the central metal ion, Pt(II), is 4. In the complex ion $[Ag(NH_3)_2]^+$, two N atoms are coordinated to Ag(I), so the C.N. of the central ion is 2. In the complex ion $[Co(NH_3)_6]^{+3}$, the C.N. of the central metal ion, Co(III), is 6.

The central atom or ion of a complex and the groups coordinated to it constitute the *coordination sphere.* Any group that is coordinated to the central element is said to be *inside the coordination sphere.* A group that is not coordinated to the central element is said to be *outside the coordination sphere.* For example, in the complex compound $[Co(NH_3)_5Cl]Cl_2$, the 5 NH_3 molecules and the one coordinated Cl^- ion *within* the bracket are "inside the coordination sphere"; the two free Cl^- ions *outside* the bracket are "outside the coordination sphere."

A coordination compound can be a *neutral complex* or an *ionic complex* (positively or negatively charged). A complex is neutral when the ionic charges of the coordinated ligands and the ionic charge of the central atom or ion exactly compensate for one another—that is, add up to zero. For example, in the complex $[Co^{III}(NO_2)_3(NH_3)_3]^0$, the tripositive charge of the central metal ion, Co(III), is balanced by the sum of the negative charges of the 3 mononegative NO_2^- ligands (the 3 NH_3 ligands being neutral). Alternatively, a complex is neutral when both the central atom or ion and the ligands have no ionic charge of their own. An example is $[Ni(CO)_4]^0$, in which the central atom is nickel in the zero oxidation state, Ni(O), and the ligands are neutral CO molecules. In an ionic complex the algebraic sum of the oxidation number of the central atom or ion and the charge of the coordinating groups is the net ionic charge of the complex. For example, the +2 net charge of $[Pt(NH_3)_4]^{++}$ results from the +2 oxidation number of the central Pt(II) and the zero charge of the 4 NH_3 molecules.

33-2 Nomenclature of Coordination Compounds

The systematic nomenclature of coordination compounds follows the same general rules given in Chapter 5 for the nomenclature of "simple" inorganic compounds. Using the systematic name of a coordination compound presupposes knowing its structure; otherwise a "trivial" name should be used. Here are the fundamental rules for writing the formulas and names of coordination compounds.

1. *Writing Formulas of Coordination Compounds*

a. Enclose the formula of a complex (whether a neutral molecule, a cation, or an anion) in square brackets [ ].

b. Within the square brackets, first write the symbol of the central atom or ion, then the symbols or formulas of all the ligands. Show the number of ligands of each kind as a subscript following the symbol or formula of the ligand, enclosing di- or polyatomic ligands in parentheses ( ). Examples: $[Co(NH_3)_6]^{+3}$, $[PtCl_4]^{=}$, and $[Cu(CN)_4]^{=}$.

c. Following the symbol of the central element, write the ligands (usually) in this order: negative ligands, neutral ligands, positive ligands. Examples: $[CoCl(NH_3)_5]^{++}$ and $[NiBr_2(NH_3)_4]^0$.

d. If a coordination compound is ionic, as usual write first the positive ion and then the negative ion. Examples: $K_2[PtCl_4]$, $[Co(NH_3)_6]Cl_3$, and $[Pt(NH_3)_4][PtCl_4]$.

2. *Writing Names of Coordination Compounds*

a. First, give the name of the ligands, using the Greek prefixes *di-*, *tri-*, *tetra-*, etc., to designate the number of identical ligands when the ligands are simple molecules or ions. If the ligands are rather complicated, enclose their names in parentheses and use the prefixes *bis, tris, tetrakis,* etc., to indicate their number (for examples, see Table 33-2). The names of the ligands are generally derived from the names of the corresponding "free" molecules or ions. The names of a number of common ligands are listed in Table 33-1.

b. Next, give the name of the central atom or ion, with its oxidation num-

TABLE 33-1 SOME COMMON LIGANDS

Ligand	Name
F^-	fluoro
Cl^-	chloro
Br	bromo
I^-	iodo
$O^{=}$	oxo
OH^-	hydroxo
CN^-	cyano
SCN^-	thiocyanato (S-bonded)
SCN^-	isothiocyanato (N-bonded)
NO_2^-	nitro (N-bonded)
NO_2^-	nitrito (O-bonded)
NO_3^-	nitrato
$C_2O_4^{=}$	carbonato
H_2O	aquo
NH_3	ammine
en*	ethylenediamine
CO	carbonyl
PF_3	trifluorophosphine
$NH_2{-}\overset{+}{N}H_3$	hydrazinium

* $H_2NCH_2CH_2NH_2$

TABLE 33-2 FORMULAS AND NAMES OF SOME COORDINATION COMPOUNDS

Formula	Name
COMPLEX CATIONS	
$[Ag(NH_3)_2]^+$	diamminesilver(I) ion
$[Be(H_2O)_4]^{++}$	tetraaquoberyllium(II) ion
$[CoCl(NH_3)_5]^{++}$	chloropentaamminecobalt(III) ion
$[CoCl(NO_2)(NH_3)_4]^+$	chloronitrotetraamminecobalt(III) ion
COMPLEX ANIONS	
$[BF_4]^-$	tetrafluoroborate(III) ion
$[Fe(CN)_6]^{-4}$	hexacyanoferrate(II) ion
$[Fe(CN)_6]^{-3}$	hexacyanoferrate(III) ion
$[Cr(C_2O_4)_3]^{-3}$	tris(oxalato)chromate(III) ion
NEUTRAL COMPLEXES	
$[PtCl_2(H_2NCH_2CH_2NH_2)]$	dichloro(ethylenediamine)platinum(II)
$[Ni(CO)_4]$	tetracarbonylnickel(0)
$[Fe(PF_3)_5]$	pentakis(trifluorophosphine)iron(0)
$[Zn(SO_4)_2(NH_2\overset{+}{N}H_3)_2]$	disulfatobis(hydrazinium)zinc(II)
$[Cu(H_2NCH_2COO)_2]$	bis(glycinato)copper(II)
SALTS OF COMPLEX CATIONS AND COMPLEX ANIONS	
$[Ag(NH_3)_2]Cl$	diamminesilver(I) chloride
$[CoCl(NH_3)_5](NO_3)_2$	chloropentamminecobalt(III) nitrate
$K_3[Fe(CN)_6]$	potassium hexacyanoferrate(III)
$[Pt(NH_3)_4][PtCl_4]$	tetraammineplatinum(II) tetrachloroplatinate(II)

ber indicated by a Roman numeral in parentheses: for example, diamminesilver(I).

c. In naming a neutral complex or a complex cation, leave the name of the central atom or ion unchanged. In naming a complex anion, indicate the central atom by the stem of its Latin name followed by the ending *-ate* and by its oxidation number in Roman numerals (in parentheses). As an illustration, the formulas and names of some coordination compounds are listed in Table 33-2.

THE DENTICITY OF LIGANDS

Denticity is the number of donor atoms of a ligand. Ammonia, NH_3, is a familiar example of monodentate ligand (denticity = 1). The molecule ethylenediamine, $H_2NCH_2CH_2NH_2$, has two nitrogen atoms, each of which donates a lone pair to a metal ion; thus the molecule is an example of a bidentate ligand (denticity = 2). A ligand that forms only *one* coordinate bond is called a *monodentate ligand.* Ligands that form 2, 3, 4, and so on coordinate bonds are called *bidentate, tridentate, tetradentate,* and so on *ligands,* or, generally, *polydentate ligands.* (Both the word *denticity* and the suffix *-dentate* come from the Latin *dentatus*, meaning "having (so many) teeth, or tooth-like projections.")

CHELATE COMPLEXES

A *di-* or *polydentate ligand* in which 2 (or more) donor atoms are so arranged that they can both coordinate to the same central element is called a *chelating ligand* (from the Greek *chele,* meaning "claw"). A chelating ligand forms with the central atom or ion one (or more) chelate ring(s), and the resulting complex is called a chelate complex, or simply a chelate.

For example, the complex formed when 2 molecules of ethylenediamine coordinate to a Pt^{++} ion is the chelate $[Pt(NH_2CH_2CH_2NH_2)_2]^{++}$. The structural formula of this bis(ethylenediamine)platinum(II) chelate complex ion, $[Pt(NH_2CH_2CH_2NH_2)_2]^{++}$, is schematically shown in the accompanying diagram.

For a molecule or ion to act as a chelating ligand, 2 or more of its donor atoms must be so situated that they may simultaneously occupy adjacent coordination positions about a single metal ion, without requiring too much distortion of the original bond angles of the ligand. In general, complexes that contain 5-membered chelate rings (each ring including the metal ion and 4 atoms of the ligand) are particularly stable, because the distortions of the bond angles of the ligand are very small. The strain on the bond angles is further relieved because the chelate rings usually assume a puckered rather than a flat arrangement. For example, in the chelate complex ion $[Pt(NH_2CH_2CH_2NH_2)_2]^{++}$, the 4 ligating N atoms of the 2 $H_2NCH_2CH_2NH_2$ chelating groups lie in the same plane as the central Pt(II) shown above; the 2 C atoms of the ethylenediamine ligand, however, lie one above and one below the plane of coordination, so that the 2 C—C—N tetrahedral (109°) angles are virtually undistorted.

AMBIDENTATE LIGANDS

In some ligands 2 (or more) *different* potential donor atoms are so arranged that they *cannot* both coordinate to the *same* metal atom or ion. Such ligands can coordinate to a single metal atom or ion only as monodentate ligands, binding either through one or through the other of their potential donor atoms. Hence these ligands are called *ambidentate ligands* (from the Latin *ambi* meaning "on both sides," and *dentatus*). An example of an ambidentate ligand is the SCN^- ion. This ion has the linear structure $:N{\equiv}C{-}\ddot{\underset{\cdot\cdot}{S}}:^-$ and therefore *cannot* coordinate to the *same* metal ion through both the N and the S atoms, even though both atoms have lone pairs available for coordination. Notice, in fact, that if one atom, say the N atom, is coordinated to a metal ion, M^{+n}, the S atom is far removed from this metal ion (see accompanying diagram); the orbitals of the lone pairs of this S donor atom then point away from the M^{+n} ion, and no M-to-S bond can be formed. Thus, the SCN^- ion coordinates to a (single) metal ion through either the N atom (only) or the S atom (only) depending on the characteristics of the particular metal ion, M^{+n}. For example, the SCN^- ligand coordinates to Co(II) through its N atom in the complex ion $[Co(NCS)_4]^=$; hence this complex is called tetra*iso*thiocyanatocobaltate(II) (see Table 33-1). On the other hand, the SCN^- ligand coordinates to Hg(II) through its S atom in the complex ion $[Hg(SCN)_4]^=$; accordingly, this complex is called tetrathiocyanatomercurate(II).

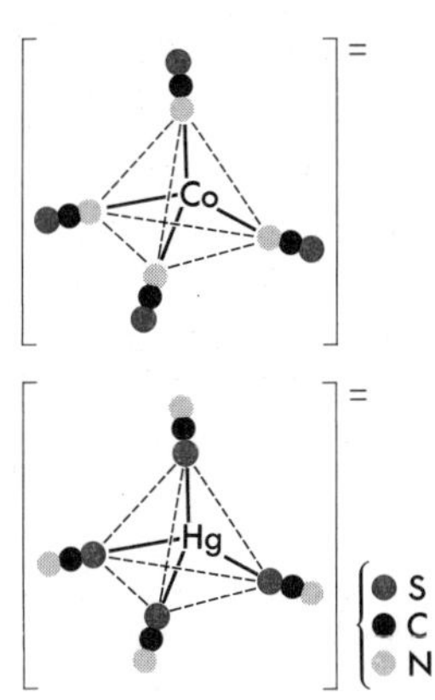

BRIDGING LIGANDS

Some molecules and ions can act as bidentate ligands, not toward the *same* (one) metal ion, but toward *two* central metal ions. A ligand that coordinates in this manner and thereby links together the two central metal ions, forms a "bridge" between them. Such a ligand is then said to be a *bridging ligand,* and the complex is called a bridged *complex,* or a *di-, tri-, . . . polynuclear complex.* In general, a molecule or ion can act as a bridging ligand when it has (1) one atom with two or more lone pairs of electrons (for example, $:\ddot{\text{Cl}}:^-$ and $:\ddot{\text{O}}:\text{H}^-$) or (2) two (identical or different) donor atoms in such positions that they are unable to form a chelate ring with the same central element. Examples are $:\text{N}{\equiv}\text{C}{-}\ddot{\text{S}}:^-$ and $:\text{C}{\equiv}\text{N}:^-$. Simple and common bridging ligands are $:\ddot{\text{Cl}}:^-$, $:\ddot{\text{Br}}:^-$, $:\ddot{\text{I}}:^-$, $:\ddot{\text{O}}:^=$, $:\ddot{\text{O}}:\text{H}^-$, $:\ddot{\text{S}}:^=$, $:\text{C}{\equiv}\text{N}:^-$, and $:\text{N}{\equiv}\text{C}{-}\ddot{\text{S}}:^-$. Two examples of compounds which are often written for simplicity as "simple salts" are silver(I) thiocyanate, "AgSCN," and palladium(II) chloride, "$PdCl_2$." These compounds, however, are bridged complexes, whose structures are schematically shown:

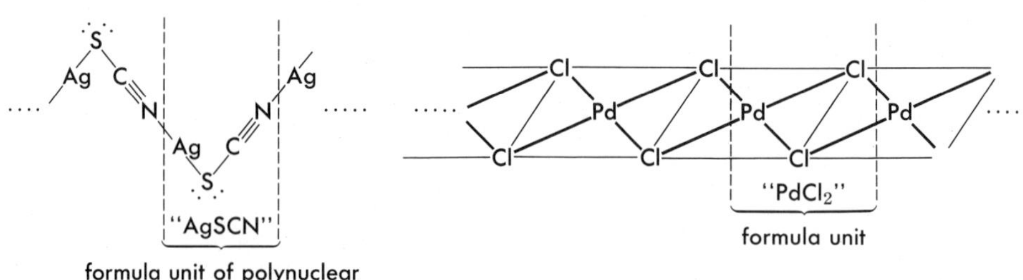

formula unit of polynuclear bridged complex

formula unit

33-3 Coordination Number of Complexes

In most complexes the C.N. is an even number, usually 2, 4, 6, and (though less commonly) 8, 10, and 12. Complexes with odd coordination numbers of 5, 7, and 9 are also known, the 5-coordinate complexes being the more common.

In general, when a given metal atom or ion joins with a given type of ligand, the resulting complex has a certain preferred coordination number. For example, the Be(II) ions will coordinate with 4 H_2O molecules to form the complex ion $[Be(H_2O)_4]^{++}$ but not $[Be(H_2O)_6]^{++}$, even if an extremely large excess of H_2O molecules is present. And, regardless of how much ammonia, NH_3, is added to a solution of Ni(II) ions, only the 6-coordinate complex $[Ni(NH_3)_6]^{++}$ has been obtained. On the other hand, when Ni metal reacts with carbon monoxide gas, CO, only the 4-coordinate $[Ni(CO)_4]$ is formed; no carbon monoxide complexes of Ni(O) with coordination numbers either lower or higher than 4 have been reported. Sometimes a certain metal ion (or atom) and a certain ligand will combine to form complexes with different coordination numbers, depending on the reaction conditions. For example, the 4-coordinate complex $[Zn(NH_3)_4]^{++}$ is formed when an aqueous solution of Zn(II) is treated with an excess of aqueous ammonia, whereas the 6-coordinate complex $[Zn(NH_3)_6]^{++}$ is formed when solid, anhydrous $ZnCl_2$ is treated with an excess of gaseous ammonia.

So many factors decide the preferred coordination number of the central element of a complex that their relative importance is generally difficult to assess. As a useful generalization, however, we can say that a metal atom or ion will tend to coordinate with as many ligands as possible, compatible with (1) the electroneutrality principle, (2) the size of the ligands, and (3) for transition metal ions, the most stable electron configuration of the *d* electrons (see Sections 33-7 and 33-8). The size of the ligands is a particularly important factor when the metal ion is small. For example, Al(III) (ionic radius, 0.50 A) coordinates with 6 F^- ions (ionic radius, 1.36 A) in $[AlF_6]^{-3}$; but with only 4 of the larger Cl^- ions (ionic radius, 1.81 A) in $[AlCl_4]^-$. If the central metal ion is large, the size requirement is of course less important. For example, the Pt(IV) ion, which is quite large, forms 6-coordinate complexes with Cl^-, and even with the still larger Br^- (ionic radius, 1.95 A); the complexes are $[PtCl_6]^=$ and $[PtBr_6]^=$.

33-4 Stereochemistry of Complexes

An interesting aspect of coordination chemistry concerns the geometrical arrangement of the donor atoms of the ligands about the central metal—what we may call the "stereochemistry of the coordination sphere." For coordination compounds in which the central metal ion has a symmetrical electron configuration, the stereochemistry is determined by the number of sigma-bond pairs (there being no lone pairs), according to the general rules given in Chapter 13. Thus, the $[Be(H_2O)_4]^{++}$ complex has a tetrahedral stereochemistry, as we would expect since the central Be(II) has a helium-like electron configuration ($1s^2$) and is associated with 4 bond pairs, each donated by an O atom of a H_2O ligand. And the $[Ag(NH_3)_2]^+$ cation, as well as the $[AgCl_2]^-$ and $[Ag(CN)_2]^-$ anions are linear, as we would expect for complexes of Ag(I) (outer electron configuration: $4s^2\,4p^6\,4d^{10}$) with 2 bond pairs. In the $[Ag(CN)_2]^-$ complex the bond pairs are donated by the C atom of the 2 CN^- ligands.

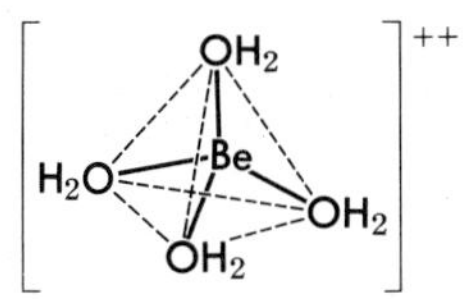

$[H_3N—Ag—NH_3]^+$
$[Cl—Ag—Cl]^-$
$[N{\equiv}C—Ag—C{\equiv}N]^-$

For a complex in which the central element is a transition metal atom or ion having incompletely filled outer *d* orbitals (see Section 33-7), the coordination number alone does not permit us to infer the stereochemistry of a complex. For example, a compound of Ni(II) with C.N. = 4 can have either a tetrahedral stereochemistry (e.g. $[NiCl_4]^{=}$) or a square planar stereochemistry (e.g. $[Ni(CN)_4]^{=}$), depending on the kind of ligands (Cl^- or CN^-) attached to the central Ni(II) (see Section 33-7). For complexes of transition metal ions, the more favorable stereochemistry generally depends, in a rather complicated manner, on the balance of many independent factors. The elucidation of these factors and of their relative importance, and the study of stereochemical isomerism, is one of the topics of current interest in chemical research.

STEREOCHEMICAL ISOMERS. When 2 (or more) forms of a complex differ only in the stereochemical arrangement of the donor atoms about the central element, they are called *stereochemical isomers.* In general, the term isomers indicates compounds with the same composition—that is, with the same molecular formula—but with some difference in their structure, in this case, a difference in stereochemistry. As a result of differences in structure, 2 or more compounds with the same molecular formula may exhibit different physical and chemical properties. The 2 compounds are called *isomers* of one another, and the phenomenon itself is known as *isomerism.*

33-5 Geometrical Isomerism of Complexes

GEOMETRICAL ISOMERS OF SQUARE PLANAR AND TETRAHEDRAL COMPLEXES

In the square planar stereochemistry all 4 donor atoms of the ligands are located at the corners of the square having the metal ion at the center. When 2 kinds of ligands are present in the same square planar complex, 2 different arrangements are possible. If 2 like ligands are at the corners of the same side of a square, the structure is described as a *cis*-structure (from the Latin *cis,* on the same side). If the 2 like ligands are at opposite corners of a square, the structure is called a *trans* structure (from the Latin *trans,* across). These 2 different spatial arrangements give rise to 2 isomeric complexes, known as *cis-trans* isomers, or as *geometric* isomers. The 2 forms of *cis-trans* isomers usually differ somewhat in certain physical and chemical properties, in particular their solubility and color.

The 2 general spatial arrangements of a square planar complex with the formula $[Ma_2b_2]$, where M is the central metal atom of the complex and a and b are the monodentate coordinating groups, are shown below.

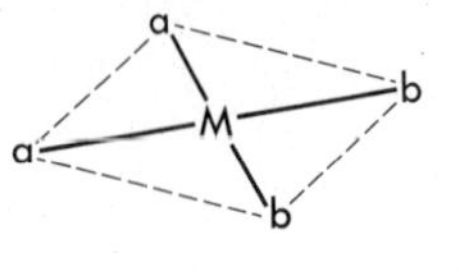

cis-[Ma_2b_2]

trans-[Ma_2b_2]

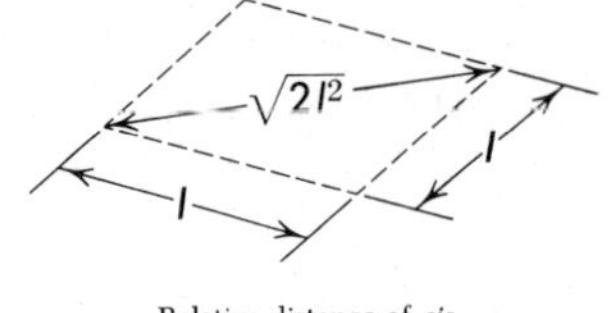

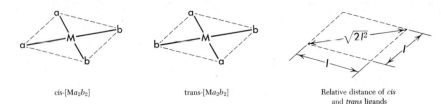

Relative distance of *cis* and *trans* ligands

Geometrical isomerism is possible in square planar complexes because, although the 4 coordinating groups are equidistant from the central atom, they are not equidistant *from one another*. Thus, in the complex [Ma_2b_2], the *b*-to-*b* distance (l) in the *cis* isomer is different from the *b*-to-*b* distance ($\sqrt{2l^2}$) in the *trans* isomer. In a tetrahedral arrangement, however, all 4 coordinating groups are equidistant *from one another*. Thus, *cis-trans* isomerism is not possible when a complex of the type [Ma_2b_2] has a tetrahedral structure.

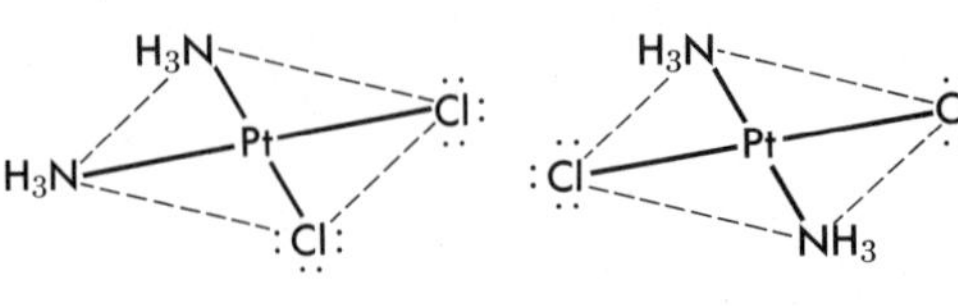

cis-dichlorodiammine-platinum(II) *trans*-dichlorodiammine-platinum(II)

An example of *cis*-trans isomerism is provided by the 2 isomeric square planar compounds of Pt(II), of formula [$PtCl_2(NH_3)_2$].

GEOMETRICAL ISOMERS OF OCTAHEDRAL COMPLEXES

For octahedral complexes which contain 2 or more different ligands, again geometric isomerism is possible. To indicate the various isomers systematically, the positions occupied by the 6 coordinating groups are numbered as shown in Fig. 33-1. Any 2 positions in an octahedral stereochemistry are either adjacent or diagonal to each other. Two identical ligands (x) situated in adjacent positions—for example, positions 1 and 2 in Fig. 33-1(b)—are obviously closer to one another than two ligands situated in diagonal positions—for example, positions 1 and 6 in Fig. 33-1(c). Since the distance between the 2 identical ligands is different in the 2 arrangements, geometrical isomerism can arise. If the identical ligands are in positions 1 and 2, they are *cis* to one another; if the identical ligands are in positions 1 and 6, they are *trans* to one another.* An example of geometrical isomerism for an octahedral complex is the ion [$CoCl_2(NH_3)_4$]$^+$, which exists as a *cis* isomer (violet) and a *trans* isomer (green) (Fig. 33-1(d) and (e)).

CONFORMATION AS AN ASPECT OF STEREOCHEMISTRY

In discussing the stereochemistry of molecules and polyatomic ions, we must consider two points. First, we are interested in the way bonds are arranged around each particular atom—that is to say, in the *stereochemistry*. Second, we want to know the relative spatial arrangement of the atoms in the *molecule as a whole*—that is to say, the *conformation*. As an illustration, let us consider the molecule B_2Cl_4 ($Cl_2B—BCl_2$). The Lewis electron-dot formula of this molecule is given in Fig. 33-2(a). The bonds of each central B atom with the 2 Cl atoms and the other B atom form angles of 120°, as illustrated in Fig. 33-2(b). The two boron atoms are labeled B_1 and $_2B$ in Fig. 33-2(c) for the purpose of the following discussion. There is more than one way in which the atoms of the $Cl_2B—BCl_2$ molecule can be arranged, still preserving the 120° bond angles. In one possible arrangement all 6 atoms lie in the same plane (Fig. 33-3(a)). Another possible arrangement is represented by Fig. 33-3(b), in which the plane containing boron atom $_2B$ and the 2 Cl atoms attached to it is at right angles to the plane containing boron atom B_1 and the 2 Cl atoms attached

* Equivalent *cis* positions are: 1,2; 1,3; 1,4; 1,5; 2,6; 3,6; 4,6; 5,6; 2,3; 2,5; 3,4; and 4,5. Equivalent *trans* positions are: 1,6; 2,4; and 3,5. *Cis* positions usually are indicated as 1,2 and *trans* positions as 1,6.

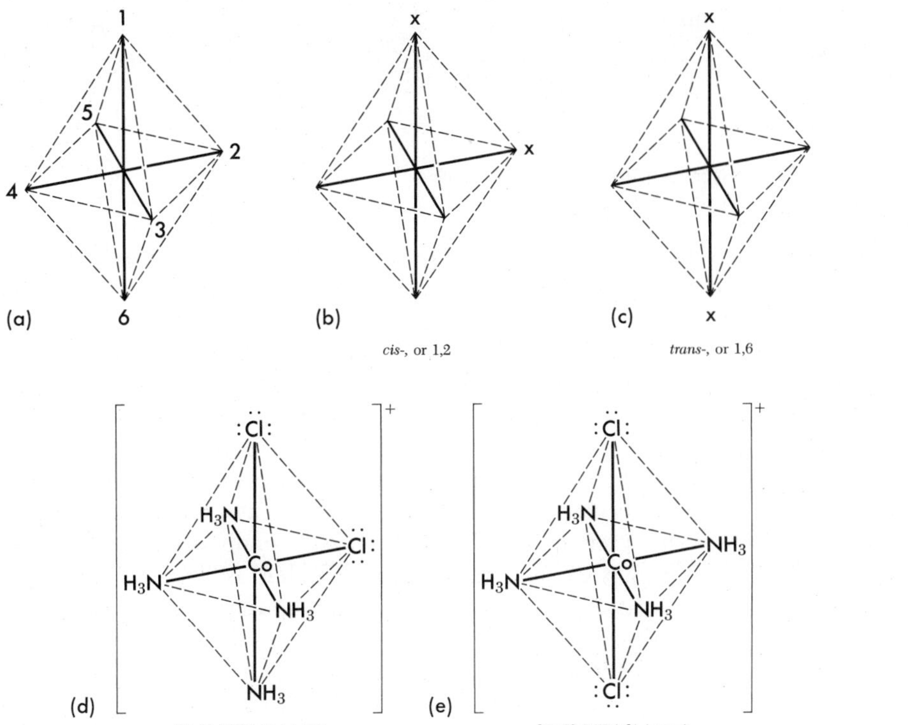

FIGURE 33-1 Geometrical isomers of octahedral complexes.

to it. These 2 arrangements, together with the various possible intermediate arrangements are called *conformations* of the molecule. The rules governing these arrangements are fairly simple. Just as the arrangement of *bonds* around a central atom is decided primarily by the repulsion of the lone *pairs* and the bonding *pairs* of electrons present on the central atom, so the arrangement of *atoms* in a molecule is decided by their tendency to *keep as far apart from one another as possible.* In fact, in the *gaseous phase* the B_2Cl_4 molecules are free from constraining forces and therefore assume the conformation shown in Fig. 33-3(b), in which the 2 Cl atoms bound to boron atom B_1 are as far apart as possible from the 2 Cl atoms bound to boron atom $_2B$. In the solid state, however, crystal forces can induce a change in the conformation of a molecule. Thus, X-ray studies of *crystalline* B_2Cl_4 indicate that the conformation shown in Fig. 33-3(a), in which all 6 atoms lie in the same plane, characterizes the solid state.

A simple example of a complex ion which illustrates the various possible conformations is $[Ag(NH_3)_2]^+$. In this complex cation the N—Ag—N bonding is linear and *each* N atom (N_1 and $_2N$) is at the center of a tetrahedron with an H atom at each of 3 corners and the Ag atom at the fourth. In the complex $[H_3N—Ag—NH_3]^+$ there are several possible ways in which the 2 coordi-

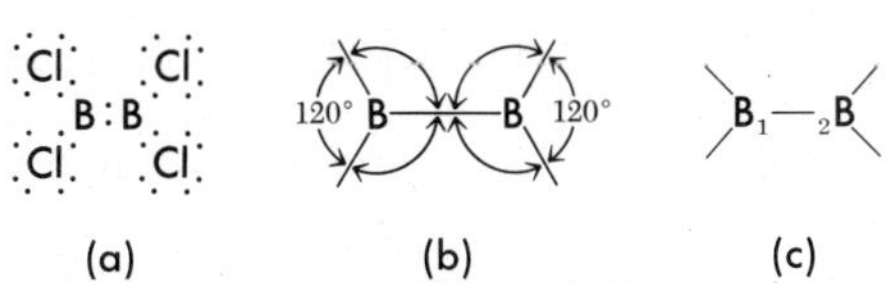

FIGURE 33-2 Electron-dot formula and the shape of the B_2Cl_4 molecule.

FIGURE 33-3 Two conformations of the B_2Cl_4 molecule.

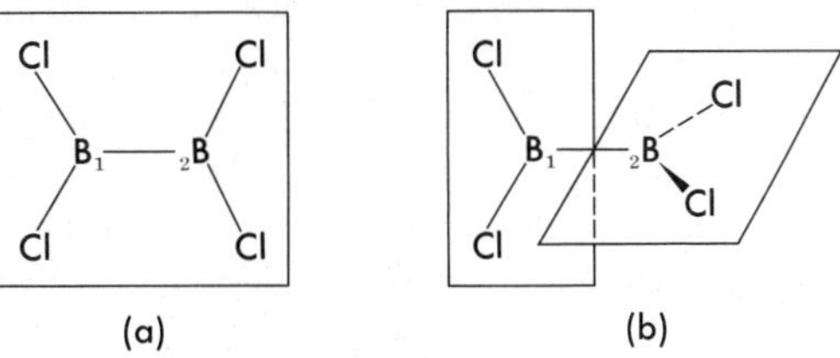

(a) (b) (c)

FIGURE 33-4 Conformations of the $[Ag(NH_3)_2]^+$ complex.

nate $—NH_3$ groups can be arranged with respect to one another while still retaining the tetrahedral arrangement around each N atom and the linear arrangement about the central Ag(I). If we label the 2 N atoms N_1 and $_2N$ for the purpose of this discussion, we can represent 2 of the possible conformations of this complex ion as shown in Fig. 33-4(a) and (b). In (a), group H_3N_1—(Ag) is staggered with respect to group (Ag)—$_2NH_3$ so that the H atoms of the H_3N_1— group occupy positions corresponding to empty spaces between 2 H atoms of the —$_2NH_3$ group. In this conformation, therefore, the H atoms belonging to the H_3N_1— group are as far apart as possible from the H atoms of the —$_2NH_3$ group, and mutual repulsion is at a minimum. The strongest mutual repulsions between the H atoms of the H_3N— groups occur when the H atoms of the 2 groups occupy positions opposite to one another, as illustrated in Fig. 33-4(b). Even in this conformation, however, the mutually repulsive forces are so very weak that there is virtually no interference among the H atoms. Consequently, each $—NH_3$ group is free to rotate independently around the N—Ag—N axis, and no definite isomers of $[H_3N—Ag—NH_3]^+$ have been discovered. Chemists usually describe this condition by saying that there is "free-rotation" of the $—NH_3$ groups around the N—Ag—N axis, as schematically represented in Fig. 33-4(c).

33-6 Ligands That Act Essentially as σ Donors

In Chapter 15 we defined a sigma (σ) bond between atom A and atom B as a covalent bond in which the electron density of the bond pair is concentrated along the A—B internuclear axis, and is cylindrically symmetrical about this axis (see diagram in margin). Ligands that coordinate to metal ions by donating a lone pair in a σ-type bond are called σ-donor ligands or σ-bonding ligands. The most common σ-donor ligands are: water, H_2O; ammonia, NH_3; a variety of organic amines, RNH_2; the halide ions, F^-, Cl^-, Br^-, and I^-; and the anions of oxoacids, such as nitrate, NO_3^- and carbonate, $CO_3^=$.

Electron density of AB σ bond

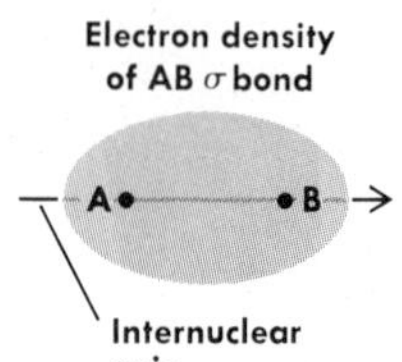

Ligands of the σ-donor type have two chief features in common: (1) *the donor atom has at least one lone pair available for donation to an acceptor* (the ligand is a Lewis base), and (2) *the valence shell orbitals of the donor atom are all occupied by electron pairs*—whether lone pairs or bond pairs. For example, the donor N atom of ammonia, $:NH_3$, has a lone pair (available for coordination) in the $n = 2$ shell. Also, all four $n = 2$ orbitals of the N atom (one $2s$ orbital and three $2p$ orbitals) are occupied by electron pairs (one lone pair; three N—H bond pairs). And in the H_2O molecule, the donor O atom has two available lone pairs, and all its four outer, $n = 2$ orbitals are occupied by these two lone pairs and by the two O—H bond pairs.

When a σ-donor ligand forms a coordinate bond to a metal ion, the electron pair which originally belonged solely to the ligand becomes shared with the metal ion. The metal ion then acquires a certain amount of negative charge, and the ligand an equal amount of positive charge (see Chapter 14, p. 276). Now, the negative charge acquired by the metal ion through coordination with the σ-bonding ligands will tend to neutralize, partially or completely, its original ionic charge. The central metal then approaches a state of effective "electroneutrality" which greatly increases the stability of the complex. If more ligands coordinate to the central metal, the metal will acquire an effective negative charge—and the stability of the complex will again decrease (for example, the central metal would be readily oxidizable). Other factors being favorable, therefore, a metal ion will tend to coordinate with just as many σ-donor ligands as are necessary to bring the metal close to a state of electroneutrality.

To summarize: The σ-donor ligands coordinate almost exclusively to a metal in its positive oxidation state; the central metal ion thus attains electroneutrality. The coordinate σ-bonds formed by monoatomic negatively charged ligands, e.g. F^-, $O^=$, have a marked ionic character; those of the neutral ligands (e.g., the N atom of NH_3) are to a large extent covalent.

AQUO COMPLEXES

As we have seen, metal ions exist in water in the hydrated form. These hydrated ions may be regarded as complex ions in which water molecules act as σ-donor ligands. The number of water molecules that can coordinate with a given metal ion to form a complex depends chiefly on the size and oxidation state of the metal ion. For most transition metal ions, this number is 6, e.g. $[Fe(H_2O)_6]^{+3}$, $[Cr(H_2O)_6]^{+3}$, $[Ni(H_2O)_6]^{++}$. For other metal ions, it is generally difficult to determine the exact coordination number of the aquo-complexes in solution. Still, there is some experimental evidence to indicate that often the preferred C.N. of the central metal ion in the aquo-complexes is equal to twice the oxidation number of the central metal ion. For example: $[Ag(H_2O)_2]^+$, $[Be(H_2O)_4]^{++}$, and $[Al(H_2O)_6]^{+3}$.

AMMINE COMPLEXES

Ammonia, NH_3, is another very common σ-donor ligand. Many transition metal ions and post-transition metal ions form complexes with ammonia in aqueous solution. The alkali-metal ions, and the alkaline-earth metal ions form ammine-complexes in the solid state but not in aqueous solution. For the ammine-complexes of the metal ions of the First Transition Series, as for the aquo-complexes, the C.N. is 6. For other metal ions, the C.N. varies from 2 (e.g., $[Ag(NH_3)_2]^+$) to 4 (e.g., $[Li(NH_3)_4]^+$, $[Pt(NH_3)_4]^{++}$), to 6 ($[Mg(NH_3)_6]^{++}$). The diagrams of Fig. 33-5 show the overlap of atomic orbitals involved in the formation of a $M \leftarrow NH_3$ coordinate bond in $[Pt(NH_3)_4]^{++}$, as well as a schematic representation of the actual electron cloud distribution of this bond.

Many ammine-complexes can be prepared simply by adding an ammonia solution to an aqueous solution of the hydrated metal ion:

$$[Ag(H_2O)_2]^+ + 2\ NH_3 \longrightarrow [Ag(NH_3)_2]^+ + 2\ H_2O$$

As this equation shows, the formation of the ammine-complex is actually a displacement reaction of water by ammonia. If the hydroxide of the metal ion is insoluble, the drop-by-drop addition of the ammonia solution to the solution of the hydrated metal ion may first produce a precipitate of the metal hydroxide. Then, as more ammonia is added, the metal hydroxide dissolves, forming the ammine complex ion in solution.

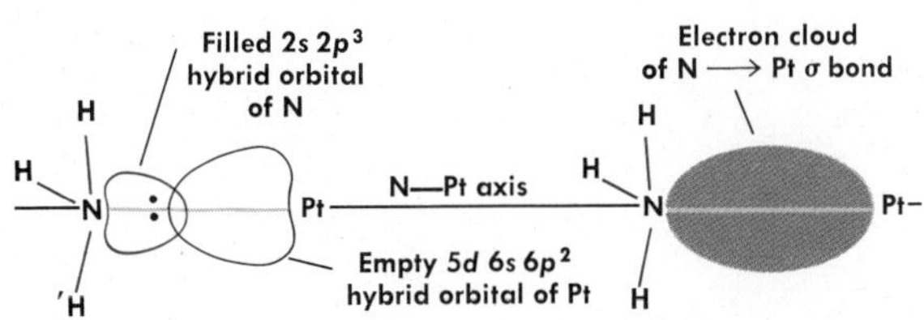

FIGURE 33-5 The $H_3N \rightarrow Pt$ σ bond in $[Pt(NH_3)_4]^{++}$.

33-7 Electron Configuration of the Central Metal in Complexes (Valence-Bond Approach)

In this section we shall apply to coordination compounds the concepts of hybridization of atomic orbitals that we studied in general in Chapter 15. We shall discuss which orbitals of the central atom or ion in the complex are occupied by the bonding electrons supplied by the donor atoms of the ligands, and which orbitals of the central atom or ion are occupied by the non-bonding electrons present in the central atom or ion before coordination. We shall see that, in some cases, when a metal atom or ion accepts one or more bond pairs to form a complex, the non-bonding electrons in its outer orbitals do not undergo a rearrangement, whereas in other cases they do. The resulting electron configuration of the central atom or ion is related to the stereochemistry that the complex assumes. In order to illustrate this point, we shall now consider some examples.

THE ARRANGEMENT OF ELECTRONS IN 3*d* AND 4*s* ORBITALS. First, let us review the distribution of electrons in the five 3*d* orbitals and in the one 4*s* orbital of the elements $_{25}Mn$ to $_{30}Zn$. The outer electron configuration of the $_{25}Mn$ (gaseous) atom is: $3d^5, 4s^2$. The two electrons in the completely filled 4*s* orbital are paired, but in the 3*d* orbitals the five electrons are unpaired, with parallel spins, and each electron occupies a separate orbital (see diagram in margin.) As usual, in this diagram each circle represents an orbital and each arrow represents an electron. (Recall that according to Hund's Rule, each orbital of a given sub-shell is first occupied by a single electron, and only after each of the degenerate orbitals has one electron does a second electron enter any orbital of that subshell.) In the $_{26}Fe$ (gaseous) atom, which has one more electron than $_{25}Mn$, the sixth 3*d* electron pairs up with another 3*d* electron to form an electron pair (see diagram in margin). Similarly, we can write the electron configurations for the (gaseous) atoms, M, and for the (gaseous) dipositive ions, M^{++}, of the other elements of the First Transition Series, as well as of the two following elements, copper and zinc (Table 33-3). Notice that the atoms of $_{24}Cr$ and $_{29}Cu$ have only one 4*s* electron; notice too that in the formation of all these dipositive ions the 4*s* electrons are lost from the atoms.

$_{25}Mn$
3*d* 4*s*
(↑)(↑)(↑)(↑)(↑) (↑↓)

$_{26}Fe$
3*d* 4*s*
(↑↓)(↑)(↑)(↑)(↑) (↑↓)

THE TETRAAMMINEZINC(II) ION, $[Zn(NH_3)_4]^{++}$

Let us first review the electron configuration and bonding in a complex, such as $[Zn(NH_3)_4]^{++}$, in which the central metal ion has a completely filled *d* subshell. The electron configurations of the (gaseous) Zn atom, of the (gaseous) Zn^{++} ion,

TABLE 33-3 OUTER ELECTRON CONFIGURATIONS OF SOME GASEOUS TRANSITION METAL ATOMS AND IONS

Atom, M			Ion, M^{++}		
	3*d*	4*s*		3*d*	4*s*
$_{24}Cr$:	(↑)(↑)(↑)(↑)(↑)	(↑)	Cr^{++}:	(↑)(↑)(↑)(↑)( )	( )
$_{25}Mn$:	(↑)(↑)(↑)(↑)(↑)	(↑↓)	Mn^{++}:	(↑)(↑)(↑)(↑)(↑)	( )
$_{26}Fe$:	(↑↓)(↑)(↑)(↑)(↑)	(↑↓)	Fe^{++}:	(↑↓)(↑)(↑)(↑)(↑)	( )
$_{27}Co$:	(↑↓)(↑↓)(↑)(↑)(↑)	(↑↓)	Co^{++}:	(↑↓)(↑↓)(↑)(↑)(↑)	( )
$_{28}Ni$:	(↑↓)(↑↓)(↑↓)(↑)(↑)	(↑↓)	Ni^{++}:	(↑↓)(↑↓)(↑↓)(↑)(↑)	( )
$_{29}Cu$:	(↑↓)(↑↓)(↑↓)(↑↓)(↑↓)	(↑)	Cu^{++}:	(↑↓)(↑↓)(↑↓)(↑↓)(↑)	( )
$_{30}Zn$:	(↑↓)(↑↓)(↑↓)(↑↓)(↑↓)	(↑↓)	Zn^{++}:	(↑↓)(↑↓)(↑↓)(↑↓)(↑↓)	( )

and of Zn(II) in the $[Zn(NH_3)_4]^{++}$ complex ion are shown in the diagram below.

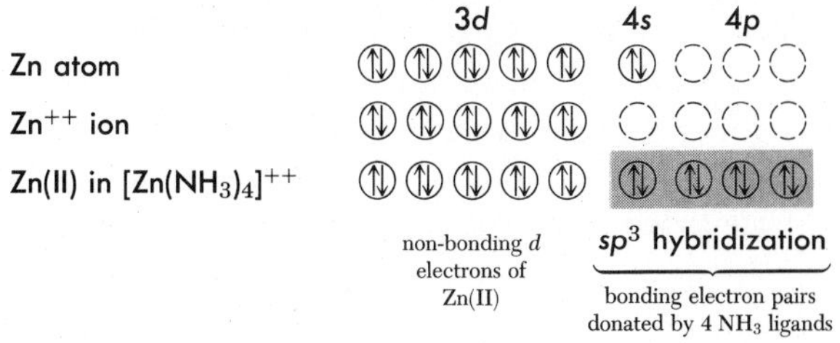

	3*d*	4*s*	4*p*
Zn atom	⇅ ⇅ ⇅ ⇅ ⇅	⇅	○ ○ ○
Zn^{++} ion	⇅ ⇅ ⇅ ⇅ ⇅	○	○ ○ ○
Zn(II) in $[Zn(NH_3)_4]^{++}$	⇅ ⇅ ⇅ ⇅ ⇅	⇅	⇅ ⇅ ⇅
	non-bonding *d* electrons of Zn(II)	sp^3 hybridization: bonding electron pairs donated by 4 NH_3 ligands	

When the Zn atom forms the Zn^{++} ion, the two 4*s* electrons are removed. Thus, the 4*s* orbital in the Zn^{++} ion becomes vacant. What happens to the vacant orbitals of the Zn^{++} ion when each of the nitrogen atoms of the four NH_3 molecules donates its lone electron pair to the Zn^{++} ion, forming the $[Zn(NH_3)_4]^{++}$ complex ion? These donated electron pairs occupy the one empty 4*s* orbital and the three empty 4*p* orbitals of the Zn^{++} ion. Since we know from experiments that the N atoms of the four NH_3 molecules are arranged tetrahedrally around the central Zn(II) atom, and that all four Zn—N bonds are identical, we say that the four outer orbitals of Zn(II)—the one 4*s* orbital and the three 4*p* orbitals—mix to yield *four* equivalent $4s\,4p^3$ hybrid orbitals. As we learned in Chapter 15, four equivalent sp^3 hybrid orbitals are arranged tetrahedrally around the central element, in agreement with the experimentally observed tetrahedral stereochemistry of the $[Zn(NH_3)_4]^{++}$ complex.

Each Zn—N bond of the complex ion $[Zn(NH_3)_4]^{++}$ is a *sigma* bond; each bond electron pair may be thought to occupy a hybrid $4s\,4p^3$ orbital of the central Zn(II) overlapping with a hybrid $2s\,2p^3$ orbital of the N atom of NH_3. Each N—H bond of the NH_3 ligand

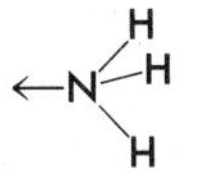

←N(H)(H)(H)

is also a *sigma* bond; the bond electron pair may be thought to occupy a hybrid $2s\,2p^3$ orbital of the N atom overlapping with a 1*s* orbital of the H atom. The accompanying figures show the overlapping of the orbitals involved in the formation of each Zn—N bond and each N—H bond in the complex ion $[Zn(NH_3)_4]^{++}$. Note that both the free (gaseous) Zn^{++} ion and Zn(II) in the $[Zn(NH_3)_4]^{++}$ complex ion have no unpaired electrons, and that there is no rearrangement of the $3d^{10}$ electrons when the complex is formed, because of the five 3*d* orbitals of Zn^{++} are completely filled.

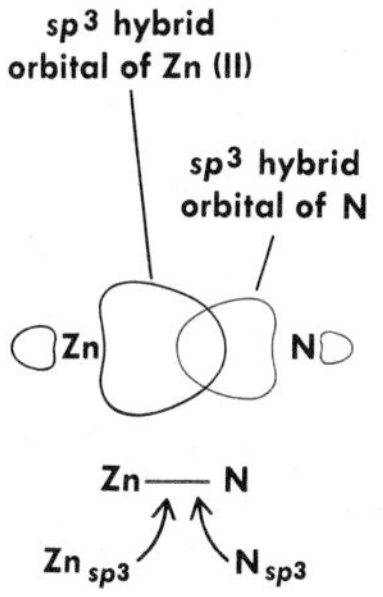

HIGH-SPIN AND LOW-SPIN COMPLEXES

Now let us consider some examples of complexes of transition metal ions, where the central metal ion does not have a complete d^{10} subshell and rearrangement of the electron distribution may or may not take place when a complex is formed.

DIAMAGNETIC AND PARAMAGNETIC SUBSTANCES. To help us find out what rearrangement of the electrons has taken place, if any, we determine by experiments the behavior of the complex in a magnetic field. Most substances when placed in a magnetic field are very slightly repelled—that is, slightly pushed out of the field. Substances that behave in this manner, called *diamagnetic, do not contain unpaired electrons.* Some substances, on the other hand, when placed in a magnetic field are pulled into it. If the attraction is proportional to the strength of the magnetic field, these substances are said to be paramagnetic. *Paramagnetic substances contain unpaired electrons.* From the extent to which a paramagnetic compound is attracted by a certain magnetic field (of constant field strength and at a constant temperature), we can calculate the number of unpaired electrons per formula weight of the compound.

THE TETRACHLORONICKELATE(II) ION, $[NiCl_4]^=$. Consider the $[NiCl_4]^=$ ion, which may be thought to result from the union of a Ni^{++} ion and 4 Cl^- ions. Experimental data show that the $[NiCl_4]^=$ ion has a regular tetrahedral stereochemistry and is paramagnetic, with two unpaired electrons per each Ni(II) ion. How can we interpret these facts in terms of our theories of electron configurations, hybridization, overlap of atomic orbitals, and coordinate bonding? The outer electron configurations of the gaseous Ni atom, of the gaseous Ni^{++} ion, and of Ni(II) as the central element of the tetrahedral $[NiCl_4]^=$ complex ion follow:

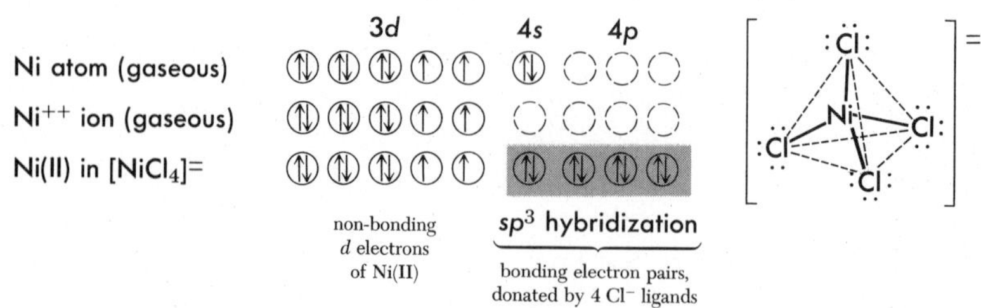

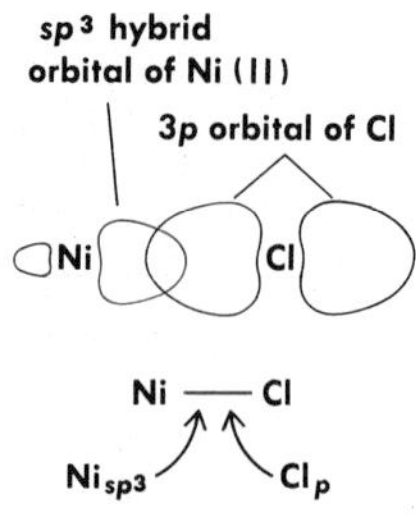

We see that both the gaseous Ni atom and the gaseous Ni^{++} ion have two unpaired electrons (in the latter the two 4*s* electrons were removed by the ionization, $Ni \longrightarrow Ni^{++} + 2\,e^-$). The Ni^{++} ion has available four empty low-energy orbitals —the one 4*s* and the three 4*p* orbitals—which can accept four electron pairs from four Cl^- ligands, thus forming the $[NiCl_4]^=$ complex. In the tetrahedral $[NiCl_4]^=$ complex, all four Cl ligands are equivalent and all four Ni—Cl bond distances are equal; thus we can say that the central Ni(II) forms bonds to the four Cl^- ions through four equivalent $4s\,4p^3$ (tetrahedral) hybrid orbitals. Each of these four $4s\,4p^3$ hybrid orbitals of Ni(II) overlaps with a 3*p* orbital of a Cl^- ligand, to form a Ni—Cl σ bond, as shown schematically in the diagram in the margin.

In the $[NiCl_4]^=$ complex, the central Ni(II) has the same number of unpaired electrons (two) as has the gaseous Ni^{++} ion, and we express this condition by saying that Ni(II) in $[NiCl_4]^=$ has a *high-spin configuration* or that $[NiCl_4]^=$ is a *high-spin complex.* In general, all complexes in which the central metal ion has the same number of unpaired electrons as the isolated gaseous ion are called high-spin complexes.

THE TETRACYANONICKELATE(II) COMPLEX, $[Ni(CN)_4]^=$. In the complex ion $[Ni(CN)_4]^=$, as we know from experiments, the Ni(II) ion is at the center and the four CN^- ligands are at the corners of a square, as shown below. Also, there are no unpaired electrons in $[Ni(CN)_4]^=$—the complex is diamagnetic. How can we explain the formation of the diamagnetic complex $[Ni(CN)_4]^=$ from the paramagnetic Ni^{++} ion and four diamagnetic CN^- ions? Consider the outer electron configuration of the (gaseous) Ni^{++} ion, shown below. If we promote one of the two unpaired 3*d* electrons of the Ni^{++} ion from one 3*d* orbital to the other 3*d* orbital containing a single electron, these two electrons pair up, and one empty 3*d* orbital becomes available. (Recall that two electrons paired up in the same orbital repel each other more strongly than two single electrons in two degenerate orbitals.) Hence, in order to pair up two electrons in the same orbital, we must supply energy to overcome the increase of electron-

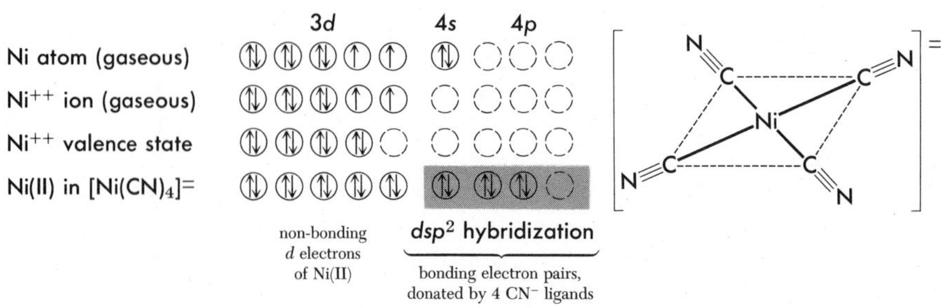

electron repulsion. This promoted Ni^{++} ion (valence state) has one vacant $3d$ orbital, so it is now possible for four lone pairs of four $:CN^-$ ligands to occupy four equivalent dsp^2 orbitals of Ni(II), resulting from the hybridization of the lowest-energy available orbitals—the $3d$, the $4s$, and two $4p$ orbitals.

As we saw in Chapter 15, p. 301, the four equivalent dsp^2 hybrid orbitals lie in a plane and form angles of 90° with one another—that is, they are directed from the center to the corners of a square. Hence this type of hybridization accounts for the square planar structure of $[Ni(CN)_4]^=$, as well as for the fact that this complex ion has no unpaired electrons (is diamagnetic), unlike the free (gaseous) Ni^{++} ion which has two unpaired electrons (is paramagentic). The central Ni(II) of the $[Ni(CN)_4]^=$ complex is said to have a *low-spin electron configuration,* and the $[Ni(CN)_4]^=$ complex is called a *low-spin complex.* In general, complexes in which the central metal ion has *fewer* unpaired electrons than the free (gaseous) ion are called *low-spin complexes.*

To have a complete picture of the bonding and electron distribution in the $[Ni(CN)_4]^=$ complex, we must also keep in mind that each CN^- ligand has the electron dot formula shown in the margin, and that the arrangement of each Ni—C≡N group is linear. This means that not only the central Ni(II) and the four C ligating atoms of the CN^- ligands lie in the same plane, but also the four N atoms, as shown in the above diagram. And each Ni—CN sigma bond may be thought to result from the overlap of a $3d\ 4s\ 4p^2$ hybrid orbital of Ni(II) and a $2s\ 2p$ hybrid orbital of the C atom of CN^-, as schematically shown in the diagram.

$[:C{\equiv}N:]^-$

3d 4s 4p² hybrid orbital of Ni

2s 2p hybrid orbital of C

Ni C≡N:

Ni — C≡N:

Ni_{dsp^2} C_{sp}

THE HEXAAMMINECOBALT(III) COMPLEX ION $[Co(NH_3)_6]^{+3}$. As another example of a low-spin complex, let us consider the ion $[Co(NH_3)_6]^{+3}$. This complex is experimentally found to be octahedral, with the Co(III) at the center, and each N atom of a coordinated NH_3 ligand at one of the six corners. Also, the $[Co(NH_3)_6]^{+3}$ ion is experimentally found to be diamagnetic (no unpaired electrons). How do we relate these facts to the electron configuration of the central Co(III) in this complex? Consider the outermost electron configuration of the gaseous Co^{+3} ion, shown below. Notice that one of the five $3d$ orbitals of the (gaseous) Co^{+3} ion is completely filled (two electrons) and that each of the other four $3d$ orbitals contains one unpaired electron. If two of these unpaired electrons are promoted to pair up with the other two unpaired electrons in two d orbitals, the resulting excited (valence) state of the Co^{+3} ion has three electron pairs in three $3d$ orbitals, and two vacant $3d$ orbitals. The six lone pairs of the N atoms of the six ammonia molecules $(:NH_3)$ can now occupy the six lowest-energy, unoccupied orbitals of the Co^{+3} ion in this excited (valence) state—the two empty $3d$ orbitals, the one $4s$ orbital, and the three $4p$ orbitals—all hybridized to form six equivalent $3d^2\ 4s^2\ 4p^3$ hybrid orbitals:

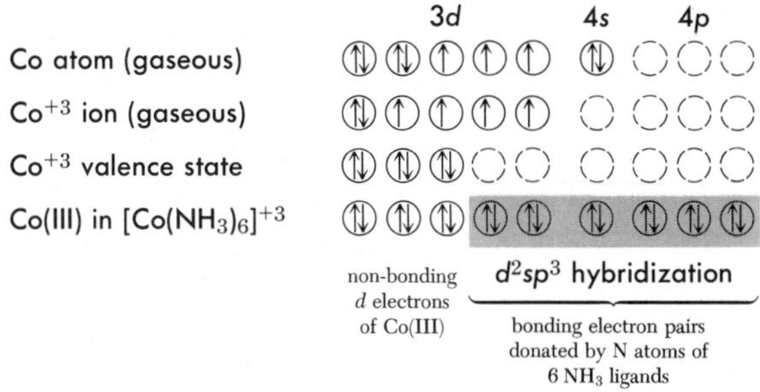

Each Co—N bond in $[Co(NH_3)_6]^{+3}$ is a *sigma* bond which results from the overlap of a hybrid $3d^2\ 4s\ 4p^3$ orbital of the central Co(III) with a hybrid $2s\ 2p^3$ orbital of the N atom of NH_3. And each N—H bond of each coordinated NH_3 molecule is a *sigma bond* resulting from the overlap of a hybrid $2s\ 2p^3$ orbital of the N atom and a $1s$ orbital of the H atom, just as we discussed previously for the $[Zn(NH_3)_4]^{++}$ complex.

33-8 Ligands That Act Both as σ-Donors and as π-Acceptors

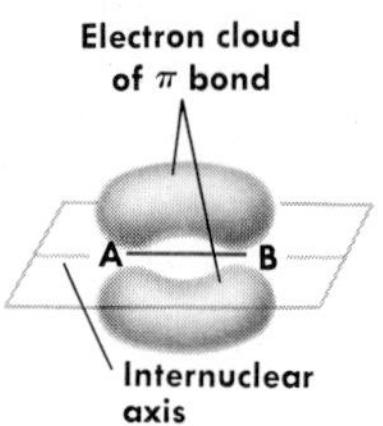

In Chapter 15 we defined a *pi* (π) bond between two atoms, A and B, as a covalent bond in which the electron density of the bond pair is concentrated in two equal regions, symmetrically situated above and below a plane containing the A—B internuclear axis (see accompanying diagram). And we have seen that when two atoms, A and B, form both a σ and a π bond—that is, a "double" bond—the strength of the A-to-B link is particularly high.

These general considerations hold, of course, also for coordination compounds. To visualize one of the most common examples of "double bonding" in complexes, let us consider the coordination compound $[Ni(PF_3)_4]$, composed of the ligand phosphorus trifluoride, $:PF_3$, with the central metal nickel in the zero oxidation state, Ni(0). Experiments show that $[Ni(PF_3)_4]$ has a tetrahedral stereochemisty about the central Ni(0); also, the complex is diamagnetic (no unpaired electrons). We can explain these properties on the basis of the electron configurations of the gaseous Ni atom, in the ground and valency states, and of Ni(0) in $[Ni(PF_3)_4]$:

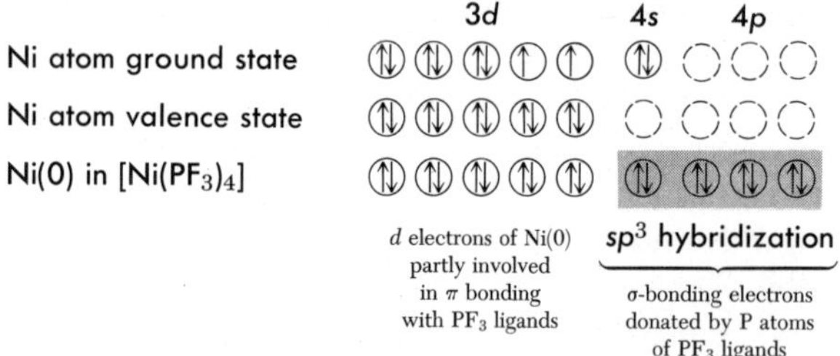

In the valence state of the Ni atom, the electron pair which in the ground state occupies the 4*s* orbital is promoted to two of the 3*d* orbitals so that the Ni atom now has available four low-energy orbitals—the 4*s* orbital and the three 4*p* orbitals. In the formation of the $[Ni(PF_3)_4]$ complex, each P atom of a PF_3 ligand donates an electron pair to the central nickel atom, Ni(0), giving rise to a σ coordinate bond: $Ni \leftarrow PF_3$ (P donor, Ni acceptor). These σ-bonding electron pairs donated by the ligands occupy the four equivalent sp^3 orbitals obtained from the hybridization of the 4*s* and 4*p* orbitals. Thus, the use of these hybrid orbitals of the central Ni(0) explains the tetra-

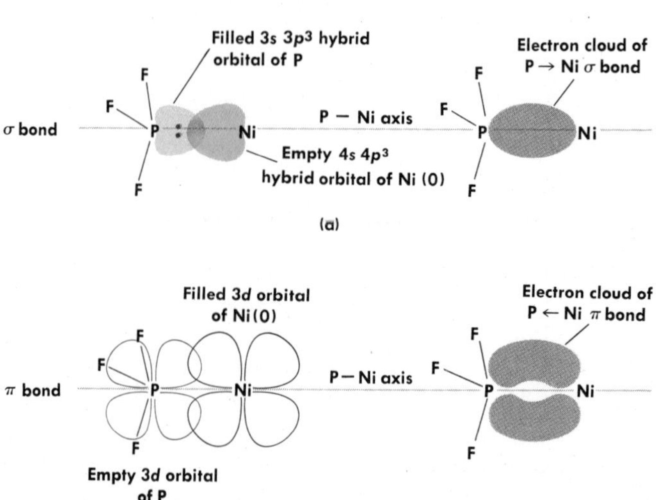

FIGURE 33-6 The σ bond and the π bond between PF_3 and Ni(O) in the $[Ni(PF_3)_4]$ complex.

hedral stereochemistry of the complex. Notice, also, that in the complex $[Ni(PF_3)_4]$ the central Ni(0) attains the electron configuration of the next noble gas, krypton, and has no unpaired electrons.

Now, as the above diagram shows, the central Ni(0) in $[Ni(PF_3)_4]$ has a filled 3*d* subshell; since the 3*d* orbitals are quite diffuse, it is possible for a filled 3*d* orbital of Ni to overlap with one of the vacant 3*d* orbitals of the P atom of the ligand PF_3. A $Ni \rightarrow PF_3$ coordinate bond results (Ni donor, P acceptor), in which the electron cloud has a π-type distribution. Figure 33-6 shows the overlap of the orbitals involved in the formation of the σ bond and of the π bond between Ni(0) and PF_3, as well as the shape of the resulting bond electron clouds. In the complex $[Ni(PF_3)_4]$, the central Ni(0) atom acts as an electron-pair acceptor (in the $Ni \leftarrow P$ σ bonds) and also as an electron-pair donor (in the $Ni \rightarrow P$ π bonds). The P atom of each PF_3 ligand, on the other hand, acts as an electron-pair donor in the $Ni \leftarrow P$ σ bond and as an electron-pair acceptor in the $Ni \rightarrow P$ π bond.

In general, the formation of a metal→ligand π bond can take place when the following requirements are satisfied. (1) The ligand must have available empty orbitals of suitable low energy and proper orientation—these are usually empty *p* or *d* orbitals of the same *n* quantum number as the valence electrons. For example, the P atom of PF_3 has available the five 3*d* orbitals, while the 3*s* and 3*p* orbitals are used for the lone pair and the three P—F bond pairs. The most common ligands that can act as both σ donors and π acceptors are the compounds of P(III) and As(III), the CN^- ion, and carbon monoxide, CO. (2) The central metal atom or ion must have filled *d* orbitals of the next-to-outermost shell; for example, the Ni(0) atom in its valence state has available five filled 3*d* orbitals. The metal atoms or ions which have the greatest tendency to act as π donors are therefore those with the greater number of *d* electrons —such as the transition metal atoms and ions at the end of the Transition Series (e.g., Co(0), Ni(0), Ni(II), Pt(0), and Pt(II)) and the post-transition metal ions of group IB (e.g., Cu(I) and Ag(I)). Of course, for each element, the tendency to act as a π donor increases as the oxidation number decreases; for example, Ni(0) has a greater π-bonding tendency than Ni(II).

When a metal M and a ligand L form a *double bond*—that is, a σ bond ($M \leftarrow L$) together with a π bond ($M \rightarrow L$)—the fraction of negative charge transferred from the ligand to the metal in the $M \leftarrow L$ σ bond can be partly or completely returned to the ligand through the $M \rightarrow L$ π bond. This effect, often called "back donation," explains why ligands that can act as π acceptors, such as PF_3, $P(CH_3)_3$, CN^-, and CO, can coordinate not only to positively charged metal ions, but also to metals in the zero oxidation state. Back donation, in fact, helps the originally neutral central metal of oxidation state zero to maintain a state of effective electroneutrality, and thus contributes to the stability of the complex.

COMPLEXES OF CARBON MONOXIDE. CARBONYLS

The two most important contributing electronic structures, I and II, of the carbon monoxide molecule, CO, are illustrated in Fig. 33-7(a). We see that the C atom of the CO molecule has a lone pair—and hence is a potential σ donor. In addition, in resonance structure II, the C atom of CO also has an empty low-energy 2*p* orbital, which can accept an electron pair from a suitable metal atom or ion in a π bond. Carbon monoxide, a gas virtually insoluble in water, does not have a tendency to form complexes with those metal ions that can act solely as electron-pair acceptors. For example, CO does not form complexes with the Be^{++} and Al^{+3} ions, nor with any other positively charged ion with a noble-gas electron configuration. But with the atoms of the transition metals (oxidation state = zero), carbon monoxide forms an important series of complexes called "carbonyls." In a carbonyl complex—for example the tetrahedral $[Ni(CO_4]$ (Fig. 33-7(b))—the C atom of the CO molecule donates its lone pair to the central metal, M, in a $M \leftarrow CO$, σ bond (Fig. 33-7(c)). In addition, a

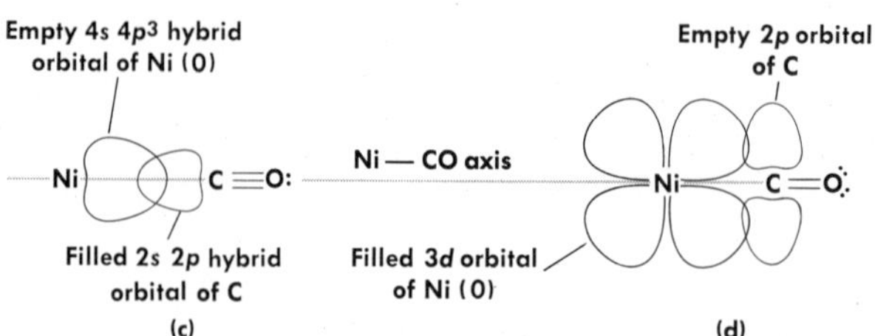

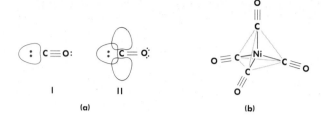

FIGURE 33-7 (a) Two resonance structures of CO. (b) Stereochemistry of $[Ni(CO)_4]$. (c) Atomic orbitals involved in the Ni←CO σ bond. (d) Atomic orbitals involved in the Ni→CO π bond.

filled d orbital of the transition metal extends over and overlaps with the empty p orbital of the C atom of CO, forming a M→CO π bond (Fig. 33-7(d)). The M←CO σ bond and the M→CO π bond mutually strengthen one another, as each bond serves to redistribute the total electron charge so that the metal atom remains in a state of effective electroneutrality.

The simplest known carbonyls of the elements of the First Transition Series follow:

Group V	Group VI	Group VII	Group VIII		
$[V(CO)_6]$	$[Cr(CO)_6]$	$[Mn_2(CO)_{10}]$	$[Fe(CO)_5]$	$[Co_2(CO)_8]$	$[Ni(CO)_4]$

The different formulas of these carbonyls may be logically explained on the basis that in these complexes the central metal atom tends to attain an electron configuration similar to that of the next noble gas, krypton. For example, the nickel atom $_{28}Ni$, $3d^8$, $4s^2$, has 8 electrons less than krypton, $_{36}Kr$, $3d^{10}$, $4s^2\,4p^6$, and it coordinates 4 CO molecules, each donating one electron pair. In the resulting carbonyl, $[Ni(CO)_4]$, the central Ni(0) has a krypton-like electron configuration $(28 + (4 \times 2) = 36$ electrons). Similarly, the iron atom, $_{26}Fe$, $3d^6$, $4s^2$, coordinates with 5 CO molecules to form $[Fe(CO)_5]$ $(26 + (5 \times 2) = 36$ electrons); and chromium, $_{24}Cr$, $3d^5$, $4s^1$, forms a carbonyl with 6 CO molecules, $[Cr(CO)_6]$ $(24 + (2 \times 6) = 36$ electrons). The atoms V, Mn, and Co, which have an odd number of electrons, cannot, however, attain the electron configuration of the next noble gas solely by coordination of CO molecules. For example, the manganese atom, $_{25}Mn$, $3d^5$, $4s^2$, would reach a total of 35 electrons (one less than krypton) if it coordinated only 5 CO molecules, and with 6 CO molecules it would have one electron more than krypton. What actually happens is that each Mn(0) atom coordinates with 5 CO molecules, and the two resulting $Mn(CO)_5$ entities pair up their single electrons in a co-

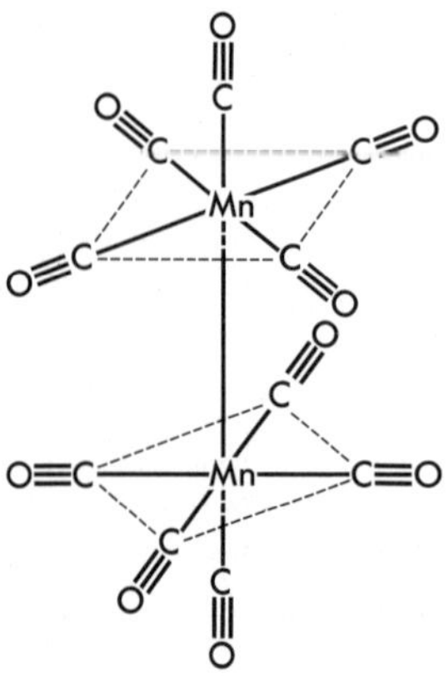

valent bond. The resulting Mn-carbonyl is a dimer, $[(CO)_5Mn—Mn(CO)_5]$, containing a metal-to-metal bond between the two Mn atoms. In a similar manner, Co(0) forms a carbonyl with a dimeric structure, $Co_2(CO)_8$, and a cobalt-to-cobalt (Co—Co) bond. On the other hand, vanadium(0) forms a monomeric carbonyl, $[V(CO)_6]$, with one unpaired electron, in which the central V(0) does not attain a krypton-like electron configuration.

33-9 Stability and Inertness of Coordination Compounds

Coordination compounds, like all other compounds, are stable under a specified set of conditions if their free energy of formation from the elements, $\Delta G^\circ_{\text{form}}$, is negative. Since the ligands themselves often are thermodynamically stable molecules or ions, it is generally convenient to use as the criterion of stability of a complex the free energy change of the reaction:

$$\text{Central Atom or Ion} + \text{Ligands} \longrightarrow \text{Complex}$$

For example, when metallic nickel, $Ni_{(s)}$, reacts with carbon monoxide gas, $CO_{(g)}$, at 1 atm and 25°C, to form liquid tetracarbonylnickel(0), $[Ni(CO)_4]_{(l)}$, we can represent the reaction by the equilibrium equation:

$$Ni_{(s)} + 4\,CO_{(g)} \rightleftharpoons [Ni(CO)_4]_{(l)}$$

For the forward reaction, $\Delta G = -5.4$ kcal/mole-eqn. Hence, $[Ni(CO)_4]$ at 25°C and 1 atm is thermodynamically stable with respect to dissociation into its components, Ni metal and CO gas.

In aqueous solution, the formation of a metal complex is essentially the replacement of the H_2O molecules coordinated to the metal ion in the aquo-complex, by molecules or ions of the ligand. For example, the formation of the hexaaminenickel(II) ion in aqueous solution is correctly represented by the equilibrium equation:

$$[Ni(H_2O)_6]^{++}{}_{(aq)} + 6\,NH_{3(aq)} \rightleftharpoons [Ni(NH_3)_6]^{++}{}_{(aq)} + 6\,H_2O_{(l)}$$

Since for the forward reaction $\Delta G^\circ = -11.7$ kcal/mole-eqn, the hexaamminenickel(II) complex, $[Ni(NH_3)_6]^{++}$, is stable in aqueous ammonia solution toward the replacement of coordinated NH_3 by H_2O molecules.

Often it is convenient to indicate the stability of complexes in aqueous solution relative to the replacement of coordinated ligands by H_2O molecules, by the value of the equilibrium constant of the reaction. As we have learned in Chapter 25, the equilibrium constant, K, of a reaction and its ΔG are related by the expression $\Delta G^\circ = -2.303\,RT \log K$. For the equilibrium of the hexaamminenickel(II) complex in aqueous solution, since the H_2O concentration is practically a constant (~55.5 moles/l.), and the "free" Ni^{++} ion is present as $[Ni(H_2O)_6]^{++}$, we can write simply:

$$Ni^{++} + 6\,NH_3 \rightleftharpoons [Ni(NH_3)_6]^{++} \qquad K = \frac{[[Ni(NH_3)_6]^{++}]}{[Ni^{++}] \times [NH_3]^6} = 4.1 \times 10^8\ (\text{mole/l.})^{-6}$$

This large value of K tells us that if we mix 1 mole of Ni^{++} with 6 moles of NH_3 in aqueous solution, almost all the Ni^{++} will react to form the $[Ni(NH_3)_6]^{++}$ complex ion. Conversely, if we dissolve in water the solid complex $[Ni(NH_3)_6]SO_4$, only a relatively small fraction of the complex cation $[Ni(NH_3)_6]^{++}$ will dissociate to give hydrated Ni^{++} and hydrated NH_3.

In general, the tendency of a complex $[ML_y]^{+n}$ to be formed in aqueous solution from the (hydrated) metal ion, M^{+n}, and the (hydrated) ligands, L, is expressed by the numerical value of the equilibrium constant, K, of the reaction:

$$M^{+n} + yL \rightleftharpoons [ML_y]^{+n} \qquad K = \frac{[[ML_y]^{+n}]}{[M^{+n}][L]^y}$$

TABLE 33-4 STABILITY CONSTANTS OF SOME COMPLEXES

Complex	Stability Constant
$[Ag(NH_3)_2]^+$	1.4×10^7
$[Ag(CN)_2]^-$	1.0×10^{21}
$[Fe(CN)_6]^{-4}$	1.0×10^{24}
$[Fe(CN)_6]^{-3}$	1.0×10^{31}
$[Co(NH_3)_6]^{+2}$	1.3×10^5
$[Co(NH_3)_6]^{+3}$	2.3×10^{34}
$[Co(CN)_6]^{-3}$	1.0×10^{64}
$[Co(en)_3]^{+2}$	9.1×10^{13}
$[Co(en)_3]^{+3}$	4.8×10^{48}

en = $H_2NCH_2CH_2NH_2$

The larger the value of K, the greater the tendency of the compound to form, and the smaller its tendency to dissociate—that is, the greater the stability of the complex. Hence, these equilibrium constants, K, are often called *stability constants*. Table 33-4 lists the values of the stability constants for a number of complexes. As these values show, the stabilities of different complexes of a *given* metal vary greatly depending on the oxidation state of the metal, the type of ligands, and, to a lesser extent, the presence of chelate rings.

CHEMICAL REACTIONS DEPENDENT ON STABILITY

The stability constant of a complex can help us understand why a given reaction can occur under a particular set of conditions. For example, the extent to which the $[Ag(NH_3)_2]^+$ ion dissociates in aqueous solution is one of the factors that determine whether an aqueous ammonia solution of a soluble Ag(I) salt can or cannot form a precipitate of silver chloride, AgCl, upon addition of (a) a neutral solution containing Cl^- ions (e.g., from NaCl) and (b) an acid solution containing Cl^- ions (e.g., from HCl). When a solution containing $[Ag(NH_3)_2]^+$ ions is mixed with a solution containing Cl^- ions, no precipitate of AgCl is formed. The reason is that the equilibrium

$$Ag^+_{(aq)} + 2\ NH_{3(aq)} \rightleftharpoons [Ag(NH_3)_2]^+_{(aq)} \qquad K = \frac{[[Ag(NH_3)_2]^+]}{[Ag^+][NH_3]^2} = 1.4 \times 10^7\ (\text{mole/l.})^{-2}$$

is greatly shifted to the right, and consequently the Ag^+ ion concentration is not high enough to exceed the solubility product of AgCl ($K_{sp} = [Ag^+] \times [Cl^-] = 2 \times 10^{-10}$ (mole/l.)^2). However, when H^+ ions are also added to the solution, AgCl precipitates. The reason is that the equilibrium

$$NH_{3(aq)} + H^+_{(aq)} \rightleftharpoons NH^+_{4(aq)} \qquad K = \frac{[NH_4^+]}{[NH_3][H^+]} = 7 \times 10^{11}\ (\text{mole/l.})^{-1}$$

is shifted to the right far more than the equilibrium for the $[Ag(NH_3)_2]^+$ complex. Thus, when H^+ ions are added, the NH_3 in equilibrium with $[Ag(NH_3)_2]^+$ is converted to NH_4^+ ions. The equilibrium $Ag^+ + 2\ NH_3 \rightleftharpoons [Ag(NH_3)_2]^+$ is then shifted to the left, and the Ag^+ ion concentration increases until the K_{sp} of AgCl is exceeded and AgCl precipitates. In other words, the addition of an acid (H^+) to an ammonia solution containing Ag^+ and Cl^- causes AgCl to precipitate because the complex $[NH_4^+]$ is about 10,000 times more stable towards dissociation than is the $[Ag(NH_3)_2]^+$ complex.

OXIDATION-REDUCTION POTENTIALS OF COMPLEXES

The oxidation-reduction behavior of a metal ion in a given oxidation state may be very different in different complexes. This is not surprising, since each complex is a different chemical compound, characterized by its own value of ΔG of formation. A striking example of the change in oxidation-reduction behavior for the same metal ion in different complexes is given by the $Hg_{(l)},Hg^{++}_{(aq)}$ and the $Hg_{(l)},[Hg(CN)_4]^=_{(aq)}$ couples:

$$Hg_{(l)} + 4\ CN^-_{(aq)} = [Hg(CN)_4]^=_{(aq)} + 2\ e^- \qquad E^\circ = +0.37\ \text{v}$$

$$Hg_{(l)} = Hg^{++}_{(aq)} + 2\ e^- \qquad E^\circ = -0.85\ \text{v}$$

Thus, the standard H_2,H^+ couple cannot oxidize metallic mercury, $Hg_{(l)}$, to hydrated mercury(II) ions, $Hg^{++}{}_{(aq)}$, but in the presence of CN^- ions it can oxidize metallic mercury, $Hg_{(l)}$, to the tetracyanomercurate(II) ion, $[Hg(CN)_4]^=$.

LABILE AND INERT COORDINATION COMPOUNDS

For coordination compounds, as for all compounds, the rates of reaction vary within very wide limits. A complex that reacts "rapidly" under a specified set of conditions is called *labile;* a complex that reacts "slowly" is called *inert. Labile* and *inert* are only relative terms and do not give us precise information about reaction rates. However, these terms are often used to describe qualitatively the kinetic behavior of complexes.

If a given complex is thermodynamically stable but kinetically labile, what happens to the complex when some "free" ligand is added to the solution? The "coordinated" ligands and the "free" ligands continuously exchange with one another within and without the coordination sphere of the complex. We can show that this exchange takes place by adding some labeled ligand (for example, a ligand containing a radioactive isotope), and then measuring how fast the radioactivity becomes distributed between the ligands within and without the coordination sphere. To give you some idea of the different rates at which ligands exchange, here are the approximate times required to reach equilibrium in the exchange of labeled water, H_2O^*, within some aquo-complexes: for $[Fe(H_2O)_6]^{++}$, *less* than 10^{-4} seconds; for $[Al(H_2O)_3]^{+3}$, about 1 second; and for $[Cr(H_2O)_6]^{+3}$, *more* than one week.

THE CHELATE EFFECT

In general, chelate ligands form more stable complexes than do monodentate ligands having the same donor atoms. Also, chelate complexes are less labile than the analogous complexes of monodentate ligands with respect to dissociation in water solution. For example, the stability constant of $[Ni(NH_3)_6]^{++}$ is 4.1×10^8 whereas that of $[Ni(H_2NCH_2CH_2NH_2)_3]^{++}$ is 2.5×10^{18}. And the rate at which one H_2O molecule replaces one monodentate NH_3 ligand within the coordination sphere of $[Ni(NH_3)_6]^{++}$ is about 20 times greater than the rate at which 2 H_2O molecules replace one bidentate $H_2NCH_2CH_2NH_2$ ligand of $[Ni(H_2NCH_2CH_2NH_2)_3]^{++}$.

Several factors contribute to the greater stability and inertness of chelate complexes. One is the increase in entropy that accompanies the formation of a complex containing chelate rings. As an illustration, consider the following reaction:

$$[Zn(NH_3)_4]^{++} + 2\ H_2NCH_2CH_2NH_2 \longrightarrow [Zn(H_2NCH_2CH_2NH_2)_2]^{++} + 4\ NH_3$$

$$\Delta H^\circ = +1.7\ \text{kcal/mole-eqn};\ \Delta S^\circ = +18.6\ \text{cal/deg} \times \text{mole-eqn};\ \Delta G^\circ = -3.8\ \text{kcal/mole-eqn}$$

The standard free energy change, ΔG°, of this reaction is favorable to the replacement of NH_3 with $NH_2CH_2CH_2NH_2$ within the coordination sphere of the Zn(II) ion, because the entropy of the system increases markedly in the reaction. And the entropy increases because when *one* bidentate ligand replaces *two* monodentate ligands in a complex, the number of particles in the system increases by one.

Another important factor in the chelate effect is the mechanism by which a ligand dissociates from the complex, to be replaced by the H_2O molecules. If the donor atom of a monodentate ligand is replaced by a H_2O molecule within the coordination sphere of a complex, the monodentate ligand will diffuse away from the complex and "be lost" within the very much larger number of H_2O (solvent) molecules. Thus, the probability is very small that the ligand may again encounter the complex from which it was originally detached and replace the H_2O molecule. On the other hand, when *one* of the two donor atoms of a bidentate ligand becomes momentarily replaced by a H_2O molecule, this "free" donor atom cannot move away (as long as the other donor atom is coordinated) and will remain in the vicinity of its original coordination position. Eventually, this donor atom will then replace the H_2O molecule within the coordination sphere of the metal, reforming the chelate ring, and the bidentate ligand as a whole does not "dissociate." A bidentate chelating ligand, in other words, will "dissociate" only when both donor atoms become detached from the metal at the same time, and the probability that this may occur is rather small. For example, in the $[Ni(H_2NCH_2CH_2NH_2)_3]^{++}$ complex ion one of the N donor atoms of $H_2NCH_2CH_2NH_2$ detaches itself from, and reattaches to, the central Ni(II) about 100 times—before finally both N donor atoms become detached and the entire $H_2HCH_2CH_2NH_2$ molecule leaves the complex, being replaced by two H_2O molecules.

Both the entropy effect and the favorable-mechanism effect become more and more important as the number of chelate rings formed by one molecule of a polydentate ligand increases. A good example is the polydentate chelating ligand ethylenediamine-tetraacetate ion, $(^{-}OOCCH_2)_2NCH_2CH_2N(CH_2COO^{-})_2$, which forms stable complexes with most metal ions, even those, such as the alkaline-earth ions, which generally show only a slight tendency to form complexes. The formula of the ethylenediamine-tetraacetate calcium(II) complex is shown schematically in the margin (only the donor atoms are shown explicitly). The ethylenediamine-tetraacetate ion and similar polydentate chelating ligands are called *sequestering agents,* because once a metal ion is coordinated to such a ligand, the probability that the metal ion may react with other ligands present in the surrounding solution (for example, the molecules of the solvent, water) is very small. The polydentate chelating ligand is, in fact, effectively "wrapped around" the metal ion and the probability that all donor atoms will be replaced by H_2O molecules at the same time is very small. So the metal ion cannot readily escape from the "flexible cage" provided by the sequestering ligand.

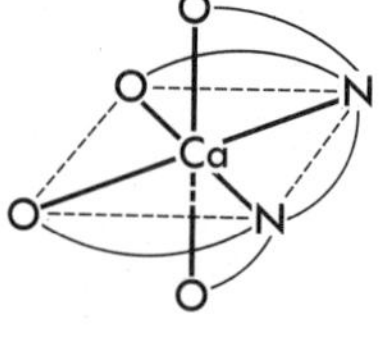

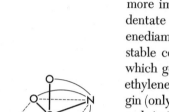

Exercises

33-1 Name the following complexes:
(a) $[Cd(NH_3)_4]^{++}$
(b) $[Cu(NH_3)_4]^{++}$
(c) $[Co(NH_3)_5Cl]^{++}$
(d) $[Ni(NH_3)_6]^{++}$
(e) $[Cr(NH_3)_5NO_2]^{++}$
(f) $[Co(NH_3)_3Cl_3]^0$
(g) $[Co(NH_3)_4CO_3]^+$
(h) $[Pd(NH_3)_2Cl_2]^0$
(i) $[CuCl_2(H_2O)_2]^0$
(j) $[FeF_6]^{-3}$
(k) $[Co(NO_2)_6]^{-3}$
(l) $[Ag(CN)_2]^-$
(m) $K_2[PtCl_4]$
(n) $Cu[Pt(NO_2)_4]$
(o) $Na_2[Zn(CN)_4]$
(p) $Ba_3[Fe(CN)_6]_2$
(q) $K_2[PtCl_6]$
(r) $[Zn(NH_3)_4]_3[PO_4]_2$
(s) $Ni_2[Fe(CN)_6]$
(t) $K_4[Ni(CN)_4]$
(u) $K_2[Ni(CN)_4]$

33-2 Write formulas for the following compounds:
(a) Bromopentaammine cobalt(III) phosphate
(b) Dinitrotetraamminechromium(III) sulfate
(c) Tetraamminegold(III) nitrate
(d) Potassium tetracyanozincate(II)
(e) Sodium tetrachloroaluminate(III)
(f) Trichlorotriamminecobalt(III)
(g) Hexaamminecobalt(III) dicyanoargentate(I)
(h) Tetracarbonylnickel(0).

33-3 Indicate the number of geometrical isomers possible for the following hypothetical compounds (M = central atom; a,b,c,d = ligands).
(a) Planar $[Ma_2b_2]$
(b) Planar $[Ma_2bc]$
(c) Planar [Mabcd]
(d) Tetrahedral $[Ma_2b_2]$
(e) Tetrahedral [Mabcd]
(f) Pyramidal $[Ma_2b]$
(g) Trigonal bipyramidal $[Ma_4b]$
(h) Trigonal bipyramidal $[Ma_3b_2]$
(i) Octahedral $[Ma_5b]$
(j) Octahedral $[Ma_4b_2]$
(k) Octahedral $[Ma_4bc]$
(l) Octahedral $[Ma_3bcd]$

33-4 Sketch the likely geometrical isomers for the following (M = central atom, a and b are monodentate ligands; $\widehat{aa}$ symmetrical bidentate chelate and $\widehat{ab}$, unsymmetrical bidentate chelate). (a) Planar complexes: (1) Ma_3b, (2) Ma_2b_2,

(3) Mab $\widehat{aa}$, (4) Mab $\widehat{ab}$, (5) M $\widehat{aa}$ $\widehat{ab}$. (b) Octahedral complexes, (1) Ma_4b_2, (2) Ma_4 $\widehat{ab}$, (3) M a_2 $(\widehat{aa})_2$ (4) Ma_2 $(\widehat{ab})_2$.

33-5 Write the electron configurations of $_{24}Cr$, $_{25}Mn$, $_{26}Fe$, $_{27}Co$, $_{28}Ni$, $_{29}Cu$, $_{30}Zn$. Using the system illustrated on p. 728, indicate the electronic distribution of the 3*d* and 4*s* electrons in (a) the atoms listed above, (b) the gaseous dipositive ions of these atoms, and (c) the known gaseous tripositive ions.

33-6 Give the shapes of the following molecules or ions and indicate the hybrid orbitals used by the central atom in bonding.

(a) $[NH_4]^+$	(d) $[Ag(CN)_2]^-$	(g) $[PCl_4]^+$
(b) $[PtCl_2(NH_3)_2]$	(e) $AsCl_3$	(h) $[PCl_6]^-$
(c) $[PtCl_2(NH_3)_4]^{++}$	(f) $[BH_4]^-$	(i) PCl_5

33-7 Indicate the number of unpaired electrons present in the *ground state* of the following atoms and ions (a) Ni^0, Ni^{++}; (b) Ag^0, Ag^+; (c) Pt^0, Pt^{++}; (d) Mn^0, Mn^{++}, Mn^{+3}; (e) Pd^0, Pd^{++}.

33-8 Indicate the number of unpaired electrons present in the following: (a) The valency state of Ni(O) to form the diamagnetic complex $Ni(CO)_4$. (b) The valency state of Co(III) to form the low-spin complex, $[Co(NH_3)_6]^{+3}$. (c) The valency state of Fe(III) to form the low-spin complex $[Fe(CN)_6]^{-3}$. (d) The valency state of Ni(II) to form the low-spin complex $[Ni(CN)_4]^{-2}$.

33-9 The complex ion $[Ag(NH_3)_2]^+$ contains no unpaired electrons. (a) In this $[Ag(NH_3)_2]^+$ complex ion each Ag—N bond consists of the overlap of the ______ hybrid orbitals of Ag(I) and the ______ hybrid orbitals of the N (atom of the NH_3 ligand). (b) Each N—H bond consists of the overlap of ______ hybrid orbitals of N and ______ orbital of H (of the NH_3 ligand).

33-10 The complex $[PdCl_4]^{-2}$ has no unpaired electrons. Each Pd—Cl bond consists of (the overlap of the) ______ hybrid orbitals of Pd(II) and the ______ orbital of the Cl ligand.

33-11 Classify the following complexes as low spin or high spin (a) $[Ni(CN)_4]^{-2}$ (no unpaired electrons), (b) $[Co(NH_3)_6]^{+2}$ (5 unpaired electrons), (c) $[Cu(NH_3)_2]^+$ (no unpaired electrons), (d) $[Mn(CN)_6]^{-4}$ (1 unpaired electron), (e) $[Mn(CN)_6]^{-3}$ (2 unpaired electrons), (f) $[Fe(dipyridyl)_3]^{2+}$ (no unpaired electrons), (g) $[CoCl_4]^{-2}$ (3 unpaired electrons), (h) $[CoF_6]^{-2}$ (3 unpaired electrons).

33-12 The complex ion $[Pt(NH_3)_4]^{+2}$ has no unpaired electrons. (a) Write its Lewis electron dot formula. (b) Using circles to represent orbitals and arrows for electrons, show the *outer* electrons of (1) Pt atom in ground state (2) Pt^{+2} ion in the ground state (3) Pt(II) in promoted state to form the diamagnetic complex $[Pt(NH_3)_4]^{+2}$ (4) Give the hybridization of the central Pt(II). (5) Each Pt—N bond consists of the (overlap of the) ______ hybrid orbitals of Pt(II) and the ______ hybrid orbital of the N (atom of the NH_3 ligand). (6) Each N—H bond of the NH_3 ligand in the complex) consists of the (overlap of) the ______ hybrid orbitals of the N atom and an ______ orbital of H. (7) The (approximate) N—Pt—N bond angle is ______. (8) The (approximate) H—N—H bond angle is ______. (9) The Pt(II) is at the center of a ______ (figure or shape). (10) Each N atom is at the center of a ______ (figure or shape).

33-13 $[Ni(NH_3)_6]^{+2} + 3\,en \rightleftharpoons [Ni(en)_3]^{+2} + 6\,NH_3$. $\Delta H^\circ = -6.0$ kcal/mole-eqn; $\Delta G^\circ = -13.2$ kcal/mole-eqn: (a) Calculate the ΔS° of this reaction, explaining the meaning of its sign. (b) Compare the contribution of ΔH° and $T\,\Delta S^\circ$ to the spontaneity of this reaction.

THE TRANSITION METALS

34

As we found in our discussion of the electron configurations of the elements, the 8 elements from Scandium, $_{21}Sc$ (Group IIIA), through nickel, $_{28}Ni$ (Group VIII), have a progressively greater number of electrons in the inner 3*d* sub-shell; these are called *transition elements* and constitute the *First Transition Series,* or 3*d* Transition Series. Note that these elements have an incomplete 3*d* sub-shell.

IIIA	IVA	VA	VIA	VIIA	VIII		
Sc	Ti	V	Cr	Mn	Fe	Co	Ni
Y	Zr	Nb	Mo	Tc	Ru	Rh	Pd
La-Lu	Hf	Ta	W	Re	Os	Ir	Pt

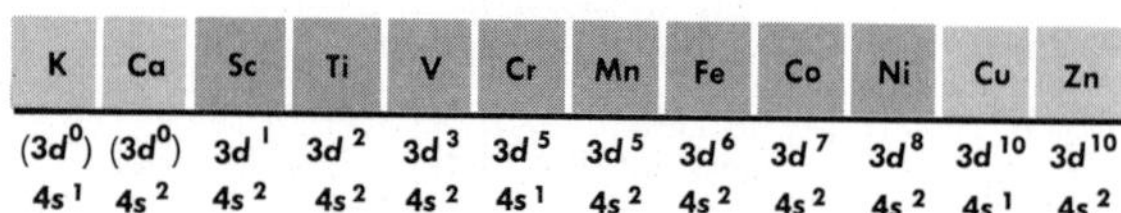

K Ca Sc Ti V Cr Mn Fe Co Ni Cu Zn
$(3d^0)$ $(3d^0)$ $3d^1$ $3d^2$ $3d^3$ $3d^5$ $3d^5$ $3d^6$ $3d^7$ $3d^8$ $3d^{10}$ $3d^{10}$
$4s^1$ $4s^2$ $4s^2$ $4s^2$ $4s^2$ $4s^1$ $4s^2$ $4s^2$ $4s^2$ $4s^2$ $4s^1$ $4s^2$

In two other series of elements, the additional electrons enter the 4*d* and 5*d* orbitals, respectively. The *Second Transition Series* includes the 8 elements from yttrium, $_{39}Y$, through palladium $_{46}Pd$; the *Third Transition Series* begins with lanthanum, $_{57}La$, runs through the next 14 elements (the rare earth elements), and continues with the next 7 elements, ending with platinum, $_{78}Pt$. In this chapter we shall consider only the elements of the First Transition Series, but we shall look at them in some detail.

34-1 Physical Properties of the First Transition Series

At ordinary conditions, all transition elements are solid metals, generally of a white or light-grey color, which can be polished to a beautiful shine. Many transition elements occur in more than one crystal form; iron, Fe, for example, can exist either in a cubic close-packed or in a body-centered cubic form, depending on the thermal conditions to which it has been submitted during its crystallization and on the presence of traces of impurities. The transition metals are generally hard, malleable, and ductile, with excellent mechanical properties. For these reasons, they find extensive applications in many areas of technology.

As the data in Table 34-1 show for the First Transition Series, the transition elements have relatively high densities, very high melting and boiling points, and very high heats of atomization. These properties indicate that the atoms of these elements are held together by very strong metallic bonds, which persist even in the molten state. As we have seen in earlier discussions, the strength of the bonding between the atoms of metals depends on the interaction between the electrons in their outermost shell. If the valence shell is half-filled or less, the valence electrons are available for bonding, and the greater the number of valence electrons available, the stronger is the resulting bonding. Also, electrons in *d* orbitals form stronger metallic bonds than electrons in *s* or *p* orbitals because, as we learned in Chapter 11, they are more diffuse, and hence can give rise to a more effective overlap. The atoms of the transition elements have *three or more electrons* available for interaction, and at least one of these electrons is a *d* electron; consequently, the interatomic bonding is very strong.

K	Ca	Sc	Ti	V	Cr	Mn	Fe	Co	Ni	Cu	Zn

It is instructive to compare the electronic structure and physical properties of potassium, K, and calcium, Ca, which precede the 3*d* Transition Series, with the structure and properties of the transition elements. An atom of potassium, $_{19}K$, has one outer 4*s* electron, $4s^1$, and an atom of calcium, $_{20}Ca$, has two outer 4*s* electrons, $4s^2$; neither atom has any 3*d* electrons. Each atom of a transition element, however, from $_{21}Sc$ to $_{28}Ni$, contains two 4*s* electrons, $4s^2$ (except for Cr, which has only one, $4s^1$), and one or more 3*d* electrons. It is the presence of both the *d* electrons and of one or more unfilled *d* orbital(s) that, to some extent, gives rise to the stronger interatomic

TABLE 34-1 SOME PHYSICAL PROPERTIES OF THE ELEMENTS OF THE FIRST TRANSITION SERIES

Element	$_{21}Sc$	$_{22}Ti$	$_{23}V$	$_{24}Cr$	$_{25}Mn$	$_{26}Fe$	$_{27}Co$	$_{28}Ni$
Atomic Weight	44.96	47.90	50.94	52.00	54.94	55.85	58.93	58.71
Outer Electron Config.	$3d^1\ 4s^2$	$3d^2\ 4s^2$	$3d^3\ 4s^2$	$3d^5\ 4s^1$	$3d^5\ 4s^2$	$3d^6\ 4s^2$	$3d^7\ 4s^2$	$3d^8\ 4s^2$
Atomic Radius, A*	1.64	1.47	1.35	1.29	1.37	1.26	1.25	1.25
Density at 20°C, g/cm^3	3.0	4.51	6.1	7.19	7.43	7.86	8.90	8.90
Melting Point, °C	1,540	1,670	1,900	1,870	1,250	1,540	1,490	1,450
Boiling Point, °C	2,730	3,260	3,450	2,660	2,150	3,000	2,900	2,730
$\Delta H_{atomiz.}$ (kcal/mole)	91.0	112.5	122.8	94.8	67.0	99.7	101.6	102.8

* Metallic radius for 12-coordination.

bond of the transition metals and, consequently, to their higher density and higher melting points as compared with the non-transition metals, potassium and calcium.

Table 34-1 shows that the density virtually triples in passing from the first element of the 3*d* Transition Series (Sc, 3.0 g/cm^3) to the last (Ni, 8.9 g/cm^3). Also, the metallic radii of these elements decrease slightly along the Transition Series, because the effective nuclear charge felt by the added 3*d* electrons increases from $_{21}$Sc to $_{28}$Ni. This relationship also holds for the elements of each of the other two Transition Series.

IONIZATION ENERGIES

Since the electron configurations of successive elements of the First Transition Series differ only by one electron in the 3*d* orbital, there are only slight differences in the ionization energies of adjacent elements, differences which are not nearly so marked as those between successive elements in a non-transition series. Along the First Transition Series from Sc to Ni, there is a slight increase in ionization energy, which corresponds to a slight decrease in atomic size and slight increase in effective nuclear charge. The energy required for the formation of the dipositive ions, M^{++}, and of the tripositive ions, M^{+3}, for the elements of this series are listed in Table 34-2. For comparison, this table also lists the values for calcium, $_{20}$Ca, the element immediately preceding the series, and for copper, $_{29}$Cu, and zinc, $_{30}$Zn, which follow. Notice that Cr and Cu both diverge from the pattern of gradually increasing values of the ionization energy for $M \longrightarrow M^{++} + 2\,e^-$. The ionization energies of Cr and Cu are abnormally high probably because the half filled *d* shell (d^5) of Cr and the completely filled *d* shell (d^{10}) of Cu are particularly stable and resist breaking up.

COLOR

As a general rule the transition elements form colored compounds, a characteristic that is associated with the incompletely filled *d* orbitals of the ions of these elements. The following considerations explain why most compounds of the transition-metal ions are colored, while almost all compounds of metal ions with a noble gas-like electron configuration are colorless.

LIGHT ABSORPTION AND COLOR. An electromagnetic radiation (such as radiowave, light, and X-ray) can be characterized by its particular wavelength, *lambda*, λ (measured in cm or A), or by its wavenumber, *nu*, ν (the reciprocal of the wavelength, $\nu = 1/\lambda$, commonly expressed in reciprocal centimeters, 1/cm, or cm^{-1}). Each unit of radiation (a photon) corresponds to a *quantum* of radiant energy, *E*,

TABLE 34-2 IONIZATION ENERGIES, IONIC RADII, AND HEATS OF HYDRATION OF THE IONS OF THE FIRST TRANSITION SERIES

		Ca	Sc	Ti	V	Cr	Mn	Fe	Co	Ni	Cu	Zn
Outer Electron Config.		$4s^2$	$3d^1 4s^2$	$3d^2 4s^2$	$3d\, 4s^2$	$3d^5 4s^1$	$3d^5 4s^2$	$3d^6 4s^2$	$3d^7 4s^2$	$3d^8 4s^2$	$3d^{10} 4s^1$	$3d^{10} 4s^2$
Ioniz. Energy for $M \longrightarrow M^{++} + 2\,e^-$ (kcal/mole)		+415	+446	+470	+493	+536	+532	+554	+574	+594	+646	+631
Ioniz. Energy for $M \longrightarrow M^{+3} + 3\,e^-$ (kcal/mole)		+1590	+1018	+1107	+1104	+1274	+1316	+1246	+1359	+1424	+1521	+1553
Ionic Radius, A*	M^{++}	0.99	—	0.80	0.73	—	0.90	0.85	0.80	0.76	0.69	0.74
	M^{+3}	—	0.69	0.63	0.62	0.62	0.63	0.63	0.56	—	—	—
ΔH_{hydr} (kcal/mole)	M^{++}	−395	—	−453	−464	−468	−454	−480	−497	−516	−516	−503
	M^{+3}	—	−904	−984	−1010	−1062	−1055	−1027	−1083	—	—	—

* The ionic radii are calculated from the M-O internuclear distances in the oxides MO for the M^{+2} ions, and in the mixed oxides $LaMO_3$ for the M^{+3} ion.

which is directly proportional to the wavenumber, ν. Since chemical calculations are founded on a mole basis, in studying the relationship between radiant energy and chemical processes it is convenient to express radiant energy in kcal/mole of photons. We can do so according to this simple relationship: the radiant energy in 1 mole of photons, with $\nu = 350\ \text{cm}^{-1}$, is equal to 1 kcal. (For the derivation of this relationship see Appendix 34-1). Thus, we can obtain the energy (expressed in kcal/mole) for photons of a given wavenumber simply by multiplying the value of ν expressed in cm^{-1} by the conversion factor $\dfrac{1\ \text{kcal/mole of photons}}{350\ \text{cm}^{-1}}$. For example, the energy of light photons with $\nu = 20{,}000\ \text{cm}^{-1}$ is:

$$\text{energy} = 20{,}000\ \cancel{\text{cm}^{-1}} \times \frac{1\ \text{kcal/mole of photons}}{350\ \cancel{\text{cm}^{-1}}} = 57.1\ \text{kcal/mole of photons}$$

And the energy of a single photon of $\nu = 20{,}000\ \text{cm}^{-1}$ is:

$$\text{energy of 1 photon} = \frac{57.1\ \text{kcal}/\cancel{\text{mole of photons}}}{6.02 \times 10^{23}\ \text{photons}/\cancel{\text{mole of photons}}} = 9.48 \times 10^{-23}\ \text{kcal/photon}$$

The wavenumber, and hence the energy, of electromagnetic radiations varies within an extremely wide range—$\nu = 10^{14}\ \text{cm}^{-1}$ for the γ-rays emitted in nuclear reactions to $\nu = 10^{-6}\ \text{cm}^{-1}$ for radiowaves. In between these two extremes, there is a continuum of radiations of intermediate wavenumbers. The human eye is sensitive only to light photons in a relatively narrow region of wavenumbers—the "visible region," which extends approximately from $27{,}000\ \text{cm}^{-1}$ to $13{,}500\ \text{cm}^{-1}$. What we commonly call "white light" is a combination of all the radiations of the visible region, each with the same relative intensity. When white light is refracted through a prism, a "spectrum" is obtained which appears to the eye as a smoothly blended sequence of colors, each color corresponding approximately to a certain interval of wavenumbers, as shown in Fig. 34-1.

In general, when white light encounters a substance, part of the light is absorbed and part is transmitted (if the substance is transparent) or part is reflected (if the substance is opaque). If only a small fraction of the incident white light is absorbed and if all the photons of the visible spectrum are equally absorbed, the compound looks "white" or, more appropriately, "colorless." (A substance that absorbs *all* of the in-

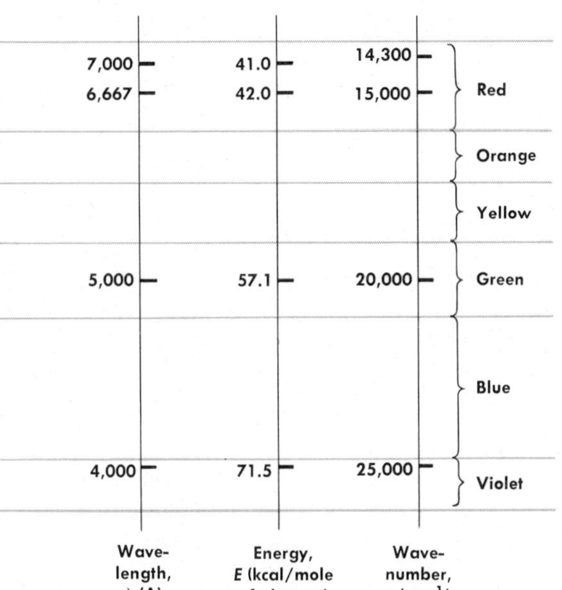

FIGURE 34-1 **Colors corresponding approximately to the various regions of the visible spectrum.**

cident light would of course appear "black.") On the other hand, a substance may absorb preferentially the light photons of one (or more) region(s) of the visible spectrum, so that the transmitted light or the reflected light is relatively richer in the radiations of the remaining regions. The combined effect of these remaining radiations is perceived as a particular color. For example, a substance that, when exposed to white light, absorbs almost all photons in the entire yellow-to-violet region (say from 17,000 to 27,000 cm^{-1}) will "appear red," because only the radiations in the red region of the spectrum (13,500 to about 17,000 cm^{-1}; see Fig. 34-1), which are not absorbed, remain to be perceived. As another example, assume that white light shines on a substance which absorbs the photons in the red-to-yellow region of the spectrum (13,500 to 19,000 cm^{-1}) as well as those in the blue-violet region (21,000 to 27,000 cm^{-1}). The light transmitted or reflected by this substance, lacking the radiations that have been absorbed, will consist chiefly of the remaining radiations of the visible spectrum, those between 19,000 cm^{-1} and 27,000 cm^{-1}—which constitute green light (see Fig. 34-1). The viewer then perceives the substance as having a green color. Similarly, a substance that "appears yellow" absorbs photons of both the green-to-violet region (from 19,000 cm^{-1} to 27,000 cm^{-1}) and the red region (from 13,500 to 16,000 cm^{-1}) of the visible spectrum. However, the color of a substance does not always tell us directly, even if approximately, what photons of the visible light the substance absorbs. For example, a substance that absorbs from white light all photons except those of the violet region (25,000 to 27,000 cm^{-1}) looks violet, but so does another substance that absorbs the photons of the orange-to-green region (16,000 to 21,000 cm^{-1}), reflecting the blue-violet radiations (21,000 to 27,000 cm^{-1}) as well as the red radiations (13,500 to 16,000 cm^{-1}). This is so because a blend of blue and red radiations is perceived as a violet color, just as violet radiations themselves are. Therefore the color of a substance does not necessarily tell us which regions of the visible spectrum are absorbed. However, the *absorption spectrum* of a substance, obtained with an instrument called a spectrophotometer, does tell us exactly which radiations are absorbed and also the relative amounts of each radiation.

Since light is energy, absorption of light is absorption of energy; so it is reasonable to assume that, if a substance absorbs light, the corresponding absorbed energy may be used to promote the atoms, ions, or molecules of the substance from their ground state to an excited state. For example, an atom, ion, or molecule which absorbs a photon of a given wavenumber takes on a *quantum* of energy that may serve to promote one electron from a lower energy orbital to an available higher-energy orbital. In general, different electronic transitions involve the absorption of different *quanta* of energy, and if the *quanta* absorbed are in the energy range of visible light, the electronic transitions may be observed visually as "different colors." As an illustration, let us consider a salt of a non-transition metal—for example, an alkaline-earth metal salt such as calcium perchlorate, $Ca(ClO_4)_2$. An aqueous solution of $Ca(ClO_4)_2$ contains hydrated Ca(II) ions, $Ca^{++}{}_{(aq)}$ or $[Ca(H_2O)_6]^{++}$, and hydrated ClO_4^- ions. For the Ca^{++} ion, which has an argon-like electron configuration ($3s^2\,3p^6$), the energy difference between a $3p$ orbital of the filled $3p$ sub-shell and the next available orbital, $4s$, is very large—685.8 kcal/mole of Ca^{++} ions. To undergo the electronic transition $3s^2\,3p^6$ (ground state) $\longrightarrow$ $3s^2\,3p^5\,4s^1$ (excited state), 1 mole of Ca^{++} ions must absorb exactly this quantity of energy, 685.8 kcal. This energy corresponds to 1 mole of photons with $\nu = 685.8\ \cancel{\text{kcal/mole}} \times 350\ \text{cm}^{-1}/\cancel{\text{kcal/mole}} = 240{,}000\ \text{cm}^{-1}$. (Thus, for this electronic transition to take place, each Ca^{++} ion must absorb a photon with wavenumber $= 240{,}000\ cm^{-1}$.) This wavenumber is outside the range of visible light (27,000 to 13,500 cm^{-1}), and in fact none of the photons of visible light has sufficient energy to promote the Ca^{++} ion to even this lowest of its possible excited electronic states. In other words, $Ca^{++}{}_{(aq)}$ does not absorb any photons of visible light, and hence it appears colorless. The $ClO^-_{4(aq)}$ ion is also colorless, because it does not absorb any photons of the visible light; in fact, the ClO_4^- ion absorbs photons which have frequencies either higher or lower than that of visible light.

Now let us consider an aqueous solution of titanium(III) perchlorate, in which the transition-metal ion, Ti^{+3}, is present as an octahedral complex, $[Ti(H_2O)_6]^{+3}$. A solution containing $[Ti(H_2O)_6]^{+3}$ and $ClO^-_{4(aq)}$ has a violet color; a spectrophotometer reveals that the solution absorbs the photons of the green region of the visible spectrum, between 19,000 and 21,000 cm^{-1} (the absorption is most intense at 20,300 cm^{-1}). Since both water and the ClO_4^- ion are colorless, it must be the $Ti^{+3}{}_{(aq)}$ ion which absorbs this part of the visible light. What does this mean in terms of the possible electronic transitions of the Ti^{+3} ion from its ground state to an excited state? The Ti^{+3} ion has the electron configuration $3s^2\,3p^6\,3d^1$. An electronic transition such as $3s^2\,3p^6\,3d^1$ (ground state) $\longrightarrow$ $3s^2\,3p^6\,4s^1$ (excited state) would require about 229 kcal/mole of Ti^{+3} ions. By using the conversion factor given above, we can calculate what photons are necessary to bring about this transition: $\nu = 229\,(\cancel{\text{kcal/mole}}) \times 350\,(\text{cm}^{-1}/\cancel{\text{kcal/mole}}) = 80{,}000\ \text{cm}^{-1}$. Again, this value of ν is beyond the upper limit of visible light. What kind of electronic excitation can then be responsible for the observed absorption at about 20,300 cm^{-1}? As we learned in Chapter 11, all five $3d$ orbitals have the same energy in the isolated gaseous Ti^{+3} ion. But, as soon as the Ti^{+3} ion becomes part of a compound, the set of five degenerate $3d$ orbitals splits into two (or more) sets of different energies. For the octahedral $[Ti(H_2O)_6]^{+3}$ ion, the splitting of the $3d$ orbitals can be represented as follows:

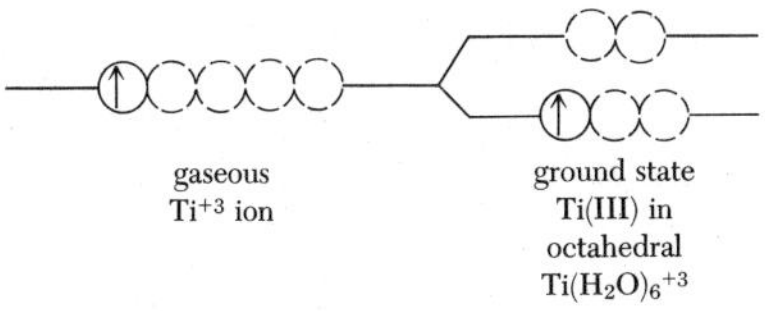

gaseous Ti^{+3} ion — ground state Ti(III) in octahedral $Ti(H_2O)_6^{+3}$

In the ground state of the octahedral $[Ti(H_2O)_6]^{+3}$, the one d electron of Ti(III) will of course occupy one of the d orbitals of lower energy, so we have the configuration shown above. Now we see that it is possible for the Ti(III) in $[Ti(H_2O)_6]^{+3}$ to absorb a quantity of energy just sufficient to promote its $3d$ electron from a lower-energy to a higher-energy $3d$ orbital.

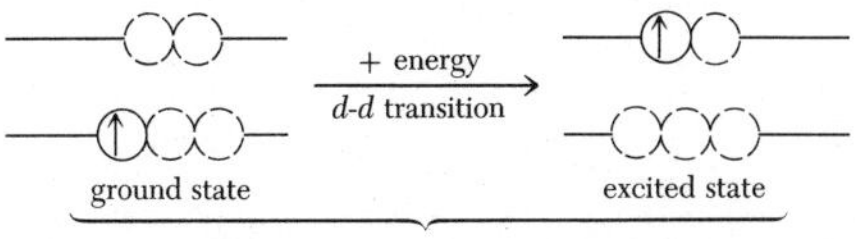

ground state — + energy, *d-d* transition → — excited state

Ti(III) in octahedral $Ti(H_2O)_6^{+3}$

The energy separation between the two sets of $3d$ orbitals in $[Ti(H_2O)_6]^{+3}$ is relatively small, for the $3d$ orbitals still belong to the same sub-shell, having the same principal quantum number, $n = 3$, and the same orbital quantum number, $l = 2$. It so happens that the energy associated with those photons that have wavenumbers in the neighborhood of 20,300 cm^{-1} is just what is required to bring about this particular *d-d* electronic transition. Thus, when exposed to white light, the $[Ti(H_2O)_6]^{+3}$ complex ion absorbs these photons at about 20,300 cm^{-1} (in the green region of the visible spectrum) and hence it appears violet.

The case we have just considered is, of course, a simple one, for the Ti^{+3} ion has only one d electron. For transition-metal ions with more than one d electron, the possible *d-d* electronic excitations are more numerous and more complicated. But in principle we have the same explanation; in the compounds of the transition-metal ions the five d orbitals no longer have the same energy, but are split into two or more different energy levels. And the promotion of an electron from a low- to a higher-energy d orbital just happens to require energies within the range of visible light.

Thus, the transition-metal compounds are colored; and their different colors arise from the fact that the energy separation between the *d* orbitals varies from one compound to another. For each compound of a transition element, in fact, the *d-d* energy separation depends on the oxidation state, coordination number, and stereochemistry of the central metal ion, as well as on the nature (size, electronegativity, polarizability) of the ligating atoms surrounding the central metal ion in the compound.

MAGNETIC PROPERTIES

Another characteristic property of the compounds of the transition metals is their paramagnetism. As we saw in Chapter 33, a substance is said to be paramagnetic if it is attracted by a magnetic field with a force proportional to the intensity of the field, and paramagnetic substances contain unpaired electrons (p. 729). The compounds of the transition-metal ions, which have partly filled *d* orbitals, are often paramagnetic. For the First Transition Series, the extent of the paramagnetism, expressed by the magnetic moment, μ, is given with good approximation by the formula $\mu = \sqrt{n(n+2)}$, where n is the number of unpaired electrons per each metal ion. Table 34-3 shows the values of the magnetic moments for a number of compounds of the elements of the First Transition Series.

34-2 Chemical Properties of the Transition Elements

OXIDATION STATES

All transition elements, except scandium, Sc, and the heavier elements of Group IIIA (yttrium, Y, and lanthanum, La), exhibit a variety of oxidation states. Scandium exhibits only one oxidation state, +3, but each of the other elements of the First Transition Series has two or more oxidation states, ranging from the positive

TABLE 34-3 MAGNETIC MOMENTS OF SOME COMPLEXES OF DIVALENT TRANSITION-METAL IONS

Metal Ion	Complex: High Spin	Complex: Low Spin	No. of d electrons	No. of unpaired electrons	Stereo-chemistry	Magnetic moment, μ*: Calculated from $\mu = \sqrt{n(n+2)}$	Magnetic moment, μ*: Experimentally Found
Ti^{+3}	$K_3[TiF_6]$	—	1	1	octahedral	1.73	1.70
V^{+3}	$[VF_3(H_2O)_3]$	—	2	2	octahedral	2.83	2.79
Cr^{+3}	$[Cr(NH_3)_6]Br_3$	—	3	3	octahedral	3.88	3.77
Cr^{+2}	$[Cr(NH_3)_6]Br_2$	—	4	4	octahedral	4.90	4.70
Mn^{+2}	$K_4[Mn(NCS)_6]$	—	5	5	octahedral	5.92	5.06
Mn^{+2}	—	$K_4[Mn(CN)_6]$	5	1	octahedral	1.73	2.18
Fe^{+3}	$K_3[FeF_6]^-$	—	5	5	octahedral	5.92	5.85
Fe^{+3}	$(NH_4)[FeCl_4]$	—	5	5	tetrahedral	5.92	5.99
Fe^{+2}	$[Fe(NH_3)_6]Cl_2$	—	6	4	octahedral	4.90	5.45
Fe^{+2}	$Cs_2[FeCl_4]$	—	6	4	tetrahedral	4.90	5.40
Co^{+3}	$Na_3[CoF_6]$	—	6	4	octahedral	4.90	5.39
Co^{+3}	—	$[Co(NH_3)_6]Cl_3$	6	0	octahedral	0	diamagn.
Co^{+2}	$[Co(NH_3)_6]Cl_2$	—	7	3	octahedral	3.88	5.05
Co^{+2}	$Cs_2[CoCl_4]$	—	7	3	tetrahedral	3.88	4.54
Ni^{+2}	$[Ni(NH_3)_6]SO_4$	—	8	2	octahedral	2.83	3.32
Ni^{+2}	$Cs_2[NiCl_4]$	—	8	2	tetrahedral	2.83	3.89
Ni^{+2}	—	$K_2[Ni(CN)_4]$	8	0	square planar	0	diamagn.
Pt^{+2}	—	$[Pt(NH_3)_4]Cl_2$	8	0	square planar	0	diamagn.

* The magnetic moment is expressed in a conventional unit called the Bohr Magneton (B.M.).

value corresponding to the periodic group number of the element, down to lower positive values, and finally to zero (or even to the negative values -1 and -2).

In their highest oxidation states, $+5$, $+6$, and $+7$, the transition elements form complex anions—usually with fluoride ions, F^-, or oxide ions, $O^=$, as the ligands. In the complex oxoanions the metal-to-oxygen bond has a largely covalent character, so that the transition metals in the higher oxidation states somewhat resemble the nonmetallic elements of the corresponding B Groups. For example, the $CrO_4^=$ ion is structurally similar to the $SO_4^=$ ion (Cr belongs to Group VIA and S to Group VIB) and the MnO_4^- ion is structurally similar to the ClO_4^- ion (Mn belongs to Group VIIA and Cl to Group VIIB). And, similar to $SO_4^=$ and ClO_4^-, the $CrO_4^=$ and MnO_4^- ions behave as the anions of strong acids, although the pure anhydrous acids H_2CrO_4 and $HMnO_4$ are not known.

In the $+2$ and $+3$ oxidations states, the transition elements form essentially ionic compounds with the most electronegative elements; the oxides MO and the fluorides MF_3, for example, are essentially ionic solids. However, with more polarizable, less electronegative elements, the transition metals in the $+2$ and $+3$ oxidation states form bonds having an appreciable covalent character. This holds especially for coordination compounds of neutral ligands—for example, the hexaammine metal(III) complexes $[M(NH_3)_6]^{+3}$.

The lower oxidation states are found exclusively in coordination compounds, usually with ligands capable of acting as π acceptors, as we discussed in the preceding chapter. Typical examples are the transition-metal carbonyls (p. 733).

ELECTROPOSITIVE CHARACTER AND REACTIVITY

The chemistry of the transition elements is characterized by an extreme variety. Not only does the chemical behavior differ markedly from one element to the next within the same Transition Series, but each element usually exhibits several possible oxidation states. And each element in a given oxidation state is characterized by a different set of properties—a certain value of the charge/radius ratio, a certain preferred coordination number and stereochemistry, a certain oxidation-reduction potential, and so forth. Yet both the varied behavior of each transition element and the differences among the transition elements can be related logically to the two main factors that determine in general the behavior of all substances—the thermodynamic and kinetic properties. In the study of the transition metals, we must keep in mind that their positively charged ions have a very great tendency to form coordination compounds with virtually all electron-pair donors, so that their chemistry always involves the reactions of complex species. The transition elements have properties intermediate between the very highly electropositive Group IA and Group IIA metals (the alkali metals and the alkaline-earth metals) and the less electropositive elements of Group IB (the coinage metals; see next chapter).

All the elements of the First Transition Series are electropositive, as shown by their positive standard oxidation potentials listed in Table 34-2, and they form stable oxides and halides. At ordinary temperatures, however, and particularly in compact form, these metals are kinetically unreactive, because of a high activation energy, related in part to their high heats of atomization (Table 34-1). The degree to which the metal is divided, the nature of the particle surface, and the thermal treatment to which the metal has been submitted during its preparation are often the factors that determine the kinetic reactivity of the transition metals. For example, a piece of compact nickel metal, with a highly polished surface, does not oxidize in air at room temperature but begins to oxidize only at red heat. However, fine nickel powder, obtained from the reduction of the oxide NiO by H_2 gas at 200°C, spontaneously ignites in air, with a violent exothermic reaction. But if this same nickel powder is first heated to 400°C in an inert atmosphere, it does not begin to oxidize in air until heated well above 300°C.

The chemistry of the transition elements is usually best understood by considering the behavior of the metallic elements and of their solid compounds separately from that of their ions in solution. The reason is that the behavior of the metallic elements and of their solid compounds is determined to a very large extent by kinetic factors; for example, a reaction that is thermodynamically favorable may not occur under certain conditions because the activation energy is too high. When we consider the metallic transition elements and their solid compounds, very seldom do we have systems in equilibrium. In solutions, on the other hand, a majority of the compounds of the transition elements react sufficiently fast, so that thermodynamically favorable reactions actually take place within a reasonably short time, and we are therefore considering systems which attain equilibrium. We shall find illustrations of this essential difference between solid state chemistry and solution chemistry in this chapter.

34-3 Reactions of the Transition Metals

All elements of the First Transition Series are electropositive, as shown by the positive $E°$ values in Table 34-2, and hence they can dissolve in aqueous solutions of non-oxidizing acids (and some even in pure water) with the evolution of hydrogen gas. In section 34-5 we shall consider this aspect of their behavior in detail.

The elements of the First Transition Series combine directly with a number of elements—such as the halogens, oxygen, nitrogen, sulfur, and phosphorus—to form a variety of binary compounds, whose formulas often depend on the conditions under which the reaction occurs. In general, these reactions occur only very slowly at ordinary temperatures, even though they are thermodynamically permitted and have large negative ΔH values. At suitably high temperatures, however, these reactions proceed rapidly with the evolution of heat. Here are some examples for iron, Fe.

Reaction	$\Delta H°$, *kcal/mole-eqn*
$3\,Fe + 2\,O_2 \longrightarrow Fe_3O_4$	−267.0
$Fe + \frac{3}{2}\,Cl_2 \longrightarrow FeCl_3$	−96.8
Fe (excess) $+ Br_2 \longrightarrow FeBr_2$	−60.0
$Fe + Br_2$ (excess) $\longrightarrow FeBr_3$	−70.1
$Fe + I_2$ (any ratio) $\longrightarrow FeI_2$	−29.9
$Fe + S \longrightarrow FeS$	−22.7
$Fe + Si \longrightarrow FeSi$	−19.2
$3\,Fe + P \longrightarrow Fe_3P$	−40.0

At high temperatures the transition elements also react with a number of gaseous compounds, for example, HCl, SO_2, NH_3, H_2O, and with molten compounds such as KNO_3, $KHSO_4$, and NaOH. Some examples, again for iron, are:

$$Fe + 2\,HCl\,(gas) \longrightarrow FeCl_2 + H_2$$
$$2\,Fe + 3\,H_2O\,(steam) \longrightarrow Fe_2O_3 + 3\,H_2$$
$$2\,Fe + 6\,KHSO_4\,(molten) \longrightarrow Fe_2(SO_4)_3 + 3\,K_2SO_4 + 3\,H_2$$

Notice that the product of the reaction of Fe metal with HCl gas is $FeCl_2$ whereas the reaction with Cl_2 gas, listed above, yields $FeCl_3$; similarly, with H_2O vapor (steam) Fe metal reacts to form Fe_2O_3, whereas by combustion in oxygen or air the oxide Fe_3O_4 is formed.

As an illustration of the variety of formulas and behaviors of the solid compounds of the transition elements, we shall now discuss their oxides.

34-4 Oxides of the Transition Elements

FORMULAS AND CRYSTAL STRUCTURE

The elements of the First Transition Series form a variety of oxides, of formulas MO, M_2O_3, M_3O_4 (or $MO \cdot M_2O_3$), MO_2, M_2O_5, and MO_3.

Oxides of the +2 oxidation state are known for all elements of the series, except for Sc and Cr; the divalent oxides, MO, have a crystal lattice of the NaCl-type, with each M^{++} ion octahedrally surrounded by 6 $O^{=}$ ions, and each $O^{=}$ ion octahedrally surrounded by 6 M^{++} ions.

Oxides of the +3 oxidation state, M_2O_3, are known for all elements of the series except for Co and Ni; these oxides have ionic lattices in which each M^{+3} ion is also octahedrally surrounded by 6 $O^{=}$ ions, whereas each $O^{=}$ ion is surrounded tetrahedrally by 4 M^{+3} ions.

Oxides of the +4 oxidation state, MO_2, are known for Ti, V, and Mn; they have the rutile structure with a 6:3 cation-to-anion crystal coordination.

Oxides of the formula M_3O_4 (or $MO \cdot M_2O_3$) contain one-third of the metal atoms in the +2 oidation state and two-thirds in the +3 oxidation state. The structure of these oxides consists of ionic lattices in which M^{++} ions, M^{+3} ions, and $O^{=}$ ions alternate in a variety of regular patterns.

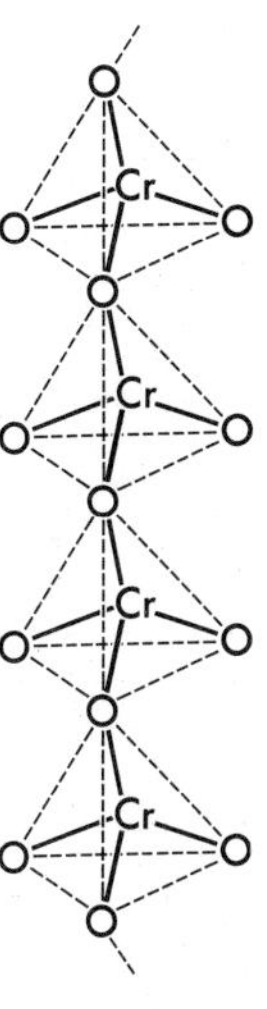

In the First Transition Series, the only well-known oxide of the type M_2O_5 is that of vanadium; in the three-dimensional network of V_2O_5 each V atom in the +5 oxidation state is surrounded by 5 $O^{=}$ ions in a rather irregular arrangement.

Chromium trioxide, CrO_3, which occurs as low-melting red crystals (m.p. 197°), is the only well-defined oxide of an element of the First Transition Series in the +6 oxidation state. In the solid state, CrO_3 consists of chains of $\{CrO_4\}$ tetrahedra joined at the corners; the chains are held together in the crystal by weak van der Waals forces, thus explaining the low melting point of this solid.

At ordinary temperature and pressure all the oxides listed above are thermodynamically stable with respect to decomposition to the metal and oxygen gas. Oxides of the same metal in different oxidation states have different relative stabilities and therefore have the capacity to partially dissociate or to disproportionate; however, such reactions do not usually take place to any detectable extent at ordinary temperature. For example, of the two oxides Fe_2O_3 and Fe_3O_4, the former is the more stable at room temperature; the thermodynamically permitted reaction

$$2\ Fe_3O_4 + \tfrac{1}{2}\ O_2 \longrightarrow 3\ Fe_2O_3 \qquad \begin{cases} \Delta H^\circ = -55\ \text{kcal/mole-eqn} \\ \Delta G^\circ = -46\ \text{kcal/mole-eqn} \end{cases}$$

does not actually proceed at room temperature, because the activation energy is too high. The values of $\Delta H^\circ_{\text{form}}$ for some of the most common oxides of the First Transition Series are given in Table 34-4.

BEHAVIOR OF THE OXIDES IN WATER

The divalent oxides, MO, are insoluble in water but soluble in aqueous solutions of strong non-oxidizing acids—thus, all oxides, MO, have a basic character. Their reaction with acids usually yields a solution of the divalent hexaaquocomplex ions, $[M(H_2O)_6]^{++}$. In some cases, these divalent aquo-complexes are not stable and reduce water, evolving H_2 gas and forming the aquo-complex of the metal in a higher

TABLE 34-4 HEATS OF FORMATION (KCAL/MOLE) OF TRANSITION-METAL OXIDES

Oxide	Sc	Ti	V	Cr	Mn	Fe	Co	Ni
MO	—	−124	−100	—	−92	−64	—	−57
M_2O_3	−411	−363	−296	−273	−229	−197	−57	—
M_3O_4	—	—	—	—	−331	−268	—	—
MO_2	—	−225	−171	−142	−124	—	−204	—
M_2O_5	—	—	−373	—	—	—	—	—
MO_3	—	—	—	−138	—	—	—	—

oxidation state. For example, titanium(II) oxide, TiO, reacts with an aqueous solution of a non-oxidizing acid to form the aquo-complex of Ti(III):

$$TiO_{(s)} + 3\ H^{+}_{(aq)} \longrightarrow Ti^{+3}_{(aq)} + \tfrac{1}{2}\ H_2 + H_2O$$

All the trivalent oxides, M_2O_3, are insoluble in water; they generally have a basic character. The oxides Ti_2O_3, V_2O_3, and Mn_2O_3 dissolve readily in acids, especially when the anions of the acid are good ligands (as, for example, Cl^-); crystalline Cr_2O_3 and Fe_2O_3, however, do not dissolve in aqueous acids.

The dioxides, MO_2, have varied behavior. Titanium dioxide, TiO_2, is insoluble in water and in cold aqueous acids, unless the anions of the acid form complexes with titanium in the +4 oxidation state. For example, crystalline TiO_2 dissolves in cold dilute hydrofluoric acid to form complexes of the type $[TiF_6]^=$ and $[TiF_4(H_2O)_2]^0$. Vanadium dioxide, VO_2, is soluble in aqueous solutions of acids, forming solutions of the hydrated vanadyl cation, $[VO]^{++}_{(aq)}$, and is soluble in bases forming complex oxoanions; thus, VO_2 is amphoteric. Manganese dioxide, MnO_2, is insoluble in water and also in cold aqueous acids and alkali; it dissolves, however, in hot concentrated hydrochloric acid because it oxidizes the Cl^- ion to gaseous chlorine, with reduction of Mn(IV) to Mn(II):

$$MnO_{2(s)} + 4\ H^{+}_{(aq)} + 2\ Cl^{-}_{(aq)} \longrightarrow Mn^{++}_{(aq)} + Cl_{2(g)} + 2\ H_2O_{(l)}$$

The oxides M_3O_4 are generally insoluble in water and in aqueous solutions of acids, but at very high temperatures they are attacked by fused $KHSO_4$ in the presence of air; for example:

$$2\ Fe_3O_{4(s)} + 6\ KHSO_{4(l)} + \tfrac{3}{2}\ O_{2(g)} \longrightarrow 3\ Fe_2(SO_4)_{3(s)} + 3\ H_2O_{(g)} + 3\ K_2SO_4$$

Divanadium pentoxide, V_2O_5, is amphoteric; it is almost insoluble in water but dissolves in aqueous solutions of acids and alkali.

Finally, chromium trioxide, CrO_3, is extremely soluble in water (it is deliquescent) and forms a reddish solution which is strongly acidic. This solution contains H^+ and $Cr_2O_7^=$ ions, together with some other polynuclear anions; it is a powerful oxidizing agent.

The behavior of the transition-metal oxides in water illustrates the general rule that for each element the character of the oxides becomes less and less basic (more and more acidic) as the oxidation state of the transition metal increases.

34-5 Chemistry of the Transition Elements in Aqueous Solution

For each transition element, the chemical behavior in aqueous solution depends on many factors, the most important being the oxidation-potential diagram of the element and the relative tendency of its ions to form complexes with the various ligands present in solution. Of course, these two factors are related, for in each case the system will tend to form the products that are thermodynamically most stable under the conditions considered. And, as we saw in Chapter 33, the formation of a very stable complex often reverses the order of stability of two oxidation states of the same element. In the following sections we shall relate these two factors to some important aspects of the behavior of the elements of the First Transition Series in aqueous solution. To understand the oxidation-reduction behavior of the transition elements in aqueous solution, we must compare their Latimer oxidation-potential diagrams with those of oxygen and hydrogen—the components of water:

For hydrogen:

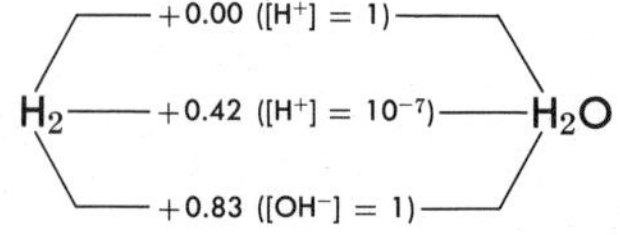

For oxygen:

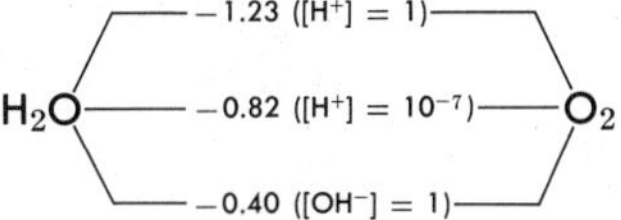

SCANDIUM

As we have already mentioned, scandium is the only element of the First Transition Series which does not exhibit variable oxidation states. The only known oxidaton state of scandium in aqueous solution is +3; the calculated oxidation potential for the Sc,Sc^{+3} couple is $E° = +2.08$ v—that is, scandium metal is strongly electropositive and has the capacity to decompose water with the evolution of H_2 gas. The Sc^{+3} ion has an electron configuration similar to that of the noble gas argon ($1s^2$, $2s^2\ 2p^6$, $3s^2\ 3p^6$), and in its properties it resembles Al^{+3}—the similar ion of the preceding element of Group III—rather than Ti^{+3} and V^{+3}—the trivalent ions of the following transition metals. In acid and neutral aqueous solutions Sc(III) is present as hexaaquoscandium(III) cations, $[Sc(H_2O)_6]^{+3}$, which upon addition of OH^- ions form an insoluble, gelatinous hydrated oxide, $Sc_2O_3 \cdot x\ H_2O$. This oxide is soluble in aqueous solutions of acids, reforming the $[Sc(H_2O)_6]^{+3}$ ion, and is also soluble in aqueous solutions of alkali, forming the complex anion, $[Sc(OH)_6]^{-3}$.

TITANIUM

The following Latimer oxidation-potential diagram summarizes the behavior of Ti in aqueous solution:

$$Ti \overset{+1.63}{\text{———}} Ti^{++} \overset{+0.37}{\text{———}} Ti^{+3} \overset{-0.20}{\text{———}} Ti(IV)$$

This oxidation-potential diagram tells us several things:

1. The oxidation of Ti metal to $Ti^{++}_{(aq)}$ has an $E°$ value of +1.63 volts; hence, titanium metal, Ti, can dissolve in solutions of non-oxidizing acids ($E°$ for H_2,H^+ couple = 0.00 v):

$$Ti_{(s)} + 2\ H^+_{(aq)} \longrightarrow Ti^{++}_{(aq)} + H_{2(g)}$$
$$E° = +1.63\ v - 0.00\ v = +1.63\ v\ (\text{in } 1\ M\ [H^+])$$

Titanium metal also has the capacity to decompose water with the evolution of hydrogen gas ($E°$ for the H_2O,H_2 couple in neutral solution = +0.42 v).

$$Ti_{(s)} + 2\ H_2O \longrightarrow Ti^{++}_{(aq)} + H_{2(g)} + 2\ OH^-_{(aq)}$$
$$E° = +1.63\ v - 0.42\ v = +1.21\ v\ (\text{for } [H^+] = 10^{-7})$$

This thermodynamically permitted reaction, however, does not occur at an appreciable rate at room temperature.

2. In aqueous acid solution, Ti^{++} can reduce O_2 gas (for example, from the atmosphere) to H_2O:

$$2\ Ti^{++}_{(aq)} + \tfrac{1}{2}\ O_2 + 2\ H^+ \longrightarrow 2\ Ti^{+3}_{(aq)} + H_2O$$

$$E° = +0.37\ v + 1.23\ v = +1.60\ v\ (\text{for } [H^+] = 1)$$

Also, $Ti^{++}_{(aq)}$ can reduce the H^+ ions to H_2 gas, while it itself is oxidized to Ti^{+3}:

$$Ti^{++}_{(aq)} + H^+ \longrightarrow Ti^{+3}_{(aq)} + \tfrac{1}{2}\ H_{2(g)}$$
$$E° = +0.37\ v + 0.00\ v = +0.37\ v\ (\text{for } [H^+] = 1)$$

3. Titanium in the +3 oxidation state cannot reduce the hydrogen atoms of water to H_2 gas, but it can reduce oxygen gas to water in acid solution, while it itself is oxidized to Ti(IV):

$$2\ Ti^{+3}_{(aq)} + \tfrac{1}{2}\ O_{2(g)} + 2\ H^+ \longrightarrow 2\ Ti^{+4}_{(aq)} + H_2O$$
$$E° = -0.20\ v + 1.23\ v = +1.03\ v\ (\text{for } [H^+] = 1)$$

Thus, the most stable oxidation states of titanium in aqueous solution are +3 and +4. The Ti^{+3} exists in water as the hexaaquocomplex, $[Ti(H_2O)_6]^{+3}$. On the other hand, Ti(IV) does not exist as the simple aquocomplex, but rather as hydroxoaquocomplexes —for example, $[Ti(OH)_2(H_2O)_4]^{++}$ and $[Ti(OH)_3(H_2O)_3]^+$. These hydroxo species are present even in acid solutions because the Ti^{+4} ion has such a large charge/radius ratio that it strongly repels the protons of the coordinated H_2O molecules.

VANADIUM

The Latimer oxidation-potential diagram for vanadium also tells us a lot.

$$V \xrightarrow{+1.18} V^{++} \xrightarrow{+0.25} V^{+3} \xrightarrow{-0.33} VO^{++} \xrightarrow{-1.0} VO_2^+$$

1. Vanadium metal can dissolve in acid solutions, as well as in pure water, with the evolution of H_2 gas (the reaction with pure water, however, is extremely slow at room temperature), the V^{++} and V^{+3} species can be formed. The species corresponding to the +2 oxidation state is $[V(H_2O)_6]^{++}$; the species corresponding to the +3 state is $[V(H_2O)_6]^{+3}$, part of which is hydrolyzed to form hydroxocomplexes such as the $[V(OH)(H_2O)_5]^{++}$ cation.

2. The V^{++} ion can reduce water in 1 M acid solution, forming the V^{+3} ion and evolving H_2 gas; also, V^{++} can reduce O_2 gas (of air) to H_2O in neutral as well as in acidic or basic solutions.

3. In the absence of an oxidant, the V^{+3} ion is stable in water, but even mild oxidants can oxidize V^{+3} to vanadium(IV).

4. The species corresponding to the +4 oxidation state is the *vanadyl* cation, VO^{++}, in which the oxygen atom is joined by a double bond to the V(IV) atom: $(V{=}O)^{++}$. The vanadyl cation, VO^{++}, is quite stable with respect to oxidation.

CHROMIUM

From the Latimer oxidation-potential diagram for chromium we see that in aqueous solution the most stable oxidation state of chromium is +3. In aqueous solution, the species of oxidation state +2 is $[Cr(H_2O)_6]^{++}$, a strong reducing

$$Cr \xrightarrow{+0.91} Cr^{+2} \xrightarrow{+0.41} Cr^{+3} \xrightarrow{-1.33\ ([H^+]\,=\,1)} Cr_2O_7^{=}$$
$$Cr \xrightarrow{+0.74} Cr^{+3}$$

agent which can be oxidized to $[Cr(H_2O)_6]^{+3}$ by atmospheric oxygen and also by the H^+ ions of an acidic aqueous solution. The $[Cr(H_2O)_6]^{+3}$ ion is slightly hydrolyzed to form hydroxocomplexes, such as $[Cr(OH)(H_2O)_5]^{++}$. As usual, in basic solutions the formation of hydroxocomplexes is more favorable, and in strongly basic solutions Cr(III) is probably present as hydroxo anions of the type $[Cr(OH)_4(H_2O)_2]^-$.

In acid solution, the species of oxidation state +6 is the dichromate ion, $Cr_2O_7^=$; whereas in basic and neutral solutions the $CrO_4^=$ ion is present. The $Cr_2O_7^=$ ion is a very strong oxidant, with the capacity to oxidize even water to oxygen gas while itself being reduced to Cr(III); this reaction, however, does not take place under normal conditions because of a very high activation energy.

As an illustration of the varied properties of transition elements in different oxidation states, let us now consider some compounds of Cr(II), Cr(III) and Cr(VI).

THE +2 OXIDATION STATE. Finely divided chromium metal dissolves in dilute solutions of non-oxidizing acids—for example, dilute sulfuric acid—to form the Cr^{++} ion while liberating H_2 gas:

$$Cr + 2\,H^+ + SO_4^= \longrightarrow Cr^{++} + SO_4^= + H_2$$

From the solution, chromium(II) sulfate crystallizes as the blue hydrate, $[Cr(H_2O)_6]SO_4 \cdot H_2O$. Since Cr^{++}, as we have seen, is very easily oxidized to Cr^{+3} by the oxygen of air, in the preparation of Cr^{++} compounds air must be excluded from the solutions. In fact, the oxidation of Cr^{++} to Cr^{+3} is so rapid, as well as energetically favorable, that traces of oxygen may be removed from a gas by bubbling it through a Cr^{++} solution.

A solution of Cr^{++} may also be prepared by the reduction of a Cr^{+3} salt with zinc metal in the presence of an acid, with all air excluded:

$$Cr^{+3}{}_{(aq)} + Zn_{(s)} + H^{+}{}_{(aq)} \longrightarrow Cr^{++}{}_{(aq)} + Zn^{++}{}_{(aq)} + \tfrac{1}{2}\,H_{2(g)}$$

Treatment of a solution of Cr^{++} with hydroxide ions, OH^-, yields a brownish-yellow, gelatinous precipitate, $Cr(OH)_2$, which is readily oxidized by O_2 of the air to form green $Cr(OH)_3$. These gelatinous hydroxides contain a variable number of bound water molecules, so that their formulas should be written more appropriately as $Cr(OH)_2 \cdot xH_2O$ and $Cr(OH)_3 \cdot xH_2O$. Chromium(II) forms both complex cations and complex anions; the hexaamminechromium(II) chloride, $[Cr(NH_3)_6]Cl_2$, is an example of a compound containing a chromium(II) complex cation; the potassium hexacyanochromate(II), $K_4[Cr(CN)_6]$, is an example of a compound containing a chromium(II) complex anion.

THE +3 OXIDATION STATE. Chromium(III) exists in aqueous solutions chiefly as the violet hexaaquochromium(III) ion, $[Cr(H_2O)_6]^{+3}$; the solution is acidic as a result of hydrolysis:

$$[Cr(H_2O)_6]^{+3} + H_2O \rightleftharpoons [Cr(H_2O)_5OH]^{++} + H^+ \cdot H_2O$$

The addition of OH^- ions shifts this hydrolysis equilibrium to the right and also favors the formation of compounds containing more than one OH^- ligand per Cr(III) ion. In fact, the addition of 3 OH^- ions (from an alkali-metal hydroxide or ammonia solution, for example) for each $[Cr(H_2O)_6]^{+3}$ ion results in the formation of the insoluble, gelatinous, green chromium(III) hydroxide, $Cr(OH)_3$.

The addition of an alkali-metal carbonate to a solution containing Cr(III) ions also precipitates the highly insoluble hydroxide, $Cr(OH)_3$, instead of Cr(III) carbonate. And a solution of $(NH_4)_2S$ added to a Cr(III) solution again precipitates $Cr(OH)_3$ rather than Cr(III) sulfide. Chromium(III) hydroxide is formed because in water the $CO_3^{=}$ and the $S^{=}$ ions are hydrolyzed to such an extent that the concentration of OH^- ions exceeds the K_{sp} of the insoluble $Cr(OH)_3$. If we add OH^- ions in high concentration, the precipitate of $Cr(OH)_3$ dissolves, forming the complex anion $[Cr(OH)_4(H_2O)_2]^-$. Thus, chromium(III) hydroxide dissolves both in basic solutions to form hydroxochromates(III) and in acid solution to form chromium(III) salts, and is therefore amphoteric.

Most Cr(III) salts crystallize from aqueous solution in a hydrated form. For example, from an aqueous solution containing Cr(III) and Cl^- ions, 3 crystalline compounds of the simple formula $CrCl_3 \cdot 6\,H_2O$ can be obtained: $[Cr(H_2O)_6]Cl_3$ (violet), $[CrCl(H_2O)_5]Cl_2 \cdot H_2O$ (pale green), and $[CrCl_2(H_2O)_4]Cl \cdot 2\,H_2O$ (dark green). In general, anhydrous Cr(III) salts cannot be obtained by dehydration of the hydrated salts, because extensive hydrolysis occurs. The Cr(III) anhydrous salts are usually prepared in the absence of water. For example, anhydrous chromium(III) chloride, $CrCl_3$, a reddish-violet substance insoluble in water, may be prepared by passing Cl_2 gas over chromium metal at a high temperature: $2\,Cr + 3\,Cl_2 \longrightarrow 2\,CrCl_3$.

Chromium(III) has a marked tendency to form complexes, usually with coordination number 6 and octahedral stereochemistry; some examples are $[Cr(NH_3)_6]^{+3}$, $[Cr(NH_3)_5Cl]^{++}$, $[Cr(CN)_6]^{-3}$, and $[Cr(CNS)_6]^{-3}$. Unlike most complexes of the elements of the First Transition Series, those of Cr(III) are very inert; for this reason, it has been possible to isolate an extremely large number of "mixed complexes" of Cr(III) in which one or more of the 6 H_2O molecules of $[Cr(H_2O)_6]^{+3}$ are replaced by other ligands. For example, in addition to the chloroaquocomplexes mentioned above, the following series of aquoamminecomplexes is known: $[Cr(H_2O)(NH_3)_5]^{+3}$, $[Cr(H_2O)_2(NH_3)_4]^{+3}$, $[Cr(H_2O)_3(NH_3)_3]^{+3}$, $[Cr(H_2O)_4(NH_3)_2]^{+3}$, and $[Cr(NH_3)_6]^{+3}$.

THE +6 OXIDATION STATE. Chromium(VI) oxide, CrO_3, may be prepared by treating a cooled concentrated solution of potassium dichromate, $K_2Cr_2O_7$, with an excess of cold concentrated H_2SO_4; the compound CrO_3, which is only slightly soluble in the cold strongly acidic solution, crystallizes as deep-red needles:

$$K_2Cr_2O_{7(aq)} + 2\ H_2SO_{4(aq)} \longrightarrow 2\ CrO_{3(s)} + 2\ KHSO_{4(aq)} + H_2O_{(l)}$$

As we have already seen, CrO_3, which contains chromium in its highest oxidation state, +6, is an acidic oxide; it is very soluble in water, forming an acid solution:

$$2\ CrO_3 + H_2O \rightleftharpoons 2\ H^+ + Cr_2O_7^=$$

In basic solutions, CrO_3 dissolves, forming the $CrO_4^=$ ion:

$$CrO_3 + 2\ OH^- \longrightarrow CrO_4^= + H_2O$$

Thus, CrO_3 is the anhydride of both dichromic acid, $H_2Cr_2O_7$, and chromic acid, H_2CrO_4. Both dichromic acid, and chromic acid exist only in solution, but their salts may be obtained in the solid state; examples are $Na_2Cr_2O_7$, sodium dichromate, and $PbCrO_4$, lead chromate. The dichromate ion, $Cr_2O_7^=$, is orange-red, while the chromate ion, $CrO_4^=$, is yellow.

THE CHROMATE-DICHROMATE EQUILIBRIUM. Chromium(VI) tends to exist as the $Cr_2O_7^=$ ion in acid solutions and as the $CrO_4^=$ ion in basic or neutral solutions. When we add a little acid, such as sulfuric acid, to an aqueous $CrO_4^=$ solution, the yellow color of the solution changes to orange-red, owing to the formation of $Cr_2O_7^=$ ions. The resulting solution contains the ions $CrO_4^=$, H^+, and $Cr_2O_7^=$ in equilibrium:

$$\underset{\text{(yellow)}}{2\ CrO_4^=} + 2\ H^+ \rightleftharpoons \underset{\text{(orange)}}{Cr_2O_7^=} + H_2O$$

The addition of H^+ ions will shift the equilibrium to the right, with the formation of $Cr_2O_7^=$ ions, whereas the addition of OH^- ions will shift the equilibrium to the left, with the formation of $CrO_4^=$ ions.

If we add lead acetate, $Pb(CH_3COO)_2$, to an aqueous solution of potassium dichromate, $K_2Cr_2O_7$, a precipitate of lead chromate, $PbCrO_4$, forms rather than lead dichromate, $PbCr_2O_7$. The reason is that the solubility product, K_{sp}, of $PbCrO_4$ is much lower than that of $PbCr_2O_7$. Thus, even though there may be more $Cr_2O_7^=$ ions than $CrO_4^=$ ions in solution, $PbCrO_4$ still precipitates. $PbCrO_4$ dissolves in solutions of strong acids owing to the reaction:

$$2\ CrO_4^= + 2\ H^+ \rightleftharpoons Cr_2O_7^= + H_2O$$

On the other hand, the $[H^+]$ in a solution of a weak acid, such as acetic acid, CH_3COOH, is not sufficient to lower the $[CrO_4^=]$ below the value required for the K_{sp} of $PbCrO_4$. Thus, $PbCrO_4$ dissolves in solutions of HNO_3 and H_2SO_4, but not in solutions of CH_3COOH. The yellow insoluble compound $PbCrO_4$ is an important pigment, known as "chrome yellow."

The chief source of Cr(VI) compounds is sodium dichromate-2 hydrate, $Na_2Cr_2O_7 \cdot 2\ H_2O$. This salt is prepared by first roasting chromium(III) oxide, Cr_2O_3, mixed with sodium carbonate and some calcium oxide (lime), in air at 1000–1300°:

$$Cr_2O_3 + 2\ Na_2CO_3 + 3\ O_2 \longrightarrow 2\ Na_2CrO_4 + 2\ CO_2$$

The molten mass, after cooling, is leached with water to dissolve the soluble Na_2CrO_4. The solution is then treated with H_2SO_4 to convert the $CrO_4^=$ ion to $Cr_2O_7^=$, and upon concentration the salt $Na_2Cr_2O_7 \cdot 2\ H_2O$ crystallizes out.

The Latimer oxidation-potential diagrams of manganese are:

In 1 M acid solution:

$$Mn \xrightarrow{+1.18} Mn^{+2} \xrightarrow{-1.51} Mn^{+3} \xrightarrow{-0.95} MnO_2 \xrightarrow{-2.26} MnO_4^{=} \xrightarrow{-0.56} MnO_4^-$$

(Mn^{+2} — -1.5 — MnO_4^-; Mn^{+3} — -1.69 — MnO_4^-)

In 1 M basic solution:

$$Mn \xrightarrow{+1.55} Mn(OH)_2 \xrightarrow{-0.1} Mn_2O_3 \xrightarrow{+0.2} MnO_2 \xrightarrow{-0.6} MnO_4^{=} \xrightarrow{-0.6} MnO_4^-$$

(MnO_2 — -1.23 — MnO_4^-)

From these potential diagrams we can see that the oxidation-reduction behavior of manganese in aqueous solution, in the absence of ligands stronger than the H_2O molecules and the OH^- ions, is as follows:

1. The metal, Mn, can dissolve in acidic as well as in basic aqueous solutions, and even in pure water, forming Mn(II) and evolving hydrogen gas.

2. In acid and neutral solutions, the most stable oxidation state is +2, present as the pale pink $[Mn(H_2O)_6]^{++}$ ion. In basic solutions, on the other hand, the oxidation state +2 is rather unstable, because even the oxygen of air is capable of oxidizing white MnO to dark-brown MnO_2. This oxidation reaction is relatively slow because MnO is a solid and its reaction with O_2 gas is heterogeneous.

3. Manganese in the +3 oxidation state tends to disproportionate to Mn^{++} and MnO_2; and $MnO_4^{=}$ tends to disproportionate to MnO_2 and MnO_4^-. Thus, owing to disproportionation, Mn(III) and Mn(VI) are unstable in aqueous solutions, even in the absence of reducing or oxidizing agents.

4. The dioxide, MnO_2, does not decompose in the presence of water alone, because it is insoluble; in acid solutions, however, MnO_2 is a strong oxidant and is reduced to Mn^{++}.

5. The deep purple permanganate ion, MnO_4^-, is an extremely strong oxidant, capable of oxidizing water with the evolution of oxygen; the reaction actually does not occur at room temperature because of kinetic factors. The MnO_4^- ion is an even stronger oxidant in basic solutions than it is in acid solutions; the reduction product of the MnO_4^- ion is Mn^{++} in acid solutions and MnO_2 in neutral and basic solutions. This is only a general statement, however, for such powerful reducing agents as KI and H_2S, further reduce MnO_2 to Mn^{++} even in neutral or basic solutions. In very strongly basic solutions, the reduction product of the MnO_4^- ion is the dark green manganate ion, $MnO_4^{=}$.

THE +2 OXIDATION STATE. When we mix a solution containing Mn^{++}, as the pink, octahedral hexaaquocomplex, $[Mn(H_2O)_6]^{++}$, with OH^- ions (from ammonia or an alkali-metal hydroxide), the rose-pink, gelatinous manganese(II) hydroxide, $Mn(OH)_2$, precipitates. In the presence of NH_4Cl, however, $Mn(OH)_2$ does not precipitate when an ammonia solution is added, because a high $[NH_4^+]$ reduces the $[OH^-]$ below the value required to exceed the K_{sp} of manganese(II) hydroxide, $Mn(OH)_2$. In the presence of atmospheric oxygen, MnO slowly darkens, owing to the formation of the hydrated Mn(III) and Mn(IV) oxides, $Mn_2O_3 \cdot nH_2O$ and $MnO_2 \cdot nH_2O$.

THE +3 OXIDATION STATE. As we have seen, Mn(III) is very unstable in aqueous solution, for it tends to disproportionate into Mn(II) and Mn(IV). For example, crystalline manganese(III) fluoride, MnF_3, which is formed by the direct reaction of manganese metal with fluorine gas, disproportionates in the presence of water to Mn^{++} and MnO_2:

$$2\ MnF_{3(s)} + 2\ H_2O_{(l)} \longrightarrow Mn^{++}{}_{(aq)} + MnO_{2(s)} + 6\ F^-{}_{(aq)} + 4\ H^+{}_{(aq)}$$

We would expect, therefore, that only the Mn(III) compounds that yield a very small concentration of Mn^{+3} would be stable in solution. And in fact the known Mn(III) compounds are either very insoluble (which means that they yield only a low Mn^{+3} ion concentration) or else they are complexes which dissociate to only a very slight extent (again producing only a very low concentration of Mn^{+3} ions). Examples are the insoluble oxide, Mn_2O_3, and the soluble, very stable complex salt, $K_3[Mn(CN)_6]$.

THE +4 OXIDATION STATE. The Mn^{+4} ion does not exist in aqueous solution, because of its high charge/radius ratio. The most important compound of manganese in the +4 oxidation state is the dioxide, MnO_2, an insoluble dark solid which has strong oxidizing properties. As we have seen above, MnO_2 is a stronger oxidant in acid solutions than it is in basic solutions; an important application of its oxidizing properties is the laboratory preparation of chlorine:

$$MnO_{2(s)} + 4\ HCl_{(aq)} \longrightarrow Cl_{2(g)} + MnCl_{2(aq)} + 2\ H_2O_{(l)}$$

THE +6 OXIDATION STATE. Potassium manganate(VI), K_2MnO_4, is produced by the fusion of MnO_2 with KOH in the presence of an oxidizing agent such as KNO_3:

$$2\ MnO_2 + 4\ KOH + [O] \longrightarrow 2\ K_2MnO_4 + 2\ H_2O$$

Potassium manganate(VI) is bright green in color and is readily soluble in water to give a green solution. As we have seen above, in acid or neutral solutions the manganate ion, $MnO_4^{=}$, disproportionates to the permanganate ion, MnO_4^-, and MnO_2:

$$3\ MnO_4^{=} + 4\ H^+ \longrightarrow 2\ MnO_4^- + MnO_2 + 2\ H_2O$$

In this reaction the color of the solution changes from the green of the manganate ion, $MnO_4^{=}$, to the purple of the permanganate ion, MnO_4^-. Even carbonic acid brings about this disproportionation. The manganates are stable only in basic solutions.

THE +7 OXIDATION STATE. The best-known compound containing manganese in the +7 oxidation state is potassium permanganate, $KMnO_4$, which has a very intense purple color. In acid solutions $KMnO_4$ is a very powerful oxidant, widely used in analytical chemistry. Examples of the oxidizing properties of the MnO_4^- ion in the presence of H^+ ion have been considered in Chapter 27.

Because of the very strong oxidizing property of the MnO_4^- ion, only very powerful oxidizing agents are capable of oxidizing the Mn^{++} ion to MnO_4^-. Sodium bismuthate(V), $NaBiO_3$, or lead dioxide, PbO_2, in the presence of HNO_3, are examples of such oxidizing agents:

$$2\ Mn(NO_3)_2 + 5\ NaBiO_3 + 14\ HNO_3 \longrightarrow 2\ NaMnO_4 + 5\ Bi(NO_3)_3 + 3\ NaNO_3 + 7\ H_2O$$

$$2\ Mn(NO_3)_2 + 5\ PbO_2 + 4\ HNO_3 \longrightarrow Pb(MnO_4)_2 + 4\ Pb(NO_3)_2 + 2\ H_2O$$

Permanganic acid, $HMnO_4$, exists only in solution. It may be prepared by the reaction of $Ba(MnO_4)_2$ with dilute H_2SO_4, which forms insoluble $BaSO_4$:

$$Ba(MnO_4)_2 + H_2SO_4 \longrightarrow 2\ HMnO_4 + BaSO_4$$

IRON

The oxidation potential diagrams of iron are:

In 1 M acid solution: $Fe \overset{+0.44}{\text{—}} Fe^{++} \overset{-0.77}{\text{———}} Fe^{+3}$

In 1 M basic solution: $Fe \overset{+0.89}{\text{—}} Fe(OH)_2 \overset{-0.56}{\text{—}} Fe(OH)_3$

Both diagrams tell us that in the presence of water the more stable oxidation state of iron is +2, but in the presence of both water and air (oxygen) the more stable oxidation state is +3. In aqueous acid solutions, the species of oxidation state +2 and +3 are $[Fe(H_2O)_6]^{++}$ and $[Fe(H_2O)_6]^{+3}$, respectively; the latter hydrolyzes extensively to form hydroxocomplexes, for example, $[Fe(OH)(H_2O)_5]^{++}$. The oxidation of

$[Fe(H_2O)_6]^{++}$ to $[Fe(H_2O)_6]^{+3}$ in 1 molar $[H^+]$ can be accomplished simply by the oxygen of the air, the rate of oxidation increasing as the acidity of the solution decreases. In basic solutions, the air-oxidation of white $Fe(OH)_2$ to black $Fe(OH)_3$ is extremely rapid.

THE +2 OXIDATION STATE. An aqueous solution of iron(II) can be obtained by dissolving Fe metal in a non-oxidizing acid, such as hydrochloric acid, in the absence of oxygen. In aqueous acid solutions, Fe(II) is present as the green $[Fe(H_2O)_6]^{++}$ ion.

Iron(II) hydroxide, $Fe(OH)_2$, is obtained as a white gelatinous precipitate by mixing air-free solutions of an iron(II) salt with an alkali-metal hydroxide. When this white hydroxide comes into contact with air, it rapidly turns a dirty green, and finally becomes reddish-brown, with the formation of $Fe(OH)_3$. Thus, $Fe(OH)_2$ serves as an effective reducing agent. The addition of an ammonia solution to an iron(II) solution partially precipitates the $Fe(OH)_2$. If, however, there are excess NH_4^+ ions present from, say, NH_4Cl, no precipitate of $Fe(OH)_2$ forms, because the presence of the common ion, NH_4^+, shifts the equilibrium to the left, $NH_3 + H_2O \rightleftharpoons NH_4^+ + OH^-$, and the concentration of OH^- accordingly decreases and is no longer sufficient to exceed the K_{sp} of $Fe(OH)_2$.

THE +3 OXIDATION STATE. In aqueous solution the hexaaquoiron(III) ion, $[Fe(H_2O)_6]^{+3}$ is extensively hydrolyzed because of the high charge/radius of the Fe^{+3} ion. Cold aqueous solutions of iron(III) chloride or sulfate are yellow; on boiling, these solutions turn brown to red, probably because of the presence of colloidal $Fe(OH)_3$, which results from complete hydrolysis. The oxidation of an aqueous solution of iron(II) chloride by chlorine, Cl_2, followed by the partial evaporation of the solution, results in the crystallization of the yellow hydrate, $FeCl_3 \cdot 6\,H_2O$, which cannot be dehydrated by heating. Anhydrous Fe(III) chloride, is prepared by passing a stream of dry Cl_2 gas over heated iron, in the absence of moisture. When this anhydrous iron(III) chloride is sublimed, vapor density measurements indicate that its molecular weight corresponds to the formula Fe_2Cl_6; the structure of this molecule is similar to that of Al_2Cl_6. Anhydrous iron(III) chloride is soluble in alcohol, ether, and acetone; it also readily dissolves in water to produce a solution that has the same properties as an aqueous solution of $FeCl_3 \cdot 6\,H_2O$, described above. The addition of OH^- ions (from ammonia, an alkali-metal hydroxide, or an alkali-metal carbonate) to an iron(III) solution produces a reddish-brown gelatinous precipitate of iron(III) hydroxide.

COBALT

The Latimer oxidation-potential diagrams are:

In 1 M acid solution: $Co \overset{+0.23}{—} Co^{++} \overset{-1.84}{—} Co^{+3}$

In 1 M basic solution: $Co \overset{+0.73}{—} Co(OH)_2 \overset{-0.17}{—} Co(OH)_3$

Thus, both in acid and in basic solutions, the more stable oxidation state of cobalt is +2. The hydrated Co^{+3} ion is a very powerful oxidizing agent that can even oxidize H_2O, liberating O_2 and forming the Co(II) ion. Consequently, only compounds that yield a very low Co^{+3} ion concentration in solution—such as insoluble salts and soluble complexes with a very high stability constant—are stable in the presence of water. For example, in an aqueous ammonia solution the oxidation, $[Co(NH_3)_6]^{++} = [Co(NH_3)_6]^{+3} + e^-$ ($E° = +0.1$) occurs spontaneously in the presence of the oxygen of the air, because of the extremely high stability constant of $[Co(NH_3)_6]^{+3}$ ($K = 10^{35}$ (mole/l.)$^{-6}$). Cobalt(II) is also easily oxidized to the +3 state in basic solutions, forming an insoluble hydroxide of formula close to $Co(OH)_3$ ($K_{sp} = 3 \times 10^{-41}$ (mole/l.)^4).

Aqueous solutions of soluble Co(II) salts, in the absence of strong ligands, contain the octahedral, pink hexaaquocobalt(II) ion, $[Co(H_2O)_6]^{++}$, which is only very slightly hydrolyzed. A change in color from pink to bright blue occurs when concentrated hydrochloric acid and a solvent such as ethanol or acetone are added to an aqueous solution containing $[Co(H_2O)_6]^{++}$. This change in color results when the 6 H_2O molecules octahedrally surrounding the Co(II) ion of the pink cation, $[Co(H_2O)_6]^{++}$, are replaced by 4 Cl^- ions forming the blue anion, $[CoCl_4]^=$:

$$\underset{\text{pink, octahedral}}{[Co(H_2O)_6]^{++}} + 4\ Cl^- \rightleftharpoons \underset{\text{blue, tetrahedral}}{[CoCl_4]^=} + 6\ H_2O$$

This equilibrium is shifted to the right by addition of Cl^- together with a solvent—such as ethanol or acetone—which decrease the effective concentration of H_2O molecules. The equilibrium is shifted to the left by the addition of H_2O; cooling the solution also favors the formation of the pink $[Co(H_2O)_6]^{++}$ ion. All reactions involving Co(II) and its complexes are extremely fast; that is, Co(II) is a *labile* system. On the other hand, Co(III), like Cr(III), forms octahedral complexes which are relatively inert—that is, they react slowly. Very many complexes of Co(III) have been extensively studied; examples are $[Co(NH_3)_6]^{+3}$, $[Co(NH_3)_5Cl]^{++}$, $[Co(CN)_6]^{-3}$, and $[Co(NO_2)_6]^{-3}$.

NICKEL

The Latimer oxidation-potential diagrams of nickel are:

In 1 M acid solution: $Ni \xrightarrow{+0.25} Ni^{++} \xrightarrow{-1.68} NiO_2$
In 1 M basic solution: $Ni \xrightarrow{+0.72} Ni(OH)_2 \xrightarrow{-0.49} NiO_2$

These oxidation-potential diagrams tell us that in acid, neutral, as well as basic solution, the more stable oxidation state of nickel is +2. Acidic and neutral solutions contain the green, hexaaquonickel(II) ion, $[Ni(H_2O)_6]^{++}$, which is only very slightly hydrolyzed. When a Ni(II) solution is treated with an alkali-metal hydroxide, nickel(II) hydroxide, $Ni(OH)_2$, separates as an apple-green gelatinous precipitate.

The oxidation of Ni(II) in an alkaline solution by a strong oxidant—for example, the hypochlorite ion, ClO^-—produces a black insoluble oxide of formula varying between Ni_2O_3 and NiO_2. These oxides of higher oxidation states are very strong oxidants, especially in the presence of acids; in fact, in acid solutions, NiO_2 can decompose water to give O_2 gas, re-forming the green $[Ni(H_2O)_6]^{++}$ ion.

34-6 Coordination Number and Stereochemistry in the Compounds of Transition Elements

As we mentioned earlier, the compounds of the transition elements are characterized by an extreme variety of coordination number, stereochemistry, mode of bonding, and electron configuration. We have discussed these aspects in general in Chapter 33. Here, as an illustration, we shall briefly summarize the different types of compounds that can be obtained with nickel, $_{28}Ni$, the last element of the First Transition Series.

COMPOUNDS OF Ni(0). Nickel forms many compounds in which it exhibits the oxidation state zero. Examples are tetracarbonylnickel(0), $[Ni(CO)_4]$, a colorless volatile liquid, and potassium tetracyanonickelate(0), $K_4[Ni(CN)_4]$, a yellow crystalline solid. In these complexes, the central nickel(0) attains the electron configuration of the next noble gas, krypton. In fact, both complexes are diamagnetic and have a tetrahedral stereochemistry—as would be expected for 4-coordinate compounds containing a central atom with a symmetrical core:

	3d	4s	4p
Ni(O) gaseous atom	(↑↓)(↑↓)(↑↓)(↑)(↑)	(↑↓)	( )( )( )
Ni(O) valence state	(↑↓)(↑↓)(↑↓)(↑↓)(↑↓)	( )	( )( )( )
Ni(O) in [$Ni(CO)_4$]	(↑↓)(↑↓)(↑↓)(↑↓)(↑↓)	(↑↓)	(↑↓)(↑↓)(↑↓)
	electrons of Ni(O) partly involved in π-back-donation to CO ligands	sp^3 hybridization σ-bonding electrons donated by C atoms of CO ligands	

COMPOUNDS OF NICKEL(II). In its compounds, nickel(II) most commonly has the coordination numbers 4 and 6; some compounds with coordination number 5 are also known, but we shall not consider them here.

The compounds of coordination number 4 can have either a tetrahedral stereochemistry with a high-spin electron configuration (2 unpaired electrons) or a square planar stereochemistry with a low-spin electron configuration (no unpaired electrons). Simple examples are the tetrahedral, paramagnetic, blue complex anion $[NiCl_4]^{=}$ and the square planar, diamagnetic, yellow complex anion $[Ni(CN)_4]^{=}$, which we discussed in detail in Chapter 33 (p. 730).

The compounds of Ni(II) with coordination number 6 have an octahedral stereochemistry almost exclusively, and the electron configuration is of the high-spin type (2 unpaired electrons). The following paramagentic complexes are examples: $[Ni(H_2O)_6]^{++}$ (green), $[Ni(NH_3)_6]^{++}$ (blue-violet), $[Ni(NO_2)_2(NH_3)_4]^0$ (violet), and $[Ni(NO_2)_6]^{-4}$ (purple).

Often, nickel(II) attains a coordination number of 6 and an octahedral stereochemistry by sharing 1, 2, or even 3 of the ligating atoms as bridges in a dimeric or polymeric structure. For example, the blue-green, paramagnetic complex of the simple formula $NiCl_2(NH_3)_2$ is a polymer, $\{NiCl_2(NH_3)_2\}_n$, with a chain-like structure:

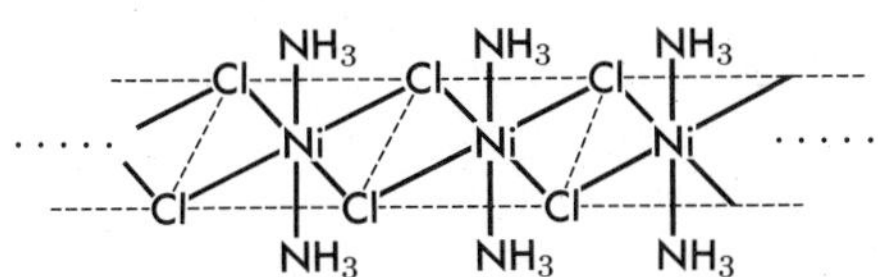

In this structure each Ni atom is surrounded by 4 Cl atoms in a plane, and by 2 N atoms (of NH_3 molecules) above and below this plane, giving rise to a distorted octahedral arrangement. In turn, each Cl atom acts as a "bridging ligand," being shared by 2 adjacent Ni atoms.

Similarly, even solid nickel(II) chloride, usually written as $NiCl_2$, may be regarded as an octahedral Ni(II) complex, since in its three-dimensional lattice each Ni atom is surrounded octahedrally by 6 Cl atoms, and in turn each Cl atom is shared by 3 neighboring Ni atoms.

34-7 Occurrence in Nature and Uses

Sc

Scandium, a rather rare element, is present in traces in many oxide minerals containing lanthanum and other elements of Group IIIA. Scandium has scarce practical applications and is far less important than the other members of the First Transition Series.

Ti

Titanium is the eleventh most abundant element in the earth's crust, and is far more abundant than some of the metals that we tend to think of as common, such as copper, nickel, and zinc. The most important titanium ores are the dioxide, TiO_2, *rutile,* whose crystal structure we discussed in Chapter 10 (p. 175), and the mixed oxide $FeO \cdot TiO_2$ (or $FeTiO_3$), *ilmenite.* Because of its desirable properties—its low density, high resistance to corrosion, and great mechanical strength even at relatively high temperatures—pure titanium metal is widely used for the manufacture of reaction vessels, pipes, and autoclaves in the chemical industry. The dioxide, TiO_2, is largely used as a white pigment, especially for enamels and paper.

V

Vanadium is also a rather abundant element; some representative vanadium minerals are: *vanadinite,* $3\ PbO \cdot V_2O_5 \cdot PbCl_2$; *dechenite,* $(Pb, Zn)\ O \cdot V_2O_5$; and *carnotite,* $K_2O \cdot 2\ VO_3 \cdot V_2O_5 \cdot 3\ H_2O$. Carnotite, incidentally, is also an important source of uranium. Vanadium is an important component of many alloys; very large quantities of vanadium are used in the manufacture of special steels. Vanadium(V) oxide, V_2O_5, is largely used as the catalyst in the oxidation of SO_2 to SO_3, which is the essential step in the preparation of H_2SO_4 by the *contact-process* (p. 638).

Cr

Chromium exists in nature almost exclusively in combination with oxygen. The principal chromium ore, *chromite,* $FeO \cdot Cr_2O_3$, contains iron in the divalent state and chromium in the trivalent state. Other ores contain chromium in a +6 oxidation state; an example is $PbCrO_4$, lead(II) chromate. The two distinguishing properties of chromium metal—its brilliant, pleasing luster, and its resistance to corrosion—are responsible for its wide use as a protective plating material for other metals. In such alloys as the chrome steels, it is used extensively in the manufacture of ball bearings, armor plate, and projectiles. Also, chromium-alloy steels are widely used in processes involving high temperature and pressures. What is known as "stainless steel" is actually an alloy of 74 per cent iron, 18 per cent chromium, and 8 per cent nickel. Many chromium salts, which have brilliant colors and are highly insoluble and stable, are used as pigments. An example is chromium(III) oxide, Cr_2O_3, which is used as a beautiful green pigment, called "chrome green." Some Cr(VI) salts are used in industry as oxidants.

Mn

Manganese occurs in many oxide ores, the most important of which is *pyrolusite,* MnO_2, a black mineral. Less important ores are: *braunite,* Mn_2O_3; *manganite,* $Mn_2O_3 \cdot H_2O$; and *hausmannite,* $MnO \cdot Mn_2O_3$. Manganese is also present as a fairly abundant impurity in most iron ores. Metallic manganese, as such, is not used to any appreciable extent in industry. But an iron-manganese alloy called ferromanganese, which contains 75 to 80 per cent manganese, is largely used in the manufacture of special steels. The addition of small quantities of ferromanganese improves the quality of steel by removing traces of oxygen and sulfur in forming MnO_2 and MnS, which are separated in the slag. The addition of larger quantities of ferromanganese forms steel of great toughness. Manganese dioxide, MnO_2, is used as a drier for paints, since it catalyzes the oxidation (drying) of the paint oils by the oxygen of the air; as a decolorizer of glass, since it oxidizes any green Fe(II) compound present to a much paler yellow Fe(III) compound; and as a depolarizer in dry cells, since it reacts with the H_2 liberated at the carbon cathode. Potassium permanganate, $KMnO_4$, finds some use as a strong oxidant, especially in analytical procedures.

Fe

Iron has been known from prehistoric times. The isolation of iron metal from its oxide ores has been carried out since pre-Roman times; the blast furnace, however, seems to have been developed only about 1500 A.D. Iron is the fourth most abundant element in the earth's crust, and the second most abundant metal, after aluminum. In nature iron occurs only in chemical combination, chiefly an oxide or carbonate, less commonly a sulfide. The principle oxide ores are *hematite,* Fe_2O_3; *magnetite,* $FeO \cdot Fe_2O_3$; and a hydrated iron(III) oxide called *limonite,* $Fe_2O_3 \cdot xH_2O$. The principal carbonate ore is *siderite,* $FeCO_3$. The most important sulfide ore is *iron pyrite,* FeS_2. In addition, nearly all rocks and soils contain at least traces of iron. Compounds of iron play an extremely important role in life processes. Most of the iron in the human body is present in the hemoglobin of the blood, which transports the oxygen of the air from the lungs to tissues throughout the body. In plants, small amounts of iron appear to be necessary for normal growth. Pure iron metal is rarely used in industry, but steel—which is an alloy of iron with other metals (chromium, nickel, vanadium, manganese) containing small percentages of carbon—is used in enormous quantities in the construction of everything from bridges, buildings, and machines down to tiny bolts and nuts. Iron(III) oxide, which has a pleasing rust color and is insoluble in water and acids, is largely used as a pigment for weather-resistant paints.

Co

Cobalt nearly always occurs in combination with arsenic and sulfur; nickel, iron, and copper are often present in the same ores. Important minerals of cobalt are $CoAs_2$, *smaltite;* CoAsS, *cobaltite;* Co_3S_4, *linnaeite;* and $Co_3(AsO_4)_2 \cdot 8\ H_2O$, *erythrite.* The chief use of cobalt is in the manufacture of corrosion-resistant alloys.

Nickel is found both in sulfide and arsenide ores—for example, *niccolite,* NiS; *millerite,* NiAs; *bravoite,* $(Ni, Fe)S_2$;—and in a variety of oxide and silicate ores, where it usually accompanies magnesium(II) and iron(II). Nickel metal, like platinum (and palladium), is an excellent catalyst, especially in reactions involving hydrogen gas. The other principal uses of nickel are as a constituent of a wide variety of alloys and in electroplating.

34-8 Preparation of the Metals

Metallic scandium can be prepared by the electrolysis of molten scandium(III) chloride, $ScCl_3$, in the presence of some LiCl and KCl to lower the melting point of the electrolyte. The method is similar to that used in the preparation of calcium metal (p. 685).

Ti

Commercial methods of producing pure Ti are based on the reduction at high temperatures of titanium(IV) chloride, $TiCl_4$, with a reducing metal, such as Na, K, Mg, or Ca, in the absence of O_2, N_2, H_2, C, and any other substance that would react with the free metal. For example, pure Ti metal is produced commercially by the reaction of $TiCl_4$ with molten Mg in an inert atmosphere of argon or helium:

$$TiCl_4 + 2\ Mg \longrightarrow Ti + 2\ MgCl_2$$

The reduction of TiO_2 with carbon in an electric furnace produces a mixture of Ti metal and titanium carbide, TiC_2, which can be used directly for the manufacture of alloys.

V

It is possible to produce vanadium metal of 99 per cent (or higher) purity by heating vanadium(V) oxide, V_2O_5, with a mixture of Ca metal and $CaCl_2$ in a steel bomb at 900–950°C.

Cr

Chromium metal may be prepared by the reduction of Cr_2O_3 with aluminum, by means of a method known as the *thermite process:*

$$Cr_2O_3 + 2\ Al \longrightarrow 2\ Cr + Al_2O_3 \qquad \Delta H = -109\ \text{kcal/mole-eqn at } 25^\circ$$

An initial heating of the Cr_2O_3-Al mixture is necessary to start the reaction; however, once the reaction has begun, enough heat is liberated to raise the temperature of the mixture above the melting point of chromium, thus producing the metal in a compact form. Pure chromium metal may also be produced by the reduction of Cr_2O_3 with carbon in an electric furnace. An iron-chromium alloy known as ferro-chrome, which is chiefly used in making chrome steel, is prepared by the reduction of chromite, $FeCr_2O_4$, with carbon in an electric furnace:

$$FeCr_2O_4 + 4\ C \longrightarrow 2\ Cr + Fe + 4\ CO$$

Mn

The most convenient method of preparing relatively pure metallic manganese is through the reduction of Mn_3O_4 with metallic aluminum. The oxide Mn_3O_4, rather than the pyrolusite ore, MnO_2, is used in this process because the reaction of Mn_3O_4 with Al is less exothermic and therefore easier to control. So the MnO_2 ore is first partially decomposed to Mn_3O_4 by heating it to redness: $3\ MnO_2 \longrightarrow Mn_3O_4 + O_2$.

The Mn_2O_3 is then reduced with Al powder, as described previously for chromium: $3\ Mn_3O_4 + 8\ Al \longrightarrow 9\ Mn + 4\ Al_2O_3$. Less pure manganese, containing carbon in the form of Mn_3C, may be prepared by the thermal reduction of MnO_2 by carbon.

Since iron and the many kinds of iron alloys are more widely used than any other metal or alloy, we shall consider the commercial preparation of iron and some of its common alloys (steels) in some detail. A number of interesting chemical reactions are involved in the commonly used methods of preparing iron. All these methods involve the following steps: (1) The reduction of an oxide of iron with CO to form "pig iron." (2) The treatment of the pig iron, to remove some constituents and to add others. (3) The tempering and/or annealing of the product to produce a material with the desired physical properties.

Production of pig iron. The starting material is a mixture of iron(III) oxide, Fe_2O_3; coke, C; and limestone, $CaCO_3$. The proportions of iron ore, coke, and limestone vary depending on the composition of the iron ore, but an excess of coke is always provided. This mixture is charged into a furnace and a blast of preheated oxygen or air is forced into the base of the furnace. The coke reacts with the oxygen present in the heated air and is converted chiefly to CO; the heat liberated by this exothermic reaction raises the temperature of the furnace. The region of the furnace where this combustion occurs, near the base, has the highest temperature, and as the gases rise through the charge they are gradually cooled. A furnace in stable operation shows a temperature gradient from about 1,930°C at the bottom to about 200°C at the top. Now, starting at the *top* of a furnace let us follow the various reactions that take place. Near the top of the furnace, where the temperature is about 200°C, the most important chemical reaction is the reduction of Fe_2O_3 to Fe_3O_4 by the CO:

$$3\ Fe_2O_3 + CO \longrightarrow 2\ Fe_3O_4 + CO_2$$

At a point lower down, where the temperature is about 350°C, Fe_3O_4 is further reduced to FeO:

$$Fe_3O_4 + CO \longrightarrow 3\ FeO + CO_2$$

Still farther down, where the temperature is higher than 350°C, FeO is reduced to metallic iron as a spongy solid:

$$FeO + CO \longrightarrow Fe + CO_2$$

The Manufacture of Steel. Iron alloys with carbon contents ranging from about 0.1 to 1.5 per cent are known commercially as steels. In the manufacture of steel, pig iron is the usual starting material. Since steel contains less carbon (0.1 to 1.5 per cent) and fewer impurities than pig iron, the removal of these materials is an essential step in steel manufacture; it is usually accomplished by either the Bessemer process or the open-hearth process.

The Bessemer process. The molten pig iron from the blast furnace is poured into the Bessemer converter, which is a large egg-shaped steel vessel lined with refractory brick and provided at the base with air inlets. Oxygen, air, or a mixture of oxygen and air under pressure is blown in through small inlets at the base. As the O_2 gas rises through the molten metal, the silicon and manganese present as impurities in the pig iron, together with the carbon of iron carbide, Fe_3C, and some of the iron itself, are oxidized:

$$\begin{aligned} Si + O_2 &\longrightarrow SiO_2 \\ 2\ Mn + O_2 &\longrightarrow 2\ MnO \\ 2\ Fe_3C + O_2 &\longrightarrow 6\ Fe + 2\ CO \\ 2\ Fe + O_2 &\longrightarrow 2\ FeO \end{aligned}$$

The SiO_2 reacts with the MnO and the FeO to form a slag:

$$MnO + SiO_2 \longrightarrow MnSiO_3$$
$$FeO + SiO_2 \longrightarrow FeSiO_3$$

When almost all the carbon of Fe_3C has been burned out, the oxygen or air intake is immediately turned off, to prevent additional Fe from being oxidized to FeO.

The Bessemer process removes almost all the carbon from the molten metal; and yet some carbon is desired, for limited amounts improve the mechanical and chemical properties of the steel. Consequently, the desired quantity of carbon is now added to the charge. (It is easier to remove all the carbon that was originally present and then to add the exactly required quantity than it is to remove just the excess.) A calculated amount of manganese is added also to reduce any FeO that may still be present and to form slag with the remaining SiO_2.

In addition to these reduction reactions involving the iron oxide ore, various other reactions are also important. The $CaCO_3$ dissociates to CaO and CO_2, and the CO_2 thus produced reacts with the excess of coke to produce more CO:

$$CaCO_3 \longrightarrow CaO + CO_2$$
$$C + CO_2 \longrightarrow 2\ CO$$

In turn, the CaO reacts with the solid SiO_2 and Al_2O_3, present as impurities in the iron ore, to form the readily fusible $CaSiO_3$ and $Ca(AlO_2)_2$:

$$CaO + SiO_2 \longrightarrow CaSiO_3$$
$$CaO + Al_2O_3 \longrightarrow Ca(AlO_2)_2$$

Near the bottom of the furnace, the combustion of the coke generates sufficient heat to raise the temperature to 1,930°C, thus melting both the iron and the slag, which form two distinct layers and can be tapped off separately. As these molten materials are removed at the bottom, the solid materials in the furnace drop down into areas of higher temperatures and more charge is added to the top of the furnace, so that the operation runs on continuously. The exhaust gases which leave at the top of the furnace consist of about 60 per cent N_2, 25 per cent CO, about 10 per cent CO_2, and about 5 per cent H_2. This flue gas has a temperature of about 200°C and is used to preheat the blast of oxygen or air that is introduced at the bottom. The CO content can also be burned to CO_2, liberating additional heat energy.

The open-hearth process. This process produces a higher-quality steel than the Bessemer process, though it is not so rapid. The open-hearth furnace consists essentially of a shallow, saucer-like hearth, in which molten iron is heated by flames from combustible gases in contact with the iron. For a charge that is relatively low in phosphorus and sulfur impurities, a lining of silica brick is used. This process is called the *acid* open-hearth process. The silica brick acts only as a fire brick, and takes no chemical part in the process. For a charge that is relatively high in phosphorus and sulfur impurities, a lining of some basic material is used, such as magnesia brick, MgO, which reacts with such impurities as the acid oxide, P_4O_{10}. This process is called the *basic* open-hearth process.

In the *basic* process the average charge consists of pig iron, scrap iron, and hematite, Fe_2O_3, in amounts calculated to produce the desired steel. (The oxygen present in Fe_2O_3 combines with the carbon of Fe_3C, and the scrap iron provides the desired quantities of additional elements, chiefly chromium and nickel.) The furnace is heated at a temperature of about 1,600°C by burning fuel gas in air. At this very high temperature, any silicon, phosphorus, and sulfur that are present in the charge form SiO_2, P_4O_{10}, and SO_2, which react with the basic lining of the furnace to form a slag. The carbon present as Fe_3C reacts with the hematite to form CO gas, the evolution of which helps to keep the charge stirred:

$$3\ Fe_3C + Fe_2O_3 \longrightarrow 11\ Fe + 3\ CO$$

When analysis of the charge shows that the desired carbon content has been reached, the proper amounts of ferromanganese, or spiegeleisen, and other alloys, are added to form a steel of the desired composition. The molten steel and slag are then tapped from the bottom of the hearth and separated.

Co Ni

Cobalt and nickel are very often present together in their ores, especially the sulfide and arsenide ores; other metals, such as iron and copper, are also present. A common process for the preparation of cobalt and nickel from their arsenide and sulfide ores is the following. The ore is first heated at high temperatures in the presence of oygen, in a process known as "roasting." The arsenic and sulfur are removed as their volatile oxides, As_2O_3 and SO_2, and the oxides of the metals are formed. The mixture of metal oxides is then reduced with $H_2 + CO$ (water gas) at high temperatures, to give an alloy that contains varying proportions of cobalt, nickel, and iron. This alloy can be used directly for the manufacture of special steels. If pure nickel is desired, the alloy is finely powdered and heated to 50°C in a stream of carbon monoxide, which converts nickel metal to volatile nickel carbonyl, $Ni(CO)_4$ (b.p., 43.2°C), but does not react under these conditions with iron and cobalt. Nickel carbonyl is then carried along with the excess carbon monoxide through tubes heated to 150–200°C and decomposes into pure nickel and carbon monoxide. Cobalt metal is generally purified by electrolysis is slightly acid solution.

Exercises

34-1 Discuss the general properties of the transition elements in regard to (a) size of the atoms, (b) interatomic bonding and melting points, (c) ionization potentials, (d) electropositive character, (e) color, and (f) magnetic properties.

34-2 (a) Which oxidation state of titanium is the most stable? (b) Write an equation to illustrate: (1) the strong reducing properties of the +2 oxidation state of titanium; (2) the disproportionation of the +3 oxidation state of titanium, (c) Does TiO_2 react with (1) hydrochloric acid? (2) hydrofluoric acid? Write equations.

34-3 Vanadium metal, like titanium metal, is very difficult to obtain in the metallic state. Explain.

34-4 Illustrate the strong reducing properties of dipositive vanadium by means of its reaction with water. Explain the formation of the vanadyl ion, whenever a V(IV) compound, for example VCl_4, is dissolved in water.

34-5 (a) Chromium metal is more electropositive than iron, yet it is used as a protective coating. Explain. (b) Write the equation for the thermite process for the preparation of chromium. (c) List the important oxidation states of chromium and indicate their relative stabilities. (d) Indicate the acidic or basic character of the oxides CrO, Cr_2O_3, and CrO_3. (e) Write equations for the reaction of chromium metal with HCl.

34-6 Starting with chromium metal, indicate how you would prepare the following compounds: (a) $CrSO_4 \cdot 7\,H_2O$, (b) $Cr(OH)_2$, (c) $Cr(OH)_3$.

34-7 Write equations to illustrate the amphoteric property of $Cr(OH)_3$.

34-8 (a) List the principal oxidation states of manganese. (b) Write equations for the reaction of HCl with (1) MnO, (2) MnO_2. Compare the oxidizing power of (1) MnO_2 and (2) $KMnO_4$ in acid and in basic solutions. Illustrate with equations.

34-9 Starting with iron as one of the reactants, describe by equations how you would prepare the following compounds either in the solid state or in solution: (a) Fe_3O_4, (b) $FeCl_2$, (c) $Fe(OH)_2$, (d) $FeCO_3$, (e) iron(III) chloride, (f) FeS, (g) $Fe_2(SO_4)_3$, (h) $Fe(OH)_3$.

34-10 State the principal oxidation states of cobalt. Give examples, and discuss their relative stabilities in (a) water, (b) acid solution, (c) basic solution, and (d) aqueous solutions containing NH_3.

34-11 (a) State the principle oxidation state of nickel. Give examples of compounds with coordination numbers 4 and 6. (b) Explain how nickel metal is obtained from its ore.

THE POST-TRANSITION ELEMENTS

35

In this chapter we shall discuss the elements of Group IB—copper, Cu; silver, Ag; and gold, Au—and the elements of Group IIB—zinc, Zn; cadmium, Cd; and mercury, Hg. These elements are generally called post-transition elements since they immediately follow the transition metals in each long period of the Periodic Table. The post-transition elements are metallic in character, and their physical and chemical properties show close similarities within each Group.

35-1 Copper; Silver; Gold —The Coinage Metals

NATURAL OCCURRENCE

The familiar metals Cu, Ag, and Au have been known since the time of the earliest civilizations. This is remarkable, because these elements are not abundant. Copper, the most abundant of the three, is present in the earth's crust to the extent of only about 0.0001 per cent and ranks twenty-fifth in abundance of all the elements. Silver occurs to the extent of 10^{-8} per cent, and gold to the extent of 10^{-9} per cent. Two factors that favored the widespread use of these three relatively rare metals are that their deposits are often concentrated and the metals themselves are easily extracted from their ores. Since copper, silver, and gold have been used since ancient times in the manufacture of coins, they are often called the "coinage metals."

Although copper sometimes occurs as the relatively pure, free metal, industrial copper is obtained principally from ores containing copper compounds. The most important of these ores contain copper combined with oxygen or sulfur. Examples are Cu_2O, cuprite; $CuFeS_2$, chalcopyrite; and Cu_2S, chalcocite. Silver is found frequently as the free metal. Its most important minerals are the sulfide Ag_2S, argentite, and the chloride, AgCl, horn silver. Silver is also present, in small concentrations, in many ores of copper, lead, and zinc, and is recovered as an important by-product in the metallurgy of these metals. Gold is found principally as the free metal, but in such very small concentrations that it has to be separated by mechanical or chemical processes. Much of the world's gold is obtained as a by-product in the refining of copper, zinc, lead, and silver.

THE PHYSICAL PROPERTIES OF Cu, Ag, AND Au

Stable State at 25°C, 1 atm	IB
reddish metal	Cu
white metal	Ag
yellow metal	Au

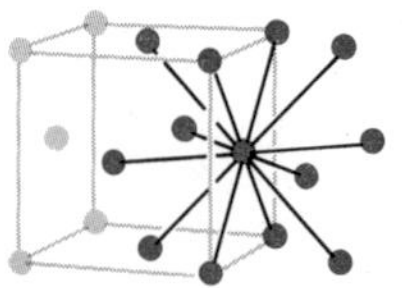

All have face-centered cubic structures

The gaseous atoms of Cu, Ag, and Au have an outer $d^{10}s^1$ electron configuration, as shown in Table 35-1. The valence electron of the coinage metals is, therefore, an ns^1 electron, as in the alkali metals. However, in the alkali metals the electron shell underlying the ns^1 electron is the $(n-1)s^2(n-1)p^6$ shell (a noble-gas configuration), whereas in the coinage metals the underlying shell is $(n-1)d^{10}$. This difference in the underlying electron shell is the reason for the very marked difference in properties and behavior between the alkali metals (Group IA) and the coinage metals (Group IB). Some important properties of the coinage metals are listed in Table 35-1; their ionization energies and oxidation potentials are given in Table 35-2.

The coinage metals are highly malleable and ductile, with gold ranking first, silver second, and copper third. In fact, gold, which is the most malleable and ductile of all metals, can be beaten into a sheet so thin that it becomes translucent to green light. The thermal and electrical conductivities of these metals are the highest of all the elements, with silver this time ranking first, copper second, and gold third. Because of its high thermal and electrical conductivity and its relatively low cost, copper is extensively used to manufacture electrical wiring.

The ΔH_{atomiz}, and consequently the melting and boiling points of the coinage metals, follow an irregular trend—first decreasing markedly from Cu to Ag, then increasing markedly from Ag to Au (see Table 35-1). On the other hand, for the ionic radii of the M^+ ions with the $(n-1)d^{10}$ electron configuration, we see that the ionic sizes regularly increase from Cu^+ (0.96 A) to Ag^+ (1.26 A) to Au^+ (1.37 A). Thus, the observed trend in the strength of the metallic bond for Cu, Ag, and Au, as well as the trend of their first ionization energy ($M_{(g)} \longrightarrow M^+_{(g)} + e^-$, where the ns^1 electron is removed), arises not from a size effect, but from changes in the effective nuclear charge of these elements. In fact, as we pass from Cu to Ag, which both have a $(n-1)d^{10}$ underlying shell, and hence have comparable effective nuclear charges,

TABLE 35-1 SOME PROPERTIES OF Cu, Ag, AND Au (GROUP IB ELEMENTS)

Element	Outer Electron Config.	Atomic Weight	Atomic[a] Radius A	Ionic Radius A	Density 20°C, g/cm³	Melting Point °C	Boiling Point °C	$\Delta H_{atomiz.}$ (kcal/mole)	Electro-negativity (Pauling)	Electron Affinity (kcal/mole)
$_{29}Cu$	$3d^{10},4s^1$	63.54	1.28 (12)	0.96 (Cu^+); 0.69 (Cu^{++})	8.96	1,083	2,600	81.1	1.8	27.7
$_{47}Ag$	$4d^{10},5s^1$	107.87	1.44 (12)	1.26 (Ag^+)	10.5	961	2,210	68.0	1.9	23.1
$_{79}Au$	$(4f^{14}),5d^{10},6s^1$	196.97	1.44 (12)	1.37 (Au^+)	19.3	1,063	2,970	87.5	2.4	48.4

[a] Metallic radius; the number in parentheses indicates the crystal coordination number.

TABLE 35-2 IONIZATION ENERGIES AND OXIDATION POTENTIALS OF Cu, Ag, AND Au

Element	Ionization Energy (kcal/mole)			Oxidation Potentials, $E°$ (volts)		
	1st	2nd	3rd	M, $M^+_{(aq)}$	M, $M^{++}_{(aq)}$	M, $M^{3+}_{(aq)}$
Cu	178	468	875	−0.52	−0.34	—
Ag	176	497	800	−0.80	−1.39	—
Au	212	470	690	~1.7	—	−1.50

the strength of the metallic bond and the first ionization energy decrease as expected with increasing size. But when we pass from Ag to Au, the nature of the underlying shell changes, since Au alone has an f^{14} filled shell, as well as the d^{10} filled shell. And since the f electrons have poorer screening properties than the d electrons, the effective nuclear charge of Au will be correspondingly greater than that of Ag. Hence the $6s^1$ valence electron of Au is held more strongly by its nucleus than the $5s^1$ valence electron of Ag, resulting in gold's stronger metallic bonding and higher ionization energy (see Figure 35-1).

COMPARISON BETWEEN THE GROUP IB AND THE GROUP IA ELEMENTS. Unlike the alkali metals, which have very low melting points (the highest being Li, 180°C), the coinage metals have very high melting points (the lowest being Ag, 960°C). Also, the densities of the coinage metals (Group IB) are about 10 times greater than those of the corresponding alkali metals (Group IA). This indicates that the metallic bonding is stronger in the coinage metals than in the alkali metals, and suggests that in the coinage metals some of the $(n-1)d$ electrons participate in the metallic bonding, in addition to the ns^1 electron.

The first ionization energies of Cu, Ag, and Au, corresponding to the removal of the ns^1 valence electron, are much higher than those of the corresponding alkali metals, K, Rb, and Cs, because of two cooperating factors: (1) The

FIGURE 35-1 Comparative properties of copper, silver, and gold.

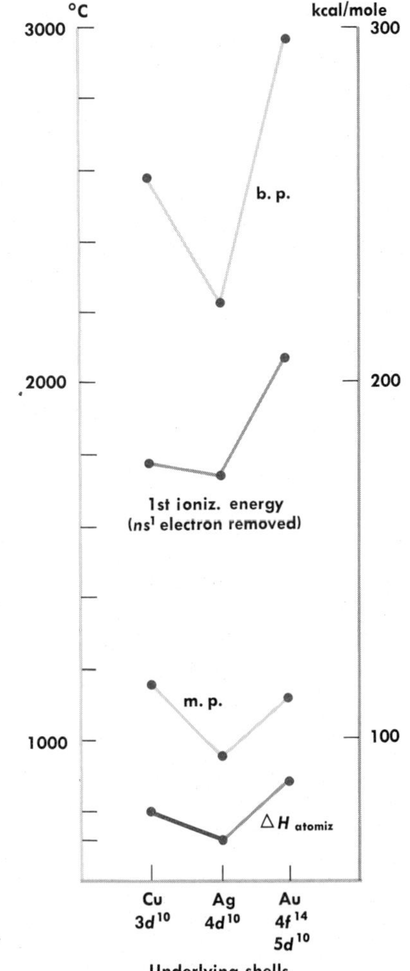

size of Cu^+, Ag^+, and Au^+ is appreciably smaller than that of K^+, Rb^+, and Cs^+, respectively. (2) The effective nuclear charge of Cu^+, Ag^+, and Au^+ is greater than that of the corresponding alkali metal ion, M^+, because the $(n - 1)d^{10}$ shell, and even more so the $4f^{14}$ shell present in Au^+, have poor shielding properties as compared with the noble gas electron configuration of the alkali-metal ions, M^+. And since the coinage metals have such high ionization energies, they are among the *least* electropositive of all metals—actually, we may consider them as being electronegative—whereas the alkali metals are among the *most* electropositive.

35-2 The Chemical Properties of Cu, Ag, and Au

The chemical properties of Cu, Ag, and Au can be related to their high ionization energies, high heats of atomization, and relatively low heats of hydration, which together determine their negative oxidation potentials and in general their low reactivity (noble character). For example, copper is the only member of Group IB that reacts directly with oxygen, forming two oxides, Cu_2O and CuO; silver oxide, Ag_2O, even though stable at room temperature ($\Delta G_{form} = -2.7$ kcal/mole), decomposes into its elements at about 200°C. Finally, gold does not form an oxide at all. Furthermore, copper, silver, and gold generally react very slowly even when the reactions are thermodynamically permitted—as are, for example, the reaction of fluorine gas with copper and silver metals. The very high activation energy of reactions involving metallic Cu, Ag, and Au is related to their very high heats of atomization.

All coinage metals exhibit the oxidation state +1, corresponding to the loss of the outer ns^1 electron. In addition, Cu, Ag, and Au also form compounds with oxidation states +2 and +3, corresponding to the removal of one and two of the $(n - 1)d$ electrons, respectively.

Copper occurs mostly in Cu(I), cuprous, and Cu(II), cupric compounds, those of Cu(II) being more common in water solution. Silver forms preferably Ag(I) compounds and gold forms Au(I), aurous, and Au(III), auric, compounds, the latter being more common. Of the coinage metals, it appears that only gold does not form M(II) compounds. The few compounds whose formulas apparently correspond to Au(II)—for example, "AuS"—contain Au(I) and Au(III) in equal proportions. It is important to remark that the compounds of Cu(I), Ag(I), and Au(I) contain metal ions with a completely filled $(n - 1)d^{10}$ shell—a symmetrical core—whereas the compounds with oxidation states +2 and +3 contain metal ions with a partially filled $(n - 1)d$ shell, which therefore act as transition metal ions. Thus, Au(III) is isoelectronic with Pt(II), and like Pt(II) forms compounds preferably with coordination numbers 4 and a square planar stereochemistry (involving dsp^2 hybrid orbitals).

The ions of the coinage metals, because of their relatively high charge/radius ratio, are strongly polarizing and tend to form compounds in which the bonding has an appreciable covalent character. For this same reason, the coinage metal ions have a very strong tendency to form complexes with the more polarizable ligands, both negative (for example, Cl^-, Br^-, CN^-) and neutral (for example, molecules with S or P as donor atoms). This tendency is especially true in the case of gold, for which a stable hydrated cation, $Au^+_{(aq)}$ or $Au^{+++}_{(aq)}$, is not known. Notice that in this respect gold and cesium exhibit extremely different behaviors, even though they have the same $6s^1$ outer electron configurations; Cs is the metal with the least tendency to form complexes, and Au exists most commonly in coordination compounds.

We saw above that the coinage metals might be considered to have a certain electronegative character. Indeed, the electronegativity value of gold is not far from that of a typically electronegative non-metal such as bromine (Au, 2.4; Br, 2.8). Furthermore, gold has a high negative electron affinity—about one-half that of bromine (Au, 48.4; Br, 81.4). And, in fact, gold exists as a mononegative Au^- ion (having a $6s^2$ outer electron configuration) in the crystalline compound cesium auride, Cs^+Au^-.

OXIDATION POTENTIALS OF Cu, Ag, AND Au

Many chemical reactions of copper, silver, and gold can be understood in terms of the oxidation potentials of these metals. First, since Cu, Ag, and Au have negative $E°$ values for the formation of their hydrated cations, $M^{+n}{}_{(aq)}$, these metals do not dissolve in solutions of non-oxidizing acids, unless the anion of the acid is a very good ligand or forms a highly insoluble salt with the metal cation.

Metallic Cu dissolves in all concentrations of nitric acid, and as we would expect from the $E°$ values of the couples (Cu,Cu^+; Cu,Cu^{++}; and NO,HNO_3), the Cu^{++} ion and not the Cu^+ ion is formed in the process. Silver also dissolves in solutions of nitric acid to form Ag^+, but gold does not dissolve. An oxidant as strong as aqua regia is necessary to oxidize Au metal.

For the coinage metals, as for the transition metals and in general for all metals that form stable complexes, the presence of a good ligand in solution tends to make the reaction more favorable—that is, the oxidation potential becomes more positive. As we mentioned above, the oxidation potential also becomes more positive if the solution contains an anion that forms a very insoluble salt with the metal ion. The oxidation potentials of some couples involving either a stable complex or an insoluble salt of a coinage-metal ion are given alongside. These $E°$ values tell us that copper metal can dissolve in aqueous solutions of NH_3 if oxygen gas is passed into the solution ($E°_{basic}$ for O_2, OH^- couple, -0.40 v).

Couple	$E°$ *(volts)*
$Cu, [Cu(NH_3)_6]^{++}$	$+0.07$
$Cu, [Cu(CN)_2]^-$	$+0.43$
$Ag, AgCl_{(s)}$	-0.22
$Ag, AgBr_{(s)}$	-0.03
$Ag, AgI_{(s)}$	$+0.15$
$Ag, [Ag(CN)_2]^-$	$+0.31$
$Au, [Au(CN)_2]^-$	$+0.60$
$Au, [AuCl_4]^-$	-1.00

$$2\,Cu_{(s)} + 12\,NH_{3(aq)} + O_{2(g)} + 2\,H_2O_{(l)} \longrightarrow 2[Cu(NH_3)_6]^{++}{}_{(aq)} + 4\,OH^-{}_{(aq)}$$

Also, metallic Ag, which does not dissolve in 1 M H^+ solution containing 1 M Cl^- ions, will dissolve in 1 M H^+ solution with 1 M I^- ions, or in a 1 M Na^+CN^- solution.

Many self oxidation-reduction reactions involving the coinage metals and their compounds can be understood on the basis of the Latimer oxidation-potential diagrams of the species considered. Thus, the oxidation diagram for the hydrated ions:

$$Cu \overset{-0.52}{\text{———}} Cu^+ \overset{-0.15}{\text{———}} Cu^{++}$$

tells us that if solid anhydrous copper(I) sulfate, Cu_2SO_4, is added to water the Cu^+ ion disproportionates, forming metallic copper, Cu, and hydrated Cu^{++} ions:

$$2\,Cu^+ + SO_4^= \longrightarrow Cu + Cu^{++} + SO_4^=$$

However, Cu(I) in the complex salt $[Cu(NH_3)_2]_2SO_4$ does not disproportionate:

$$Cu \overset{+0.12}{\text{———}} [Cu(NH_3)_2]^+ \overset{+0.01}{\text{———}} [Cu(NH_3)_4]^{++}$$

Similarly, the Latimer oxidation potential of gold:

$$Au \overset{-1.68}{\text{———}} Au^+ \overset{-1.41}{\text{———}} Au^{+++}$$

tells us that AuCl disproportionates when added to water:

$$3\,AuCl \longrightarrow 2\,Au + AuCl_3$$

Let us now consider the various oxidation states of the coinage metals.

THE +1 OXIDATION STATE

Most of the compounds of Cu(I), Ag(I), and Au(I) with monoatomic anions are insoluble in water; examples are CuCl, AgCl, AuCl, and the corresponding bromides, MBr, and iodides, MI. The cyanides, MCN; cyanates, MOCN; and thiocynates, MSCN, are also insoluble in water. In these compounds, the bonding has a more or less marked covalent character because of the relatively high charge/radius ratio of the Cu(I), Ag(I), and Au(I) cations and the polarizable character of the anions. The crystal structure of these compounds depends on both the cation and the anion. For example, AgCl and AgBr have a sodium chloride structure (6:6 octahedral crystal coordination), CuCl has a zinc blende structure (4:4 tetrahedral crystal coordination), whereas AgCN and AgSCN consist of linear and zig-zag covalent chains, respectively.

—Ag—C≡N—Ag—C≡N—Ag—C≡N—

"AgCN" linear chain

S, Ag, C, N, 104°, Ag, C, S, 104°, N, Ag, C, S, 104°, N, Ag

"AgSCN" zig-zag chain

The chloride, bromide, and iodide of silver(I) all darken when exposed to light, the chloride being the most sensitive and the iodide the least. Because of its photosensitivity, pale-yellow silver bromide, AgBr, is the principal constituent of photographic emulsions.

There are a few soluble salts of Ag(I)—for example, the fluoride, AgF; the nitrate, $AgNO_3$; and the perchlorate, $AgClO_4$—but the corresponding Cu^+ and Au^+ compounds are not known. Among the best studied complexes of Cu(I), Ag(I), and Au(I) are the ammine-complexes $[Cu(NH_3)_2]^+$, $[Ag(NH_3)_2]^+$, $[Au(NH_3)_2]^+$; the halo-complexes $[CuCl_2]^-$, $[AgCl_2]^-$, $[AuCl_2]^-$; and the cyano-complexes $[Ag(CN)_2]^-$, $[Au(CN)_2]^-$.

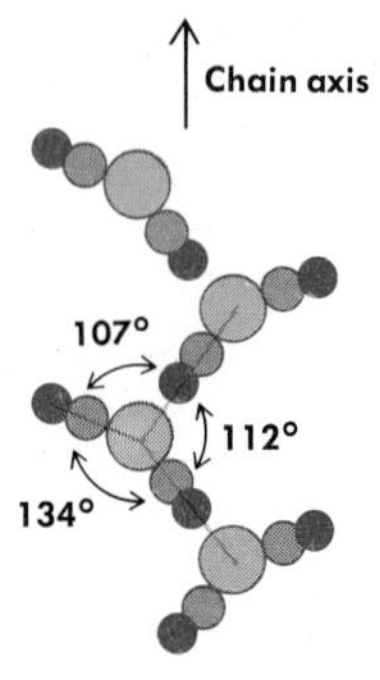

The formation of the diamminesilver(I) complex ion, $[Ag(NH_3)_2]^+$, is important in relation to the precipitation-solution equilibria of silver halides as was discussed in Chapter 24, p. 537. When a solution of ammonia is added to a solution of any soluble silver salt—e.g., silver fluoride—the NH_3 molecule reacts with the Ag^+ ion to form the stable diamminesilver(I) complex ion $[Ag(NH_3)_2]^+$. The NH_3 also reacts with insoluble AgCl to form the soluble $[Ag(NH_3)_2]^+ Cl^-$ complex. It reacts similarly with AgBr, though only to a limited extent, and does not react at all with AgI, which is too insoluble. In all these complexes with C.N. = 2, the central M(I) ion has a linear stereochemistry (two bond pairs and no lone pairs associated with a symmetrical nd^{10} core). On the other hand, it is interesting that in crystalline $K[Cu(CN)_2]$, the structure of the anion consists of infinite chains, in which each Cu(I) is bonded to two C atoms of two CN^- groups and to one N atom of another CN^- group, giving rise to a distorted non-planar trigonal stereochemistry (see upper sketch in margin). Other anionic complexes of Cu(I), Ag(I), and Au(I) are $[CuCl_3]^=$ and $[AgCl_3]^=$. In aqueous solution these very likely exist as the aquo-complexes $[CuCl_3(H_2O)]^=$ and $[AgCl_3(H_2O)]^=$; in the solid state they consist of chains of $\{CuCl_4\}$ and $\{AgCl_4\}$ tetrahedra joined by bridging Cl (see lower sketch in margin). These complexes of the coinage metals are a good illustration of the inadvisibility of drawing conclusions about the structure of a compound on the basis of its formula alone.

Cl Cu

THE +2 OXIDATION STATE

As we have already pointed out, the +2 oxidation state is the more common for copper; for silver, the oxidation state +2 occurs in a few simple compounds and in a number of complexes. No compounds containing Au(II) are known.

In the majority of its compounds Cu(II) has a coordination number of 6, but compounds with coordination numbers of 4 and 5 are also known. In the 6-coordinate compounds, the central Cu(II) is surrounded by 6 donor atoms in a distorted octahedral arrangement; the 4 donor atoms in the equatorial plane are equidistant from the central Cu(II), whereas the 2 donor atoms in the axial positions are farther apart from the Cu(II). This distorted octahedral stereochemistry is called tetragonal and is illustrated in the margin.

2 "long" bonds in the axial positions

Cu^{++}

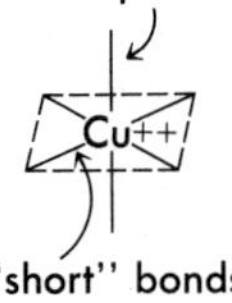

4 "short" bonds in the equatorial plane

The most familiar copper(II) salt is probably the bright blue compound $CuSO_4 \cdot 5\ H_2O$, commonly known as blue vitriol. In the crystal lattice of this salt, the central Cu(II) is surrounded by the 4 O atoms of 4 H_2O molecules at equal distances in a plane, while an O atom of an $SO_4^=$ ion lies above the central Cu(II) ion, and an O atom of another $SO_4^=$ ion is situated at an equal distance below. The Cu(II)-to-oxygen($SO_4^=$) distances are longer than the Cu(II)-to-oxygen(H_2O) distances in the plane, giving rise to a tetragonally distorted octahedral environment of O atoms about the central Cu(II). The fifth H_2O molecule of $CuSO_4 \cdot 5\ H_2O$ is not directly bound to the Cu(II) ion, but is hydrogen-bonded to the $SO_4^=$ ion and the other water molecules. Hence, the formula $CuSO_4 \cdot 5\ H_2O$ is more appropriately written as $Cu(H_2O)_4SO_4 \cdot H_2O$. Other common hydrated Cu(II) salts are the blue nitrates, $Cu(NO_3)_2 \cdot 6\ H_2O$ and $Cu(NO_3)_2 \cdot 9\ H_2O$; the green chloride, $CuCl_2 \cdot 2\ H_2O$; and the green bromide, $CuBr_2 \cdot 4\ H_2O$. Attempts to dehydrate these salts by heat alone cause them to hydrolyze to basic salts, and at high temperatures the black oxide, CuO, is formed.

In most of its hydrated salts, Cu(II) is surrounded by 6 donor atoms—for example, O atoms of H_2O molecules or of oxoanions, halide ions, and so forth—in the usual tetragonal arrangement. Copper(II) tends to attain this stereochemistry even in simple anhydrous salts. Copper(II) chloride, $CuCl_2$, for example, consists of infinite chains, in which each Cu(II) is surrounded by 4 Cl at the corners of a square. These chains are stacked in the crystal lattice so that each Cl of each chain also forms two longer bonds to two Cu(II) of the adjacent chains. An example of a simple compound in which Cu(II) has coordination number 4 is the bright yellow cesium tetrachlorocuprate(II), $Cs_2[CuCl_4]$. In this compound the $[CuCl_4]^=$ ion has a flattened tetrahedral stereochemistry. Water solutions of Cu(II) are blue from the presence of the hydrated Cu^{++} ion. The probable formula of the hydrated Cu^{++} ion in dilute aqueous solutions is $[Cu(H_2O)_6]^{++}$, hexa-aquocopper(II) ion, although it is often written as $[Cu(H_2O)_4]^{++}$, tetra-aquocopper(II) ion, omitting the fifth and sixth H_2O molecules which are less tightly bound to the central Cu(II). Solutions of Cu(II) ions containing a high concentration of Cl^- ions are greenish-yellow and will turn yellow if concentrated hydrochloric acid solution is added to the solution. This yellow solution, on the other hand, reverts to blue if it is diluted with water. In such water solutions that contain a high concentration of Cl^- ions, the color observed arises from a mixture of the blue tetragonal complex ion $[Cu(H_2O)_6]^{++}$, of the yellow distorted tetrahedral $[CuCl_4]^=$, and of other intermediate species in equilibrium with one another. The equilibrium can be represented in a simplified manner by the equation:

$$\underset{\text{blue}}{[Cu(H_2O)_6]^{++}} + 4\ Cl^- \rightleftharpoons \underset{\text{yellow}}{[CuCl_4]^=} + 6\ H_2O$$

A high Cl^- concentration shifts the equilibrium to the right, whereas dilution with H_2O will shift it to the left.

Copper(II) hydroxide, $Cu(OH)_2$, is a blue insoluble compound which is formed by adding a solution of a soluble Cu(II) salt to a solution of a strong base (OH^- ions). Copper(II) hydroxide, $Cu(OH)_2$, is also first formed when a solution of ammonia, which contains $NH_{3(aq)}$ molecules in equilibrium with some $NH^+_{4(aq)}$ and $OH^-_{(aq)}$ ions, is slowly added to a solution of a soluble Cu(II) salt. When an excess of ammonia solution is added, however, the NH_3 molecules present react with the insoluble $Cu(OH)_2$ to form the deep-blue hexaamminecopper(II) ion:

$$Cu(OH)_{2(s)} + 6\ NH_{3(aq)} \longrightarrow [Cu(NH_3)_6]^{++}{}_{(aq)} + 2\ OH^-{}_{(aq)}$$

The intense blue color, which arises from the $[Cu(NH_3)_6]^{++}$ ion, is sometimes used as a qualitative test for the presence of copper(II). When an aqueous suspension of $Cu(OH)_2$ is boiled for some time, or when the blue solid $Cu(OH)_2$ is heated at about 300°C, water is lost and the black copper(II) oxide, CuO, is formed. Crystalline CuO is another example of 4-coordinated copper(II); here, however, Cu(II) has a square planar stereochemistry. In the lattice of CuO, each Cu(II) ion is surrounded by 4 oxide ions, $O^=$, at the corners of a square, and in turn each $O^=$ ion is surrounded tetrahedrally by 4 Cu(II) ions. When black copper(II) oxide is heated at very high temperatures (about 1,000°C), the red copper(I) oxide, Cu_2O, is formed:

$$4\ CuO_{(s)} \longrightarrow 2\ Cu_2O_{(s)} + O_{2(g)} \qquad \Delta H = +34.7 \text{ kcal/mole-eqn at } 25°\text{C, 1 atm}$$

THE +3 OXIDATION STATE

Compounds of Cu(III) and Ag(III) can be obtained by oxidation under extremely drastic conditions, but they are unstable. Gold(III), on the other hand, forms a large number of compounds, which are all covalent in character. Gold(III) halides, "$AuCl_3$," "$AuBr_3$," and "AuI_3," for example, actually consist of planar dimeric molecules Au_2X_6, in the vapor, in a solution of benzene and also in the crystalline state. In the Au_2X_6 molecule, Au(III) has square planar coordination, being bound to two "terminal" X atoms, and two "bridging" X atoms. Thus, gold(III) halides resemble aluminum(III) halides except for the stereochemistry of the metal—tetrahedral for Al(III) and planar for Au(III). Gold(III) halides also resemble Al(III) halides in some of their reactions. For example, they react with an excess of halide ions, X^-, to form the square planar tetrahalogenoaurate(III) complex anions, $[AuX_4]^-$:

$$Au_2Cl_6 + 2\ Cl^- \longrightarrow 2[AuCl_4]^-$$

With basic solutions, gold(III) halides hydrolyze to form an insoluble hydroxide, which may be represented simply as $Au(OH)_3$. This hydroxide reacts with concentrated basic solutions, for example, NaOH solutions, to give the insoluble Na_2HAuO_3. However, $Au(OH)_3$ does not dissolve in basic solutions, nor does it dissolve in acids except when their anions form complexes with Au(III).

METALLURGY OF THE COINAGE METALS

The metallurgy of copper consists essentially of roasting the ore in air to convert any sulfides to oxides, and then reducing the oxides with carbon at high temperature in the presence of sand (SiO_2) as a flux. In this way copper metal of about 97 per cent purity is obtained; the remaining 3 per cent consists of other metals such as Ag, Au, Zn, Fe, and traces of the platinum metals. This 97 per cent copper is further purified by electrolysis, essentially as described in Chapter 23, p. 519. The less electropositive metals (Ag, Au, and traces of the platinum metals) are not oxidized at the anode because their $E°$ values are far too negative; they simply fall to the bottom of the cell as the anode dissolves and are recovered. The copper metal deposited on the cathode is more than 99.9 per cent pure.

Gold, as we have said, occurs in nature mostly as the free metal but at such low concentrations that a chemical process is often required to extract it. This process involves the oxidation of Au metal by oxygen of the air, in the presence of a solution of sodium cyanide, Na^+CN^-:

$$2\ Au + \cancel{4\ Na^+} + 4\ CN^- + H_2O + \tfrac{1}{2}\ O_2 \longrightarrow 2[Au(CN)_2]^- + \cancel{4\ Na^+} + 2\ OH^-$$

Metallic gold dissolves as the soluble sodium dicyanoaurate(I), $Na[Au(CN)_2]$, from which the metal is then recovered by treatment with an acid. Silver is usually obtained, as we have already mentioned, as a by-product in the refinery of other metals, especially copper, lead, and zinc.

35-3 Zinc, Zn; Cadmium, Cd; and Mercury, Hg (Group IIB)

NATURAL OCCURRENCE

Stable State at 25°C, 1 atm	IIB
white metal (hexagonal lattice)	Zn
white metal (hexagonal lattice)	Cd
gray liquid metal	Hg

The elements Zn, Cd, and Hg, known as the zinc subgroup or Group IIB elements, occur principally as their sulfide ores, MS. Neither zinc nor cadmium, because of their positive oxidation potentials, occurs as free elements in nature. Zinc is a relatively abundant element, for it constitutes about 0.02 per cent of the earth's crust and is about 100 times more abundant than copper. The chief sulfide ore of zinc, ZnS, is called zincblende or sphalerite; ZnS also occurs in nature in a less common crystalline form called wurtzite. The ore sphalerite may contain copper, lead, iron, cadmium, arsenic, and antimony. The chief sulfide mineral of cadmium is CdS, called greenocite; however, the principal source of cadmium is the CdS which accompanies ZnS in the sphalerite ore. Mercury, which is about as abundant as cadmium (10^{-4} per cent of the earth's crust) has one important ore—HgS, cinnabar. Small deposits of metallic, liquid mercury have also been found.

PHYSICAL PROPERTIES OF Zn, Cd, AND Hg

The elements Zn, Cd, and Hg have the outer electron configuration $(n-1)d^{10},ns^2$. Their valence electrons, therefore, are the ns^2 electrons, as for the alkaline-earth elements, but the presence of the underlying filled $(n-1)d^{10}$ sub-shell gives rise to marked differences in properties and behavior. Some of the important properties of Zn, Cd, and Hg are listed in Tables 35-3 and 35-4.

Zinc is a white metal with a distorted hexagonal close-packed crystal structure. Each Zn atom has 6 equidistant nearest neighbors in a plane, and 6 other neighbors—3 above and 3 below this plane—at slightly greater distance (see margin illustration). Zinc is moderately hard but brittle at ordinary temperatures. Zinc metal, because of a tenacious basic carbonate layer that forms on its surface, withstands corrosion and hence is used as a protective coating for steel. The "galvanizing" process consists of treating steel with molten zinc or of coating steel with zinc by electrolytic deposition. Zinc is also used as a component of various alloys, one of the most important is brass.

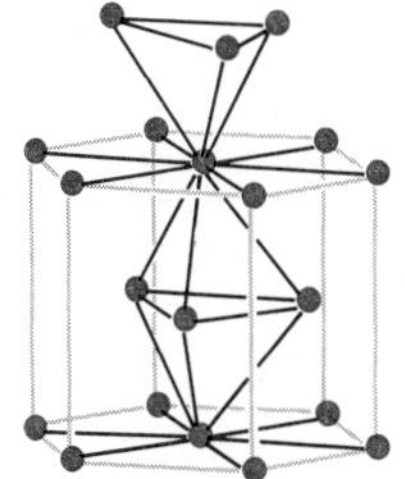

Portion of distorted hexagonal close-packed lattice of zinc

Cadmium is a white metal with a crystal structure similar to that of zinc. It is softer and more malleable than zinc. Cadmium melts at a relatively low temperature,

TABLE 35-3 SOME PROPERTIES OF Zn, Cd, AND Hg (GROUP IIB ELEMENTS)

Element	Outer Electron Config.	Atomic Weight	Atomic[a] Radius A	Ionic Radius M^{++} Ion, A	Density at 20°C, g/cm^3	Melting Point °C	Boiling Point °C	ΔH_{atomiz} (kcal/mole)	Electro-negativity (Pauling)
$_{30}Zn$	$3d^{10},4s^1$	65.37	1.37 (12)	0.74	7.14	419	906	31.2	1.6
$_{48}Cd$	$4d^{10},5s^1$	112.40	1.52 (12)	0.97	8.65	321	765	26.8	1.7
$_{80}Hg$	$(4f^{14}),5d^{10},6s^1$	200.59	1.55 (6)[b]	1.10	13.6	−38	357	14.6	1.9

[a] Number in parentheses is crystal coordination number. The metallic radii of Zn and Cd are average values since interatomic distances to nearest neighbors are not all equal.

[b] Value is for solid mercury, below −38°C, which has a rhombohedral structure (6 nearest neighbors).

TABLE 35-4 IONIZATION ENERGIES AND OXIDATION POTENTIALS OF ZINC, CADMIUM, AND MERCURY

Element	Ionization Energy (kcal/mole)			Oxidation Potential, E° (volts)	
	1st	2nd	Total for M^{++}	M, M_2^{++}	M, M^{++}
Zn	217	414	631	—	+0.76
Cd	207	388	595	—	+0.40
Hg	240	430	670	−0.79	−0.85

321°C, and is widely used in combination with lead, tin, and bismuth to make low-melting alloys. Cadmium is also used for plating other metals, and is especially useful as a protective coating in basic solutions because, unlike zinc, it is not amphoteric and hence does not oxidize to form a complex hydroxo-anion.

Mercury, as we know, is liquid at room temperature and has the lowest melting point of any metal (the next lowest are cesium, 28.5°C, and gallium, 29.8°C). Mercury also has an exceedingly low boiling point (357°C) for a metal of such high atomic weight. It does not wet glass. Both as a liquid and as a solid, mercury is an effective conductor of electric current. Many metals dissolve in mercury to some extent to form solutions called "amalgams," which may be solids or liquids. Mercury is a cumulative poison and inhalation of mercury vapor should be avoided. Since liquid mercury has an appreciable vapor pressure even at room temperatures, *liquid mercury should always be treated as a potentially hazardous material, especially when heated.*

We see from Table 35-3 that the melting points, boiling points, and ΔH_{atomiz} of Zn, Cd, and Hg decrease regularly with increasing sizes (the radii of the M^{++} ions are here a better guide than the metallic radii, since mercury is a liquid at room temperature, and in the solid state it has a structure different from that of Zn and Cd). It is interesting to notice that Zn, Cd, and Hg are among the metals with the lowest ΔH_{atomiz}. Actually, mercury has the lowest heat of atomization (14.6 kcal/mole of atoms) of all elements except the noble gases. (The element with the next lowest heat of atomization is cesium—18.7 kcal/mole of atoms—which as we saw above is also second to Hg in melting point.) Table 35-4 lists the first and second ionization energies of Zn, Cd, and Hg, together with the total ionization energy for the reaction $M_{(g)} \longrightarrow M^{++}_{(g)} + 2\,e^-$. The ionization energy first decreases from Zn to Cd, because of the increase in size, then again increases from Cd to Hg, because of the poor screening properties of the $4f^{14}$ underlying shell present in mercury. This is the same pattern observed for the first ionization energies of the Group IB elements.

COMPARISON OF GROUP IIB ELEMENTS WITH THE GROUP IB AND GROUP IIA ELEMENTS. Each atom of the Group IIB elements has one more electron in the *ns* orbital than the atom of the immediately preceding coinage metal (Group IB). Since *s* electrons screen one another incompletely from the nuclear charge, the atoms of Zn, Cd, and Hg are smaller than the atoms of the corresponding coinage metals. However, the densities of the zinc sub-group metals are lower than the densities of the preceding coinage metals, partly because of a less close packing of the atoms and partly because of weaker interatomic bonding. (The metallic bonding involving the *s* electrons of the completed s^2 orbitals of Zn, Cd, and Hg is weaker than that involving the *s* electrons of the half-filled s^1 orbitals of the corresponding coinage metals.) This decrease in the strength of the metallic bonding is also evident from the much lower values of the ΔH_{atomiz} (for example, Au, 87.5; Hg, 14.6 kcal/mole) and of the melting and boiling points (for example, Au, m.p. 1063°C, b.p., 2970°C; Hg, m.p. −38°C, b.p. 357°C).

The only similarity that can be found between the metals of the IIB Group (the zinc sub-group) and the metals of the IIA Group (the alkaline-earth metals) is that all these elements exhibit an oxidation number of +2. The standard oxidation potentials, $E°$, of the Group IIB elements, Zn, Cd, and Hg, are much less positive than those of the corresponding elements of Group IIA, Ca, Sr, and Ba. (Actually, the Hg,Hg^{++} couple has a negative oxidation potential.) Thus, the Group IIB elements are much less electropositive than the Group IIA elements. Accordingly, the zinc sub-group metals form compounds with an appreciably covalent character whereas the alkaline-earth metals form predominantly ionic compounds. Again, this difference in behavior is explained by the greater polarizing ability of Zn^{++}, Cd^{++}, and Hg^{++}, which are smaller and also have higher effective nuclear charges than Ca^{++}, Sr^{++}, and Ba^{++}.

35-4 The Chemical Properties of Zn, Cd, and Hg

Unlike the coinage metals, all of which exhibit variable oxidation states, zinc has exclusively an oxidation state of +2; cadmium forms compounds with the oxidation state +2, although there is evidence that the Cd_2^{++} ion also exists in solution; and mercury forms compounds with both the +1 and the +2 oxidation states. All compounds of Zn(II), Cd(II), and Hg(II) have a metal ion with a symmetrical core—the d^{10} shell—and their stereochemistry conforms to the usual rules. Zinc and cadmium are moderately electropositive metals and have closely similar chemical properties. Mercury is not an electropositive metal, and its general chemical behavior departs appreciably from that of Zn and Cd.

Zinc and cadmium have positive $E°$ values (Zn,Zn^{++}, $E° = +0.76$; Cd,Cd^{++}, $E° = +0.40$). These metals therefore react with solutions of non-oxidizing acids to form the dipositive metal ion M^{++} and H_2 gas. Mercury, on the other hand, has a negative $E°$ value (Hg,Hg^{++}, $E° = -0.85$). Therefore the simple Hg(II) salts, $Hg(NO_3)_2$ and $HgSO_4$, can be obtained only by the reaction of the metal with the oxidizing acids HNO_3 and hot concentrated H_2SO_4 respectively.

$$3\,Hg + 8\,HNO_3 \longrightarrow 3\,Hg(NO_3)_2 + 2\,NO + 4\,H_2O$$
$$Hg + 2\,H_2SO_4 \longrightarrow HgSO_4 + SO_2 + 2\,H_2O$$

Of course, the presence of good ligands or of anions which form insoluble salts with the M^{++} ions will lower the value of the oxidation potential. For example, mercury dissolves in a concentrated solution of hydriodic acid, HI, liberating H_2, because the formation of the very stable $[HgI_4]^{=}$ complex ion make the following half reaction thermodynamically favorable:

$$Hg + 4\,I^- = [HgI_4]^{=} + 2\,e^- \qquad E° = +0.04\text{ v}$$

When finely divided zinc metal is heated in air or oxygen above its melting point, the metal burns with a bluish flame to form the white oxide, ZnO. Cadmium metal undergoes a similar reaction, forming brown CdO. Both ZnO and CdO sublime at about 1,800°C without decomposing. When mercury metal is heated at about 300°C, it too reacts with oxygen and forms the red oxide HgO; this, however, decomposes into Hg and O_2 if heated to about 100° higher than the temperature at which it begins to form at an appreciable rate. Notice that the different thermal stabilities of ZnO, CdO, and HgO parallel the values of their $\Delta H°_{form}$, given in the margin.

	$\Delta H°_{form}$ (kcal/mole)
ZnO	−83.2
CdO	−60.9
HgO	−21.7

The oxides ZnO, CdO, and HgO are insoluble in water but dissolve in acids, forming the salt of the acid and water. The nitrates, sulfates, acetates, and perchlorates of Zn(II), Cd(II), and Hg(II) are soluble in water and form colorless solutions.

In a water solution, the soluble Zn(II) salts of non-coordinating anions probably contain the octahedral complex $[Zn(H_2O)_6]^{++}$, hexaaquozinc(II) ion, which exists also in the crystalline salt $Zn(ClO_4)_2 \cdot 6\ H_2O$. Because of the relatively high effective nuclear charge of the small Zn^{++}, the aquo complex, $[Zn(OH_2)_6]^{++}$ tends to hydrolyze, giving an acid solution:

$$[Zn(OH_2)_6]^{++} + H_2O \rightleftharpoons [Zn(OH_2)_5(OH)]^{+} + H^{+} \cdot H_2O$$

If OH^- ions—for example, from a NaOH solution—are added to a water solution of a Zn(II) salt, the above equilibrium reaction is shifted to the right; the final product is a white gelatinous precipitate of zinc hydroxide whose formula is generally written as $Zn(OH)_2 \cdot nH_2O$ or simply $Zn(OH)_2$. (The symbol n indicates that the quantity of water present in the gelatinous precipitate is variable.) Thus, the reaction of a base (OH^- ions) with a soluble Zn(II) salt in water produces insoluble $Zn(OH)_2$, according to the following simplified equation:

$$Zn^{++}{}_{(aq)} + 2\ OH^{-}{}_{(aq)} \longrightarrow Zn(OH)_{2(s)}$$

When additional OH^- ions are added to the solution containing the $Zn(OH)_2$ precipitate, the precipitate dissolves and forms the tetrahedral tetrahydroxozincate(II) anion, $[Zn(OH)_4]^{=}$. The hydroxide $Zn(OH)_2$ is therefore amphoteric. Cadmium(II) salts do not hydrolyze appreciably in water, and the insoluble Cd(II) hydroxide, $Cd(OH)_2 \cdot n(H_2O)$, does not dissolve in basic solutions. Mercury(II) salts also do not hydrolyze in water; the reaction of OH^- ions with Hg(II) salts yields a variety of insoluble basic salts. For example, white Hg_3OCl_4, black $Hg_3O_2Cl_2$, or the insoluble yellow mercuric oxide HgO can be obtained from a solution of $HgCl_2$ under different conditions.

Zinc(II) forms complexes with a variety of ligands, for example, ammonia and the cyanide ion. Thus, when a water solution containing ammonia is added to a solution containing Zn^{++} ions or to the insoluble $Zn(OH)_2$, the complex cation, hexaamminezinc(II), $[Zn(NH_3)_6]^{++}$, is formed. Similarly, the tetracyanozincate(II) anion, $[Zn(CN)_4]^{=}$, is formed if a solution containing CN^- ions is added to a solution containing Zn^{++} ions or $Zn(OH)_2$. Cadmium(II) forms similar ammine- $[Cd(NH_3)_6]^{++}$ and cyano- $[Cd(CN)_4]^{=}$ complexes, but mercury(II) does not. In fact, when a Hg(II) salt reacts with ammonia, a compound of a completely different type is formed, containing the amido group, NH_2^-, covalently bound to Hg(II). For example:

$$HgCl_2 + 2\ NH_3 \longrightarrow HgNH_2Cl + NH_4^{+} + Cl^{-}$$

The compound $HgNH_2Cl$ is a white solid, insoluble in water, and has a structure consisting of positively charged zig-zag chains of covalently bonded $—NH_2^+—$ groups and —Hg— atoms:

$$\diagdown \overset{+}{N}H_2 \diagup Hg \diagup \overset{+}{N}H_2 \diagdown Hg \diagdown \overset{+}{N}H_2 \diagup$$

These chains are connected in the crystal lattice by the Cl^- ions. Also, in contrast to Zn(II) and Cd(II), a solution of Hg(II) reacts with CN^- ions to form a very stable cyanide, $Hg(CN)_2$, but does not form a cyano-complex anion. $Hg(CN)_2$ is a covalent compound; it is very soluble in water, but its solutions do not appreciably conduct an electric current.

MERCURY(I) COMPOUNDS

Of all the zinc sub-group elements, only mercury exhibits a +1 oxidation number. As we have already mentioned, Hg(I) exists exclusively as the dimeric ion $(Hg)_2^{++}$, in which the two Hg^+ ions are held together by a covalent bond, $Hg^+:Hg^+$, involving one s electron from each mercury(I). Mercury(I) chloride (mercurous chloride), Hg_2Cl_2, is formed by heating $HgCl_2$ with Hg, or by adding chloride ions to a soluble salt of mercury(I). Mercury(I) chloride, Hg_2Cl_2, is a white powder, insoluble in water, which consists of linear Cl—Hg—Hg—Cl covalent molecules. When Hg_2Cl_2 reacts with a solution containing ammonia, NH_3, half of the Hg(I) is oxidized to Hg(II) and half is reduced to metallic mercury, Hg. This disproportionation reaction is:

$$Hg_2Cl_2 + 2\ NH_3 \longrightarrow HgNH_2Cl_{(s)} + Hg + NH_4^+ + Cl^-$$

As we have seen before, $HgNH_2Cl$ is a white solid, but the product of the above reaction appears black because of the presence of very finely divided metallic mercury, which is deep black and is adsorbed on the surface of the white $HgNH_2Cl$.

THE METALLURGY OF Zn, Cd, AND Hg

Zinc and cadmium ores, which contain Zn(II) and Cd(II) compounds mixed with useless materials called the gangue, are first enriched by a process called *flotation*. This process makes use of the fact that ZnS and CdS are not easily wetted by water whereas the gangue is. The zinc ore, finely ground, is treated with water and with small amounts of appropriate surface-active substances, and then air is bubbled through the mixture. Most of the ZnS and CdS collect with the oily foam at the surface of the mixture and can be collected as a highly concentrated material even if the original ore is a very low grade. The ZnS (together with CdS) is then roasted in air to produce the metal oxide and SO_2.

$$2\ ZnS + 3\ O_2 \longrightarrow 2\ ZnO + 2\ SO_2 \qquad \Delta H = -105.7\ \text{kcal/mole-eqn}$$

The ZnO (together with CdO) thus formed is then reduced to the metal by heating with excess coke to about 1,100°C, which is above the boiling points of Zn (907°C) and Cd (768°C). Carbon monoxide gas is formed, and the Zn and Cd, which vaporize, are collected as crystalline powders in cooling chambers.

$$ZnO + C \longrightarrow Zn + CO \qquad \Delta H = +56.8\ \text{kcal/mole-eqn}$$

Mercury is prepared simply by roasting its ore, HgS, in air:

$$HgS + O_2 \longrightarrow Hg + SO_2 \qquad \Delta H = -57.1\ \text{kcal/mole-eqn}$$

This reaction, which is carried out above the relatively low boiling point of mercury (357°C), yields mercury vapor which is then condensed to its liquid. Mercury(II) oxide, HgO, is not obtained, because at the high temperature of the roasting process it would be unstable towards decomposition into its elements.

Exercises

35-1 Discuss the elements Cu, Ag, and Au with respect to (a) atomic size, (b) size of the M^+ ions, (c) effective nuclear charge, (d) ionization energy, (e) heat of atomization, (f) oxidation potential, (g) electronegativity. Correlate observed trends in the above properties with the electron configurations of the elements.

35-2 Compare the coinage metals (Group IB) with the alkali metals (Group IA) in regard to (a) outer electron configuration, (b) density, (c) melting point and heat of atomization, (d) ionization energy, (e) oxidation potential, (f) electronegativity, (g) character of bonding in compounds, (h) tendency to form coordination compounds.

35-3 Which is the most stable oxidation state, in aqueous solution, of (a) copper, (b) silver, (c) gold?

35-4 Which are the most common coordination numbers and stereochemistries for the compounds of (a) copper(II), (b) silver(I), (c) gold(III)?

35-5 Explain the following observations: (a) Copper does not react with dilute HCl solution but does react with dilute HNO_3 solution. (b) When NaOH solution is added to $CuSO_4$ solution, a blue precipitate is formed which does not dissolve on adding an excess of NaOH. (c) When an ammonia solution is added to a $CuSO_4$ solution, the blue precipitate which forms initially redissolves on the addition of an excess of ammonia solution. (d) Gold does not dissolve in HNO_3 solution or HCl solution alone, but it does dissolve in aqua regia. (e) Cu metal slowly dissolves in an ammonia solution in the presence of air. Write the equation for this reaction. (f) Gold metal dissolves in a solution of sodium cyanide, NaCN, in the presence of air. Write the equation for this reaction. (h) Silver does not dissolve in a 1 *M* solution of HCl, but dissolves slowly in a 1 *M* solution of HI (liberating hydrogen gas).

35-6 What is the stereochemistry of the following: $[Ag(NH_3)_2]^+$, $[Ag(CN)_2]^-$, $[CuCl_4]^=$, $[Cu(H_2O)_6]^{++}$, $K_2[Cu(CN)_3]$ (solid), $[AuCl_2]^-$, $[AuCl_4]^-$, Au_2Cl_6.

35-7 Write equations for the reactions involved in the metallurgy of (a) copper, (b) gold. Briefly describe and explain the conditions under which such reactions take place.

35-8 Compare in general the physical and chemical properties of Zn, Cd, and Hg (Group IIB) with those of (a) the coinage metals Cu, Hg and Au (Group IB), (b) the alkaline-earth metals, Ca, Sr, and Ba (Group IIA).

35-9 How do you explain the fact that Hg, the heaviest metal of Group IIB, has the lowest melting and boiling points and the lowest ΔH_{atomiz} of the elements of this group?

35-10 Discuss the metals of Group IIB in regard to (a) oxidation state, (b) oxidation potential, (c) type of bonding in compounds, (d) preferred coordination number and stereochemistry.

35-11 Write equations for the reactions with ammonia solution of (a) $Zn(NO_3)_2$, (b) $Cd(OH)_2$, and (c) $HgCl_2$. Describe the structure of each product.

35-12 Write the equation of the reaction which takes place when mercury metal is heated with nitric acid.

35-13 Explain why mercury dissolves in a concentrated solution of hydroiodic acid, HI, but not in a concentrated solution of HCl.

ORGANIC CHEMISTRY

36

Organic chemistry is concerned with the compounds of carbon, principally the hydrocarbons and their derivatives. Organic chemistry is commonly considered a separate topic of study because of the vast number and variety of carbon compounds. The atoms of carbon are uniquely capable of combining with one another and with the atoms of a few other elements—usually hydrogen, oxygen, nitrogen, and sulfur; indeed, the total number of known organic compounds exceeds a million. The total number of known inorganic compounds —those formed by all the other elements together —is about 100,000; we studied the most important and simple of these in Chapters 27 through 35. The same fundamental principles of bonding, energetics, and kinetics that explain the chemistry of inorganic compounds explain those of organic compounds.

We constantly come in contact with organic compounds in our everyday life. All living organisms, plant and animal, consist of highly complicated, organized assemblages of carbon compounds. The term *organic chemistry* derives from this fact, for there would be no life as we know it without carbon and its compounds. Here are some of the familiar materials in which carbon compounds appear. (1) All food products with the exception of a few mineral salts and water. (2) Fuels of all types, including coal, oil, gasoline, natural gas, and wood. Actually, with a few exceptions, such as hydrogen and fissionable materials, all fuels consist of organic compounds. (3) Lubricants and all other petroleum products. (4) All the common solvents, except water. (5) Textiles and fibers, including such synthetic fibers as nylon, Orlon, and Dacron, and such natural fibers as cotton, silk, and wool. (6) Leather and furs. (7) Dyes of all kinds, both natural and synthetic. (8) Vitamins and medicinal drugs. Virtually all medicinal drugs are composed of organic compounds, which, for the most part, are manufactured synthetically. (9) Insecticides and fungicides. (10) Soaps, detergents, and cosmetics. (11) Elastomers—that is, elastic materials, including natural and synthetic rubber, resins, and plastics. (12) Paper and wood products. (13) Most explosives. (14) Asphalt and tar.

In this tremendous variety of substances, which have vastly different structures and properties, the key element is always carbon. And carbon, as we have already learned, displays only *three* stereochemical arrangements—tetrahedral, trigonal, or linear. In this chapter we shall see how this simple generalization can help us correlate and explain the properties and behavior of vast classes of organic compounds.

36-1 General Properties of Organic Compounds

Each class of organic compounds has a set of characteristic physical and chemical properties related to their molecular structure, but almost all organic compounds have two very important properties in common. One is their sensitivity to heat. Most organic compounds decompose when they are heated vigorously even in an inert atmosphere (such as nitrogen gas) and char when they are heated above 400°C. For example, after a few minutes of gentle heating in a test tube, glucose (grape sugar), $C_6H_{12}O_6$, first melts, then begins to give out fumes (chiefly water vapor), and finally chars, leaving a black residue of carbon. Charring, even though it usually consists of a very complicated sequence of chemical reactions, is essentially the break-down of the organic compound into carbon as an amorphous solid and the other constituents (chiefly hydrogen, oxygen, and nitrogen) as gaseous molecules—for example, H_2O, H_2, O_2, CO_2, CO, N_2, NH_3, and H_2S. Thus, when a solid organic compound chars, the entropy of the system increases. At high temperatures this entropy effect becomes the predominant factor, overcoming the effect of the bond energy.

The other important common characteristic property of organic compounds is their combustibility—that is, they can react with oxygen to form chiefly CO, CO_2, and H_2O. Most organic substances exist at room temperature in the presence of the oxygen of air, only because their combustion usually has a high activation energy. At high temperatures, of course, the activation-energy barrier is overcome, and combustion then occurs rapidly with, the evolution of a large quantity of heat. The fact that the combustion of organic compounds in air or oxygen has a favorable free energy change is extremely important. The energy necessary for most life processes is, in fact, furnished by the controlled biological combustion of organic substances within the cells of living organisms. And, apart from life processes, one of the most important uses of organic compounds is their combustion—as sources of energy—in furnaces, internal combustion engines, jets, and rockets.

36-2 Carbon-Carbon Linkage and Bond Energy

The main reason why the compounds of carbon are far more numerous than the compounds of all the other elements together is that carbon atoms are far more able to bind with one another through covalent bonds, forming chains. Any carbon atom can form 1, 2, 3, or 4 covalent bonds with other carbon atoms, each of which can also form up to 4 covalent bonds with other carbon atoms, and so on; thus carbon atoms can unite with one another to form not only linear chains (of different lengths) but also branched chains and cyclic chains. Since carbon atoms can also form covalent bonds with the atoms of many other elements—especially hydrogen, oxygen, chlorine, nitrogen, and sulfur, but also other non-metals and even metals—the possible carbon compounds are almost endless. The strong tendency of carbon to catenation is related to its central position in the first short Series of the Periodic Table. As the typical element of Group IVB, it has the outer electron configuration $2s^2\ 2p^2$ (a total of 4 valence electrons) and 4 outer orbitals (one $2s$ and three $2p$ orbitals) that can be used for bond formation. Each C atom, therefore, can form 4 covalent bonds with 4 like or unlike partner atoms. Since the C atom is small, its orbitals can overlap very effectively with the orbitals of the partner atoms, forming strong covalent bonds. Also, a C atom that forms 4 covalent bonds has no lone electron pairs, so the interelectron repulsion between the bonded atoms is minimized. This explains, for example, why the C—C bond is one of the strongest *single covalent* bonds between identical atoms, as indicated by the values of the bond energies listed in the accompanying chart.

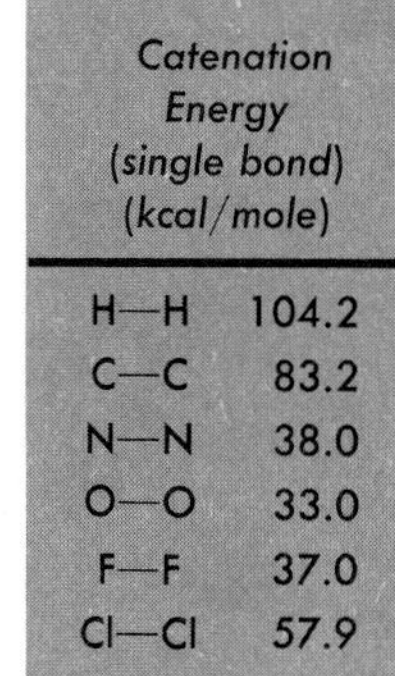

Catenation Energy (single bond) (kcal/mole)	
H—H	104.2
C—C	83.2
N—N	38.0
O—O	33.0
F—F	37.0
Cl—Cl	57.9

We learned in Chapters 28 and 32 that a few other elements in the central region of the Periodic Table, chiefly sulfur and silicon, also have some tendency to catenation. For these elements, too, the single bond energy between their atoms is relatively high (S—S, 51; Si—Si, 42 kcal/mole of bonds) but still much lower than that for carbon. In fact, no other element is capable of forming such a range of *stable* atom-to-atom links as carbon does. Compounds that contain rings or chains of the atoms of other elements are rare and, with few exceptions, markedly unstable.

STEREOCHEMICAL ARRANGEMENTS OF THE CARBON ATOM. The three stereochemical arrangements of carbon—tetrahedral, trigonal, or linear—can be correlated to the number of sigma bonds (or coordination number) and the electron configuration of the carbon atom, as we shall discuss in the following sections.

36-3 Carbon with Four Sigma Bonds (C.N. = 4): Tetrahedral Stereochemistry

As we discussed in detail in Chapter 14, when a C atom is covalently bonded to 4 partner atoms, its stereochemistry is tetrahedral (regular or distorted depending on whether the 4 partner atoms are or are not all equal). The C atom may be described as using sp^3 hybrid orbitals for the formation of its 4 bonds (see Chapter 15). As an example, the bonds in methane, CH_4, are illustrated here by (a) the electron-dot formula, (b) the dash formula, (c) a three-dimensional representation, and (d) the sigma-bonding orbitals.

109°

1.08 A

C_{sp3} — H_s sigma bond

(a) (b) (c) (d)

The electron configurations of the gaseous C atom in its ground and valency states, and of the C atom in methane, follow:

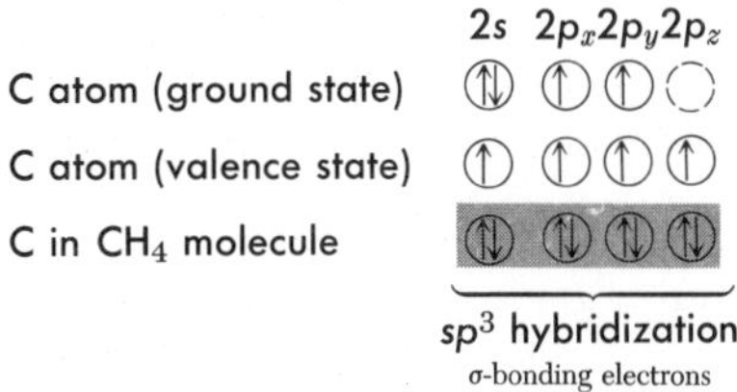

CARBON-CARBON SINGLE COVALENT BOND: ETHANE, C_2H_6

The simplest organic compound containing 2 carbon atoms joined together by a single covalent bond is ethane, C_2H_6 (a gas, b.p. of $-88°C$). Its electron-dot formula and dash formula are shown below in (a) and (b). In a molecule of ethane, C_2H_6, the 2 carbon atoms share an electron pair in a σ covalent bond, to which each atom contributes one electron; in addition each C atom shares an electron pair, in a σ bond, with 3 H atoms. Each C atom of ethane has a tetrahedral stereochemistry; the atomic orbitals involved in bond formation are shown in (c).

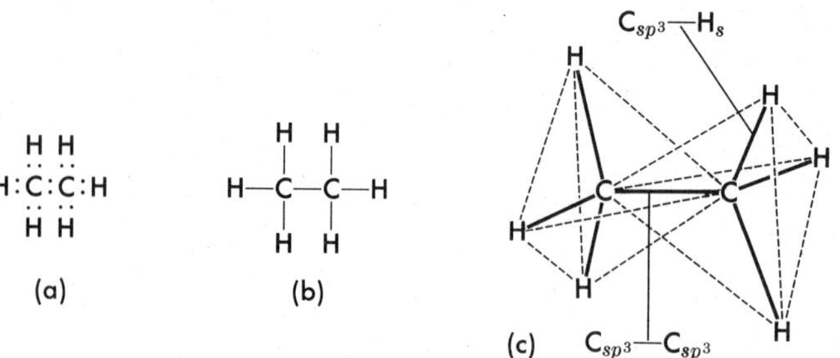

It is often convenient to represent the molecule of ethane by a "structural formula" such as H_3C—CH_3 or CH_3—CH_3, which draws attention to the carbon-carbon single covalent band that links together the 2 CH_3 groups. We shall often use structural formulas of this kind to represent organic compounds whose full structural formula (either the electron-dot or the dash kind) would be cumbersome.

In Chapter 33 we cited examples of conformations of some inorganic molecules and ions. The existence of various conformations is very common for organic compounds. The ethane molecule, CH_3—CH_3, is a simple example. As Fig. 36-1 illustrates, there are numerous possible ways in which the two—CH_3 groups of ethane can

(a) (b) (c)

FIGURE 36-1 Conformations of the H_3C—CH_3 molecule.

be arranged with respect to one another, while still retaining the C—C covalent bond and a tetrahedral arrangement around each C atom. Each of the 3 H atoms attached to one of the carbon atoms, ①C, in one H_3C— group can be positioned opposite to one of the 3 H atoms attached to the carbon atom, ②C, in the other —CH_3 group, as in Fig. 36-1(a). As another possible arrangement, 3 H atoms of one —CH_3 group can occupy positions corresponding to the empty spaces between the H atoms of the other —CH_3 group. In this case the two —CH_3 groups are staggered with respect to one another, as in (b). In addition, all the various conformations intermediate between the two shown are possible and can be schematically represented as in (c). The staggered conformation (b) involves the least mutual repulsion between the 2 sets of H atoms attached to the C atoms; it is therefore the most stable conformation. Although at any one time the majority of ethane molecules have a staggered conformation, the difference in energy among the forms is relatively small and the various forms interconvert extremely rapidly. In fact, it is not possible to isolate conformational isomers of ethane.

36-4 Carbon with Three Sigma Bonds (C.N. = 3): Trigonal Planar Stereochemistry

As an example of an organic compound in which the C atom has a trigonal planar stereochemistry, let us consider ethylene, a colorless gas (b.p. $-104°C$) composed of C_2H_4 molecules. (An inorganic compound in which the C atom has trigonal

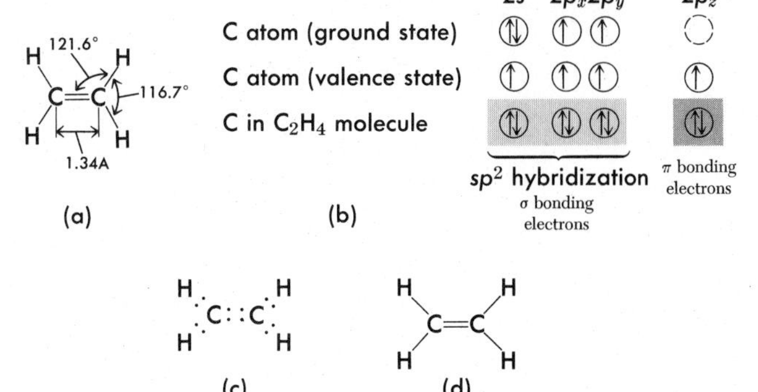

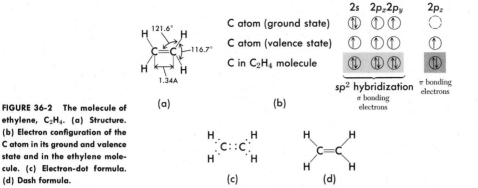

FIGURE 36-2 The molecule of ethylene, C_2H_4. (a) Structure. (b) Electron configuration of the C atom in its ground and valence state and in the ethylene molecule. (c) Electron-dot formula. (d) Dash formula.

planar stereochemistry is the carbonate ion, $CO_3^{=}$, p. 294.) Experiments show that all 6 atoms of the C_2H_4 molecule lie in the same plane—that is, the C_2H_4 molecule is planar—and that each C atom is linked to 2 equivalent H atoms and to the other C atom. The carbon-carbon bond length in ethylene (1.34 A) is less than in ethane (1.54 A), and the experimentally determined bond energy for the carbon-carbon link in ethylene, 146.8 kcal/mole, is greater than the C—C single bond strength of ethane (83.2 kcal/mole). In ethylene the H—C—H bond angles are 116.7° and the H—C—C bond angles are 121.6°, as shown in Fig. 36-2(a). Both gaseous and liquid ethylene are *diamagnetic*, a property which indicates that the ethylene molecule contains no unpaired electrons. Taken together, all these experimental data give us an insight into the type of bonding present in the C_2H_4 molecule. Since each C atom in ethylene is bonded to 3 other atoms, we may say that 2 of its valence electrons pair up with the 1*s* electrons of 2 H atoms forming 2 C—H sigma bonds and that 1 electron of 1 carbon atom pairs up with 1 electron of the other C atom forming a C—C sigma bond. The C—H and C—C σ bonds, therefore, account for the pairing up of 3 of the 4 valence electrons of each C atom (Fig. 36-2(b)). But since there are no unpaired electrons in ethylene, we may conclude that the remaining valence electrons also paired up with each other—forming a C—C π bond. We can picture the 2 C atoms of C_2H_4 as being effectively joined by a double bond (2 shared electron pairs), thus accounting for the greater carbon-carbon bond strength and the shorter bond length in ethylene as compared with the single C—C bond of ethane.

The molecule of ethylene, C_2H_4, is often represented simply by the electron-dot formula (c) or by the dash formula (d). These formulas show the carbon-carbon double bond; however, the 2 electron pairs (: :) and the 2 dashes (=) do not differentiate between the σ bond and the π bond. One way to represent the 2 different carbon-carbon bonds of ethylene is to show explicitly the electron configuration of the C atom in ethylene and the atomic orbitals that take part in the bonding. Figure 36-2(b) shows that the 2*s* orbital and 2 of the 2*p* orbitals of the carbon atom in the valence state may hydridize to form three sp^2 hybrid orbitals, symmetrically oriented about 3 trigonal axes which lie in the same plane and make angles of about 120° with one another. The framework of the σ bonds in the ethylene molecule, C_2H_4, can then be visualized as follows: one sp^2 trigonal orbital of one C atom overlaps with one sp^2 orbital of the other C atom forming a carbon-carbon σ bond. Each of the other two sp^2 hybrid orbitals of each C overlaps with the 1*s* orbital of one H atom, forming one carbon-hydrogen σ bond. Each C atom thus forms 3 σ bonds—one with its partner C atom and one with each of its 2 partner H atoms (Fig. 36-3(a)). For each C atom, there is one remaining *p* orbital, say the p_z orbital, which is not involved in this sp^2 hybridization, and has its axis at right angles to the plane containing the 3 axes of the sp^2 hybrid orbitals. The electron in each p_z orbital of each C atom can also pair up with each other as shown, resulting in another carbon-carbon covalent bond. As Fig. 36-3(b) illustrates, the electron distribution of this bonding pair consists of 2 regions of high electron density—one above

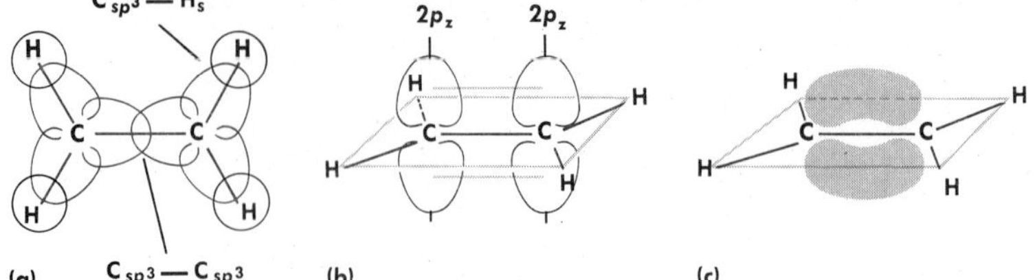

FIGURE 36-3 **(a) Orbitals interacting to form the σ bonds of the ethylene molecule. (b) Orbitals interacting to form the carbon-carbon π bond. (c) Electron distribution of the π bonding pair.**

the plane of the 6 atoms of the C_2H_4 molecule and the other below. (In the molecular plane containing the C and H atoms the electron density of this carbon-carbon π bond is virtually zero.) It must be emphasized that the region of electron density above the molecular plane (of the C_2H_4 molecule) and the region of electron density below it, taken together, constitute the π bond, just as the 2 lobes of the original p_z orbital of each C atom constitute the total electron cloud of the p_z orbital.

Even though the carbon-carbon double bond in ethylene is usually represented simply as C=C, it must be kept in mind that the 2 shared pairs of electrons have different electron-cloud distributions about the carbon-carbon internuclear axis. The electron cloud of the σ bond resulting from the overlap of two sp^2 hybrid orbitals of the 2 C atoms is concentrated along the C—C axis. The electron cloud of the π bond formed by the overlap of the two p_z orbitals is symmetrically distributed over 2 equal lobes, one above and one below the molecular plane of the C_2H_4 molecule. Even though, as we have seen, a carbon-carbon double bond (σ + π) is stronger than a carbon-carbon single bond (σ), the double bond is not twice as strong as the single bond. In fact, it requires 83 kcal/mole to break the C—C single σ bond of ethane, $H_3C—CH_3$, and 147 kcal/mole (that is, only 64 additional kcal/mole) to completely break the C=C double (σ + π) bond of ethylene, $H_2C=CH_2$.

Finally, let us consider how the presence of the C=C double bond explains why the H—C—H bond angle (116.7°) and the H—C—C bond angle (121.6°) in the ethylene molecule differ from the regular 120° value, expected for sp^2 hybridization. On the basis of electrostatic repulsions between electron pairs, we may expect a double bond to act as a "more concentrated" single bond, since it consists of 2 electron pairs. Consequently, we may expect that in C_2H_4 the electron cloud of the C=C double bond will push the 2 C—H bond pairs of each C atom closer together than would a single bond pair, so that the H—C—H bond angle will be smaller than 120°. In fact, the H—C—H bond angle is found to be 116.7°.

36-5 Carbon with C.N. = 2: Linear Stereochemistry

An example of an organic compound in which the C atom has a linear stereochemistry is acetylene, a colorless gas (b.p. −81.5°C). (An inorganic compound in which the C atom has linear stereochemistry is carbon dioxide, CO_2, p. 289.) Experimentally we find that in the acetylene molecule, C_2H_2, each C atom is bonded to the other C atom and to one H atom. Also, the molecule is linear, with a carbon-carbon distance of 1.20 A (Fig. 36-4(a)), and is diamagnetic—that is, it contains no unpaired electrons. From considerations similar to those developed for ethylene, we conclude that each C atom forms 2 σ bonds, 1 to the partner C atom and 1 to an H atom. In addition each C atom forms 2 π bonds with the partner C atom.

In the formation of the 2 σ bonds each C atom makes use of sp (linear) hybrid orbitals, as shown in Fig. 36-4(b). If we assume that the $2p$ orbital of C involved in the sp hybridization is the $2p_y$ orbital, the C—C σ bond lies along the y axis of the 2 C atoms, which is also the molecular axis. One of the 2 C—C π bonds then derives from the pairing of the electrons in the $2p_x$ orbitals of the 2 C atoms, and the other C—C π bond derives from the pairing up of the two $2p_z$ electrons. Thus, in acetylene,

C_2H_2, the 2 C atoms are bound by a triple bond, consisting of 1 σ bond and 2 π bonds as shown simply by the electron-dot formula or by the dash formula in the margin. Figure 36-4(d) shows the overlapping p orbitals of the 2 carbon atoms in the 2 π bonds. The electron density of each of the carbon-carbon π bonds in acetylene, HC≡CH, similar to that of the single carbon-carbon π bond in ethylene, $H_2C{=}CH_2$, is composed of 2 equal regions of electron density—one above and one below a nodal plane. For these 2 π bonds of HC≡CH, which we may indicate as π_x and π_z, the nodal planes are at right angles to one another, just as the p orbitals from whose interactions the π bonds result.

H:C⋮⋮C:H

H—C≡C—H

The bond energy of the carbon-carbon triple bond in HC≡CH is 190.5 kcal/mole. Compare this value with that for the bond energy of the C=C double bond in ethylene, $H_2C{=}CH_2$ (146.8 kcal/mole) and that of the C—C single bond in ethane, $H_3C{-}CH_3$ (83.2 kcal/mole). The formation of one carbon-carbon π bond, in addition to the carbon-carbon σ bond, increases the total bond energy by 63.6 kcal/mole, but the formation of a second π bond only increases the total bond energy by an additional 43.7 kcal/mole.

SUMMARY OF CARBON STEREOCHEMISTRY

(a) Carbon atoms that form 4 σ bonds have a tetrahedral stereochemistry. The electron densities of the 4 σ bonds (sp^3 hybridization) are arranged tetrahedrally about the central carbon atom. Examples are CH_4 and $CH_3{-}CH_3$.

(b) Carbon atoms that form 3 σ bonds and 1 π bond have a trigonal planar stereochemistry; the electron densities of the 3 σ bonds (sp^2 hybridization) are arranged trigonally about the central carbon atom, and the electron density of the fourth bond—a π bond—extends above and below the plane of the molecule (nodal plane). Examples are ethylene, $H_2C{=}CH_2$, and its chloro-derivative, tetrachloroethylene, $Cl_2C{=}CCl_2$.

(c) Carbon atoms that form 2 σ bonds and 2 π bonds have a linear stereochemistry. The electron densities of the σ bonds (sp hybridization) are arranged linearly about the central carbon atom; the electron densities of the 2 π bonds extend above and below 2 nodal planes containing the C—C internuclear axis; these nodal planes are perpendicular to each other.

FIGURE 36-4 **The acetylene molecule, C_2H_2. (a) Structure. (b) Electron configuration of the C atom in its ground and valence state and in the C_2H_2 molecule. (c) Orbitals involved in the σ bonds. (d) Orbitals involved in the formation of the carbon-carbon π bonds. (e) Electron distribution of the π bonding electrons.**

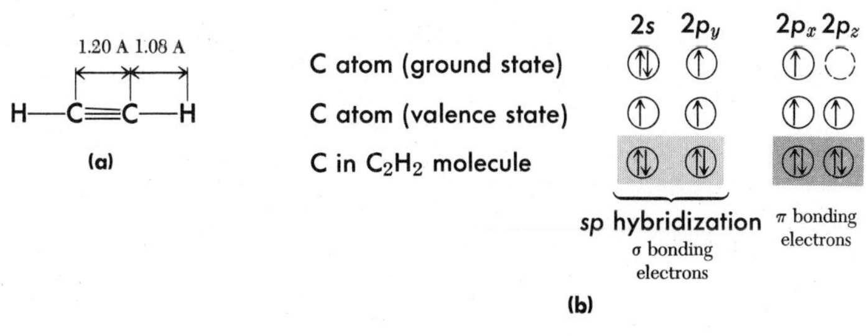

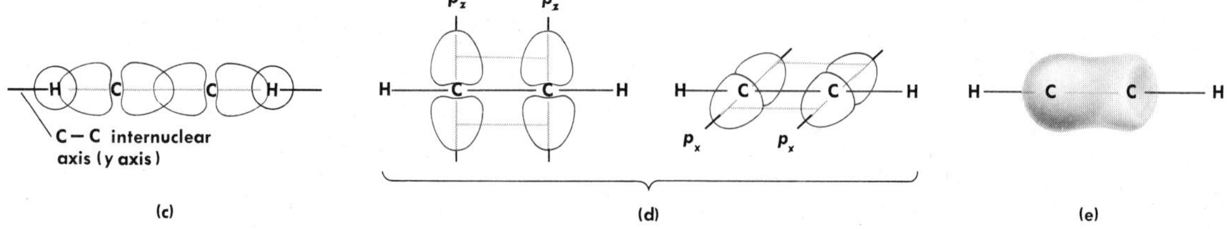

The electron configurations of the C atom in each of these 3 kinds of bond arrangements are summarized below:

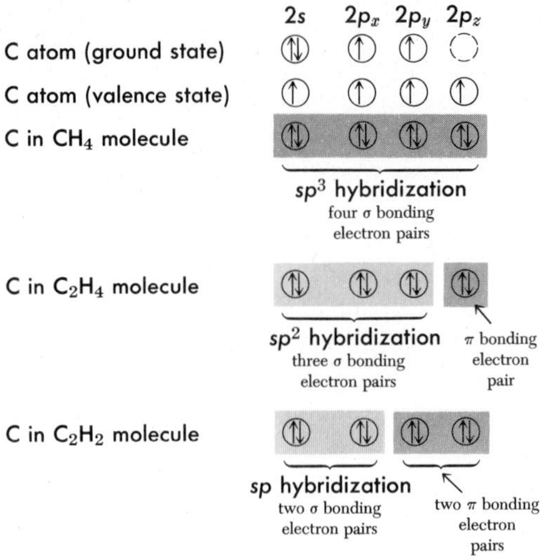

	2s	$2p_x$	$2p_y$	$2p_z$
C atom (ground state)	⇅	↑	↑	○
C atom (valence state)	↑	↑	↑	↑
C in CH_4 molecule	⇅	⇅	⇅	⇅

sp^3 hybridization: four σ bonding electron pairs

C in C_2H_4 molecule: ⇅ ⇅ ⇅ ⇅

sp^2 hybridization: three σ bonding electron pairs; π bonding electron pair

C in C_2H_2 molecule: ⇅ ⇅ ⇅ ⇅

sp hybridization: two σ bonding electron pairs; two π bonding electron pairs

36-6 Carbon Skeletons in Organic Compounds

We have seen that carbon atoms, because of their small size and electronic arrangements (4 valence electrons) have a unique tendency to bind together to form chains. Now let us consider some of the structural properties of these chains of carbon atoms, beginning with those in which each carbon atom forms 4 single σ covalent bonds (sp^3 hybridization). For 1, 2, and 3 such tetrahedrally bonded carbon atoms we can write the following dash formulas to show the carbon-carbon linkages:

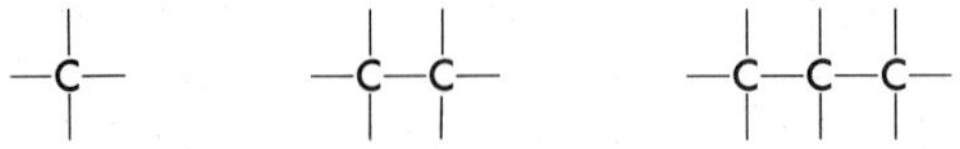

—C— —C—C— —C—C—C—

When we consider a combination of 4 (tetrahedrally bonded) carbon atoms, we see that there are 2 possible arrangements of the carbon-carbon bonding:

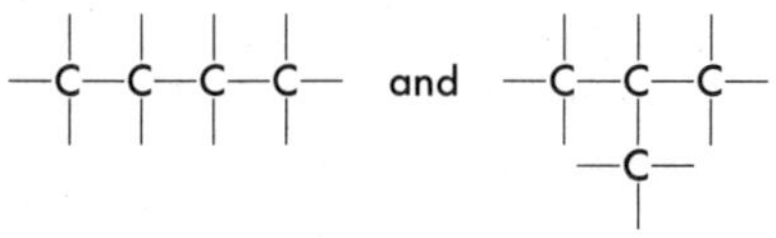

—C—C—C—C— and —C—C—C— (with a —C— branch on the middle carbon)

And for a combination of 5 (tetrahedrally bonded) carbon atoms, there are 3 possible bonding arrangements:

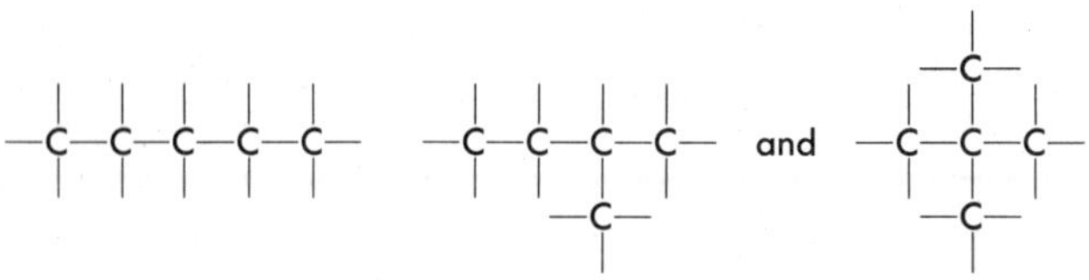

—C—C—C—C—C— —C—C—C—C— (with a —C— branch on the second carbon) and —C—C—C— (with —C— branches above and below the middle carbon)

We call these combinations "carbon skeletons." Carbon skeletons *are not molecules and are not capable of independent existence,* because some or all of the carbon atoms have unshared valencies (represented as a dash not connected to a partner atom). Carbon skeletons, however, are very convenient when we wish to illustrate the different ways by which carbon atoms can link up with one another, and with other atoms, while still maintaining the same tetrahedral bond arrangement about each C atom.

Suppose now that in one of the carbon skeletons shown above, wherever there is an unshared carbon valence, a hydrogen atom (with its one unpaired electron) binds to a carbon atom (with its unpaired electron). When all carbon valences not already taken up in carbon-carbon bonds are used to form a bond with a hydrogen atom, the carbon skeleton is said to be "saturated" with hydrogen atoms and we obtain compounds having the formulas I–VIII. In two dimensions the atoms in formulas V, VII,

```
    H          H  H          H  H  H           H  H  H  H           H     H     H
    |          |  |          |  |  |           |  |  |  |           |     |     |
 H—C—H     H—C—C—H      H—C—C—C—H       H—C—C—C—C—H       H—C—————C—————C—H
    |          |  |          |  |  |           |  |  |  |           |     |     |
    H          H  H          H  H  H           H  H  H  H           H  H—C—H  H
                                                                          |
                                                                          H
I. methane  II. ethane   III. propane       IV. n-butane          V. isobutane
```

```
                                                              H
                                                              |
    H  H  H  H  H          H  H     H     H             H H—C—H H
    |  |  |  |  |          |  |     |     |             |     |     |
 H—C—C—C—C—C—H      H—C—C—————C—————C—H      H—C—————C—————C—H
    |  |  |  |  |          |  |     |     |             |     |     |
    H  H  H  H  H          H  H  H—C—H  H             H  H—C—H  H
                                     |                        |
                                     H                        H
    VI. n-pentane           VII. isopentane            VIII. neopentane
```

and VIII appear to be overcrowding one another, but keep in mind that the formulas represent three-dimensional molecules, and models of these show that the atoms fit in quite well. These structural formulas now represent actual compounds, the first members of a series of carbon-hydrogen compounds in which each C atom forms its maximum number, 4, of covalent σ bonds. Such compounds are called "saturated hydrocarbons." The chains of C atoms in saturated hydrocarbons, and in the corresponding carbon-skeletons, are usually written out "straight" for convenience, but it is important to remember that any two bonds of a tetracoordinated (tetrahedral) carbon atom make an angle of about 109°. Also, since there is almost completely free rotation about each C—C single bond, as we have seen in the discussion of the formula of ethane, a great variety of conformations is possible for each compound. These conformations may differ not only in the relative positions of the H atoms attached to adjacent C atoms, but also, and more importantly, in the relative positions in space of the carbon atoms themselves. For example, if we consider the hydrocarbon *n*-pentane, CH_3—CH_2—CH_2—CH_2—CH_3, two limiting conformations are (a) and (b):

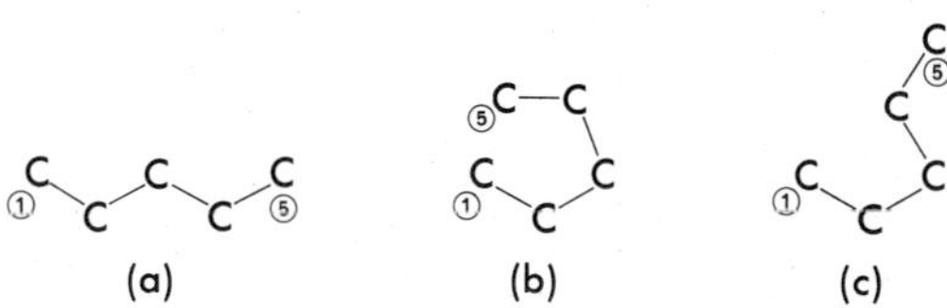

In both conformations the C atoms lie all in the same plane, but in (a) the atom labeled ①C is as far as possible from the labeled ⑤C, whereas in (b) the two terminal atoms, ①C and ⑤C, are as close as they can be compatibly with the tetrahedral angle (~109°) of all C—C—C bonds. Of course, the various conformations intermediate between (a) and (b), in which ①C and ⑤C are no longer in the same plane, can also exist.

In general, all organic molecules in which there are single C—C bonds can exist in a variety of conformations. Usually, one or more conformations are more stable than the others, although the energy differences among the various conformations are quite small. Hence, the internal energy of the molecules is sufficient to enable different parts of the molecule to rotate relative to one another about the C—C single bonds (free rotation about single C—C bonds). The interconversion of the different conformations occurs very rapidly, so that the molecular configuration changes continuously. Because of the C—C—C tetrahedral bond angle, and of the free rotation about each C—C single bond, the actual shapes of organic molecules generally are quite different from the schematic two-dimensional representations. For example, *n*-pentane is usually written as in VII, or more simply as CH_3—CH_2—CH_2—CH_2—CH_3, but a molecule of *n*-pentane may actually have either of the two limiting conformations (a) and (b), as well as any intermediate one—for example, (c).

Inspection of formulas I–VIII shows that all these saturated hydrocarbons can be represented by the general formula C_nH_{2n+2}, where n is the number of C atoms and $(2n + 2)$ the number of H atoms in the molecule. From the structural formulas II, III, IV, and VI we see that these molecules are built up of 2 kinds of tetrahedrally bonded C atoms, with different environments: (a) Carbon atoms that are joined only to 1 other C atom; these are the C atoms which are at the end of the chain and hence are called terminal C atoms. These terminal C atoms, bonded to only 1 other C atom (and to 3 H atoms) are known as *primary* C atoms. (b) Carbon atoms bonded to 2 other C atoms (and to 2 H atoms); these are called *secondary* C atoms.

The chains of C atoms in II, III, IV, and VI are "unbranched" or "normal," and hydrocarbons with unbranched chains of C atoms are referred to as "normal hydrocarbons." A small "*n*" (for normal) is prefixed to the name (e.g., *n*-pentane for $CH_3CH_2CH_2CH_2CH_3$). The compounds of formulas V and VII contain, in addition to primary and secondary C atoms, 1 (or more) C atom(s) joined to 3 other C atoms (and 1 H atom); these are called *tertiary* C atoms. And in VIII there is 1 C atom which is joined to 4 other C atoms, and is therefore called a *quaternary* C atom. Tertiary or quaternary C atoms or both are always present in branched-chain hydrocarbons.

STRUCTURAL ISOMERISM OF SATURATED HYDROCARBONS

The hydrocarbons of formulas IV and V both have the same molecular formula, C_4H_{10}, but their molecules have different structures. Compound IV, *n*-butane, has an unbranched carbon chain, and compound V, *iso*-butane, has a branched carbon chain. These 2 hydrocarbons are definite and distinct compounds; for example *n*-butane boils at 0.5°C and isobutane at −11.7°C. Here, then, is an example of isomerism—the phenomenon exhibited by substances which have the same molecular formula but different *bond arrangements* of the atoms within each molecule. Inspection shows that 3 possible isomers—VI, VII, and VIII—correspond to the molecular formula C_5H_{12}. In general, the greater the number of carbon atoms present in the molecule, the greater are the possibilities of isomerism, and furthermore, the number of isomers possible for each molecular formula increases markedly as the number of carbon atoms increases. For example, for the molecular formula $C_{10}H_{22}$, with twice as many C atoms as in formula C_5H_{10}, there are 75 possible isomers, and for the molecular formula $C_{12}H_{26}$ the number of possible isomers is 355. This type of isomerism, which arises from the ways in which the carbon atoms are linked together, is often called skeleton or chain isomerism. As we shall see later, there are other ways in which isomerism can occur in organic compounds.

INTERCONVERSION OF STRUCTURAL ISOMERS. The 2 structural isomers of formula C_4H_{10}, *n*-butane and *iso*-butane, differ very little in their thermodynamic stability. At 25C° the most stable state for a substance of molecular formula C_4H_{10} is an equilibrium mixture in which the 2 isomers *n*-butane and *iso*-butane coexist in comparable concentrations (the equilibrium constant for the reaction *n*-butane $\rightleftharpoons$ *iso*-butane, is $K = 2.5$ at 25°C). However, the activation energy for both the forward and reverse reaction in this equilibrium is quite high because the reaction involves the breaking of strong C—C σ covalent bonds. Hence, the interconversion of *n*-butane and *iso*-butane to give an equilibrium mixture does not actually take place, even though it is thermodynamically favored. This is generally true of all organic compounds that exist as structural isomers. If, by an appropriate method of preparation, we can obtain a certain structural isomer, this does not necessarily convert rapidly to a more stable structural isomer or to an equilibrium mixture of various structural isomers. And often one isomer can be kept indefinitely without noticeable change, provided the temperature is sufficiently low and no catalyst is present.

CHEMICAL PROPERTIES OF SATURATED HYDROCARBONS

The saturated hydrocarbons constitute a family of chemically similar compounds called a *homologous series* (from the Greek word *homologos*, meaning "assenting" or "agreeing"). The members of this series have the general formula C_nH_{2n+2} and show regular gradation in physical properties (e.g., rise in boiling point) as the molecular weight increases. This regular gradation in properties is understandable, since in the homologous series C_nH_{2n+2} the difference in formula between one member and the next heavier member is 1 additional C and 2 additional H atoms bonded together in a $-CH_2-$ group. Saturated hydrocarbons are distinguished by a remarkable inertness to most chemical reagents. For example, *n*-hexane, $CH_3-CH_2-CH_2-CH_2-CH_2-CH_3$, is unreactive towards concentrated sulfuric acid, boiling nitric acid, molten sodium hydroxide, and also to the strong oxidant potassium permanganate. Because of their scarce reactivity, the saturated hydrocarbons are sometimes called *paraffins*—a name derived from two Latin words meaning "little affinity." The polythene and polypropylene plastics are substances composed of very large molecules of the saturated hydrocarbon type, and their lack of chemical reactivity makes them valuable as materials for chemical containers, food packaging, tubing, and so on.

The saturated hydrocarbons undergo only 2 important chemical reactions. One is combustion in air or oxygen to form carbon dioxide and water with the evolution of a very large quantity of heat. Indeed, modern civilization is possible only because of the enormous amounts of energy we derive from the combustion of fuels, much of which are saturated hydrocarbons from natural oil. The other important reaction of saturated hydrocarbons is with the halogens to form compounds called alkyl halides.

36-7 Alkyl Halides

The halogens—fluorine, chlorine, and bromine (but not iodine except under very special conditions)—can attack the molecules of saturated hydrocarbons. The first product of this reaction results from the exchange of one hydrogen atom by a halogen atom (e.g., chlorine)—that is, the substitution of a C—H σ bond by a C—Cl σ bond. Thus, when methane, CH_4, reacts with chlorine, Cl_2, the first product formed is the compound CH_3Cl, mono-chloro-methane, also commonly called methyl chloride. A molecule of gaseous hydrogen chloride is also formed:

$$\begin{array}{c}\text{H}\\|\\\text{H—C—H}\\|\\\text{H}\end{array} + \text{Cl—Cl} \longrightarrow \begin{array}{c}\text{H}\\|\\\text{H—C—Cl}\\|\\\text{H}\end{array} + \text{H—Cl}$$

A reaction of this type is generally called a "halogenation reaction"—in this particular example a "chlorination reaction."

In halogenation reactions, a carbon-bonded hydrogen atom (C—H) is substituted by a carbon-bonded halogen atom (C—X); hence the reaction is often called a "substitution" reaction. For a hydrocarbon such as *n*-pentane, C_5H_{12}, in which there are 3 kinds of carbon atoms with different environments (2 primary carbon atoms, ①C and ⑤C; 2 secondary carbon atoms, ②C and ④C, each linked to 1 primary and 1 secondary carbon atom; and 1 secondary carbon atom ③C, linked to 2 secondary carbon atoms) the substitution of 1 H atom by 1 Cl atom can lead to any one of 3 different products or to a mixture of 2 or 3 of them:

I. 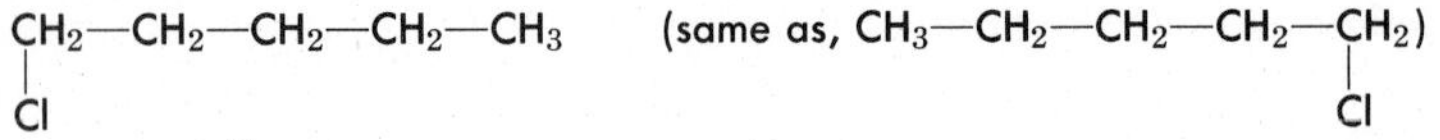 $CH_2—CH_2—CH_2—CH_2—CH_3$ with Cl on C-1 (same as, $CH_3—CH_2—CH_2—CH_2—CH_2$ with Cl on the terminal C)

1-chloropentane

II. $CH_2—CH—CH_2—CH_2—CH_3$ with Cl on C-2 (same as, $CH_3—CH_2—CH_2—CH—CH_3$ with Cl on the CH)

2-chloropentane

III. 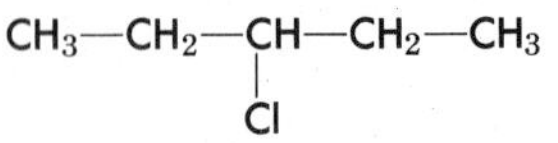 $CH_3—CH_2—CH—CH_2—CH_3$ with Cl on C-3

3-chloropentane

Compounds, I, II, and III, which go under the general name of mono-chloro-*n*-pentanes, all have the same molecular formula, C_4H_9Cl, and each contains the same (normal chain) carbon skeleton (—C—C—C—C—C—). In this case, the isomerism arises from the different positions taken by the substituting Cl atom. This kind of isomerism is called *position isomerism.*

The chlorine-substituted products of a saturated hydrocarbon are much more reactive than the parent hydrocarbon, and in all cases the reactive center is the

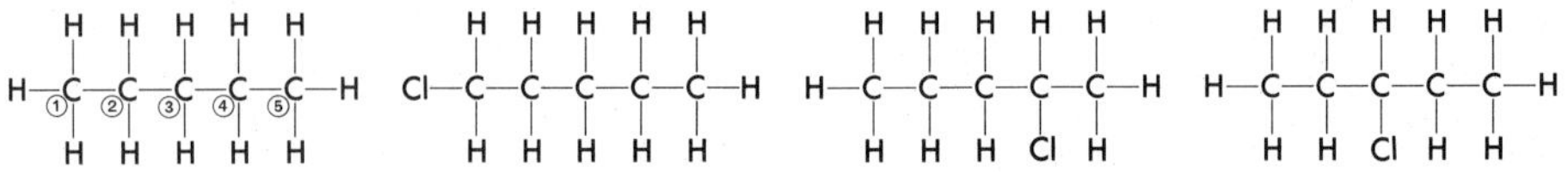

H—C—C—C—C—C—H (carbons numbered ①–⑤, each with H above and below)

n-pentane

Cl—C—C—C—C—C—H (all other positions H) — 1-chloropentane

H—C—C—C—C—C—H (Cl below the third carbon from left... i.e. lower row H H H Cl H) — 2-chloropentane

H—C—C—C—C—C—H (lower row H H Cl H H) — 3-chloropentane

three isomeric chloropentanes

C—Cl bond. For example, it is not possible to substitute directly one H atom of *n*-pentane with a —OH group, or with other groups such as $—NH_2$, —SH, and —C≡N. However, any one of the mono-chloro-*n*-pentanes will react—even though rather slowly—with appropriate reagents to form compounds in which the Cl atom is substituted by another group:

$CH_3—CH_2—CH_2—CH_2—CH_2—OH$ $\qquad$ $CH_3—CH_2—CH_2—CH_2—CH_2—SH$

$CH_3—CH_2—CH_2—CH_2—CH_2—NH_2$ $\qquad$ $CH_3—CH_2—CH_2—CH_2—CH_2—CN$

Notice that in these compounds the carbon skeleton (—C—C—C—C—C—) remains intact, and the C—H bonds remain unchanged; only the C—Cl bond of the parent chloropentane has been affected. Therefore, in representing these substitution reactions, it is often convenient to write the chloropentane simply as R—Cl, where R represents the whole group of C and H atoms (C_nH_{2n+1}) that remains intact in the reaction considered. In general, R represents any group of bonded atoms which is not capable of long independent existence but survives intact during a certain chemical change. This group R is called a *radical*—in this case an *alkyl* radical since it derives from a saturated hydrocarbon, *alkane.*

If we replace one H atom by a Cl atom in the molecules of the homologous series of saturated hydrocarbons C_nH_{2n+2}, or R—H, the resulting compounds form a homologous series of *alkyl chlorides* C_nH_{2n+1}—Cl, or R—Cl. As the above examples of *n*-pentane and chloro-*n*-pentanes illustrate, there are very many more possible isomers in the alkyl-chloride series, R—Cl, than in the saturated hydrocarbon series, R—H. However, since all isomers have the same C—Cl bond, they all undergo the same type of reactions characteristic of this bond. Thus, if we know how any one member of this homologous series behaves chemically, we can predict quite accurately how any other member of the series will behave when similarly treated. An enormous number of different facts can then be correlated and classified into a few simple generalizations.

Some general and important reactions of the alkyl halides, R—Cl, can be schematically represented as follows:

$$R{-}Cl + H_2O \longrightarrow R{-}OH + H{-}Cl \qquad R{-}Cl + NH_3 \longrightarrow R{-}NH_2 + H{-}Cl$$
$$R{-}Cl + H_2S \longrightarrow R{-}SH + H{-}Cl \qquad R{-}Cl + AgCN \longrightarrow R{-}CN + AgCl$$

For any alkyl chloride, R—Cl, these reactions proceed essentially in the same manner; there are, however, some marked differences in the *rates* of reaction. The "reactive" C—Cl bond is a higher relative percentage of a molecule of, say, methyl chloride, CH_3—Cl, than of a molecule of, say, *n*-pentyl chloride, $CH_3CH_2CH_2CH_2$-CH_2—Cl. Therefore, when a molecule of a reagent (e.g., an ammonia molecule, NH_3) seeking to attack the C—Cl bond encounters a molecule of the alkyl chloride, the probability of its coming sufficiently near the "reactive" C—Cl bond is greater for CH_3—Cl than for $CH_3CH_2CH_2CH_2CH_2$—Cl. On the basis of the encounter frequency, ammonia can react much more *rapidly* with methyl chloride than with *n*-pentyl chloride.

When we examine the chemical behavior of the new substitution compounds of saturated hydrocarbons mentioned above, we again find the reactivity largely concentrated in the bonds (C—OH; C—SH; C—NH_2; and C—CN) that link the new substituting group to a C atom of the alkyl radical, not in the C—C or C—H bonds. Also, all the compounds of the general formula R—X, where X represents the substituting group, constitute an homologous series of compounds which have very similar chemical properties and show regular gradations of physical properties as their molecular weight increases in the series. For example, the substitution compounds of the general formula R—NH_2, called *alkyl amines,* all have weakly basic character, similar to the inorganic ammonia, NH_3. The basic properties of alkyl amines, RNH_2, just as for ammonia, NH_3, arise from the presence on the nitrogen atom of a lone electron pair that can be donated to a proton, H^+, forming a substituted ammonium ion (a mono-alkylammonium ion):

$$H_3N{:}\ + H_2O \rightleftharpoons [H_3N{\rightarrow}H]^+ + OH^-$$
$$RH_2N{:}\ + H_2O \rightleftharpoons [RH_2N{\rightarrow}H]^+ + OH^-$$

Not only the basic character but most other reactions of alkayl amines involve the —NH_2 group. We call this a "functional" group, because its presence is what determines the manner in which the alkyl amines behave, or function, toward chemical reagents.

In general, it is very helpful to consider organic chemistry as the chemistry of many homologous series of compounds, each homologous series being characterized by the presence of a certain "functional" group or groups. Thus, organic chemistry is concerned with the ways of introducing various functional groups into organic molecules, and with the manner in which such functional groups, once they are part of the organic molecule, react with different reagents.

In our preceding discussion we have looked upon the various alkyl compounds, R—X, as being derived from the corresponding saturated hydrocarbons, R—H, by substitution of a H atom by the functional group X, and we have stated that the general behavior of the homologous series can be related to that of the parent saturated hydrocarbons, modified by the presence of the functional group. Because of the importance of functional groups in determining the reactivity of organic compounds, it is also enlightening to look upon the different types of organic compounds as being derived from an inorganic parent compound of the functional group, by substitution of a H atom by an alkyl radical. For example, ammonia, NH_3, can be considered the parent compound of the functional amine group, —NH_2. Thus, CH_3—NH_2, methyl amine (note single m), can be thought to be derived from ammonia (note double m), NH_3, by substitution of one H atom by the methyl group, —CH_3, that is, by substitution of one N—H bond with one N—CH_3 bond. On this basis, we can expect the alkyl amines to have a chemical behavior similar to that of ammonia, although modified by the presence of an alkyl group R, in place of an H atom.

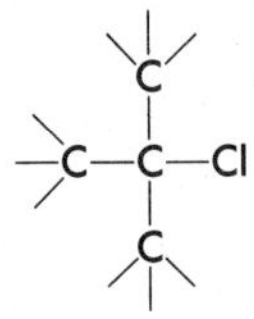

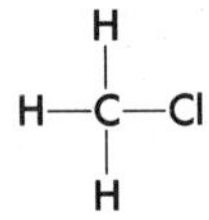

You must also keep in mind that the environment of a group in an organic molecule affects to some extent its reactivity. For example, a C—Cl bond of a tertiary carbon atom (see figure in margin) is different in its reactivity from a C—Cl bond of a primary carbon atom. In general, environmental conditions always affect, at least to some extent, the chemical properties of the bond between an organic radical and a functional group. We shall meet several examples of this effect in the following sections.

POLYSUBSTITUTED SATURATED HYDROCARBONS

So far we have discussed the compounds formed by the substitution of *one* hydrogen atom of a saturated hydrocarbon by *one* atom or group of atoms (functional group), say a chlorine atom:

$$R—CH_3 + Cl_2 \longrightarrow R—CH_2Cl + HCl$$

Substitution is not restricted to the replacement of only 1 atom by 1 functional group. For example, in the chlorination of normal pentane, $CH_3—CH_2—CH_2—CH_2—CH_3$, we can replace 2 H atoms by 2 Cl atoms—that is, we can replace 2 C—H bonds by 2 C—Cl bonds. We have seen that the reactivity of a certain functional group (or of a certain C—X bond) is influenced to some extent by the environment. Consequently, in a disubstituted chloro-compound the 2 C—Cl bonds will react independently and similarly if they are very far apart and belong to the same environment (for example, if both Cl atoms are attached to a primary C atom). Or, the 2 C—Cl bonds may react independently but differently (for example, if they are far apart and one Cl atom is attached to a primary C atom whereas the other Cl atom is attached to a tertiary C atom). A third possibility is that the 2 C—Cl bonds are so situated in the organic molecule that they can react together; we shall now consider an important example of this kind of behavior.

SATURATED RING COMPOUNDS—CYCLOALKANES

Let us consider dichloro-*n*-pentane, $C_5H_{10}Cl_2$, in which the two Cl atoms are attached to the 2 terminal C atoms of the carbon chain: $Cl—CH_2—CH_2—CH_2—CH_2—CH_2—Cl$. Because of the C—C—C tetrahedral angles and of the free rotation about each C—C bond, it is possible for the 2 dichloro-*n*-pentane molecule to assume a conformation in which the 2 C—Cl bonds come into close proximity of each other. What happens then if a compound such as dichloro-*n*-pentane is treated with a reagent such as finely divided sodium metal, which tends to cause the breaking of the two C—Cl bonds (forming sodium chloride, Na^+Cl^-)? The 2 Cl atoms are eliminated, each with its unpaired electron, leaving each of the 2 terminal C atoms of the *n*-pentane skeleton with 1 unpaired electron. If this skeleton has an appropriate conformation, the 2 unpaired electrons on the 2 C atoms pair up in a C—C σ bond, and a ring (*cyclic*) hydrocarbon C_5H_{12}, is formed (see diagram in margin). Similar to the saturated hydrocarbons (alkanes), the saturated ring hydrocarbons, called *cyclo-alkanes*, contain only C—H σ bonds and C—C σ bonds. In fact, the cyclo-alkanes can be thought of as being derived from the corresponding alkanes by the removal of 2 hydrogen atoms from *non-neighboring* carbon atoms, and the linking together of these carbon atoms to form a ring:

$$C_nH_{2n+2}\ (n\text{-alkane}) \longrightarrow C_nH_{2n}\ (\text{cyclo-alkane}) + H_2$$

If we consider that the C—C—C bond angle for tetrahedral carbon atoms is about 109°, we can see that a 5-carbon chain can be linked to form a ring (cyclic) structure with very little distortion of the bond angles (the internal angle of a regular pentagon is 108°). It is also possible to prepare cyclic hydrocarbons containing more than 5 C atoms in the ring; these larger rings, however, are puckered so that the

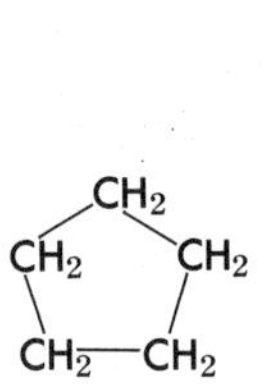

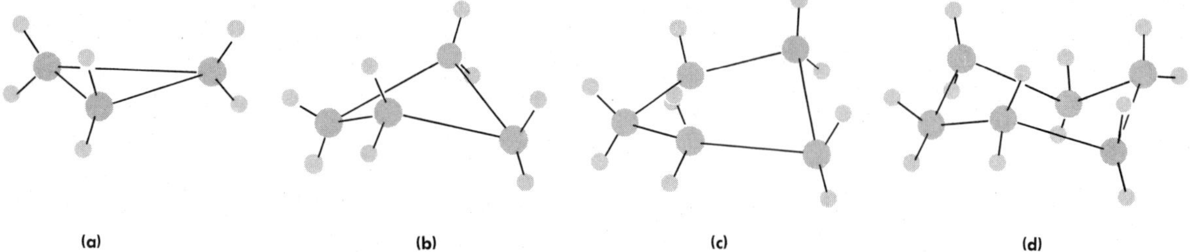

FIGURE 36-5 Schematic representation of the molecules of the simplest cycloalkanes. (a) Cyclopropane, C_3H_6. (b) Cyclobutane, C_4H_8. (c) Cyclopentane, C_5H_{10}. (a) Cyclohexane, C_6H_{12} (the chair form, one of the possible conformations).

C—C—C bond angles are close to 109°, and the strain of the C—C—C bond angles of a planar cyclic structure is relieved. (A flat 6-membered ring would have internal angles of 120°.) In the puckered molecules of cycloalkanes, the bond angle about each carbon atom is the same as in the chains of alkanes—that is, the puckered rings are *strainless.*

It is of interest to note that 5- and 6-membered ring compounds are more common in nature (for example, in petroleum compounds) and easier to prepare than either the larger or the smaller cyclic molecules. This is so because the terminal C atoms of normal carbon chains consisting of 5 and 6 atoms can, as we have just seen, come close enough to join together, under the action of an appropriate reagent. The probability that the 2 terminal C atoms of the original normal chain molecule may come together decreases rapidly as the chain length increases, and for this reason large ring molecules are less common, even though they are still strainless. On the other hand, smaller carbon rings, 4- and 3-membered rings, are less common because the C—C—C bond angles are badly distorted (the deviation from the 109° tetrahedral angle is about 20° in a 4-membered ring and as high as 50° in a 3-membered ring). The molecules of the first 4 members of the cycloalkane series are shown in Fig. 36-5.

36-8 Unsaturated Hydrocarbons: The Olefin Series

Hydrocarbons that contain a C=C double bond, are called *olefins.* Ethylene, which we have already studied, is the simplest of the olefins. Olefins belong to a class of compounds called *unsaturated hydrocarbons,* because they contain less than the maximum possible number of hydrogen atoms that can be bonded to the carbon skeleton. For example, the olefin C_2H_4, ethylene ($H_2C{=}CH_2$) has only 4 H atoms, as compared to 6 H atoms in the saturated hydrocarbon C_2H_6, ethane ($H_3C—CH_3$). Any hydrocarbon that contains a carbon-carbon double bond (C=C) is an unsaturated hydrocarbon.

DEHYDROGENATION AND OLEFIN FORMATION. Olefins, with the general formula C_nH_{2n}, may be formed by the removal of a hydrogen atom from each of 2 adjacent carbon atoms of a saturated hydrocarbon. Ethylene, C_2H_4, for example, is prepared from ethane, C_2H_6, by the removal of 2 hydrogen atoms on adjacent carbon atoms at temperatures of about 500°C, and in the presence of a catalyst such as chromium(III) oxide:

$$\text{H}_3\text{C—CH}_3 \longrightarrow \text{H}_2\text{C{=}CH}_2 + \text{H—H}$$

The 2 indicated H atoms are eliminated, together with their single electrons, and the remaining single electrons on the adjacent C atoms then rearrange themselves by pairing up to form a carbon-carbon π bond. This example again illustrates that a chemical reaction in organic chemistry generally involves the breaking of one or more covalent bonds and the formation of one or more new covalent bonds. In this example in the reactant, C_2H_6, two C—H σ bonds are broken, and in the products C_2H_4 and H_2, one C—C π bond as well as one H—H σ bond are formed. In general, a reaction can involve the formation, or breaking, of bonds of either the σ type, or the π type, or both.

The process of removing 2 hydrogen atoms from 2 adjacent carbon atoms to form a C=C double bond is known as *dehydrogenation.* Under appropriate conditions, all saturated hydrocarbons with 2 or more C atoms can undergo dehydrogenation; in general, the hydrocarbons with 4 or more C atoms can give rise to isomeric olefins. In ethane, C_2H_6, there are only 2 carbon atoms present; consequently, there is only one way of removing 2 hydrogen atoms from adjacent carbon atoms and bringing about the formation of a C=C double bond, as shown above. Similarly, the dehydrogenation of propane, $CH_3—CH_2—CH_3$, can give only 1 olefin, $CH_2=CH—CH_3$. But in the dehydrogenation of the saturated hydrocarbon $CH_3—CH_2—CH_2—CH_3$ there are 2 different ways by which this molecule may lose 2 hydrogen atoms from adjacent carbon atoms, forming 2 possible olefin position isomers, $CH_2=CH—CH_2—CH_3$, and $CH_3—CH=CH—CH_3$. Thus, in the olefin series isomerism may arise from the different positions of the C=C double bond in the olefin.

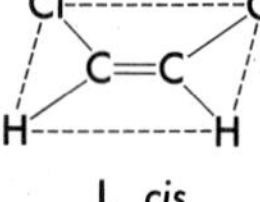

I. *cis*

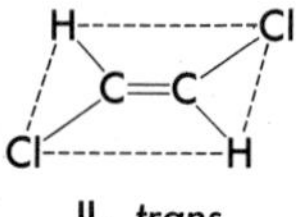

II. *trans*

CIS-TRANS ISOMERISM IN OLEFINS. Another way in which isomerism may occur in olefins is illustrated by the following example. The olefin of molecular formula ClHC=CHCl exists as 2 isomers having the structures I and II shown in the accompanying diagrams. These isomers differ in the relative positions of the 2 H atoms and of the 2 Cl atoms relative to the C=C double bond. If we draw a rectangle in the plane of the molecule, with the C=C double bond at the center, then in isomer I the 2 Cl atoms occupy adjacent corners (as do the H atoms), and we say that they are in *cis* positions. In isomer II, on the other hand, the 2 Cl atoms occupy opposite corners (as do the H atoms), and we say that they are in *trans* positions. This type of isomerism, and the name given to the isomers, is analogous to what we studied in Chapter 33 for square-planar metal complexes of the general formula $[Ma_2b_2]$.

Cis-trans isomers exist in olefins because there is no free rotation about the C=C double bond as there is about a C—C single bond. The accompanying diagrams illustrate this difference. In the ethane molecule, $CH_3—CH_3$, if we keep one $CH_3—$ group

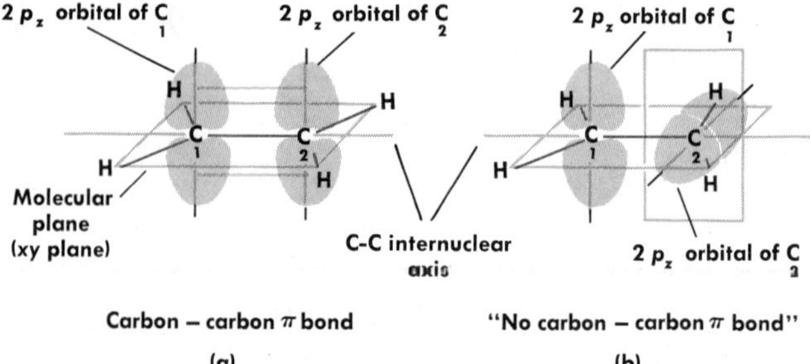

Carbon – carbon π bond (a) "No carbon – carbon π bond" (b)

fixed in a certain position and rotate the other about the C—C internuclear axis, the electron cloud of the C—C σ bond remains essentially unaltered. Now consider the ethylene molecule, $CH_2=CH_2$. Suppose we keep one planar CH_2 group (labeled ①CH_2) in a certain fixed position, while rotating the other planar CH_2 group (labeled ②CH_2) about the C—C internuclear axis. The orientation of the p_z orbital of the ①C atom then remains fixed, whereas that of the p_z orbital of the ②C atom changes its orientation (since it must remain perpendicular to the plane of the 3 σ bonds). The overlap of the $2p_z$ orbitals, which leads to the carbon-carbon π bond, thus becomes less and less effective the more we rotate the plane of the ②CH_2 group from its original position. Finally, when the plane of the 2 —CH_2 groups are at right angles, no carbon-carbon π bonding is possible. In effect, rotating one CH_2 group with respect to the other CH_2 group means breaking the carbon-carbon π bond. We saw earlier that the total energy of the C═C double bond, 147 kcal/mole, exceeds by 64 kcal/mole the energy of the C—C single bond (83 kcal/mole). Thus, to rotate one CH_2 group relative to the other CH_2 group about the C—C axis, we would need to supply this large quantity of energy necessary to break the π bond. The vibrational energy of the olefin molecules at ordinary temperatures is much too low to bring this about, and thus there is no free rotation about a C═C double bond.

ADDITION REACTIONS OF OLEFINS. The reactions of the olefins usually involve the C═C double bond. Thus, in studying the chemical reactivity of olefins, it is often convenient to consider them as substituted hydrocarbons containing a particular kind of functional group—a C═C double bond. As we have seen, a saturated hydrocarbon can be dehydrogenated to form an olefin. We can also reverse this process to form a saturated hydrocarbon by the *addition* of hydrogen to an olefin. A chemical reaction that involves the addition of the atoms of a molecule of H_2 to a molecule containing a C═C double bond (or, as we shall see later, a C≡C triple bond) is called an *addition reaction.* Examples of addition reactions are the reactions of ethylene, $H_2C{=}CH_2$: with (a) H_2 to form $H_3C{-}CH_3$, ethane; with (b) Cl_2 to form $ClH_2C{-}CH_2Cl$, ethylene dichloride; with (c) HCl to form $CH_3{-}CH_2Cl$, ethyl chloride; and (d) with H_2O to form $CH_3{-}CH_2OH$, ethyl alcohol.

The reactivity of the C═C double bond, as that of most functional groups, depends on its environment. If 2 C═C double bonds are present in the same molecule but are far apart from each other, then each reacts more or less independently and the olefin has the behavior resulting from 2 *isolated* C═C double bonds. But if the 2 C═C double bonds are close to each other, then the reactivity of one C═C group is affected by the proximity of the other. This interaction is particularly pronounced when 2 or more C═C double bonds are on alternating pairs of C atoms, for example —C═C—C═C—. Such C═C double bonds are said to be "conjugated." A characteristic example of the reactivity of conjugated double bonds is the addition of 1 molecule of Cl_2 to a molecule of the diolefin $CH_2{=}CH{-}CH{=}CH_2$, butadiene:

$$CH_2{=}CH{-}CH{=}CH_2 + Cl{-}Cl \longrightarrow \underset{\displaystyle Cl}{\underset{|}{CH_2}}{-}CH{=}CH{-}\underset{\displaystyle Cl}{\underset{|}{CH_2}}$$

As this equation shows, the 2 C═C double bonds of the conjugated system —C═C—C═C— actually behave as a unit; a Cl atom adds at each C atom at the *ends* of the conjugated system, while a new C═C double bond forms between the 2 middle C atoms.

The interaction between conjugated C═C double bonds is even more pronounced when they are part of a ring system of appropriate size. This leads us to the study of unsaturated ring systems, of which the most important is benzene.

36-9 Benzene

Benzene is a colorless liquid (b.p. 84°C) of molecular formula C_6H_6. In the benzene molecule, the 6 C atoms are linked to one another in a flat ring (regular hexagon) and each of the 6 H atoms is linked to a C atom in the same plane as the ring. All carbon-carbon distances are identical, 1.39 A, and so are all carbon-hydrogen distances, 1.08 A; also, all the C—C—C and all the C—C—H bond angles are identical, 120°. The value of the carbon-carbon distance in benzene, C_6H_6, is appreciably less than the value of the 1.54 A for the C—C single bond in alkanes such as ethane,

$H_3C{-}CH_3$, and is only slightly greater than the value of 1.34 A for the C=C double bond in olefins such as ethylene, $H_2C{=}CH_2$. Finally, benzene is a diamagnetic substance—that is, its molecules have no unpaired electrons.

On the basis of experimental data, we can explain the bonding present in the benzene molecule as follows. Each C atom forms 3 σ bonds—one to each of the 2 adjacent C atoms in the ring and one to a H atom. For these 3 σ bonds, which as we have seen are in the same plane and form angles of 120°, the C atom utilizes three sp^2 hybrid orbitals (Fig. 36-6(a)) formed from the $2s$, $2p_x$ and $2p_y$ orbitals. In addition, each C atom has one electron in its $2p_z$ orbital, not engaged in the formation of a σ bond; thus in the benzene molecule there are 6 electrons in 6 equally oriented p_z orbitals of the 6 C atoms, (Fig. 36-6(b)). We have seen that in the ethylene molecule, $H_2C{=}CH_2$, one electron in the p_z orbital of one C atom pairs up with 1 electron in the p_z orbital of the partner C atom, forming a carbon-carbon π bond. Similarly, in benzene the electron in the p_z orbital of one C atom pairs up with the electron in the p_z orbital of an adjacent partner C atom, forming a carbon-carbon π bond. In this way, 3 carbon-carbon π bonds may be formed in benzene. But since in benzene all carbon-carbon distances are identical, we cannot localize the 3 π bonds in any fixed positions in the ring, (if the 3 C=C double bonds were localized, then 3 of the carbon-carbon distances would be different from the other 3). That is to say, the electron in the p_z orbital of one carbon atom may pair up with the electron in the p_z orbital of *either* adjacent partner carbon atom. Thus, we must think of the 3 π bonds as being delocalized over the entire 6-carbon ring. That is to say, the 6 π-bonding electrons of benzene are free to move around the hexagonal ring of the 6 C atoms. The electron cloud of the π-bonding electrons can be represented as consisting of 2 identical regions of electron density, symmetrically situated above and below the plane of the ring as shown in (c). The formula of benzene can then be written as (d), or as the resonance hybrid of 2 equivalent contributing structures I and II (Fig. 36-6 (e)).

The carbon-carbon bonds in benzene, therefore, are intermediate between single and double bonds and would be expected to have properties different from single σ bonds and also different from localized double $\sigma + \pi$ bonds. Compare these

FIGURE 36-6 The benzene molecule. (a) Framework of the σ bonds. (b) The 6 p_z orbitals of the 6 C atoms. (c) Electron-cloud distribution of the 6 π bonding electrons. (d) Schematic formula showing the system of the π bonding electrons as a dashed circle. (e) Schematic representation of the contributing structures I and II.

(a) (b) (c)

(d) (e)

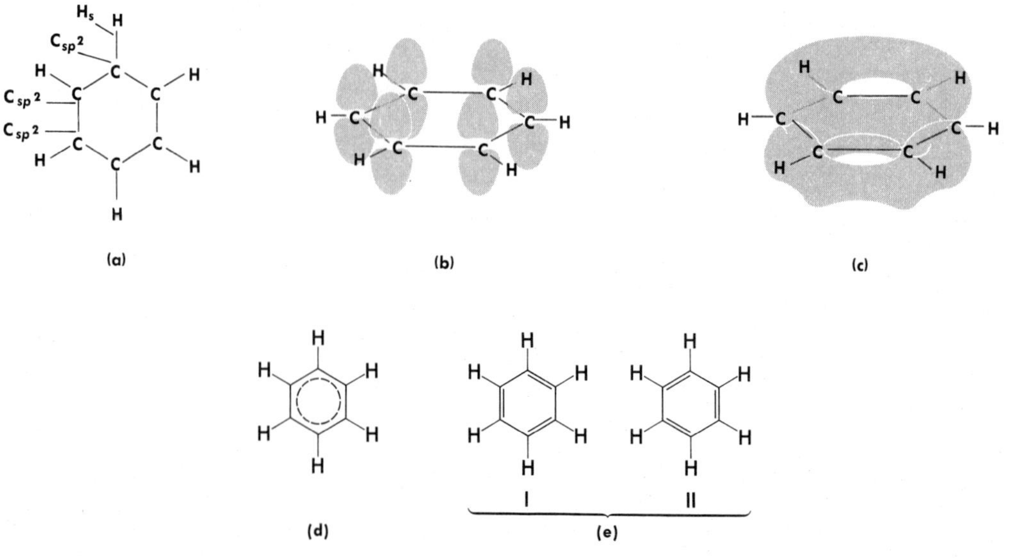

reactions with bromine, Br_2: Ethylene, $H_2C{=}CH_2$, an unsaturated olefin containing localized π electrons, undergoes an *addition* reaction with Br_2 to form ethylene dibromide, $BrH_2C{-}CH_2Br$; but benzene, C_6H_6, containing delocalized π electrons, undergoes a *substitution* reaction with Br_2 (a Br atom substitutes for a H atom) to form bromobenzene, C_6H_5Br. In general the chemical behavior of benzene does not resemble that of the unsaturated (olefins) compounds.

36-10 Unsaturated Hydrocarbons: The Alkyne Series

In a preceding section we discussed the structure and bonding of acetylene,

$$H{:}C{\vdots}{\vdots}C{:}H \qquad H{-}C{\equiv}C{-}H \qquad HC{\equiv}CH$$

a gas with a boiling point of $-84°C$, which is the simplest member of a homologous series of general formula C_nH_{2n-2}. The presence of a $C{\equiv}C$ triple bond in a hydrocarbon is indicated by the ending *-yne;* thus the general name of the C_nH_{2n-2} series is *alkynes,* and acetylene is also called ethyne (*eth*ane + *yne*).

We have seen that in olefins the chemical reactivity is associated chiefly with the $C{=}C$ double bond; similarly, for alkynes, the $C{\equiv}C$ triple bond is the point of attack of most chemical reagents. And, in general, the triple bond of alkynes shows the same kind of behavior as the double bond of olefins. For example, acetylene, $HC{\equiv}CH$, reacts with chlorine, Cl_2, to form $ClHC{=}CHCl$; to this we can then add more Cl_2 (in the presence of finely divided nickel catalyst) to form $Cl_2HC{-}CHCl_2$. Similarly, acetylene, $HC{\equiv}CH$, combines with hydrogen iodide, HI, as well as the other hydrogen halides, to form $H_3C{-}CHI_2$ as the *final* product:

$$HC{\equiv}CH + HI \longrightarrow H_2C{=}HCI + HI \longrightarrow H_3C{-}CHI_2$$

Note that the second HI adds to the double bond of $H_2C{=}CHI$ in such a way that the second H atom becomes attached to the same carbon atom as the first.

ALCOHOLS

The compounds derived from the hydrocarbons by the substitution of an H atom by an —OH group are called alcohols. The replacement of one H atom in the methane, CH_4, molecule, by one —OH group produces the compound CH_3OH, called methyl alcohol, or methanol. Similarly, the replacement of one H atom in the ethane molecule, $CH_3{-}CH_3$, by one —OH group produces the compound $CH_3{-}CH_2OH$, called ethyl alcohol, or ethanol.

ETHYL ALCOHOL, C_2H_5OH. The compound represented by the formula C_2H_5OH (b.p. + 78°C) is frequently called grain alcohol, for it can be produced by the fermentation of grain. It may also be made synthetically by the addition of H_2O to ethylene, $CH_2{=}CH_2$, under suitable conditions: $H_2C{=}CH_2 + H_2O \longrightarrow H_3C{-}CH_2(OH)$. In this reaction, 1 hydrogen atom from the water molecule joins with 1 carbon atom of the ethylene molecule, and the OH group joins with the other carbon atom. This type of reaction involves the "breaking" of the carbon-carbon π bond of ethylene, with the formation of two σ bonds—a C—H bond and a C—OH bond in the product CH_3CH_2OH.

PROPYL ALCOHOL AND HIGHER ALCOHOLS. When 1 hydrogen atom of the compound $CH_3{-}CH_2{-}CH_3$ is replaced by 1 —OH group, 2 different alcohols can be formed which are "position isomers." If a hydrogen atom attached to 1 of the terminal (primary) carbon atoms of propane, $CH_3{-}CH_2{-}CH_3$, is replaced by a —OH group, the alcohol formed is $CH_3{-}CH_2{-}CH_2{-}OH$, normal propyl alcohol. If a hydrogen atom attached to the central (secondary) carbon atom of propane, $CH_3{-}CH_2{-}CH_3$, is replaced, the alcohol formed is $CH_3{-}CH(OH){-}CH_3$, *iso*-propyl alcohol.

CARBOXYLIC ACIDS

We have already learned that the presence of a functional group in a molecule affects to some extent the bonds present on the same and on neighboring atoms. A notable example is the following. A saturated hydrocarbon, R—CH_3, is extremely inert toward oxidizing agents; for example, it is not attacked by potassium permanganate. However, if 1 H atom of the saturated hydrocarbon is substituted with a —OH group to form a primary alcohol, R—CH_2—OH, the carbon atom to which the —OH group is linked can now be oxidized easily by a suitable oxidizing agent (represented schematically as [O]). The final product of the oxidation is a carboxylic acid: $RCH_2OH + [O] \longrightarrow RCOOH$. The ease of oxidation of primary alcohols as compared to the corresponding hydrocarbons points out that the carbon-hydroxyl bond, C—OH, affects appreciably the two C—H bonds of the same C atom.

The functional group —COOH (see margin) is called the *carboxylic acid group.* Organic compounds which contain the —COOH group are known as *carboxylic acids*. The formula of the simplest carboxylic acid, formic acid, is HCOOH; the next member of the series is acetic acid, CH_3—COOH, which we have encountered many times. Carboxylic acids are generally weak acids—that is, they ionize only to a slight extent in aqueous solution; as we have learned in Chapter 20, only the H atom of the —OH group of carboxylic acids can ionize. As we would expect, acetic acid and the other carboxylic acids can react with the electropositive metals to liberate H_2; with metal oxides, hydroxides, and carbonates, they react to yield metal salts and water.

ALDEHYDES

When the oxidation of ethyl alcohol, CH_3CH_2OH, by an appropriate oxidizing agent, represented simply as [O], is carried out under carefully controlled conditions, the compound acetaldehyde, CH_3CHO, is formed (together with H_2O):

$$CH_3CH_2OH + [O] \longrightarrow CH_3CHO + H_2O$$

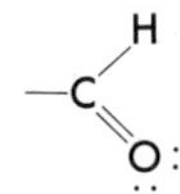

Aldehydes are organic compounds whose molecules contain the —CHO functional group (see margin). Further oxidation of an aldehyde, R—CHO, produces the corresponding carboxylic acid, RCOOH, as discussed above.

KETONES

We have just seen that the oxidation of a primary alcohol, RCH_2OH, yields first an aldehyde, R—CHO, and then a carboxylic acid, R—COOH. But if the —OH group in the alcohol is bonded to a secondary carbon atom, then the oxidation product of this secondary alcohol is a *ketone:*

$$\underset{\displaystyle\text{OH}}{\text{R—}\underset{|}{\text{CH}}\text{—CH}_3} + [O] \longrightarrow \text{R—}\underset{\displaystyle\text{O}}{\underset{\|}{\text{C}}}\text{—CH}_3 + H_2O$$

For example, on oxidation the secondary alcohol $CH_3CH(OH)CH_3$ produces the ketone CH_3COCH_3, called dimethylketone or simply acetone. The characteristic functional group of a ketone is the carbon-to-oxygen double bond called a carbonyl group (see margin), present on a non-terminal position on the carbon chain. Notice that both aldehydes and ketones contain the carbonyl group, C=O, although in different positions on the carbon chain. Reactions that depend only on the presence of a C=O group are therefore the same for both classes of compounds, and in fact aldehydes and ketones have a great many properties in common.

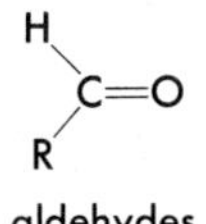

aldehydes

ketones

DEHYDRATION OF ALCOHOLS

In general, organic compounds that contain hydroxyl groups, —OH, can be dehydrated—that is, they may lose a H atom and an —OH group in the form of water. This generalization holds good for alcohols in which the dehydration involves either the same single alcohol molecule or two alcohol molecules. Dehydration involving only one alcohol molecule is referred to as *intra*-molecular dehydration, and dehydration involving more than one molecule is referred to as *inter*-molecular dehydration.

INTRA-MOLECULAR DEHYDRATION. An example of *intra*-molecular dehydration is the elimination of 1 H_2O molecule from 1 molecule of an alcohol to form a molecule of an olefin. The intra-molecular dehydration of ethyl alcohol, CH_3CH_2OH, to produce the olefin, ethylene, can be represented as:

$$\underset{\boxed{\text{H}\quad\text{OH}}}{\text{H}_2\text{C—CH}_2} \longrightarrow \text{H}_2\text{C}{=}\text{CH}_2 + \text{H}_2\text{O}$$

INTER-MOLECULAR DEHYDRATION. An example of an *inter*-molecular dehydration is the elimination of 1 H_2O molecule from 2 molecules of ethyl alcohol:

$$\text{CH}_3\text{—CH}_2\boxed{\text{OH} + \text{H}}\text{O—CH}_2\text{—CH}_3 \longrightarrow \text{CH}_3\text{—CH}_2\text{—O—CH}_2\text{—CH}_3 + \text{H}_2\text{O}$$

In the inter-molecular dehydration, the H_2O is formed from the OH group of 1 molecule and a H atom from the OH group of the other molecule, as represented schematically by the above equation. The compound $CH_3—CH_2—O—CH_2—CH_3$ is called diethyl ether. This is the familiar anesthetic commonly referred to as "ether." It boils at +34°C.

The products of the inter-molecular dehydration of alcohols are known in general as *ethers*. They are characterized by the presence of an oxygen atom covalently bonded to 2 carbon atoms, as shown in the margin.

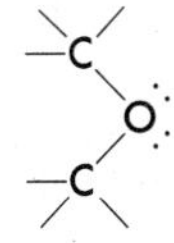

The above examples show that by carefully controlling the temperature and pressure and by choosing the proper catalyst, we can dehydrate ethyl alcohol, $CH_3—CH_2OH$, by intra-molecular dehydration to form the olefin ethylene, $CH_2{=}CH_2$, or by inter-molecular dehydration to form diethyl ether, $CH_3—CH_2—O—CH_2—CH_3$. These reactions illustrate a principle that we have already discussed in Chapter 26, one that is especially important in organic chemistry: *Starting with the same reactants, we can obtain different products by varying the experimental conditions.*

SYSTEMATIC NOMENCLATURE OF ORGANIC COMPOUNDS

In organic chemistry, just as we saw in Chapter 5 for inorganic chemistry, it is often necessary to give trivial names to those compounds whose structures have not yet been established. In fact, a trivial name is preferable to a name assigned on the basis of an assumed, incorrect structure. Once the structure of a compound is established, the trivial name is replaced by a systematic name following a precise and logical set of rules. The purpose of systematic nomenclature is to designate a compound by a name that can apply only to one possible structure—that of the compound considered—and in addition gives sufficient information so that from the name we can write the correct structural formula.

The systematic nomenclature of organic compounds, as recommended by the I.U.P.A.C. (Internal Union of Pure and Applied Chemistry) is illustrated here for the alkanes. Consider the saturated hydrocarbon represented by the semi-structural formula:

```
 ①     ②     ③     ④     ⑤     ⑥
CH3—CH——CH2—CH——CH2—CH3
 6     5|    4     3|    2     1
       CH3         CH2
                    |
                   CH3
```

Rule 1. Examine this formula and pick out the *longest continuous* chain of C atoms. The name of the normal chain of the saturated hydrocarbon having as many C atoms as this longest chain forms the *basis* of the name of the entire compound.

In our example, the longest chain includes 6 carbon atoms and the basis of the name is "hexane."

Rule 2. Number the C atoms in this longest continuous chain, starting at one end, so that the C atoms with substituents attached to them have the *lower numbers*. (In our example, we chose the series of numbers on top of the C atoms. Notice that the numbers below the atoms have cancel marks through them, because we discarded this numbering series).

Rule 3. All other carbon atoms, attached to the numbered atoms of the longest carbon chain, are part of branched chains. The names of these substituents are included in the name of the compound together with their position number, corresponding to their point of attachment to the longest chain. In our example, the substituent CH_3, methyl, is attached to carbon atom number 2, and thus this substituent is called 2-methyl; the substituent ($—CH_2—CH_3$) or C_2H_5, ethyl, is on carbon atom number 4, and thus this substituent is called 4-ethyl.

Rule 4. All the substituents (branched chains) are named in *alphabetical* order (not necesarily in the order of their lowest numbered positions in the longest chain). Thus, the name of our compound is 4-ethyl-3-methyl-hexane (not, 3-methyl-4-ethyl-hexane).

Reaction of Methane with Chlorine To Form Methyl Chloride and Hydrogen Chloride, at 25°C, 1 atm:

$CH_{4(g)}$ + $Cl_{2(g)}$ ——

Physical State:

$CH_{4(g)}$	$Cl_{2(g)}$
Colorless gas; b.p. = −161.5°C; m.p. = −184°C; sparingly soluble in water.	*Green-yellow gas; b.p. = −34.6°C; m.p. = −101.6°C; moderately soluble in water to give an equilibrium reaction:* $Cl_{2(g)} + H_2O \rightleftharpoons HClO + HCl$

Structure of Molecule:

tetrahedral

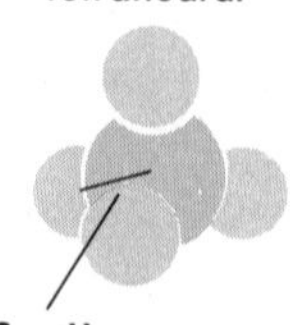

C—H
1.54 A

linear

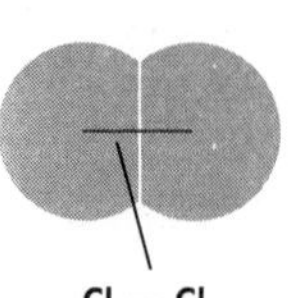

Cl — Cl
1.98 A

Bonding:

C—H σ bonds: covalent with some dipolar character owing to different electronegativities of C(2.5) and H(2.1), and to different sizes of C and H atoms.

Cl—Cl σ bond: purely covalent (identical atoms).

Atomic Orbitals Used in Bonding:

1s orbitals of H
2s 2p^3 hybrid orbitals of C

3p orbitals of Cl atoms

36-11 Anatomy of the Reaction of CH_4 with Cl_2 To Form CH_3Cl and HCl

We shall now discuss in some detail the chlorination of methane to form methyl chloride, to illustrate how the fundamental principles of bonding, stereochemistry, energetics, rates, and mechanism of reactions, which we have studied in the chapters on general chemistry, apply to an organic reaction. We will show the basic similarity, as well as some differences, between inorganic and organic reactions.

When the colorless gas methane, $CH_{4(g)}$, and the greenish gas chlorine, $Cl_{2(g)}$, are mixed and kept in the dark at room temperature, no perceptible chemical reaction occurs. But if the gaseous mixture is heated in the dark above 250° C, or is exposed to sunlight, a rapid and exothermic reaction takes place; the first products formed are the colorless gaseous compounds methyl chloride (chloromethane), $CH_3Cl_{(g)}$, and hydrogen chloride, $HCl_{(g)}$. The experimentally determined value of the standard enthalpy of the reaction is $\Delta H° = -23.7$ kcal/mole CH_3Cl. Following are the equations for this reaction, a summary of the properties of the reactants and products, and pertinent structural and thermodynamic data.

$$\longrightarrow CH_3Cl_{(g)} + HCl_{(g)} \quad \begin{cases} \Delta H° = -23.7 \text{ kcal/mole-eqn} \\ \Delta S° = +0.5 \text{ cal/mole-eqn} \times \text{deg} \\ \Delta G° = -23.9 \text{ kcal/mole-eqn} \end{cases}$$

Colorless gas; b.p. = −24° C; m.p. = −97.7° C; slightly soluble in water (400 cm^3/100 cm^3 H_2O); soluble in ether, chloroform, acetone.

Colorless gas; b.p. = −85° C; m.p. = −111° C; extremely soluble in water to give a colorless acidic solution, containing $H^+_{(aq)}$ ions and $Cl^-_{(aq)}$ ions.

tetrahedral

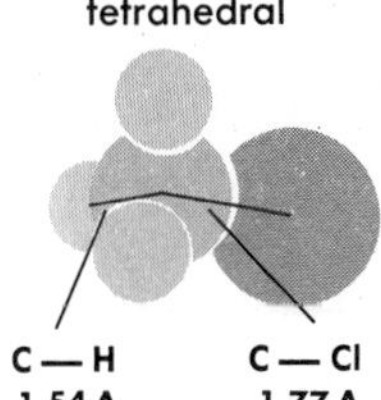

linear

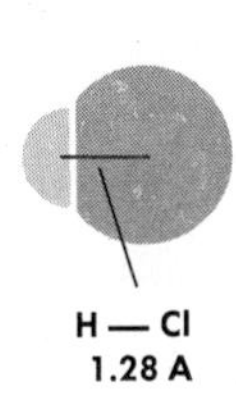

C—H σ bonds: (as for CH_4). C—Cl σ bond: covalent with marked dipolar character owing to different electronegativities of C(2.5) and Cl (3.0), and to different sizes of C and Cl atoms.

H—Cl σ bonds: covalent with marked dipolar character owing to different electronegativities of H(2.1) and Cl(3.0), as well as to very different sizes of H and Cl atoms.

1s orbitals of H atoms
3p orbital of Cl atom
2s $2p^3$ hybrid orbitals of C

1s orbital of H atom
3p orbital of Cl atom

The net result of this substitution reaction, $CH_{4(g)} + Cl_{2(g)} \longrightarrow CH_3Cl_{(g)} + HCl_{(g)}$, is that 2 σ bonds are broken in the reactions—1 of the 4 covalent C—H bonds of the CH_4 molecule, and the covalent Cl—Cl bond of the Cl_2 molecule, while 2 (new) σ covalent bonds are formed in the products—the C—Cl bond in the CH_3Cl molecule and the H—Cl bond in the HCl molecule. The breaking of the indicated covalent bonds in the reactants, and the formation of the (new) covalent bonds of the products, can be imagined to take place by the following hypothetical steps, as illustrated in the accompanying enthalpy diagram (Fig. 36-7):

Step 1. The Cl—Cl bond is broken, forming 2 Cl atoms.
Step 2. The H_3C—H bond is broken, forming the H_3C radical and the H atom.
Step 3. The H_3C radical and the Cl atom combine to form H_3C—Cl.
Step 4. The H atom combines with the Cl atom to form H—Cl.

The enthalpy of the net reaction calculated from the enthalpy diagram ($\Delta H° = -23$ kcal/mole-eqn) agrees well with the experimentally determined value ($\Delta H = -23.7$ kcal/mole-eqn).

In the equation $CH_{4(g)} + Cl_{2(g)} \longrightarrow CH_3Cl_{(g)} + HCl_{(g)}$, the number of moles of the gaseous reactants and the number of moles of the gaseous products are equal; hence, we can predict that the entropy change, $\Delta S°$, accompanying the reaction should be very small. In fact, $\Delta S°$ is about +0.5 cal/mole-eqn × deg. For this reaction, at 25°C, the $T\,\Delta S°$ energy term has therefore relatively little effect on the value of the free energy change:

$$\Delta G° = \Delta H° - T\,\Delta S° = -23.7 \text{ kcal/mole-eqn} \times -(298 \text{ deg} \times +0.5 \text{ cal/mole-eqn} \times \text{deg})$$
$$\Delta G° = -23.9 \text{ kcal/mole-eqn}$$

Thus, the spontaneous character of this substitution reaction is determined essentially by the favorable enthalpy change, which in turn simply reflects the fact that the 2 new σ bonds formed in the products are more stable than the 2 old σ bonds broken in the reactants. The following is a schematic representation of how we could

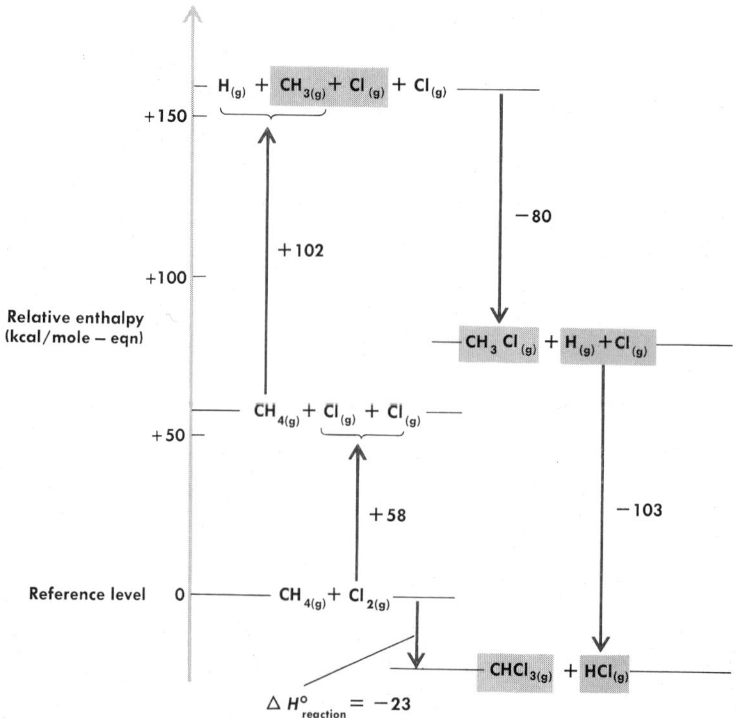

FIGURE 36-7 Enthalpy diagram for the reaction, $CH_{4(g)} + Cl_{2(g)} \longrightarrow CH_3Cl_{(g)} + HCl_{(g)}$.

calculate rapidly the enthalpy change of this reaction from the values of the bond energies (in kcal/mole) of the bonds broken and formed:

$$\underset{102}{H_3C{-}H} + \underset{58}{Cl{-}Cl} \longrightarrow \underset{80}{H_3C{-}Cl} + \underset{103}{H{-}Cl}$$

$$+102 + 58 = +160 \qquad -80 - 103 = -183$$

This quantity of energy is absorbed (+ sign) when the indicated bonds are broken.

This quantity of energy is released (− sign) when the indicated bonds are formed.

Total enthalpy change: $-183 + 160 = -23$ kcal/mole-eqn

VALUES OF $\Delta G°$ AND K FOR THE REACTION

Equation: $CH_{4(g)} + Cl_{2(g)} \longrightarrow CH_3Cl_{(g)} + HCl_{(g)}$ $\qquad \Delta G° = -23.9$ kcal/mole-eqn

Equilibrium Constant: $K = \dfrac{[CH_3Cl] \times [HCl]}{[CH_4] \times [Cl_2]} = 1 \times 10^{18}$

The very large value of $K(1 \times 10^{18})$ and the negative value of $\Delta G°(-23.9$ kcal/mole-eqn) tell us that the reaction of methane with chlorine to form methyl chloride and hydrogen chloride can proceed to completion. Of course, the value of the free energy change, $\Delta G°(-23.9$ kcal/mole-eqn), and the value of the equilibrium constant, $K(1 \times 10^{18})$, of a given reaction are related by the expression, $\Delta G° = -2.303\ RT \log K$, as we learned in Chapter 25. Thus, $\Delta G°$ and K give us essentially the same information, although in different forms.

RATE AND MECHANISM OF THE REACTION

The thermodynamic factors that we have just considered tell us that the reaction of $CH_{4(g)}$ with $Cl_{2(g)}$ to form $CH_3Cl_{(g)}$ and $HCl_{(g)}$ can take place spontaneously and can proceed practically to completion. However, as we have already pointed out, no perceptible reaction actually takes place as long as the mixture of the reactants is kept in the dark, and at temperatures below 250°C. But if the mixture of CH_4 and Cl_2 is heated above 250°C, or if it is exposed to strong direct sunlight at room temperature, then the reaction occurs rapidly. Actually, the light-induced (photochemical) reaction will even proceed explosively if the concentrations of the reactants have certain appropriate values. Obviously, some energy—the activation energy—must be supplied to the reactants, either as heat or as light, in order to initiate the spontaneous reaction.

For the photochemical reaction, the mechanism that best explains all experimental data is a chain-mechanism very similar to that discussed in Chapter 26 for the reaction of $Cl_{2(g)}$ and $H_{2(g)}$ to form $HCl_{(g)}$. Again, the reaction can be initiated photochemically because one of the reactants, $Cl_{2(g)}$, absorbs light photons in the violet and near-ultraviolet region of the spectrum. (The fact that chlorine is greenish-yellow tells us that its molecules absorb from the white sunlight the light photons of the blue-violet region.) When a Cl_2 molecule absorbs a photon of appropriate energy, the Cl—Cl covalent bond is broken and 2 extremely reactive Cl atoms are formed. This is the first step of the chain-reaction, which may be represented as follows:

1. *Chain-initiation step:* The light photon which is absorbed supplies the energy required to break the Cl—Cl bond:

$$:\ddot{Cl}{-}\ddot{Cl}: \xrightarrow{\text{light energy}} 2\ \cdot\ddot{Cl}:$$

2. *Chain propagation steps:*

(a) A Cl atom with sufficient kinetic energy comes in contact with a CH_4 molecule; a C—H bond is broken, while a H—Cl bond is formed. By losing a H atom, the

CH_4 molecule becomes a $\cdot CH_3$ radical:

$$:\ddot{\underset{..}{Cl}}\cdot + H_3C{-}H \longrightarrow \underset{\text{activated complex}}{[H_3C{-}{-}H{-}{-}Cl]} \longrightarrow H_3C\cdot + H{-}\ddot{\underset{..}{Cl}}:$$

(b) A methyl radical $\cdot CH_3$ comes in contact with a Cl_2 molecule; a Cl—Cl bond is broken while a C—Cl bond is formed. The products are a CH_3Cl molecule and a chlorine atom:

$$H_3C\cdot + Cl{-}Cl \longrightarrow \underset{\text{activated complex}}{[H_3C{-}{-}Cl{-}{-}Cl]} \longrightarrow H_3C{-}Cl + \cdot\ddot{\underset{..}{Cl}}:$$

These two chain-propagation steps, (a) and (b), are repeated very many times before the chain reaction is finally broken by one of the following chain-termination steps:

$$H_3C\cdot + \cdot Cl \longrightarrow H_3C{-}Cl$$

$$Cl\cdot + \cdot Cl \longrightarrow Cl{-}Cl; \qquad H_3C\cdot + \cdot CH_3 \longrightarrow H_3C{-}CH_3$$

INFLUENCE OF CONCENTRATION ON THE CHLORINATION PRODUCT

The first product in the chlorination of methane, CH_4, is, as we have just seen, methyl chloride, CH_3Cl. But the substitution can proceed further, forming the di-, tri-, and finally the tetra-chloro-compound, CH_2Cl_2, $CHCl_3$, and CCl_4. Experiments show that a H atom of CH_3Cl is more readily substituted by a Cl atom than is a H atom of methane, CH_4. In turn, a H atom of CH_2Cl_2 is more susceptible to further substitution by a Cl atom than a H atom of CH_3Cl, and similarly for $CHCl_3$. This is not surprising, since we know that chemical bonds are, to some extent, influenced by their environment. In this case, the C—H bond becomes more readily susceptible to substitution by a C—Cl bond as the number of Cl atoms already attached to the C atom increases. To put it in terms of energetics, the compound CH_3Cl is thermodynamically stable with respect to a mixture of CH_4 and Cl_2, but the di-, tri-, and tetra-substituted compounds, CH_2Cl_2, $CHCl_3$, and CCl_4, are even more stable (see values in the margin), their stability increasing with the number of Cl atoms in the molecule. How, then, can we carry out the chlorination of methane so that the least stable of the chlorination products—the monosubstituted CH_3Cl—is formed preferentially?

	$\Delta H°$ form (kcal/mole)
CH_4	−17.9
CH_3Cl	−19.6
CH_2Cl_2	−21.0
$CHCl_3$	−24.0
CCl_4	−25.5

To obtain CH_3Cl as the major chlorination product, we must take advantage of some kinetic factor, since from the viewpoint of energetics the reaction would tend to form the most stable, fully substituted compound, CCl_4. We cannot, however, control the reaction simply by changing reaction rates, because CH_3Cl, CH_2Cl_2, $CHCl_3$, and CCl_4 all form at about the same rate under comparable conditions and by similar mechanisms. What we can actually do is to start with an initial mixture of the reactants containing a very large excess of methane over chlorine. At the start, under these conditions, the Cl atoms come into contact only with CH_4 molecules, and the product of each fruitful collision between a CH_4 molecule and a Cl atom is a molecule of CH_3Cl. As the reaction proceeds and CH_3Cl molecules are formed, it is possible that a Cl atom may collide with a CH_3Cl molecule forming the disubstituted compound: $CH_3Cl + Cl_2 \longrightarrow CH_2Cl_2 + HCl$. However, if a sufficiently large excess of CH_4 is always present, so that even at the end of the reaction when the last remaining Cl_2 molecules are present, the number of CH_4 molecules greatly exceeds the number of CH_3Cl molecules, it is still more probable for a Cl atom to collide with a CH_4 molecule (to form CH_3Cl) than with a CH_3Cl molecule (to form CH_2Cl_2). Hence, under these conditions, CH_3Cl is still the main product of the chlorination of methane, although the more substituted products may also be formed in much smaller yields. In this manner, by taking advantage of the fact that *each fruitful collision of the reactants results in the substitution of only one H atom by one Cl atom*, we can direct the reaction to form chiefly the desired product, CH_3Cl, rather that the thermodynamically more stable CH_2Cl_2, $CHCl_3$, and CCl_4.

EXERCISES

36-1 Write the electronic and structural formulas of the following organic compounds: (a) C_2H_6, (b) C_2H_4, (c) C_2H_2, (d) C_2H_5Cl, (e) C_2H_5OH.

36-2 Write at least 6 structural formulas each for compounds that have the general formula (a) C_5H_8, (b) $C_4H_8Br_2$.

36-3 There are 2 position isomers of each of the compounds with the following molecular formulas: $C_2H_4Cl_2$ and $C_2H_3Br_3$. Write the structural formulas of these isomers.

36-4 When $AgNO_3$ is added to an aqueous solution of NaCl, a precipitate of AgCl forms. When $AgNO_3$ is added to liquid CCl_4, no precipitate of AgCl forms. Explain.

36-5 Write balanced equations for the following:
(a) ethane + Br_2 (all possible mono-brominated product(s))
(b) propane + Br_2 (all possible mono-brominated product(s))
(c) *n*-butyl bromide + Na
(d) iso-butyl bromide + Na
(e) ethylene + HBr
(f) propylene + H_2 (Ni catalyst)
(g) preparation of $CH_3—CH_2—CH{=}CH_2$ from $CH_3—CH_2—CH(OH)—CH_3$
(h) preparation of $CH_3—CH{=}CH—CH_3$ from $CH_3—CH_2—CH(OH)—CH_3$

36-6 Write all possible cis-trans isomers of: (a) $H_3C—CH{=}CH—CH_3$, (2-butene); (b) $Cl_2C{=}CH_2$ (1,1-dichloroethane); (c) $ClHC{=}CHCl$ (1,2-dichloroethane).

36-7 How many cm^3 of a 0.10 *M* solution of HCl are required to (completely) neutralize the following: (a) 0.001 mole of *n*-propylamine, $CH_3CH_2CH_2—NH_2$; (b) 0.02 mole of ethylenediamine, $NH_2—CH_2—CH_2—NH_2$; (c) 0.01 mole of aniline, $C_6H_5—NH_2$.

36-8 Write balanced equations to show: (a) Two possible products that could be formed by the dehydration of isopropyl alcohol, $CH_3CH(OH)CH_3$. (b) The reaction with sodium metal of (1) CH_3CH_2OH and (2) $CH_3CH(OH)CH_3$ (c) The oxidation, [O], of isopropanol, $CH_3—CH(OH)—CH_3$.

36-9 Write balanced equations to show the reactions of *n*-propyl iodide, $CH_3—CH_2—CH_2I$, to form (a) *n*-hexane, (b) *n*-propyl alcohol, (c) $CH_3—CHI—CH_3$.

36-10 Write balanced equations for the reaction of acetic acid with (a) AgOH; (b) NH_3; (c) $Ba(OH)_2$; (d) $(C_2H_5)_3N$.

36-11 Write balanced equations to show how it is possible to form the following from CH_3CH_2OH: (a) acetic acid; (b) CH_3COCH_3, acetone; (c) ethane; (d) CH_3CH_2Cl.

36-12 (a) The molecular weights of ethane, C_2H_6, and methanol, CH_3OH, are nearly equal. Explain the extreme difference in their boiling points ($C_2H_5OH = +78.5°C$; $C_2H_6 = -88.3°C$). (b) Compare the melting points of methyl chloride, CH_3Cl (−97.7°C), and sodium chloride (+800°C) and explain. (c) How do the members of a homologous series differ in boiling points?

36-13 Write structural formulas for the following reactions: (a) Reaction of ethylene with H_2. (b) Reaction of ethane with Cl_2 (write 3 equations showing 3 possible products). (c) Reaction of propylene with H_2O. (d) Reaction of 1 mole of acetylene with 1 mole of H_2, and the reaction of this product with 1 mole of Cl_2.

36-14 Write the equation for the *inter*molecular dehydration of isopropyl alcohol to form di-isopropyl ether.

36-15 Compare the *relative* ΔH values for the general reaction: $H_3C—H + X_2 \longrightarrow H_3C—X + H—X$ ($X_2 = F_2, I_2$; bond dissociation energy: $F_2 = 37$; $I_2 = 36$).

36-16 In the reaction of $CH_{4(g)}$ with $Cl_{2(g)}$ to form $CH_3Cl_{(g)}$, explain on the basis of energetics why mechanism (a) is more likely than (b).
(a) $H_3C—H + \cdot Cl \longrightarrow H_3C\cdot + H—Cl$
(b) $H_3C—H + \cdot Cl \longrightarrow H_3C—Cl + .H$

36-17 Predict the *relative* ΔH values for the general reaction:
(a) $H_3C—H + \cdot X \longrightarrow H_3C—X + \cdot H$ ($\cdot X = \cdot F, \cdot Cl, \cdot Br, \cdot I$ atoms)
(b) $H_3C\cdot + X—X \longrightarrow CH_3—X + \cdot X$ ($X—X$ = F—F, Cl—Cl, Br—Br, I—I)
(c) $H_3C\cdot + \cdot X \longrightarrow H_3C—H$
Explain your answers.

36-18 On the basis of conformation and reaction probability explain the following. Normal $ClCH_2CH_2CH_2CH_2CH_2CH_2Cl$ reacts with Na(metal): (a) in very dilute solutions to form the ring compound, C_6H_{12}, cyclohexane (and Na^+Cl^-);

and (b) in concentrated solutions, these same reactants produce normal $ClCH_2$—$(CH_2)_{10}$—CH_2Cl (and other linear compounds, and Na^+Cl^-).

36-19 The net reaction of a saturated hydrocarbon, with the halogens, X_2, is shown schematically as follows: R—C—H + X—X ⟶ R—C—X + H—X. Predict the relative values of ΔH of this substitution reaction for $X_2 = F_2$, Cl_2, Br_2, and I_2. Explain your answer on the basis of (a) the bond strength of X—X; (b) the relative bond strengths of C—X (taking into account the possible overlap of the sp^3 hybrid orbital of the C atom with the p orbital of the X atom and the size and the electronegative values of the halogen); (c) the strength of the H—X bond.

APPENDIX

APPENDIX

2-1 Scientific Notation

Any number may be expressed as the product of two other numbers, one of which may be a power of 10. For numbers 10 and larger, the power is positive, and for numbers 0.1 and smaller, the power is negative. Some positive powers of ten follow.

$1 = 1 \times 10^0$	$100{,}000 = 1 \times 10^5$
$10 = 1 \times 10^1$	$1{,}000{,}000 = 1 \times 10^6$
$100 = 1 \times 10^2$	$10{,}000{,}000 = 1 \times 10^7$
$1000 = 1 \times 10^3$	$100{,}000{,}000 = 1 \times 10^8$
$10{,}000 = 1 \times 10^4$	$1{,}000{,}000{,}000 = 1 \times 10^9$

The superscript indicating the power of ten is called the *exponent*. Notice that in each case the positive exponent equals the number of places the decimal point of the large number must be moved to the *left* to yield the number 1. Thus, $10 = 1 \times 10^1$ (or 1.0.); $100 = 1 \times 10^2$ (1.00.); and $1000 = 1 \times 10^3$ (1.000.).

Numbers less than 1 can also be expressed as powers of 10. Some of the negative powers of ten are listed below:

$0.1 = 1 \times 10^{-1}$	$0.000001 = 1 \times 10^{-6}$
$0.01 = 1 \times 10^{-2}$	$0.0000001 = 1 \times 10^{-7}$
$0.001 = 1 \times 10^{-3}$	$0.00000001 = 1 \times 10^{-8}$
$0.0001 = 1 \times 10^{-4}$	$0.000000001 = 1 \times 10^{-9}$
$0.00001 = 1 \times 10^{-5}$	$0.0000000001 = 1 \times 10^{-10}$

Each negative exponent indicates the number of places the decimal point of the small number must be moved to the *right* to yield the number 1. Thus, $0.1 = 1 \times 10^{-1}$ (0.1.); $0.01 = 1 \times 10^{-2}$ (0.01.); and $0.001 = 1 \times 10^{-3}$ (0.001.).

Now let us use this system to express some numbers other than multiples or submultiples of 1. First, we shall take a fairly large number, 245,000. We can express this number as a product of two numbers, one of which is a multiple of 10. For example, $245{,}000 = 2.45 \times 10^5$ ($2.45000. = 2.45 \times 10^5$).

Thus, the number representing the quantity of atoms of iron in 1 g of iron is:

$$10{,}800{,}000{,}000{,}000{,}000{,}000{,}000. = 1.08 \times 10^{22}$$

Now let us try a small number: 0.0042 can be expressed in exponential form as 4.2×10^{-3} ($0.004\,2 = 4.2 \times 10^{-3}$). Thus, the number that indicates the weight of one atom of iron is:

$$0.000{,}000{,}000{,}000{,}000{,}000{,}000{,}009{,}26 = 9.26 \times 10^{-24}$$

Here is a good general rule to follow: *To express any large or small number, write the number with one digit to the left of the decimal point. The exponent of 10 corresponds to the number of places the decimal point is moved. If the decimal point of the original number is moved to the left, the exponent is positive; if the decimal point is moved to the right, the exponent is negative.* Some additional examples follow:

$6{,}000{,}000 = (6\,000000.) = 6 \times 10^{6}$ $\quad$ $0.000{,}000{,}298 = (0.0000002\,98) = 2.98 \times 10^{-7}$

$84{,}500{,}000 = (8\,4500000.) = 8.45 \times 10^{7}$ $\quad$ $360{,}000 = (3\,60000.) = 3.6 \times 10^{5}$

$0.000{,}521 = (0.0005\,21) = 5.21 \times 10^{-4}$ $\quad$ $0.004{,}79 = (0.004\,79) = 4.79 \times 10^{-3}$

MULTIPLICATION AND DIVISION OF EXPONENTIAL NUMBERS

To multiply numbers expressed as powers of 10, *add the exponents;* for example, $(10^3) \times (10^2) = 10^5$. Additional examples are:

$(2 \times 10^6) \times (4 \times 10^3) = 8 \times 10^9$ $\quad$ $(3 \times 10^8) \times (2 \times 10^{-3}) = 6 \times 10^5$

$(3 \times 10^{-4}) \times (3 \times 10^{-8}) = 9 \times 10^{-12}$ $\quad$ $(4 \times 10^{-5}) \times (1 \times 10^7) = 4 \times 10^2$

To divide numbers expressed as powers of 10, *subtract the exponents.* Examples:

$$\frac{8 \times 10^7}{4 \times 10^2} = 2 \times 10^5 \qquad \frac{12 \times 10^6}{3 \times 10^{-2}} = 4 \times 10^8$$

$$\frac{18 \times 10^{-4}}{6 \times 10^{-6}} = 3 \times 10^2 \qquad \frac{6 \times 10^{-5}}{2 \times 10^3} = 3 \times 10^{-8}$$

It is customary to express an answer in exponential form with one digit to the left of the decimal point, as shown in the following examples:

$$\frac{18 \times 10^{-4}}{1.2 \times 10^{-6}} = 15 \times 10^2 = 1.5 \times 10^3$$

$$1.80 \times 10^5 \times 8.50 \times 10^2 = 15.3 \times 10^7 = 1.53 \times 10^8$$

Solve the following problems:

(a) $(3.6 \times 10^{-8}) \times (4.7 \times 10^6) =$

(b) $\dfrac{7.81 \times 10^{-7}}{3.2 \times 10^{-10}} =$

(c) $4 \times (10^3)^2 =$

(d) $4^2 \times 10^3 =$

(e) $(4 \times 10^3)^2 =$

(f) $(2.7 \times 10^3) + (1.4 \times 10^2) =$

(g) $(6.5 \times 10^{-7}) - (4.3 \times 10^{-6}) =$

(h) $(9.8 \times 10^{12}) - (4.2 \times 10^{-12}) =$

4-1 Calculations

The following problem shows that solving an everyday problem on the dozen basis involves the same type of thinking as solving a chemical problem on the mole basis.

FAMILIAR PROBLEM (DOZEN BASIS)

PROBLEM. If 18 pencils cost 48 cents, how many dozen pencils can be bought for 64 cents?

SOLUTION. Since 12 = 1.0 dozen, the number of dozen pencils in 18 pencils is $\frac{18}{12}$ dozen:

$$\frac{\frac{18 \text{ pencils}}{12 \text{ pencils}}}{1 \text{ dozen pencils}} = 18 \cancel{\text{pencils}} \times \frac{1 \text{ dozen pencils}}{12 \cancel{\text{pencils}}} = 1.5 \text{ dozen pencils}$$

$$\frac{1.5 \text{ dozen pencils}}{48 \text{ cents}} = \text{the number of dozen pencils that can be bought for 1 cent}$$

Thus, the number of dozen pencils that can be bought for 64 cents is 64 times this value.

$$\frac{1.5 \text{ dozen pencils}}{48 \cancel{\text{cents}}} \times 64 \cancel{\text{cents}} = 2 \text{ dozen pencils}$$

(Also, $2 \cancel{\text{dozen pencils}} \times \frac{12 \text{ pencils}}{1 \cancel{\text{dozen pencils}}} = 24$ pencils) (the number that can be bought for 64 cents)

ADDITIONAL PROBLEMS

PROBLEM. Calculate the number of grams of oxygen that react with 60 g of carbon to form carbon dioxide.

SOLUTION.

C	+	O_2	$\longrightarrow$	CO_2
1 mole carbon		1 mole oxygen		1 mole carbon dioxide
12 g carbon		32 g oxygen		44 g carbon dioxide

Calculation on Weight (Gram) Basis

The equation shows that 32 g oxygen is the number of grams of oxygen that react with 12 g of carbon.

$$\frac{32 \text{ g oxygen}}{12 \text{ g carbon}} = \text{number of grams of oxygen that react with 1 g of carbon}$$

Thus, the number of grams of oxygen that react with 60 g of carbon is 60 times this value:

$$\frac{32 \text{ g oxygen}}{12 \cancel{\text{g carbon}}} \times 60 \cancel{\text{g carbon}} = 160 \text{ g oxygen}$$

Calculation on Mole Basis

$$\frac{\frac{60 \text{ g carbon}}{12 \text{ g carbon}}}{1.0 \text{ mole carbon}} = 60 \cancel{\text{g carbon}} \times \frac{1.0 \text{ mole carbon}}{12 \cancel{\text{g carbon}}}$$

$$= \frac{60}{12} \text{ mole carbon} = 5 \text{ moles carbon}$$

Now the equation shows that 1 mole of oxygen, or 32 g oxygen is the number of grams of oxygen that react with 1 mole of carbon:

$$\frac{32 \text{ g oxygen}}{1 \text{ mole carbon}} = \text{the number of grams of oxygen that react with 1 mole of carbon}$$

Thus, the number of grams of oxygen that combine with 5 moles of carbon is 5 times this value:

$$\frac{32 \text{ g oxygen}}{1 \cancel{\text{mole carbon}}} \times 5 \cancel{\text{moles carbon}} = 160 \text{ g oxygen}$$

PROBLEM. If 36 g of carbon react with oxygen, how many (a) grams and (b) moles of carbon dioxide are formed?

SOLUTION.

C	+	O_2	$\longrightarrow$	CO_2
1 mole carbon		1 mole oxygen		1 mole carbon dioxide
12 g carbon		32 g oxygen		44 g carbon dioxide

Calculation on Gram Basis

(a) 44 g carbon dioxide = the number of grams of carbon dioxide that are formed when 12 g of carbon react.

$$\frac{44 \text{ g carbon dioxide}}{12 \text{ g carbon}} = \text{the number of grams of carbon dioxide formed when 1 g of carbon reacts}$$

Thus, the number of grams of carbon dioxide formed when 36 g of carbon react is 36 times this value:

$$\frac{44 \text{ g carbon dioxide}}{12 \cancel{\text{g carbon}}} \times 36 \cancel{\text{g carbon}} = 132 \text{ g carbon dioxide (formed from 36 g of carbon)}$$

(b) $\frac{1 \text{ mole carbon dioxide}}{44 \text{ g carbon dioxide}}$ = the number of moles of carbon dioxide in 1 g of carbon dioxide.

Thus, the number of moles of carbon dioxide in 132 g of carbon dioxide is 132 times this value:

$$\frac{1 \text{ mole carbon dioxide}}{44 \cancel{\text{g carbon dioxide}}} \times 132 \cancel{\text{g carbon dioxide}} = 3 \text{ moles carbon dioxide}$$

Calculation on Mole Basis

(b) 12 g carbon = 1 mole carbon.

$$36 \cancel{\text{g carbon}} \times \frac{1 \text{ mole carbon}}{12 \cancel{\text{g carbon}}} = 3 \text{ moles carbon (moles of carbon in 36 g carbon)}$$

Since, according to the above chemical equation, 1 mole carbon produces 1 mole carbon dioxide, 3 moles carbon produces 3 moles carbon dioxide.

(a) $\frac{44 \text{ g carbon dioxide}}{1 \text{ mole carbon dioxide}}$ = the number of g of carbon dioxide in 1 mole of carbon dioxide.

Thus, the number of g of carbon dioxide in 3 moles carbon dioxide is 3 times this value:

$$\frac{44 \text{ g carbon dioxide}}{1 \cancel{\text{mole carbon dioxide}}} \times 3 \cancel{\text{mole carbon dioxide}} = 132 \text{ g carbon dioxide}$$

PROBLEM. If 76 g of carbon dioxide are formed from carbon and oxygen, how many grams and moles of oxygen have reacted?

SOLUTION.

C	+	O_2	$\longrightarrow$	CO_2
1 mole carbon		1 mole oxygen		1 mole carbon dioxide
12.0 g carbon		32.0 g oxygen		44.0 g carbon dioxide

Calculation on Gram Basis

32 g oxygen = the number of grams of oxygen that react to form 44 g of carbon dioxide.

$$\frac{32 \text{ g oxygen}}{44 \text{ g carbon dioxide}} = \text{the number of grams of oxygen that react to form 1 g of carbon dioxide}$$

Thus, the number of grams of oxygen that react to form 76 g of carbon dioxide is 76 times this value:

$$\frac{32 \text{ g oxygen}}{44 \cancel{\text{ g carbon dioxide}}} \times 76 \cancel{\text{ g carbon dioxide}} = 55 \text{ g oxygen (the number of grams that react to form 76 g of carbon dioxide)}$$

Also:

$$\frac{1 \text{ mole oxygen}}{32 \text{ g oxygen}} = \text{the number of moles of oxygen present in 1 g of oxygen}$$

Therefore, the number of moles of oxygen present in 55 g of oxygen is 55 times this value:

$$\frac{1 \text{ mole oxygen}}{32 \cancel{\text{ g oxygen}}} \times 55 \cancel{\text{ g oxygen}} = 1.7 \text{ moles of oxygen}$$

Calculation on Mole Basis

$$76 \text{ g of carbon dioxide} = \frac{76 \text{ g carbon dioxide}}{\dfrac{44 \text{ g carbon dioxide}}{1 \text{ mole carbon dioxide}}}$$

$$= 76 \cancel{\text{ g carbon dioxide}} \times \frac{1 \text{ mole carbon dioxide}}{44 \cancel{\text{ g carbon dioxide}}} = \frac{76}{44} \text{ mole carbon dioxide}$$

Therefore,

$$\frac{76}{44} \text{ moles of oxygen reacted} = 1.7 \text{ moles oxygen}$$

Also: The number of grams of oxygen that reacted is:

$$\frac{76}{44} \cancel{\text{ mole oxygen}} \times \frac{32 \text{ g oxygen}}{1 \cancel{\text{ mole oxygen}}} = 55 \text{ g oxygen.}$$

PROBLEM. How many grams and how many moles of magnesium oxide, MgO, will be formed when 36.48 g of magnesium, Mg, react with oxygen (Mg = 24.31; O = 16.00)?

SOLUTION.

2 Mg	+	O_2	$\longrightarrow$	2 MgO
2 moles		1 mole		2 moles
48.62 g		32.00 g		80.62 g
magnesium		oxygen		magnesium oxide

Calculation on Gram Basis

80.62 g magnesium oxide = the number of grams of magnesium oxide formed from 48.62 g of magnesium.

$$\frac{80.62 \text{ g magnesium oxide}}{48.62 \text{ g magnesium}} = \text{the number of grams of magnesium oxide formed from 1 g of magnesium}$$

Thus, the number of grams of magnesium oxide formed from 36.48 g of magnesium is 36.48 times this value:

$$\frac{80.62 \text{ g magnesium oxide}}{48.62 \cancel{\text{ g magnesium}}} \times 36.48 \cancel{\text{ g magnesium}} = 60.49 \text{ g magnesium oxide (formed from 36.48 g of magnesium)}$$

Also: 1 mole magnesium oxide = 40.31 g magnesium oxide:

$$\frac{1 \text{ mole magnesium oxide}}{40.31 \text{ g magnesium oxide}} = \text{the number of moles of magnesium oxide present in 1 g of magnesium oxide}$$

Therefore, the number of moles of magnesium oxide present in 60.49 g magnesium oxide is 60.49 times this value:

$$\frac{1 \text{ mole magnesium oxide}}{40.31 \cancel{\text{ g magnesium oxide}}} \times 60.49 \cancel{\text{ g magnesium oxide}} = 1.500 \text{ moles magnesium oxide}$$

Calculation on Mole Basis

$$36.48 \text{ g magnesium} = \frac{36.48 \text{ g magnesium}}{\dfrac{24.31 \text{ g magnesium}}{1 \text{ mole magnesium}}}$$

$$= 36.48 \cancel{\text{ g magnesium}} \times \frac{1 \text{ mole magnesium}}{24.31 \cancel{\text{ g magnesium}}} = 1.500 \text{ moles magnesium}$$

Therefore, according to the above equation 1.500 moles of magnesium oxide are formed. Also:

$$1.500 \cancel{\text{ moles magnesium oxide}} \times \frac{40.31 \text{ g magnesium oxide}}{1 \cancel{\text{ mole magnesium oxide}}}$$

$$= 60.49 \text{ g magnesium oxide}$$

Here is yet another variation of this type of chemical problem.

PROBLEM. Calculate the number of (a) grams and (b) moles of mercuric oxide, HgO, needed to produce 8.00 g of oxygen according to the decomposition reaction $2\ HgO \longrightarrow 2\ Hg + O_2$ (Hg = 200.6; O = 16.00).

SOLUTION.

$2\ HgO$	$\longrightarrow$	$2\ Hg$	$+$	O_2
2 moles		2 moles		1 mole
433.2 g		401.2 g		32.00 g
mercuric oxide		mercury		oxygen

Calculation on Gram Basis

(a) 433.2 g of mercuric oxide = the number of grams of mercuric oxide needed to produce 32.00 g of oxygen

$$\frac{433.2\text{ g mercuric oxide}}{32.00\text{ g oxygen}} = \text{the number of grams of mercuric oxide needed to produce 1 g of oxygen}$$

Thus, the number of grams of mercuric oxide needed to produce 8.00 g of oxygen is 8.00 times this value:

$$\frac{433.2\text{ mercuric oxide}}{32.00\ \cancel{\text{g oxygen}}} \times 8.00\ \cancel{\text{g oxygen}} = 108.3\text{ g mercuric oxide}$$

(b) 1 mole mercuric oxide = 216.6 g mercuric oxide

$$\frac{1\text{ mole mercuric oxide}}{216.6\text{ g mercuric oxide}} = \text{the number of moles of mercuric oxide present in 1 g of mercuric oxide}$$

Therefore, the number of moles of mercuric oxide present in 108.3 g mercuric oxide is 108.3 times this value

$$\frac{1\text{ mole mercuric oxide}}{216.6\ \cancel{\text{g mercuric oxide}}} \times 108.3\ \cancel{\text{g mercuric oxide}} = 0.50\text{ mole mercuric oxide}$$

Calculation on Mole Basis

(b) $8.00\text{ g oxygen} = \frac{8.00}{32.00}\text{ mole oxygen} = \frac{1}{4}\text{ mole oxygen}$

(a) $0.50\ \cancel{\text{mole mercuric oxide}} \times \frac{216.6\text{ g mercuric oxide}}{1\ \cancel{\text{mole mercuric oxide}}} = 108.3\text{ g mercuric oxide}$

Therefore, according to the above equation, $\frac{1}{2}$ mole of mercuric oxide is needed to produce 8.00 g of oxygen.

$$8.00\ \cancel{\text{g oxygen}} \times \frac{1\text{ mole oxygen}}{32.00\ \cancel{\text{g oxygen}}} = \frac{1}{4}\text{ mole oxygen}$$

$$\frac{2\text{ mole mercuric oxide}}{1\ \cancel{\text{mole oxygen}}} \times \frac{1}{4}\ \cancel{\text{mole oxygen}} = 0.50\text{ mole mercuric oxide}$$

7-1 Determining Equivalent Weights

COMBINATION OF AN ELEMENT WITH OXYGEN

As an example of this procedure, let us consider what happens when 1.0020 g of calcium are heated in the presence of oxygen gas. The equation for this reaction (though not required to solve the problem) is:

$$2\ Ca + O_2 \longrightarrow 2\ CaO$$

The calcium oxide, CaO, formed is found to weigh 1.4020 g. Thus, 1.0020 g of calcium react with 0.4000 g of oxygen (1.4020 g–1.0020 g).

$$\frac{1.0020\text{ g calcium}}{0.4000\text{ g oxygen}} = \text{the weight of calcium that combines with 1 g of oxygen}$$

The gram equivalent weight of calcium, the weight that combines with exactly 8 g of oxygen, is:

$$\frac{1.0020\text{ g calcium}}{0.4000\ \cancel{\text{g oxygen}}} \times 8.000\ \cancel{\text{g oxygen}} = 20.04\text{ g calcium (gram equivalent weight of calcium)}$$

Many other elements, both metals and non-metals, also combine directly with oxygen. The gram equivalent weights of such elements can be found by determining the weight of each element that combines with 8 g of oxygen. The procedure is the same as that involving the reaction of calcium with oxygen.

REDUCTION OF A METAL OXIDE TO THE FREE METAL

Some metal oxides can be thermally decomposed to form the free metal and oxygen. For example, we find experimentally that 1.083 g of an oxide of mercury can be decomposed thermally to form 1.003 g of mercury.* Thus, 1.003 g of mercury

* The equation for this reaction (though not required to solve the problem) is $2\ HgO \longrightarrow 2\ Hg + O_2$.

are combined with 0.080 g of oxygen (1.083 g − 1.003 g), as in the following:

$$\frac{1.003 \text{ g mercury}}{0.080 \text{ g oxygen}} = \text{the weight of mercury that combines with 1.0 g of oxygen}$$

Since the equivalent weight of mercury is the weight that combines with 8.00 g of oxygen, the equivalent weight of mercury in this compound is:

$$\frac{1.003 \text{ g mercury}}{0.080 \text{ g oxygen}} \times 8.00 \text{ g oxygen} = 1.0 \times 10^2 \text{ g mercury}$$

$$= \text{(equivalent weight of mercury in this oxide of mercury)}$$

The oxides of many metals may be reduced by using various reducing agents such as hydrogen gas, carbon, or carbon monoxide gas. If we reduce 3.194 g of an iron oxide by heating it in a stream of hydrogen gas, we find that it produces 2.234 g of pure iron.* Thus, 2.234 g of iron were combined with 0.960 g of oxygen in the oxide (3.194 g − 2.234 g). The equivalent weight of iron in this oxide is:

$$\frac{2.234 \text{ g iron}}{0.960 \text{ g oxygen}} \times 8.00 \text{ g oxygen} = 18.6 \text{ g iron}$$

$$= \text{(equivalent weight of iron in this iron oxide)}$$

FORMATION OF HYDROGEN FROM A METAL AND AN ACID

If a metal reacts with an acid to form hydrogen, we can calculate the equivalent weight of the metal by measuring the quantity of hydrogen evolved from a known weight of the metal. For example, if 3.5 g of aluminum react with an acid to yield 0.39 g of hydrogen, we can calculate the equivalent weight of aluminum:

$$\frac{3.5 \text{ g aluminum}}{0.39 \text{ g hydrogen}} = \text{the weight of aluminum that displaces 1.0 g of hydrogen}$$

$$\frac{3.5 \text{ g aluminum}}{0.39 \text{ g hydrogen}} \times 1.008 \text{ g hydrogen} = 9.0 \text{ g is the equivalent weight of aluminum in this compound}$$

8-1 Solutions of Problems in Chapter 8

PROBLEM. If 0.300 g of oxygen gas occupies a particular volume at 30°C and exerts a particular pressure, at what temperature would 0.200 g of oxygen gas exert the same pressure in the same volume?

SOLUTION. T (in °K) = 273 + 30° = 303°K

	T	N	P	V
Initial state:	303°K	0.300 g	constant	constant
Final state:	T_f	0.200 g	constant	constant

$$T_{final} = T_{initial} \times \frac{\text{fraction to correct for change}}{\text{in number of molecules}}$$

$$T_f = T_i \times \frac{N_i}{N_f} \qquad (P \text{ and } V \text{ constant})$$

Since a higher temperature is required for the smaller weight (0.200 g) of oxygen gas to exert the same pressure in the same volume, we place the larger weight in the numerator of the fraction N_i/N_f.

$$T_f = 303°\text{K} \times \frac{0.300 \text{ g}}{0.200 \text{ g}} = 455°\text{K}$$

$$T_f \text{ (in °C)} = 455° - 273 = 182°\text{C}$$

Now since a smaller weight of a gas contains fewer molecules than a larger weight of the same gas, the smaller number of molecules must strike the walls of the container

* The equation for this reaction (though not required to solve the problem) is $Fe_2O_3 + 3\ H_2 \longrightarrow 2\ Fe + 3\ H_2O$.

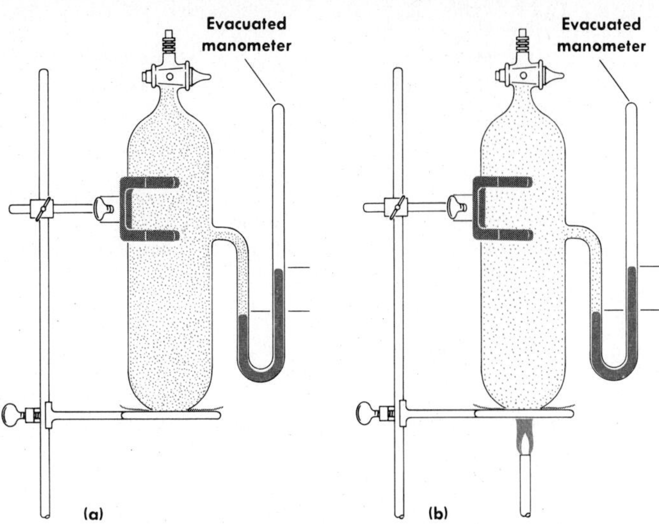

FIGURE 8A-1 **Pressure maintained constant by increasing *T* and decreasing *N*; *V* is constant.**

harder and more often in order to keep the pressure constant. That is to say, the temperature of these molecules must be increased, as indicated in Fig. 8A-1.

PROBLEM. To what pressure must 500 ml of gas at a pressure of 700 torr be changed to reduce the volume to 400 ml, with no change in temperature or weight of gas?

SOLUTION.

	P	V	N	T
Initial state:	700 torr	500 ml	constant	constant
Final state:	P_f	400 ml	constant	constant

$$P_{final} = P_{initial} \times \frac{\text{fraction to correct for}}{\text{change in volume}}$$

$$P_f = P_i \times \frac{V_i}{V_f} \qquad (N \text{ and } T \text{ constant})$$

Since V is decreased, P must increase, because the gas molecules now strike the walls of the container more often in a given time. Consequently, the larger value for V goes in the numerator:

$$P_f = 700 \text{ torr} \times \frac{500 \cancel{\text{ml}}}{400 \cancel{\text{ml}}} = 875 \text{ torr}$$

PROBLEM. If a fixed weight of gas in a fixed volume exerts a pressure of 2.0 atm at 20°C, at what temperature will the same weight of gas in the same volume exert a pressure of 0.50 atm?

SOLUTION.

	T	P	V	N
Initial state:	293°K	2.0 atm	constant	constant
Final state:	T_f	0.50 atm	constant	constant

$$T_{final} = T_{initial} \times \frac{\text{fraction to correct for}}{\text{change in pressure}}$$

$$T_f = T_i \times \frac{P_f}{P_i} \qquad (V \text{ and } N \text{ constant})$$

$$T_f = 293°\text{K} \times \frac{0.50 \cancel{\text{atm}}}{2.0 \cancel{\text{atm}}} = 73°\text{K}$$

$$T_f \text{ (in °C)} = 73 - 273 = -200°\text{C}$$

PROBLEM. If a given weight of a gas in a volume of 5.000 l. exerts a pressure of 1 atm at 30°C, at what temperature will the same weight of gas occupy a volume of 400 ml and exert the same pressure?

SOLUTION. $T_i = 273 + 30 = 303°\text{K}$ 5.000 l. = 5000 ml

	T	V	N	P
Initial state:	303°K	5000 ml	constant	constant
Final state:	T_f	400 ml	constant	constant

$$T_{\text{final}} = T_{\text{initial}} \times \frac{\text{fraction to correct for}}{\text{change in volume}}$$

$$T_f = T_i \times \frac{V_f}{V_i}$$

In order for the same weight of a gas to occupy a smaller volume and still exert the same pressure, the molecules must be slowed down, and the only way in which this can be done is by decreasing the temperature. Therefore, the smaller volume must go into the numerator of the fraction, V_f/V_i:

$$T_f = 303°\text{K} \times \frac{400\ \cancel{\text{ml}}}{5000\ \cancel{\text{ml}}} = 24.2°\text{K}$$

$$T_f\ (\text{in }°\text{C}) = 24.2° - 273° = -249°\text{C}$$

PROBLEM. If 5.00 g of gas A (1 mole = 150 g) occupy a certain volume and exert a certain pressure at 40°C, at what temperature will 6.00 g of gas B (1 mole = 90.0 g) occupy the same volume and exert the same pressure?

SOLUTION. First, we calculate the number of moles present in each quantity of gas.

The number of moles in gas A is: $\dfrac{5.00\text{ g}}{150\text{ g/1 mole}} = \dfrac{5}{150}\text{ mole} = \dfrac{1}{30}\text{ mole}$

The number of moles in gas B is: $\dfrac{6.00\text{ g}}{90.0\text{ g/1 mole}} = \dfrac{6}{90}\text{ mole} = \dfrac{1}{15}\text{ mole}$

The absolute temperature is: $T = 273 + 40° = 313°\text{K}$

	T	n	V	P
Initial state:	313°K	$\frac{1}{30}$ mole	constant	constant
Final state:	T_f	$\frac{1}{15}$ mole	constant	constant

The number of molecules present in $\frac{1}{15}$ mole of gas B is greater than the number of molecules present in $\frac{1}{30}$ mole of gas A. The temperature of gas B must be decreased if it is to exert the same pressure as gas A. Thus, the smaller value is placed in the numerator of the fraction n_i/n_f:

$$T_{\text{final}} = T_{\text{initial}} \times \frac{\text{fraction to correct for}}{\text{change in number of moles}}$$

$$T_f = T_i \times \frac{n_i}{n_f}$$

$$T_f = 313°\text{K} \times \frac{\frac{1}{30}\ \cancel{\text{mole}}}{\frac{1}{15}\ \cancel{\text{mole}}} = 156°\text{K}$$

$$T_f\ (\text{in }°\text{C}) = 156 - 273 = -117°\text{C}$$

12-1 The Spatial Distribution of *p* Orbitals

As stated in the text (p. 242), the *point* electron density in a p orbital depends on two factors—the distance r of the point from the nucleus and the orientation in space relative to a reference system (for example, a set of Cartesian axes, x, y, and z, having the origin at the nucleus). As Fig. 12A-1(a) shows, the position of a point A in space may be specified by giving its distance $r = OA$ from the origin, and also the values of the angles theta, θ, and phi, ϕ. (θ is the angle between the line OA and the z axis, and ϕ is the angle between the x axis and the projection of the line OA on the xy plane.)

Let us now consider separately how the point electron density of a p orbital depends on the two factors mentioned above. The dependence of the point electron density of a p orbital on the distance r from the nucleus, regardless of the direction, is

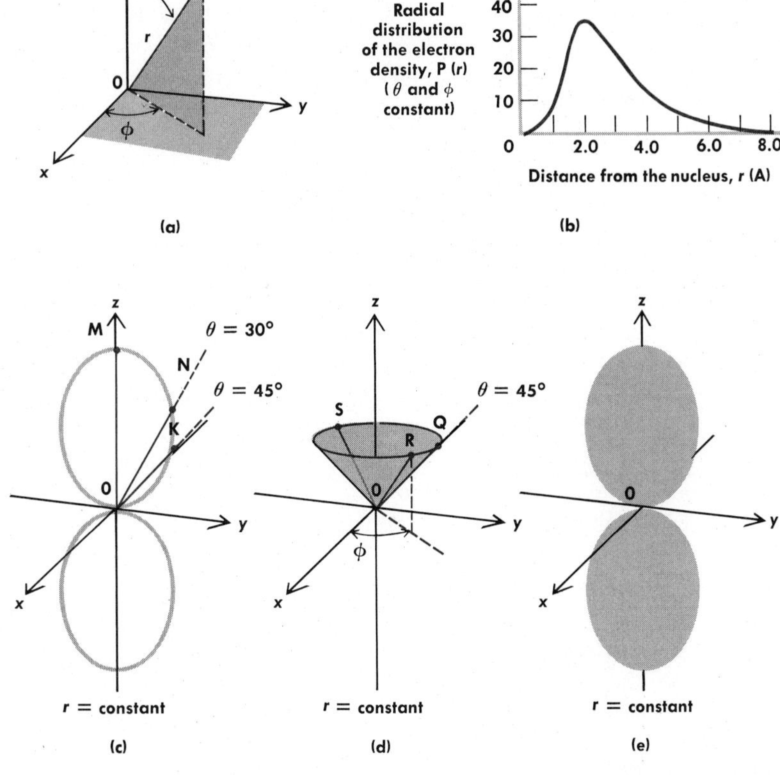

FIGURE 12A-1 (a) Position of a point in space. (b) Radial distribution, $P(r)$, as a function of r, for θ and ϕ constant. (c) Variation of the electron density of a 2p orbital with ϕ, for r = constant and $\phi = 0$. (d) Electron density as a function of ϕ, for r = constant and θ = constant. (e) Three-dimensional representation of the angular distribution of a p orbital as a function of θ and ϕ, for r = contant.

called the *radial dependence* or *radial distribution* and is shown in Fig. 12A-1(b). As r increases in any given direction, the electron density first increases rapidly to a maximum, then gradually decreases and finally becomes practically zero.

Next let us consider how the point electron density of a p orbital is dependent on the orientation in space (given by the values of the angles θ and ϕ). Assume that we determine the electron density for all points which have the same given distance r from the nucleus but differ in their orientation in space. First let us keep constant the angle ϕ and determine the electron density for all the possible values of the angle θ. (For example, for $\phi = 90°$, we are considering only the points on the yz cartesian plane.) We find that for a point with $\phi = 90°$, and $\theta = 0°$—that is, a point on the z axis—the electron density has a certain value, which we represent as the OM segment in Fig. 12A-1(c). Then we determine the electron density for another value of θ, say 30°, and we find that the electron density is only $\frac{3}{4}$ of that found in the direction $\theta = 0°$. This we represent by the ON segment ($ON = \frac{3}{4}\ OM$), in the direction $\theta = 30°$. For still another value of θ, say 45° (and the same value of r, and $\phi = 90°$), we find that the electron density is about $\frac{1}{2}$ of that for $\theta = 0°$, and we represent this with the OK segment ($OK = \frac{1}{2}\ OM$) in the direction $\theta = 45°$. Finally, when $\theta = 90°$—that is, along the y axis—the electron density is zero. Proceeding in this way for all values of θ (always for the same r, and $\phi = 90°$) the lengths of the segments, OM, ON, OK, $\cdots$, represent the electron densities; and the ends of the segments, the $M, N, K, \cdots$ points, outline the two-lobed figure shown in the diagram. For $\theta = 0°$ (z axis) the electron density is the maximum possible for that given value of r; for $\theta = 90°$ (y axis) the electron density is zero; and for intermediate values of θ the density decreases rapidly as θ approaches 90°. If now we determine the electron density for the same value of r by keeping θ constant and gradually varying ϕ, we find that the electron density remains a constant. So if we represent, as before, the electron density in each direction by an appropriate segment, the ends of all these segments, OQ, OR, OS, $\cdots$ (the points $Q, R, S \cdots$) outline a circle concentric with the z axis, as shown in Fig. 12A-1(d). By repeating such determinations for each value of θ, we obtain the two-lobed surface shown in Fig. 12A-1(e), which represents the *angular distribution* or *directional dependence* of the p orbital. (Notice that this surface is derived from the outline of Fig. 12A-1(c) by rotation about the z axis). For each point on this surface the distance from the origin O represents the electron density of all those points of space around the nucleus which have the same given values of θ and ϕ—that is, all the points in the same (θ, ϕ) direction. This electron density in the θ, ϕ direction is expressed as a fraction of the maximum electron density possible for the distance r considered. For any given r, the electron density has a maximum value, which is only a function of r, along the axis of the orbital ($\theta = 0°$). The electron density then decreases as the value of θ increases from 0° to 90°, as shown in the diagram, finally becoming zero in all directions along the xy plane ($\theta = 90°$). If we repeat this procedure for another value of r, we find that the maximum electron density along the axis of the orbital ($\theta = 0$) is different from what we had previously found, because, as we have said, this maximum electron density depends only on r, and actually is the value of the radial density distribution, $P(r)$ given in Fig. 12A-1(b). Similarly, for this new value of r, the electron density at each point in space not situated on the axis of the orbital is different from what we had found for the previous value of r, but it is still the same fraction of the maximum electron density. In other words, for each direction in the space around the nucleus (for all points with a given θ and a given ϕ) the electron density is always the same fraction of the maximum possible electron density, which in turn depends only on r. Therefore, the surface of Fig. 12A-1(e) represents how the electron density depends on the orientation in space for all values of r. To summarize: For all points in space along the axis of a p orbital, the electron density depends only on the value of the radial probability; for the points with $\theta = 90°$, the electron density is zero for all values of r, whereas for all other points in space the electron density depends both on r and on the direction (θ and ϕ).

12-2 The Spatial Distribution of *d* Orbitals

As is the case for the p orbitals, the *point* electron density of the d orbitals depends on both the distance from the nucleus and the orientation in space relative to a reference system (a set of Cartesian axes, x, y, and z, having the origin at the nucleus). The dependence of the electron density on the distance from the nucleus only (*radial distribution*) is similar to that of the p orbitals, and is shown in Fig. 12A-2. There is a region of zero electron density at the nucleus; the density then increases to a maximum and gradually decreases again, becoming practically zero at relatively large distances. The dependence of the electron density of a d orbital on the direction (*angular distribution*) is more complicated than for the p orbitals, and is shown as boundary surfaces in the text in Fig. 12-7(a).

From these diagrams you can accept that in an isolated atom the three d orbitals, d_{xy}, d_{yz}, and d_{xz}, are completely equivalent, because their shapes are equal and they are similarly oriented with respect to the Cartesian axes, their electron density being

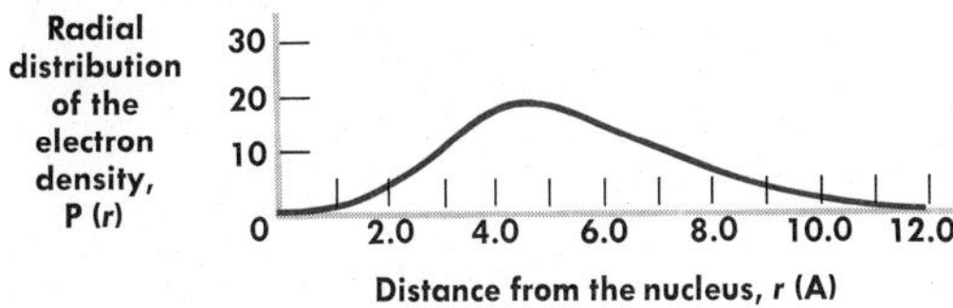

FIGURE 12A-2 Radial distribution of the electron density of a 3*d* orbital (equal for all five *d* orbitals).

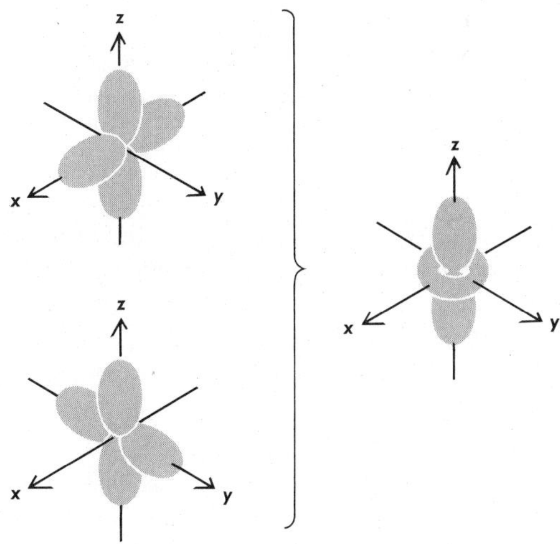

concentrated between the axes. These considerations may be extended to include the $d_{x^2-y^2}$ orbital which also has the same shape as the d_{xy}, d_{yz}, and d_{xz} orbitals, although differing in its orientation with respect to the Cartesian axes (in fact, its electron density is concentrated along the x and y axes). On the other hand, it is not evident from Fig. 12-7(a) that the d_{z^2} orbital is equivalent to the four other d orbitals, because it differs not only in orientation but also in shape. This point may be clarified only by recourse to mathematics. An approximate pictorial idea may be obtained by considering that the shape of the d_{z^2} orbital results from the combination of two shapes identical to that of the $d_{x^2-y^2}$ orbital, but oriented along the x,z and y,z axes respectively, as shown alongside.

17-1 Calculation of the Pressure-Volume Work in a Reversible Expansion of an Ideal Gas

GRAPHICALLY

We know from Boyle's Law that for an ideal gas the PV product is a constant at constant temperature (see p. 121). This relationship can be represented graphically by a hyperbola as shown in Fig. 17A-1. Now consider the expansion of (1 mole of) an ideal gas at a constant temperature, $T = 298°K$, from an initial state represented in the diagram by the point A ($P_i = 2.000$ atm, $V_i = 12.2$ l.) to a final state represented by the point B ($P_f = 1.000$ atm, $V_f = 24.4$ l.). Notice that from Boyle's Law, $P_iV_i = P_fV_f$ (2.000 atm $\times$ 12.2 l. = 1.000 atm $\times$ 24.4 l.).

We may imagine this expansion to take place by a continuous series of extremely small "elements of expansion"—so small that during each element of expansion the opposing pressure may be considered to be constant and only just slightly lower than the pressure of the gas itself. We can then calculate the "element of work" done by the system against the opposing pressure during each of these elements of expansion by using the formula $dw = -P\,dV$, where dw indicates the very small "element of work" and dV the very small volume change—in this case, the "element of expansion." Notice that in the formula $dw = -P\,dV$, P is the external opposing pressure, whereas in Boyle's Law, $PV =$ const, P is the pressure exerted by the gas itself. Only because we are considering a reversible process can we equate the pressure of the gas with the external opposing pressure which determines the amount of work done.

The element of work, $dw = -P\,dV$, is represented graphically as the rectangular area having dV as the base and the corresponding pressure P as the height. For example, the element of work performed during the element of expansion from the initial volume V_i to a slightly larger volume $(V_i + dV)$, is represented by the small

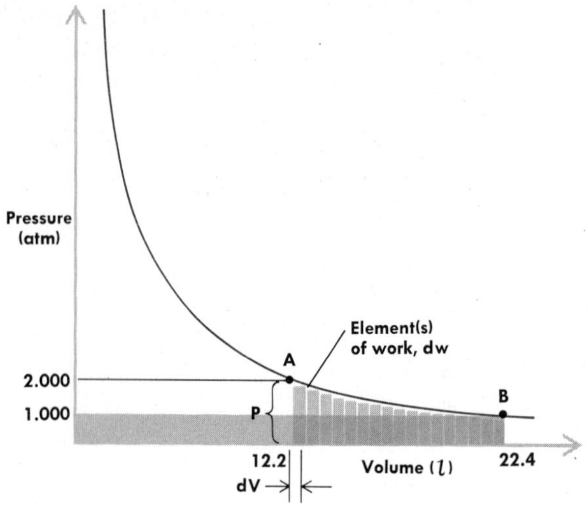

FIGURE 17A-1 Graphic representation of the pressure-volume work for the reversible expansion of an ideal gas.

vertical rectangular area next to point A. The entire work done by the system during the expansion is the sum of all these miniscule elements of work done in each tiny successive element of expansion against a gradually decreasing opposing pressure, which is always just slightly lower than the pressure of the gas itself. Notice that the total area representing the sum of all the elements of work is less than the area under the curve of the hyperbola, because as we have said, the opposing pressure against which the system performs its expansion work is at all instants just slightly less (however small the difference may be) than the pressure exerted by the gas itself. The smaller the elements of expansion considered, the more closely the total work done in the step-wise expansion approaches the total work which would be done if the expansion were carried out *reversibly*—that is, by a series of extremely small expansions represented as a series of vertical lines. In fact, we have seen that in a reversible expansion the system performs the maximum work possible for the transformation considered. Hence, the maximum work that the gas is capable of doing in passing from the initial state represented by A to the final state represented by B is the area under Boyle's hyperbola, between A and B.

MATHEMATICALLY

A student who has studied the elements of calculus knows that the area under the curve (Fig. 17A-1) between point A (representing V_i) and point B (representing V_f) is given by $\int_{V_i}^{V_f} P\,dV$. We have just seen that this area represents the work, w, done by the system on the surroundings when it undergoes a transformation from its initial state to its final state, and we know that if the transformation is carried out isothermally, this work is a maximum. Hence, bearing in mind our convention on the sign of w, we can write:

$$1.\quad w_{max} = -\int_{V_i}^{V_f} P\,dV$$

Now, from the ideal gas law, $PV = nRT$, we have $P = \frac{nRT}{V}$, and substituting this expression for P in (1) we obtain:*

$$2.\quad w_{max} = -\int_{V_i}^{V_f} \frac{nRT}{V}\,dV$$

* In $P\,dV$, P is the external opposing pressure; in $PV = nRT$, P is the pressure exerted by the gas. For a reversible change, these two terms are only infinitesimally different.

Since n, R, and T are all constants, we finally have the following formula:

$$3.\quad w_{max} = -nRT\int_{V_i}^{V_f}\frac{dV}{V} = -nRT\ln\frac{V_f}{V_i} = -2.303\ nRT\log\frac{V_f}{V_i}$$

This is the formula given in the text (p. 355) to calculate the maximum work involved in a (reversible) volume change of an ideal gas at constant temperature. From Boyle's Law, $P_iV_i = P_fV_f$, it follows that $\frac{V_i}{V_f} = \frac{P_f}{P_i}$; hence equation (3) can also be written as:

$$4.\quad w_{max} = -2.303\ nRT\log\frac{P_i}{P_f}$$

This latter expression permits us to calculate the maximum work involved in an isothermal volume change of an ideal gas at temperature T, if we know the values of the initial and final pressure.

17-2 Approximate Calculation of the Entropy Change, ΔS, for Transformations at Variable Temperature

Consider a system consisting of 1 mole of an ideal monoatomic gas, contained in a cylinder of fixed volume and in thermal contact with the surroundings. If the surroundings are initially at a higher temperature than the system, heat is transferred from the surroundings to the system, whose temperature is gradually raised until the system attains the same temperature as the surroundings. Therefore, let us consider that the temperature of the 1 mole of ideal gas is raised by, say, 10 degrees, from 273°K to 283°K, during the transformation. We know that the heat capacity at constant volume of a monoatomic ideal gas is: $C_V = 3.00$ cal/mole × deg K; that is to say, in order to increase the temperature of 1 mole of an ideal monoatomic gas by 1 degree K at constant volume, we need to add 3.00 cal. Thus the (total) quantity of heat that the system takes on from the surroundings at constant volume in this transformation from 273°K to 283°K is: $q = (3.00 \times 10 =)$ 30 cal. Notice that since no work is being done, all this heat goes to increase the internal energy (temperature) of the system, $\Delta E = q$.

The energy-distribution curves of Fig. 17-6 may help to visualize the increase in "energetic disorder" (increase in entropy) resulting from this temperature increase. The value of the entropy change, ΔS, which accompanies the transformation of 1 mole of an ideal monoatomic gas from an initial state, V_i,P_i,T_i ($T_i = 273$°K) to a final state, V_f,P_f,T_f ($V_f = V_i$, $T_f = 283$°K) is calculated approximately as follows. We assume the transformation to occur by a series of successive steps, each step corresponding to a very small increment of temperature, dT. For example, let us say that $dT = 1$°K increase in temperature. In each of such steps, the system absorbs from the surroundings 3.00 cal of heat, while its temperature increases by one degree. Since during each step the temperature increase is relatively small ($dT = 1$°K), we may as a first approximation consider these 3.00 cal of heat to be taken on by the system at constant temperature—for example, the initial temperature of the step. Thus, the small entropy increase of the system during the first step of the transformation may be expressed by the formula which holds for a transformation at constant temperature:

$$\text{Approximate small entropy increment}_{273°\text{K}\rightarrow 274°\text{K}} = \frac{q}{T_1} = \frac{C_V}{T_1}$$

$$= \frac{3\ \text{cal/mole} \times \text{deg K}}{273\ \text{deg K}} = 0.01099\ \text{cal/mole (for 1 degree temp. change)}$$

In a similar manner, we can calculate the approximate small entropy increments for each of the successive "one-degree steps" of the transformation, up to the final temperature, $T_f = 283$°K. Note that in the above expression, the small approximate entropy increment of the step is given by the product of two terms: the ratio $\frac{C_V}{T}$, and the "one-degree" temperature increment ($dT = 1°K$). Hence, if we plot the value of the ratio $\frac{C_V}{T}$ versus the temperature T, we can use the line graph thus obtained to calculate graphically the approximate entropy change of each "one-degree" step. The procedure is the same as used to calculate approximately the pressure-volume work involved in a reversible (isothermal) expansion of an ideal gas (Appendix 17-1). The small approximate increment of entropy of each step, corresponding to a small temperature increment, dT, is represented by the rectangular area having dT as the base and the corresponding value of $\frac{C_V}{T}$ as the height. The temperature, T, actually varies within the step considered, but we can make the approximation of taking T (in the ratio $\frac{C_V}{T}$) to be constant and equal to, let us say, the initial temperature of each step. Thus, the small entropy increment for the first step of the transformation considered is represented by the first shaded rectangular area in Fig. 17A-2. In a similar manner, the small entropy increase of each successive one-degree step is given by the rectanglar area having $dT = 1°K$ as the base, and $\frac{C_V}{T_{\text{initial of step}}}$ as the height. Notice that the area of the rectangle, that is, the entropy increase of each successive step, gradually becomes smaller as we pass from $T_i = 273°K$, to $T_f = 283°K$. This is so because —as we know—the entropy change resulting from the absorption of a certain fixed quantity of heat (in this example 3.00 cal) depends on the temperature at which the heat is absorbed, and decreases as this temperature increases. An approximate estimate of the total entropy change of the transformation is then given by the sum of all the small entropy changes of each single step. In this manner we obtain an approximate value of the total entropy change (shown as the total area under the purple stepwise line in the diagram) which is larger than the actual ΔS of the transformation, because we have assumed that in each step the heat is absorbed at a *constant temperature* lower than the actual (gradually decreasing) temperature of the system.

FIGURE 17A-2 Approximate graphic calculation of the entropy change, ΔS, for a transformation at constant volume.

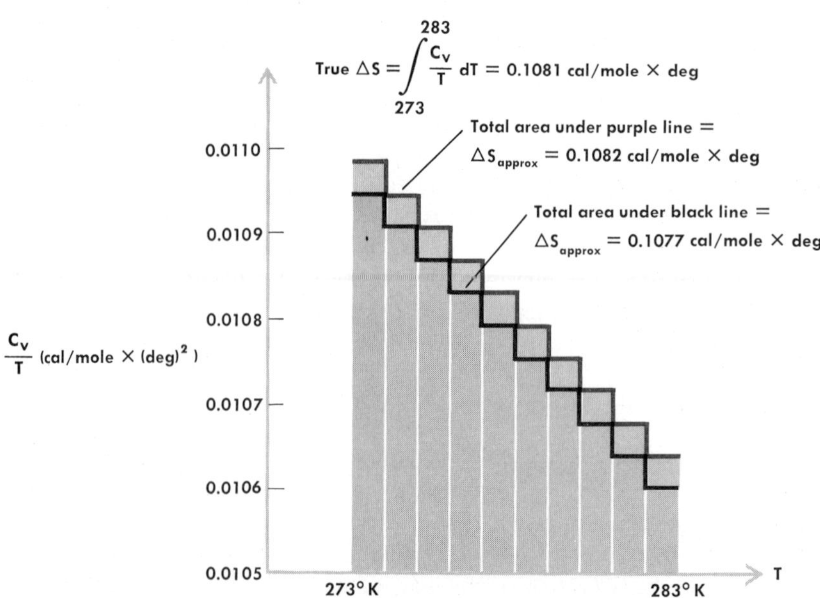

We could also calculate an approximate value of the entropy change by assuming that in each step the heat is absorbed at the higher temperature of the step. The entropy change for the first step, 273°K → 274°K, would then be: $\frac{3 \text{ cal/mole}}{274°\text{K}} =$ 0.01094 cal/mole × deg. The approximate total value of the entropy change calculated in this manner (represented by the total area under the black stepwise line in the diagram) would be smaller than the one calculated above, and also, of course, smaller than the true value of ΔS, because now we have assumed that in each step the same quantity of heat is taken on at the higher temperature of the step. If we were to repeat this calculation in a similar manner, but considering the transformation to take place by a succession of smaller steps, each corresponding, let us say, to a temperature increase of 0.5 degrees, we would find two other approximate values of the entropy change—one again larger and the other smaller than the true ΔS—but these values would now be closer to one another, and hence to the true ΔS value, than in the previous case. Similarly, we would find that as the steps by which we imagine the transformation to take place become smaller and smaller, the approximate values of the entropy change—the one larger and the other smaller than the true ΔS—become closer and closer to one another. At the limit, if the transformation is imagined to take place reversibly by a series of infinitesimally small steps, in each of which the system absorbs an infinitesimally small "element of heat" from the surroundings while its temperature also changes by an infinitesimally small increment, we obtain the true value of ΔS for the specified transformation.

The true value of ΔS for any transformation involving a temperature change from T_i to T_f at constant volume is the area under the curve between T_i and T_f. As the student familiar with calculus will no doubt recognize, this true value of ΔS can be calculated by the formula

$$\Delta S = \int_{T_i}^{T_f} \frac{C_v}{T} \times dT = C_v \ln \frac{T_f}{T_i}$$

In our case, $\Delta S_{273°K \to 283°K} = C_v \ln \frac{T_f}{T_i} = 3.00 \text{ cal/mole} \times \text{deg} \times \ln \frac{283}{273}$
$= 0.108 \text{ cal/mole} \times \text{deg}.$

34-1 Conversion Factor between cm^{-1} and kcal/mole

The energy of a photon with a given wavenumber, ν, is given by the expression:

$$E = h \times c \times \nu$$

In this expression, h is Planck's constant ($h = 6.62 \times 10^{-27}$ erg × sec) and c is the velocity of light ($c = 3.00 \times 10^{10}$ cm/sec), and ν is expressed in cm^{-1}. Thus, the *quantum* of energy corresponding to a photon of a given wavenumber ν is:

$$E = 6.62 \times 10^{-27} \text{ erg} \times \cancel{\text{sec}} \times 3.00 \times 10^{10} \cancel{\text{cm/sec}} \times \nu \cancel{\text{cm}^{-1}} = 1.99 \times 10^{-16} \times \nu \text{ erg}$$

We can express this *quantum* of energy in the more familiar kcal unit by using the conversion factor 1 erg = 2.39×10^{-11} kcal:

$$E = 1.99 \times 10^{-16} \times \nu \cancel{\text{erg}} \times 2.39 \times 10^{-11} \text{ kcal/}\cancel{\text{erg}} = 4.75 \times 10^{-27} \times \nu \text{ kcal}$$

And the energy in 1 mole of photons (6.02×10^{23} photons) is:

$$E = 6.02 \times 10^{23} \times 4.75 \times 10^{-27} \times \nu \text{ kcal/mole}$$
$$E = 2.86 \times 10^{-3} \times \nu \text{ kcal/mole} = (\nu/350) \text{ kcal/mole}$$

The conversion factor between cm^{-1} and kcal/mole is therefore:

$$350 \text{ cm}^{-1} = 1 \text{ kcal/mole (of photons)}$$

TABLE I STANDARD OXIDATION POTENTIALS OF HALF-REACTIONS IN ACID SOLUTIONS

The E° values are a measure of the tendency of the indicated half-reaction to take place, relative to the half-reaction $H_2 = 2\ H^+ + 2\ e^-$ at 25°C and 1 atm, when all species involved have activity equal to unity (ionic species have approximately 1 molar concentration). All species in solution are hydrated.

Couple	*Half-Reaction*	*E° (volts)*
Li,Li^+	$Li = Li^+ + e^-$	+3.05
K,K^+	$K = K^+ + e^-$	+2.93
Rb,Rb^+	$Rb = Rb^+ + e^-$	+2.92
Cs,Cs^+	$Cs = Cs^+ + e^-$	+2.92
Ra,Ra^{++}	$Ra = Ra^{++} + 2\ e^-$	+2.90
Ba,Ba^{++}	$Ba = Ba^{++} + 2\ e^-$	+2.91
Sr,Sr^{++}	$Sr = Sr^{++} + 2\ e^-$	+2.89
Ca,Ca^{++}	$Ca = Ca^{++} + 2\ e^-$	+2.87
Na,Na^+	$Na = Na^+ + e^-$	+2.71
La,La^{+++}	$La = La^{+++} + 3\ e^-$	+2.52
Mg,Mg^{++}	$Mg = Mg^{++} + 2\ e^-$	+2.37
Sc,Sc^{+++}	$Sc = Sc^{+++} + 3\ e^-$	+2.08
Pu,Pu^{+++}	$Pu = Pu^{+++} + 3\ e^-$	+2.07
$Al,[AlF_6]^{=}$	$Al + 6\ F^- = [AlF_6]^{=} + 3\ e^-$	+2.07
Be,Be^{++}	$Be = Be^{++} + 2\ e^-$	+1.85
Al,Al^{+++}	$Al = Al^{+++} + 3\ e^-$	+1.66
Ti,Ti^{++}	$Ti = Ti^{++} + 2\ e^-$	+1.63
Zr,Zr^{+4}	$Zr = Zr^{+4} + 4\ e^-$	+1.53
Mn,Mn^{++}	$Mn = Mn^{++} + 2\ e^-$	+1.18
Zn,Zn^{++}	$Zn = Zn^{++} + 2\ e^-$	+0.76
Cr,Cr^{+++}	$Cr = Cr^{+++} + 3\ e^-$	+0.74
Ga,Ga^{+++}	$Ga = Ga^{+++} + 3\ e^-$	+0.56
Fe,Fe^{++}	$Fe = Fe^{++} + 2\ e^-$	+0.47
Cr^{++},Cr^{+++}	$Cr^{++} = Cr^{+++} + e^-$	+0.41
Cd,Cd^{++}	$Cd = Cd^{++} + 2\ e^-$	+0.40
Ti^{++},Ti^{+++}	$Ti^{++} = Ti^{+++} + e^-$	+0.37
Pb,PbI_2	$Pb + 2\ I^- = PbI_2 + 2\ e^-$	+0.37
Tl,Tl^+	$Tl = Tl^+ + e^-$	+0.34
Co,Co^{++}	$Co = Co^{++} + 2\ e^-$	+0.28
V^{++},V^{+++}	$V^{++} = V^{+++} + e^-$	+0.26
$Sn,[SnF_6]^{=}$	$Sn + 6\ F^- = [SnF_6]^{=} + 4\ e^-$	+0.25
Ni,Ni^{++}	$Ni = Ni^{++} + 2\ e^-$	+0.27
Cu,CuI	$Cu + I^- = CuI + e^-$	+0.19
Ag,AgI	$Ag + I^- = AgI + e^-$	+0.15
Sn,Sn^{++}	$Sn = Sn^{++} + 2\ e^-$	+0.14
Pb,Pb^{++}	$Pb = Pb^{++} + 2\ e^-$	+0.13
Fe,Fe^{+++}	$Fe = Fe^{+++} + 3\ e^-$	+0.05
$Hg,[HgI_4]^{=}$	$Hg + 4\ I^- = [HgI_4]^{=} + 2\ e^-$	+0.04
H_2,H^+	$H_2 = 2\ H^+ + 2\ e^-$	+0.00
$Ag,[Ag(S_2O_3)_2]^{\equiv}$	$Ag + 2\ S_2O_3^{=} = [Ag(S_2O_3)_2]^{\equiv} + e^-$	−0.01
$Cu,CuBr$	$Cu + Br^- = CuBr + e^-$	−0.03
UO_2^+,UO_2^{++}	$UO_2^+ = UO_2^{++} + e^-$	−0.05
$Ag,AgBr$	$Ag + Br^- = AgBr + e^-$	−0.09
Ti^{+++},TiO^{++}	$Ti^{+++} + H_2O = TiO^{++} + 2\ H^+ + e^-$	−0.10
H_2S,S	$H_2S = S + 2\ H^+ + 2\ e^-$	−0.14
Sn^{++},Sn^{+4}	$Sn^{++} = Sn^{+4} + 2\ e^-$	−0.15
Cu^+,Cu^{++}	$Cu^+ = Cu^{++} + e^-$	−0.16
$H_2SO_3,SO_4^{=}$	$H_2SO_3 + H_2O = SO_4^{=} + 4\ H^+ + 2\ e^-$	−0.17
$Hg,[HgBr_4]^{=}$	$Hg + 4\ Br^- = [HgBr_4]^{=} + 2\ e^-$	−0.21
$Ag,AgCl$	$Ag + Cl^- = AgCl + e^-$	−0.22
UO^{+4},UO_2^{++}	$U^{+4} + 2\ H_2O = UO_2^{++} + 4\ H^+ + 2\ e^-$	−0.33
Cu,Cu^{++}	$Cu = Cu^{++} + 2\ e^-$	−0.34
$Ag,AgIO_3$	$Ag + IO_3^- = AgIO_3 + e^-$	−0.35
$[Fe(CN)_6]^{-4},[Fe(CN)_6]^{-3}$	$[Fe(CN)_6]^{-4} = [Fe(CN)_6]^{\equiv} + e^-$	−0.36
V^{+++},VO^{++}	$V^{+++} + H_2O = VO^{++} + 2\ H^+ + e^-$	−0.36
Ag,Ag_2CrO_4	$2\ Ag + CrO_4^{=} = Ag_2CrO_4 + 2\ e^-$	−0.45
Cu,Cu^+	$Cu = Cu^+ + e^-$	−0.52
I^-,I_2	$2\ I^- = I_2 + 2\ e^-$	−0.54
I^-,I_3^-	$3\ I^- = I_3^- + 2\ e^-$	−0.54

TABLE I (CONT'D)

Couple	Half-Reaction	E° (volts)
$CuCl,Cu^{++}$	$CuCl = Cu^{++} + Cl^- + e^-$	−0.54
$Ag,AgNO_2$	$Ag + NO_2^- = AgNO_2 + e^-$	−0.56
$MnO_4^=,MnO_4^-$	$MnO_4^= = MnO_4^- + e^-$	−0.58
$Ag,Ag(CH_3COO)$	$Ag + CH_3COO^- = Ag(CH_3COO) + e^-$	−0.64
Ag,Ag_2SO_4	$2\ Ag + SO_4^= = Ag_2SO_4 + 2\ e^-$	−0.65
H_2O_2,O_2	$H_2O_2 = O_2 + 2\ H^+ + 2\ e^-$	−0.68
Fe^{++},Fe^{+++}	$Fe^{++} = Fe^{+++} + e^-$	−0.77
Hg,Hg_2^{++}	$2\ Hg = Hg_2^{++} + 2\ e^-$	−0.79
Ag,Ag^+	$Ag = Ag^+ + e^-$	−0.80
Rh,Rh^{+++}	$Rh = Rh^{+++} + 3\ e^-$	ca. −0.8
Hg_2^{++},Hg^{++}	$Hg_2^{++} = 2\ Hg^{++} + 2\ e^-$	−0.92
PuO_2^+,PuO_2^{++}	$PuO_2^+ = PuO_2^{++} + 2\ e^-$	−0.93
HNO_2,NO_3^-	$HNO_2 + H_2O = NO_3^- + 3\ H^+ + 2\ e^-$	−0.94
NO,NO_3^-	$NO + 2\ H_2O = NO_3^- + 4\ H^+ + 3\ e^-$	−0.96
$Au,[AuCl_4]^-$	$Au + 4\ Cl^- = [AuCl_4]^- + 3\ e^-$	−1.00
I_2,ICl_2^-	$\frac{1}{2}\ I_2 + 2\ Cl^- = ICl_2^- + e^-$	−1.06
Br^-,Br_2	$2\ Br^- = Br_2 + 2\ e^-$	−1.09
H_2O,O_2	$2\ H_2O = O_2 + 4\ H^+ + 4\ e^-$ (or $4\ OH^- = O_2 + 2\ H_2O + 4\ e^-$)	−1.23
Mn^{++},MnO_2	$Mn^{++} + 2\ H_2O = MnO_2 + 4\ H^+ + 2\ e^-$	−1.23
Tl^+,Tl^{+++}	$Tl^+ = Tl^{+++} + 2\ e^-$	−1.25
Co^{++},Co^{+++}	$Co^{++} = Co^{+++} + e^-$	−1.30
$Cr^{+++},Cr_2O_7^=$	$2\ Cr^{+++} + 7\ H_2O = Cr_2O_7^= + 14\ H^+ + 6\ e^-$	−1.33
Cl^-,Cl_2	$2\ Cl^- = Cl_2 + 2\ e^-$	−1.40
Mn^{++},Mn^{+++}	$Mn^{++} = Mn^{+++} + e^-$	−1.51
Mn^{++},MnO_4^-	$Mn^{++} + 4\ H_2O = MnO_4^- + 8\ H^+ + 5\ e^-$	−1.51
$Cl_2,HClO$	$\frac{1}{2}\ Cl_2 + H_2O = HClO + H^+ + e^-$	−1.62
MnO_2,MnO_4^-	$MnO_2 + 2\ H_2O = MnO_4^- + 4\ H^+ + 3\ e^-$	−1.70
H_2O,H_2O_2	$2\ H_2O = H_2O_2 + 2\ H^+ + 2\ e^-$	−1.77
Ag^+,Ag^{++}	$Ag^+ = Ag^{++} + e^-$	−2.00
F^-,F_2	$2\ F^- = F_2 + 2\ e^-$	−2.87

Oxidation potentials of half-reactions not involving H^+ ions are independent of the hydrogen ion concentration of the solution.

TABLE II STANDARD OXIDATION POTENTIALS OF HALF-REACTIONS IN BASIC SOLUTIONS

The $E°$ values are a measure of the tendency of the indicated half-reaction to take place, relative to the half-reaction $H_2 = 2\ H^+ + 2\ e^-$, at 25°C and 1 atm, when all species involved have activity equal to unity (ionic species have approximately 1 molar concentration). All species in solution are hydrated.

Couple	Half-Reaction	E° (volts)
$Ca,Ca(OH)_2$	$Ca + 2\ OH^- = Ca(OH)_2 + 2\ e^-$	+3.03
$Sr,Sr(OH)_2$	$Sr + 2\ OH^- + 8\ H_2O = Sr(OH)_2 \cdot 8\ H_2O + 2\ e^-$	+2.99
$Mg,Mg(OH)_2$	$Mg + 2\ OH^- = Mg(OH)_2 + 2\ e^-$	+2.69
$Mn,Mn(OH)_2$	$Mn + 2\ OH^- = Mn(OH)_2 + 2\ e^-$	+1.55
$Cr,Cr(OH)_3$	$Cr + 3\ OH^- = Cr(OH)_3 + 3\ e^-$	+1.30
$Zn,Zn(OH)_2$	$Zn + 2\ OH^- = Zn(OH)_2 + 2\ e^-$	+1.24
$Zn,[Zn(OH)_4]^=$	$Zn + 4\ OH^- = [Zn(OH)_4]^= + 2\ e^-$	+1.22
$Zn,[Zn(NH_3)_4]^{++}$	$Zn + 4\ NH_3 = [Zn(NH_3)_4]^{++} + 2\ e^-$	+1.03
$Fe,Fe(OH)_2$	$Fe + 2\ OH^- = Fe(OH)_2 + 2\ e^-$	+0.88
H_2,OH^-	$H_2 + 2\ OH^- = 2\ H_2O + 2\ e^-$ (or $H_2 = 2\ H^+ + 2\ e^-$)	+0.83
$Cd,[Cd(NH_3)_4]^{++}$	$Cd + 4\ NH_3 = [Cd(NH_3)_4]^{++} + 2\ e^-$	+0.60
O_2^-,O_2	$O_2^- = O_2 + e^-$	+0.56
$S^=,S$	$S^= = S + 2\ e^-$	+0.48
$Ag,[Ag(CN)_2]^-$	$Ag + 2\ CN^- = [Ag(CN)_2]^- + e^-$	+0.31
HO_2^-,O_2	$HO_2^- + OH^- = O_2 + H_2O + 2\ e^-$	+0.08
$Mn(OH)_2,MnO_2$	$Mn(OH)_2 + 2\ OH^- = MnO_2 + 2\ H_2O + 2\ e^-$	+0.05
$[Co(NH_3)_6]^{++},[Co(NH_3)_6]^{+++}$	$[Co(NH_3)_6]^{++} = [Co(NH_3)_6]^{+++} + e^-$	−0.10
$Ag,[Ag(NH_3)_2]^+$	$Ag + 2\ NH_3 = [Ag(NH_3)_2]^+ + e^-$	−0.37
OH^-,O_2	$4\ OH^- = O_2 + 2\ H_2O + 4\ e^-$ (or $2\ H_2O = O_2 + 4\ H^+ + 4\ e^-$)	−0.40

TABLE III FOUR-PLACE LOGARITHM TABLE

N	0	1	2	3	4	5	6	7	8	9
10	0000	0043	0086	0128	0170	0212	0253	0294	0334	0374
11	0414	0453	0492	0531	0569	0607	0645	0682	0719	0755
12	0792	0828	0864	0899	0934	0969	1004	1038	1072	1106
13	1139	1173	1206	1239	1271	1303	1335	1367	1399	1430
14	1461	1492	1523	1553	1584	1614	1644	1673	1703	1732
15	1761	1790	1818	1847	1875	1903	1931	1959	1987	2014
16	2041	2068	2095	2122	2148	2175	2201	2227	2253	2279
17	2304	2330	2355	2380	2405	2430	2455	2480	2504	2529
18	2553	2577	2601	2625	2648	2672	2695	2718	2742	2765
19	2788	2810	2833	2856	2878	2900	2923	2945	2967	2989
20	3010	3032	3054	3075	3096	3118	3139	3160	3181	3201
21	3222	3243	3263	3284	3304	3324	3345	3365	3385	3404
22	3424	3444	3464	3483	3502	3522	3541	3560	3579	3598
23	3617	3636	3655	3674	3692	3711	3729	3747	3766	3784
24	3802	3820	3838	3856	3874	3892	3909	3927	3945	3962
25	3979	3997	4014	4031	4048	4065	4082	4099	4116	4133
26	4150	4166	4183	4200	4216	4232	4249	4265	4281	4298
27	4314	4330	4346	4362	4378	4393	4409	4425	4440	4456
28	4472	4487	4502	4518	4533	4548	4564	4579	4594	4609
29	4624	4639	4654	4669	4683	4698	4713	4728	4742	4757
30	4771	4786	4800	4814	4829	4843	4857	4871	4886	4900
31	4914	4928	4942	4955	4969	4983	4997	5011	5024	5038
32	5051	5065	5079	5092	5105	5119	5132	5145	5159	5172
33	5185	5198	5211	5224	5237	5250	5263	5276	5289	5302
34	5315	5328	5340	5353	5366	5378	5391	5403	5416	5428
35	5441	5453	5465	5478	5490	5502	5514	5527	5539	5551
36	5563	5575	5587	5599	5611	5623	5635	5647	5658	5670
37	5682	5694	5705	5717	5729	5740	5752	5763	5775	5786
38	5798	5809	5821	5832	5843	5855	5866	5877	5888	5899
39	5911	5922	5933	5944	5955	5966	5977	5988	5999	6010
40	6021	6031	6042	6053	6064	6075	6085	6096	6107	6117
41	6128	6138	6149	6160	6170	6180	6191	6201	6212	6222
42	6232	6243	6253	6263	6274	6284	6294	6304	6314	6325
43	6335	6345	6355	6365	6375	6385	6395	6405	6415	6425
44	6435	6444	6454	6464	6474	6484	6493	6503	6513	6522
45	6532	6542	6551	6561	6571	6580	6590	6599	6609	6618
46	6628	6637	6646	6656	6665	6675	6684	6693	6702	6712
47	6721	6730	6739	6749	6758	6767	6776	6785	6794	6803
48	6812	6821	6830	6839	6848	6857	6866	6875	6884	6893
49	6902	6911	6920	6928	6937	6946	6955	6964	6972	6981
50	6990	6998	7007	7016	7024	7033	7042	7050	7059	7067
51	7076	7084	7093	7101	7110	7118	7126	7135	7143	7152
52	7160	7168	7177	7185	7193	7202	7210	7218	7226	7235
53	7243	7251	7259	7267	7275	7284	7292	7300	7308	7316
54	7324	7332	7340	7348	7356	7364	7372	7380	7388	7396
N	0	1	2	3	4	5	6	7	8	9

N	0	1	2	3	4	5	6	7	8	9
55	7404	7412	7419	7427	7435	7443	7451	7459	7466	7474
56	7482	7490	7497	7505	7513	7520	7528	7536	7543	7551
57	7559	7566	7574	7582	7589	7597	7604	7612	7619	7627
58	7634	7642	7649	7657	7664	7672	7679	7686	7694	7701
59	7709	7716	7723	7731	7738	7745	7752	7760	7767	7774
60	7782	7789	7796	7803	7810	7818	7825	7832	7839	7846
61	7853	7860	7868	7875	7882	7889	7896	7903	7910	7917
62	7924	7931	7938	7945	7952	7959	7966	7973	7980	7987
63	7993	8000	8007	8014	8021	8028	8035	8041	8048	8055
64	8062	8069	8075	8082	8089	8096	8102	8109	8116	8122
65	8129	8136	8142	8149	8156	8162	8169	8176	8182	8189
66	8195	8202	8209	8215	8222	8228	8235	8241	8248	8254
67	8261	8267	8274	8280	8287	8293	8299	8306	8312	8319
68	8325	8331	8338	8344	8351	8357	8363	8370	8376	8382
69	8388	8395	8401	8407	8414	8420	8426	8432	8439	8445
70	8451	8457	8463	8470	8476	8482	8488	8494	8500	8506
71	8513	8519	8525	8531	8537	8543	8549	8555	8561	8567
72	8573	8579	8585	8591	8597	8603	8609	8615	8621	8627
73	8633	8639	8645	8651	8657	8663	8669	8675	8681	8686
74	8692	8698	8704	8710	8716	8722	8727	8733	8739	8745
75	8751	8756	8762	8768	8774	8779	8785	8791	8797	8802
76	8808	8814	8820	8825	8831	8837	8842	8848	8854	8859
77	8865	8871	8876	8882	8887	8893	8899	8904	8910	8915
78	8921	8927	8932	8938	8943	8949	8954	8960	8965	8971
79	8976	8982	8987	8993	8998	9004	9009	9015	9020	9025
80	9031	9036	9042	9047	9053	9058	9063	9069	9074	9079
81	9085	9090	9096	9101	9106	9112	9117	9122	9128	9133
82	9138	9143	9149	9154	9159	9165	9170	9175	9180	9186
83	9191	9196	9201	9206	9212	9217	9222	9227	9232	9238
84	9243	9248	9253	9258	9263	9269	9274	9279	9284	9289
85	9294	9299	9304	9309	9315	9320	9325	9330	9335	9340
86	9345	9350	9355	9360	9365	9370	9375	9380	9385	9390
87	9395	9400	9405	9410	9415	9420	9425	9430	9435	9440
88	9445	9450	9455	9460	9465	9469	9474	9479	9484	9489
89	9494	9499	9504	9509	9513	9518	9523	9528	9533	9538
90	9542	9547	9552	9557	9562	9566	9571	9576	9581	9586
91	9590	9595	9600	9605	9609	9614	9619	9624	9628	9633
92	9638	9643	9647	9652	9657	9661	9666	9671	9675	9680
93	9685	9689	9694	9699	9703	9708	9713	9717	9722	9727
94	9731	9736	9741	9745	9750	9754	9759	9763	9768	9773
95	9777	9782	9786	9791	9795	9800	9805	9809	9814	9818
96	9823	9827	9832	9836	9841	9845	9850	9854	9859	9863
97	9868	9872	9877	9881	9886	9890	9894	9899	9903	9908
98	9912	9917	9921	9926	9930	9934	9939	9943	9948	9952
99	9956	9961	9965	9969	9974	9978	9983	9987	9991	9996
N	0	1	2	3	4	5	6	7	8	9

INDEX

INDEX

H

T

ELECTRON CONFIGURATIONS OF THE ELEMENTS

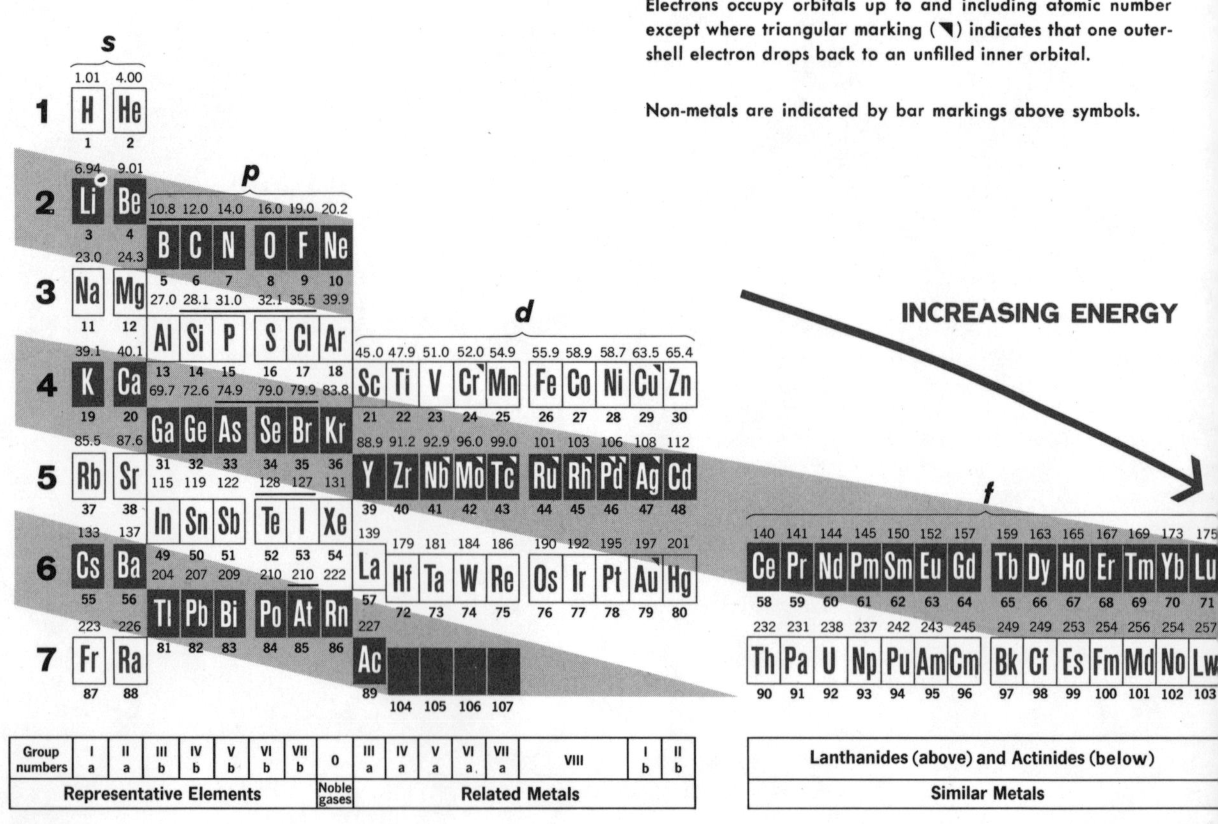

References: H. C. Longuet-Higgins, Journal Chemical Education 34, Page 30 (1957); J. W. Eichinger, Jr., Journal Chemical Education 34, Page 77 (1957).

In this Electron Chart, the numbers 1, 2, 3 . . . 7 at the left are the principal quantum numbers, n, and the letters s, p, d, f at the top represent the orbitals corresponding to the values 0, 1, 2, 3 of the orbital quantum number, m_l. Each number at the left of the chart applies to the elements of the adjacent white or purple row slanting downward. White is used for the quantum numbers $n = 1, 3, 5, 7$; purple for the quantum numbers $n = 2, 4, 6$. The letters s, p, d, f apply to all elements bracketed below them. The *row numbers* and *column letters* are the keys to the electronic configurations of the atoms in their ground states.

Here is how to use the chart. Both $_1$H and $_2$He fall in row 1 and column s. The electron configuration of the $_1$H atom is written as $1s^1$. The number 1 (corresponding to the row number at the left) indicates quantum level 1; the letter s indicates the s orbital of this quantum level; the superscript ^{1} means that one electron is present in this s orbital. Helium, $_2$He, is also in row 1 and column s, and its electron configuration is $1s^2$.

The next element, $_3$Li, has one more electron than $_2$He. The first two electrons of $_3$Li are in the 1s orbital, $1s^2$, as in $_2$He. But Li is located in slanting row 2, which means that the third electron must be present in the $n = 2$ quantum level. Since Li is in column s, this